CARNEGIE INSTITUTION OF WASHINGTON

PUBLICATION NO. 376

1931

INTRODUCTION
TO THE
HISTORY OF SCIENCE

VOLUME II

FROM RABBI BEN EZRA TO ROGER BACON

BY
GEORGE SARTON
Associate in the History of Science
Carnegie Institution of Washington

IN TWO PARTS

PUBLISHED FOR THE
CARNEGIE INSTITUTION OF WASHINGTON
BY
THE WILLIAMS & WILKINS COMPANY
BALTIMORE

Reprinted 1950, 1953

PART II

The Thirteenth Century

BOOK III

The Time of Robert Grosseteste, Ibn al-Baiṭār and Jacob Anaṭoli (First Half of Thirteenth Century)

Chapter XXVIII

Chapter XXIX

Chapter XXX

Chapter XXXI

Chapter XXXII

Chapter XXXIII

Chapter XXXIV

Chapter XXXV

CHAPTER XXXVI

CHAPTER XXXVII

CHAPTER XXXVIII

CHAPTER XXXIX

BOOK IV

The Time of Roger Bacon, Jacob ben Maḥir ibn Tibbon, and Quṭb al-dīn al-Shīrāzī. (Second Half of Thirteenth Century)

CHAPTER XLII

Chapter XLV

Chapter XLVI

Chapter LIII

Chapter LIV

Chapter LV

Indices

PART II
THE THIRTEENTH CENTURY

BOOK THREE

The time of Robert Grosseteste, Ibn al-Baiṭār, and Jacob Anatoli

(*First Half of Thirteenth Century*)

Mihi certe multum auferre temporis solet contemplatio ipsa sapientiae: non aliter illam intueor obstupefactus quam ipsum interim mundum, quem saepe tamquam spectator novus video. Veneror itaque inventa sapientiae inventoresque: adire tamquam multorum hereditatem iuvat. Mihi ista adquisita, mihi laborata sunt. Sed agamus bonum patrem familiae: faciamus ampliora quae accepimus. Maior ista hereditas a me ad posteros transeat. Multum adhuc restat operis multumque restabit, nec ulli nato post mille saecula praecludetur occasio aliquid adhuc adiciendi . . . Multum egerunt qui ante nos fuerunt, sed non peregerunt. —*L. A. Seneca*

(Ad Lucilium epist. 64)

CHAPTER XXVIII

SURVEY OF SCIENCE AND INTELLECTUAL PROGRESS IN THE FIRST HALF OF THE THIRTEENTH CENTURY

I. INTRODUCTION

During the second half of the twelfth century the contributions of the Christians, Muslims, and Jews were substantially equal. By the middle of the thirteenth century that equality was entirely disrupted in favor of Christendom. And yet Islām and Israël were still doing a large share of the world's intellectual work.

We may call this time, The time of Robert Grosseteste, Ibn al-Baiṭār, and Jacob Anaṭoli. These three men represent the three main streams of culture in their order of importance. The three covered the period completely; all three were born in the twelfth century; Ibn al-Baiṭār died in 1248, Grosseteste in 1253, and Anaṭoli probably a few years later. All three were westerners, and the center of gravity of the world was now undoubtedly in the West; yet Ibn al-Baiṭār, who spent the latter half of his life in the East, is a good symbol of that East and especially of Syria—of Damascus—which was then one of the main cultural centers.

The three heroes of the preceding period were connected with Spain, but for this period only one is a Spaniard, Ibn al-Baiṭār. This symbolizes the relative decadence of that country.

Grosseteste was not the greatest Christian scientist. Fibonacci and Jordanus Nemorarius were both greater; the former originated the new European mathematics, and the latter, the new mechanics; but they both died before the middle of the century, Jordanus in 1237, Fibonacci after 1240. Grosseteste's spirit was less profound than theirs, but more comprehensive. He illustrates the English Franciscan tradition which would culminate somewhat later in the activity of his most famous disciple, Roger Bacon. It is no disparagement of the latter to say how much he owed to his master.

Moreover, Grosseteste represents also England, which was one of the most productive countries of that time and probably the most original. On the other hand, Anaṭoli reminds us of Southern France, and Ibn al-Baiṭār of Spain and Syria.

Grosseteste and Anaṭoli helped to create the new intellectual milieu, the former by his Aristotelian studies, the latter by his popularization of Maimonides and Ibn Rushd. Ibn al-Baiṭār, on the contrary, was a herbalist and physician, one primarily interested in concrete and limited problems. In this respect too these three men complete one another very well, and together they give us as fair an image of this age as any three names could evoke.

It is not part of my program to include any summary of political history in this survey, yet it is worthwhile to recall four capital events of this period:

(1) *1204*. Constantinople taken and sacked by the Crusaders. That was almost a death blow to Greek culture.

(2) *1214*. Battle of Bouvines (near Lille), won by Philip Augustus over the emperor Otto IV, supported by English and Flemish contingents.

(3) *1238-1241.* Tartar invasion of Russia, Hungary, Bohemia, and Poland. Kiev and Cracow destroyed, Pesth besieged. The Mongol tide was stopped by the battle of Wahlstatt (near Liegnitz) in 1241.

(4) *1236-1248.* The Moors are slowly driven out of Spain. Cordova being reconquered by the Christians in 1236, Seville in 1248. By the middle of the century the Moors were restricted to the little Kingdom of Granada.

I shall have various opportunities of referring to these events, but it is well to bear them always in mind.

II. RELIGIOUS BACKGROUND

1. *Christendom*—The greatest events were undoubtedly the creation of the two leading orders of friars, the Seraphic Order and the Order of Preachers, the former in 1210 by St. Francis of Assisi, the latter by St. Dominic of Caleruega five years later. The importance of these events, not only from the religious point of view, but also with regard to the intellectual development of Christendom, will be sufficiently proved by the whole of my account (I have inserted on p. 548 a list of the main Franciscans and Dominicans dealt with; it is very impressive). For example, it is impossible to explain the vicissitudes of mediaeval philosophy from this time on without paying attention to the complications and to the new incentives and rivalries caused by the existence of these two militant organizations.

To begin with, they took part in the immense educational expansion which was then taking place in western Europe. Our own age has witnessed a tremendous increase in the number of university students, but this change, in so far as it concerned the men, has been quantitative rather than qualitative, and even the higher education of women has not been a novelty. To understand properly the educational revolution of the thirteenth century one must try to imagine the creation of some fifteen universities in four countries at a time when such opportunities were not only unknown except in a very few places but were undreamt of. The Friars were not slow in realizing the possibilities of the new institutions and they soon tried to obtain footholds in them. They generally succeeded, though not without struggle and bickering. The Dominicans obtained two chairs in the Faculty of Theology of Paris in 1229 and 1231, and soon afterwards the Franciscans obtained a third one. They made many other conquests, but these were the most conspicuous and far-reaching, for the Parisian faculty was then the leading center of Christian theology in the West. Any doctrine which was taught from one of these Parisian chairs was widely broadcast and bound to have international repercussions if there was the slightest pretext for them.

The rivalries between Franciscans and Dominicans were not restricted to those which will naturally occur between two strong and aggressive organizations covering the same field. They were emphasized and duplicated by the misunderstandings caused by divergent tendencies. Of these we shall say more further on, for the present it may suffice to express the differences in their thought and behavior in terms of one of the oldest philosophical distinctions; the Franciscans were Platonists, the Dominicans, Aristotelians.

The Franciscans, or Grey Friars, and the Dominicans, or Black Friars, are and have always been the most important of the "Four mendicant orders." The two others originated at about the same time. The Carmelites, or White Friars, date back their beginnings on Mt. Carmel to the middle of the twelfth century, but they received their earliest constitution only c. 1210. Thus as an established order the White Friars are not older than the Grey ones. Their first leader in Palestine had been Berthold of Calabria, but the organization did not prosper considerably until it had moved to the West. Strangely enough, the first general chapter occurred in England (1245) and their first great leader was the Englishman St. Simeon Stock. The order was especially successful in England, at least until the second half of the sixteenth century when it was regenerated in Spain. The fourth mendicant order, that of the Augustinians, dates only from the middle of the thirteenth century; it was the latest, it was also the least important. However, the historian of culture cannot forget that it was from among the Augustinians that there sprang forth, less than three centuries later, the foremost champion of the Reformation, that Thuringian prophet, Martin Luther. Such are the vagaries of life. Out of these four orders, three were initiated by Italians, one by a Spaniard, but all of them soon became truly international institutions.

Two smaller orders belong to the same fervid age; the Order of our Lady of Mercy, and the Order of the Servants of Mary. Their names are characteristic of an increasing devotion to the Mother of God. The Mercedarians' main purpose was to ransom captives fallen into Moorish hands. The Servites had no purpose except to cultivate in common their asceticism and their devotion to Mary. The former were organized by the Languedocian, St. Peter Nolasco, at Barcelona, in 1218; the latter, by seven merchants of Florence, in 1233.

Thus far I have explained only the constructive work, and its abundance would suggest that this age was less rebellious than the previous one. It certainly was, but not as much as my account would make one believe. In fact, I have told thus far only one part of the story. The spiritual unrest which had waxed during the twelfth century continued. And what else would one expect? The same evils which inspired in certain minds the foundation of new religious orders, caused others to revolt against the church. That was simply a different kind of reaction against the same stimulus, and as long as there are different kinds of men we must expect different types of reaction.

The most interesting heretics of this period were Amaury of Bêne and David of Dinant, who carried a step further the ideas of Scot Erigena and reached pantheistic conclusions. These views were deemed so obnoxious that every trace of them was obliterated, and we only know them through inimical accounts and the reports of various condemnations. In spite of persecution, the Amalricians continued to flourish secretly, their faith being fortified by the Joachimite ideals of the Eternal Evangel which were then percolating across the Alps.

Other heresies are also known through contemporary writings dedicated to their destruction; for example, the Anti-haereses of Eberhard of Bethune against the Waldensians, and the epic poem De triumphis ecclesie in which John of Garland exulted over the defeat of the Albigenses.

The Albigenses, so called after their main center, the town of Albi in Languedoc, were a variety of those Cathari, of whom I have already spoken. During the course of the twelfth century their numbers and power had increased so much in southern France that pope Innocent III was frightened and considered it necessary to fight them into submission. In 1208 he ordered a crusade against them, and that order was obeyed with special alacrity by Simon of Montfort and other captains, who were thus given a splendid opportunity of dispossessing in the name of religion the lawful lords of that heavenly country. This war lasted until 1229; it destroyed the power of the southern aristocracy, but it failed to destroy the heresy itself. Another means was then devised, more terrible than the war itself, the Inquisition! It was organized c. 1231, and its realization was intrusted to the fanatical zeal of the Dominicans. In 1252 Innocent IV approved the use of torture to obtain the confessions of heretics. Thus was this sinister instrument perfected. On the whole, it was not used considerably in the thirteenth century; it was not brought fully into play until the end of the fifteenth century; but we must remember that the atrocities of later times were prepared by the well-meaning popes and Dominicans of the first half of the thirteenth century.

To complete this account of religious life in western Christendom, we might say a few words of three leading Dominicans who represent three different countries and three different types. The Italian, John of Vicenza, was primarily a politician. He tried to pacify northern Italy, and his success was amazing but short lived. He might be considered one of the heralds of a unified Italy, or even one of the humble pioneers of the international peace movement. The Catalan, Raymond of Peñafort, was more of a theologian. He it was who edited the Decretals for Gregory IX; he was one of the organizers of the Inquisition, and at the same time one of the founders of the Order of our Lady of Mercy. Mercy for good Christians; as to the heretics it was more merciful to confound them! Hugh of Saint Cher, the Dauphinois, was the type of the scholar. He was one of the greatest Biblical scholars of his time in Christendom. He directed a revision of the Vulgate and the compilation of the first concordance to it. Like Raymond, he spent much of his time investigating heresies and making sure of their condemnation.

As compared with the intensity of religious life which obtained in western Christendom, the activity of Greek churchmen was exceedingly poor. But we must bear in mind that in 1204 Constantinople had been ruined and wrested out of their hands by their Latin brethren in Christ. The extent and depth of that calamity cannot be exaggerated, and the poverty of Greek life and thought from this time on is a measure of it. The only important work written by a Greek theologian of this time of national humiliation is the Treasure of orthodoxy compiled soon after the catastrophe by the historian Nicetas Acominatos. It contains valuable information on the Greek heresies.

2. *Israel*—Outside of the Qabbalists, who will be dealt with in the philosophical section, the Jewish theologians of this time were not very important. I have selected four of them as the best representatives of various tendencies; two Frenchmen (the one from the south, and the other from the north), a Bohemian and a southern Italian. The Languedocian, Abraham ben Nathan ha-Yarḥi, wrote in 1204 a guide of ritual observance, Sefer ha-manhig, which offers some ethnographic or archaeologic interest. This work was composed in Toledo, where Abraham had finally settled after years of wandering; this is curious, for most Jews were then traversing the Pyrénées in the opposite direction. The other Frenchman, Moses ben Jacob of Coucy, wrote the Sefer ha-miẓwot (or "Semag") some forty years later. Moses' work seems to have been appreciated, and a summary of it, the "Semaq," was published in 1277 by Isaac ben Joseph of Corbeil. In 1234 a Bohemian Talmudist, Abraham ben Azriel, wrote a commentary on the Maḥzor, which is the first literary fruit of Slavonic Jewry. These three men are really of little importance, and I quote them partly faute de mieux; but my fourth rabbi, Isaiah ben Mali of Trani, was of far nobler stature. He was a typical Talmudist, moderate in his views, but with little originality. However his commentaries remained authoritative in Italy for centuries, and he was compared by his admirers to Jacob ben Meir Tam, and even—God bless their loyalty—to Maimonides.

Even as a good part of Christian endeavor consisted in the denunciation and punishment of heresies or other faiths, a large and increasing part of the Jewish energy was spent in resisting persecution and in recuperation.

I have already had occasion to explain that the anti-Jewish outbreaks of the eleventh and twelfth centuries were mainly caused by the Crusading fervor, and as it turned out that the Crusades were not a paying business—neither morally nor financially (except for Venice!)—the persecutions of the Jews tended to become more vicious and more petty. A good example of the petty kind is the wearing of a yellow badge enforced upon the Jews by the Fourth Lateran Council in 1215, under Innocent III. The psychological effects of such measures, upon the oppressors as well as upon the victims, are easy to imagine. The segregation of the Jews into ghettos, voluntary at first for mutual protection, obligatory later, was almost a natural consequence of that branding;[1] and the ghetto unfortunately could not but envenom the vicious conditions from which it sprang.

Thus was continued that evil stream of consequences: persecutions begetting hatred and treachery, which in their turn begat more persecutions, and so forth. But one cannot persecute people without reason, and new reasons were needed all the time. It was hoped that a critical examination of the Jewish writings, and especially of their beloved Talmud, would prove their radical perversity and justify their treatment as outcasts. Such examination could not have been accomplished without the complicity of Jewish renegades, for there was not then a single Christian who could have wound his way unassisted through the rabbinical labyrinths. One blushes to have to admit that such renegades were found, and that they were found repeatedly whenever the need of them arose. I suppose that in the whole history of Jewish persecution, black as it is, there is nothing more painful (especially to the Jews themselves) than this recurrence of traitors and blackmailers. Judas was always waiting behind a curtain, ready for any emergency.

The most conspicuous of these renegades in the first half of the thirteenth century was the Franciscan, Nicholas Donin of La Rochelle, who denounced the Talmud to Gregory IX as the main source of Jewish antagonism to Christendom. The pope ordered the confiscation of all the Talmuds, and his order was confirmed and aggravated in 1240 by St. Louis. In the same year a public debate on the subject was arranged between Donin on one side and four rabbis on the other. A great number of Talmuds and other Hebrew books were burned in Paris in 1242.

It is interesting to report in this connection that a few years before, in 1234, copies of the works of Maimonides had also been destroyed by Christian authorities, but at the instigation of the conservative rabbis of southern France. This may help us to remember that the love of persecutions and autos-da-fé is not the monopoly of any group of men, but a very general weakness which we must always be prepared to repress.

Turning to the East we find there but one Jewish scholar worth mentioning, and one Samaritan. Tanḥum ben Joseph Yerushalmi, sometimes called the Ibn Ezra of the East, deserves to arrest our attention if only because he was the last great Jewish scholar of the Orient. He was primarily a grammarian, but he composed various Biblical commentaries in Arabic. Unfortunately the dates of his activity are very uncertain. The Samaritan, Ṣadaqa ben Munaja', was a distinguished

[1] Some ghettos may be anterior to it. It is difficult to say. It all depends upon one's definition of a ghetto. It is clear that Jewish streets may have existed for centuries in Christian communities, without being ghettos in any real sense.

court physician, but his medical activities left him time to compose a number of theological treatises. Some of these may be apocryphal, for he had obtained so much fame in Samaritan and Muslim circles that it was found expedient to attach his name to many writings.

All of the western theologians wrote in Hebrew exclusively. It is probable that they did not even know Arabic, except perhaps the two southerners, Abraham ben Nathan and Isaiah ben Mali. The two easterners wrote in Arabic. The meaning of this was that Israel was now broken in two sections, East and West, even as Christendom.

3. *Islām*—The Egyptian, Abū-l-Baqā' composed in 1221 a refutation of Christianity and Judaism which was sent by the Ayyūbid king of Egypt to the Roman emperor. This defense of Islām was republished in a slightly different form by another author more than three centuries later.

The leading theological efforts were made in the east by two Shāfi'ite doctors and one Mālikite. The Shāfi'ites were 'Umar al-Suhrawardī, a Sūfī of Baghdād, who was already dealt with in the previous chapter, but died only in 1234; and Ibn al-Ṣalāḥ, whose work on traditions was very popular.

The Mālikite, Ibn al-Ḥājib, was equally famous as a grammarian and as a theologian. He had the merit of harmonizing the teachings of Mālikite theologians of East and West, and this gave much prestige to his treatises, especially in the Maghrib.

4. *Buddhism*—The tranquil continuation of Chinese Buddhism is attested by Hui Hung's work of 1227, including a collection of Buddhist biographies and an account of the five schools, or tsung, of the Sung period.

Japanese Buddhism was still in its creative stage. Two new schools were founded during the first half of the thirteenth century, and these schools have remained to this day by far the most popular. The first of these, the Zen-shū, was founded by Eisai in 1202. It was the development of a tradition going back to Bodhidharma, a tradition of almost seven centuries stretched from southern India to Japan. No sect has influenced Buddhist thought and Buddhist art more deeply. The second, the Shin-shū, was established by Shinran in 1224. It was a reform of the Pure Land sect and it carried Amidaism to the extreme.

Thus these two great sects were almost opposites. The former was nearer to primitive Buddhism, even to the extent of being almost atheistical. The latter insisted above everything upon salvation by faith in God and by His grace. The fact that they were both immensely successful shows that these two opposite tendencies were almost equally represented in the Japanese soul. In that respect there was a striking contrast between the Japanese on one side and the Christians and Muslims on the other.

Summary

To sum up, the main religious events were the foundation of the Franciscan and Dominican Orders in the West, and of the Zen-shū and Shin-shū in the Far East. These European and Japanese events, however different, were comparable in magnitude and pregnancy. It would be equally impossible to tell the intellectual history of the West without reference to the disciples of St. Francis and St. Dominic, or that of Japan without mentioning Zen and Jōdo-shin.

The foremost persecution was that of the Albigenses, which was exceedingly cruel. Incidentally it brought southern France within the sphere of the royal government established in the north. Its most evil by-product was the creation of the Inquisition, c. 1231. The same period was cursed by many other persecutions, chiefly the branding of Israel with a yellow badge, a measure which entailed sooner or later the creation of ghettos, and the attempts to undermine the spiritual resistance of the Jews by destroying the sacred depository of their traditions, the holy Talmud.

As I have mentioned the ugliest Dominican undertaking, the Inquisition, I must also mention for the sake of fairness other and better fruits of their activity. It was one of them, Raymond of Peñafort, who edited the Decretals; and another, Hugh of Saint Cher, who revised the Vulgate and compiled a concordance to it.

From the theological point of view this was a poor age, but we must not forget that the philosophers, of whom we shall speak later on, were also, most of them, theologians. In some cases it is almost impossible to draw the line between philosophical and theological interests, and in most cases it is difficult and somewhat arbitrary.

III. THE TRANSLATORS

1. *From Arabic into Latin*—Though this period saw no giant comparable to Gerard of Cremona, many distinguished scholars still devoted the whole or part of their activity to translating Arabic treatises into Latin. For a correct appraisal of their effort, one must bear in mind that by this time the main works were already translated, and that, irrespective of genius or persistency, it would have been impossible to duplicate Gerard's amazing performance.

It is convenient to divide these translators into four groups: English and Scotch, Spanish, Italian, and Syrian.

The first of these groups was by far the most remarkable, though like the others it included only two men, the Englishman Alfred Sareshel, and the Scotchman Michael Scot. Alfred translated the De plantis ascribed to Nicolaos Damascenos, and the alchemical part of Ibn Sīnā's Shifā'. His own treatise De motu cordis was derived largely from Arabic sources. Michael's contributions were far more important; he translated al-Biṭrūjī's astronomy (1217), the zoology of Aristotle (before 1220), the De coelo et mundo and other Aristotelian texts together with Ibn Rushd's commentaries. Finally he wrote at least one treatise derived from Arabic sources. In other words Michael introduced into the Latin world three novelties of the very first order: Aristotelian zoology, Alpetragian astronomy, Averroistic philosophy. At a time when many would have felt that there was nothing left to translate, he managed to discover three works of a revolutionary nature. Of course it would have been hardly possible to translate the works of Ibn Rushd earlier. These were novelties in every sense, and for the first time the Latin world was allowed to know of a Muslim achievement while it was really fresh and alive. Indeed, we may say that thanks to Michael Scot, to the awakening of Latin intelligence, and to the increasing drowsiness of Islām, Averroism reached and influenced western philosophy at a time when the majority of Muslims were still unaware of it.

Alfred and Michael represent distinctly a new type of translators; translation is no longer the whole of their activity, but only a part of it; they are less slavish, more interested in original research. Both were trained in Spain; Michael did his best work as translator in Toledo. In that sense, they continued the glory of Gerard's school, but with a difference—a greater eagerness for knowledge itself irrespective of its source.

The internationalism of the Spanish school of translators is very remarkable. To be sure, John of Seville, Domingo of Segovia, Hugh of Santalla, Marc of Toledo, were Spaniards, but all others thus far considered were foreigners, who had been attracted to Spain as the best center of Arabic research. I may now name two more Spaniards, though of secondary importance: Stephen of Saragossa, and Peter Gallego, a Galician. Stephen translated the Kitāb i'timād, a medical treatise of Ibn al-Jazzār. Peter translated the Aristotelian zoology from an Arabic abridgment, taking advantage of Scot's earlier version, and a treatise on economy, probably the one ascribed to Galen.

The Italians were even less important than the Spaniards. Salio of Padua translated astrological treatises; the Neapolitan, William of Lunis, some of Ibn Rushd's commentaries on the Organon and a book on algebra.

Unlike the great medical translator, Stephen of Antioch (first half of the twelfth century), who was really a Pisan, Theodore of Antioch and Philip of Tripoli were apparently genuine Syrians. Theodore was said to be a Jacobite Christian; he entered the service of Frederick II, and translated for him a treatise on falconry and medical extracts from the Sirr al-asrār. Philip translated the whole of that work. The transmission of the Sirr al-asrār to the Latin world is interesting, but far less from the scientific than from the ethnologic standpoint.

2. *From Arabic into Hebrew*—The Jewish translators of the second half of the twelfth century, Joseph Qimḥi and Judah ibn Tibbon, had been interested only in Jewish works; but the situation was very different in the thirteenth century, which was the golden age of Arabic-Hebrew translations.

The translators of the first half of the thirteenth century were all of them, as we would expect, western Jews. Two were born in Spain, Judah ben Solomon al-Ḥarizi and Solomon ibn Ayyub, but the latter spent the best part of his life in Béziers. Al-Ḥarizi translated Aristotle's Ethics and Politics, two Galenic (or pseudo-Galenic) treatises, the Sayings of the philosophers, Maimonides' Moreh nebukim and his Mishnah commentary, and finally a gynaecological treatise by an older contemporary, Sheshet Benveniste (d. c. 1209). Solomon's activity belongs mainly to the second half of the century, but as early as 1240 he had translated the Book of commandments of Maimonides.

There was only one Catalan translator, who without being one of the greatest translators was certainly one of the most remarkable. Abraham ben Samuel ibn Ḥasdai, who flourished in Barcelona, translated an ethical treatise by al-Ghazzālī and two treatises by Maimonides, the story of Barlaam and Ioasaph, and two interesting works, both of which are lost in Arabic, the pseudo-Aristotelian Book of the apple (Sefer ha-tappuaḥ), and the treatise on the elements ascribed to Isḥāq al-Isrā'īlī.

The most important work was done in Provence and in Languedoc; for example, in such places as Béziers, Lunel, and Narbonne. We have already seen that the Spaniard, Solomon ibn Ayyub, did most of his work in Béziers. Abraham ben Nathan ha-Yarḥi (i.e., of Lunel) translated a responsum by Saadia Gaon (or at any rate included such translation in his Manhig). This is not very significant, but we now come to two of the greatest translators of mediaeval times, Samuel ibn Tibbon and Jacob Anaṭoli.

Samuel came from Lunel but he flourished also in Béziers, in Provence, Catalonia, and Spain. His greatest translation, that of the Moreh nebukim, was completed at Arles in 1204. He had been able to avail himself of Maimonides' own advice while preparing it. It was certainly one of the most influential translations ever made. Samuel translated other treatises by Maimonides, and by Ibn Rushd, Aristotle's Meteorology (1213), and 'Alī ibn Riḍwān's commentary on Galen's Tegni (1199).

The illustrious Ibn Tibbon family increased its fame by taking into itself Jacob Anaṭoli;—he married Samuel's daughter. Jacob was born probably in Marseilles, but he flourished in Languedoc and later at the court of Frederick II. He was even a greater translator than his father-in-law. Even as Samuel was the main introducer of the Moreh nebukim to the Hebrew-speaking world, Jacob was the first translator of Ibn Rushd's commentaries (1232). That is, he rendered to the Jews the same service as his colleague at the Neapolitan court, Michael Scot, rendered to the Christians. But he did not limit himself to that; he also translated Ptolemy's Almagest (c. 1233), Ibn Rushd's summary of it (lost in Arabic), and al-Farghānī's astronomy.

The simultaneous and parallel activities of Anaṭoli and Scot form the best illustration of the double channel through which the Greco-Arabic culture penetrated Western Europe. Both introduced Averroism at the same time, one in Latin, the other in Hebrew. It is certain that they knew one another, but it is impossible to appreciate the extent of their collaboration. There is no way of substantiating the story according to which they prepared together a Latin version of the Moreh nebukim.

One thing is sure—and it is full of significance—Jacob was as familiar with the Latin language as with the Arabic, and his translation of al-Farghānī was made on the basis of both the Latin and the Arabic texts. This is symptomatic of a new age. Not only do the Western Jews lose their Arabic, they are beginning to know Latin. The consequences of this change of orientation need not be emphasized. It illustrates more vividly than anything else the rise of Latin prestige.

3. *From Persian into Arabic*—The Persian historian, al-Bundārī, translated Firdawsī's Shāhnāma into Arabic c. 1222. I mention this to show the prestige which the Arabic language continued to enjoy in Persian lands, even in lay matters. I suppose a Persian was proud to be able to exhibit the national epic of his people to the "Arabs," and such a translation afforded Persian gentlemen a pleasant means of obtaining more familiarity with the learned language imposed upon them by their faith.

4. *From Greek into Latin*—The fine series of direct translations from Greek into Latin, which was one of the more distinguished achievements of western Christendom in the second half of the twelfth century, was almost completely interrupted for more than half a century. This is the more surprising in that the establishment of the Latin Empire (1204–1261) seemed to open a splendid opportunity for such investigations. Even as the conquest of Toledo by the Christians (1085) had made that city the main center of Arabic studies in the West, even so we might have expected the fall of Constantinople to have initiated a revival of Greek studies. The fact that no such revival happened is an excellent proof of the intellectual baseness of that Latin interregnum. Was this due to Nemesis? For indeed no conquest could have been more contemptible than that of the great Christian metropolis of the East by western Crusaders whose boast it was to deliver Christendom from the infidels. They had failed to redeem Jerusalem, which remained in Muslim hands except for two short periods (1229–1239, 1243–1244); but they almost succeeded in destroying the second Rome.

About the efficacy of their destructive power there can be no doubt. Our school histories insist upon the terrible consequences of the capture of Constantinople by the Turks in 1453; but the truth is that its capture by the Crusaders in 1204 was far more disastrous to Greek culture. Quantities of works of art and manuscripts did then disappear, and most of them did not reappear in other places; they were lost for ever. And this was not yet the worst, for the Crusaders did not simply destroy the glorious remains of a culture which they could not understand, but the blow which they delivered to the culture which was still alive was so staggering that it could never recover from it.

It is not that the Crusaders did not realize the superiority of Byzantine civilization; some of them did realize it, but they hated their eastern brothers the more because of it; the riches of Constantinople awakened no feeling in them except greed. How can one say that the Crusades were an undertaking of love? Hatred was far more conspicuous; hatred, jealousy, greed, and lust.

The fall of Constantinople did not promote Greek studies, except indirectly. For example, Athens had now become a Frank seigniory. A young Englishman, John Basingstoke, was able to go and study there and thus obtain a first-hand knowledge of Greek. He brought back Greek MSS. to England, and translated a grammar, the Donatus Graecorum. The only other Hellenist of the period was, strange to say, also an Englishman and, as we shall have occasion to see later, one of the greatest—Robert Grosseteste. About 1241 he produced the first complete Latin translation of the Nicomachean Ethics, together with the commentaries of Eustratios of Nicaea and Michael of Ephesus; he also wrote a summary of it, and translated various other works (or extracts) by Aristotle, Dionysios Areopagita, John of Damascus and Suidas. Grosseteste and Basingstoke were friends; thus we may assume that the former's Hellenism was, partly at least, a distant consequence of the Latin conquest of Constantinople.

On the other hand, the Crusaders destroyed many MSS., and the remains of ancient Greek literature were certainly less considerable after 1204 than before.[2]

Summary

Let us now consider which Greek and Arabic works became available in the West during the first half of the thirteenth century.

We shall naturally begin with Aristotle. The De coelo et mundo and probably the De anima were translated into Latin by Michael Scot; the Zoology by the same (before 1220), and a little later by Peter Gallego; the Ethics, by Robert Grosseteste, c. 1241. The Ethics and Politics were translated into Hebrew by al-Ḥarizi, and the Meteorology, by Samuel ibn Tibbon. All these translations were derived from the Arabic except Grosseteste's which was made from the original Greek. The Meteorology had been available before in Latin; about the middle of the thirteenth century it was translated from Latin into French by Matthieu le Vilain.

The increase in Aristotelian knowledge was thus considerable as well in Israel as in Christendom. We have indirect proofs of it in the anti-Aristotelian reaction which began to manifest itself in Paris in 1210, and waxed rapidly.

Passing to other Greek works, the De plantis of Nicholaos Damascenos was translated into Latin by Alfred Sareshel; a treatise on economics, by Peter Gallego; a Greek grammar, by John Basingstoke. This is very little indeed. The trans-

[2] M. R. James: The wanderings and homes of manuscripts (14, London 1919).

lations into Hebrew were more important. The Almagest and Ibn Rushd's summary of it were translated by Jacob Anaṭoli (c. 1233); pseudo-Galenic treatises by al-Ḥarizi; the story of Barlaam and Ioasaph, by Ibn Ḥasdai. The translation of the Almagest was important only from the Jewish point of view, for that great work had been given to the Latin world more than half a century earlier (1160, 1175).

Before considering the Arabic works credited to known authors, let us deal with a few anonymous ones. The Sirr al-asrār was translated into Latin, partly by Theodore of Antioch, completely by Philip of Tripoli; an Arabic algebra was translated by William of Lunis; a treatise on falconry, by Theodore of Antioch. The book of the apple has come down to us in the Hebrew version of Ibn Ḥasdai.

A medical treatise of Ibn al-Jazzār was translated into Latin by Stephen of Saragossa, and the alchemical part of Ibn Sīnā's Shifā', by Alfred Sareshel. The Hebrew translations include al-Farghānī's astronomy by Jacob Anaṭoli; 'Alī ibn Riḍwān's commentary on the Tegni, by Samuel ibn Tibbon; Isḥāq al-Isrā'īlī's treatise on the elements and an ethical treatise of al-Ghazzālī both by Ibn Ḥasdai. In this case the Hebrew translations are more valuable, and this is especially true because two of those texts, the Sefer ha-tappuaḥ and Isḥāq's treatise on the elements, are lost in the Arabic original.

We are now coming to the most important texts, not even excluding the Aristotelian ones with which they were intimately connected. I mean the treatises of al-Biṭrūjī, Ibn Rushd, and Maimonides. It is highly significant that all of these texts were new at the beginning of the thirteenth century. For the first time the most important texts to be translated were the latest. Al-Biṭrūjī's astronomy was published in Latin by Michael Scot in 1217. Ibn Rushd's commentaries were translated into Latin by Scot and by William of Lunis, and into Hebrew by Jacob Anaṭoli and Samuel ibn Tibbon. Maimonides' Moreh nebukim was translated into Hebrew by Samuel ibn Tibbon (1204) and by al-Ḥarizi; the Mishnah commentary, by al-Ḥarizi; the Sefer ha-miẓwot, by Solomon ibn Ayyub (1240); other treatises, by Samuel ibn Tibbon and Ibn Ḥasdai. These Hebrew translations were especially important because they superseded the original Arabic texts which fell almost into oblivion except in the East.

Finally I may recall for the sake of curiosity that, c. 1222, Firdawsī's Shāhnāma was translated from Persian into Arabic by al-Bundārī.

IV. EDUCATION

1. *Christendom*—The universities born in the preceding century continued their vigorous growth, and many new ones were established. The period of unconscious development was now almost over. Universities had become something tangible and definite, of which the possibilities were not only recognized but eagerly capitalized by Church and State. Their further growth was thus conditioned not only by genuine educational needs but by theological and political aspirations.

Among the new universities of the first half of the thirteenth century, the most important were Padua, a daughter of Bologna, born in 1222; Naples, deliberately established by Frederick II in 1224; the law schools of Orleans and Angers; Cambridge, issued from Oxford in 1209; and Salamanca, which survived a delicate infancy to become the leading intellectual center of Spain. The international aspect of this movement is one of its most remarkable features. Not only did new universities appear in four countries (Italy, France, England, Spain), but the circumstances of their birth or growth often involved the international authority of the Pope. Finally, students and teachers moved from one university to another with surprising ease. This continual va-et-vient across the frontiers will be so frequently illustrated in the course of my study that it is unnecessary to insist upon it at this moment.

2. *Israel*—A valuable account of the ordinary course of studies in the Jewish schools of Spain has been given by Judah ibn 'Abbas in his ethical work entitled Shebeṭ Yehudah. This helps us to understand the superiority of the Spanish Jews. They received a very solid instruction, including scientific training; their moral education was attended to with special care; they were well disciplined; and learned many languages as a matter of course. If they were gifted with intelligence, it is clear that such rich equipment gave them a tremendous advantage over their Christian contemporaries.

3. *China*—The great organizer of Mongol education was a Tartar called Yeh-lü Ch'u-ts'ai. Yeh-lü was well acquainted with Chinese traditions and apparently also with Chinese science. He served under the Mongol rulers, Chingiz Khān and Ogotāy, and was in the same relation to them as Alcuin was to Charlemagne. During Chingiz's campaign against Persia in 1219, in which he took part, whenever herbs, books and instruments were found in the booty they were kept for him. In 1233 he established literary colleges at Yen-ching, near Peking, and at P'ing-yang, in Shansi.

4. *Japan*—In 1241 a school was attached to the shōgunal government for the training of the officers' children. The education was essentially Chinese, but much attention was paid to physical exercises and to games.

V. PHILOSOPHIC AND CULTURAL BACKGROUND

1. *Frederick II*—It is neither possible nor expedient in this survey to enlarge upon the political background, but the reader may be helped if I remind him that this was the age of John and Henry III in England; of Philip Augustus, Louis VIII, St. Louis, and Blanche of Castile in France, and that Innocent III, Honorius III, Gregory IX and Innocent IV succeeded one another in St. Peter's seat. I have already spoken of the situation in the eastern empire; Baldwin, count of Flanders, became emperor of Constantinople in 1204 and was followed within half a century by a whole series of other rulers and regents.

However, there are two potentates whose cultural influence was at once so singular and so great that we must pause a little longer to consider them: Chingiz Khān and Frederick II Hohenstaufen. We shall deal with the former at the end of this section. As to Frederick, one could not choose a better symbol of that new European civilization which was to be the synthesis of so many different streams: Greek and Latin, Jewish, Christian, and Muslim. Indeed all of these streams were combined in his own strange personality. Like the Spanish hero, el Cid el Campeador, he was half Muslim in his ways. His court became the leading intellectual center of Europe; thanks to the co-operation of such men as Michael Scot and Jacob Anaṭoli it superseded Toledo and was for a while the foremost clearing house for cultural exchanges of all kinds. In 1224 he created a new university at Naples to offset Bologna, that Guelph nursery. He promoted the diffusion of Averroism. He was not simply a patron; the genuineness of his philosophical and scientific curiosity is sufficiently proved by the questions he submitted to Michael Scot and Ibn Sab'īn, by his contempt of superstition, and above all by his own scientific activity.

Frederick was one of the most romantic figures of European history. Unfortunately, he was so far ahead of his people (and not always in the right direction), so little in touch with the more urgent necessities of his time, so erratic, that his influence was considerably smaller than it might have been. To be sure, Averroism developed, but that was bound to happen sooner or later even without his patronage; nor were Scot's and Anaṭoli's translations the only ones.

2. *English Philosophers*—We have seen that the most distinguished group of Christian philosophers in the second half of the twelfth century was the English. That supremacy was not only continued but much enhanced in the first half of the thirteenth century. The two leading philosophers of Christendom were Michael Scot and Robert Grosseteste, and both were English. That is, from the continental point of view; Grosseteste came from Suffolk, and Scot was a Scotchman.

To be sure, Scot's main activity took place in Spain and Italy, but that does not alter the fact of his origin. His main title to fame is that he was the father of Christian Averroism.

The encyclopaedist, Alexander Neckam, dealt with in the previous chapter, lived until 1217. John of London was one of the first exponents of the new Aristotelian knowledge in Oxford. However, the glory of the English philosophy of that time was almost entirely due to the Franciscans, four of whom were men of great distinction: Alexander of Hales, Adam Marsh, Robert Grosseteste[2a], and Bartholomew the Englishman. They were not equally distinguished. Alexander's Summa was despised by Bacon, yet Alexander was the first incumbent of the Franciscan chair of theology in Paris, and he was one of the very first in the West to attempt a synthesis of the new Aristotelian, Muslim, and Jewish philosophy available in Latin. Adam Marsh was the real founder of the Franciscan school of Oxford; he was one of those men whose fame is greater than their writings would justify, because writing is only a part, and not the best, of their activity. The greatest of the four was Robert Grosseteste, bishop of Lincoln, in many ways Bacon's forerunner, one of the most original thinkers of mediaeval times, a man endowed with imagination and with courage. He insisted upon the importance of linguistic and mathematical studies, upon the fundamental value of experimentation. His many works include commentaries on the Posterior Analytics and the Physics.

The fourth Franciscan was of a much humbler type, yet by far the most popular. He composed for the plain people an encyclopaedia, De proprietatibus rerum, which remained one of the favorite books of Europe for three centuries (none of our own "best sellers" will last as long!). Bartholomew's encyclopaedia was not on a very high level, nor was it generally up-to-date (much of it was distinctly out-of-date), but it was for a considerable time the main source of scientific knowledge of most laymen.

3. *French Philosophers and Writers*—All of the English wrote in Latin, but some of the French had the idea of using their own language, which was then the leading vernacular of Europe. Thus we shall divide the latter into two groups, the Latin-French and the pure French; the distinction, as we shall see, is not simply linguistic; it goes much deeper.

Two men belong to the first group, William of Auvergne and John of La Rochelle. Both of them flourished in Paris, and both were engaged in the same undertaking

[2a] Grosseteste did not assume the Franciscan habit but he was intimately associated with the Franciscan school of Oxford; he was their first lecturer in 1224.

as Alexander of Hales, that is, in the assimilation of the new knowledge made available by the Latin translators. But they did it in very different ways. To put it briefly, John's point of view was Augustinian and neo-Platonic, while William was almost a Thomist. Even as Robert Grosseteste was a forerunner of Bacon, William of Auvergne anticipated to some extent St. Thomas Aquinas. Their different points of view are partly explained by their different circumstances. William was a secular priest who became bishop of Paris; John was a Franciscan who succeeded Alexander of Hales, c. 1238, in the chair of theology. While the English Franciscans were preparing the advent of a Roger Bacon, the French were gradually making possible the teachings of St. Bonaventure.

As we would expect, the purpose and the tone of the French writings were as different as could be from the Latin. For the treatises written by William of Auvergne and John of La Rochelle, Latin was by far the most natural language; I assume that William and John would have been hardly able to discuss their own views in French, and Latin is not yet obsolete even to-day for similar publications. The writings now to be considered were popular, and it was equally natural to compose them in French. I imagine that a man like Bartholomew the Englishman would have been induced for similar reasons to write in English, if the glorious tradition begun by Alfred the Great had not been brutally interrupted by the Norman Conquest. At any rate three important works of this time were written in French with the view of reaching a larger public than that of the clerks. The earliest, the Bible of Guiot of Provins (c. 1205), a satirical poem, which is a good mirror of contemporary life and thought. Then the Romance of Sidrach (c. 1243?), a sort of encyclopaedia in the form of a catechism, which obtained considerable success in spite (or because) of its extreme puerility. Its origin is obscure; it is not even known whether the French text is original or a translation. Finally, Walter of Metz composed, c. 1246, another popular encyclopaedia in French verse entitled L'image du monde. Two other editions of the same work (the one in verse, the other in prose) appeared before the middle of the century. The Image du monde was far superior to the Romance of Sidrach in every respect; its popularity was not restricted to the French laity, for it was translated into Hebrew and into English.

Before proceeding to other countries it is well to point out the great importance taken by the University of Paris, not only for a French audience but for an international one. The influence of Paris, however, was not necessarily or exclusively French; it was itself of an international nature, for many foreigners came there to teach as well as to study.

4. *Italian Philosophers*—There is but little to be said about Italians, though the energy of Frederick II had transformed his court in southern Italy into one of the main intellectual focuses of the time. If we spoke of the University of Paris as an international institution, how much more true would this not be of the imperial court? For after all, the internationalism of Paris (and of other universities) was restricted within the confines of Latin Christendom, and Christian science and philosophy had not yet come of age. Frederick surrounded himself not only with Christians, but with Jews and Muslims; he had Arabic and Greek secretaries as well as Latin ones, and there is no evidence that Italians were in any way privileged. Scot was a Scotchman, Anaṭoli a Provençal. The only Italian known by name was William of Lunis; it is possible but not certain that he belonged to Frederick's entourage. This William, it will be remembered, translated Ibn Rushd's commentaries on the Organon.

The only other Italian who belongs a little to this period is St. Bonaventure, who was already teaching philosophy in Paris in 1248, succeeding John of La Rochelle. As to St. Thomas, he was only twenty-five years old in 1250.

5. *German Philosophers*—German thought is represented by two popular encyclopaedists, Arnold the Saxon, and Thomas of Cantimpré. Arnold's encyclopaedia, De finibus rerum naturalium, was smaller and less important. Thomas' work, De natura rerum, was comparable to that of Bartholomew the Englishman, though exceedingly different. The publication of these two compilations at almost the same time, and independently, the one by an English Franciscan, the other by a German Dominican, is very interesting. It clearly proves that the time was calling for such compilations, but it is unfortunate that these two works which emerged from among many others as the most important and the most popular, and which were consulted for centuries as we ourselves consult our own encyclopaedias, were already hopelessly out-of-date when they appeared. They represented not the new knowledge which had been pouring in in increasing quantities for more than a century, but the earlier mediaeval—the good old—knowledge, which they helped to perpetuate in the face of dangerous novelties. The hold which such antiquated books kept on an overwhelming majority of readers helps us to understand the unprogressiveness of mediaeval thought. There were progressive thinkers then, even as now, but it was infinitely more difficult for them to obtain a hearing, and their views were more completely submerged by the accepted and comfortable ones than can ever be the case to-day.

Another Dominican, Albert the Great, was active long before the middle of the century, but as his main activity occurred later, we shall deal with him in the following chapter. Yet it is well to bear in mind that his immense knowledge was growing throughout this period. It is well to remember his presence in the background, as of one who waits. A giant who slowly prepares himself to enter into the arena.

6. *Scandinavian Knowledge*—The encyclopaedic spirit was felt even in the northern countries; witness the Konungs skuggsjá, which was written in old Norwegian about the middle of the century. Of all the contemporary encyclopaedias this is perhaps the most original; besides the information borrowed in the usual style from earlier works, it also contains a surprising number of facts, which must have been drawn from the author's own experience or from unknown Scandinavian sources, for they are certainly not derived from the literature with which we are familiar. Moreover, many of these facts are peculiar to the northern climates.

It is interesting that the only vernaculars used for philosophic or encyclopaedic purposes were French and Norwegian.

7. *Western Muslim*—To appreciate the efforts made in the western part of Islām, one must remember that by this time the Muslim hold on Spain had been enormously reduced. James I of Aragon annexed the Baleares in 1232, and Valencia in 1238; Frederick III of Castile conquered Cordova in 1236, Murcia in 1243, Jaen in 1246, Seville in 1248. Before the middle of the century, the Moors, who had once ruled over the whole peninsula except the northwestern and northeastern corners, were restricted to the little kingdom of Granada. To be sure, the Magrib remained in Muslim hands, but Spain had always been the fountain head of western Islām. Thus it is not very surprising that the glorious days of Ibn Ṭufail and Ibn Rushd were not repeated.

Before speaking of the Spaniards, let us dispose rapidly of an Algerian, al-Būnī, who enjoyed (and continues to enjoy to this day) a great reputation as an occultist.

His writings are one of the best sources for the study of the darker sides of Muslim thought.

Three distinguished men hailed from eastern Spain: Ibn Ṭumlūs, from Alcira; Ibn 'Arabī and Ibn Sab'īn, from Murcia. Ibn Ṭumlūs wrote a logical treatise. Ibn 'Arabī was the main representative of the Ishrāqī school of philosophy, a mystical school which had originated in Cordova in the first half of the tenth century. In addition to their value for the history of neo-Platonism and of the later Augustinianism, his writings are interesting because they contain curious anticipations of the Divina Commedia. His love poems may have inspired indirectly the "dolce stil nuovo" of the Convito. Ibn Sab'īn was also a mystic, and a new ṣūfī sect was even named after him, but he is chiefly known because of his answers to the so-called Sicilian questions, asked by Frederick II (c.1240). Both Ibn 'Arabī and Ibn Sab'īn died in the East. The former's recollections would suggest that even in its last days Muslim Spain was intellectually superior to Syria, but we must make allowance for the author's nostalgia and for his deep loyalty to his old teachers. Moreover, he had been young in Spain, and in the East he was old.

8. *Eastern Muslim*—At any rate the state of affairs revealed by my investigations does not confirm Ibn 'Arabī's contempt of the East. But it may be that what shocked him was rather the luxury, laziness, and the moral laxity of the Syrians. Five Easterners deserve mention in this section; it is true, only one or two of them belonged to the Near East; the others came from the Tigris valley or from Transoxiana.

Of al-Zarnūjī we know practically nothing, except that he was the author (c. 1203) of a philosophical primer which enjoyed some popularity, especially in Turkish lands. Al-Āmidī, who died at Bukhārā in 1218, wrote a treatise on the microcosmos and macrocosmos said to be an adaptation of an unidentified Sanskrit work. He also composed a treatise on dialectics, which was used considerably.

Two of these Easterners, the Baghdādite 'Abd al-Laṭīf, and Kamāl al-dīn Ibn Yūnus of Mūṣul, were encyclopaedists. At one time they worked together in Mūṣul. Both wrote abundantly on many subjects. 'Abd al-Laṭīf flourished a long time in Egypt, and his main work is an account of that country containing many original observations. None of Kamāl al-dīn's writings calls for special mention here, but it is interesting to note that, even as his Moorish contemporary, Ibn Sab'īn, he was asked to answer some questions propounded by the emperor Frederick II. This shows that the latter was really trying to obtain information from independent sources. Kamāl al-dīn attained considerable prestige as a learned man and teacher, and a college was named after him in Mūṣul.

At this time the greatest ṣūfī poet writing in Arabic, Ibn al-Fāriḍ, was flourishing in Cairo.

9. *Persian*—Two of the Eastern Muslims deserve separate treatment because they were bold enough to write in Persian. This may be compared to the use of the French vernacular by a few of the Christians, instead of Latin. The purpose was similar in both cases. Of course every Persian having any pretension to learning knew Arabic, but these formed only a part of the Persian audience; it is possible that even then many educated Persians (not only women of course, but also men) were unable to read much Arabic outside of the Holy Qur'ān. One can conceive that some Persians were tempted to write in their national language for the larger audience, in spite of the fact that by so doing they risked being considered a little vulgar.

I spoke a moment ago of the poet, Ibn al-Fāriḍ, who wrote in Arabic. The greatest ṣūfī poets, however, wrote in Persian. A magnificent renaissance of Persian poetry occurred in the second half of the thirteenth century; it was heralded by Fāriḍ al-dīn 'Aṭṭār, who hailed, like 'Umar al-Khayyāmī, from Nīshāpūr. Though less famous than his successors, Jalāl al-dīn Rūmī and Sa'dī, Fāriḍ al-dīn was a poet of considerable power. His main work, memoirs of the ṣūfī saints, was written in prose. His best known poem is the Manṭiq al-ṭayr (Reasoning of the birds), a mystical allegory.

Another Persian writer, Muḥammad al-'Awfī, compiled a history of the Persian poets (some three hundred of them being quoted!), and a vast collection of anecdotes.

10. *Syriac*—As I have done before, I am using here the adjective "Syriac" with reference to language, in opposition to "Syrian" relative to nationality or race. Most Syrians, even those who were Christians, wrote in Arabic; but a few of the latter remained loyal to their old ecclesiastical language, Syriac. Small as it was, that Syriac community was very soon divided against itself on theological grounds. There were at least three hostile groups, the Orthodox, the Nestorians (vol. 1, 381), and the Monophysites (who claimed that there is but a single nature in Christ, at once human and divine). However, after the fifth century, there remained only two important Syriac groups, the Nestorian and the Monophysite, the Orthodox being represented only by the Maronites and Melkhites, who continued to use their language for liturgical purposes, but otherwise identified themselves more or less, the former with the Roman Church, the latter with the Greek Church.

Thus the mediaeval Syriac literature to be considered in my survey is either Nestorian or Monophysite. For example, there were two outstanding writers in the first half of the thirteenth century, Solomon of al-Baṣra and Jacob bar Shakkō. Solomon was a Nestorian; Jacob a Jacobite (Monophysite). The former, who came from Lake Vān, compiled a collection of stories entitled the Book of the bee. The second, who was born near Mūṣul, wrote a popular encyclopaedia called the Dialogues, and a theological treatise, the Book of treasures. These similar efforts to popularize knowledge, made simultaneously by Solomon and Jacob, did not duplicate each other, because they were made for two sets of readers, which however near, were absolutely distinct.

To emphasize the distinctness of these two publics, I may add that it is very easy to distinguish Nestorian texts from the Jacobite, even at first sight, because, though the language is essentially the same, the script is different. Remember what I said of the religious importance of script vs. language in volume I (152, 333). The oldest Syriac texts were written in the script called esṭrangelā (i.e., στρογγύλη, roundish). About the eighth and ninth century that script was developed independently by the Western Syrians and the Eastern ones. The Eastern or Nestorian script remained closer to the ancient esṭrangelā; the Western or Jacobite script, called serṭō, was more divergent. The differences between the vocalized texts were even greater, for the Nestorians developed under Arabic influence a system of vowel points, while the Jacobites, influenced by their Greek neighbors, used little symbols derived from the Greek vowels.

11. *Hispano-Jewish*—Most of the Jewish philosophers of this time came from Spain, Catalonia, or southern France. They were of two very different types: the Maimonideans or Averroists and the Qabbalists; or more simply, the rationalists and the mystics.

The former group was by far the most important. It included such men as Joseph ibn 'Aqnīn, Maimonides' favorite disciple, who went east and died in Aleppo as late as 1226. Or as Judah ben Solomon ha-Kohen of Toledo, who was in scientific correspondence with "the philosopher of Frederick II." Joseph ibn 'Aqnīn, who spent his years of maturity in Egypt and Syria, wrote naturally in Arabic. Judah ben Solomon symbolizes the transition; he began the compilation of an encyclopaedic treatise in Arabic, but completed it in Hebrew or translated it into that language (Midrash ha-ḥokmah).

All the other Jews wrote in Hebrew. There is first of all the great theologian and grammarian, David Qimḥi; I dealt with him in the previous book but he must be named again here for he died only in 1235, at Narbonne. Towards the end of his life the communities of Lunel and Narbonne sent him to Spain to explain the Maimonidean philosophy. Then there is the whole group of translators from Arabic into Hebrew, of whom we have already spoken as translators: the poet, al-Ḥarizi, who composed the Taḥkemoni upon the model of al-Ḥarīrī's Maqāmāt; Abraham ibn Ḥasdai, Solomon ibn Ayyub, Samuel ibn Tibbon, Jacob Anaṭoli. It is not necessary to speak again of all of their translations, except of two which cannot be mentioned too often, Samuel's translation of the Dalālat al-ḥā'irīn (Arles, 1204) and Jacob's translation of Ibn Rushd's commentaries (Naples, 1232). It is these translations more than any others which introduced Maimonides and Ibn Rushd to the western Jews. Thus their dates of publication, 1204 and 1232, may be used to date the beginnings, respectively, of Maimonidism and Averroism in the Hebrew-speaking world.

Before passing to the Qabbalists, brief mention must be made of Judah ibn 'Abbas, whose Shebeṭ Yehudah is a valuable document for the understanding of the intellectual achievements of the Spanish Jews.

And now the Qabbalists! I have already spoken of them before, and though the Qabbalah was not completely organized until the end of the century, one might easily detect such tendencies at almost any period of Jewish evolution. They belong to the Jewish soul, even as Ṣūfism to the Muslim. We might simply say that Qabbalism is the extreme form of Jewish mysticism.

It is natural enough that the very progress of rationalism would stimulate a recrudescence of mysticism. The Catalan, Azriel ben Menahem, who is sometimes called the founder of the Qabbalah, elaborated the theory of emanation (already outlined in the Yeẓirah and the Bahir) as a means of reconciling the Aristotelian notion of the eternity of the world with the Biblical dogma of creation. This theory of emanation was refined by other philosophers and dreamers, sometimes to a fantastic extent, and became one of the central theories of the Qabbalah. I do not propose to describe its endless ramifications, but the student of Jewish thought must always bear in mind that background of Qabbalistic ideas and visions, for no Jewish philosopher escaped altogether their influence. Isaac the Blind, who had been Azriel's tutor, found another distinguished pupil in his own nephew, Asher ben David. A third contemporary Qabbalist was Isaac ibn Laṭīf of Toledo. This Isaac was one of the first of a good many tortured spirits who tried to harmonize Qabbalistic vagaries with scientific knowledge. Indeed the belief in the Qabbalah originated a new kind of pseudo-problems, and a new kind of scholasticism, which was worse than the former, in proportion as the Qabbalah was more artificial than the Torah. These three Qabbalists represented respectively Catalonia, Languedoc, and Spain, three countries among which there was then constant intercourse, especially in so far as their Jewish populations were concerned.

12. *Germano-Jewish*—The best proof that in spite of its artificiality the Qabbalah answered a genuine need of the Jewish soul, is that it appeared also at about the same time in Germany. The German form of Qabbalah was very different from the Spanish; it was more directly connected with early Jewish (Babylonian) mysticism, and largely independent of foreign (Greek and Arabic) influences. This is of course what we would expect, for the German Jews were as remote from these influences as their Spanish brethren were exposed to them. The leaders of these German mystics were Judah ha-Ḥasid of Ratisbon, and his disciple, Eleazar of Worms. Whether Judah was the author or not of the Sefer ha-ḥasidim, and whoever was the real author, it is a good mirror of Jewish culture. Eleazar's main Qabbalistic work was his Book of the perfumer (Sefer ha-roqeaḥ). Both Judah and Eleazar were primarily interested in morality.

13. *Samaritan*—When one remembers that Maimonides died at Cairo in 1204, the almost complete interruption of Eastern Jewish philosophy is very remarkable. In fact the only Jewish philosopher deserving mention was Maimonides' pupil, Joseph ibn 'Aqnīn; but Joseph was not an Egyptian, but a Spaniard, and has already been dealt with as such.

Besides this Joseph, I can only name the Samaritan, Ṣadaqa ben Munaja'. Ṣadaqa was primarily a physician, but he wrote (in Arabic of course) a number of philosophical and theological treatises, and many more were ascribed to him.

14. *Mongol and Chinese*—The great conqueror, Chingiz Khān, deserves to be remembered in this survey on the same grounds as many other rulers who were not simply generals and statesmen but cultural promoters of the very first order, such as Alexander, Justinian, T'ai Tsung, Charlemagne, Hārūn al-Rashīd, al-Ma'mūn, 'Abd al-Raḥmān III of Cordova. The Tatar, Chingiz, has every right to be included in that small company. The fact that he was the organizer of a stupendous empire extending from Korea to Asia Minor (and later to Russia and Hungary) does not impress us. But it was largely thanks to his energy and vision that the conquering Mongols attempted to raise themselves to the cultural level of their victims. We may speak of a Mongol civilization originated by Chingiz Khān, which was essentially a combination of elements derived from China, Central Asia, and Islām, and adapted to their own needs. He showed much toleration of foreign faiths.

The mathematician, Ts'ai Ch'ên, a disciple of Chu Hsi, wrote a commentary on the Shu Ching, which has itself become a classic. Another work of his deals with number mysticism.

Summary

As compared with the second half of the twelfth century this was a period of retrogression, but it is fair to remember that the extraordinary climax due to the genius of Ibn Rushd and Maimonides was bound to be followed by an anti-climax. The leading philosophers of this period were two Christians, Robert Grosseteste and Michael Scot, and strangely enough both hailed from that remote island in the Far West, Great Britain. No Jew could compare with them, not even Jacob Anaṭoli, who was almost exclusively a translator. The most original of the Muslims was perhaps 'Abd al-Laṭīf, but we might name also the foremost representative of the Ishrāqī school, Ibn 'Arabī; and the two great Ṣūfī poets, Ibn al-Fāriḍ, who wrote in Arabic, and Fāriḍ al-dīn 'Aṭṭār, who wrote in Persian.

VI. MATHEMATICS AND ASTRONOMY

1. *Latin and Vernacular*—From our special point of view, nothing was more hopeful than the presence among the philosophers of this time of such a man as Robert Grosseteste. It indicated that a radical improvement of intellectual method was being prepared, nay, had already begun. It meant that Western Christendom was finally groping its way in the right direction.

That promise and that hope were abundantly confirmed by the activities of two great mathematicians: Fibonacci and Jordanus Nemorarius. Fibonacci had been brought up in Bugia, on the Barbary Coast, and had received some Arabic training. He was thus influenced by Muslim examples, but he was an original mathematician; his was a truly creative mind, and he took full advantage of the Greek and Muslim knowledge available to him, in an independent manner. His first and main work, the Liber abaci, appeared in 1202, and that date may be considered the birthdate of European mathematics. The Liber abaci contains many novelties, e.g., the earliest example of the so-called series of Lamé, and new theorems on prime numbers; also the first complete explanation in Latin of the Hindu numerals and their use. In 1220 he wrote a treatise on geometry, Practica geometriae, in which algebra was applied to the solution of geometrical problems. Five years later he published two smaller works, the Flos and Liber quadratorum, wherein the originality of his mind was even more conspicuous. The Flos was chiefly devoted to Diophantine analysis, but perhaps the most striking novelty in it, humble as it may seem, was the interpretation of a negative solution as a debt. The Liber quadratorum dealt with similar problems and with the theory of numbers.

Jordanus Nemorarius was more important as a mechanician than as a pure mathematician; yet his mathematical contributions were considerable. He wrote two arithmetical treatises which were very different from Fibonacci's in that they were independent of Muslim influence and simply continued the ancient tradition of Nicomachos and Boetius. He used letters instead of numerals for the sake of generality; Fibonacci did this at least in one case, but Nemorarius did it constantly. He discovered some new propositions in the theory of numbers. He also composed one algebraical and two geometrical treatises. One of these, the Planisphaerium, dealing with mathematical astronomy, included the first general proof of the fundamental property of stereographic projection (circles remain circles).

A contemporary arithmetical treatise, the Algorismus demonstratus, has sometimes been ascribed to Nemorarius; it belongs probably to his school, but we cannot be sure that it was composed in the first half of the thirteenth century; it may be somewhat later. The author was probably one Magister Gernardus about whom we know nothing. The Algorismus demonstratus is essentially Boetian, like Nemorarius' treatises; it is divided into two parts treating respectively of integers and fractions. It contained no important novelties but deserves mention because of its great popularity.

The reality of a mathematical revival in the Christian West is proved beyond doubt by the contemporary activities of many smaller men. The existence of two mathematicians of genius, like Fibonacci and Nemorarius, is not in itself a sufficient proof, for genius is too accidental. We feel strongly that, while mathematical standards can be determined by various circumstances, the occurrence of mathematical genius remains a sort of miracle.

Among these smaller mathematicians two are exceptionally conspicuous, not because of any great merit of their own, but because of their immense popularity which lasted centuries: Alexander of Villedieu, and John of Halifax (Sacrobosco). Villedieu was the author of an arithmetical poem (Carmen de algorismo), explaining the Hindu-Arabic methods, which was widely read in the original and also in English, French, and Icelandic versions. Sacrobosco wrote elementary treatises on astronomy, arithmetic, and the calendar. The first of these, his Sphaera, was perhaps the most popular, witness the number of manuscripts, editions, commentaries, and translations into many languages, including Hebrew. The arithmetic was of a very practical nature, which helped its considerable success; it originated the common belief expressed by the phrase "Arabic numerals," as if these numerals were really a Muslim invention.

Some of the other mathematicians we have already met. Robert Grosseteste was one of the first to discuss the need of a new calendar, and his opinion on the subject was repeatedly quoted by the pioneers who prepared the Gregorian reform (1582). William of Lunis translated an algebraical treatise from the Arabic. A compotus is ascribed to the English grammarian, John of Garland. Finally, some contemporary algorisms were composed by unidentified authors, e.g., the Hanover and Salem Latin algorisms. The most remarkable of these anonymous treatises is the Oxford French algorism, which is probably the earliest algorism in any vernacular.

We may now consider a group of men whose interest was astronomical and astrological rather than mathematical. John of London lectured on astronomy and meteorology in Oxford. Michael Scot introduced the upsetting Alpetragian ideas in the Latin West (Toledo, 1217), and later (after 1227) during his stay at the court of Frederick II he wrote astrological treatises for his imperial patron. William the Englishman (alias William of Marseilles) devoted himself chiefly to the interpretation of al-Zarqālī, and he thus helped to transmit the erroneous ideas on the trepidation of the equinoxes. He wrote a summary of the Almagest and a treatise on medical astrology. He was the first Latin writer to publish the Greco-Arabic views on the size of the solar system explained by al-Farghānī.

More astrological treatises were translated or composed by Salio of Padua, Leopold of Austria (though he belongs more probably to the second half of the thirteenth century), and Henrik Harpestraeng. It is pleasant to recall in this connection that the Dominican, John of Vicenza, was bold enough to denounce the practice of judicial astrology.

It is impossible to dissociate astronomical from astrological work, for every astronomer was of necessity an astrologer (astrology was his means of subsistence), and every astrologer was of necessity an astronomer. For example, the need of better astronomical tables was felt equally by the genuine astronomer and by the maker of horoscopes. I have spoken above of Raymond of Marseilles, who, c.1140, adapted al-Zarqālī's Toledan tables to the coordinates of Marseilles. Raymond's task was continued by William the Englishman, c.1231. London tables were compiled, c.1232, by an anonymous astronomer.

2. *Western Muslim*—It is possible that Muḥammad al-Ḥaṣṣār, with whom I dealt in the previous chapter, flourished in the thirteenth century, because all we know is that he was anterior to Ibn al-Bannā'.

Magic squares were naturally considered, as every other magic thing, by the Algerian occultist, al-Būnī. This is simply quoted for the sake of curiosity; it hardly concerns the history of mathematics.

The greatest astronomer of the time, al-Ḥasan al-Marrākushī, was then flourishing in Morocco. His main work, Jāmi' al-mabādī wal-ghāyāt (1229), was perhaps the best mediaeval treatise on practical astronomy; it explained the mathematical and experimental methods to be employed, giving good accounts of the instruments; it also was the best general treatise on gnomonics. It contained a catalogue of 240 stars. The mathematical part was equally important, the methods explained being in part trigonometrical, in part graphical. It was the most elaborate work of its kind in the Muslim West. It included trigonometrical tables, not only of sines, but also of versed sines, arc sines, and arc cotangents. Thus, while the Christian mathematicians were opening new paths, the Muslims were continuing along the trigonometrical road which they had made so conspicuously their own.

Another mathematician of far less importance, Ibn Badr, was living probably in the thirteenth century in Seville. He wrote an algebraical treatise wherein the main theories were illustrated by means of numerical examples.

3. *Eastern Muslim*—While no eastern Muslim was at all comparable to Ḥasan al-Marrākushī, four of them distinguished themselves in various ways.

Al-Muẓaffar al-Ṭūsī wrote treatises on algebra and on the astrolabe, and invented a linear astrolabe called Ṭūsī's staff (not to be confused with Jacob's staff). His pupil, the famous Kāmal al-dīn Ibn Yūnus of Mūṣul, dealt with a number of mathematical subjects, and solved a mathematical problem for Frederick II. One of Kamāl al-dīn's pupils, Qaiṣar ibn Abī-l-Qāsim, was primarily a musician and engineer; in 1225 he constructed a celestial globe which is extant to this day in the Museum of Naples. He dedicated a discussion of Euclid's postulates to Nāṣir al-dīn al-Ṭūsī (1201–1274). This reminds us that this great mathematician, to be studied in our next chapter, was already famous before the middle of the century. Finally Ibn al-Lubūdī compiled astronomical tables, and wrote various mathematical and astrological treatises. Nothing of all this is of great significance, but it shows that mathematics and astronomy were not neglected in the eastern caliphate.

4. *Syriac*—The Nestorian, Solomon of al-Baṣra, wrote a treatise on the shape of the heavens and earth, which is lost, and another on the calendar.

A part of the Dialogues of the Monophysite theologian, Jacob bar Shakkō, deals with mathematics and music. The fourth section of his Book of treasures contains an account of his cosmological views.

5. *Western Jewish*—Very little work was done by Jews, and that little exclusively in the West. Aaron ben Meshullam of Lunel made a comparative study of the Christian and Jewish calendars. An astrological treatise, Gemaṭriot, is ascribed to the German mystic, Judah ha-Ḥasid. Jacob Anaṭoli translated the Almagest (c. 1231) and Ibn Rushd's summary of it (lost in the Arabic original), also al-Farghānī's astronomy. It is typical of the prestige of Hebrew translations that J. Christmann's Latin edition of al-Farghānī (1590) was derived from Anaṭoli's version, though this text had been translated twice into Latin before Anaṭoli, by John of Seville and by Gerard of Cremona. In fact, Anaṭoli used one of these Latin versions, probably Gerard's, together with the Arabic text. The most important Hebrew work on mathematics and astronomy was the relevant part of the Midrash ha-ḥokmah, an encyclopaedic treatise compiled by Judah ben Solomon ha-Kohen of Toledo. This Judah was one of the mathematical correspondents of Frederick II, whom he met in Toscana, in 1247.

Of course Anaṭoli's translations were very important from the Jewish point of view; from a more general point of view they were far less important because they were posterior to the Latin translations. These Hebrew translations were of great convenience to the Jews, but they were not indispensable for the transmission of Greek and Arabic knowledge to modern astronomers.

6. *Hindu*—A grandson of Bhāskara, Caṅgadeva, founded in 1205 a school for the study of the Ṣiddhāntaśiromaṇi. No mathematical or astronomical contribution can be definitely credited to it. It is probable that the main purpose was astrological. This is not surprising considering that similar conditions obtained in the West. However, in the West there was a surplus energy devoted to pure mathematics and pure astronomy, and henceforth that energy would go on increasing throughout the ages, while by this time, the mathematical genius of India was apparently exhausted.

7. *Chinese*—The great educator, Yeh-lü Ch'u-ts'ai, proposed a reform of the calendar in 1220. This was accomplished by Chingiz Khān. Ts'ai Chên's commentary on the Shu Ching contains a description of a decimal number system, but that was an old story in China. The same Ts'ai Chên indulged in number mysticism, showing that that kind of aberration was well-nigh universal and answered definite needs of the human soul.

It is very curious that two of the very greatest mathematicians of this period—two out of five—were Chinese. Indeed, Ch'in Chiu-shao and Li Yeh must be counted among the most original mathematicians of all times. Note that they had, as far as we can know, no contact, for Ch'in was in the service of the southern Sung on the Yang-tze, while Li was flourishing under the Nü Chên Tartars in northern China.

Ch'in Chiu-shao composed his main work, Shu-shu chiu-chang, in 1247. It is a collection of problems solved by means of an exceedingly original method called t'ien yüan shu. His way of solving numerical equations of any degree was an astounding anticipation of the Ruffini-Horner procedure.

The Ts'ê-yüan hai-ching, Li Yeh's main work, appeared in the following year, 1248, and he published a second work in 1259. As opposed to the arithmetical tendencies of Ch'in, Li Yeh was primarily an algebraist. His first work dealt with measurements analogous to our trigonometrical measurements. He also used the t'ien yüan method, but somewhat differently from Ch'in. This is most interesting for it suggests that both derived the t'ien yüan shu from a common origin. For that origin we would have to look in Central Asia or India, but we do not yet know of any such method outside of the Far East.

The great mathematical school which developed in China in the thirteenth century is thus very mysterious. We shall come back to it in Book IV.

Summary

This period witnessed the activities of five outstanding mathematicians: Fibonacci, Nemorarius, al-Ḥasan al-Marrākushī, Ch'in Chiu-shao, and Li Yeh. These men represent four very different countries, Italy, Germany, al-Maghrib, and China; we might even say five countries, counting China as two, for Ch'in hailed from the southern part of it, and Li from the northern part, and these were indeed separate countries, unlike in many respects.

The spirit bloweth where it listeth. Is it not remarkable that the progress of mathematics (and for that matter of any science) should be due to the efforts of men of genius not only independent of one another but widely separated and very unlike? When we think of science as a tree, we must complete this otherwise excellent comparison by postulating the existence of many roots, roots finding their nourishment all over the earth. To be sure, the Chinese efforts remained exotic and did not fulfill their promises. The astounding thing, however, is not that some efforts were apparently wasted, but that most of them were soon utilized and became an integral part of human knowledge.

The main accomplishments of this period were:

(1) The publication of the Liber abaci, 1202, marking the beginning of European mathematics.

(2) The diffusion of Hindu-Arabic methods in Europe, by Fibonacci and by many smaller mathematicians of whom the most popular were Villedieu and Sacrobosco.

(3) Fibonacci's interpretation of a negative solution as a debt (1225).

(4) His problems of Diophantine analysis (1225).

(5) General proof of the fundamental theorem of stereographic projection, by Nemorarius.

(6) Contributions to the theory of numbers by Fibonacci and Nemorarius.

(7) Publication of astronomical tables in Marseilles and London (c. 1231–1232). However, we must not forget that the needs which brought these tables into being were astrological rather than astronomical.

(8) The Jāmi' of al-Ḥasan al-Marrākushī (1229), which was the most elaborate trigonometrical treatise of the western caliphate, the best mediaeval treatise on practical astronomy, on gnomonics, the best explanation of graphical methods.

(9) Introduction of Alpetragian astronomy into the Latin world by Michael Scot (1217).

(10) Translation of the Almagest into Hebrew by Jacob Anaṭoli (c. 1231).

(11) Development of the t'ien yüan shu by Ch'in Chiu-shao and Li Yeh (1247–1248).

(12) Numerical solution of equations of any degree by Ch'in Chiu-shao (1247).

VII. PHYSICS AND MUSIC

1. *Mechanical Rebirth in the West*—If the mathematical developments, with which we have just dealt, indicated the existence of a genuine scientific revival in the West, such impression is considerably strengthened by the study of contemporary mechanics. In fact we witness in western Europe a real mechanical rebirth. With the exception of a brief interlude in the days of Philoponos and Simplicios (first half of the sixth century), nothing at all comparable to it had happened since the almost legendary age of Archimedes. It is difficult to account for these great events; we can only say that the progress in mathematics and philosophy made them easier and almost prepared them.

The founder of that new mechanical school was Jordanus Nemorarius. His commentary on Aristotelian mechanics led him to formulate the notion of "gravitas secundum situm" (component of gravity along the trajectory) and the axiom "that which can lift a certain weight up to a certain height, can also lift a weight k times heavier to a height k times smaller." Another mechanical treatise, De ratione ponderis, contains the fundamental notion of statical moment and its application to the study of the angular lever and the inclined plane, and we may find in it the germ of the principle of virtual displacements. This second treatise is so advanced that one hesitates to ascribe it also to Nemorarius, though one has no good reason for crediting it to somebody else. If it was not composed by Nemorarius himself, it was the work of a direct or indirect pupil, for it belongs certainly to the same school.

The notion of impetus vaguely used by Philoponos and Simplicios, had been introduced with hardly more clearness by al-Biṭrūjī, and the Latin world became familiar with it through Michael Scot's translation (1217). Some Alpetragian ideas appear already in the writings of the great English philosopher, Robert Grosseteste, but the latter was more interested in astronomy and in optics than in mechanics.

The Fleming, Gerard of Brussels, who flourished probably in the thirteenth century, tried to solve the difficulties involved in the difference between linear and angular velocity. He failed to solve them, but it was quite an achievement to be aware of them.

Thus we see that after centuries of somnolence, this school was finally laying the foundations of cinematics and dynamics, and beginning the immense travail which would culminate later in the discoveries of Galileo and Newton.

2. *Meteorology and Optics*—Under the influence of Greek and Arabic knowledge the more scientifically minded of the Latin philosophers were much interested in a complex collection of problems, which does not correspond to any single science of to-day, and was represented by the words perspective and meteorology. It included the whole of optics, geometrical and physiological, all the problems connected with light and darkness, shadows, vision, color, etc., meteorology proper, and finally the miscellaneous astronomical, geological, even chemical queries, discussed in Aristotle's Meteorologica.[3]

In fact, the contents of mediaeval "meteorology"—a subject in some ways more comprehensive than our own, in others, less—were largely determined by Aristotle's treatise. I may recall that the Meteorologica was available in Latin before the beginning of the thirteenth century; not only had it been translated from the Arabic (the first three books by Gerard of Cremona), but it had also been translated directly from the Greek. There was a Hebrew translation by Samuel ibn Tibbon. Finally, about the middle of the thirteenth century, Matthieu le Vilain had translated it into French. To the translations must still be added the commentaries; for example, such a commentary by Alfred of Sareshel was used by Roger Bacon. In short we may assume that every scientific man was acquainted with the Meteorologica. The foremost contemporary student of these questions was Robert Grosseteste, who devoted to them a number of treatises. Grosseteste was well aware of the magnifying properties of lenses; in this respect, as in others, he was the forerunner of Roger Bacon.

It is possible that these optical and meteorological studies were stimulated by the translation of the Ptolemaic optics from the Arabic into Latin by Eugene the Amīr (about 1154), though this cannot be proved; it is certain that they were influenced by the translation of Ibn al-Haitham by Gerard of Cremona.

3. *Compass*—The use of a compass in navigation was probably a Muslim invention derived from idle Chinese observations. At any rate mention of it appeared at the end of the twelfth and the beginning of the thirteenth century in the Latin writings of Alexander Neckam, and of James of Vitry, and in the French "Bible" of Guiot of Provins. It is curious that the earliest Persian and Arabic references to it are somewhat later than the Latin. This is explainable if one realizes that

[3] See Isis, 6, 138.

such a discovery would not be published by the pilots who made it, nor by their associates, who had every reason for keeping it secret; if it were published at all, this would be done—and only later—by outsiders. The mention of the compass which is probably the earliest of all, by Alexander Neckam, refers to it but not as to a novelty. In fact, the invention dates back at least to the end of the eleventh century, but it must have taken some time before it became known in the West.

4. *Ḥammāmāt*—A curious consequence of the Crusades was the introduction of public bathing places in the main cities of the West, comparable to those existing in the Muslim East.

5. *Physics in the Eastern Caliphate*—Eastern Muslims were chiefly concerned with the invention or making of automata and contrivances such as were described by Heron of Alexandria and other Hellenistic mechanicians. Ibn ab-Sā'ātī of Damascus repaired the clock which his father had constructed in the Bāb Jairūn, and in 1203 he wrote a book explaining its structure and use. Two years later al-Jazarī completed at Āmid, on the upper Tigris, a treatise describing a whole series of apparatus, most of them hydraulic, such as clepsydras and fountains of various sorts. This treatise is the most elaborate of its kind and may be considered the climax of this line of Muslim achievement. The mathematician, Qaiṣar ibn Abī-l-Qāsim, constructed (c. 1236) water-mills on the Orontes in Ḥamāh, a locality which has remained famous for them until our own days.

It is curious that what might be considered a revival of Hellenistic invention should coincide with the beginning of a higher mechanical tradition in the West. This shows once more that the Christian West was awakening, and that if it was still inferior to the Muslim East in the matter of accomplishments, it was now decidedly on the upward path; its inferiority was no longer intrinsic, it was but the inferiority of youth as compared with middle age, an inferiority which is bound to be transformed pretty soon into the opposite.

6. *Muslim Music*—A treatise on music, Kitāb al-samā', was composed by 'Abd al-Laṭīf. The mathematician and engineer, Qaiṣar ibn Abī-l-Qāsim, was reputed to have a deep knowledge of music which he had obtained from Kamāl al-dīn Ibn Yūnus in Mūṣul. It is interesting to note that according to the Arabic account[4] Qaiṣar began a comprehensive program of study under Kamāl al-dīn with music. This suggests the scientific importance which Muslims attached to it.

Passing to the West, Ibn Sab'īn of Murcia, one of Frederick II's correspondents, wrote a book on the musical modes. Another treatise by Muḥammad al-Shalāḥī of Seville (1221) is a good representative of a typical department of Arabic literature. We might call it a musico-theological treatise. It is a discussion of the lawfulness of music. Is it a sin or not to play music or listen to it? Is every kind of music sinful or not, is it sinful only at certain times and in certain places, or is it sinful always and everywhere, etc. A good theologian with a secret love for music would have no difficulty in developing this theme indefinitely.

7. *Music in Western Christendom*—In the meanwhile Christian music was well under way. The Compendium discantus ascribed to Franco of Cologne may be a production of this century. It contains a full account of mensural music and of the so-called Franconian notation. Another treatise is credited to John of Garland. But the best proof of the maturity of Western music is given not by these treatises, but by the music itself, chiefly by that little masterpiece, Sumer is icumen in, which was created before 1240.

[4] Ibn Khallikān (vol. 3, 471).

VIII. CHEMISTRY

No spectacular progress was made in the field of chemistry, unless gunpowder was invented in this period, which is possible but unproved. I shall discuss the question of gunpowder in the following book.

1. *Western Europe*—Alfred of Sareshel translated the alchemical part of Ibn Sīnā's Shifā', the so-called Avicennae Mineralia; this may have been done before the beginning of the century, though he was still living c. 1210. He wrote a commentary on Aristotle's Meteorologica, a work which was generally available to Latin scholars at the beginning of the century. Now these two books, the Meteorologica and the Mineralia, were extensively used by almost every Latin author touching chemical or geological subjects. Alchemical treatises are ascribed to Michael Scot, to John of Garland, and to Richard of Wendover. Scot's treatises—there are two of them, a larger and a smaller one—are probably genuine. They contain interesting evidence of collaboration with Jewish and Muslim experimenters. The Compendium alchemiae bearing Garland's name is certainly a much later work.

Materia medica was another source of chemical knowledge. The most valuable contributions were probably due to Hugh Borgognoni, who founded the surgical school of Bologna, and to his son Theodoric. It is difficult to dissociate father and son, as discoveries are ascribed indifferently to each or to both. They sublimated arsenic, made experiments with other chemicals, chiefly mercury, and improved the technique of narcosis.

2. *Eastern Islām*—An amusing source of information on the shady side of Muslim alchemy has come down to us from this time. That is a treatise written by the Syrian, al-Jawbarī, c. 1226, to expose the frauds and deceptions of quacks, alchemists, and other rascals. Al-Jawbarī was not alone in this fight; the philosopher 'Abd al-Laṭīf did not fail to denounce alchemical superstitions.

The historian 'Umar Ibn al-'Adīm wrote a guide for the making of perfumes, which may offer some chemical interest.

3. *India*—A Hindu physician who flourished about this time, Śārṅgadhara, is the author of a treatise on materia medica, of which the chemical part is particularly interesting. It contained older traditions of which it is as yet impossible to trace the development. As it is, it gives one the impression that the iatrochemical reforms of Europe were anticipated in India.

4. *Japan*—The art of making glazed earthenware (faïence) was introduced from China into Japan in 1228 by Katō Shunkei. Katō was thus the founder of a great Japanese industry which was directed for seven centuries by members of his own family.

IX. GEOGRAPHY

1. *English*—The main Latin geographical writer of the second half of the twelfth century, Gerald the Welshman, came from Great Britain. In the first half of the thirteenth century the Latin geographical writings, as distinguished from the accounts of pilgrims and missionaries, were contributed by three Englishmen and one Dane.

The three Englishmen were Gervase of Canterbury, Gervase of Tilbury, and the friar Bartholomew. The first Gervase, a monk at Christ Church, wrote a description of England, shire by shire, which he called Mappa mundi. The second Gervase composed for Otto IV, c. 1211, the Otia imperialia, a collection of anecdotes which included much geographical information, e.g., on the topography of Rome. Two out of the nineteen books of Bartholomew's De proprietatibus rerum dealt with physical and political geography. Of course the other encyclopaedias contained also geographical information, but much less than Bartholomew's, except the Konungs skuggsjá (which was not written in Latin).

2. *Scandinavian*—The Dane was Saxo Grammaticus. This Saxo was primarily a historian, but his Gesta Danorum contains geographical data of unique value, e.g., observations of the glaciers of Iceland, and the earliest mention of the motion of glaciers. Saxo wrote at the beginning of the century, and his work, which was quite popular in mediaeval times, was for centuries the main source of information on the northern countries. More information was published some forty years later by the unknown author of the Konungs skuggsjá, but as it was given in Norwegian it remained utterly unknown outside of Scandinavia until the eighteenth century. This was doubly unfortunate, for this author gave not only new descriptions of the northern countries and of their many peculiarities, but his general geographical conceptions were uncommonly broad; for example, he believed in the sphericity of the earth and conceived the possibility that the south temperate zone was inhabited.

In the meanwhile, Scandinavian travelers continued their bold undertakings. Rafn Sveinbjörnsson, an Icelandic chieftain, visited England, France, and Spain. Various expeditions were made toward the east, in the direction of the White Sea. Ogmund of Spånheim, who took part in one of these expeditions, traveled from the White Sea across Russia to the Black Sea and Palestine and then back to Norway! It is clear that for these men inured to the most severe climate, traveling abroad was less of a hardship, and if they directed their steps towards the southern regions they had the joy of discovering comforts and beauties of which they had been deprived in their own homeland. Indeed it is surprising that not more of them were tempted to migrate southwards, if only temporarily.

3. *Christian Pilgrims*—As I have had previous occasions of explaining the geographical and historical importance of mediaeval pilgrimages and other journeys to the Holy Land, it will now suffice to enumerate very briefly the main travelers of this period. Wolfger of Ellenbrechtskirchen in 1195–1198 (he is quoted in this chapter because of later travels); an anonymous pilgrim of Soissons, before 1205; Wilbrand of Oldenburg, in 1211; one Thietmar, c. 1217; Ogmund of Spånheim, after 1217; St. Sabbas, c. 1225; an unknown Frenchman, c. 1231. These travelers are distributed by nationality as follows: three Germans, two Frenchmen, one Norwegian, and one Serb. Most accounts were in Latin; one in Scandinavian, one in Slavonic, one in French. To this last one might be added two French descriptions of Jerusalem and Palestine, the one by the historian Ernoul, the other by an unknown author.

4. *Christian Travelers to the Mongol Empire*—We now come to the most significant achievements of this period, from the geographical standpoint. I am referring to the journeys made by the diplomats sent to the Mongols by Innocent IV and St. Louis. Being stimulated on the one hand by the repeated failures of the Crusaders and by the increasing Muslim danger, on the other hand by the old dreams relative to Prester John, the pope decided to send missions to the Mongols with the hope of obtaining their adhesion to Christendom and their help against the Infidels. The first mission was headed by the Italian Franciscan, John of Pian del Càrpine. He left Lyon in 1245, went as far as Qaraqorum and was back

home two years later. The Latin account of his travels and of the Mongols is by far the most important geographical work of the first half of the thirteenth century, and one of the most important of mediaeval times. At about the time of Pian del Càrpine's home-coming, a second mission was sent by Innocent IV, this time a Dominican one, led by the Lombard, Ascelin. They do not seem to have gone farther than the Mongol outposts of Armenia, and they returned in 1250; the indirect account of their journeys is far less interesting than the Franciscan relation. One of Ascelin's companions, the French Dominican, Andrew of Longjumeau, was sent on a similar errand by St. Louis in 1248, returning to his master in 1251.

As far as their political purpose was concerned these missions were made in vain. But thanks to them the western Christians obtained a far better knowledge of Asia; in fact, a new world was revealed to them, and their general conception of the Ptolemaic οἰκουμένη was at once enlivened and deepened. It is not too much to say that these missions opened a new period in the history of geography. Moreover, irrespective of their results, they were heroic achievements of the first order.

5. *Eastern Muslim*—The greatest geographer of the previous period was a Western Muslim, the Spaniard, al-Idrīsī; the greatest of this period was an Eastern one, Yāqūt. Or rather, Yāqūt was born a Greek but had been educated by the Muslims as one of them. It is rather startling to observe that by far the most eminent Greek of this time had become, by the force of circumstances, a Muslim! Yāqūt had traveled considerably in Asia from the Syrian coast to Marw, but he is far less known as a traveler than as a geographical encyclopaedist.

Traveling to accomplish the Pilgrimage was a duty; traveling in search of knowledge (fī ṭalab al-'ilm) was a secondary duty, a means of obtaining merit, and it became an obsession with them; the immensity and variety of the Arabic-speaking countries were perpetually inducing wandering students of all ages to move on from place to place. On the other hand, when the Muslims had conquered and colonized large territories they had felt the need of geographical knowledge to establish their dominion. It is to such political requirements that we owe those typical roadbooks (Kitāb al-masālik wal-mamālik) which appeared in the ninth and tenth centuries (see, e.g., vol. 1, 606, 636). They were by-products of the organization of postal systems, taxation offices, and intelligence services by the governments concerned. Later, as such knowledge accumulated, as the Muslim community of each locality had more points of contact with others, near and distant; as more of the faithful had become ḥujjāj[5] and had brought back home not only their own recollections but those of fellow pilgrims hailing from every clime, there developed naturally a need for geographical encyclopaedias. We have already spoken of such compilations, the two most important being the Murūj al-dhahab of al-Mas'ūdī and the Rujārī of al-Idrīsī. The Mu'jam al-buldān of Yāqūt, completed in 1228, was another one having the same encyclopaedic purpose, but arranged in alphabetic order. Though very different from the works of al-Mas'ūdī and al-Idrīsī, the Mu'jam must be placed near them as one of the greatest geographical treatises not only of Islām but of all mediaeval civilizations. The dictionary proper is preceded by a treatise dealing with geography in general from every point of view.

Another Eastern work, much more narrow in its scope, but in a way more

[5] A ḥājj is one who has accomplished the Pilgrimage to Mecca.

important because more original, was 'Abd al-Laṭīf's account of Egypt, apparently completed about the beginning of the century.

6. *Western Muslim*—The geographical activities of Western Islām were relatively insignificant. The great astronomical treatise of al-Ḥasan al-Marrākushī contains the latitudes and longitudes of 135 places, partly established by his own observations. Though Ibn al-Baiṭār was primarily a herbalist, he traveled extensively from Spain and North Africa to the east probably as far as Mūṣul, and we find in his works many traces of these wanderings. The Kitāb al riḥla of Abū-l-'Abbās al-Nabātī, describing his journey to the east, is also primarily botanical.

7. *Western Jewish*—Pilgrimages were not restricted to Christians and Muslims; some Jews were impelled by a similar anxiety to visit the Holy Land. However we have but very few narratives of Jewish pilgrims, and what one might call more generally geographical literature is much smaller in Hebrew than in Arabic or Latin.

In 1210 Samuel ben Samson accompanied by three other rabbis traveled to the Holy Land and as far east as Mūṣul. He wrote an account of his journey. In the following year some three hundred English and French Jews, inspired by Samuel's relation, went to Palestine to settle there.

Jacob Anaṭoli added to his translation of al-Farghānī's astronomy three original chapters of which the last is geographical. It quotes the coordinates and lengths of days of a number of places.

8. *Syriac*—The Book of treasures, a theological treatise, composed in 1231 by the Jacobite, Jacob bar Shakkō, includes a summary of geographical knowledge.

9. *Chinese*—The splendid efforts of Sung geographers were continued during the thirteenth century. We owe to them some of our best knowledge on Central Asia. The information derived from Chinese sources is particularly valuable because it completes that given by the Muslims and Christians, and enables us to some extent to check it. To begin with, we have the accounts of journeys to Central Asia, which were caused by Chingiz Khān's expeditions into Persia in 1219 and following years. One of these itineraries was written by the great educator Yeh-lü Ch'u-ts'ai, another by Wu-ku-sun Chung-tuan, a third by Ch'iu Ch'ang-ch'un. This last one, called Hsi yu chi, is particularly valuable.

Another work of a different kind and without equivalent in any contemporary literature is the Chu fan chih (Records of foreign nations) compiled, c. 1225, by Chao Ju-kua. This Chao was a trade inspector in the cosmopolitan harbor of Ch'üan-chow in Fukien; his commercial handbook gives information, largely derived from his own experience, on foreign countries and peoples and on the main articles of merchandise.

Summary

The outstanding geographical works of the first half of the thirteenth century were those of Saxo Grammaticus and of John Pian del Càrpine, in Latin; the Konungs skuggsjá, in Norwegian; the treatises of Yāqūt and 'Abd al-Laṭīf, in Arabic; and last but not least, those of Ch'iu Ch'ang-ch'un and Chao Ju-kua, in Chinese. The richness, the abundance, and the variety of these works are equally remarkable.

It is curious to compare these seven outstanding personalities with the seven outstanding personalities of the previous period. In each case there were two Chinese, but the five other geographers were very different, four Spaniards and one

Welshman, or three Muslims, one Jew, and one Christian in one case, against two Scandinavians, two Muslims, and one Italian in the other. The most striking facts are the eclipse of Spain and the reappearance of Scandinavia. The lonely Italian did represent more than his own undaunted spirit; he was the standard bearer of the great religious orders to which we owe many geographic discoveries and the memory of so much heroism and charity.

The main additions to geography were the exploration of the region south of the White Sea, a better understanding of arctic conditions, a deeper knowledge of Central Asia. That knowledge was due to the convergent efforts of Christian, Muslim, and Chinese geographers.

X. NATURAL HISTORY

1. *Latin*—Among Latin contributions we must count first of all the Greek texts which then became available through translations from the Arabic. The De plantis ascribed to Nicholas of Damascus was translated by Alfred Sareshel; and the same author wrote a commentary on the Parva naturalia. The three zoological treatises of Aristotle were translated by Michael Scot, at Toledo, probably before 1220. Some twelve years later Michael dedicated to Frederick II a translation of Ibn Sīnā's summary of Aristotelian zoology. Another Arabic abridgment of it was translated a little later by the Galician, Peter Gallego. Thus by the middle of the century Aristotle's zoology must have been known, at least in its outline, to any Latin scholar who was sufficiently curious.

Michael Scot's own writings contain valuable information, not found in other contemporary ones, on the hot sulphur springs of Italy and the volcanic phenomena of the Lipari islands.

The translation of the alchemical part of the Shifā', Avicennae Mineralia, which Alfred of Sareshel completed, c. 1200, was an important source of geological knowledge. Alfred had derived from the Arabic literature some clear ideas on the formation of mountains.

The De proprietatibus rerum of Bartholomew the Englishman was one of the most popular books on natural history of mediaeval times. Out of its nineteen parts, at least five dealt with the three kingdoms of nature. Bartholomew's natural history was more advanced than his astronomy; it is full of descriptions wherein fact and fancy are delightfully blent. Its popularity was largely due to that blending which satisfied the mediaeval imagination. Of course the other encyclopaedic publications of the period contained their share of natural history. It is not necessary to name them again, except two; the De finibus rerum naturalium of Arnold of Saxony, of which the mineral part or lapidary was especially popular; and the De natura rerum of Thomas of Cantimpré, which contained not less than six zoological, three botanical, and two mineralogical books; to which might still be added one anthropological book; that is, twelve books on natural history out of nineteen, constituting the main bulk of the whole work. It is impossible to go into the details of such comprehensive surveys, but two outstanding peculiarities of Thomas' encyclopaedia may be mentioned; his description of herring fisheries, and the anthropological section, the first of its scope in Latin. Unfortunately Thomas' accounts were even less critical than those of Bartholomew, and a great part of his work was distinctly folkloric instead of scientific, even if one makes full allowance for the limitations of his time and environment.

For Latin treatises on falconry, see below, under Falconry.

2. *Vernacular*—Besides these Latin works, western Christians derived scientific intelligence from a few books written in vernaculars. However, only two kinds of vernaculars were thus employed: Scandinavian and French.

The Scandinavian writings were the most important. The Danish physician, Henrik Harpestraeng, wrote a herbal, and perhaps a lapidary. He had been educated in France and perhaps also in Italy, and of course could write in Latin as well as in his own language. It is almost impossible to say in which language each opus ascribed to him was originally written, for we have manuscripts of them in Icelandic, Swedish, Norwegian, Danish, and Latin.

The Norwegian encyclopaedia Konungs skuggsjá was one of the most precious contributions to natural history; it included descriptions of the walrus and of various kinds of whales and seals, and of life in arctic regions. It was much nearer to nature than any of the Latin treatises.

French literature was represented by the Hosebondrie, a treatise on husbandry composed about the middle of the century by an English bailiff, Walter of Henley. This was soon translated into Latin and English and remained the standard book on the subject in England for three centuries. However, it did not begin to compare with the Kitāb al-falāḥa, which Ibn al-ʿAwwām had published in Spain toward the end of the previous century. The Hosebondrie referred to the practice of marling.

3. *Falconry*—By far the greatest contribution to zoology was due, mirabile dictu, to the emperor Frederick II. His treatise on falconry, De arte venandi cum avibus, was completed by 1248; later his son Manfred prepared a revision of it. It is an astounding work, taking into account the Greek and Arabic literature on the subject, but essentially based upon the author's own observations and experiments, and upon the information elicited by himself from his Muslim advisers. It set forth a number of new anatomical facts—e.g., the pneumaticity of the bones of birds—and discussed bird migrations and the mechanical conditions of flight. Frederick even instituted experiments to determine how vultures were attracted to their prey. His interest in zoology, though centered on falconry, was not by any means restricted to it. He kept menageries in South Italy, and traveled across the Alps with some of his animal treasures. The first giraffe to appear in Europe did so under his patronage! We might say that the first animal circus to travel along the roads of Italy and Germany was organized by the emperor himself, Stupor mundi.

I said that Frederick's knowledge was partly derived from Muslim writings. Indeed an Arabic treatise was translated for him by his astrologer and secretary, Theodore of Antioch, and another in Persian was also known to him. Later both treatises were retranslated from Latin into French by Daniel of Cremona for Frederick's son Enzio. Frederick's own work was translated into French before the end of the century.

As the noblemen who hunted with birds could not be expected to be scholars, it is not surprising that treatises on falconry were written in vernaculars or translated into them. Besides the French versions already mentioned, we have contemporary treatises in Provençal and in Catalan.

This polyglot literature testifies to the international interest in that noble sport. As falcons and other hunting birds were valuable, difficult to breed, to train, and to keep in good health, it is natural enough that some men, hunters or gamekeepers, began to study them more closely. Thus is zoology indebted to sport. "La science pour la science" was an impossible ideal in the Middle Ages; to study anything there must needs be some good reason, theological or practical; knowledge of it must be found to be indispensable for this life or the next. In this case the requirements of falconers were reasons good enough, and it thus happened that ornithology was the most progressive branch of zoology in the thirteenth century.

4. *Eastern Muslim*—'Abd al-Laṭīf's account of Egypt contains information on plants and animals; the botanical part is particularly important. The Syrian physician, Ibn al-Ṣūrī, was also a great botanist, who herborized considerably in the country around Damascus and the Lebanon. He was accompanied by an artist who made colored pictures of the plants at different stages of their growth.

The Egyptian, al-Tīfāshī, was the author of an elaborate lapidary.

To these three men must be added two more who wrote in Persian. First the Ṣūfī poet, Fārid al-dīn 'Aṭṭār, whose poem on birds, Manṭiq al-ṭayr, is one of the classics of Persian literature. Of course the zoological interest of such a poem is but very small. Second, Muḥammad al-'Awfī, whose Jawāmi' al-ḥikāyāt, a collection of stories, includes a number of zoological items.

5. *Western Muslim*—Even as the greatest naturalist of the East was a botanist, even so Western Islām was then represented by two botanists, who upheld the glorious tradition consecrated by al-Ghāfiqī and Ibn al-'Awwām. Abū-l-'Abbās al-Nabātī of Seville and Ibn al-Baiṭār of Malaga were two very distinguished botanists indeed, and both traveled considerably to find plants in their own habitat and be able to examine them with their own eyes at various seasons. Both traveled east, but Abū-l-'Abbās returned finally to Spain; Ibn al-Baiṭār died in Damascus. As much of their experience was obtained in the East, it would have been proper to consider them together with 'Abd al-Laṭīf and Ibn al-Ṣūrī. And what a fine group of men!

Ibn al-Baiṭār was primarily a medical man, but Abū-l-'Abbās seems to have been interested in plants for their own sake, though naturally enough he was also a pharmacist. A pure botanist would have been inconceivable in those days. He described some new plants; e.g., those growing along the shores of the Red Sea. Ibn al-Baiṭār's Jāmi' refers to some two hundred plants which had not been dealt with before, except perhaps by al-Ghāfiqī.

6. *Hindu*—Śārṅgadhara's medical treatise dealt with a number of herbs (e.g., bertram root), though it was perhaps more remarkable because of its insistence upon mercurial and other metallic preparations.

7. *Chinese*—We generally expect the Chinese contributions to be out of the ordinary, and we shall certainly not be disappointed this time. To begin with, we have that commercial treatise composed, c. 1225, by the trade inspector, Chao Ju-kua. This provides information on a number of articles. such as camphor, frankincense, myrrh, dragon's blood, etc.

Two other works are more directly devoted to natural history. Ch'ên Jên-yü published in 1245 a treatise on the culture of mushrooms, eleven kinds being dealt with. General Chia Ssŭ-Tao wrote a treatise on crickets! While western people, including the Muslims, were more interested in larger animals and in those of which they had special need, such as horses, dogs, and falcons, the Chinese paid special attention to insects. It is thus natural enough that it was they, and not westerners, who discovered the wonderful industry of the silkworm and learned to take advantage of it. At an early time they were aware of the mysterious metempsychosis of the cicada, and used it as an emblem of resurrection. Their familiarity with various insects is fully revealed by their language which contains a number of special terms without equivalents in Arabic or Latin or in the European vernaculars. The most conspicuous aspect of their interest in insects, outside of sericulture, was their extraordinary fancy for crickets. They soon distinguished various kinds of chirping, and learned to breed and nurse the best musicians. They also originated the sport of cricket-fights, which increased fantastically the value of their pets. Thus there developed a cricket literature of which Chia's treatise, the Ts'u chih ching, was the earliest.

Summary

In this summary we shall leave out of account the encyclopaedic works and those which were purely literary. It is well to remember that they are there in the background but we need not drag them all the time behind us.

Let us consider the three kingdoms of nature in succession. Some geological progress was due to Michael Scot, to Alfred Sareshel's translation of Ibn Sīnā, and to the Konungs skuggsjá. The lapidaries of Harpestraeng and al-Tīfāshī were of little importance.

With regard to botany and husbandry, the Hosebondrie of Walter of Henley was a very influential work, and we were pleased to come across that treatise on mushrooms by Ch'ên Jên-yü, yet by far the main contributions were due to Muslims. Not less than four great Muslim botanists flourished at this time: 'Abd al-Laṭīf, Ibn al-Ṣūrī, Abū-l-'Abbās, and Ibn al-Baiṭār.

As to zoology, the outstanding work was undoubtedly Frederick's treatise on falconry. Not only the best zoological treatise of that time, but one of the best of the Middle Ages. Frederick's traveling menagerie must have been a very unusual object lesson to all the people who were privileged to gaze on it. Of hardly less importance to the West was the transmission of Aristotelian zoology, chiefly through Michael Scot's translation (before 1220). First-hand zoological information was given in the Konungs skuggsjá; unfortunately that work remained unknown outside of Scandinavia. Finally we have the astounding cricket lore explained by Chia Ssŭ-tao.

The outstanding naturalists were ten in number: three westerners, Frederick II, Michael Scot, and Walter of Henley; one Scandinavian, the author of the Konungs skuggsjá; in all, four Christians; then four Muslims, all of them botanists, 'Abd al-Laṭīf, Ibn al-Ṣūrī, Abū-l-'Abbās, Ibn al-Baiṭār; finally two Chinese, Ch'ên Jên-yü and Chia Ssŭ-tao, mushrooms and crickets.

A new husbandry was written in French by an Englishman; botany was fostered by Muslims; ornithology by an Italian; entomology by a Chinese.

XI. MEDICINE

1. *Translators from Arabic into Latin*—Before dealing with the more original productions of Western Christendom, it is well to consider the translations. These were relatively insignificant. The Sirr al-asrār was translated by Theodore of Antioch and Philip of Tripoli; the Kitāb i'timād of Ibn al-Jazzār, by Stephen of Saragossa. That is all. As we shall see later, the medical translations into Hebrew were hardly more important. The age of translations was passing and pretty soon the tide would begin to move the other way. Many of the Latin treatises of this period were eventually translated into Hebrew.

2. *Italian*—The balneological poem ascribed to Alcadino of Girgenti and to

others may be a production of the first half of the thirteenth century. Same remark with respect to Magister Maurus and Joannes Ferrarius already dealt with in the previous book. It is difficult to apportion their activities among the two centuries; Maurus died in 1214, and one Ferrarius died only in 1232.

Adam of Cremona composed for Frederick II a treatise on the hygiene of an army or of a large body of pilgrims. The lessons of the Crusades were beginning to tell.

Another result of the Crusades was the stimulation of surgical efforts. War is the mother of surgery. The surgical renaissance initiated by Roger of Salerno was brilliantly continued by other Italians: Roland of Parma, author of the Chirurgia rolandina, and the four anonymous doctors who discussed his work. As compared with Roger, their surgery is more Arabic; the Arabic lessons obtained in the West and perhaps also in the Near East have had more time to sink down. Another commentator on Roger's Practica was the South Italian, Jamatus.

Our knowledge of the Salernitan school is completed by the study of the regulations of medical teaching and practice promulgated by Frederick II in 1240. These regulations were the very first of their kind, and they were remarkably comprehensive. Unfortunately they came too late; to begin with, the school was no longer in the thirteenth century what it had been before 1193; Frederick's very measures to enhance the medical prestige of Salerno do but confirm our impression that its prestige had suffered, that something had to be done to revive it; finally the school did not survive the Hohenstaufen rule which came to an end less than thirty years later.

Roland of Parma had transmitted the Salernitan tradition to Bologna. Soon afterward a new surgical tradition was established in that learned city by a veteran Crusader, Hugh Borgognoni, and his son Theodoric. It would seem that transplantation affects ideas as it often does plants; it excites them and gives them a new scope. The result may be good or evil, but nothing can be worse than stagnation, and by this time the school of Salerno had already passed its climax. The Bolognese surgeons showed at once more initiative; they introduced new methods in the treatment of luxations, fractures, and wounds, in the use of anaesthetics and other drugs. Other physicians of Europe and India had used mercury salts before him, but Theodoric was apparently the first to observe the resultant salivation. As Bologna was one of the main intellectual centers of Christendom, these new medical ideas had a good chance of being propagated. Theodoric's Cyrurgia was soon translated into Catalan.

3. *French*—The introducer of Salernitan medicine into Paris, Giles of Corbeil, died only c. 1222. His influence may be detected in the abundant writings of Walter Agilinus, who was probably a Frenchman. The teachings of the Italian school of surgery were transmitted beyond the Alps by William of Congenis, a master of Montpellier, and probably by other doctors, for it would seem that the Glossulae quatuor magistrorum were also composed in France.

4. *Spanish*—Though Christian Spain had grown considerably, Spanish medicine was still very rudimentary. The only physician I came across was Stephen of Saragossa, who translated Ibn al-Jazzār's treatise on simples.

5. *English*—The English school, on the contrary, was quite remarkable. In fact, if we make a distinction between general medicine and surgery (and such distinction was as legitimate then as it is now), we may say that the Italian school was the leading surgical school of Europe, while the English was the leading medical one.

Alfred of Sareshel wrote an original treatise, De motu cordis (c. 1210), derived from Greek and Arabic sources. He was deeply steeped in Aristotle, and unfortunately defended some erroneous views of the master concerning the supremacy of the heart over the brains. In spite of that reactionary tendency, Alfred was really scientifically minded; that is, he was bent on finding scientific rather than theological explanations.

The unavoidable mixture of truth and error is well illustrated by Michael Scot's Physionomia, the most popular of his works. The gynaecological introduction to it was probably the origin of the fantastic division of the womb in seven chambers, which recurred in many later writings.

Astrology was then inseparable from medicine; every physician needed some astrological knowledge in the same way as they now need physical and chemical training. No treatment could be prescribed without astrological considerations. A contemporary treatise on medical astrology was the work of the mathematician, William the Englishman, who was established in Marseilles.

Thus far I have spoken only of secondary matters; the two outstanding figures of medical England were Richard of Wendover and Gilbert the Englishman. The former wrote a medical summary entitled Micrologus. A contemporary anatomy, the Anatomia Ricardi anglici (alias, De anatomia vivorum), was probably also his work. Gilbert was the author of many medical writings, by far the most important being the Compendium (or Lilium) medicinae. It is a very comprehensive outline including good pathological descriptions and two chapters on the hygiene of travel.

Comparing the teachings of these two men we find that Richard was well acquainted with the Greek and Arabic literature available in Latin; in his anatomy he curiously upheld Aristotelian views against the sounder Galenic; this was probably done under the influence of Alfred of Sareshel. On the other hand, Gilbert was more up-to-date, more familiar with Salernitan medicine. The introducer of that medicine in England was Robert Grosseteste; we would place Gilbert a little later than Richard and Robert because of his superior Salernitan knowledge, but not much later because his surgery was derived from Roger, not from Roland. It must be added that the Lilium contained more magic than would be allowable even in those days, but this must be ascribed to Gilbert's own perversity; one can date nothing with magic.

It is interesting to note that with the exception of Grosseteste, who spent most of his life in his own country, these Englishmen spent much time abroad: Alfred of Sareshel in Spain, Michael Scot in Spain and Italy, Richard in Rome and Paris, Gilbert in Montpellier, William in Marseilles. It is typical enough that three of them, Richard, Gilbert, and William, were called Anglicus, the Englishman. This underlines the insularity of England. Many Englishmen distinguished themselves, and some of them became the leaders of their time; yet in most cases this implied living abroad for a long period, and on the continent they remained somewhat distant and outlandish and were soon singled out—a little like the Americans or Australians of to-day.

I have had many occasions to observe that in science as in other fields it takes some time to establish a reputation; it often takes so much time that a reputation is only obtained when it has ceased to be completely deserved. For example, Salernitan medicine was not fully appreciated abroad until its climax had been passed. The earlier Latin publications were too near to Arabic and other sources to be taken very seriously, but this situation changed gradually, and by the beginning of the thirteenth century, the cumulative effect of many valuable publications was already sufficient to increase considerably the prestige of each. The best proof of this is afforded by a series of Hebrew translations, including the Rolandina, and other writings by Theodoric Borgognoni, Walter Agilinus, William of Congenis, and Gilbert the Englishman. Most of these translations are undated, and presumably rather late; two dated ones are from the end of the thirteenth century and from the year 1362. Of course, their coming into being was due partly to the fact that Jewish physicians knew less and less Arabic and more and more Latin; yet these translations would not have been made if there had been no demand for them.

6. *Welsh*—After this survey of the main sources of the new European medicine in Italy, France, and England, we may consider medical activities in other countries, i.e., in Wales, Germany, and Scandinavia. It is possible that further investigations would make it possible to extend these notes to still other countries, but this would hardly affect our conclusions.

The case of Wales is especially interesting, though perhaps more so from the folkloristic than from the purely medical standpoint. Welsh medicine is represented by a series of Celtic texts entitled Meddygon Myddvai (the physicians of Myddvai). The earliest is traditionally ascribed to the physician, Rhiwallon, who flourished about the middle of this century.

7. *German*—For the understanding of German medical thought we have only a few collections of recipes.

8. *Scandinavian*—We are much better informed with regard to Scandinavia. I have already spoken of that Icelandic chieftain, Rafn Sveinbjörnsson, who traveled not only to Norway but to southern countries as far as Spain, and finally returned to Iceland. He is said to have performed the stone operation according to the Celsus method.

Salernitan knowledge was introduced into northern Europe by the famous Danish physician, Henrik Harpestraeng (d.1244). He explained it in various treatises dealing with medicine, astrology, and related subjects. However, the knowledge which he imported was a little less recent than that which Gilbert the Englishman and William of Congenis were transmitting at about the same time to Western Europe. His writings were derived from the earlier Salernitan literature, anterior to the second half of the twelfth century, while those of Gilbert and William represented the following stage, that of Roger of Salerno.

9. *Eastern Muslim*—There were quite a number of distinguished physicians in the Egyptian and the Eastern Caliphate, though none very great.[6] Most of them have already been mentioned in this survey, as philosophers, or mathematicians, or in some other capacity, for the practice of medicine was but one of their accomplishments—the paying one.

Ibn al-Sā'ātī, mechanician of Damascus, wrote a commentary on the Qānūn and a supplement to Ibn Sīnā's treatise on gripes. Najīb al-dīn al-Samarqandī was the author of many medical treatises, one of which enjoyed some popularity, and was the object of Arabic and Persian commentaries. 'Abd al-Laṭīf, who is best known for his account of Egypt, was also a physician and even an anatomist of astounding originality; he was able to examine a quantity of human remains with his own eyes, not with Galen's, and he noticed that the lower maxillary and the

[6] However, Aḥmad ibn 'Uthmān al-Qaisī, who flourished in Cairo in the fifth decade, was an outstanding eye-doctor. I had forgotten him, but repaired the omission in an appendix.

sacrum are single bones. The great botanist, Ibn al-Ṣūrī, wrote a treatise on simples. Ibn al-Lubūdī's writings include various medical ones. A more ambitious work was the Tadhkirat al-hādiya, a medical encyclopaedia compiled by Ibn Ṭarkhān out of many hundreds of Arabic authors. Ibn Ṭarkhān's Tadhkirat was twice abbreviated in the sixteenth century.

We now come to a very enigmatic personality, the author of a treatise on surgery, presumably composed in Arabic, but known only through Latin and Hebrew translations. This treatise was obviously derived from Arabic sources, but was it really written in Arabic? Or was the Arabic label simply a publicity trick? The treatise was ascribed to one Mesuë, whom we shall call Mesuë the Third, to distinguish him from two other famous physicians, Arabic-writing Christians, bearing the good name of Māsawaih. We can conceive many possibilities. For example, the author may have been of Arabic origin, and may have belonged to the Māsawaih family, and yet have called himself Mesuë and written in Latin. That would not be an unusual case; how many Arabic-writing Yūsufs did not become Latin-writing Josephs? The Crusades had put a premium on surgeons, and the superior ability of some Arabic surgeons must have been recognized in many instances. When the Cross was fighting the Crescent would it be an unnatural thing for an Arabic-speaking Christian to engage in the service of western Christians, to assimilate himself to them, and finally to write in Latin and to Latinize his name? It would be idle to enlarge on this. The important point is that this treatise, whatever its original language, still represents Arabic knowledge as contrasted with the newer surgery of Salerno, Bologna, and Montpellier.

Two other physicians were primarily historians, Ibn al-Qifṭī and Ibn abī Uṣaibi'a. The former composed a collection of biographies of ancient and Muslim physicians, men of science, etc., which is one of our main sources for the history of Muslim science and helps us to realize to what extent Greek achievements were understood and valued by the Muslims. Ibn abī Uṣaibi'a wrote a similar work, but restricted to physicians, and of such importance that without it our knowledge of Muslim medicine would be considerably more imperfect than it is. His work is especially valuable because he was himself a medical man and had known personally many of the leading physicians of his times.

With the exception of Najīb al-dīn, who flourished in Samarqand and Khurāsān (he was killed by the Tartars in Herāt, 1222), all of these physicians flourished in Syria and Egypt. The city most often quoted in their biographies is Damascus, which was then, in spite of much turbulence, one of the leading metropoleis of the East.

10. *Western Muslim*—As compared with that fine array of Syrians, there is but one Spaniard to name, Ibn al-Baiṭār of Malaga, and he became half Syrian himself. He had left his country, c. 1219, never to return; he died in Damascus in 1248.

However, this single gift of Spain was a great one. Ibn al-Baiṭār was unquestionably the greatest herbalist or apothecary among the Muslims, nay, the greatest of the Middle Ages, for no one surpassed him outside of Islām. From the time of Dioscorides and Galen down to the sixteenth century no contributions equalled his in bulk and quality.[6a] Unfortunately they came too late, when Arabic influence

[6a] Since writing this, Meyerhof's studies on al-Idrīsī and al-Ghāfiqī seem to prove that Ibn al-Baiṭār's borrowings from them were so extensive that they might more properly be called plagiarisms. If this is confirmed Ibn al-Baiṭār's merit and fame will wane considerably.

was already on the decline, and thus they failed to be integrated in the main stream of western knowledge and to affect materially its progress.

11. *Western Jewish*—The Jewish physicians of Spain and Languedoc produced a few Hebrew translations of no great importance. The Spaniard, al-Ḥarizi, translated two Galenic or pseudo-Galenic books, and what is more interesting, the gynaecological treatise written in Arabic by his older contemporary, the Catalan, Sheshet Benveniste. This is typical of the linguistic change which was then taking place; even Spanish Jews were losing their hold on Arabic. 'Alī ibn Riḍwān's commentary on Galen's Tegni was translated by Samuel ibn Tibbon, at Béziers in 1199, this being Samuel's earliest dated work.

An interesting sidelight on the practice of medicine by Jews is the case of the eye-doctor Abraham of Aragon. The crusade against the Albigenses had been also to a smaller extent a crusade against the Jews of southern France. The council held at Béziers in 1246 forbade them to practice medicine among Christians. In spite of this prohibition, Alphonse, count of Poitou, obliged Abraham to treat him.

12. *Egyptian Jewish*—In my paragraph on Eastern Muslim medicine I remarked that most of these Eastern physicians flourished in Syria and Egypt which formed then one single dominion ruled by the Ayyūbid dynasty. Of course most of them would visit Egypt and spent there more or less time, yet Syria, and chiefly Damascus, seemed to be their main center of attraction. Even an Egyptian born, like Ibn al-Qifṭī, would establish himself finally in Syria. This may be explained by the fact that Egyptian medicine was largely dominated by Jewish physicians who continued the glorious tradition begun by Maimonides. In the chapter on the second half of the twelfth century, I had to deal with no less than six Egyptian Jewish physicians. On the other hand, we do not hear of eminent Jewish physicians established in Damascus. It would thus seem that a separation had gradually taken place, consciously or not, the Jews remaining masters of Cairo, the Muslims and a few Samaritans gathering in Damascus.

However, the Jewish physicians of Egypt formed a far less conspicuous group in the first half of the thirteenth century than in the previous period. To begin with, Maimonides died in 1204, and there was nobody to replace him. His son-in-law, Abū-l-Ma'ālī, lived probably a little longer, but then he died altogether as far as Israel was concerned, for his children became Muslims. And yet it was probably one of these, Yūsuf ibn 'Abdallāh, who had edited in 1204 the last chapter of Maimonides' Fuṣūl fī-l-ṭibb.

There were only two who belonged entirely to this period, al-As'ad al-Maḥallī and David ben Solomon, and the latter was a Qaraite. Both were distinguished physicians highly praised by Ibn abi Uṣaibi'a. Al-As'ad wrote various medical works, one of them being a collection of questions submitted to his Samaritan colleague, Ṣadaqa ben Munaja'. David ben Solomon, the Qaraite, was the author of a famous antidotary, Al-dastūr al-māristānī, and of a commentary on Galen's treatise on causes and symptoms.

I forgot to say, though it goes almost without saying, that all of these writings were in Arabic.

13. *Samaritan*—The little Samaritan colony established in Damascus produced two physicians, Ṣadaqa ben Munaja' and Abū-l-Ḥasan ben Ghazāl. Both of them wrote in Arabic, as by this time the Samaritans had almost forgotten their own language, a kind of Aramaic, and used it only for religious purposes. Sadaqa was

the author of a number of treatises, medical and others; one was composed in answer to the Jew, al-As'ad al-Maḥalli. Abū-l-Ḥasan, who eventually embraced Islām and became a wazīr, was a great collector of books, and it was to him that the 'Uyūn al-anbā' of Ibn abī Uṣaibi'a was dedicated.

14. *Hindu*—Śārṅgadhara wrote a medical treatise wherein great importance was paid to mercurial and other metallic preparations. It contains among other things an elaborate analysis of the pulse. The popularity of this work is proved by many manuscripts, editions, and translations in various Hindu vernaculars.

The Kashmirian physician, Narahari, composed a dictionary of materia medica.

15. *Chinese*—Ch'ên Tzŭ-ming wrote a treatise on external troubles, and c. 1237, one on women's diseases. The treatise on mushrooms written by Ch'ên Jên-yü in 1245 contains an antidote at the end.

The most important Chinese publication of this time was the medico-legal treatise entitled Instructions to coroners, composed about the middle of the century (c. 1247) by Sung Tz'ŭ. This treatise has exerted a tremendous influence, for revised editions have been used to our own days. In this the Chinese were again pioneers, for nothing at all comparable to it appeared in Europe until almost three centuries later.

Summary

The main achievements were the following:

(1) Surgical novelties introduced by Hugh and Theodoric Borgognoni.

(2) Medical regulations promulgated by Frederick II.

(3) Further transmission of Salernitan medicine: to Montpellier, by William of Congenis and the Four Masters; to England, by Robert Grosseteste and Gilbert the Englishman; to Scandinavia, by Henrik Harpestraeng.

(4) New descriptions of human bones (lower maxillary and sacrum) by 'Abd al-Laṭīf.

(5) Hygienic rules for armies and crusaders, by Adam of Cremona, and for travelers, by Gilbert the Englishman.

(6) Instructions for coroners, by Sung Tz'ŭ.

(7) Last but not least, a new synthesis of materia medica, by Ibn al-Baiṭār.

The leading personalities were Roland of Parma, Hugh and Theodoric Borgognoni, Richard of Wendover, Gilbert the Englishman, Henrik Harpestraeng, 'Abd al-Laṭīf, Ibn al-Baiṭār, and Sung Tz'ŭ. Six Christians, two Muslims, one Chinese. Or otherwise, three Italians, two Englishmen, one Dane, one Spaniard, one 'Irāqian flourishing in Egypt, and one Chinese. The most important languages, as far as the transmission of new medical ideas was concerned, were Latin and Arabic.

The main centers were: in Christendom—Salerno, Bologna, and Montpellier, but Salerno was dying and its prestige was rather of the past than of the present; in Islām—Cairo and Damascus, Cairo's medical fame being due to Jewish efforts, while Damascene medicine was Muslim or Samaritan. In short, the main Christian centers were Bologna and Montpellier; the main Muslim center, Damascus; the main Jewish center, Cairo.

XII. HISTORIOGRAPHY

1. *French*—While the finest group of historians of the second half of the twelfth century was the English, the leading historians of Christendom in the first half of the thirteenth century were French, and next to them came the Scandinavians.

"A tout seigneur, tout honneur." Let us begin with Villehardouin, who was not simply the greatest French historian, but one of the very greatest historians of that time. He was one of the organizers of the Fourth Crusade, that wretched undertaking which ended in the fighting of other Christians instead of Infidels, and in the taking of Constantinople instead of Jerusalem. His account of it was written in French, after 1207, and is one of the masterpieces of early French literature and of mediaeval historiography. It was continued by Henry of Valenciennes. Other French narratives of the same Crusade were given by Robert of Clari and by Ernoul, and we have a Latin one in the Historia orientalis of James of Vitry. This shows that the Crusades continued to be a French specialty (see my remarks on p. 138). Though other nationalities were associated with them, the French were the main leaders, even as the Venetians were the main profiters.

Another crusade, even more tragic and more cruel, was then taking place on French soil against the Albigenses. We have various accounts of it, notably a chronicle in French verse by William of Tudela, another by an unknown author, and a Latin one by Peter of Vaux Cernay. Needless to say, in the case of crusades directed against a minority of heretics, the point of view of the orthodox persecutors is generally far better known than that of their victims. For that reason the anonymous narrative is especially precious, for it acquaints us with the views of the oppressed people of southern France.

Three more historians must still be quoted. Rigord and William the Breton indited chronicles of the reign of Philip II, whom they called Philip Augustus. These works have the usual merits and faults of official chronicles; the authors were witnesses of many of the events they described, or they could obtain first-hand information from such witnesses; authentic documents were available to them; on the other hand, they could not be expected to be impartial. Finally the Tournaisien, Philip Mousket, devoted an immense French poem to the history of France from the Trojan war to his own days. The final part of it contains valuable information.

It is striking that among these ten chroniclers, not less than six wrote in French (two of them, it is true, in langue d'oc).

2. *Spanish*—One of these chroniclers, William of Tudela, hailed from Spanish Navarra, south of the Pyrénées. I dealt with him in section 1, because it was natural to speak of him together with the other chroniclers of the Crusade against the Albigenses. This may help us to remember that the Pyrénées were then far less of a separation than they became later. To begin with, two distinct races, the Basques in the West and the Catalans in the East, always lived astride of the mountains. These were no more of an obstacle to them than a hill is to the castellan who lives at the top of it and holds the passes. Thanks to those people and also to some restless Jews, there was far more communication between, say, Languedoc and Aragon, than between Languedoc and northern France. This situation was somewhat modified when the southern provinces were subordinated to the French crown, but this was a much slower process than is generally realized. To speak only of the southernmost provinces, Languedoc was annexed to the crown under Philip III (1270–1285), Provence under Louis XI (1461–1483), Gascony, Béarn, and Foix under Henry IV (1589–1610), while Roussillon was not finally integrated until 1659 (Paix des Pyrénées). The complete amalgamation of the provinces, and the diffusion of the northern manners and language, took more than four centuries.

To return to Christian Spain, besides William of Tudela, there was but one historian, Rodrigo Jiménez de Rada, who wrote histories of Spain and of the Moors. Being archbishop of Toledo he was well placed to obtain information from Arabic as well as from Latin or Spanish sources.

3. *Italian*—The only Italian historian was the Franciscan, Giovanni Pian del Càrpine, whose history of the Mongols has already been praised in our geographical section.

4. *English*—Layamon's semi-Saxon paraphrase of the Roman de Brut, composed at the beginning of this century, marked an English revival. However, as contrasted with the French historians, the majority of whom used their own language, all the historical works written by Englishmen of this period were in Latin. This is not surprising, if one considers that since the Norman Conquest, English had fallen into disfavor.

Gerald the Welshman lived until c. 1223, and his historical works were revised by himself within the new century. The Otia imperialia were put together by Gervase of Tilbury, c. 1211, for the emperor Otto IV. Chronicles of England and of Canterbury were composed by Gervase of Canterbury. A little later a general chronicle was compiled by Roger of Wendover, who worked in St. Albans. Roger was not a great chronicler, but he prepared the achievements of his successor, Matthew Paris.

5. *Scandinavian*—Two of the greatest historians lived in northern Europe; Saxo Grammaticus in Denmark, and Snorri Sturluson in Iceland. Saxo's work, being written in Latin, was available to the scholars of other parts of Europe and was in fact quite popular among them. It is of unique value for the study of Danish origins, and contains many items which appear here for the first time; e.g., a reference to prehistoric graves.

Snorri's writings, being in Icelandic, remained unknown outside of Scandinavia for more than four centuries. Their mediaeval influence was thus strictly Scandinavian. Yet their intrinsic importance is considerable. Snorri continued in an admirable manner the work begun by Ari Fróði Þorgilsson, and may be called one of the founders of the Icelandic literature and civilization.

6. *German*—Arnold of Lübeck continued Helmold's chronicle, dealing with the progress of German colonization in Slavonic countries.

The Sächsische Weltchronik is a universal chronicle in Low German extending to the year 1225 and following. It was formerly ascribed to Eike of Repgow. It is the earliest historical work of its scope in German prose.

7. *Other Latin*—One of the earliest chronicles of Poland was composed by Vincent of Cracow. A history of Livonia was written by Henry the Lett, who was a witness of many events, or could obtain direct information about them.

8. *Byzantine*—While so many historical works were being published in Latin, only one Greek chronicle deserves to be mentioned. This was written by Nicetas Acominatos. It contains an account of the conquest of Constantinople, which is of considerable value for comparison with the Latin relations.

9. *Armenian*—John Vanagan had been enslaved by the Mongols, but later manumitted. He founded the monastery of Khoranashat and spent there the rest of his life. He wrote a chronicle containing an account of the Mongol invasion; unfortunately most of it is lost.

10. *Syriac*—The Nestorian metropolitan, Solomon of al-Baṣra, compiled a collection of historical and theological anecdotes, entitled Book of the bee.

11. *Hispano-Jewish*—The Sha'ar ha-shamayim composed by Ibn Laṭīf, c. 1244, includes a brief history of Jewish science down to Maimonides.

12. *Western Muslim*—Out of four historians, two were Africans, the two others Spaniards.

Ibn Ḥammād wrote chronicles of the Fāṭimid rule in Africa, and of the Algerian town of Bougie, which was then far more important than it is now and had known many vicissitudes. 'Abd al-Wāḥid al-Marrākushī wrote a chronicle of the Almohades.

The works of the Spaniards were of the biographical type, so popular in Islām. The famous mystic, Ibn 'Arabī of Murcia, who spent the second half of his life in the East, was full of nostalgia when he thought of his old teachers in Spain. His Al-durrat al-fākhira contains biographies of them and of other Western scholars and saints who had inspired him. The Valencian, Ibn al-Abbār, continued Ibn Baskhuwāl's Kitāb al-ṣila and composed another work of the same kind. After the conquest of Valencia (1238) he had emigrated to Tunis, where he died. Ibn 'Arabī died in Damascus. Thus were the Spanish seeds scattered abroad; it was other countries' gain, but Spain's irreparable loss.

13. *Eastern Muslim*—Under the Ayyūbid rule of Egypt, Damascus, Ḥalab, Ḥamāh, Ḥimṣ, Arabia, and Mesopotamia, a number of historians found opportunities of distinguishing themselves.

We may first recall one of the previous period, Yūsuf ibn Rāfi' of Mūṣul, who wrote histories of Ṣalāh al-dīn and of Ḥalab, for he lived until 1234. The immense geographical work of Yāqūt is full of historical and ethnographical information. He also composed a dictionary of learned men. 'Abd al-Laṭīf's account of Egypt is as valuable for the historian as for the geographer.

By far the greatest Arabic historian of the period was Ibn al-Athīr. Indeed Ibn al-Athīr was one of the best historians of mediaeval times; he was far above all of the Christians of this period, except perhaps Villehardouin, whose distinction was of an entirely different kind. Ibn al-Athīr composed a universal chronicle down to 1231, a history of the Atābeg rulers of Mūṣul, and biographical and genealogical works. His chronicles are of considerable value to the student of the Crusades, as they enable him to give sufficient weight to the Muslim point of view.

I must speak more briefly of the others. Ibn abī-l-Dam of Ḥamāh wrote histories of Islām. 'Umar Ibn al-'Adīm devoted all of his energy to compile the annals of his native city, Ḥalab. Finally we have two historians of unusual interest to us, the Egyptian, Ibn al-Qifṭī, and the Damascene, Ibn abī-Uṣaibi'a, who published biographies of men of science, Greek and Muslim. We might call them historians of science, and to be sure, without their help our knowledge of Muslim science would be much smaller. I have already explained their fundamental importance in the medical section.

14. *Persian*—Al-Bundārī of Ispahan, better known as the translator of the Shāhnāma into Arabic, abridged the history of Saljūq rule written by 'Imād al-dīn al-Iṣfahānī. Al-Nasawī wrote an excellent biography of Jalāl al-dīn Khwārizmshāh. Muḥammad al-'Awfī compiled an enormous collection of anecdotes of all kinds.

The first two wrote in Arabic, the third in Persian.

15. *Chinese*—Ts'ai Ch'ên wrote a commentary on the Shu Ching, which has become itself a secondary classic. Yeh-lü Ch'u-ts'ai, whom we might call "primus Mongolorum praeceptor," wrote an account of Chingiz Khān's campaign against

Persia. Yeh Lung-li was the author of a history of the Kitan Tartars, and perhaps also of a history of the Chin Tartars.

16. *Japanese*—The Hōjō-ki of Kamo Chōmei, a classic of Japanese literature, contains valuable historical information.

Summary

Among the many historians of this period—I have dealt with almost half a hundred—it will suffice to recall those who were of outstanding importance. I believe almost every scholar would agree upon the following choice: Villehardouin, Pian del Càrpine, Saxo Grammaticus, Snorri Sturluson, Ibn al-Athīr, 'Abd al-Laṭīf, Yāqūt, Ibn al-Qifṭī, Ibn abī Uṣaibi'a. Out of these nine, five were Muslims, four Christians. Five wrote in Arabic, two in Latin, one in French, one in Icelandic. They came from nine different countries; one was a Greek slave brought up as a Muslim, the eight others hailed from France, Italy, Denmark, Iceland, Syria, Egypt, 'Irāq, Jazīrah.

XIII. LAW AND SOCIOLOGY

1. *Italian*—The legal revival begun in the first half of the twelfth century had slackened a little in the second half of that century, but in the thirteenth century a new and greater activity set in. The second part of the Canon Law, the Decretals, was published by Gregory IX in 1234. It was more independent of Roman law than the Decretum. Indeed the opposition of the Curia to the legists increased continually.

Yet this was a golden age in the history of Roman law. The school of Bologna, which was already famous at the beginning of the century, was now illustrated by the labor and prestige of many professors, such as Azo, Hugolinus, Francesco Accorso, Odofredus. The master of all was Accorso whose Glossa ordinaria became a sort of legal Bible, and remained the supreme authority for almost two centuries.

The teachings of Bologna were diffused all over Europe not only by the students who flocked there from every Christian country, but also by some of the professors. Remember Vacarius. Another missionary of Roman law in England was the eldest of Accorso's sons, Francesco II. Odofredus taught in France. Some Bolognese legists were even attracted to the papal court, e.g., Accorso's third son, Guglielmo; and Francesco II was there for a time as the representative of Edward I.

It is hardly necessary to say that without a full appreciation of this legal development one cannot understand the political events of the age, and chiefly the struggle between the popes and emperors, the growing organization of governments, the crystallization of thousands of institutions and offices. But I must once more insist that the growth of law influenced also, and very deeply, the growth of science. To begin with, the legists helped to dethrone the theologians; in many cases it appeared that the former were far more important than the latter; in the second place, they helped to clarify thoughts and methods. If the legal arguments were often artificial, they were much less so than the theological; legal realities were much closer to nature after all; this was a step forward.

What we said above of the conflict between Roman and Canon law must not be misunderstood. This conflict was but the age-old one between the sacred and profane conceptions of knowledge and of duty. But for all that, Bologna was a hotbed of Guelf politics, and the lawyers were naturally inclined to take the pope's side against the emperor; it was partly on that account that Frederick II founded the University of Naples. But just because the civilians were not in any sense antipapal, it was easier for them to disentangle law from theology and to establish it so to say on its own legs.

At the same time one cannot emphasize too much that this was a parting of the ways between East and West. In Islām the distinction between theological and legal thought was hardly made until almost our own days; in Christendom it was made with increasing vigor from the twelfth century on, and this was but the opening wedge which prepared many other differentiations and unlimited ramifications. In Islām, intellectual progress was completely inhibited by the theological supremacy; it is as if a spell had been thrown upon all but the freest minds; in Christendom, legal endeavor opened an avenue of deliverance. But I must not anticipate, for even in the West the fight between theology and lay knowledge was a protracted one and the human spirit was not entirely freed until the end of the seventeenth century.

To return to Italian law, a few words must still be said of the protagonists in the supreme legal contest of that time, Frederick II Hohenstaufen and Innocent IV. Frederick II gave in 1231 to the Sicilies a remarkable code of laws; the wise regulations which he devised for the safeguarding of the Salernitan school have already been praised. His main legal adviser was Peter of Vinea. Innocent IV, who caused Frederick to be excommunicated, and began a life and death struggle with him, was himself a jurist. He is said to have been the first to speak of a corporation as a persona ficta.

2. *Spanish*—Peter Gallego translated the treatise on economy ascribed to Galen.

3. *English*—Before speaking of individual activities, let us recall that it was during this period, in 1215, that the Magna Carta was granted by king John to his barons. This great charter is one of the most important monuments in the constitutional history of the British Empire.

Gerald the Welshman wrote a treatise on the education of princes and a similar work, the Oculus pastoralis, was composed, c. 1222, probably by the Florentine, Boncompagni. William of Drogheda, who was teaching in Oxford, wrote, c. 1239, a treatise on canon law, which was very popular, not only in England but abroad, even in Bologna. This illustrates the speed of diffusion of legal studies in Europe.

4. *German*—The most important code of mediaeval Germany was put together by Eike of Repgow; he wrote it first in Latin but translated it into Low German before 1235. It was best known under its German name, Sachsenspiegel. It was very popular and exerted a deep influence upon a number of other codes published in High German, Dutch, and even Polish, but chiefly upon the Deutschenspiegel and the Schwabenspiegel (c. 1259). One result of this strong autochthonous development was the relative unpopularity of Roman law in German lands.

5. *Icelandic*—The dialogue entitled The king's mirror, of which we have already spoken—e.g., apropos of its geographical items—contains an account of royal duties and customs. It is curious that one of the earliest European treatises on the theory of the state should have been written in Icelandic.

6. *Hispano-Jewish*—Al-Ḥarizi translated Aristotle's Ethics and Politics from Arabic into Hebrew.

7. *Egypto-Muslim*—The grammarian Ibn al-Ḥājib wrote treatises on Mālikī law wherein he harmonized the teachings of Egypt with those of the Maghrib. Mālikī

law was essentially the law of the western caliphate, and it has remained so until this day.

8. *Chinese*—The great Mongol organizer, Chingiz Khān, gave his peoples a new code of laws.

Sung Tz'ŭ's Instructions to coroners have already been discussed in the medical section. This has remained a standard work in Chinese criminal procedure until our own days.

9. *Japanese*—A new code, the Jōei-shikimoku, was promulgated in 1232. It was meant to consecrate the novel feudal conditions obtaining in Japan, and to complete from that special point of view, rather than supersede, previous codifications.

Summary

Of course every code and every legal effort is of paramount importance to the countries wherein they were made. But if we consider only the efforts which were truly of international scope, we find that by far the greatest achievements of this period were the Magna Carta, a sacred covenant for the English peoples but an inspiration to the whole world, and the growth of Roman law in Bologna.

XIV. PHILOLOGY

1. *Latin*—The two grammarians, Hugutio of Pisa and Alexander Neckam, continued their task in this century, for Hugutio died only in 1212, and Alexander in 1217.

Two grammatical poems, Graecismus and Labyrinthus, were composed by the Fleming, Eberhard of Bethune. The former was used by Erasmus as a primer. John of Garland's Dictionarius was a list of words similar to the De utensilibus of Alexander Neckam, but more elaborate. Incidentally this title represents the first use of the word dictionary. John was one of the first speculative grammarians or "modistae," whose efforts tended to lift grammar up to a higher philosophical level. Down to this time, Donatus and Priscian had been the main authorities; if one keeps in mind the almost infantile character of their grammars, one is better able to appreciate the renaissance initiated by John of Garland. In the meanwhile, the old grammar held its own—and held it for centuries—for one of the most popular books of the Middle Ages, Villedieu's poem, Doctrinale puerorum, was largely derived from Donatus and Priscian.

The didactic treatises composed by Albertano of Brescia exerted a deep influence on many Christian generations. This was especially true of his Ars loquendi et tacendi (1245) which was translated into many vernaculars, including Icelandic.

2. *French*—Though no grammarian was as yet ready to fossilize the French language, that language deserves special consideration, for it is clear that it was coming of age and that its international importance was already considerable.

One pregnant result of the crusade against the Albigenses was to carry the northern French language, the langue d'oïl, down to the foot of the Pyrénées and to the Mediterranean shores. At the same time the crushing defeat suffered by the heretics thwarted the growth and the crystallization of their own language, the beautiful langue d'oc, and the future of the most promising literature of southern Europe was thus irremediably jeopardized.

A curious monument of the linguistic situation of that time in southern France is the chronicle composed by William of Tudela. Remember that William hailed from Spanish Navarra. He was more familiar with the southern idiom, but tried to write in French. His verse is a mixture of langue d'oc and langue d'oïl. The growing relations between the north and south are also illustrated by Guiot of Provins, who lived not only in Mayence, Clairvaux, and Cluny, but also in Arles.

The English Dominican, Walter of Henley, wrote his husbandry in French. This is not very remarkable; but what is more so, the Icelandic Konungs skuggsjá recommended the study of Latin and French "for those idioms are most widely used." French was thus placed by this impartial and wise observer upon the same level as Latin! This was going perhaps a little too far, but future events would almost justify the prophecy.

Some valuable information on the contemporary French pronunciation may be derived from Hebrew-French glossaries containing vocalized transliterations of French words in Hebrew script.

3. *Italian*—Provençal literature found a strong echo at the Sicilian court, that strange assemblage kept together by Frederick's genius. We hear so much of the Greeks, Jews, and Muslims, who were attracted there, that we might overlook the obvious fact that after all the majority of the Sicilians were Italian-speaking people. Under the stimulation of these polyglot influences the Italians became conscious of their own language, and thus it is not surprising that its final emancipation from the Latin took place in South Italy. However, the Sicilian court was too artificial a "milieu" to insure a healthy development, even if it had survived Frederick's death long enough. From the Provençal and Muslim seeds which had been sown upon the receptive Italian soil, little plants had grown, as frail as they were precious. If they had remained there, they would certainly have died, but happily they were transplanted to Tuscany, and it was there that their development was to be completed in the following century. The Italian literary language was born in Naples, but it reached its maturity in Florence.

4. *Scandinavian*—By this time the Icelandic language was fully developed; witness not only the chronicles already dealt with, but also conscious grammatical efforts. The Edda edited by Snorri Sturluson contains a prosody composed by himself, and four grammatical treatises by other authors. Two of them date from the twelfth century; one was written by Snorri's nephew, Ólafr Thórðarson, and another is later still.

The old Norwegian language had also reached its maturity, as is proved by the encyclopaedic treatise Konungs skuggsjá, written about the middle of the century (probably before).

Though the Swedish and Danish languages were somewhat younger, their earliest monuments date also from this century.

5. *Greek*—The presence of an abundant Greek population in South Italy is sufficiently established by the fact that Frederick's code of law, originally published in Latin, had soon to be translated into Greek. When we think of the transmission of Greek knowledge to the West, we must ever keep that population in mind. Indeed the surprising thing is not that some Greek knowledge filtered through Italy, but that so little of it reached western Europe by that way. This failure can be explained only by the backwardness and illiteracy of that population.

The Latins themselves became better acquainted with the Greek language, though the progress was slow and in the hands of so few people that it was exceedingly precarious. The best Hellenists of these days were two Englishmen, John Basingstoke and Robert Grosseteste. John had obtained part of his education in Athens, and thus we may assume that his knowledge of Greek was genuine. He translated a Greek grammar, the Donatus Graecorum. We have already spoken of Robert's translations; he added a number of grammatical notes to the Nicomachean Ethics; his extracts from Suidas are other evidences of his philological curiosity.

6. *Armenian*—An Armenian dictionary and a treatise on the art of writing were composed by Aristaces, disciple of Gregory of Sgevrha.

7. *Hebrew*—I have sufficiently insisted upon the significance of the Hebrew translations from the Arabic, and of the linguistic reconstruction which was implied, to make further commentaries unnecessary. The work begun by Judah ibn Tibbon was worthily continued by such men as Samuel ibn Tibbon and Jacob Anaṭoli. The more specifically grammatical activity of David Qimḥi must be recalled, because David died only in 1235.

The 'Arugat ha-bosem of Abraham ben Azriel was the earliest literary fruit of Slavonic Jewry; it contains many Bohemian glosses. Another commentary ascribed to this same Abraham, contains French glosses, but we are not sure of its authenticity.

The connections between Hebrew and European vernaculars, chiefly French, are revealed by a number of glossaries. The most extensive of the early Hebrew-French glossaries is the one composed by Joseph ben Samson in 1240. Jews had good reasons for studying French (or eventually other vernaculars), practical reasons to begin with; moreover there was not the same religious objection to the neutral vernaculars as there could be to the ecclesiastical language of western Christendom.

So much for Western Jewry. The only grammarian of the East was Tanḥum Yerushalmi, and we are not sure that he flourished exactly at this time. He compiled a Hebrew-Arabic dictionary to Maimonides' Mishneh Torah, and other writings of his (in Arabic) show that he was deeply concerned with Hebrew grammar.

Hebrew scholarship in Christendom was still at a very low ebb. Just as we have Hebrew-French glossaries written in Hebrew script by Jews, we have others written in Roman script by Christians. These documents have but little philological value, but they prove that a few Christians were trying to read God's own words. Grosseteste, whom we have met everywhere among the pioneers, was one of those Christians.

8. *Arabic*—Yāqūt's Mu'jam al-buldān, though primarily geographical, contains abundant items of philological interest. For example, Yāqūt took pains to vocalize proper names, and he often discussed points of grammar. These grammatical tendencies, which would never be dormant in an Arabic mind, appear even more clearly in other works of his.

I have already had many occasions of underlining the lexicographical aspect of treatises on materia medica or herbals. It was natural enough to quote the names of herbs in various languages, and their synonyms, inasmuch as this was an inevitable by-product of the author's work. Ibn al-Baiṭār not only gave the Arabic synonyms, but also their equivalents in Greek, in the Latin and Arabic dialects of Spain, in Persian and Berber.

To pass to works specifically devoted to grammar, two were composed by the Egyptian, Ibn al-Ḥājib; and a more elaborate one, dealing also with rhetoric, by al-Sakkākī of Khwārizm. These books were very popular. Al-Sakkākī's authority was also felt indirectly through later commentaries and elaborations; his influence upon Arabic letters may be compared to Quintilian's upon the Latin.

It will not surprise the readers who have followed us thus far, that these grammatical efforts were made by people who were not by any means pure Arabs. Ibn al-Ḥājib was of Kurdish, and al-Sakkākī of Turkish origin. Of course they felt the need of rules and guides more strongly than those who were to the manner born. (See my remarks in vol. I, 179, 502, etc.)

9. *Sanskrit*—The Kashmirian physician, Narahari, compiled a dictionary of materia medica.

10. *Chinese*—Chingiz Khān introduced the use of the Uighūr alphabet, and later of the Chinese script to write Mongolian. He carried out a number of educational reforms, and deserved to be called the first instructor of his people.

11. *Japanese*—The gradual emancipation of the Japanese language and script is shown by the fact that the new samurai code of 1232, Jōei-shikimoku, was written, not in Chinese characters, but in the Japanese syllabary.

Summary

The main facts considered in this section are the following:

(1) The birth of a new grammatical movement under the influence of John of Garland.

(2) The priority of the French vernacular among others.

(3) The beginning of Italian literature in Sicily.

(4) The continuation of the golden age of Icelandic and (Old) Norwegian literature.

XV. CONCLUSIONS

OUTSTANDING SCIENTIFIC ACHIEVEMENTS

In this summary I shall speak only of scientific achievements proper, though of the less relevant facts three are of such pregnancy that they must be mentioned once more: the foundation of the Franciscan and Dominican orders, the promulgation of the Magna Carta, and the development of Roman Law in Bologna.

(1) Material increase of Aristotelian knowledge through Latin and Hebrew versions (zoology, de coelo et mundo, ethics, politics).

(2) Translations of al-Biṭrūjī into Latin; of Ibn Rushd into Latin and Hebrew; of Maimonides into Hebrew.

(3) Fibonacci's Liber abaci, 1202; beginning of European mathematics, derived from the Arabic, yet original.

(4) Treatise on trigonometry, gnomonics, graphical methods, and astronomical instruments by al-Ḥasan al-Marrākushī.

(5) Development of t'ien yüan shu by Ch'in Chiu-shao and Li Yeh.

(6) Mechanical renaissance initiated by Jordanes Nemorarius.

(7) Descriptions of Asia by Pian del Càrpine, Ch'iu Ch'ang-ch'un, and Chao Ju-kua; of Egypt, by 'Abd al-Laṭīf; of northern regions, by Saxo Grammaticus and the Konungs skuggsjá.

(8) Yāqūt's geographical dictionary.

(9) Popular encyclopaedias of natural history, etc., by Bartholomew the Englishman, and Thomas of Cantimpré.

(10) Walter de Henley's Hosebondrie.

(11) Ibn al-Baiṭār's botanical and medical synthesis.

(12) Frederick's treatise on falconry, including new anatomical observations.

(13) Development of surgery, chiefly in Bologna and Montpellier.

COMPARATIVE ACHIEVEMENTS OF VARIOUS GROUPS

For the sake of easy comparison, we shall follow the same plan as before, beginning with Japan and traveling westwards. The outstanding names are italicized throughout.

Japanese (4)

Religious founders (2): Shinran-Shōrin and Dōgen.
Historian: Kamo Chōmei.
Technician: Katō Shunkei.

Chinese (14)

Educators (2): Chingiz Khān, Yeh-lü Ch'u t'sai.
Mathematicians (3): Ts'ai Ch'ên, *Ch'in Chiu-shao, Li Yeh.*
Geographers (3): *Ch'iu Ch'ang-ch'un*, Wu-ku-sun, *Chao Ju-kua.*
Naturalists (2): *Chia Ssŭ-tao, Ch'ên Jên-yü.*
Physicians (2): Ch'ên Tzŭ-ming, *Sung Tz'ŭ.*
Historians (2): Hui Hung, Yeh Lung-li.
The Chinese contributions were still very superior to the Japanese.

Hindu (3)

Mathematician: Caṅgadeva.
Physicians (2): *Śārṅgadhara* and Narahari. The latter was a Kashmirian.
A contemporary Arabic treatise by al-Āmidī on the microcosm and macrocosm was said to be translated from the Sanskrit, but the Sanskrit original (if any) is unknown.

Muslim (42)

Eastern Muslim,[7] (30)

Theologians (2): Ibn al-Ṣalāḥ, Abū-l-Baqā'.
Philosophers (7): al-Zarnūjī, Muḥammad al-'Awfī**, al-Āmidī, Farīd al-dīn 'Aṭṭār**, *'Abd al-Laṭīf*, Ibn al-Fāriḍ, Kamāl al-dīn Ibn Yūnus.
Mathematicians (3): al-Muẓaffar al-Ṭūsī, Qaiṣar ibn abī-l-Qāsim, Ibn al-Lubūdī.
Physicists (2): al-Jazarī, Ibn al-Sā'ātī.
Geographer: *Yāqūt* (of Greek origin).
Naturalists (2): *Ibn al-Ṣūrī*, al-Tīfāshī.
Physicians (3): Najīb al-dīn al-Samarqandī, Ibn Ṭarkhān, Mesuë the third (?).
Historians (8): al-Jawbarī, *Ibn al-Athīr*, al-Bundārī, Ibn abī-l-Dam, al-Nasawī, *Ibn al-Qifṭī*, Ibn al-'Adīm, *Ibn abī Uṣaibi'a.*
Philologists (2): al-Sakkākī, Ibn al-Ḥājib.
It is clear that the more literary kind of scholars were more abundant than the others, though my enumeration is a little deceptive. As each man is named but once, the group of "philosophers" includes distinguished specialists, such as 'Abd al-Laṭīf and Kamāl al-dīn Ibn Yūnus. Of these thirty men only two wrote in Persian; all of the others, many of whom were Persians, wrote in Arabic. One, al-Sakkākī, is said to have used also the Turkish language.

Distribution of the Eastern Muslims: How were these men geograpically distributed? We may try to classify them according to their native countries,

[7] In this section two asterisks following a name mean "wrote exclusively in Persian;" one means "wrote in Persian and Arabic."

bearing in mind that such classification, though perhaps the most natural, is still very artificial.

Transoxiana (2): al-Āmidī, Najīb al-dīn al-Samarqandī.

Khurāsān (4): Muḥammad al-'Awfī**, al-Muẓaffar al-Ṭūsī, Fāriḍ al-dīn 'Aṭṭār**, al-Nasawī.

Khwārizm (1): al-Sakkākī.

Jibāl (1): al-Bundārī.

Kurdistān (1): Ibn al-Ṣalāḥ.

'Irāq and Jazīrah (4): Al-Jazarī, *'Abd al-Laṭīf*, *Ibn al-Athīr*, Kamāl al-dīn Ibn Yūnus.

Syria (9): Al-Jawbarī, Ibn al-Sā'ātī, *Ibn al-Ṣūrī*, Ibn abī-l-Dam, Ibn al-'Adīm, Ibn al-Lubūdī, *Ibn abī Uṣaibi'a*, Ibn Ṭarkhān. I am adding to this group *Yāqūt*, who was of Greek origin.

Egypt (6): Abū-l-Baqā', Qaiṣar ibn abī-l-Qāsim, Ibn al-Fāriḍ, *Ibnal-Qifṭī*, Ibn al-Ḥājib, al-Tīfāshī.

Unknown origin (2): Mesuë the Third, al-Zarnūjī.

The most remarkable fact was the superiority of Egypt and above all of Syria. After these two, the main nurseries of men were Mesopotamia and Khurāsān; the latter sent her sons not only westward but also eastward—Muḥammad al-'Awfī flourished in India. The superiority of Egypt and Syria would be greater still if we had considered them as one single group, for these two countries were closely united under the Ayyūbids. Then we would see that half of the Eastern Muslims and two-thirds of the leading ones belonged to that single group.

A simpler classification of these 28 men would be the following:

Mesopotamian (that is, 'Irāq and Jazīrah) 4.

Easterners ("Persians") 9.

Westerners (Syro-Egyptians) 15.

The conclusion of this classfication would be the same.

Western Muslim (12)

Philosophers (4): Ibn Ṭumlūs, al-Būnī, *Ibn 'Arabī*, Ibn Sab'īn.

Mathematicians (2): *al-Ḥasan al-Marrākushī*, Ibn Badr.

Musician (1): Muḥammad al-Shalāḥī.

Botanists and Physicians (2): *Abū-l-'Abbās al-Nabātī*, *Ibn al-Baiṭār*.

Historians (3): 'Abd al-Wāḥid al-Marrākushī, Ibn Ḥammād, Ibn al-Abbār.

This group is much smaller than the Eastern one, which is not surprising considering that Islām was being slowly driven out of Spain. Yet Spain was still the main nursery in the West, as will be seen presently.

Distribution of Western Muslims: These twelve men may be distributed according to their native countries as follows:

Seville (3): Muḥammad al-Shalāḥī, *Abū-l-'Abbās al-Nabātī*, Ibn Badr.

Malaga (1): *Ibn al-Baiṭār**.

Murcia (2): *Ibn 'Arabī**, Ibn Sab'īn*.

Valencia (2): Ibn Ṭumlūs, Ibn al-Abbār.

Morocco (3): 'Abd al-Wāḥid al-Marrākushī*, Ibn Ḥammād, *al-Ḥasan al-Marrākushī*.

Algeria (1): al-Būnī.

Those whose names are followed by an asterisk died in the East: four out of twelve, three Spaniards out of eight. Moreover the Valencian, Ibn al-Abbār, died in Tunis. Thus was the Spanish decadence slowly prepared.

Samaritan (2)

Physicians (2): Ṣadaqa ben Munaja' and Abū-l-Ḥasan ben Ghazāl, both of whom flourished in Damascus.

Jewish (23)

Eastern Jewish (3)

Philosopher (1): Tanḥum Yerushalmī.
Physicians (2): al-As'ad al-Maḥallī, David ben Solomon, both of Cairo.
These three wrote in Arabic.

Western Jewish (20)

Theologians (5): Abraham ben Nathan ha-Yarḥi, Abraham ben Azriel, Moses ben Jacob of Coucy, Isaiah ben Mali of Trani, and the renegade, Nicholas Donin.
Translators (3): *Samuel ibn Tibbon*, Ibn Ḥasdai, *Jacob Anaṭoli*.
Philosophers (8): Judah ha-Ḥasid, al-Harizi, Azriel ben Menahem, Asher ben David, Eleazar of Worms, Judah ben Solomon ha-Kohen, Ibn Laṭīf, Judah ibn 'Abbās.
Mathematician (1): Aaron ben Meshullam.
Traveler (1): Samuel ben Samson.
Physician (1): Abraham of Aragon.
Philologist (1): Joseph ben Samson.
All of these men wrote in Hebrew, but Judah ben Solomon wrote also in Arabic, and Joseph ben Samson in French.

Distribution of Western Jews: Geographically these Jews can be classified as follows:

Spain (5): al-Ḥarizi, Judah ben Solomon ha-Kohen, Abraham of Aragon, Ibn Laṭīf, Judah ibn 'Abbās.
Catalonia (2): Azriel ben Menahem, Ibn Ḥasdai.
Languedoc (5): Abraham ben Nathan ha-Yarḥi, Aaron ben Meshullam, Samuel ben Samson (?; at any rate his traveling companion to the East was a Languedocian), *Samuel ibn Tibbon*, Asher ben David.
Provence (1): *Jacob Anaṭoli*.
Other parts of France (3): Moses ben Jacob of Coucy, Joseph ben Samson, Nicholas Donin.
South Italy (1): Isaiah ben Mali.
Germany (2): Judah ha-Ḥasid, Eleazar of Worms.
Bohemia (1): Abraham ben Azriel.
Egypt (2): al-As'ad al-Maḥalli, David ben Solomon.
Palestine (1): Tanḥum Yerushalmī.

As contrasted with Muslim conditions, Israel was much stronger in the West than in the East. However, the Jewish group was far inferior in its totality to the Muslim one. There were only two Jews of outstanding importance and both were primarily translators; that is, transmitters rather than creators.

Christian (96)

Eastern Christian (6)

The Eastern group may be divided into four sub-groups: Greek, Slavonic, Syriac, and Armenian.

Greek (1)

Historian: Nicetas Acominatos.

To this might be added *Yāqūt*, who was of Greek race, but was captured by Muslims and educated by them. Compare the similar case of al-Khāzinī (first half of the twelfth century). However we feel that it would be a little deceptive to put Yāqūt to the Greek credit. The decadence of the Greek-speaking world was terrible.

Slavonic (1)

St. Sabbas of Servia.

Syriac (2)

Nestorian (1): Solomon of al-Baṣra.

Jacobite (1): Jacob bar Shakkō.

Armenian (2)

Historian (1): John Vanagan.

Philologist (1): Aristaces.

The total activity of Eastern Christendom was very small.

Western Christian (90)

All wrote in Latin except the few whose names are followed by an asterisk; these few did not write, or they used a vernacular, as indicated between parentheses.

I have divided the Western Christians into a number of groups forming convenient geographical units, as follows: Italy; France; the Hispanic peninsula; Great Britain and Ireland; Low Countries; Germany, Poland and Latvia; Scandinavia; Syria. Two Syrian authors writing in Latin are quoted here because they really were representatives of Western, not of Eastern, Christendom.

Italy (22)

Religious leaders (4): Francis of Assisi, Clara of Assisi*, John of Vicenza*, Filippo Benizzi*.

Translators (3): Salio of Padua, William of Lunis, Daniel of Cremona* (Fr.).

Mathematician (1): *Fibonacci.*

Travelers (2): *Pian del Càrpine*, Ascelin.

Naturalist (1): *Frederick II Hohenstaufen.*

Physicians (5): *Roland of Parma*, John Jamatus, Adam of Cremona, *Hugh Borgognoni*, *Thedoric Borgognoni.*

Jurists (5): Azo, Hugolinus, Peter Vinea, *Accorso*, Odofredus.

Educator (1): Albertano of Brescia.

France (20)

Religious leaders (3): Amaury of Bêne*, Peter Nolasco, Hugh of St. Cher.

Philosophers and polygraphs (5): Guiot of Provins* (Fr.), John of La Rochelle, Walter of Metz, William of Auvergne, John Peter of Lyon* (Prov. ?).

Mathematician (1): Alexander of Villedieu.

Physicist (1): Matthieu le Vilain* (Fr.).

Traveler (1): Andrew of Longjumeau.

Physicians (2): *William of Congenis* (?), Walter Agilinus (?).

Historians (7): *Villehardouin** (Fr.), Robert of Clari* (Fr.), Rigord, William the Breton, Peter of Vaux-Cernay, Ernoul* (Fr.), James of Vitry.

Hispanic Peninsula (6)

Religious leaders (2): St. Dominic, Raymond of Peñafort.

Translators (2): Stephen of Saragossa, Peter Gallego.

Historians (2): William of Tudela* (Fr.), Rodrigo Jiménez de Rada.

Raymond of Peñafort was a Catalan, the others hailed from other parts of Spain.

Great Britain and Ireland (20)

Religious leader (1): Simeon Stock.

Translators (2): *Alfred of Sareshel,* John Basingstoke.

Philosophers (6): John of London, *Bartholomew the Englishman, Michael Scot,* Adam Marsh, *Robert Grosseteste,* Alexander of Hales.

Mathematicians (2): William the Englishman, Sacrobosco.

Geographer (1): Gervase of Tilbury.

Agriculturist (1): *Walter de Henley** (Fr.).

Physicians (2): *Richard of Wendover, Gilbert the Englishman.*

Historians (2): Gervase of Canterbury, Roger of Wendover.

Jurist (1): William of Drogheda.

Philologist (1): *John of Garland.*

All of these were Englishmen, except Michael Scot who was a Scotchman, and William of Drogheda who was an Irishman. To these might be added the Welsh author (or authors) of the Meddygon Myddvai* (Celtic).

Low Countries (5)

Religious leaders: David of Dinant* (Fr.).

Philosopher: *Thomas of Cantimpré.*

Mechanician: *Gerard of Brussels.*

Historian: Philip Mousket* (Fr.).

Philologist: Eberhard of Bethune.

Germany, Poland, and Latvia (8)

Philosopher: Arnold the Saxon.

Mathematician, mechanician: *Jordanus Nemorarius.*

Travelers (3): Wolger of Ellenbrechtskirchen, Wilbrand of Oldenburg, Benedict the Pole.

Historians (2): Vincent of Cracow, Henry of Latvia.

Jurist: *Eike of Repgow** (Ge.).

All of these were Germans, except Benedict the Pole and Vincent of Cracow, who were Poles, and Henry of Latvia.

Scandinavia (7)

Philosophy: Author of the *Konungs skuggsja** (Norw.).

Travelers (2): Rafn Sveinbjörnson*, Ogmund of Spånheim*.

Physician: *Harpestraeng**.

Historians (2): *Saxo Grammaticus, Snorri Sturluson** (Icelandic).

Philologist: Ólafr Thorðarson.

Syria (2).

Translator: Philip of Tripoli.

Naturalist: Theodore of Antioch.

To these might possibly be added the historian, Ernoul, who flourished in Syria, though the chances are that he was French born.

Summary[8]

Far East	18 (7):	Japanese	4
		Chinese	14 (7)
Hindus	3 (1)		3 (1)
Muslims	42 (10):	Eastern Muslims	30 (6)
		Western Muslims	12 (4)
Samaritans	2		2
Jews	23 (2):	Eastern Jews	3
		Western Jews	20 (2)
Christians	96 (25):	Eastern Christians	6
		Western Christians	90 (25)
Total	184 (45)	Total	184 (45)

The two Christian groups may be subdivided as follows:

Eastern		Western	
Syriac	2	Italy	22 (7)
Armenian	2	Great Britain	20 (8)
Greek	1	France	20 (2)
Slavonic	1	Central Europe	8 (2)
		Scandinavia	7 (4)
Total	6	Spain	6
		Low Countries	5 (2)
		Syria	2
		Total	90 (25)

The Christian group was now not only the most important, but it was even more important than all the others put together (96 against 88). This was entirely due to Western Christendom, for Eastern Christendom was on a very low level.

The two following tables afford other comparisons between the main groups. In each case the groups are put in the order of numerical importance.

Main Groups		Smaller Groups	
Christians	96 (25)	W. Christians	90 (25)
Muslims	42 (10)	E. Muslims	30 (6)
Jews, Sam.,	25 (2)	W. Jews	20 (2)
Chin., Jap.,	18 (7)	Chinese	14 (7)
Hindus	3 (1)	W. Muslims	12 (4)
		E. Christians	6
Total	184 (45)	Japanese	4
		Hindus	3 (1)
		E. Jews	3
		Samaritans	2
		Total	184 (45)

[8] The figures between parentheses indicate the number of outstanding personalities. See next section.

Among the Christians, the main groups were the Italian, English, and French (see table, Western Christians). Then came Central Europe, Scandinavia, Spain, etc. But for a proper appreciation of the work done, not by special races, but within certain countries, we have to combine the data in other ways.

The following tables explain themselves.

France

Christians	20 (2)
Jews	9 (2)
Total	29 (4)

Italy

Christians	22 (7)
Jews	1
Total	23 (7)

Spain

Muslims	8 (3)
Jews	7
Christians	6
Total	21 (3)

Syria

Muslims	9 (3)
Syriac	2
Latin	2
Samaritan	2
Jews	1
Total	16 (3)

Egypt

Muslims	6 (1)
Jews	2
Total	8 (1)

Central Europe

Christians	8 (2)
Jews	3
Total	11 (2)

Taking all these figures into account, the various nations may be arranged as follows:

Order of Nations

France	29 (4)
Italy	23 (7)
Spain	21 (3)
Great Britain	20 (8)
Syria	16 (3)
China	14 (7)
Central Europe	11 (2)
Egypt	8 (1)
Scandinavia	7 (4)
Low Countries	5 (2)
Japan	4
India	3 (1)

This table is very interesting indeed, but needless to say one should not attach too much importance to it, and one should bear in mind the many qualifications without which it could be grossly misunderstood. To begin with, it does not refer to units of comparable size and population. Then some groups were far more homogeneous than others.

However, we can safely deduce from it that the five leading countries were France, Italy, Spain, England, and Syria. Spain was still one of the leading countries, though no longer the leading one. She was now the third or fourth in importance. The place taken by Syria is very remarkable, and if we had put Syria and Egypt together they would have reached the second rank.

The superiority of France is still clearer if we consider the language. French was thus by far the most important vernacular, the only one which could at all compete with Latin, though it stood a long way behind it. It was truly international, for it was used by Italians like Daniel of Cremona, by Spaniards like William of Tudela, by Englishmen like Walter of Henley, by Jews like Joseph ben Samson, and it was not unknown in Scandinavia.

COMPARATIVE ACHIEVEMENTS OF VARIOUS GROUPS IF ONLY THE OUTSTANDING PERSONALITIES ARE CONSIDERED

Some idea of this question has already been given in the preceding tables, wherein the figures between brackets are the numbers of outstanding personalities. Out of 184 personalities I have selected 45, which may be distributed as follows:

Translators (3): Alfred Sareshel, Samuel ibn Tibbon, Jacob Anaṭoli.

Philosophers and Encyclopaedists (7): Michael Scot, Robert Grosseteste, Bartholomew the Englishman, Thomas of Cantimpré, author of Konungs skuggsjá, 'Abd al-Laṭīf, Ibn 'Arabī.

Mathematicians, Astronomers, Mechanicians (6): Fibonacci, Jordanus Nemorarius, Gerard of Brussels, al-Ḥasan al-Marrākushī, Ch'in Chiu-shao, Li Yeh.

Travelers and Geographers (4): Pian del Càrpine, Yāqūt, Ch'iu Ch'ang-ch'un, Chao Ju-kua.

Naturalists (6): Frederick II, Walter of Henley, Abū-l-'Abbās al-Nabātī, Ibn al-Ṣūrī, Ch'ên Jên-yü, Chia Ssŭ-tao.

Physicians (10): Roland of Parma, Hugh and Theodoric Borgognoni, William of Congenis, Gilbert the Englishman, Richard of Wendover, Harpestraeng, Ibn al-Baiṭār, Śārṅgadhara, Sung Tz'ŭ.

Historians (6): Villehardouin, Snorri Sturluson, Saxo Grammaticus, Ibn al-Athīr, Ibn al-Qifṭī, Ibn abī Uṣaibi'a.

Jurists (2): Accorso, Eike of Repgow.

Philologist (1): John of Garland.

It will be noticed that every group is international. Perhaps the most characteristic fact is the preponderance of Englishmen in the philosophical group. If we consider the geographical distribution of these leaders (see table, Order of Nations), we are also struck by the superiority of the English. Though France and Spain produced each of them more scholars than England, England gave birth to more leaders than these two great nations combined. The most original of the nations was thus England, Italy following close behind. This cannot be accounted for by insularity, for many of the English scientists flourished abroad.

The leadership of China is less surprising, for as its development was almost entirely independent of ours, it was of necessity original. Yet China showed considerably more originality and creative power than Japan.

The originality of Scandinavia is also partly explained by aloofness, but only partly—the main explanation is genius. Compare the publications of these northern peoples in their own vernaculars, with, say, the publications of all the

Eastern Christians combined. What a difference! The explanation is, no doubt, that the Scandinavians were quick, while the Greeks and others were asleep.

If I were pressed to name the ten most important men from our point of view, I would name with some hesitation (for such questions are a little foolish) Villehardouin, Yāqūt, Michael Scot, Jordanus Nemorarius, Fibonacci, Ibn al-Baiṭār, Frederick II, Pian del Càrpine, Robert Grosseteste, Jacob Anaṭoli (they are named in the order of death years). This selection, arbitrary as it is, is a good representation of the age: one Jew, two Muslims, seven Christians; or otherwise, three Italians, two Englishmen, two Frenchmen, one German, one Spaniard, and then Yāqūt, the Muslim Greek!

CHAPTER XXIX

RELIGIOUS BACKGROUND

(First Half of Thirteenth Century)

I. CHRISTENDOM

FRANCISCANS AND DOMINICANS

The two greatest orders of friars (Christian mendicant monks) were founded in the first quarter of the thirteenth century, and they played so prominent a part in the history of civilization, so many of their members contributed to the development of science and philosophy, that it is impossible to understand the thought of their time and of many subsequent centuries without paying considerable attention to them. The Franciscan Order was founded in 1210, and the Order of Preachers in 1215. Before speaking of each of them in particular, their common characteristics may be noticed. While the majority of Christian monks ran away from the people, and tried to spend their lives in secluded monasteries, as far away from the world as possible, the Friars went to the people; they established themselves, not in solitary places deep in the country, but in the growing towns where they could preach to multitudes. They were not attached to monasteries, but simply to their Order, being like independent soldiers of Christ fighting each in his own way for the redemption of the people. They soon realized that it would be impossible to redeem the masses without controlling the education of the leaders, and thus they tried to obtain chairs in the universities, notably in Paris, and this was to be the cause of abundant trouble between them and the other professors of theology.

THE FRANCISCANS (1210)

The earliest of these orders was that of the Franciscans, also called Grey Friars, Friars Minor, or Minorites (The Seraphic Order), founded by St. Francis.

Saint Francis of Assisi, one of the most lovable of men who ever lived, was born in 1181 or 1182 at Assisi, Umbria. Soon after 1202 he experienced a profound spiritual crisis. He began to preach to the poor at Assisi in 1209. As soon as he had gathered eleven disciples they went to Rome and obtained the pope's (Innocent III) sanction. On their return to Assisi they obtained from the Benedictine Abbey on Mount Subasio the use of the chapel of St. Mary of the Angels (Portiuncula) in the plain below Assisi. The order was there inaugurated in 1209 or more probably in 1210. This was the "First Order of St. Francis," restricted to men having vowed to imitate the life of Christ, especially his poverty.

A similar order for women was founded in 1212 when Saint Clara was professed by St. Francis at the Portiuncula. This is the "Second Order of St. Francis" (Poor Clares, Clarisses). St. Clara, born at Assisi in 1194, was the true spiritual sister of St. Francis, and probably of all his disciples the one who understood him best. She was abbess of the convent of St. Damian's, near Assisi—the earliest house of Poor Clares—and died there August 11, 1253.

A third organization, a sort of extension of the Franciscan movement into the lay world, was initiated by St. Francis about 1221. This is the "Third Order of St. Francis."[1] The Third Order was exceedingly successful all over Western Europe, and it became the model of similar extensions of the other mendicant orders, the Tertiaries being in every case controlled by the First and Second Orders.[2] Some of the Tertiaries live together in a community (Regular Tertiaries), others remain in the world, pursuing their ordinary vocations and living with their family (Secular Tertiaries). The Franciscan Tertiaries are submitted to a "Rule of Life" which dates back essentially to St. Francis' original rule of 1221.

The order was sanctioned by the Fourth Lateran Council in 1215. By 1219 it had already grown so much that it was necessary to divide it into Provinces, and that its government far exceeded St. Francis' administrative ability. In 1220 a bull was granted by Pope Honorius III sanctioning anew the organization of the order and appointing Cardinal Hugolino of Ostia (afterwards Gregory IX) its official protector. Soon after (September 1220) St. Francis abdicated as minister-general. He died at the Portiuncula October 3, 1226.

The history of the order after Francis' death is extremely complicated, and cannot be told here. The rule was too severe for many, especially with regard to poverty, both individual and corporate. Thus in the course of time the Franciscan movement branched off in various directions, according to the interpretation of the original rule: Conventuals, whose application of the rule was less severe; Observants, 1370, whose application was more severe; Capuchins (so-called from their hood, capuchon), founded in 1520–1529, more severe still.

The Franciscans are by far the most numerous of all the Christian orders. The Capuchins form the chief branch of Franciscanism; they possess the Portiuncula, and most of the Franciscans of to-day are either Capuchins or Capuchines (the latter organization was founded at Naples in 1538; they are also called Sisters of Suffering).

The Franciscans have devoted themselves mainly to missionary enterprises in distant countries, and among the poor who live near us yet away from us. Their contributions to knowledge and progress have been considerable, as will be shown in the course of my work.

They established themselves in Paris in 1219, and obtained a chair of theology in the University about 1232, the first incumbent being Alexander of Hales. They organized studia particularia in each province, and studia generalia in the main centers—e.g., Paris, Oxford, Toulouse. These studia generalia were intrinsic parts of the university organization in these places. They arrived in England in 1224 (four years later than the Dominicans) and soon obtained there considerable influence.

Bibliography—Andrew George Little: A guide to Franciscan studies (64 p., London 1920).

Luke Wadding (1588–1657): Annales Minorum seu trium ordinum a S. Francisco institutorum (Rome 1625–1654). Editio 2, locupletior et accuratior opera et studio Josephi Mariae Fonseca ab Ebora (25 vols., Rome 1731–1886).

[1] The Tertiaries, Brothers and Sisters of the Order of Penance. A similar organization, that of the Humiliati, was earlier—certainly earlier than 1178—but ended in failure (see second half of twelfth century).

[2] Thus there are Dominican, Carmelite, Augustinian, Servite, Premonstratensian . . . . Tertiaries.

Luke Wadding: Scriptores ordinis Minorum. Quibus accessit syllabus eorum, qui ex eodem ordine pro fide Christi fortiter occubuerunt: Priores atramento, posteriores sanguine christianam religionem asserverunt (Rome 1650). New edition (243 p., Rome 1906). Supplement by Giovanni Giacinto Sbaraglia (Rome 1908 sq.). Girolamo Gobulovich: Biblioteca biobibliografica della Terra Santa e dell'Oriente francescano (Firenze 1906, etc.; new series, 1921, etc.).

St. Francis' Writings—Opera omnia secundum editionem fr. Lucae Waddingi edidit, vitam a Sancto Bonaventura concinnatam textu recognito adjecit Joh. Jos. von der Burg (442 p., Cologne 1849). Scritti, edited by Vittorino Facchinetti (Milano 1921). Franziskus und Dominikus, Leben und Schriften (125 p., Breslau 1926).

Paschal Robinson: The writings of St. Francis (240 p., Philadelphia 1906).

A few Biographies, ancient and modern—Le Speculum perfectionis ou Mémoires de frère Léon sur la seconde partie de la vie de St. François. Latin text edited by Paul Sabatier (382 p., Manchester 1928; Isis, 13, 159). Thomas de Celano (fl. 1257): The lives of St. Francis, translated by A. G. Ferrers Howell (384 p., London 1908). St. Bonaventura (1221–1274): Vita di S. Francesco a cura di G. Battelli (Sancasciano 1926). English translation of St. Bonaventure's life by Emma Gurney-Salter (Temple Classics, 1904). Ferdinand M. Delorme: La Legenda antiqua S. Francisci (92 p., Paris 1926). Text of MS. 1046 of Perugia edited.

Paul Sabatier: Vie de St. François (Paris 1894, often reprinted). Englished by Louise S. Houghton (New York 1894). Walter Goetz: Die Quellen zur Geschichte des hl. Franz (269 p., Gotha 1904). Father Cuthbert: Life of St. Francis (462 p., London 1912). Vittorino Facchinetti: San Francesco (Milano 1921). Luigi Salvatorelli: Vita di San Francesco (Bari 1926). Emma Gurney Salter: Sources for the biography of St. Francis (Speculum, vol. 5, 388–410, 1930).

Franciscan studies—Friedrich Glaser: Die franziskanische Bewegung, ein Beitrag zur Geschichte sozialer Reformideen im Mittelalter (176 p., Stuttgart 1903). Heribert Holzapfel: Handbuch zur Geschichte des Franziskanerordens (752 p., Freiburg i.B., 1909). Karl Balthasar: Geschichte des Armutsstreites im Franziskanerorden bis zum Konzil von Vienne (Münster i.W., 1911). David Saville Muzzey: The spiritual Franciscans (Columbia thesis, 76 p., New York 1907; reprinted, 107 p., Washington 1914). Vlastimil Kybal: Die Ordensregeln des hl. Franz und die ursprüngliche Verfassung des Minoritenordens (176 p., Leipzig 1915). Ellen Scott Davison: Forerunners of St. Francis (Boston 1927; Isis, 11, 145–147).

Henry Thode: Franz von Assisi und die Anfänge der Kunst der Renaissance in Italien (Berlin 1885; 2d ed., 670 p., Berlin 1904). French version by Gaston Lefèvre (2 vols., 64 pl., Paris c. 1910).

A. G. Little: Studies in English Franciscan history (258 p., Manchester 1917; Isis, 3, 280–282). Emma Gurney-Salter: The coming of the Friars Minor to England and to Germany, being the Chronicles of Brother Thomas of Eccleston and Brother Jordan of Giano. Translated from the critical edition by A. G. Little and H. Boehmer (234 p., ill., London 1926). Edward Hutton: The Franciscans in England, 1224–1538 (London 1926; Speculum, 216–222, 1927).

Hilarin Felder (O. M. Cap.): Geschichte der wissenschaftlichen Studien im Franziskanerorden bis zum die Mitte des 13. Jahrhunderts (568 p., Freiburg i. B., 1904). French version by Father Eusèbe of Bar-le-Duc (582 p., Paris 1908). Hilarin Felder: The ideals of St. Francis. Translated by Berchmans Bittle (534 p., New York 1925).

Main Periodicals—Études franciscaines (Paris 1899, sq.). Archivum franciscanum historicum (Ad Claras Aquas prope Florentiam, 1908 sq.). British Society of Franciscan studies (Manchester 1908, sq.). La France franciscaine (Lille 1912, sq.). Franziskanische Studien (Münster i. W., 1914 sq.). Revue d'histoire franciscaine (Paris 1924, sq.).

THE DOMINICANS (1215)

The Dominicans, Friar Preachers, or Black Friars, were founded by St. Dominic.

Saint Dominic (Domingo de Guzmán) was born in 1170 at Caleruega in the province of Burgos. He studied at Palencia, then became an Augustinian canon of the cathedral of Osma. From 1205 to 1215 he was charged by Pope Innocent III to carry on missionary work among the Albigenses of Languedoc. This gave him, in 1214 or before, the idea of creating a religious order the main purpose of which would be to preach and teach the Christian Gospel among infidels and heretics. The organization was approved by Innocent III in 1215, with reservations, then more fully the next year, and finally sanctioned by an encyclical bull in 1218. The success of the order was immediate and enormous and by the time of Dominic's death at Bologna, August 6, 1221, its influence was already felt all over Western Europe.

The Dominican ideal was easier to realize than the Franciscan, and thus the history of the Dominicans was less troubled than that of the Franciscans, though it was by no means free of vicissitudes. The rock upon which the Franciscan communion risked many times being wrecked was the question of poverty, not simply individual but also corporate, upon which St. Francis insisted. This question was far less essential from the Dominican point of view. In 1425 some Dominican houses were already allowed to hold property, and by 1475 this privilege was extended to the whole order which thus ceased to be mendicant. Considering their aim, it is natural that the Dominicans played a very important rôle in the development of mediaeval universities and the systematization of Christian philosophy. It will suffice to recall the names of the two greatest Dominicans of the thirteenth century: Albert the Great and St. Thomas Aquinas. The organization of the Inquisition was also essentially the work of Dominicans. (Hence the nickname, Domini canes.)

The First Order of St. Dominic was founded in 1215 (or 1218). The Second Order was an earlier creation, however, the first nunnery being founded by St. Dominic as early as 1206 near Toulouse. The Third Order dates only from the fifteenth century.

The most important early Dominican communities were those of Paris and Bologna. The Paris Dominicans were familiarly called Brothers of St. James, and those of Bologna, Brothers of St. Nicholas. The Dominicans were established in Paris as early as 1217, and they soon began to make efforts to obtain a chair of theology in the University. They did not succeed until 1229, when a strike of the secular teachers gave them their first opportunity; they obtained a second chair in 1231. The earliest incumbents were Roland of Cremona and John of St. Giles. As I have already observed, trouble arose between the regulars and the seculars, but this did not become serious until the second half of the century (see next book). The Dominicans arrived in England in 1220.

Bibliography—The Dominican literature, though smaller than the Franciscan, is nevertheless very considerable. I can but quote a few titles.

Jacques Quétif (1618–1698) and Jacques Echard: Scriptores Ordinis Praedicatorum recensiti (2 vols., Paris 1719–1721). Second edition, corrected and brought up-to-date by Remi Coulon (Paris 1910, sq.). Antoine Touron: Histoire des hommes illustres de l'Ordre de Saint Dominique (6 vols., Paris 1743–1749). Pierre Félix Mandonnet: Les Dominicains et la découverte de l'Amérique (Paris 1893).

Andreas Frühwirth (and others): Analecta sacra Ordinis Fratrum Praedicatorum (Rome 1893, sq.). D. A. Mortier: Histoire des maitres généraux de l'ordre (8 vols., Paris 1903–1920). Pierre F. Mandonnet: Order of Preachers (Catholic Encyclopaedia, vol. 12, 354–370, 1911). Ernest Barker: The Dominican Order and convocation, a study of the growth of representation in the church during the thirteenth century (83 p., Oxford 1913). Berthold Altaner: Die Dominikanermissionen des 13. Jahrhunderts. Forschungen zur Geschichte der kirchlichen Unionen und der Mohammedaner- und Heidenmission des Mittelalters (Habelschwerdt, Schlesien, 1924). Mrs. Georgina Rosalie (Cole-Baker) Galbraith: The constitution of the Dominican order from 1216 to 1360 (Publications of the University of Manchester, histor. series, 44; 302 p., 1925).

On Roland of Cremona, see Alexandre Birkenmajer: Le rôle joué par les médecins et les naturalistes dans la réception d'Aristote (La Pologne au VIe Congrès international des sciences historiques, Oslo, 1928; 15 p., Warsaw 1930; Isis. 15, 272).

INFLUENCE OF FRANCISCANS AND DOMINICANS ON THE PROGRESS OF CIVILIZATION

The spiritual attitude of the Franciscans and that of the Dominicans were very different, if not antagonistic. To put it as simply as possible (too simply), the former spoke to the heart, the latter to the head; the former continued the Platonic tendencies of early Christendom, the latter made it their special task to develop Aristotelian philosophy and to adapt it to Christian theology. The former had perhaps less intellectual curiosity but more intellectual freedom. It is not a mere matter of chance that Roger Bacon was a Grey Friar, and St. Thomas Aquinas a Black Friar.

Both orders aided the progress of thought to the same extent that all religious fraternities have, in creating a more disinterested attitude of the mind with regard to the material world, also in providing retreats where the more studious and wistful could be protected from that world when it became too oppressive and too ugly. Before the creation of Universities—and these remained for centuries restricted to a relatively small number of localities—the religious orders provided the main asylums for those who wanted solitude and peace to think out their problems, the main centers of research and teaching, the main focuses of human devotion and charity.

While writing this I keep in mind that their intellectual influence was sometimes a very evil one; witness the Dominican Inquisition. Thus, of all human affairs. Institutions specifically devised to foster freedom may become instruments of servitude. Our modern universities reveal sometimes obscurantist tendencies, and our democracies are not always all that they pretend to be. We must consider the main drift of events.

To complete this attempt to explain our debt to the Friars Grey and Black, it will suffice to name here all of those whose work and activity have been dealt with in my survey. They are arranged in the order of their death years.

The double list is sufficiently impressive and makes further comment unnecessary.

Dominicans[2a]	*Franciscans*
St. Dominic (d. 1221)	Giles of Corbeil (d. 1222)
	St. Francis of Assisi (d. 1226)
Jordanus Nemorarius (d. 1237)	
	Bartholomew the Englishman (fl.c. 1240)
	Alexander de Villedieu (d.c. 1240)
	Nicholas Donin of La Rochelle (fl.c. 1240)
	Alexander of Hales (d. 1245)
	John of La Rochelle (d. 1245)
Andrew of Longjumeau (fl.c. 1250)	John of Parma (?) (fl.c. 1250)
Ascelin (or Anselm) (fl.c. 1250)	
Walter de Henley (fl.m. XIII)	
	Giov. Pian del Carpine (d. 1252)
	St. Clara of Assisi (d. 1253)
	William of Rubruquis (fl.c. 1255)
	Adam Marsh (d. 1257)
	Guibert of Tournay (fl.c. 1259)
John of Vicenza (d. before 1260)	Thomas of York (d. 1260)
Hugh of St. Cher (d. 1263)	
Vincent of Beauvais (d. 1264)	
	Peter Gallego (d. 1267)
St. Thomas Aquinas (d. 1274)	St. Bonaventure (d. 1274)
Raymond of Peñafort (d. 1275)	
Thomas of Cantimpré (d.c. 1271–1280)	
Burchard of Mount Sion (fl.c. 1276)	
Ulrich of Strassburg (d. 1277)	
Martin of Troppau (d. 1278)	
Robert Kilwardby (d. 1279)	
Albert the Great (d. 1280)	
William of Moerbeke (d.c. 1286)	
Raymond Martin (d. before 1286)	
Nicholas of Poland (fl. 1279–1288)	Richard Middleton (fl.c. 1284–1288)
	Salimbene (d. before 1288)
	William of Ware (fl. last quarter of thirteenth century)
Bernard of Trilia (d. 1292)	Roger Bacon (d. 1292)
	John Peckham (d. 1292)
Theodoric Borgognoni (d. 1298)	William de la Mare (d. 1298)
	Peter Olivi (d. 1298)
Peter of Dacia (fl. end XIII)	Peter of Trabibus (fl. end XIII)
	Bernard of Verdun (fl. end XIII)
Giles of Lessines (d.c. 1304)	
	Duns Scot (d. 1308)
	Ramon Lull (Tert.) (d. 1315)
Ricoldo di Monte Croce (d. 1320)	

[2a] This double list was compiled by Miss M. C. Welborn.

CARMELITES

The order of Carmelites (or White Friars) was founded probably about the middle of the twelfth century by a Calabrian crusader named Berthold, and ten companions of his, near the cave of Elias on Mount Carmel. A Greek pilgrim, Phocas (second half of twelfth century), visiting Mount Carmel in 1185, gave some account of them. However, their earliest constitution was not given to them until c. 1210, by Albert, Latin patriarch of Jerusalem. This date, c. 1210, may be considered the date of formal foundation of the order; the early rule was strictly eremetical; it was sanctioned by the pope in 1226. The unsafe conditions obtaining in Palestine obliged the friars to move away about 1240, first to Cyprus, then to Sicily, France and England. The first general chapter of the order was held in the last named country, at Aylesford, on the Medway (Kent), in 1245, and the Englishman, St. Simeon Stock,[3] was elected general. Under his direction the rule was mitigated (1248) and transformed into a coenobitical rule of the mendicant type. The Carmelites thus became one of the four great orders of mendicant friars.

The vicissitudes of the order need not be related here. It will suffice to remark that it was subject to the same ordeal as the Franciscan order, a continuous internal strife between radicals and moderates.

The order seems to have been especially successful in England. For a long time it was restricted to men; and no Carmelite nunnery existed before the middle of the fifteenth century. Yet it is from one of these early nunneries that a new movement for reform was started, which was to lead in the course of time to the creation of an independent community.

Teresa de Cepeda (St. Theresa of Jesus, born in Avila, 1515; died in Alva, 1582), after having spent thirty years in a Carmelite convent at Avila, Old Castile, was "converted" in 1554, and gradually led to establish at Avila in 1562 a rule of greater austerity, reproducing as much as possible primitive Carmelite life. The same reform was carried through in the monasteries with the help of Juan de Yepez y Álvarez (Juan de la Cruz, born at Ontiveros, Old Castile, 1542; died at Ubeda, 1591). After considerable struggle, the new order obtained semi-independence in 1580 and complete independence in 1593. As these Carmelites wore sandals in place of shoes and stockings, they were called Descalzos (Déchaussés, Barefoots, Discalced). At the present time the Discalced Carmelites are far more numerous than the Calced ones; their intense missionary activity has carried them all over the world. St. Theresa and St. John of the Cross composed a number of mystical writings in Spanish; both were ultimately canonized, she in 1622, he in 1726.

Text—Antiquas ordinis constitutiones, acta capitulorum generalium, tractatus de prioribus generalibus, de magistris parisiensibus necnon epistolas diversas edidit Benedictus Zimmerman (Monumenta historica carmelitana, 1, Liriniae, ex typis abbatiae, 1907). Acta capitulorum generalium ordinis fratrum B. V. Mariae de Monte Carmelo. Vol. 1 ab anno 1318 usque ad annum 1593. Cum notis B. Zimmerman, auctoritate P. M. Mayer, edidit Gabriel Wessels (Rome 1912; no more published).

Criticism—San Juan de la Cruz; revista carmelitano-teresiana dirigada por los PP. Carmelitas Descalzos (Segovia 1890, etc.). Etudes carmélitaines; historiques et critiques sur les traditions, les privilèges et la mystique de l'ordre par les pères

[3] St. Simeon Stock, born c. 1165, studied in Oxford, died in Bordeaux, 1265. Propagator of the "scapular."

Carmes déchaussés de la province de France (Paris 1911, etc.). Table générale analytique, 1911–1922.

Excellent introductory article by Edward Cuthbert Butler, O. S. B., in Encyclopaedia Britannica (11th ed., vol. 5, 358, 1911). P. R. McCaffrey: The White Friars. An outline of Carmelite history with special reference to the English-speaking provinces (Dublin 1926; illustr.).

See biographies of St. Theresa of Jesus, and of St. John of the Cross.

AUGUSTINIANS

The fourth of the mendicant orders,[4] the Augustinians, was founded under papal direction about the middle of the century. The Augustinians or Augustinian Hermits, are also called, improperly, Black Friars. They ought not to be confused with the Augustinian Canons (second half of eleventh century). The Augustinian Order was largely the result of the organization of sundry small groups of Italian hermits. They followed the so-called Rule of St. Augustine and were organized on the model of the Franciscan and Dominican communities. The new order spread rapidly over Western Europe, producing a great many variations which remained loosely united under the same general. A later variation occurred in Germany, c. 1500, and separated itself entirely from the main body; it will be remembered that Luther was one of those German separatists whose congregation was dissolved in 1526. There are still a small number of convents of Augustinian Hermits (Hermitesses) to-day, and also organizations of Augustinian Tertiaries.

Davide Aurelio Perini: Augustiniani scriptores (Rome 1911, sq.). Gregorio de Santiago Vela: Ensayo de una biblioteca ibero-americana de la Orden de San Augustin (Madrid 1913–22).

MERCEDARIANS

The Order of Our Lady of Mercy (Orden de Nuestra Señora de la Merced) is a congregation of men founded in 1218 by St. Peter Nolasco. Its purpose was similar to that of the Trinitarians (second half of twelfth century), namely, to ransom captives, especially those fallen into Muslim hands. It was thus an additional illustration of the struggle between Christendom and Islām. It included both religious members or monks, and lay ones or knights.

Peter Nolasco was born in 1189 (or 1182) at Mas-des-Saintes-Puelles, near Castelnaudary (Languedoc); he was a soldier in Simon de Montfort's army fighting the Albigenses; later he was appointed tutor to the young king, James of Aragon, in Barcelona. He founded the new order in that city, with the advice and help of Raymond of Peñafort. The latter is sometimes called the founder. Raymond drew the first rule, but Peter was the first superior or Commander General, and the first Ransomer (i.e., the monk who was sent to the Moors to negotiate a ransom); Peter resigned in 1249, and died at Barcelona in 1256.

The Order was approved by Honorius III, and by Gregory IX, who granted a bull of confirmation in 1230 and prescribed the Rule of St. Augustine. It developed rapidly in France, England, Germany, Portugal, and Spain. Its great success caused various vicissitudes which do not concern us. Some Mercedarians accompanied Columbus to the New World, where they made a great many proselytes; the order has remained to this day far more important in Latin America than in Europe.

[4] The first three being the Franciscans, Dominicans, and Carmelites.

Gari y Siumell: Bibliotheca mercedaria (Barcelona 1875). Revista Mercedaria, published by the monastery of Cordova. J. M. Besse: Catholic Encyclopaedia (vol. 10, 197, 1911). Faustino D. Gazulla: Refutación de un libro titulado S. Raimundo de Peñafort, Fundator de la Orden de la Merced (Barcelona 1920).

THE SERVITES

The order of the Servites, or Servants of Mary, was founded in 1233 by seven merchants of Florence near that city. The very austere rule, promulgated in 1240, is essentially the Augustinian with some modifications inspired by the Dominican example. The order received the papal sanction in 1255. The chief organizer was the fifth general, Filippo Benizzi, who was born in Florence in 1233, studied philosophy and medicine in Paris, practiced medicine in Florence and Padua, and finally joined the order; he died in 1285, and was canonized in 1671. There is a corresponding order for women, and there are also Servite Tertiaries.

Arcangelo Giani: Annalium sacri ordinis fratrum Servorum B. Mariae Virginis a suae institutionis exordio centuriae quatuor (3 vols. folio, Lucae, 1719–1725).

AMAURY OF BÊNE AND DAVID OF DINANT

Amaury or Amalric of Bêne, or Bennes, near Chartres. Taught at the University of Paris. Died in 1206. Influenced by Scot Erigena (second half of ninth century), and by the School of Chartres; he developed a pantheistic theology (Omnia unum, quia quidquid est est Deus. Nemo potest esse salvus, nisi credat se esse membrum Christi).

Similar views were defended by another theologian, David of Dinant,[5] of whom nothing is known except that he had an interview with Pope Innocent III in 1212. Amaury left no writings; and David's works, which were especially obnoxious because they were written in the French vernacular, were burned; we know their views only indirectly from those who opposed them.

Amaury's philosophy was censored by the University of Paris in 1204, and condemned by Pope Innocent III in 1207. Yet he found many followers, the Amauricians or Amalricians, who combined the original pantheism with other mystical and apocalyptic ideas; twelve of them were condemned to death in 1210 by a Parisian synod, which ordered at the same time that Amaury's body be exhumed from consecrated ground. That this heresy continued is proved by the fact that Innocent III found it necessary to condemn it again at the Fourth Lateran Council (Rome, 1215).

It is interesting to compare this pantheistic propaganda with the mystical views which arrived at about the same time from South Italy. The writings of the Calabrian mystic, Joachim of Floris (second half of the twelfth century) became especially popular in the first half of the thirteenth century, especially among the most rigorous Franciscans, and they spread rapidly beyond the Alps. The Joachimite views were not formally condemned until 1255; they inspired directly or indirectly an enormous literature.

Text—Clemens Baeumker: Contra Amaurianos. Ein anonymer, wahrscheinlich dem Garnerius von Rochefort zugehöriger Traktat aus dem Anfang des XIII. Jahrhunderts. Mit Nachrichten über die übrigen unedierten Werke des Garnerius

[5] Dinant on the Meuse in Belgium, not Dinan in Brittany.

(Beiträge zur Geschichte der Philosophie des Mittelalters, Bd. 24, Heft 5–6, 110 p., Münster 1926). This Garnerius of Rochefort was a Cistercian who became bishop of Langres in 1192, and died at Clairvaux after 1215; Mandonnet would ascribe the same text to Rudolph of Namur.

Criticism—P. Alphandéry: Les idées morales chez les hétérodoxes latins au début de XIIIe siècle (Paris 1903). P. Duhem: Système du monde (vol. 5, 244–249, 1917). Gustave Théry: David de Dinant (Bibliothèque thomiste, 6, 150 p., Kain, 1925). M. de Wulf: Mediaeval philosophy (vol. 1, 191–195, 1926).

Auguste Jundt: L'apocalypse mystique du moyen âge et la Matelda de Dante (Leçon d'ouverture; Séance de l'Université de Paris, 17–71, 1886). Johann Chrysostomus Huck: Ubertin von Casale und dessen Ideenkreis (114 p., Freiburg 1903).

For Everard of Bethune and John of Garland, see philological chapter, below.

ORGANIZATION OF THE INQUISITION

Man is naturally intolerant with regard to the religious beliefs and spiritual attitude of his neighbors. Such intolerance is but one aspect of human gregariousness which was, and still is, an important factor of the stability of civilization, and thus a condition of progress. The primeval human herd cannot stand many leaders; it tends to exterminate all of them but the very few which it immediately needs. This is still true, though to an increasingly smaller extent, of civilized societies. Thus we must expect many forms of inquisition of "heretics," and of their persecution, private and public, to occur throughout the course of human history. The things to be explained are not the inquisitions, but the rare moments of complete toleration.

However, it is remarkable that in the early Middle Ages the persecution of heretics took but rarely (as, for example, in the case of the Manichaeans) a violent form. One can even say that religious persecution entailing the penalty of death was not generally introduced into Christian Europe until the end of the twelfth century. The one individual who must bear the heaviest responsibility with regard to that criminal introduction was Innocent III, pope from 1198 to 1216. Innocent's motives were the highest, and he showed for a time unusual forbearance,[6] yet he considered the Albigensian heresy to be so subversive of Christian civilization that it could not possibly be endured and he resolved to stamp it out (1198, 1207). This work of Innocent III was completed by others, chiefly by the Emperor Frederick II, and Gregory IX (pope from 1227 to 1241). The latter realized the use that could be made of the great number of friars already spread all over Western Europe, and may be said to have created the monastic inquisition (in 1231 or soon before). In 1233 he decided to entrust this sacred task, the discovery and repression of heresy, to the Dominicans. Later, the organization of the inquisition in various parts of the world remained entirely in the hands of friars, in most cases Dominicans. In 1252, by the bull Ad extirpanda, Innocent IV approved the use of torture to obtain confessions. The number of victims of that early inquisition remained relatively small; it did not begin to take larger proportions until the fifteenth century and later. In the meanwhile the issues of heresy and witchcraft had become more and more confused. (See my note on Witchcraft, second half of the fifteenth century).

With regard to the extirpation of the Albigensian heresy from southern France,

[6] See Isis, 11, 146.

it is well to bear in mind that this was not merely a religious question. It was almost from the beginning, and became more and more, a political war, a war of conquest against the counts of Toulouse and other feudal lords of the south, the religious issue being used as a pretext, and a fuel. One result of these persecutions and wars was a greater unification of France. After the middle of the thirteenth century southern France developed to a larger extent within the orbit of royal France.

Literature—Henry Charles Lea: History of the Inquisition of the Middle Ages (3 vols., New York 1887; this is still the best general account). J. J. I. von Döllinger: Beiträge zur Sektengeschichte des Mittelalters (2 vols., München 1890). Joseph Hansen: Zauberwahn, Inquisition und Hexenprozess im Mittelalter (554 p., München 1900); Quellen und Untersuchungen zur Geschichte des Hexenwahns (715 p., Bonn 1901). Célestin Douais: L'inquisition, ses origines, sa procédure (378 p., Paris 1906). Elphège Vacandard: The Inquisition. Transl. from the 2d. ed. (302 p., New York 1908, 1921; fair-minded account by a Catholic priest). Henri Maillet: L'église et la répression sanglante de l'hérésie (120 p., Liège 1909). Hermann Theloe: Die Ketzerverfolgungen im 11. und 12. Jahrhundert (179 p., Berlin 1913). Charles Turner Gorham: The medieval inquisition (126 p., London 1908). Arthur Stanley Tuberville: Medieval heresy and the Inquisition (London 1920). Hoffmann Nickerson: The Inquisition, a political and military study of its establishment. Preface by Hilaire Belloc (Boston 1923).

Special studies devoted to the French inquisition—Célestin Douais: Documents pour servir à l'histoire de l'Inquisition dans le Languedoc (2 vols., Paris 1900). Charles H. Haskins: Robert le Bougre and the beginnings of the inquisition in northern France (American historical review, vol. 7, 437–457, 631–652, 1902; revised in Studies in mediaeval culture (193–244, Oxford 1929; Isis, 14, 433–436). Th. de Cauzons: Histoire de l'Inquisition en France (Paris 1909, sq.). See my note on the Cathari (first half of twelfth century).

JOHN OF VICENZA

Giovanni da Vicenza. Italian Dominican, born towards the end of the twelfth century, died after 1260. In 1233 he began to preach mutual toleration and forgiveness to the people of Bologna, in order to put an end to their factions. He delivered the same message with considerable success to many other cities of northern Italy, and finally organized an immense peace meeting on the plain of Paquara, near Verona, on August 28, 1233. A peace treaty was then concluded proclaiming reciprocal forgiveness and peace for the whole of northern Italy. Giovanni denounced the practice of judicial astrology, thus incurring the hatred of Guido Bonatti (second half of the thirteenth century). Unfortunately the immense prestige which he had won for himself was soon ruined by his inordinate ambition. He tried to rule Vicenza and Verona, misused his power to obtain death sentences against sixty heretics, and was promptly obliged to retire into seclusion. In 1247 he began a new campaign against the heretics of Lombardy.

Nouvelle biographie générale (vol. 26, 565–566, 1858). John Addington Symonds: Renaissance in Italy (vol. 1, 3d ed., 474–475, 1897).

RAYMOND OF PEÑAFORT

Raimundus de Pennaforti. San Ramón (Raimundo) de Peñafort (Penyafort, Peniafort). Catalan theologian. Born in the castle of Peñafort, near Villafranca del Panadès (Barcelona), c. 1175; flourished in Barcelona, and died there in 1275.

Canonized in 1601. He studied in Bologna in 1210, etc.; assumed the Dominican habit in 1222, and was general of the order (the third one) in 1238–1240. Gregory IX (pope from 1227 to 1241) entrusted to him the compilation of the Decretales, 1228–1234 (about which, see my note on Gratian, first half of the twelfth century). He was one of the organizers of the Inquisition in Aragon and South France, and one of the founders of the religious order called la Merced (1218). It was he who organized the public disputation between Moses ibn Naḥman (q.v.) and Pablo Christiani in 1263. In 1264 he was commissioned, together with Raymond Martin (q.v.) and others, to examine and censor the Talmud.

Text—Summula sacramentorum (Cologne 1500, 1502). Summa pastoralis, in Catalogue général des manuscrits de France (vol. 1, 592–649, 1849).

Criticism—Potthast (1542, 1896). Nicolas Eymerich: Vita antiqua Sancti Raymundi (Raymundiana, part 1, 1898).

Ludwig von Rockinger: Berthold von Regensburg und Raimund von Peniafort im sogenannten Schwabenspiegel (Abhd. der bayer. Akad., 89 p., 1877). Buenaventura Ribas y Quintana: Estudios historicos y bibliográficos sobre san Ramon de Penyafort (Mem. Acad. de Buenas Letras, Barcelona 1890). Francis Balme and Ceslaus Paban: Raymundiana, seu documenta quae pertinent ad S. Raymundi de Pennaforti vitam et scripta (Monumenta ordinis fratrum praedicatorum historica, 6; parts 1–2, Rome 1898–1901; no more published). Faustino D. Gazulla: Refutación de un libro titulado San Raimundo de Peñafort, Fundador de la Orden de la Merced (by Enrique Vacas Galindo) (Barcelona 1920). Elaborate article with abundant bibliography, unsigned, in the Enciclopedia universal ilustrada (vol. 49, 405–409, 1923). E. Allison Peers: Ramon Lull (London 1929; Isis, 13, 368).

HUGH OF SAINT CHER

Hugo de Sancto Caro (Charo). Hugues de Saint Cher. Born at Saint Cher, near Vienne, Dauphiné; assumed the Dominican habit in Paris, 1225; provincial of France in 1227, and again in 1236, in the meanwhile prior of the monastery of St. James, Paris; vicar general of his order in 1240, and confidential adviser to Gregory IX, Innocent IV and Alexander IV (popes from 1227 to 1264); created cardinal priest by the second of these in 1244; apostolic legate to Germany after the death of Frederick II; died at Orvieto in 1263.

French theologian and scholar, the greatest Biblical scholar of his time in Christendom. His main title to remembrance is the first revision of the Vulgate begun in 1236 by the Dominican Order under his direction, and the edition of the first Latin concordance to the Bible, compiled by many of his brethren.

It would seem that Hugh's revision of the Vulgate was made with reference to the Hebrew and Greek texts; but this was done awkwardly in an unscientific way (it was more like a big commercial rather than a scholarly undertaking) and was rightly criticized by Bacon.

Hugh wrote abundant commentaries on the Bible, and on the Sentences of Peter the Lombard, and sermons.

He was instrumental in the condemnation of the Introductorius in evangelium aeternum by Gherardo del Borgo San Donnino (1254), and of the De periculis novissimorum temporum (1255) by William of Saint Amour (d. 1272).

The concordance to the Vulgate has also been ascribed to the Italian Franciscan, Arloto of Prato, in Tuscany, who died in Paris, 1286.

Text—The Correctorium of the Vulgate was revised in 1248, 1256, and became the Correctorium Bibliae Sorbonicum.

The Concordantiae sacrorum bibliorum (or Concordantiae S. Jacobi, or Concordiantiae bibliorum utriusque Testamenti) was often printed: Nurnberg 1485, etc. Convenient edition in 2 vols. (Avignon 1786).

Postilliae in sacram scripturam juxta quadruplicem sensum, litteralem, allegoricum, anagogicum et moralem. Many fifteenth and sixteenth century editions. Collected edition in 8 vols. (Venice 1754).

Criticism—P. C. F. Daunou: Histoire littéraire de la France (vol. 19, 38–49, 1838). Heinrich Denifle: Die Handschriften der Bibel-Correctorien des 13. Jahrhunderts (Archiv für Litteratur und Kirchengeschichte, vol. 4, 1888). Samuel Berger: Quam notitiam linguae hebraicae habuerint christiani medii aevi temporibus in Gallia (72 p., Nancy 1893); Histoire de la Vulgate pendant les premiers siècles du Moyen âge (468 p., Paris 1893).

NICETAS ACOMINATOS

See historical chapter, below.

II. ISRAEL

ABRAHAM BEN NATHAN

Abraham ben Nathan ha-Yarḥi. Called Rabn for short, from the initials of his name. French Talmudist, who was born in Lunel, Languedoc (hence the name Yarḥi; yareaḥ means lune, moon). He was educated in Lunel, and later in Dampierre, Champagne. He traveled extensively in western Europe, and finally settled in Toledo. It was in that city that he began, in 1204, his main work, Sefer ha-manhig (The guide) or Manhig 'olam (Guide of the world). The dates of his birth and death are unknown. The Manhig is a guide of ritual observances, which is historically valuable because it explains the customs of many countries (western Germany, northern France, Burgundy, Champagne, England) and illustrates their great diversity. It is divided into two parts, the first of which is a collection of his own responsa, the second a collection of extracts from the two Talmuds, the Midrashim, and many other works. It contains, among other things, the Hebrew translation of a responsum by Saadia Gaon; this would suggest (but does not prove) that Abraham had learned Arabic.

Text—First edition of the Manhig, Constantinople, 1519. Second edition with index and notes by N. A. Goldberg (Berlin 1855). The order of chapters is different in the second edition. Responsa edited in Solomon Aaron Wertheimer: Ginze Yerushalayim (Jerusalem 1896).

Criticism—E. Renan: Rabbins·français (521, 747, 1877). Louis Ginzberg: Jewish Encyclopaedia (vol. 1, 116–117, 1901). Siegfried Bernfeld: Encyclopaedia Judaica (vol. 1, 524–528, 1928).

MOSES BEN JACOB

Moses ben Jacob of Coucy. Moses of Coucy. French Talmudist. Studied in Paris; he had a good knowledge of French, Spanish, and Arabic; in 1235–1236, he lectured in various French and Spanish synagogues; in Paris, 1240, he was one of the rabbis designated to answer Donin's denunciations. A few years later he completed his main work, the Sefer ha-miẓwot. This is an attempt to codify Mosaic law under 613 headings; namely, 365 prohibitions and 248 positive commandments.[7] Judging by the number of MSS., editions, and commentaries, this work was immensely popular. The Miẓwot is often called Sefer miẓwot ha-gadol (Semag, for short; a name also given to the author), to distinguish it from an epitome compiled in 1277 by Isaac ben Joseph of Corbeil, which is called Sefer miẓwot ha-qaṭon (Semaq, for short).

Text—First edition of the Miẓwot printed at Rome (?) before 1480. Second edition, Soncino 1488. Many later editions with various commentaries.

Edition by Sebastian Münster entitled Miẓwot lo ta'aseh u-miẓwot 'aseh, with Latin translation, Praecepta Mosaica sexcenta atque tredecim cum succincta Rabbinorum expositione (Basel 1533).

The Semaq, or abbreviated edition by Isaac ben Joseph of Corbeil, was first printed in Constantinople (1510?), with notes by Pharez ben Elijah, and a preface by Mordecai ben Nathan. Many later editions.

Criticism—Max Schloessinger: Jewish Encyclopedia (vol. 9, 68–70, 1905; with facsimile of a page of the first edition of the Miẓwot). For Isaac of Corbeil see S. Kahn (ibidem, vol. 6, 623, 1904).

ABRAHAM BEN AZRIEL

Bohemian Talmudist, who flourished in the first half of the thirteenth century in Bohemia. He composed, c. 1234, a commentary on the Maḥzor (collection of prayers and piyyuṭim, varying according to place and time), entitled 'Arugat ha bosem (Bed of spices), which is culturally interesting as the earliest important literary effort of the Slavonic Jewry. It contains many Bohemian glosses. A commentary on the Seliḥot (penitential prayers), also ascribed to him, contains fewer Bohemian phrases than French ones. If this ascription is correct, it would prove that Abraham had been partly educated in France, or by French rabbis. He was also acquainted with the works of the Jewish grammarians of Spain, and with those of the German Qabbalists, Judah ha-Ḥasid and Eleazar of Worms.

Louis Ginzberg: Jewish Encyclopaedia (vol. 1, 98, 1901). S. H. Lieben: Encyclopaedia Judaica (vol. 1, 418, 1928).

ISAIAH BEN MALI OF TRANI

"Rid." Often called Isaiah of Trani, the Elder, to distinguish him from his daughter's son, Isaiah (ben Elijah) of Trani, the Younger (second half of the thirteenth century). Italian Talmudist. Born c. 1180, founded a Jewish school in Trani (on the Adriatic, north of Bari delle Puglie, Apulia), and lived probably in Venice; he died c. 1250. He was one of the foremost Italian Talmudists and remained for centuries one of their main authorities, his prestige as an exponent of the law being comparable to that which Jacob ben Meir Tam enjoyed in France, and Maimonides in the East.

His main works are: (1) a commentary on the Pentateuch, Nimmuqim (or Nimmuqe Ḥomesh), which is largely a collection of glosses on Rashi; (2) commentaries on the Talmud, in the form of tosafot, or novellae (ḥiddushim), or decisions (pesaqim); (3) a collection of ninety-two halakic discussions, Sefer ha-makri'a. He was very clear, and showed much moderation; for example, in the conflicts between the theological and philosophical points of view.

[7] These numbers were not introduced by Moses ben Jacob. The tradition that there are 613 positive and negative commandments in the Torah may be traced back at least to the ninth century and is found in various Jewish and Samaritan works. For the Samaritan tradition, see my note on Abū-l-Isḥāq Ibrāhīm (second half of the twelfth century).

Text—Nimmuqim, printed in appendix to Ḥayim Joseph David Azulai: Pene David (Leghorn 1792).

There are many partial editions of his Talmudic commentaries.

The Makri'a was first printed in Leghorn, 1779.

Criticism—Max Schloessinger: Jewish Encyclopaedia (vol. 6, 644, 1904).

DONIN

Nicholas Donin of La Rochelle. Jewish renegade, who was largely responsible for the Christian efforts to suppress the Talmud. Having been excommunicated by the synagogue in Paris, 1225, he assumed the Franciscan habit, c. 1235. He is said to have been the main artisan of the Jewish persecutions which were then committed by Crusaders in Brittany, Poitou, and Anjou (some 3000 Jews being killed, 500 baptized). In 1238 he went to Rome and denounced the Talmud to Gregory IX (pope from 1227 to 1241), charging that it contained blasphemies against God and Christianity, and was the main cause of Jewish resistance to conversion. The pope ordered that all copies of the Talmud be confiscated, and that its contents be investigated. Saint Louis (king of France from 1226 to 1270) followed up this matter vigorously, the Jews of France being compelled in 1240 to surrender their Talmuds or forfeit their lives. Moreover, he ordered a public disputation between Donin and four rabbis, Jehiel of Paris, Moses of Coucy, David of Melun, and Samuel ben Solomon of Château-Thierry. The debate was opened on June 12, 1240. It is interesting to note that William of Auvergne and Albert the Great attended it. The Talmud was finally condemned, and a great many copies of it and of other Hebrew books were burned in Paris in 1242 (or 1244). In 1247 Pope Innocent IV (1243–1254) was willing to reopen the case, but his legate condemned the Talmud a second time in 1248. This was a terrible blow to Talmudic studies in France. On the other hand, the persecutions, originated by Donin, and which were continued spasmodically for centuries, may be said to have stimulated Hebrew studies among a certain number of Gentiles.

Meir of Rothenburg (second half of the thirteenth century), who had witnessed the public burning of the Talmud, celebrated the event in an elegy which is chanted to this day in the synagogues on the ninth of Ab.

Criticism—I. Ziegler: Religiöse Disputationen im Mittelalter (Francfort 1894). I. Broydé: Jewish Encyclopaedia (vol. 4, 638, 1903). Max L. Margolis and Alexander Marx: History of the Jewish people (378, 1927).

For the Qabbalists, see the philosophical section; for Tanḥum Yerushalmi, see the philological chapter.

For the Samaritan, Ṣadaqa ben Munaja', see the medical chapter.

III. ISLĀM

ABŪ-L-BAQĀ'

Abū-l-Baqā' Ṣāliḥ ibn al-Ḥusain al-Ja'farī. In 1221–1222 he wrote a refutation of Christianity and Judaism (Kitāb al-bayān al-wāḍiḥ al-mashhūd min faḍā'iḥ al-Naṣārā wal-Yahūd) in answer to a letter sent by the Roman emperor to the Ayyūbid king of Egypt, al-Kāmil Muḥammad (ruled from 1218 to 1238). It is also called Takhjīl man ḥarrafa al-tauriya wal-injīl.

A later publication by one Abū-l-Faḍl al-Mālikī al-Su'ūdī (1536) is essentially an extract from the Takhjīl.

Text—Abū-l-Baqā's treatise was edited by F. Triebs: Liber decem quaestionum contra Christianos (Diss., Bonn 1897).

Al-Su'ūdī's, by T. J. van den Hamm: Disputatio pro religione Muhammedanorum adversus Christianos (Leiden, 1877–1890).

Criticism—Ḥājī Khalīfa (Flügel's ed., vol. 2, 249). C. Brockelmann: Arabische Litteratur (vol. 1, 430, 1898; vol. 2, 329, 1902). C. van Arendonck: Encyclopaedia of Islām (vol. 4, 572, 1928).

IBN AL-ṢALĀḤ

Abū 'Amr 'Uthmān Ibn Ṣalāḥ al-dīn Ibn al-Ṣalāḥ al-Shahrazūrī, Taqī al-dīn. Born in 1181–1182, near Shahrazūr, Kurdistān; studied in Mūṣul; taught in Jerusalem and in Damascus, where he died in 1245. Shāfi'ite doctor and traditionalist; one of the most learned men of his time. His work on traditions (ḥadīth), entitled Kitāb aqṣā' l-amal wal-shauq fī 'ulūm ḥadīth al-rasūl (The liveliest hope and desire in the knowledge of traditions of the Prophet), was exceedingly popular. Among his other works I quote only a treatise on the rites of the Pilgrimage (Kitāb ṣilat al-nāsik fī ṣifat al-manāsik).

Ibn Khallikān: de Slane's translation (vol. 2, 188–191, 1843). Ibn Khaldūn: Prolégomènes (vol. 2, 468, 1865). F. Wüstenfeld: Geschichtschreiber (121, 1881). C. Brockelmann: Arabische Litteratur (vol. 1, 358, 1898).

IBN AL-ḤĀJIB

See philological chapter, below.

IV. BUDDHISM

By the thirteenth century Buddhism was already extinct in India proper, surviving only in Ceylon, Nepal, and Burma. Chinese Buddhism continued, but without originality, being carried ahead by its own immense inertia.

HUI HUNG

Hui[4] Hung[2] (5199, 5252). Flourished, c. 1227. Chinese Buddhist. He wrote, c. 1227, the Ch'an[2]-lin[2] sêng[1]-pao[3] ch'uan[2] (348, 7157, 9617, 8720, 2740), in 30 books, containing the biographies of 81 Buddhist priests and detailed information on the Five (Buddhist) Schools of the Sung period.

Hui Hung's work should not be confused with the collections of Buddhist biographies called Kao sêng ch'uan (vol. 1, 491, 673; Isis, 13, 513).

A. Wylie: Chinese literature (210, 1902).

JAPANESE BUDDHISM

The earliest original Japanese sects of Buddhism appeared in the twelfth century; four more Buddhist sects were established during the thirteenth century. These were the latest Japanese sects, which does not mean that Buddhism ceased to develop in Japan after the thirteenth century, but simply that ulterior developments, of which there were many, occurred within these sects. The history of the great Buddhist schools is similar in that respect to that of the great Christian orders. However, the vicissitudes of each school do not concern us, and it will suffice to refer to them in a general way, and to indicate when each school began.

Out of these four thirteenth-century schools or sects, two—the Zen and Jōdoshin—belong to the first half of the century. These two are by far the most popular sects of Japan even to this day.

Zen-shū (1202)

The Zen-shū has already been mentioned in my note on Eisai (second half of the twelfth century). It is the Japanese development of the Chinese Ch'an[2] tsung[1] (348, 11976), founded by Bodhidharma, c. 520 (vol. 1, 420). Eisai returned from China for the second time in 1191, and the date 1191–1192 is sometimes considered the birthdate of Zen Buddhism. However the date more generally accepted is 1202, when the shōgun invited Eisai to settle at the Kennin-ji in Kyōto. Later Eisai was established at another monastery in Kamakura, the military capital.

In the course of time the Zen-shū was divided into four main branches. The one which continued the mother stem is called Rinzai-shū. The earliest of the three others is the Sōdō-shū (or Sōtō) introduced from China by the bonze Dōgen in 1228. This Dōgen, son of the Naidaijin Kuga Michichika, was born in 1200, educated at the Hiei-zan, traveled in China from 1223 to 1228, died in 1253. He began to preach the Sōdō reform at the Kennin-ji in 1228, and in 1244 founded the Eihei-ji (province of Echizen) which became the main temple of the sect. He is best known under his posthumous title, Shōyō-daishi, (1880). The Sōdō-shū attaches more importance to book learning than the other branches; it is now by far the most popular.

The Zen shū is perhaps nearer to the ideal of early Buddhism than any other Japanese sect. Of course its historical connection with Hindu Buddhism, through Bodhidharma, is as direct as any such connection could be. Its strong emphasis on self-discipline and its relative atheism show that it has preserved some of the fundamental teachings of the Buddha. Moreover, it has successfully assimilated Confucian ethics. This explains its great popularity with military men.

It also attaches due importance to gymnastics, and to those respiratory exercises, probably of Hindu origin, which had been developed by Chinese Taoists and Buddhists, but were practised with especial fervor by their Japanese devotees. These exercises provide an extraordinary means of controlling one's body and one's soul.

On the other hand, its emphasis on contemplation, and its mystical tendencies, have influenced the development of art to a very deep extent. No Buddhist sect has affected far-eastern thought (that is, the thought of leading men) more profoundly.

The two main branches of Zen Buddhism—Rinzai and Sōdō—were represented in Japan, c. 1917, respectively by 6,142 and 14,211 temples. A third branch, Ōbaku, introduced from China by Ingen only about the middle of the seventeenth century (1655), counted 519 temples. Thus these three Zen sects had 20,872 temples out of a grand total of 72,191; i.e., almost one-third.

Shin-shū (1224)

The Shin-shū, or Jōdo-shin-shū, meaning the New Jōdo sect; also called Ikkō-shū, or Monto-shū. It was founded in 1224 by Shinran, being a reform of the Jōdo or Pure Land sect (second half of the twelfth century).

Shinran-Shōnin, born at Kyōto in 1174 of the noble Hino family; disciple of Genkū; he rejected celibacy and took a wife unto himself; he died in 1268. He has received the posthumous title of Kenshin-daishi.

Amidaism—salvation by faith in Amida and His grace only—was carried by

Shinran to the extreme. Much emphasis was laid by him also on everyday duties, and on the harmonization of life and religion.

The Shin-shū was gradually divided into ten branches (Jōdo-shinshū jū-ha) counting the mother stem, Kongwanji-ha, as one of them. Of the nine other branches, three were founded in the thirteenth century, five in the fourteenth, and one at the beginning of the seventeenth century. Taken as a whole, the Shin-shū was almost as successful as the Zen-shū, these two sects being far ahead of all the others. It was represented, c. 1917, by 19,447 temples out of 72,191. The Zen and Shin together counted 40,369 temples; that is, more than half of all of the temples of Japan.

E. Papinot: Historical and geographical dictionary of Japan (Tōkyō, c. 1909). August Karl Reischauer: Studies in Japanese Buddhism (New York 1917).

Schūej Ōhasama: Zen, der lebendige Buddhismus in Japan. Ausgewählte Stücke des Zen-Textes übersetzt und eingeleitet (215 p., Gotha 1925). Daisetz Teitaro Suzuki: Essays in Zen Buddhism (424 p., London 1927).

On the respiratory exercises, see Vasant G. Rele: The mysterious Kundalini (112 p., 4 pl., Bombay 1927; 2d. ed., Bombay 1929; Isis, 11, 224; 13, 510). Franz Hübotter: Die chinesische Medizin (315, Leipzig 1929; Isis, 14, 255–263).

CHAPTER XXX

THE TRANSLATORS

(First Half of Thirteenth Century)

I. FROM ARABIC INTO LATIN

ALFRED OF SARESHEL

English philosopher and scientist, translator from Arabic into Latin. He flourished at the end of the twelfth century and the beginning of the thirteenth, part of the time in Spain. Dates of birth and death unknown. His name is spelled in many ways: Walafred, Alvred, Alphiatus; Sarewel, Sarchel, Serechel. He is also called Alfredus Philosophus and Anglicus. This last epithet proves that he resided abroad; Bacon's testimony and Castilianisms in his own writings prove his Spanish residence. He translated the following:

(1) The Aristotelian treatise De vegetabilibus or De plantis, ascribed to Nicolaos Damascenos (second half of the first century B.C.). This work had been translated into Arabic by Isḥāq ibn Ḥunain (second half of the ninth century), and by Ibn al-Ṭaiyib (first half of the eleventh century). Alfred's translation and commentary were dedicated to Roger of Hereford (second half of the twelfth century).

(2) The alchemical part of Ibn Sīnā's Shifā', the so-called Avicennae Mineralia (alias Liber de congelatis); this translation was completed, c. 1200, if not before; it is very imperfect.

Later (c. 1210) he wrote a treatise De motu cordis, dedicated to Alexander Neckam (d. 1217). It is based on Greek, Muslim, and Salernitan knowledge, and pre-Averroistic philosophy (Platonic, Aristotelian, and also neo-Platonic, through the Liber de causis). Considering his time, his knowledge of Aristotle was unusually large. He composed commentaries on the Meteorology (used by R. Bacon) and on the Parva naturalia. In the De vegetabilibus he quoted the De anima and the De generatione et corruptione; in the De motu cordis, the Physics, Metaphysics, and Nicomachean Ethics.

His scientific (vs. theologic) point of view was remarkable. He had some clear ideas, derived from the Arabic writings, on orogeny. For him, the heart was the seat of the vital spirit and of the soul (Cor domicilium est vitae . . . . cor igitur animae domicilium est).

Text—E. H. F. Meyer: Nicolai Damasceni de plantis libri duo Aristoteli vulgo adscripti (Leipzig 1841).

Carl Sigmund Barach: Excerpta e libro Alfredi Anglici de motu cordis. Item Costa ben Lucae de differentia animae et spiritus liber translatus a Johanne Hispalensi (Bibliotheca philosophorum mediae aetatis, 2, Innsbruck 1878). First complete edition of the De motu cordis, with commentary, by Clemens Baeumker (Beitr. zur Gesch. der Philosophie des Mittelalters, 23, 132 p., Münster 1923).

E. J. Holmyard and D. C. Mandeville: Avicennae de congelatione et conglutinatione lapidum (95 p., Paris 1927; Isis, 11, 134–135).

Criticism—R. Adamson: Dictionary of national biography (vol. 1, 285, 1885).

M. Steinschneider: Europäische Übersetzungen (4, 1904). Clemens Baeumker: Die Stellung des Alfred von Sareshel und seiner Schrift De motu cordis in der Wissenschaft des beginnenden XIII. Jahrhunderts (Sitzungsber. der bayer. Ak. der Wiss., phil. Kl., 64 p., 1913). Auguste Pelzer: Une source inconnue de R. Bacon (Archivum franciscanum historicum, 44–67, 1919). C. H. Haskins: Studies in mediaeval science (128–129, 1924). M. de Wulf: Mediaeval philosophy (vol. 1, 330–332, 1926). Martin Grabmann: Mittelalterliche lateinische Aristotelesübersetzungen und Aristoteleskommentare in Handschriften spanischer Bibliotheken (46–51, München 1928; Handschriftliche Hinweise auf den Meteorologicakommentar des Alfred von Sareshel. Aristoteleskommentare des Adam von Bocfeld und Adam de Bouchermefort; Isis, 13, 205).

MICHAEL SCOT

See philosophical chapter, below.

STEPHEN OF SARAGOSSA

Stephanus Caesaraugustanus, civis Ilerdensis. Stephen of Saragossa and Lerida. In 1233 he translated Ibn al-Jazzār's Reliable treatise on simple drugs (Kitāb i'timād fī-l-adwiya al-mufrada) from Arabic into Latin, under the title Liber fiduciae de simplicibus medicinis. The treatise De gradibus, ascribed to Constantine the African and printed in the Omnia opera Ysaac (Lyon 1515), is a free and abbreviated translation of the same Arabic work.

M. Steinschneider: Constantinus De gradibus und Ibn al-Gezzars Adminiculum (Deutsches Archiv für Geschichte der Medizin, vol. 2, 1879); Hebraeische Übersetzungen (703, 1893); Europaeische Übersetzungen (78, 1904).

PETER GALLEGO

Spanish Franciscan of the noble family of the Fajardos of Galicia. Translator from Arabic into Latin. In 1236 he was provincial of Castile (?). Confessor to Alfonso el Sabio, before the latter's accession to the throne. When Alfonso reconquered Murcia in 1241–1242, he placed Peter at the head of the church of Cartagena. Peter was the first bishop of Cartagena, from 1250 to his death in 1267. He translated the following:

(1) Aristotle's treatise on animals, from an Arabic abridgment. For this translation he certainly made use of the commentary by Ibn Rushd, and of Michael Scot's previous version.

(2) A treatise on economy, probably that of the pseudo-Galen. For this treatise, see my note on Armengaud son of Blaise, who also translated it. Both translations were soon superseded by contemporary versions of the Economy of the pseudo-Aristotle.

Auguste Pelzer: Un traducteur inconnu, Pierre Gallego (Miscellanea Ehrle, vol. 1, 407–456, 1923; Isis, 8, 743).

SALIO OF PADUA

Canon in Padua. Translator from Arabic into Latin. In 1244, 1248, or 1218 he translated, with the assistance of one David, an astrological treatise of Abū Bakr, Liber de nativitatibus; he also translated another treatise of the same kind, De stellis fixis, ascribed to Hermes Trismegistos.

Text—First edition of the De nativitatibus, Venice 1492 or before, 1501, etc. The second text may be the one printed at the end of the edition of Ptolemy's Quadripartitum, 1493: De judiciis et significatione stellarum.

Criticism—M. Steinschneider: Europäische Übersetzungen (75, 1904).

WILLIAM OF LUNIS

Wilhelmus de Lunis apud Neapolim. Italian translator from Arabic into Latin, who flourished in the thirteenth century. He translated some of Ibn Rushd's commentaries on Aristotelian logic, and on Porphyry's interpretation of it. He also translated a book on algebra (not al-Khwārizmī's); it would seem that there was also an Italian version of the same text.

G. Libri: Histoire des sciences mathématiques en Italie (vol. 2, 45, 1838). M. Cantor: Geschichte der Mathematik (vol. 2, 100, 1899). M. Steinschneider: Europäische Übersetzungen (80, 1904; 82, 1905).

THEODORE OF ANTIOCH

See chapter on natural history, below.

PHILIP OF TRIPOLI

Philipus Tripolitanus. A member of the clergy of Tripolis (or Tripoli, in Syria), who flourished during the second quarter of the thirteenth century. Being in Antioch with his bishop, Guido de Valentia,[1] they found a manuscript of the Sirr al-asrār, i.e., the pseudo-Aristotelian Secret of Secrets. (For the earlier history of this interesting text, see my vol. 1 556–557). Philip translated it from Arabic into Latin at some time during the second quarter of the thirteenth century (c. 1243?). This Latin translation was only one of the channels through which the miscellaneous folklore of the Sirr al-asrār reached Christian Europe, but it was the most important; it was the source of the printed editions.

Text—First edition. De Secretis secretorum (Cologne 1480). Many other early editions in Latin, French, etc.

Criticism—L. Leclerc: Médecine arabe (vol. 2, 446–448, 1876). M. Steinschneider: Hebräische Übersetzungen (249, 1893); Europäische Übersetzungen (60, 1904).

II. FROM ARABIC INTO HEBREW

For al-Ḥarizi, see philosophical chapter below. Solomon ibn Ayyub will be dealt with in the next book.

IBN ḤASDAI

Abraham ben Samuel ibn Ḥasdai ha-Levi. Flourished in Barcelona; died in 1240. Translator from Arabic into Hebrew. Ardent defender of Maimonides. His most important translations are the following: Sefer ha-tappuaḥ, a pseudo-Aristotelian philosophical dialogue, of which the Arabic text, Kitāb al-tuffāḥah (Book of the apple), is lost; Sefer ha-yesodot, translation of the treatise on the elements (Kitāb al-isṭaqisāt) by Isḥāq al-Isrā'īlī (lost in Arabic); Mozene ẓedeq, translation of an ethical treatise by al-Ghazzālī, Mīzān al-'amal (all quotations from Muslim scriptures being replaced by equivalent ones taken from the Jewish ones); two

[1] This bishop is not mentioned in P.D. Gams: Series episcoporum (1873–1886).

treatises by Maimonides (Sefer ha-mizwot, and Iggeret teman); the story of Barlaam and Ioasaph (see vol. I, 507). The Sefer ha-tappuaḥ was translated into Latin under the direction (and perhaps with the assistance) of Manfred, regent and king of Sicily from 1250 to 1266.

Text—Sefer ha-tappuaḥ (Venice 1519; Riva di Trento 1562; Francfort o. O., 1693?, 1800, etc.). Hebrew text with Latin translation, by Joh. Just. Losius: Biga dissertationum quarum prima exhibet Sefer ha-tappuah sive librum de pomo Aristotelis quod moribundus in manu gestaverit (Giessen 1706). German translation by J. Musen (Lemberg 1873). English translation by Hermann Gollancz (London 1908).

Sefer ha-yesodot. Hebrew text with German translation by Salomon Fried (Frankfort 1900). There is a Latin translation of the same Arabic work by Gerard of Cremona.

Mozene ẓedeq. First edition by Jacob Goldenthal, with a Hebrew introduction (Leipzig 1839).

Hebrew version of the story of Barlaam and Ioasaph, Constantinople 1518, Mantua 1557, Wandsbeck 1727, Francfort o. Oder 1766. Hebrew-Yiddish edition, Zolkiew 1771. Hebrew-German edition, Fürth 1783; etc. Nathan Weisslovits: Prinz und Derwisch, ein indischer Roman enthaltend die Jugendgeschichte Buddhas in hebräischer Darstellung aus dem Mittelalter, nebst einer Vergleichung der arabischen und griechischen Paralleltexte; mit einem Anhang von Fritz Hommel (178 p., München 1890).

Criticism—N. Weisslowits: Abraham ben Samuel sein Leben und seine Schriften (Diss., Munich 1889). Max Schloessinger: Jewish encyclopaedia (vol. 6, 247, 1904). J. Heller: Encyclopaedia judiaca (vol. 5, 352–554, 1930).

ABRAHAM BEN NATHAN

See religious chapter above.

SAMUEL IBN TIBBON

Samuel ben Judah ibn Tibbon. Son of the Andalusian scholar, Judah ibn Tibbon (second half of the twelfth century). Samuel was born at Lunel, Languedoc, c. 1150; he flourished in Béziers (1199), Arles (1204), Barcelona, Toledo, Alexandria, finally in Marseilles, where he died, c. 1232. Judeo-Provençal theologian, philosopher, and translator from Arabic into Hebrew. Admirably trained by his father, he became one of the greatest translators of his time. He translated the following works:

(1) Aristotle: Meteorology. The Arabic version of Yaḥyā ibn Baṭrīq was translated by Samuel at sea during his voyage from Alexandria in 1213, under the title Otot ha-shamayim (or 'elyonot). Extracts edited by Filipowski (c. 1860).

(2) 'Alī ibn Riḍwān (first half of the eleventh century): Commentary on Galen's Tegni. Hebrew version, Melaka qeṭana, completed at Béziers in 1199, this being Samuel's earliest dated work.

(3) Ibn Rushd: Three small treatises translated under the title Sheloshah ma'amarim. Edited by J. Hercz: Drei Abhandlungen über die Conjunction des separaten Intellects mit dem Menschen (Berlin 1869, with German translation).

(4) Maimonides: Dalālat al-ḥā'irīn. Translated by Samuel under the title Moreh nebukim, Guide of the perplexed (Enemies of Maimonides affected to call it Nebukat ha-morim, Perplexity of the guides!). This translation, completed at Arles in 1204, is Samuel's main title to fame. He obtained Maimonides' own

advice to solve certain difficulties. Another Hebrew translation of the same work, published by al-Ḥarizi a few years later, was inferior and much criticized, and yet not unsuccessful.

(5) Maimonides: Treatise on resurrection, under the title Iggeret, or Ma'amar teḥiyyat ha-metim. Printed in Constantinople, 1569, etc.

(6) Maimonides: Mishna commentary on Pirqe abot, with psychological introduction called Shemonah peraqim. Printed in Soncino, 1484, etc.

(7) Maimonides: "Thirteen articles," under the title Shelosh 'esreh 'iqqarim, or Yesodot.

(8) Maimonides: Letter to his disciple, Joseph ibn 'Aqnīn.

Besides these translations, which were his most valuable contributions, Samuel wrote Biblical commentaries, e.g., the treatise on the phrase "yiqqawu ha-mayim" (Genesis, 1, 9). In 1213 he composed at sea, on his way back from Alexandria, a glossary of the many new terms he had been obliged to introduce in his translation of Maimonides' Dalālat. This glossary, entitled Bi'ur millot ha-zarot, included Arabic words in Hebraic form, but also Hebrew words to which he had given new meanings by analogy with the Arabic.

Samuel was largely responsible for the diffusion of Maimonidean philosophy in the West, and also for the development of the Hebrew philosophical language.

Text—The Moreh nebukim and the Bi'ur millot ha-zarot were printed at Venice 1551, and many times afterwards.

Ma'amar yiqqawu ha-mayim, edited by Mordecai Loeb Bisliches (Pressburg 1837).

Some of the letters exchanged by Maimonides, Samuel ibn Tibbon, and Joseph ibn 'Aqnīn will be found in the Qobeẓ teshubot ha-Rambam (vol. 2).

Criticism—M. Steinschneider: Bodleian catalogue (2481–2493, 1860); Hebraeische Übersetzungen (1893). E. Renan: Rabbins français (573–575, 1877); Ecrivains juifs (1893). Max Schloessinger: Jewish Encyclopaedia (vol. 6, 548–550, 1904).

JACOB ANAṬOLI

Jacob ben Abba Mari ben Simson (or Simeon) ben Anaṭoli (Anṭoli, Anaṭolio). Provençal Talmudist, astronomer, philosopher. Translator from Arabic (and Latin) into Hebrew, and possibly also from Hebrew into Latin. He was born in southern France, probably at Marseilles; flourished in Narbonne and Béziers, and later (c. 1231, etc.) in Naples in the service of Frederick II. His dates of birth and death are unknown (c. 1194, c. 1256?). He was a disciple and son-in-law of Samuel ibn Tibbon; a fervent Maimonidean, and strongly opposed to qabbalistic tendencies. His two main titles to fame are that he was the first translator of Ibn Rushd's commentaries into Hebrew, and the first popularizer (or one of the first) of the Maimonidean points of view. Both titles are very significant. He and Michael Scot (and later Moses ibn Tibbon) were the main transmitters of the vast Aristotelian knowledge elaborated by Ibn Rushd.

At the age of fifty-five he composed a collection of sermons entitled Malmad ha-talmidim (Teaching of the students, or Goad to the students), wherein he showed much knowledge not only of Greek and Averroistic philosophy, but also of Christian institutions. He quotes Frederick II, and one Christian, Michael (probably Michael Scot). Of far greater importance were his translations, as follows:

(1–5) Ibn Rushd's intermediate commentaries on Porphyry's Isagoge, and on Aristotle's Categories, Interpretation, Prior and Posterior Analytics. This work was probably begun in Provence; it was completed at Naples in 1232. The first three books were translated from the Hebrew into Latin by Jacob Mantino (first half of the sixteenth century) and published in the editions of 1550 to 1553. Anaṭoli planned to translate other parts of Ibn Rushd's commentaries, but failed to do so.

(6) Ptolemy's Almagest from the Arabic, entitled in Hebrew, Ḥibbur ha-gadol ha-niqra al-magesṭi (the great composition called Almagest), c. 1231–1235.

(7) Ibn Rushd's Summary of the Almagest. Translated in 1231 (or 1235) under the title Qiẓẓur almagesṭi. This text is known only in Hebrew.

(8) Al-Farghānī (first half of the ninth century): Kitāb fī-ḥarakāt al-samāwīya. The Hebrew translation, also called Qiẓẓur almagesṭi, was apparently made (c. 1231–1235) on the basis of a Latin version but with reference to the Arabic text. There were two Latin versions, by John of Seville, and by Gerard of Cremona, and Anaṭoli probably used the latter. The printed Latin translation of Jacob Christmann (1554–1613): Muhammedis Alfragani chronologica et astronomica elementa (Francfort 1590), was made from Anaṭoli's Hebrew version. The Hebrew title, Yesodot ha-tekunah, is a later one probably inspired by the Latin one, Elementa astronomica. Anaṭoli's translation contains three additional chapters (as compared with the Arabic text). One of these, the last (or 33rd) is geographical and gives the position of a number of places, and lengths of days.

The translations of al-Fārābī's logical treatises ascribed to Anaṭoli, because they are found in the MSS. together with his translations of Ibn Rushd, may belong to other translators, e.g., Moses ibn Tibbon.

It has been suggested that Jacob Anaṭoli and Michael Scot together prepared a Latin translation of Maimonides' Dalālat al-ḥā'irīn, from the second Hebrew version by al-Ḥarizi. It has also been suggested that Jacob (or his son, Antonio) composed the anonymous commentary on the Dalālat called Ruaḥ ḥen (spirit of grace). These suggestions are plausible but unproved.

Anaṭoli's activity is a good illustration of the growing complexity of Latin-Hebrew exchanges. Consider, for example, his translation of al-Fargānī's work made from a Latin version (and later retranslated into Latin!). Western Jews knew less and less Arabic, and more and more Latin.

Text—The Sefer malmad ha-talmidim was published, incompletely, by the Meqiẓe nirdamin society (Lyck 1866).

The Hebrew translation of the summary of Ibn Rushd's logic printed at Riva di Trento in 1560, was not made by Jacob Anaṭoli, but by Jacob ben Maḥir.

The Ruaḥ ḥen was printed in Venice, 1544, 1549; Cremona 1566, Prague 1593, Lublin 1620, Jessnitz 1744, Brünn 1796; etc. Hebrew-Latin edition, Cologne 1555.

Criticism—E. Renan: Rabbins français (580–589, 1877); Ecrivains juifs (by index, 1893). M. Steinschneider: Hebraeische Übersetzungen (990, 1893; 47, 51, 58 for Ibn Rushd; 523 for the Almagest; 547 for Ibn Rushd's summary of it; 555 for al-Farghānī). H. G. Enelow: Jewish encyclopaedia (vol. 1, 562–564, 1901). Romeo Campani: Il Kitāb al-farghānī nel testo arabo e nelle versioni (Rivista degli studi orientali, vol. 3, 205–252, 1910). Important study containing samples of Anaṭoli's translation. U. Cassuto: Encyclopaedia judaica (vol. 2, 772–774, 1928).

III. FROM PERSIAN INTO ARABIC

AL-BUNDĀRĪ

See historical chapter, below.

IV. FROM GREEK INTO LATIN

JOHN BASINGSTOKE

John Basing, or Basyngstoke. Probably named after the town of Basingstoke in Hampshire. English humanist, who died in 1252. Archdeacon of Leicester (in or before 1235). He studied in Oxford, Paris, and—Athens!, and was one of the earliest Englishmen having a real knowledge of Greek. He was a friend of Grosseteste and Matthew Paris. He brought back Greek MSS. to England, and translated into Latin a Greek grammar, which he called Donatus Graecorum.

He tried to introduce a system of numeration in which the numbers were differentiated by the position and inclination of a hook at the top of an upright line. According to Matthew Paris, he had brought back the Greek numerals to England. One wonders whether the Greek numerals and the strange numerals abovementioned were not confused.

T. A. Archer: Dictionary of national biography (vol. 3, 354–356, 1885). H. Suter: Die Mathematik auf den Universitäten des Mittelalters (Zürich 1887). M. Cantor: Geschichte der Mathematik (vol. 2, 100, 1899). Ernest A. Savage: Old English libraries (219, 267, 1911). Sandys: History of classical scholarship (vol. 1,[3] 423, 576, 1921). Florence A. Yeldham: The story of reckoning in the Middle Ages (94, London 1926; Isis, 10, 259).

ROBERT GROSSETESTE

See philosophical chapter, below.

ARISTOTELIAN TRADITION IN THE FIRST HALF OF THE THIRTEENTH CENTURY

To the many translations dating from the twelfth century, quite a few important ones were added in the first half of the thirteenth century, as has been shown above. The zoological books, the De coelo et mundo, and the De anima, were translated from Arabic into Latin, together with Ibn Rushd's commentaries, by Michael Scot. Another Latin translation of the zoology was made somewhat later by Peter Gallego. The pseudo-Aristotelian treatise De plantis was translated from Arabic into Latin by Alfred Sareshel. The Organon, as elaborated by Ibn Rushd, was translated from Arabic into Latin by William of Lunis, and from Arabic into Hebrew by Jacob Anaṭoli. The Ethics was translated from Arabic into Hebrew by al-Ḥarizi, and from Greek into Latin by Grosseteste.

The case of the Meteorology is especially interesting. We have seen that it was translated from Arabic into Hebrew by Samuel ibn Tibbon. But Latin translations were available before this time, one made from the Arabic (the first three books by Gerard of Cremona); one made partly from the Arabic and partly (book 4) from the Greek; one made entirely from the Greek. Moreover, about the middle of the century, the first three books of the last mentioned Latin version (entirely from the Greek) were translated into French by one Matthieu le Vilain of Neufchâtel, in the diocese of Rouen. This is noteworthy, because it was long believed that the earliest French versions of Aristotle dated only from the rule of Charles V the Wise (1364–1380).

For this French version and what little is known of the author, see Léopold Delisle: Comptes rendus de l'Académie des Inscriptions (vol. 9, 11, 1881); Notice sur deux livres ayant appartenu à Charles V (Notices et extraits, vol. 31 (1), 1–16).

A summary of the situation obtaining in the Latin world was given by Haskins as follows: "The Physics, Metaphysics and briefer works on natural history reached Western Europe about 1200; the Politics, Ethics, Rhetoric, and Economics only in the course of the next two generations. In nearly every instance translations are found both from the Greek and from the Arabic and nearly all are undated. At present about all that can be said is that by the turn of the century traces are found of versions from the Greek in the case of the Physics, de Coelo, de Anima, and the Parva Naturalia. The Metaphysics seems to have come from Constantinople shortly after 1204."

C. H. Haskins: The Greek element in the Renaissance of the twelfth century (American historical review, 25, 612, 1920).

Another aspect of the question is offered by the attitude of the ecclesiastical authorities with regard to the teaching of Aristotelian doctrines. It should be remembered that Ibn Rushd reached western Europe close on the heels of Aristotle. The most obnoxious Aristotelian doctrine—to Christians as well as to Jews—was that of the eternity of the world, conflicting with the dogma of creation; and this very doctrine was lengthily discussed by Ibn Rushd. One can readily imagine the anxiety which the spread of such subversive ideas must have caused to the responsible leaders, and it is not at all surprising that their first reaction was antagonistic. We shall see in the following book that their attitude changed when the contents of Aristotelian knowledge were better known and its dangers circumscribed.

A provincial council held in Paris in 1210 forbade the public or private teaching of Aristotelian natural philosophy (i.e., Aristotelian physics and metaphysics), and its commentaries (of course there was no objection to the Organon). The pantheistic views of Amaury of Bêne and David of Dinant were condemned by the same council. The prohibition was renewed in 1215 with special reference to the University of Paris, by the cardinal, Robert de Courçon (d. 1219). Robert allowed the teaching of the old and new logic, and the ethics, but expressly forbade the physics and metaphysics, and the heretical views of Amaury, David, and Maurice of Spain (i.e., probably the Moor of Spain, Ibn Rushd. That prohibition was confirmed by the Fourth Lateran Council (1215) under Innocent III and by other popes in 1231, 1245, etc. Yet these later interdictions were already less absolute. For example, in 1231 Gregory IX (1227–1241) ordered three theologians, William of Auxerre, Simon of Authie, and Stephen of Provins, to censor the forbidden books "ne utile per inutile vitietur;" this implied a partial readmission. Further interdictions were more and more restricted to Averroistic exaggerations. One thing is clear: the prohibitions of 1210, 1215 and later years prove indirectly the spread of Aristotelianism.

Amable Jourdain: Recherches critiques sur l'âge et l'origine des traductions latines d'Aristote, etc. (488 p., Paris 1843; still fundamental). Georges Henri Luquet: Aristote et l'université de Paris pendant le XIIIe siècle (Bibl. de l'Ecole des hautes études, sci. relig., vol. 16, 2., 34 p., Paris 1904). Georg Kriesten: Über eine deutsche Übersetzung des pseudo-aristotelischen Secretum secretorum aus dem

XIII. Jahrh. (Diss., Berlin 1907). Martin Grabmann: Forschungen über die lateinischen Aristoteles-Übersetzungen des XIII. Jahrh. (Beitr. zur Gesch. der Philos. des Mittelalters, 17, 5, 297 p., Münster 1916; important; completing Jourdain). Lynn Thorndike: The Latin pseudo-Aristotle and medieval occult science (Journal of English and Germanic philology, 21, 229–258, 1922; Isis, 5, 214). Martin Grabmann: Mittelalterliche lateinische Aristotelesübersetzungen und Aristoteleskommentare in Handschriften spanischer Bibliotheken (Sitzungsber. der bayer. Akad., 120 p., München 1928; Isis, 13, 205). Alexandre Birkenmajer: Le rôle joué par les médecins et les naturalistes dans la réception d'Aristote aux XIIe et XIIIe siècles (La Pologne au VIe Congrès international des sciences historiques, Oslo 1928; 15 p., Warsaw 1930; Isis, 15, 272).

F. Picavet: La science expérimentale au XIIIe siècle (Le Moyen Age, 241–248, 1894; à propos of Berthelot's work). Ludwig Keller: Die Anfänge der Renaissance und die Kulturgesellschaften des Humanismus im 13. und 14. Jahrhundert (Comenius Gesellschaft, vol. 11, 2, 30 p., Berlin 1903). George von Hertling: Wissenschaftliche Richtungen und philosophische Probleme des 13. Jahrhunderts (Festrede, Akad. der Wissensch., 37 p., München 1910).

CHAPTER XXXI

EDUCATION

(First Half of Thirteenth Century)

I. CHRISTENDOM

CREATION OF NEW UNIVERSITIES

We have explained in the previous chapter that the earliest universities were not founded but simply grew. By the beginning of the thirteenth century that growth was already sufficient to show what a University was and what it could do for good or evil. The authorities, lay and ecclesiastical, became aware of the importance, actual or potential, of these new institutions and vied with one another to obtain control of them. Royal and papal recognition of universities became a matter of policy. Kings and popes granted charters to the universities which already existed or which they now created for the very purpose of extending and strengthening their influence. Each charter conceded sundry privileges and protection for the sake of submission to the authority which promulgated it.

For example, in Paris the university was controlled by the chancellor of the cathedral who alone conferred the licentia docendi, the right to teach. I have explained above that some chairs of the Faculty of theology of Paris were acquired by the Dominican Order in 1229 and 1231, and by the Franciscan, c. 1232. In this struggle against the rest of the university the Friars were naturally seconded by the popes, as the presence of Franciscans and Dominicans in the Faculty of theology was the best guarantee of orthodoxy.

The detailed history of each university does not interest us. The history of education and the history of science are two different subjects. But it is well to know when each university began, because each of them was (or might be) a new focus of scientific research.

The best general account is still that of Hastings Rashdall: The universities of Europe in the Middle Ages (2 vols. in three, Oxford 1895); a new edition is being prepared by H. H. E. Craster and F. M. Powicke. See also Heinrich Denifle: Die Universitäten des Mittelalters bis 1400 (Berlin 1885). C. H. Haskins: The rise of universities (143 p., New York 1923; a delightful summary; Isis, 6, 203).

I shall now indicate briefly the main facts.

Italy

Migrations from Bologna created new studia generalia in other Italian cities, e.g., in Modena before 1182, and in Reggio in Emilia in 1188.

Vicenza (1204)—The university of Vicenza owed its origin, in 1204, also to a migration of scholars, probably from Bologna. Its existence was exceedingly short, only a few years.

Reggio—This was clearly recognized as a studium generale in 1210, but it did not last more than a century.

Arezzo (? *1215*)—A law school was established in Arezzo in 1215 by Roffredus de Benevento, a seceder from Bologna. By the middle of the thirteenth century (1255) it was already a studium generale. It received an imperial charter from Charles IV in 1355.

Padua (*1222*)—Padua was also a daughter of Bologna and by far the greatest. Its history as a studium generale begins in 1222. The seventh centenary of its birth was celebrated in 1922 (see e.g., Nature, vol. 109, 752, 1922). A considerable body of students moved to Vercelli in 1228. During the tyranny of the Ezzelino family, 1237–1260, the university of Padua was reduced to a very low ebb. In 1260 a new start was made. Papal bulls were obtained in 1264 from Urban IV, in 1346 from Clement VI, and in 1363 from Urban V. The earliest Paduan college, the Collegium tornacense, dates only from 1363. The university reached its zenith under Venetian tutelage in the fifteenth and sixteenth centuries. It was the university town, the "quartier latin," of Venice.

Naples (*1224*)—With one partial exception (Palencia, 1212–1214; see below), Naples was the first university which was deliberately founded by an outside power, and thus it was also the first of which the date of foundation is absolutely definite. It was created in 1224 by the emperor Frederick II through his chancellor, Peter of Vinea, to offset the university of Bologna (a Guelf city). The charter of foundation (1224) forbade Neapolitan and Sicilian subjects to attend other schools. This antipapal institution did not last very long, but it had the paradoxical glory of counting St. Thomas Aquinas among its alumni.

Roman Curia (*1244–1245*)—A university attached to the papal court was founded by Innocent IV (1243–1254) in 1244 or 1245. Its seat was the same as that of the court, Rome or any other Italian residence, later for a time, Avignon. The studies were largely restricted to civil and canon law, and to theology. The theological teaching was controlled to a large extent by Dominicans. Civil law was taught, which shows that the popes were not systematically hostile to that study, though Honorius III (1216–1227) had prohibited it. Indeed some knowledge of civil law was essential to canonists. The Council of Vienne in Dauphiné (1311–1312) ordered that professors of Greek, Arabic, Chaldee, and Hebrew be maintained in five universities, of which that of the Roman Curia was one, the four others being Paris, Bologna, Oxford, and Salamanca.

Siena (*1246*, *1357*)—Taking advantage of Bologna's troubles with Frederick II, Siena started a regular teaching of civil law in 1246. A bull was granted by Innocent IV in 1252, and by that time it is probable that Siena was already a studium generale in fact. At any rate, an official document of the city of Siena, dated 1275, proclaims the existence of a studium generale within its walls. The university was considerably reinforced in 1321 and 1338 by Bolognese immigrants. After having failed to obtain a charter from the popes (who no doubt did not want to do anything which might hurt Bologna), they obtained a new charter of foundation from the emperor Charles IV in 1357. More privileges were granted to them in 1408 by Gregory XII.

Thus the university of Siena received its first recognition from the pope (1252), the second from the city itself (1275), the third from the emperor (1357), the fourth from the pope (1408): a curious example of the conflicting tendencies in the midst of which the early universities were developing, and of which they took advantage.

Piacenza (*1248*)—This university was a town school (as there were many others in Italy) which obtained a bull of foundation from Innocent IV in 1248. However, it remained insignificant till 1398, when Gian Galeazzo Visconti granted a new charter, and suppressed the university of Pavia (founded in 1361) in its favor. This new foundation failed as completely as the first, and Pavia was reestablished in 1412 as the Milanese university.

France

Paris—See preceding book. The University of Paris received its first charter only in 1200, from King Philip Augustus, and this date is claimed by itself as the true date of foundation. The earliest statutes date from 1208–1209. Papal privileges were granted in 1215 and 1231.

Ernest Wickersheimer: Les origines de la faculté de médecine de Paris (Bull. de la Soc. hist. méd., vol. 13, 249–260, 1914; earliest date, 1213; Isis, 4, 405).

Montpellier—See preceding book. The medical school is first mentioned in a document of 1137; the earliest statutes date from 1220. The law school began c. 1160; its importance increased considerably c. 1230; this increase was probably due to the political troubles from which Bologna was then suffering; the earliest statutes date from 1339; these were legatine statutes. The faculty of arts existed already in 1242. The earliest college, Valmagne, dates from 1262. Montpellier was one of the most famous universities of Europe until the middle of the fourteenth century, after which time it declined rapidly. It again enjoyed some prestige in the seventeenth century and after.

Orleans—The law school of Orleans is very ancient. The Brachylogus, composed at the beginning of the twelfth century, was possibly one of its productions. However, in the twelfth century this school seems to have been far less concerned with law than with grammar, classical literature and dictamen (the art of letter writing); the secretaries of popes Alexander III (1159–1181) and Lucius III (1181–1185) were educated there. The school of grammar of Orleans remained important until the second half of the thirteenth century. The prohibition of teaching civil law in Paris, by Honorius III in 1219, and subsequent events helped to revive the law school of Orleans. It should be noted that that prohibition jeopardized also the teaching of canon law. The earliest document concerning the law school of Orleans dates only from 1235, but that school assumed very quickly a definite preponderance; it remained the main legal school of France throughout the Middle Ages. Its organization was sanctioned by a bull granted by Clement V in 1306.

Angers—This was an ancient cathedral school which was fortified by a Parisian immigration in 1229. Its institutional development was very similar to that of Orleans. It was reorganized in 1398 on the model of the latter. It was first of all a school of law, chiefly civil law. Less important than Orleans in mediaeval times, its fame increased gradually, and in the sixteenth century it was the center of a great juridical revival and then eclipsed its rival. Until 1432 there was apparently no faculty but the legal one; in that year faculties of theology, medicine, and arts were established by a bull of Eugenius IV (1431–1447).

Toulouse (1230, 1233)—The university of Toulouse was deliberately founded in 1230 by a bull of Gregory IX (1227–1241); this being an incident in the struggle against heresy in Languedoc and Provence. The final treaty between Louis IX and the defeated count, Raymond of Toulouse, signed in Paris in 1230, obliged the latter to pay the salaries of fourteen professors. An additional bull of 1233 granted the jus ubique docendi to graduates; finally, in 1245, Innocent IV issued a charter of privilege conferring upon Toulouse all the liberties and privileges bestowed upon Paris. But in spite of all, the university decayed rapidly. John of Garland, who was one of the earliest teachers, wrote a poem in which he described the establishment of the university and its failure. Later it revived and assumed much importance as a law school, especially after the decline of the law school of Montpellier in the middle of the thirteenth century, and became the legal center of the south of France, even as Orleans was the legal center of the north.

England

Oxford—See preceding book. The history of Oxford university began, c. 1167. The earliest charter is a legatine ordinance of 1214. The organization of the university was at first modeled upon that of Paris. The first Oxford statute dates from 1252, and this was sanctioned by Innocent IV in 1254. The Dominicans appeared in Oxford in 1221, and the Franciscans in 1224, and they worked in harmony with the seculars and laymen until the beginning of the fourteenth century, when various conflicts arose between them.

None of the Oxford colleges dates from the first half of the thirteenth century, but University College, which began, c.1280, owed its foundation partly to a bequest made in 1249 by William of Durham, archbishop-elect of Rouen.

Cambridge (*1209*)—The birth of the University of Cambridge was due to a "suspendium clericorum" which occurred at Oxford in 1209, and led to the emigration of a large body of students. But many of these students returned to Oxford in 1214, and the new university remained insignificant for many years. In 1229 Henry III assigned it for residence to many of the dispersed students of Paris. Its existence was consecrated in 1318 by a bull of John XXII (1316–1334).

The Franciscans reached Cambridge in 1224 or 1225, the Dominicans in 1274. The earliest Cambridge college, Peterhouse, dates only from 1284.

Spain

Palencia (*1212–1214*)—The cathedral school of Palencia, in Old Castile, which counted St. Dominic among its pupils (c. 1184), was transformed into a university in 1212–1214 by Alfonso VIII, king of Castile. This was a deliberate foundation, but without charter of any kind. After the founder's death in 1214, the little university was suspended; in 1220 it was reestablished but its existence remained precarious; it still existed in 1243; by 1263 it had disappeared.

Salamanca (*before 1230*)—Salamanca was founded at an unknown date by Alfonso IX of Leon, who died in 1230. This failed, and a new foundation occurred in 1242, when Ferdinand III of Castile issued a charter of privilege. However, Salamanca did not attain any importance till 1254 when Alfonso X the Wise granted a new charter; this charter was confirmed by a bull of Alexander IV in 1255. The university was controlled by the cathedral. By the end of the thirteenth century it was recognized by Boniface VIII as one of the leading universities of Europe.

For Seville and Valladolid, see Book IV.

II. ISRAEL

JUDAH BEN 'ABBAS

See philosophical chapter, below.

III. CHINA

YEH-LÜ CH'U-TS'AI

Yeh[1]-lü[4]* Ch'u[3]-ts'ai[2] (12974, 7548, 2662, 11496). Posthumously ennobled and canonized. Born in 1190 of a princely family of the Liao[2] (7058) or Ch'i-tan, Eastern Tartars. He was governor of Peking in 1214, when the city was taken by Chingiz Khān. Flourished at the Mongol court under Chingiz and Ogotāy; died in 1244. Mongol astronomer, educator, and statesman. I say Mongol, both because of his origin (witness his Ch'i-tan name) and his function; but his education and traditions were Chinese. He took part in Chingiz's successful campaign against Persia in 1219, and wrote an account of it entitled Account of a journey to the West, Hsi[1] yu[2] lu[4]* (4031, 13423, 7386). During this campaign the Mongols collected books, herbs, and scientific instruments for him out of their abundant spoil. On one occasion he cured an epidemic which was menacing the horde, by means of rhubarb. In 1220 he proposed a reform of the calendar, characteristically called the Western expedition chronography of the Kêng wu epoch, Hsi[1] cheng[1] kêng[1] wu[3] yüan[2] li[4]* (4031, 689, 6001, 12769, 13744, 6923). In 1227, when Ogotāy succeeded his father, Yeh-lü became the main administrator of the empire. In 1233, he established an institution for literary composition at Yen[4]-ching[1] (13048, 2140) near Peking, and a college for classical studies at P'ing[2] yang[2] (9310, 12883) in Shansi. This college is supposed to mark the beginning of educational organization under the Mongols. In 1236 he prevailed on Ogotāy strictly to limit an issue of paper-money. Unfortunately (for the Mongols) his power came to an end when Ogotāy died in 1241.

Text—The Library of Congress has the Hsi yu lu in vol. 28 of the Ling[2] chien[1] ko[2]* ts'ung[1] shu[1] (7222, 1637, 6037, 12039, 10024). The Library also has the collected writings of Yeh-lü Ch'u-ts'ai under his style name, Chan[4] jan[2] chü[1] shih[4] wên[2] chi[2]* (313, 5551, 2987, 9992, 12633, 906) in vols. 1371–4 of the Ssŭ[4] pu[4] ts'ung[1] k'an[1] (10291, 9484, 12039, 5861).

Extracts from the Hsi yu lu have been published by E. Bretschneider: Mediaeval researches (vol. 1, 9–24, 1888).

Criticism—Abel Rémusat: Yeliu-Thsou-Thsai, ministre tartare (Nouveaux mélanges asiatiques, vol. 2, 64–88, 1829). Alexander Wylie: Chinese researches (part 3, 15, 1897). Giles: Biographical dictionary (929, 1898). Harold Lamb: Genghis Khan (228–230, New York 1927).

IV. JAPAN

The military affairs of the shōgunal government were administered by the ko-saburai-dokoro, an office established at Kamakura in 1219, and of which the superintendent (bettō) was always taken from among the Hōjō family. In 1241 a school was annexed to it, to educate the children of the officers. The education included Chinese writing and music, horsemanship, sports and games, etc.

E. Papinot: Historical dictionary (310, 1909).

CHAPTER XXXII

PHILOSOPHIC AND CULTURAL BACKGROUND

(First Half of Thirteenth Century)

I. FREDERICK II

Frederick II of Hohenstaufen. Born in Iesi, near Ancona, 1194; died in Fiorentino, South Italy, 1250; buried in Palermo. King of Sicily since 1198 (of age in 1208), head of the Holy Roman Empire since 1220, king of Jerusalem since 1229. Frederick was the most accomplished example of the mixture of Muslim and Christian civilizations which was then taking place in southern Europe, chiefly in Sicily and Spain. As Emperor, he was the highest civil authority in Christendom; yet his life and court were similar to those of a Muslim sulṭān.

He had established a Muslim colony at Lucera or Nocera (in Campania), from which he could draw a praetorian guard to execute his orders. This had far-reaching consequences. For in so doing, Frederick inaugurated a practice followed by many Italian despots of the fourteenth and fifteenth centuries. The native subjects were relieved from conscription and continued their own activities; of course, they had to pay taxes, but the fighting was done by mercenaries under the tyrant's immediate control. This meant relative peace and prosperity to the burghers and absolute power to the tyrant. On the other hand, the Muslim soldiery must have contributed to the diffusion of Muslim customs throughout the peninsula. One thing is certain; under Frederick's rule Muslim arts and lore were transmitted from Sicily to Lombardy.

He was a philosopher, a man of science and a patron of learning, and surrounded himself in Sicily with learned men, some of them Christian, such as Michael Scot and Fibonacci, but most of them Jews or Muslims. He corresponded with scholars throughout Islām. During his travels in Italy, Germany, or the Holy Land he was accompanied by learned men, chiefly Muslims.

In 1224 he founded the University of Naples, this being the first University of Europe which was founded at a definite time by a definite charter. He formed at that university a large collection of Arabic manuscripts. In 1220 (or 1232) he caused the works of Aristotle and Ibn Rushd to be translated, and sent copies of the translations to Paris and Bologna.

He devoted the leisure time of his busy life to the preparation of a treatise on falconry, De arte venandi cum avibus, which is one of the most elaborate treatises of its kind and one of the most important zoological works of the Middle Ages. The text as compiled by himself seems to have been already completed by 1248, when it was lost in a defeat which he suffered before Parma. A revision of the first two books, prepared by his son Manfred (born c. 1232; king of Sicily from 1258 to 1266), is the basis of the printed editions. It was translated into French before the end of the century. The complete treatise is very large (589 pages in the Mazarine MS.). It is based on Aristotle, but also to a large extent on Muslim examples,[1] and on direct observations and experiments. It is very methodical and technical, the work of a man of science and of a sportsman. It is divided into six books, as follows: (I) Praise of falconry. Zoological introduction, anatomy and habits of birds, and especially of birds of prey. (II) Rearing, feeding, and seeling of falcons; necessary implements, including hoods. (III) Various kinds of lures and their use; training of dogs for hunting with falcons. (IV) Hunting of cranes with gerfalcons. Habits of cranes and gerfalcons, comparison of gerfalcons with other falcons. (V) Hunting of herons with the sacred falcon. Their habits. (VI) Hunting of water birds with the peregrine falcon. Their habits. For contemporary treatises on falconry, see the chapter below devoted to natural history.

Book I contains a number of facts on the anatomy of birds which had not yet been recorded anywhere else; e.g., pneumaticity of the bones, form of the sternum, structure of the lungs, rump glands. Remarks on the mechanical conditions of flight and on bird migrations. Frederick observed, imitated, and improved the Arab practice of equipping hunting birds with hoods (book II, chapter 77). He made experiments on the artificial incubation of eggs, and to determine whether vultures find their food by sight or by smell. Much of this reveals a scientific spirit of the first order. His interest in animals was further evidenced by the menageries which he had established in Palermo and Lucera dei Pagani, and the one which followed him in Italy and even across the Alps into Germany; it included elephants, dromedaries, camels, panthers, lions, leopards, gerfalcons, white falcons, bearded owls, monkeys, and even a giraffe, the first to appear in Europe.

Frederick's genuine love of science is further revealed by the questions which he submitted to his scientific advisers; for example, to Michael Scot and Ibn Sab'īn. He also loved to explode superstitions by means of experiments or simple common sense; e.g., with regard to the generation of barnacle geese.

He tried to put a stop to the madness of the Crusades, and to reconcile Christendom and Islām.

He gave to the Sicilies in 1231 a very remarkable code of laws. The official text of these Constitutiones was in Latin, but a Greek translation was also published. In 1240 he promulgated a regulation of the practice of medicine, the first elaborate regulation of its kind, though some efforts in that direction had already been made a century before by his predecessor, Roger II. Frederick granted to Salerno the exclusive right to confer the license to practice medicine in the whole kingdom. The length of medical studies was determined: five years, plus one year of practical work under the guidance of an experienced physician, and one more year for the surgeons. The preparation of drugs, and the relations between doctors and apothecaries were also regulated. Unfortunately this was like the siren-song of the old school which ended together with the Hohenstaufen rule in 1268, and was replaced by Naples. In Petrarca's time Salerno was already legendary.

It has been said that one Martianus, protomedicus of Sicily, prevailed upon the emperor to order in 1238 that a human body be dissected publicly at Salerno every five years. This story and others of the same kind have not been proved. The history of human dissection does not begin before the second half of the thirteenth century, as far as tangible facts are concerned.

It is interesting to note that Frederick's code contains the earliest example of

[1] Observed by himself in the East, derived from Arabic books (see, e.g., my note on Theodore of Antioch), or obtained from the Muslim falconers whom he took with him to Italy.

death by burning as a penalty for the crime of heresy. This shows once more that free thought is often combined with intolerance (see my note on al-Ma'mūn, vol. 1, 557). Frederick was excommunicated at least five times during his life, and once more after his death.

It is difficult to say exactly when the Italian literary language was born. Various documents (e.g., legal documents) of the first half of the thirteenth century illustrate the pressure of the vulgar speech upon the Latin jargon of the learned. Italian poetry, and we might say Italian literature, began to blossom at Frederick's court under the combined influence of Provençal trovatori and Muslim singers. This again had very far-reaching consequences, but only after a certain transformation had taken place. Frederick's court was too artificial and too exotic a center for the creation of a national language, but it gave the initial stimulation; one which hardly survived the emperor. After his death the literary center was transferred to Tuscany, and the earlier poems were promptly "Tuscanised." For example, it would seem that Dante knew most of them only in the Tuscanised form. It is this process of toscaneggiamento—translation from the Sicilian into the Tuscan dialect—which completed the emancipation of the Italian language. The point to remember now is that Provençal and Muslim poetry and music influenced Italian music and letters through the Sicilian court; there may have been other infiltrations but this was the main channel.

Text—Of the six books of the De arte venandi cum avibus, only the first two have been edited. Reliqua librorum Frederici II imperatoris De arte venandi cum avibus cum Manfredi regis additionibus. Ex membranis vetustis nunc primum edita. Albertus Magnus de falconibus asturibus et accipitribus (414 p., Augsburg 1596; Frederick's treatise covers p. 1–358). The editor was Marcus Velser. This was reprinted with a zoological commentary by Jo. Gottl. Schneider (2 vols., Leipzig 1788–1789).

Harting quotes two earlier editions, together with a Latin version of Guillaume Tardif's French treatise on falconry (Geneva 1560, Basle 1578).

German translation of Velser's text by J. Erh. Pacius: Friedrich II. übrige Stücke des Buches von der Kunst zu Baitzen, nebst den Zusätzen des Königs Manfredus und Alberti Magni Unterricht von den Falken und Habichten (Ansbach 1756). H. Schöpffer: Des Friederichs II Bücher von der Natur der Vögel und der Falknerei mit den Zusätzen des Königs Manfred. Übersetzt und versehen mit Originalzeichnungen, sowie einem Wörterbuch der Falknereisprache (238 p., 8 pl., 40 ill., Berlin 1896). A new edition is being prepared by J. Strohl of Zurich.

One of the MSS. of this work, a Vatican codex of the thirteenth century, contains more than 900 figures of individual birds admirably done from life. See D'Agincourt: Histoire de l'art par les monuments depuis sa décadence au IVe siècle jusqu'à son renouvellement au XVIe (4 vols., Paris 1823; vol. 3, p. 78, pl. 73).

Gustav Wolff: Vier griechische Briefe Kaiser Friedrichs II (60 p., Berlin 1855). Staatsbriefe Friedrichs II (104 p., Breslau 1923).

Liber novem judicum in judiciis astrorum. Astrological compilation arranged in topical order and supposed to have been made by order of Frederick II (1st ed. Venice 1509; later edition, Basle 1571). It contains the writings of the following nine authors quoted in the order of the princeps: Mesehella (Māshāllāh, second half of eighth century), Aomar (possibly 'Umar ibn al-Farrukhān or his son, first half of ninth century), al-Kindī (first half of ninth century), Zael (probably Sahl ibn Bishr, first half of ninth century), Albenait (Abū 'Alī al-Khaiyāṭ), Dorotheus (Sidonius?), Jergis (one Jirjīs or George), Aristotle, Ptolemy. See M. Steinschneider: Europäische Übersetzungen (Wien, 61, 1905). Gustav Hellmann:

Die Wettervorhersage im ausgehenden Mittelalter (Beiträge zur Geschichte der Meteorologie, vol. 2, 201, 1917; Isis, 4, 185).

Biography and general criticism—J. L. A. Juillard-Bréholles (1817–1871): Historia diplomatica Friderici Secundi (6 vols., Paris 1852–1861). Ed. Winkelmann (1838–1896): Kaiser Friedrich II (2 vols., Leipzig 1889–1897; left incomplete; first ed. 1863–1865). Georges Blondel: La politique de Fréderic en Allemagne (486 p., Paris 1892). H. Chone: Die Handelsbeziehungen Kaiser Friederichs II in den Seestädten Venedig, Pisa, Genua (134 p., Berlin 1902). Franz Guntram Schultheiss: Die deutsche Volkssage vom Fortleben und der Wiederkehr Friedrichs II (Berlin 1911). Lionel Allshorn: Stupor mundi; life and times of Frederick II (318 p., ill., London 1912). Hans Niese: Zur Geschichte des geistigen Lebens am Hofe Kaiser Friedrichs II (Historische Z., vol. 108, 473–540, München 1912). Ernst Kantorowitz: Kaiser Friedrich II (651 p., Berlin 1927; important).

Special criticism (except zoology)—A. Del Vecchio: La legislazione de Federico II (Torino 1874). H. Rashdall: Universities of Europe in the Middle Ages (vol. 2, 22, 1895). Potthast: Bibliotheca medii aevi (470, 1896). Arthur Haseloff: Die Kaiserinnengräber in Andria. Ein Beitrag zur apulischen Kunstgeschichte unter Friedrich II (69 p., ill., Bibl. des preuss. hist. Instituts, Rom 1905). Heinrich Geymüller: Friedrich II und die Anfänge der Architektur der Renaissance (30 p., München 1908). Alfred Bäumer: Die Gesetzgebung Friedrichs II und ihre geschichtliche Grundlagen (Diss., 42 p., 1911). E. Wiedemann: Fragen aus dem Gebiet der Naturwissenschaften gestellt von Friedrich II (Archiv für Kulturgeschichte, vol. 11, 483–485, 1914). Charles H. Haskins: Michael Scot and Frederick II (Isis, 4, 250–275, 1922; 5, 216); Science at the court of Frederick II (American Historical Review, vol. 27, 669–694, 1922). H. Suter: Beiträge zu den Beziehungen Friedrichs II zu zeitgenössischen Gelehrten des Ostens und Westens (Abhdl. zur Gesch. der Naturwissensch., Heft 4, 1–8, 1922; Isis, 5, 501). Gustave Schlumberger: Voyage dans les Abruzzes et les Pouilles (Revue des Deux Mondes, février, 1916; new edition more than three times longer in Byzance et Croisades, 149–206, Paris 1927; Isis, 11, 500; contains information on Frederick's castles and menageries in Lucera dei Pagani, Firenzuola, Castel del Monte). Karl Hampe: Friedrich II als Fragensteller (Kultur- und Universalgeschichte, Festschrift für W. Goetz, 53–66, 1927). C. H. Haskins: Latin literature under Frederick II (Speculum, 3, 129–151, 1928).

Zoology—Baron Jérome Pichon: Du traité de fauconnerie composé par Frédéric II (Bulletin du bibliophile, Paris 1864). James Edmund Harting: Bibliotheca accipitraria (159–160, 167–172, London 1891). Léon Moulé: La médecine vétérinaire en Europe au Moyen âge (61–63, Paris 1900). C. B. Klunzinger: Über die Hohenstaufenkaisers Friedrich II Werk über die Vögel und die Jagd mit Falken (Journal für Ornithologie, vol. 51, 539–542, 1904). A. Hauber: Friedrich II und der langlebige Fisch (Archiv für Geschichte der Naturwissenschaften, vol. 3, 315–329, 1911) apropos of a fish supposed to have been thrown into the sea by Frederick in 1230 and fished out again in 1497! Gustave Loisel: Histoire des ménageries (vol. 1, 145–147, 1912). Charles H. Haskins: The De arte venandi of Frederick II (English historical review, 334–355, July 1921; elaborate study, Isis, 4, 403); Some early treatises on falconry (Romanic review, vol. 13, 18–27, 1922; Isis, 5, 213); Revised editions of these papers and also of those quoted above in his Studies in mediaeval science (Cambridge, Mass., 1924; Isis, 7, 121–124; see also second edition, p. xiv, 1927). Maurice Boubier: L'évolution de l'ornithologie (7, 231, Paris 1925; Isis, 8, 515). C. H. Haskins: The Latin literature of sport (Speculum, 2, 235–252, 1927).

Medicine—Of course the papers dealing with Frederick's legislation will probably include a discussion of the medical regulations or references to them. Robert von Töply: Studien zur Geschichte der Anatomie im Mittelalter (Leipzig 1898).

James J. Walsh: The popes and science (1908; Knights of Columbus edition, 419–423, 1913). K. Sudhoff: Der griechische Text der Medizinalverordnungen Friedrichs II (Mit. zur Geschichte der Medizin, vol. 13, 180–182, 1914); Ein diätetischer Brief an Friedrich II von seinem Hofphilosophen Magister Theodorus (Archiv für Geschichte der Medizin, vol. 9, 1–9, 1915); Geschichte der Medizin im Überlick (with Th. Meyer-Steineg, 3d ed., Jena 1928).

The Muslim colony of Lucera di Puglia—The only Arabic document relative to the Muslim colony which Frederick II had moved from Girgenti to Lucera di Puglia (Lucera dei Pagani) is dated 1284. It was published in facsimile by G. H. Pertz (Archiv der Gesellschaft für ältere deutsche Geschichtskunde, vol. 5, pl. 3, 1824). P. Egidi: La colonia saracena di Lucera e la sua distruzione (Archivio storico per le province napoletane, vols. 36 to 39; reprinted, Naples 1912). G. Levi Della Vida: La sottoscrizione araba di Riccardo di Lucera (Rivista degli studi orientali, vol. 10, 284–292, 1924).

The Muslim colony of Lucera was destroyed in August 1300 by Charles II of Anjou. See my note on Peter the Pilgrim (second half of thirteenth century).

II. ENGLISH PHILOSOPHERS

MICHAEL SCOT

Scot or Scott. Scotch philosopher, alchemist, astrologer, translator from Arabic into Latin. One of the founders of Latin Averroism. Born in Scotland in the last quarter of the twelfth century; educated we don't know where; we find him in Toledo in 1217, at Bologna in 1220; he was in touch with the Roman curia from 1224 to 1227; after that time he was probably at the court of Frederick II. He died at an unknown time, probably, c. 1235. He was for a long time in the service of Frederick II, as astrologer and translator; his later works were dedicated to him, and one of them (the Abbreviatio Avicenne) was in the imperial library in 1232. His writings are mainly philosophical and astrological, but they show glimpses of a genuine experimental point of view.

His writings are undated (except one, of 1217), but they can be divided into two groups according to the two main periods of Michael's life, the Spanish and the Sicilian.

Spanish Period

1. Al-Biṭrūjī (second half of twelfth century): Translation of his astronomical treatise Liber astronomiae (or De verificatione motuum coelestium), completed at Toledo in 1217. This text was soon translated into Hebrew (1259), and the Hebrew text was translated into Latin by Qalonymos ben David, junior, in 1528 (printed in Venice in 1531). Michael's version introduced Alpetragian astronomy, and incidentally the theory of the impetus, into the Latin world.

2. First Latin translation of Aristotle's Historia animalium, made in Toledo, probably before 1220. This consists of nineteen books including the De animalibus historia (with spurious book 10), De partibus animalium, De generatione animalium. This translation remained in use until the fifteenth century.

3. Translation of Aristotle's De coelo et mundo, with Ibn Rushd's commentary. Dedicated to Stephen of Provins.

4. Probably, translation of Aristotle's De anima, with Ibn Rushd's commentary. Other Aristotelian texts, with Ibn Rushd's commentaries, almost always follow these in the Latin MSS., and their translation may be tentatively ascribed to Michael: De generatione et corruptione, Meteora (book 4 of the middle com-

mentary), Parva naturalia, De substantia orbis. But these ascriptions are unproved. The same may be said of the translations of the Physics, Metaphysics, and Ethics, together with Ibn Rushd's commentaries. Michael may be the translator, but we don't know.

5. Divisio philosophica, an original treatise discussing the classification of science, based on al-Fārābī, as adapted by Domingo Gundisalvo. This is known only through fragments preserved by Vincent of Beauvais.

6. Quaestiones Nicolai peripatetici, an Averroistic compendium ascribed to Scot by Albert the Great. (It is not, and could not be, the translation of a treatise by Nicholas of Damascus.)

Sicilian Period

7. Abbreviatio Avicenne de animalibus. Translation dedicated to Frederick II. Anterior to 1232, probably not much (the date 1210 is wrong).

8–10. Three popular treatises on astrology and general science. Posterior to 1228; also dedicated to the emperor.

8. Liber introductorius. Scot's most ambitious work. It is a general introduction to astrology, divided into four parts. It includes a history of the subject.

9. Liber particularis. Also a popular introduction to astrology, but much briefer than the preceding. The last quarter of it contains a series of questions on scientific subjects asked by Frederick II, together with Michael's answers. For example, it includes a description of the hot sulphur springs of Italy, and of the volcanic phenomena of the Lipari islands.

10. Physionomia, also called Liber physiognomiae or De secretis naturis. This was the most popular of his works. It is preceded by a treatise on generation. This is possibly the origin of a fantastic division of the uterus into seven cells, which recurs in many later texts (e.g., Mondino). The physionomia includes a treatise De urinis; the only medical treatise which can be definitely ascribed to Scot.

11–12. Michael Scot was probably the author of two treatises on alchemy: Magisterium (de arte alchimie), Minus magisterium, which afford interesting evidence of collaboration with Jewish and Muslim experimenters.

Spurious Works

1. Latin translation of Maimonides' Guide of the perplexed. This translation was made from the Hebrew version in South Italy before the middle of the thirteenth century. It was suggested that Scot made it with the help of Jacob Anaṭoli; this is unproved.

2. Latin translation of Maimonides' Kitāb al-farā'iḍ, probably also from the Hebrew. Very doubtful.

3. Commentary on Sacrobosco's Sphaera, ascribed to Scot in the printed edition (Bologna 1495). Doubtful, if only because Sacrobosco probably outlived Scot.

4. Liber geomantiae. Very doubtful.

5. Mensa philosophica. This is certainly apocryphal. The author may possibly be Theobald Anguilbert, an Irish physician, under whose name it was published in Paris in 1500.

To conclude, Michael's main achievements were his translations of Aristotle, Ibn Rushd, and al-Biṭrūjī, from the Arabic. His most important translation of the Aristotelian corpus was that of the zoology; moreover he was the introducer of

Alpetragian astronomy, of Ibn Rushd's commentaries, and of Averroism in general. It should be noted, however, that in the Liber introductorius, he denied the doctrine of the eternity of the universe.

Michael had no knowledge of Greek, but he knew Hebrew; however there is no evidence that his translations were made from the Hebrew. He was helped—to a very considerable extent, said Bacon—by a Jewish dragoman named Abuteus or Andrew. This was probably the Andrew, canon of Palencia, whom Honorius III praised in 1225 for his knowledge of oriental languages; or he might be identical with Anaṭoli, with whom Michael was certainly in touch at Frederick's court.

Though his main titles to our gratitude are his activities as translator and experimental philosopher, he was especially famous in his and the following generations as an astrologer and magician. Many legends crystallized around his memory and he thus became in the popular mind one of the foremost wizards of the Middle Ages. Dante put him in Hell (XX, 116).

"Michele Scotto fu, che veramente
"Delle magiche frode seppe il gioco."

Text—Liber physiognomiae. First edition, Venice 1477. (78 leaves quarto). Later editions: Basle c. 1480; Venice 1482, 1490, etc. There were at least eighteen printed editions, in Latin, German, and Italian between 1477 and 1660. Edited with the De secretis mulierum and other treatises ascribed to Albert the Great (Amsterdam 1740).

The De animalibus is included in the Latin Aristotle published at Venice, 1496. It seems to have been printed before, separately, in 1493.

Expositio super auctorem Sphaerae cum quaestionibus (Bologna 1495, 1518, etc.).

Quaestio curiosa de natura solis et lunae (Theatrum chemicum, vol. 5, Strassburg 1622). Apocryphal. For this, see Ferguson (vol. 2, 355, 436).

Mensa philosophica. Many early editions. Cologne (1480?, 1485?, 1500?, 1508), Louvain (1481?, 1485?), Heidelberg, 1489, etc. Mensa philosophica, seu Enchiridion in quo de quaestionibus memorabilibus et variis ac jucundis hominum congressibus agitur (Francfort 1602; Leipzig 1603). English translation, The philosopher's banquet, 1614. Apocryphal.

General criticism—Arturo Graf: Miti, leggende e superstizioni del medio evo (2 vols., Torino 1892–1893; one essay is devoted to Scot). J. Wood Brown: An enquiry into the life and legend of Michael Scot (297 p., Edinburgh 1897; elaborate but a little adventurous; chronology incorrect). Sheriff Mackay: Dictionary of national biography (vol. 51, 59–62, 1897; repeating many of Brown's unwarranted statements). Charles Homer Haskins: Michael Scot and Frederick II (Isis, 4, 250–275, 1922; 5, 216; contains the text of a new series of Sicilian questions); reprinted in Studies in mediaeval science (272–298, 1924; again 1927, see p. XV of new edition). Lynn Thorndike: History of magic (vol. 2, 307–337, 1923). C. H. Haskins: Michael Scot in Spain (Homenaje a Adolfo Bonilla y San Martín, vol. 2, 129–134, Madrid 1930; Isis, 15, 406).

Translations and Averroism—Lucien Leclerc: Histoire de la médecine arabe (vol. 2, 451–459, 1876). F. Wüstenfeld: Übersetzungen arabischer Werke (99–107, 1877). E. Renan: Averroès et l'Averroïsme (3d and later editions, 205–210, 1869); Rabbins français (583, 1877; apropos of the Jew Andrew). M. Steinschneider: Hebraeische Übersetzungen (477–483; 1893); Europaeische Übersetzungen (55–58, 1904). Martin Grabmann: Mittelalterliche lateinische Aristotelesübersetzungen und Aristoteleskommentare in Handschriften spanischer Bibliotheken (37–40, München 1928; Isis, 13, 205).

Scientific criticism—John Ferguson: Bibliotheca chemica (vol. 2, 355–360, 1906; long bibliography). P. Duhem: Etudes sur Léonard de Vinci (vol. 2, 72, 1909; on the plurality of worlds and the omnipotence of God); Système du monde (vol. 3, 241–248, 1915; on astronomy). Charles Singer: Evolution of anatomy (81, 83, 1926). C. H. Haskins: The alchemy ascribed to Michael Scot (Isis, 10, 350–359; contains long extracts). Dorothea W. Singer: Michael Scot (Isis, 13, 5–15, 1929), completing Haskins's study with reference to other MSS.

Physiognomy—Richard Foerster: De translatione latina physiognomonicorum quae feruntur Aristotelis (progr., 27 p., Kiel, 1884); De Aristotelis quae feruntur Secretis secretorum (41 p., Kiel 1888); Scriptores physiognomonici (Leipzig 1893). Arthur Heinrich Querfeld: M. Scottus und seine Schrift de secretis naturae (Diss. 64 p., Leipzig 1919, long extracts; Isis, 4, 585).

JOHN OF LONDON

Lectured in Oxford, c. 1210–1213; still teaching in Oxford in 1252. He lectured on astronomy and meteorology. Teacher of John of Garland, who speaks of him very enthusiastically. He is highly praised also by Roger Bacon. He was one of the most fervent expounders of the new Aristotle.

Heinrich Denifle: Die Entstehung der Universitäten (246, Berlin 1885). Fontès: Deux mathématiciens peu connus du XIIIe siècle (Mémoires de l'Académie de Toulouse, vol. 9, 384–386, 1897). According to Fontès, John was sent by Bacon to carry books and instruments to Innocent IV (pope from 1243 to 1254) who kept him in his service. John compiled a list of stars in 1246, partly from his own observations. M. Cantor: Vorlesungen (vol. 2^2, 98, 1899). Fontès and Cantor mistook another John of London for this one; there were at least two Johns of London in this period. Montague Rhodes James: The ancient libraries of Canterbury and Dover (Cambridge 1903). Louis John Paetow: Morale scolarium of John of Garland (Memoirs of the University of California, 4, no. 2, Berkeley, 1927; Isis, 10, 126).

ALEXANDER OF HALES

Alexander de Ales, Halensis. Called Doctor irrefragabilis, Doctor doctorum, Theologorum monarcha. English Franciscan philosopher. Born in Hales, Gloucestershire; assumed the Franciscan habit in 1222; studied and taught in Paris; died there in 1245. He was the first magister regens to hold the chair of theology which was conceded to the Franciscans by the University of Paris, c. 1232; he resigned that chair, c. 1238 and was succeeded by his pupil, John of La Rochelle. He wrote, presumably in connection with his teaching, a Summa theologica, which was not entirely completed at the time of his death. This first philosophical contribution of the Franciscans was rather mediocre. Bacon spoke contemptuously of it, and furthermore maintained that Alexander had not written it! It was based on the Latin translations of Aristotle, of Muslim commentaries, chiefly Ibn Sīnā's, and of Jewish writings, chiefly those of Ibn Gabirol and Maimonides. In great contrast with the majority of his Christian contemporaries, Alexander professed considerable toleration and charity for the Jews.

Text—Expositio super tres libros Aristotelis de anima (240 leaves, Oxford 1481).

Summa, Pars 3 super tertium sententiarum (380 leaves, Venice 1475). Summa, four parts (Nürnberg 1481–1482; in four parts dated respectively 1482, 1481, 1482, 1482). New edition of the four parts (Pavia, 1489). See Gesamtkatalog der Wiegendrucke (vol. 1, 433–439, 1925). Among the later editions we may still quote the following: one in 4 vols., Venice 1576; another in 4 vols., Cologne 1611; and a critical one in the course of preparation by the Franciscans of Quaracchi, near Florence.

Criticism—Prof. Adamson: Dictionary of national biography (vol. 1, 271, 1885). J. Endres: Des Alexander von Hales Leben und psychologische Lehre (Philos. Jahrbuch, 1, 24–55, 203–296, 1888). F. Picavet: Abélard et Alexandre de Hales, createurs de la méthode scolastique (Biblioth. de l'école des hautes études, sci. religieuses, vol. 7, 1, 1896). J. Guttmann: Jewish Encyclopaedia (vol. 1, 350, 1901). P. Duhem: Système du monde (vol. 3, 399–407, 1915, astronomy; vol. 5, 316–340, 1917, philosophy). M. De Wulf: Mediaeval philosophy (vol. 1, 345–349, 1926). H. Rudy: Encyclopaedia judaica (vol. 2, 206–208, 1928).

ADAM MARSH

Adam de Marisco. Doctor illustris. English Franciscan. Born in Somerset; studied in Vercelli, Piedmont; entered the Franciscan order in Worcester, c. 1237; died in 1257 or 1258. He is not mentioned because of his writings which are lost and of no special interest to us, but rather because he was the real founder of the great Franciscan school of Oxford, the friend and counsellor of such men as Grosseteste, with whom he attended the Council of Lyon in 1245. He exerted a moderating influence on Simon de Montfort, Earl of Leicester, the main leader of the crusade against the Albigenses, and upon various statesmen and churchmen. His fame was considerable.

Text—Epistolae in J. S. Brewer: Monumenta franciscana (vol. 1, 77–489, 1858).

Criticism—J. S. Brewer: Monumenta franciscana (vol. 1, p. lxxvi-ci, 1858). Creighton: Dictionary of national biography (vol. 1, 79, 1885). A. G. Little: Grey friars in Oxford (Oxford 1892). Potthast (10, 1895). Ernest A. Savage: Old English libraries (57, 86, London 1911). A. G. Little: Studies in English Franciscan history (Manchester 1917; Isis, 3, 280–282).

ROBERT GROSSETESTE

Robert Grosthead or Greathead. Robert of Lincoln. Robertus Grosse capitis Lincolniensis. Born of humble parentage at Stradbrook, Suffolk, c. 1175; educated in Oxford and Paris (?); first chancellor of the University of Oxford; first lecturer to the Oxford Franciscans, 1224; bishop of Lincoln from 1235 to his death in 1253. English mathematician, astronomer, physicist, philosopher, translator from the Greek into Latin. He was the main organizer of philosophical studies at Oxford, and his influence was strongly felt in England for at least a couple of centuries. Nor was it limited to England. His insistence on the necessity of studying Greek and of basing natural philosophy upon mathematics and experiment was extremely beneficial and far-reaching; in this he was clearly the forerunner of his most famous pupil, Roger Bacon. We may say that he influenced the whole western world, partly through his own writings, and partly through these new tendencies emphasized by Bacon and others.

A large number of writings are ascribed to him; allowing for the fact that some are probably apocryphal, his literary activity must have been tremendous. He wrote commentaries on the Posterior Analytics, and on the Physics of Aristotle. His treatise on the compotus (c. 1232) includes a discussion of the reform of the calendar, which was repeatedly quoted by subsequent writers from Bacon to

Peter of Ailly. He insisted upon that need (calendrical reform) also in another treatise of his, the Compendium sphaerae. This Compendium was derived from Sacrobosco, but contained original additions, notably the first mention of the trepidation of the equinoxes in a non-Muslim work. (This erroneous notion had been introduced mainly by Thābit ibn Qurra, second half of the ninth century). His astronomical ideas were partly Ptolemaic, and partly Alpetragian. Besides the Sphaera already mentioned he wrote various other astronomical and astrological treatises; e.g., De generatione stellarum and De cometis. The majority of his scientific treatises deal with physical and meteorological questions. A few titles to illustrate: De luce seu de inchoatione formarum, De iride, De colore, De impressionibus aëris (de prognosticatione), De lineis angulis et figuris seu de fractionibus et reflexionibus radiorum, De impressionibus elementorum, De generatione sonorum, De calore solis, etc. He was much concerned with that complex subject called "perspective" and with optical questions in general. He was well aware of the magnifying properties of lenses, a knowledge which he probably transmitted to Bacon. (Which suggests that other items of Bacon's encyclopaedic knowledge were probably obtained from Grosseteste). Many of these physical writings were ascribed by Bacon collectively to Grosseteste and to Adam Marsh. Grosseteste was one of the earliest English authors to be acquainted with the writings of the Salernitan school; (that is, it is probable that Gilbert the Englishman became acquainted with them only a little later; but on the other hand Alfred of Sareshel preceded him). He showed interest in astrology and alchemy, but was remarkably free from magical fancies.

He had a very good knowledge of Greek. About 1240–1243, he made the first complete translation into Latin of the Nicomachean Ethics, together with the commentaries of Eustratios, metropolitan of Nicaea (c. 1050–c. 1120), of Michael of Ephesus, Psellos's pupil (second half of eleventh century), and of others, and he added to it many notes on Greek lexicography and syntax. (This very important translation was at first wrongly ascribed to William of Moerbeke). He also wrote a summary of the Nicomachean Ethics. He translated from Greek into Latin various other works by Aristotle, Dionysios Areopagita, John of Damascus, and extracts from Suidas. Through these translations he exerted a deep influence upon St. Thomas and Albert the Great.

Some Greeks came to England about 1202, and some Armenians, among them a bishop, visited St. Albans. Grosseteste seems to have been helped in his studies by one Nicholas the Greek, clerk to the abbot of that monastery. This Nicholas translated from Greek into Latin the apocryphal Testaments of the twelve patriarchs.

Grosseteste had some knowledge of Hebrew, and owned a copy of a literal Latin translation of the Old Testament with the Hebrew text. His main reason for advocating the study of Hebrew was to promote the conversion of the Jews. He was not hostile to the latter, and saved many of them from being massacred.

A translation from the French into English of Walter de Henley's husbandry was wrongly ascribed to him. A very remarkable encyclopaedia, the Summa philosophica, has also been attributed to him; it is certainly a later work, probably by a pupil of Bacon's (q.v.).

Robert was not simply a great scholar, but a courageous man. He did not fear to repress the evil tendencies of his flock, nor to reprove those of the Roman curia.

He did not assume the Franciscan habit but was the first reader to the Oxford

Franciscans and he was an intrinsic member and the chief inspirer of the Franciscan school of Oxford. The following lecturers, one Peter (Peter of Ramsey?), Roger of Wesham, Thomas of Wales were also seculars, not friars, but Adam Marsh was a friar.

Text—The main source for Grosseteste's scientific writings is Ludwig Baur: Die philosophischen Werke des Robert Grosseteste (976 p., Beiträge zur Geschichte der Philosophie des Mittelalters, vol. 9, Münster i. W., 1912). This critical edition includes 29 works, authentic and apocryphal, some very short, less than a page, others very long, like the apocryphal Summa philosophiae, and an elaborate introduction (181 p.).

Compendium sphaerae, included in the astronomical collections published in Venice, 1508, 1513 or 1514, 1518, 1531. Also in Baur (10–32).

Libellus de phisicis lineis angulis et figuris per quas omnes acciones naturales complentur (Nürnberg 1503). See Gustav Hellmann: Bibliotheca mathematica (vol. 2, 443, 1901). New edition by Maximilian Curtze: De fractionibus et reflexionibus radiorum (Bibliotheca mathematica, vol. 1, 55–59, 1900). Also in Baur (59–65).

Commentarius in Analytica posteriora. 1475?, Venice 1494, 1497, 1499, 1504, 1537.

Super libros Physicorum. Venice 1506, etc.; the printed text was translated into Hebrew by Elias ben Joseph of Nola in 1537.

Comm. in mysticam theologiam Dionysii Aeropagitae, Strassburg 1502 or 1503.

Opuscula quaedam philosophica. Venice 1514.

Some Dicta and Sermones were edited by Edward Brown, in appendix to Fasciculus rerum expetendarum et fugiendarum (250–414, London 1690).

Epistolae edited by Henry Richard Luard (Rolls series, London 1861).

Rotuli Roberti Grosseteste 1235–1253, episcopi Lincolniensis necnon Rotulus Henrici de Lexington. Edited by F. N. Davis (570 p., Publication of the Lincoln record society, vol. 11, Horncastle 1914).

Carmina anglo-normannica. Château d'amour, etc., with an English version. Edited by M. Cooke (Caxton Society, 15, London 1852). J. Murray: Le château d'amour (182 p., thèse, Paris 1918; including text, p. 89–138).

Compotus factus ad correctionem communis kalendarii nostri. Edited by Robert Steele: Opera hactenus inedita Rogeri Baconi (fasc. 6, 212–267, Oxford, 1926). Mary Catherine Welborn has prepared a new edition of the Compotus and an English translation of it to be published by the Columbia University Press.

General criticism—Samuel Pegge: The life of Robert Grosseteste, with an account of the Bishop's works (390 p., London 1793). Gotthard Victor Lechler: Robert Grosseteste (Progr., 29 p., Leipzig 1867). Joseph Felten: Grosseteste. Ein Beitrag zur Kirchen- und Culturgeschichte des 13. Jahrh. (120 p., Freiburg i. B., 1887). H. R. Luard: Dictionary of national biography (vol. 23, 275–278, 1890). Francis Seymour Stevenson: Grosseteste (364 p., London 1899). A. G. Little: Studies in English Franciscan history (Manchester 1917; the sixth lecture deals with Grosseteste and Bacon; Isis, 3, 280–282).

Scientific and Philosophic criticism—M. Steinschneider: Hebraeische Übersetzungen (476, 1893). Norman Moore: The schola salernitana. Its history and the date of its introduction into the British Isles (Glasgow medical journal, 241–268, April 1908). Ernest A. Savage: Old English libraries (219, London 1911). J. de Ghellinck: L'entrée de Jean de Damas dans le monde littéraire occidental (Byzantinische Z., vol. 21, 448–457, 1912; apropos of Grosseteste's translation of the De fide orthodoxa). P. Duhem: Système du monde (vol. 3, 277–287, 460–471, 1915, the second part devoted to the apocryphal writing Summa philosophiae; vol. 5, 341–358, 1917, philosophy). Arvid Lindhagen: Die Neumondtafel des Robertus

(Arkiv för Matematik, Astronomi och Fysik, vol. 11, 41 p., Stockholm 1916). Ludwig Baur: Die Philosophie des Grosseteste (Beitr. zur Gesch. der Philosophie des Mittelalters, vol. 18, 314 p., Münster i. W., 1917). Capital study, a good half of which is devoted to scientific questions: cosmography and astronomy; "light metaphysics" and cosmogony; mathematics; with bibliography. Ernest Wickersheimer: Robert Grosseteste et la médecine (Communication faite au 3e Congrès de l'art de guérir, 4 p., Londres 1922, Anvers 1923). Lynn Thorndike: History of magic (vol. 2, 436–453, 1923). M. de Wulf: Mediaeval philosophy (vol. 1, 241–242, 352–362, 1926). F. M. Powicke: Grosseteste and the Nicomachean ethics (Proc., British Academy, vol. 16, 22 p., 1930).

BARTHOLOMEW THE ENGLISHMAN

Bartholomaeus Anglicus, Magister de proprietatibus rerum. The name Bartholomew de Glanville, which is uncertain and probably wrong, should be avoided; it was first used perhaps because of a confusion with another English Franciscan bearing that name, who died in 1360.

Bartholomew was born in England; he flourished in Oxford, Paris (c. 1220), Magdeburg (after 1230); he was a Franciscan of the French province; he must have lived until about the middle of the century, for he quotes Michael Scot and Grosseteste; he is quoted by Bacon. He was perhaps a pupil of Grosseteste. He wrote, c. 1230–1240, for the plain people (simplices et rudes) an encyclopaedia entitled De proprietatibus rerum, which was immensely popular for about three centuries, though it was already behind the times in many respects when it was composed. Its popularity is witnessed by the number of manuscripts, translations, and editions. It was one of the books which the Paris students could hire for a definite price. The aim was primarily theological and philosophical, but Bartholomew had a genuine taste for natural history. His work is divided into nineteen books of which the contents can be roughly indicated as follows: (1) God; (2) angels and demons; (3) psychology; (4–5) physiology; (6) family life, domestic economy; (7) medicine (largely derived from Constantine the African); (8) cosmology, astrology; (9) time divisions; (10) form and matter, elements; (11) air, meteorology; (12) flying creatures; (13) waters and fishes, dolphins, whales; (14) physical geography; (15) political geography, (in 175 chapters; this contains a number of interesting remarks, notes on economic geography, etc.); (16) gems, minerals, metals; (17) trees and herbs; (18) animals; (19) color, odor, savor; food and drink; eggs; weights and measures; musical instruments.

It is clear that Bartholomew's encyclopaedia was remarkably comprehensive and methodical. But on the whole it represented a state of knowledge which was already superseded. For example, his astronomy represented the early mediaeval tradition, that of Macrobius (first half of fifth century) and of Martianus Capella (second half of fifth century), and hence it included allusions to the geo-heliocentrical system of Heraclides of Pontos. His geography and natural history were more advanced, and his descriptions of plants and animals contain original touches which are exceedingly delightful. His herbal was by far the most notable work of its kind written by an Englishman in the Middle Ages. The political geography of Europe contains a quantity of information which had not been put together before.

His account of the divisions of time is curious: the day is divided into twenty-four hours, the hour into four points or forty moments, the moment into twelve ounces, the ounce into forty-seven atoms (thus there are 22560 atoms in one hour, as compared with our 3600 seconds). An earlier encyclopaedia, the Imago mundi,[2] which shared the popularity of Bartholomew's work, explained the same division of the hour (but its hour was double, one twelfth part of the day), but also others into ten minutes, fifteen parts, sixty ostenta.

The De proprietatibus rerum was translated into Italian by Vivaldo Belcalzer of Mantova in 1309; into French, by Jean Corbechon for Charles V in 1372; into Provençal before 1391; into English by John of Trevisa in 1397 or 1398; into Spanish by Vicente (Vincent) of Burgos some time in the fifteenth century. This last named translation is a classic of the Spanish language; it is registered in the Catálogo de autoridades de la lengua.

Text—The information on incunabula editions is primarily derived from the Gesamtkatalog der Wiegendrucke (vol. 3, 411–427, 1928).

Princeps, Basel c. 1470 (220 leaves). Other early Latin editions: Cologne c. 1472; Lyon 1480; Cologne 1481; Lyon 1482 (two); Cologne 1483; Nürnberg 1483; Strassburg 1485; Heidelberg 1488; Strassburg 1491; Nürnberg 1492. Other Latin editions: Strassburg 1505; Nürnberg 1519; Venice 1571; Paris 1574; Strassburg 1575; Francfort 1601, 1609.

French translation by Jean Corbechon, edited by Pierre Farget: Lyon 1482 (330 leaves, 20 woodcuts), 1485, 1486, 1487, 1491; Paris c. 1493; Lyon c. 1500. Many later editions in Paris, 1510, 1518, 1525, 1528, c. 1530, 1539, 1556 (four); Rouen 1512.

Dutch translation: Haarlem 1485 (466 leaves, 11 woodcuts).

Spanish translation by Vincent of Burgos: complete edition (320 leaves, 18 woodcuts, 6 schematic woodcuts, Toulouse 1494). Partial edition, Tractado de los metales y piedras preciosas (Zaragoza 1495). Later edition: Toledo 1529.

English version by John of Trevisa. First printed by Wynkyn de Worde, Westminister c. 1495 (202 leaves, 10 woodcuts). Among the curious illustrations is a good drawing of a dissection scene, the earliest of its kind in a book printed in England or in an English book. Second edition printed by Berthelet, London 1535. A third edition, Batman uppon Bartholome his booke . . . newly corrected and amended, etc. (London 1582), was an arrangement by Stephen Batman (d. 1584), differing considerably from the original.

Robert Steele: Mediaeval lore, an epitome of the science, geography, animal and plant folk-lore and myth of the middle age, being classified gleanings from the encyclopaedia of Bartholomaeus Anglicus on properties of things. With a preface by William Morris (164 p., London 1893; reprinted in the King's Classics, London 1907). Derived from the second English edition, 1535).

Criticism—Ernst H. F. Meyer: Geschichte der Botanik (vol. 4, 84–91, 1857). Valentin Rose: Aristoteles de lapidibus und Arnoldus Saxo (Z. für deutsches Alterthum, vol. 18, 321–455, 1875). Miss L. Toulmin Smith: Dictionary of national geography (vol. 21, 409–411, 1890). Léon Moulé: La medecine vétérinaire en Europe au Moyen âge (Paris, 59–60, 1900). Vittorio Cian: Vivaldo Belcalzer e l'enciclopedismo italiano delle origini (Giornale storico della letteratura ital., suppl. no. 5, 192 p., 1902; including copious extracts and glossary). Edmund Voigt: Bartholomaeus. Literarhistorisches und Bibliographisches (Englische Studien, vol. 41, 338–359, 1910). Ch. V. Langlois: La connaissance de la nature et du monde au moyen âge (114–179, 1911; containing an analysis based on Corbechon's text). Arthur Schneider: Metaphysische Begriffe des Bartholomaeus (Clemens Baeumker Festgabe, 139–179, Münster 1913). P. Duhem: Système du Monde (vol. 3, 127–130, 1915). Duhem would place the composition of Barth-

[2] Probably compiled by Honorius Inclusus (second half of eleventh century. See vol. 1, 749).

olomaeus' book a little later than I do, between 1250 and 1275. G. E. Se Boyar: Bartholomaeus and his Encyclopaedia (Journal of English and Germanic philology, 19, 168–189, 1920). Gerhard Ritter: Zahnärztliches aus den encyclopädischen Werken Isidors von Sevilla und Bartholomäus (Diss., 25 p., Leipzig 1922). E. S. Rohde: Old English herbals, London 1922 (chapter 2 contains an enthusiastic account of Bartholomaeus plant-lore; Isis, 5, 457–461). Lynn Thorndike: History of magic (vol. 2, 401–435, 1923). M. de Wulf: Mediaeval philosophy (vol. 1, 333, 1926). F. S. Bodenheimer: Materialien zur Geschichte der Entomologie (vol. 1, 181, 1928).

III. FRENCH PHILOSOPHERS AND WRITERS

WILLIAM OF AUVERGNE

Guilelmus Alvernus (or Arvenus). Born c. 1180, at Aurillac, Auvergne (Cantal); bishop of Paris from 1228 to his death in 1249, hence he is sometimes called William of Paris. French philosopher, "the first great scholastic," i.e., the first great forerunner of St. Thomas. His main work, written between 1223 and 1240, is the Magisterium divinale, including many treatises of theology, metaphysics and psychology. The most interesting of these treatises is the De universo creaturarum, composed c. 1231–1236. He made use of the newly acquired works of Aristotle and was influenced also by Muslim and Jewish philosophers and above all by Ibn Gabirol, whom he believed to be a Christian (of course he knew these works only through their Latin versions). He made an effort to syncretize those philosophies and to harmonize them with the Christian dogmas. The De universo is an intermediate between the early mediaeval writings on cosmology (Isidore; Bede; Honorius Inclusus) and the encyclopaedias of the second half of the thirteenth century (Vincent of Beauvais; Albert the Great). He was genuinely interested in natural philosophy, but his knowledge of it—e.g., of astronomy—was very poor.

He was deeply versed in occult lore (for example, he was perhaps the first Latin scholar to be well acquainted with the works ascribed to Hermes Trismegistos) and the De universo is very valuable for the history of mediaeval magic. He speaks very often of "experiments," but had apparently no conception of experimental science.

The De immortalitate animae, written by him before 1228, was copied almost verbatim from Gundisalvo.

He was one of the judges who ordered the Talmud to be burned in Paris, 1242.

Text—I do not quote editions of separate writings. Opera, Nürnberg 1496 or 1497; 2 vols., Paris 1516; 2 vols., Venice 1591; 2 vols., Aureliae 1674.

Criticism—Karl Werner: Die Psychologie des Wilhelm (Akad. d. Wiss., phil. Kl., vol. 73, 257–326, Wien 1873). Noël Valois: Guillaume d'Auvergne, sa vie et ses ouvrages (Thèse, 404 p., Paris 1880). Matthias Baumgartner: Die Erkenntnislehre des Wilhelm (Beitr. zur Gesch. der Philos. des Mittelalters., II, 1, Münster 1893). Stephan Schindele: Die Metaphysik des Wilhelm (Diss., München 1900). Isaac Broydé: Jewish Encyclopaedia (vol. 6, 107, 1904). P. Duhem: Etudes sur Léonard de Vinci (vol. 2, 408–410, 1909; on the plurality of worlds); Système du monde (vol. 3, 249–260, 1915, de universo; vol. 5, 260–285, 1917, philosophy). Lynn Thorndike: History of magic (vol. 2, 338–371, 1923; elaborate account of his views on many magical subjects and on science). M. de Wulf: Mediaeval philosophy (vol. 1, 339–345; vol. 2, 109, 1926). Bernard Landry: L'originalité de Guillaume d'Auvergne (Revue d'histoire de la philosophie, vol. 3, 441–465, 1929; Isis, 14, 478). Artur Landgraf: Der Traktat De errore Pelagii des Wilhelm von Auvergne (Speculum, vol. 5, 168–180, 1930).

JOHN OF LA ROCHELLE

Joannes a Rupella. French Franciscan. Born probably at La Rochelle; pupil of Alexander of Hales, whom he succeeded in the Franciscan chair of theology of the university of Paris, c. 1238; he died in 1245;[3] he was succeeded by St. Bonaventure in 1248. He wrote various philosophical commentaries and treatises, notably a Summa de anima, which is not so much derived from Aristotle, as from Augustine, Ibn Sīnā, Alcher of Clairvaux (second half of the twelfth century) and neo-Platonic writings. It represents the Augustinian and neo-Platonic point of view. This is not very important but it helps to explain the establishment in Paris of the Franciscan tradition, a tradition which would soon culminate in the teachings of St. Bonaventure, otherwise so different.

Text—Teofilo Domenichelli: La Summa de anima di Frate Giovanni de la Rochelle (Prato 1882; poor edition).

Criticism—Daunou: Histoire littéraire de la France (vol. 19, 171–173, 1838). B. Hauréau: Nouvelle biographie générale (vol. 26, 549–550, 1858). Parthenius Minges: De scriptis quibusdam Fr. Ioannis de Rupella (Archivum franciscanum historicum, vol. 6, 597–622, 1913). M. Baumgartner: Überwegs Grundriss (vol. 2, 10th ed., 1915). M. de Wulf: Mediaeval philosophy (vol. 1, 349–351, 1926).

GUIOT OF PROVINS

Guiot or Guyot. French poet, who was in Mainz (Mayence) in 1148, and spent some time in the monasteries of Clairvaux and Cluny. He seems to have traveled considerably, for he resided some time in the south of France (e.g., at Arles) and may have reached Jerusalem. He composed in old age, c. 1205, a great satirical poem in French (2691 lines) which he entitled Bible. It is a moot question whether he is identical or not with the poet Kyot, from whom Wolfram von Eschenbach borrowed his version of the legend of Parsifal. The town of Provins is situated on the Voulzie, an affluent of the Seine. Thus Guiot was not a Provençal but he had studied and lived in the south of France, being the most remarkable example of the relations which thus already existed between the poets speaking the "langue d'oïl" and those using the "langue d'oc," i.e. between the trouvères and the troubadours. His Bible is a mirror of contemporary life; it contains some very free criticism of the clergy and monks, of the physicians, etc., and also one of the earliest western mentions of the compass. The "Bible Guiot" was very popular in the thirteenth century.

Text—The Bible and other texts have been edited by San Marte (A. Schulz) and J. F. Wolfart: Parcival Studien, 1 (Halle 1861). Oeuvres editées par John Orr (261 p., Manchester 1915).

Criticism—See my note on the history of the compass (first half of the fourteenth century).

Arthur Baudler: Guiot von Provins (91 p., Halle 1902). Ch. V. Langlois: La vie en France au moyen âge, d'après les moralistes du temps (47–87, Paris 1924; revised edition, 47–87, 1926).

THE ROMANCE OF SIDRACH

The book, called in French "Fontaine de toutes les sciences," "Livre" or "Roman" of the philosopher Sidrach, was one of the most popular mediaeval works.

[3] Other dates are given, e.g., 1254 and 1271, but 1245 seems to be the right one.

It was part of every princely library in the fourteenth and fifteenth centuries. Manuscripts of it (in one or another of many European vernaculars) exist in almost every important collection. It is an encyclopaedic treatise arranged in the form of a catechism, the number of questions varying with the MSS., from 615 to 1209 and more. It is perhaps the most puerile encyclopaedia of the Middle Ages.

Its origin has been much debated. According to its own prologue, dated 1243, the French book of Sidrach would have been translated in Toledo from a Latin version made by order of Frederick II from a "Saracen" text, which had been itself made in Spain from the Latin translation of a Greek original. Now this Oriental origin is far from being established, for no Oriental text is known. Victor Leclerc suggested[4] that it had been translated in the thirteenth century from Hebrew into Latin; this is certainly wrong. Italo Pizzi, on the other hand, would trace it back to an Iranian prototype, a Pahlawī dialogue between King Nūshīrwān and the wise Burzūya. See my note on the latter in my chapter on the second half of the sixth century (vol. 1, 449).

There is in the Bibliothèque Nationale of Paris a ninth century Latin MS. of a text ascribed to Priscian the Philosopher containing the solution of problems proposed by King Nūshīrwān. These problems are similar to those of Sidrach. I have mentioned them in my note on Priscianos (first half of the sixth century, vol. 1, 423).

See also Jules Quicherat: Solution des problèmes proposés par Chosroès (Bibliothèque de l'Ecole des chartes vol. 4, 248–263, 1853).

According to Ernest Renan and Gaston Paris, the romance of Sidrach was written directly in a Western vernacular; the original text was probably written in Lyon, in Provençal? Langlois' hypothesis, however, is more plausible: according to him, the writer was a Frenchman, who was living (or had been living) in the Latin East. The romance was not necessarily composed, or completed, in 1243; it may date only from the last quarter of the century; the Image du Monde, dated 1246–1248 is mentioned in it.

The author was possibly one "Jean-Pierre" (John Peter) of Lyon, quoted in the text. Nothing is known of him. As there are points of contact between Sidrach and the Sirr al-asrār it is just possible that Jean Pierre is a corruption of Yaḥyā ibn Baṭrīq (Johannes filius Patricii or Petri, Jean fiz Patrice, Jean Pierre). See my note on the Secretum in my chapter on the first half of the ninth century (vol. I, 556).

Text and Criticism—La fontaine de toutes sciences (Paris 1486). Victor Leclerc: L'image du monde (Histoire littéraire de la France, vol. 23, 287–335, 1856). Adolfo Bartoli: Il libro di Sidrach, testo inedito del sec. XIV. (Pt. 1, Bologna 1868). Ernest Renan et Gaston Paris: La fontaine de toutes sciences. (Histoire littéraire, vol. 31, 285–318, 1893). Italo Pizzi: Storia della poesia persiana (2 vols.; vol. 2, 452, Torino 1894); Un riscontro arabo del libro di Sidrac (Raccolta dedicata ad Al. d'Andona, 235–239, Firenze 1901). Hermann Jellinghaus: Das Buch Sidrach nach der Kopenhagener mittelniederdeutschen Handschrift v. J. 1479 (252 p., Tübingen 1904). M. Steinschneider: Europäische Übersetzungen (75, 1904; Fra Ruggiero of Palermo was sent by Frederick II to Tunis, to translate the Book of Sidrach into Italian). Ch. V. Langlois: La connaissance de la nature et du monde au moyen âge (180–264, Paris 1911; revised edition, 198–275, 1927). Containing a

[4] Histoire littéraire (vol. 23, p. 294).

summary of the text with a very clear introduction upon which my note is essentially based. Gunnar Knudsen: Sydrak, efter haandskriftet ny Kgl. saml. 236, 4° (144 p. in 2 parts, Copenhagen 1921–1925, not complete).

WALTER OF METZ

French writer who flourished c. 1246. He is known only as the author of an encyclopaedic treatise in French, L'image du monde (or Livre de clergie). It deals with cosmogony, theology, geography, natural history, meteorology, astronomy. The first edition, in 6594 verses, dates from 1246 (1245, O.S.); a second edition in verse, possibly by another author, contains 4000 more lines and dates from c. 1248. An edition in prose was composed probably at the same time as the first edition in verse. The three editions were exceedingly popular.

The Image du monde was naturally derived from other works of the same kind, chiefly the Imago mundi, probably compiled by the English Benedictine, Honorius Inclusus (second half of the eleventh century), and from the writings of Alan of Lille, James of Vitry, etc.

The author's name, Walter, or rather its French equivalent Gautier, is uncertain; it may have been Gossuin (or Gossouin). Or else Gossuin may possibly have been the author of the first editions in verse and prose, and Gautier of the second edition in verse (or vice versa).

The Image du monde was translated into Hebrew under the title Demuth ha-'olam by one David ben Moses. There is another Hebrew version entitled Ẓel ha-'olam, by Mattathias ben Solomon Delaqruṭ (or De La Crota), a Polish scholar who flourished in Italy about the middle of the sixteenth century. This version has been ascribed to Hagin Deulacres (second half of the thirteenth century) but apparently with no authority except the resemblance between the names. The Image was also translated into Yiddish.

An English translation was made by William Caxton in 1480.

Text—Prose text edited by Michel le Noir (Paris 1501), and by Alain Lotrian (Paris 1520). O. H. Prior: L'Image du monde de maitre Gossouin. Rédaction en prose. Texte du MS. de la Bibliothèque nationale, fonds français n° 574 (216 p., Lausanne 1913).

Caxton's English version was printed by him in Westminster, 1481, and again in 1490. The edition of 1481 was the first work printed in England with illustrations. It has been reprinted by Oliver H. Prior for the Early English Text Society (218 p., London 1913). A third English edition by Lawrence Andrewe of Calais (fl. 1510–1537) appeared in London, 1527.

The Ẓel ha-'olam was printed in Amsterdam, 1733; again in Warsaw, 1873.

One François Buffereau of Vendôme, published the French poem as his own (Geneva 1517) stating that he had composed it in 1514–1516 in his castle of Divonne.

Criticism—Gustav Haase: Die Reime in der Image du Monde des Walther von Metz (Diss., 23 p., Halle 1879). Fr. Fritsche: Untersuchung über die Quellen der Image du monde (Halle 1880). Carl Fant: L'image du monde. Poème inédit du milieu du XIIIe siècle, étudié dans ses diverses rédactions françaises d'après les MSS. des bibliothèques de Paris et de Stockholm (78 p., Uppsala Universitets Årsskrift, 1886, important). M. Steinschneider: Hebraeische Übersetzungen (950–951, 1893). Ch. V. Langlois: La connaissance de la nature et du monde au moyen âge (49–113, Paris 1911, analysis of both verse versions; revised edition, 135–197, 1927).

IV. ITALIAN PHILOSOPHERS

For William of Lunis, see chapter on translators from Arabic into Latin, above. For St. Bonaventure, see Book IV.

V. GERMAN PHILOSOPHERS

ARNOLD THE SAXON

Arnoldus Saxo. German encyclopaedist, who flourished in Lower Saxony c. 1225 (the epithets Saxo, Saxonicus, refer to Lower Saxony). He wrote between 1220 and 1230 a brief encyclopaedia entitled De finibus rerum naturalium, divided into five books: De coelo et mundo, de naturis animalium, de gemmarum virtutibus, de virtute universali, de moralibus. It is based on the Latin translations of Greek and Arabic writings. The third part, or lapidary, was especially popular. It quoted Aristotle, Dioscorides, and "Aaron and Evax" (i.e., Marbode). It was used by Thomas of Cantimpré, Bartholomew the Englishman, Albert the Great, and Vincent of Beauvais, but was not quoted except by the last named and by the author of the Hortus sanitatis. There is an anonymous Hebrew translation of it, Sefer ha-abanim.

According to Thorndike, instead of Bartholomew having used Arnold's lapidary, it would be the other way around. If so, Arnold's work would be somewhat younger than we said. One thing is certain, Bartholomew's lapidary is more elaborate than Arnold's.

Text—Emil Stange: Die Encyklopädie des Arnoldus Saxo zum ersten Mal nach einem Erfurter Codex hrg. (Progr., 88 p., Erfurt 1905–1906). Does not include the fifth part dealing with ethics.

Criticism—Valentin Rose: Aristoteles de lapidibus und Arnoldus Saxo (Z. für deutsches Alterthum, vol. 18, 321–455, 1875). Emil Stange: Arnoldus Saxo, der älteste Encyklopädist des XIII. Jahrhunderts (Diss., Halle, 67 p., Halle 1885). M. Steinschneider: Hebraeische Übersetzungen (957, 1893). Lynn Thorndike: History of magic (vol. 2, 260, 431–432, 469–470, 1923).

THOMAS OF CANTIMPRÉ

Thomas of Brabant. Thomas Brabantinus, de Cantiprato, Cantipratanus, Cantimpratensis. Flemish Dominican and encyclopaedist. Born in Brabant c. 1186–1210 (probably nearer to the latter date, c. 1204?); flourished in Chantimpré, near Cambrai; studied in Liége; entered the Dominican Order in 1232; was in Paris in 1238; sub-prior in Louvain, 1246; died, probably in Louvain, c. 1271–1280. It is possible that he attended some of Albert the Great's lectures, but he can hardly be called the latter's disciple. His two main works are (1) a popular encyclopaedia of science, De natura rerum, to the preparation of which he devoted some fifteen years of study and which he completed between 1228 and 1244; (2) a collection of absurd stories for the edification of the clergy, Bonum universale de apibus, written late in life.

It is interesting to observe that the Dominican, Thomas of Cantimpré, and the Franciscan, Bartholomew the Englishman, were engaged in the same kind of undertaking about the same time: The Properties of things being completed c. 1230–1240, and the Nature of things c. 1228–1244. Both works were encyclopaedic in scope and divided into nineteen books, but they were otherwise very different, and in all probability independent. Judging by the number of MSS., both works were almost equally popular (if one takes into account that there are many MSS. of Thomas' work which do not bear his name); but with regard to printed editions, Bartholomew's popularity was incomparably greater. Indeed Thomas' encyclopaedia has not yet been entirely published.

Thomas' main authorities were Aristotle, Pliny, Solinus, Ambrose and Basil, Isidore, Adelard of Bath (whom he does not mention), James of Vitry, two lost works, Liber rerum and Experimentator, which were probably contemporary or at any rate recent, and a few others to be quoted presently. The De natura rerum is divided as follows: (1) The human body; anatomy, physiology, gynaecology, derived from Galen, Cleopatra, Ibn Sīnā, William of Conches; (2) the soul, mainly after Augustine; (3) strange races of man, hermaphrodites, gymnosophists, Brahmans, etc. (a sort of anthropological treatise); (4) quadrupeds; (5) birds; (6) marine monsters, including an account of herring fisheries; (7) fishes; (8) snakes; (9) "worms," including amphibians, leeches, tortoises, etc. (these 6 zoological books, 4 to 9, fill more than half of the whole work); (10) ordinary trees; (11) aromatic and medicinal plants and trees; (12) herbs (the main authority here is Matthaeus Platearius); (13) fountains and rivers; (14) precious stones (mainly derived from Marbode); includes the description of a mariner's compass of the floating type; (15) seven metals (gold, electrum, silver, copper, lead, tin, iron); includes allusions to the transmutation of metals and to the use of lead for plumbing; (16) seven regions of the air and their humors; (17) the sphere and seven planets; (18) meteorology; (19) universe and four elements. Some MSS. have an additional book (20) De ornatu coeli et eclipsibus solis et lunae, derived from William of Conches. The structure of this work can be summed up thus: (1–3) man; (4–9) animals; (10–12) plants; (13) waters; (14–15) stones and metals; (16–18) astronomy, astrology, meteorology; (19) elements. A very logical plan, and extremely different from that of Bartholomew.

Two little treatises are included in extenso: in book I, the Letter of Alexander to Aristotle, that is, John of Seville's translation of the medical part of the Sirr al-asrār; in book 14, Thethel's discussion of seals or images on stones. This Thethel (or Zethel, Zahel, Cehel) was a Jewish astrologer presumably identical with Sahl ibn Bishr (first half of the ninth century).

The popular influence of the De natura rerum was much increased by the fact that it was soon translated into Flemish by Jacob van Maerlant (second half of thirteenth century), and into German by Conrad of Megenberg (first half of fourteenth century).

The scientific value of this compilation was vitiated by the author's excessive credulity, even from the point of view of his own time. This utter lack of critical spirit became even more apparent in the Bonum de apibus composed in his old age. His purpose was to edify his readers and to help them to a better understanding of the Scriptures, not scientific investigation even in the humblest way.

Thomas of Cantimpré was not the author of the De secretis mulierum, also ascribed to Albert the Great, nor of the somewhat different text represented by the German treatises "von den Geheimnissen der Weiber."

Apropos of the Bonum de apibus, it is interesting to note the same image (comparison with bees) in a contemporary Syriac treatise, the Kĕthābhā dhĕ-dhebbōrīthā by Solomon of al-Baṣra.

Text—The Liber de natura rerum secundum diversos philosophos has not yet been completely published. Extracts in vol. 3 of Jean Baptiste Pitra: Spicilegium Solesmense (4 vols., Paris 1852–1858). Partial editions of book 3 by Alfons Hilka: Liber de monstrosis hominibus orientis (Breslau 1911); and of book 1 by Christoph Ferckel: Die Gynäkologie des Thomas von Brabant. Ein Beitrag zur Kenntnis der mittelalterlichen Gynäkologie und ihrer Quellen (Alte Meister der Medizin und Naturkunde in Facsimile-Ausgaben und Neudrucken, vol. 5; 83 p., 24 pl., Munich 1912; Isis, 1, 271).

The Bonum universale de apibus (or Liber apum aut de apibus mysticis sive de propietatibus apum seu universale bonum tractans de prelatis et subditis ubique sparsim exemplis notabilibus) was printed at least twice before 1501, in Cologne and Strassburg. A Dutch translation, Der bien boekh, appeared in Zwolle, 1488. Critical edition of Latin text by George Colvener (Douay 1597; again, 1605, 1627).

General criticism—Daunou: Histoire littéraire de la France (vol. 19, 177–184, 1838); Léopold Delisle: ibidem (vol. 30, 365–384, 1888). A. Kaufmann: Thomas von Chantimpré (138 p., Cologne 1899). Hermann Stadler: Albertus Magnus, Thomas von Chantimpré, und Vincent von Beauvais (Natur und Kultur, vol. 4, 86–90, Munich 1906). Lynn Thorndike: History of magic (vol. 2, 372–400, 1923). Includes lists of MSS. of the De natura rerum and of Thetel's treatise on seals.

Scientific criticism—E. H. F. Meyer: Geschichte der Botanik (vol. 4, 91–96, 1857). Victor Carus: Geschichte der Zoologie (211–223, 1872). Fritz Jäger: Zahnärztliches aus den Werken Alberts des Grossen und seiner Schüler (Diss., 63 p., Mannheim 1921; superficial). Christoph Ferckel: Cantimpré über die Metalle (Studien zur Geschichte der Chemie, Festgabe v. Lippmann dargestellt, 75–80, 1927). See also Ferckel's edition of 1912 above-mentioned. Ferckel has made an elaborate study of the text and sources of the first book of the De naturis rerum. The MS. of it is kept at the Leipzig Institute for the history of medicine (Mitt. zur Geschichte der Medizin, vol. 22, 201, 1923). F. S. Bodenheimer: Materialien zur Geschichte der Entomologie (vol. 1, 168–170, 1928).

Bonum de apibus—Paul Kirsch: Das Buch der Wunder und denkwürdigen Vorbilder (Diss., 44 p., Gleiwitz 1875). Elie Berger: Thomae Cantipratensis Bonum universale de apibus quid illustrandis saeculi decimi tertii moribus conferat (Diss., 72 p., Paris 1895). W. A. van der Wet: Het bienboec en zijne exempelen ('s Gravenhage 1902). Otto Heimertz: Die mittelniederdeutsche Version des Bienenbuches. Das erste Buch (Lund 1906; including text).

Apocryphal—Friedrich Popitz: Die Versus fratris Thome de Campopratu im Codex Lipsiensis 1181 (Diss., 34 p., Leipzig 1922). Medical poem of 373 lines wrongly ascribed to Cantimpré (Isis, 5, 501). Christoph Ferckel: Versus fratris Thome de Campopratu (Archiv für Geschichte der Medizin, vol. 13, 64, 1921).

ALBERT THE GREAT

See Book IV.

VI. SCANDINAVIAN

KONUNGS SKUGGSJÁ

The Konungs skuggsjá (Speculum regale, King's mirror) is an encyclopaedic treatise written in old Norwegian by an unknown author, some time between 1217 and 1260, probably about the time of Hakon IV's coronation in 1247. The author was in all probability a priest, possibly a court chaplain, for he was very familiar with the Norwegian court of Bergen and Trondhjem. Identifications with one Master William and with Ivar Bodde, both court chaplains, are plausible but unproved. The work was composed in the region of Namdalen, northeast of Trondhjem and just south of Halogaland.

It is written in the form of a dialogue between a wise father and his son. According to its own introduction it was divided into four parts dealing with the four estates of that time in Norway: the merchants, the king and his court; the church; the peasantry; but none of the many extant MSS. has more than the first two parts. The substance is derived to a small extent from such books as Pedro Alfonso's Disciplina, the Elucidarium of Honorius of Autun, Prester John's letter, and the description of Ireland by Gerard the Welshman, also from the accounts of returned crusaders and pilgrims; but the best part is drawn from the author's own experience in the northern countries or from other Scandinavian sources unknown to us.

The author deals with physical subjects as far as they interest sailors; i.e., stars, planets, calendar, winds, tides and currents. His geographical knowledge is especially strong. He believed in the sphericity of the earth and conceived the possibility that the south temperate zone be inhabited. He describes many pecularities of Norway, Iceland, Greenland, and of the arctic regions: northern lights, glaciers, icefloes, icebergs, geysers, mineral springs, volcanoes, earthquakes; he gives much information on the fauna of these countries, mentioning twenty-one species of whales and describing some of them, six varieties of seals, describing the walrus, etc.

Next to this, the most valuable part of this work is the account of royal duties and court manners and customs, the vindication of the divine right of kings, this being one of the earliest treatises on the theory of the state in Western Christendom. Much attention is paid to the military art, these remarks being perhaps derived from the experience of Crusaders, and to ethical and ecclesiastical problems. There are sound views on education; the son is urged to learn Latin and French (besides his own tongue), "for these idioms are most widely used." There is also some valuable information on Norwegian history. The author was obviously a man not only well informed, but of superior intelligence, a good observer, who had been able to free himself from some of the current superstitions, and whose outlook on the world was relatively broad.

Text—First edition of the original Icelandic text with Danish and Latin versions by Halfdan Einersen and John Erichsen, and a commentary by Hans Finsen: Kongs-skuggsio (Sorö 1786). Second edition by Rudolf Keyser, Peter Andreas Munch and Carl R. Unger: Kongespeilet (204 p., Christiana 1848). Third edition by Otto Brenner: Speculum regale, ein altnorwegischer Dialog (Munich 1881). Fourth edition by Finnur Jónsson: Konungs skuggsjá (414 p., Copenhagen 1920).

Georg T. Flom: The Arnamagnean MS. 243 B^a folio. The main MS. of Konungs skuggsjá in phototypic reproduction with diplomatic text (320 p., Urbana, Ill., 1916).

Kongespegelen, translation into New Norse by K. Audne (Oslo 1909–1913). English translation by Laurence Marcellus Larson (404 p., New York 1917).

Criticism—Potthast (699, 1896). Fridtjof Nansen: In northern mists (2 vols., 1911, passim, many extracts quoted). Introduction to Larson's translation (1917).

VII. WESTERN MUSLIM

AL-BŪNĪ

Abū-l-'Abbās Aḥmad ibn 'Alī ibn Yūsuf al-Būnī, al-Qurashī, Muḥyī al-dīn (various other titles of honor have been given to him). Algerian occultist. Born at Bona,

Algeria; died in or after 1225. One of the most popular Muslim writers on occult subjects, even to this day. His abundant writings are one of the primary sources for the study of Muslim occultism in all of its phases: magic power of the basmala, of the divine names, of the letters of the alphabet, talismans, etc. His most important works are the Sun of knowledge (Shams al-ma'ārif wa laṭā'if al-'awārif), the Book of (magic) properties, Kitāb al-khawāṣṣ, the Secret of the sciences, Sirr al-ḥikam. His works contain examples of magic squares.

Text—Lithographic editions of the Shams al-ma'ārif have appeared in Cairo, 1291 H. and Bombay, 1296–8 H.

Criticism—Ibn Khaldūn: Prolégomènes (vol. 3, 195, 1868). C. Brockelmann: Arabische Litteratur (vol. 1, 497, 1898). H. Suter: Die Mathematiker und Astronomen der Araber (136, 218, 1900; Nachträge, 174, 1902). Carra de Vaux: Article al-Būnī in Encyclopaedia of Islām (vol. 1, 793, 1912). W. Ahrens: Die magischen Quadrate al-Būnī's (Der Islām, vols. 12, 157–177, 1922; 14,104–110, 1925). Joseph Elian Sarkis: Encyclopaedic dictionary of Arabic bibliography (p. 607, Cairo 1928).

IBN ṬUMLŪS

Abū-l-Ḥajjāj Yūsuf ibn Muḥammad ibn Ṭumlūs. Born in Alcira, in the Muslim kingdom of Valencia; flourished in Valencia and Murcia. Physician to the fourth ruler of the dynasty of Almohades, Muḥammad al-Nāṣir (who ruled from 1199 to 1214); died at Alcira in 1223–1224. Hispano-Muslim logician and physician. He wrote a treatise on logic called Kitāb al-madkhal li sinā'a-l-manṭiq (Introduction to the art of logic).

Text—The first part of his Logic dealing with the Categories and Interpretation was edited by Miguel Asín: Introducción al arte de la lógica por Abentomlús de Alcira. (294 p., Arabic and Spanish; see Isis, 11, 426).

Criticism—M. Steinschneider: Hebraeische Übersetzungen (107, 1893; apropos of the Hebrew translation of a very short text De mistione propositionis de inesse et necessariae). C. Brockelmann: Arabische Litteratur (vol. 1, 463, 1898).

IBN 'ARABĪ

Abū Bakr Muḥammad ibn 'Alī, Muḥyī-l-dīn al-Ḥātimī al-Ṭā'ī[5] al-Andalusī, Ibn 'Arabī. (In this case, better than Ibn al-'Arabī). Born at Murcia in 1165; flourished mainly in Seville until 1201–1202, when he made the Pilgrimage; he spent the rest of his life in the East, dying in Damascus in 1240. Hispano-Muslim poet and theologian; he was a Ẓāhirite, a follower of Ibn Ḥazm (first half of the eleventh century), but more essentially, a ṣūfī; the greatest representative of the Illuministic (Ishrāqī) or pseudo-Empedoclean, neo-Platonic, and pantheistic school founded by Ibn Masarra of Cordova (883–931). His most important work, The revelations of Mecca (Kitāb al-futūḥāt al-Makkīya), is a treatise on mysticism in 560 chapters, which was published toward the end of his life in Damascus. Chapter 559 is a summary of the whole.

Chapter 167 of the Futūḥāt, entitled Kīmiyā al-sa'āda (Alchemy of happiness), is an esoteric allegory of the ascension of man to heaven, anticipating Dante's Paradise. Another work of his, Kitāb al-isrā' ilā maqām al-asrā (The nocturnal

[5] Meaning descendant of the famous pre-Islāmic poet, Ḥātim al-Ṭā'ī, about whom see C. van Arendonck in Encyclopaedia of Islām (vol. 2, 290, 1916).

journey towards the station of the most magnanimous) deals with a similar theme, being a development of the Muslim tradition concerning the Prophet's ascension (mi'rāj). These works of Ibn 'Arabī are of considerable interest, as containing the most complete anticipation in many ways of the Divine Comedy. It is certain that Dante drew his inspiration to a considerable extent from Muslim sources; it is probable that Ibn 'Arabī was one, and the main one of these sources. Ibn 'Arabī's love poems, The interpreter of love (Kitāb tarjumān al-ashwāq), written in 1214–1215, and his mystical interpretation of them, The treasures of the devoted (Kitāb dhakhā'ir al-a'lāq), written the following year, may have inspired the dolce stil nuovo, Dante's Convito, and the meeting of Beatrice and Dante, an essential episode of the Divine Comedy, unprecedented in Christian legend and even foreign to the very spirit of Christianity. A parallel for that episode may be found in a poem of Shākir ibn Muslim of Orihuela (c. 1136), which is the climax of a very old Muslim tradition.

Considerable autobiographical information is included in the Futūḥāt, and in another work also written in Damascus, the Al-durrat al-fākhira (The precious pearl). The latter work contains a large number of biographies of the western scholars and saints who influenced Ibn 'Arabī's thought. He was anxious to contrast the sanctity of his old masters and friends with the spiritual decadence which his old age was condemned to witness in the East.

The philosophical views of the Ishrāqī school were transmitted from Muslim Spain to Christian Europe by the so-called Augustinian scholastics, such as Alexander Hales, Duns Scotus, Roger Bacon and Ramon Lull.

Text—The Futūḥāt was printed in Būlāq, 1274 H., 1293 H., Cairo, 1329 H.

The Isrā' is still unpublished.

The Tarjumān was edited with an English literal version and an abridged translation of the Dhakhā'ir by R. A. Nicholson (Royal Asiatic Society, London 1911). The Dhakhā'ir was printed in Beirut, 1312 H.

Minor writings edited by H. S. Nyberg (Leiden 1919).

Khan Sahib Khaja Khan: Wisdom of the prophets in the light of tasawwuf. Being a synoptical translation into English of the famous standard book on tasawwuf Fusus ul-hikam (Bezels of wisdom) with analytical notes on each fas and a life of the shayk (Madras 1928?). The Fuṣūṣ al-ḥikam were revealed to Ibn 'Arabī at Ḍamascus in 1229 (J. R. A. S., 680–681, 1930).

Ibn Arabī wrote a great many other works, the list of which may be found in Brockelmann.

Criticism—C. Brockelmann: Arabische Litteratur (vol. 1, 441–448, 1898). D. B. Macdonald: Development of Muslim theology (261–263, New York 1903); Religious attitude and life in Islam (146, 188, Chicago 1909). R. A. Nicholson: The lives of 'Umar ibnu 'l Fāriḍ and Ibnu 'l-'Arabī extracted from the Shadharātu 'l-dhahab fī akhbāri man dhahab (Journal R. Asiatic Soc., 797–824, 1906, Arabic text). T. H. Weir: Encyclopaedia of Islām (vol. 2, 361, 1916). Miguel Asín y Palacios: La escatologia musulmana en la Divina Comedia (Madrid 1919; English translation, London 1926; Isis, 10, 65–68). Richard Hartmann: Eine islamische Apokalypse aus der Kreuzzugszeit. Ein Beitrag zur jafr-Literatur (Schrift. d. Königsbergen Gelehrten Gesellschaft, 89–116, 1924; Isis, 9, 503). Miguel Asín y Palacios: El místico murciano Abenarabi (Boletín de la Real Academia de la Historia, Madrid 1925–1928; four memoirs, 347 p. in all; fundamental, see Isis, 11, 425; 13, 158). The fourth memoir contains the translation of a summary of Ibn 'Arabī's philosophy by 'Abd al-Razzāq al-Qāshāni (first half of the fourteenth century). Mehemmed-Ali Aïni: La quintessence de la philosophie de Ibn-i-Arabī

(105 p., Paris 1926). A laudatory composition without scientific value, except in so far as it illustrates Turkish opinion of to-day (Isis, 11, 426; Revue de l'histoire des religions, vol. 97, 141–142, 1928).

For Muḥammad ibn 'Abdallāh ibn Masarra, see R. Dozy: Spanish Islām (409, 535, 721, London 1913). Miguel Asín: Abenmasarra y su escuela. Orígenes de la filosofía hispano-musulmana (168 p., Madrid 1914; important; Isis, 11, 168).

IBN SAB'ĪN

Abū Muḥammad 'Abd al-Ḥaqq ibn Ibrāhīm al-Ishbīlī Ibn Sab'īn. Born in Murcia c. 1217; lived in Ceuta, committed suicide in Mecca, 1269–1270. Spanish ṣūfī, founder of the sect called after him Sab'īnīya. He is chiefly known for his answers to the so-called "Sicilian Questions," Kitāb al-ajwiba 'ani-l-as'ila al-ṣaqalīya. These questions, asked by Frederick II, had been transmitted to him by the Almohade, 'Abd al-Wāhid, who ruled from 1232 to 1242. They deal with such subjects as the eternity of the world, metaphysical and theological methods, value and number of categories, nature of the soul. Ibn Sab'īn answered them while he was in Ceuta, c. 1237–1242. His other works include a metaphysical introduction; a mystical treatise, Asrār al-ḥikma al-mashraqīya; and a musical one, Kitāb al-adwār al-mansūb (Book of the related musical modes).

Text and translations—The Arabic text of Frederick's questions and Ibn Sab'īn's answers is still unpublished. A. F. Mehren: Correspondance d'Ibn Sab'īn avec Frédéric II publiée d'après le MS. de la Bodléienne contenant l'analyse générale de cette correspondance et la traduction du quatrième traité (Journal asiatique, vol. 14, 341–454, 1879). It is very desirable to publish the complete Arabic text of these questions together with an English translation and discussion.

Criticism—Michele Amari: Questions philosophiques adressées aux savants musulmans par Frédéric II (Journal Asiatique, vol. 1, 240–274, 1853). E. Renan: Averroës (2e éd., 289, 1861). C. Brockelmann: Arabische Litteratur (vol. 1, 465, 1898). H. G. Farmer: History of Arabian music (226, 1929; Isis, 13, 375).

VIII. EASTERN MUSLIM

AL-ZARNŪJĪ

Al-Zarnūjī Burhān al-dīn (meaning, the proof of religion). Flourished c. 1203. Muslim educator. He composed, c. 1203, a philosophical primer, entitled Instruction for him who desires to learn (Ta'līm al-muta'allim), which, judging by the number of MSS., obtained considerable popularity. During the reign of Murād III ('Uthmānlī sulṭān from 1574 to 1595), a commentary was written upon it by one Ibn Ismā'īl, or one Nau'ī (1587–1588). The Ta'līm was translated into Turkish.

Text—Enchiridion studiosi. Edition by H. Reland (Utrecht 1709); again by C. Caspari (Leipzig 1838).

Criticism—Ḥājī Khalīfa: Lexicon bibliographicum (vol. 2, 325, 1837). Contains a brief analysis of the Ta'līm, but the name of the author is misspelled Zarbūjī. C. Brockelmann: Arabische Litteratur (vol. 1, 462, 1898).

AL-ĀMIDĪ

Abū Ḥāmid Muḥammad ibn Muḥammad al-Āmidī (or 'Amīdī? 'amīd means chief; Āmid is the name of a town, ancient Amida, Diyārbakr, on the Upper Tigris) al Samarqandī, Rukn al-dīn. Born in Samarqand; died in Bukhārā in 1218. Ḥanīfite theologian. He wrote a treatise on the comparison between the microcosmos and macrocosmos, offering it as an Arabic adaptation of the Persian version of a Sanskrit work called Amṛītakuṇḍa by Bahucara. (I cannot identify this author, but the Sanskrit title is plausible. It means Vessel containing nectar.) This adaptation, entitled Kitāb mir'āt (ḥayāt) al-ma'ānī fī idrāk al-'ālam al-insānī, was elaborated by Ibn 'Arabī. Al-Āmidī wrote a book on the art of controversy or dialectics which was extremely popular, Kitāb al-irshād (Direction). I must still mention a treatise on talismans, Kitāb ḥauḍ al-ḥayāt (Pond of life).

Criticism—In Khallikān: Slane's translation (vol. 2, 660–662, 1843). Ibn Khaldūn: Prolégomènes (vol. 3, 39, 1868, apropos of the Irshād). C. Brockelmann: Arabische Litteratur (vol. 1, 439, 1898); Encyclopaedia of Islām (vol. 1, 326, 1910).

'ABD AL-LAṬĪF

Abū Muḥammad 'Abd al-Laṭīf ibn Yūsuf ibn Muḥammad ibn 'Alī, Muwaffaq al-dīn al Baghdādī. Also called Ibn al-Labbād (labbād means felter, a man who makes felt or works with felt). Muslim scientist and philosopher, physician; versatile and prolific writer. Born at Baghdād in 1162; he died there in 1231. He studied in Baghdād; in 1189–1190 he went to Mūṣul, where he worked for a time under Kamāl al-dīn Ibn Yūnus; he visited Jerusalem some time after its conquest by Ṣalāḥ al-dīn (1187) and obtained from him a chair in the great mosque of Damascus. After Ṣalāḥ al-dīn's death (1193) he went to Egypt and taught at al-Azhar; he was acquainted with Maimonides. Later still, in 1207–1208, he taught at al-'Azīzīya in Damascus.

More than 160 writings are ascribed to him. Among them is one criticizing Ibn al-Haitham's views on space, another dealing with Hindu arithmetic, another on music (Kitāb al-samā'), and medical treatises.

He is chiefly known for his Account of Egypt, Al-ifādat wal-i'tibār fī-l-umūr al-mushāhadat wal-hawādith al-mu'āyanat bi arḍ Miṣr. The text transmitted to us is divided into nine chapters dealing respectively with generalities, plants, animals, ancient monuments, buildings and ships, cookery, the Nile, and the events of the years 597 and 598 (end of 1200 to end of 1202). It includes a description of the great plague and famine of 597.

'Abd al-Laṭīf had the opportunity of examining a large quantity of human ossements at al-Maks (Egypt) and he did so without Galenic prejudice: the lower maxillary consists of a single bone, not of two, and the sacrum generally of a single one too, instead of six. But he had found a specimen consisting of six bones, probably of a child. (The sacrum consists generally of five fused vertebrae but in some exceptional cases of six. The first anatomist to recognize the five vertebrae and to represent them accurately was Leonardo da Vinci).[6]

He denounced alchemical superstition. He was apparently one of the most enlightened men of his time. The botanical part of his Account seems particularly important.

Text and Translations—The Arabic text of the Account of Egypt was edited by H. E. G. Paulus (Tübingen 1789). Again, by Joseph White: Abdollatiphi historiae

[6] J. P. MacMurrich: Leonardo da Vinci as an anatomist (120, Baltimore 1930; Isis, 15, 342).

Aegypti compendium arabice et latine (Oxford 1800). Part of this Latin translation had been made a long time before by Edward Pococke, Jr.

German translation by S. F. Günther Wahl: Abdallatif's Denkwürdigkeiten Egyptens (360 p., Halle 1790; unsatisfactory). French translation by Silvestre de Sacy: Relation de l'Egypte, suivie de divers extraits d'écrivains orientaux et d'un état des provinces et des villages de l'Egypte dans le XIVe siècle, 1376. (776 p., Paris 1810). Important, including long notes and elaborate index.

Criticism—The main source of 'Abd al-Laṭīf's biography is the account of his younger contemporary, Ibn Abī Uṣaibi'a (Müller's edition, vol. 2, 201–213, 1884; an unusually long notice). This account has been edited separately by John Mousley with a Latin translation. Abdollatiphi Bagdadensis Vita, auctore Ibn Abi Osaiba (86 p., Oxford 1808). One will find a French translation of the same text in De Sacy's work quoted above, 457–494.

F. Wüstenfeld: Geschichte der arabischen Aerzte (123–127, 1840); Die Geschichtschreiber der Araber (112, 1881). Ernst H. F. Meyer: Geschichte der Botanik (vol. 3, 301–306, 1856). L. Leclerc: Médecine arabe (vol. 2, 182–188, 1876). C. Brockelmann: Arabische Litteratur (vol. 1, 481, 1898). H. Suter: Die Mathematiker und Astronomen der Araber (138, 1900). M. Th. Houtsma: Encyclopaedia of Islām (vol. 1, 47, 1908). J. E. Sarkis: Dictionnaire de bibliographie arabe (p. 1292, Le Caire 1929). A systematic study of 'Abd al-Laṭīf's works from our point of view is badly needed.

KAMĀL AL-DĪN IBN YŪNUS

Abū-l-Fatḥ (or Abū 'Imrān) Mūsā ibn Yūnus ibn Muḥammad ibn Man'a. Generally called Kamāl al-dīn Ibn Yūnus (or Kamāl al-dīn Ibn Man'a). Muslim theologian, mathematician, and encyclopaedist. Born at Mūṣul in 1156; in 1175–1176 he went to Baghdād, where he continued his studies at the Niẓāmīya; finally he returned to Mūṣul, where he taught at a college which was called afterwards in his honor, the Kamālic College. He died in Mūṣul, 1242. He was reputed to be one of the most learned men of his time, a man of encyclopaedic knowledge, a great teacher. His prestige is proved by many anecdotes, but we know little about his definite achievements. He wrote commentaries on the Qur'ān and on Ibn Sīnā, and various other treatises on such subjects as Arabic grammar, logic, astrology, arithmetic, algebra, square numbers, magic squares, regular heptagon, etc. Some questions asked by the emperor Frederick II were submitted to him by the Ayyūbid al-Kāmil (ruler of Egypt from 1218 to 1238, and of Damascus from 1237 to 1238). One of the questions solved by him was how to construct a square equivalent to a circular segment. The solution was proved by a pupil of his, al-Mufaḍḍal ibn 'Umar al-Abharī, who wrote an essay on it.

Criticism—Ibn Khallikān in De Slane's translation (vol. 3, 466–474). Ibn abī-Uṣaibi'a in Müller's edition (vol. 1, 306–308). L. Leclerc: Médecine arabe (vol. 2, 144, 1876). H. Suter: Die Mathematiker und Astronomen der Araber (140,142, 1900); Beiträge zu den Beziehungen Kaiser Friedrichs II zu zeitgenössischen Gelehrten des Ostens und Westens (Abhdl. zur Geschichte der Naturwiss., Heft 4, 1–8, 1922; Isis, 5, 501).

IBN AL-FĀRIḌ

Abū-l-Qāsim 'Umar ibn 'Alī ibn al-Fāriḍ. One of the greatest Ṣūfī poets, and the greatest among those writing in Arabic. Born of pure Arab stock in Cairo, 1180–1181; made the Pilgrimage in 1231 and remained a long time in Mecca; died in Cairo, 1234–1235.

He is quoted here partly on his own account[7], partly because of his greater Persian contemporary, Fāriḍ al-dīn 'Aṭṭār, who died probably c. 1230. (See below.) It is curious that those two great Ṣūfī poets, the one Arabic, the other Persian, lived practically at the same time. This fact and the fact that they had one name, Fāriḍ, in common, might cause them to be confused.

His Dīwān was first collected and edited by his grandson, 'Alī, c. 1329–1330. There are many commentaries on it or on single poems.

Text—Many oriental editions, see British Museum catalogues. I shall only quote that prepared by the Maronite Shaikh, Rushaid al-Daḥdāḥ ibn Ghālib, including late commentaries (Marseilles 1853; Paris 1855; Būlāq 1872).

The most famous piece of his Dīwān is the poem of the mystic's progress Naẓm al-sulūk, often called Al-tā'iyya al-kubrā (the greater ode rhyming in *t*). It was edited in Arabic and German verse by Hammer-Purgstall: Das arabische hohe Lied der Liebe (Vienna 1854); in Italian by Sac. Ignazio Di Matteo (259 p., autograph, Roma 1917).

Criticism—C. Brockelmann: Arabische Litteratur (vol. 1, 262–263, 1898). R. A. Nicholson: Literary history of the Arabs (325, 394–398, 402, 448, 462, 1907). C. A. Nallino: Il poema mistico arabo d'Ibn al-Fāriḍ (Rivista degli studi orientali, vol. 8, 1–106, 1919; criticism of Di Matteo's translation). Sac. Ignazio Di Matteo: Sulla mia interpretazione del poema mistico d'Ibn al-Fāriḍ (ibidem, 479–500, 1920). Carlo A. Nallino: Ancora su Ibn al-Fāriḍ e sulla mistica musulmana (ibidem, 501–562, 1920).

IX. PERSIAN

FĀRIḌ AL-DĪN 'AṬṬĀR

Abū Ḥāmid (or Abū Ṭālib) Muḥammad ibn Ibrāhīm, Fārid al-dīn 'Aṭṭār (the last word means a dealer in 'iṭr or essence of roses and other perfumes, but it also means a druggist, a medical practitioner). Persian poet and sūfī, who might be considered the herald of the great literary renaissance of the second half of the thirteenth century. Indeed if we assume that he died c. 1230, Jalāl al-dīn Rūmī and Sa'dī—to be dealt with in the following book—were his younger contemporaries.

The dates of his life are very uncertain. The date of his death varies from 1193 to 1234–1235; the most probable value being 1229–1230, but there is no reason to believe that he was killed by the Mongols. He was born at Nīshāpūr; spent thirteen years of his youth in Mashhad (not very far from Nīshāpūr, also in Khurāsān), traveled extensively, going as far as India and Egypt, and for thirty-nine years busied himself collecting sayings of the Ṣūfī saints. He wrote in Persian about forty works, including more than 200,000 verses. His main and longest work, however, was composed in prose; this was his Memoirs of the (Ṣūfī) saints, Tadhkirat al-awliyā'. His best known poems are the short Pandnāma (Book of counsels) a collection of maxims, and the longer Manṭiq al-ṭayr (Reasoning of the birds), a mystical allegory containing over 4600 couplets (completed in 1177–1178?). It tells of the quest of the birds (i.e., Ṣūfī pilgrims) for the mythical Sīmurgh, symbolizing the Truth. Some thirteen species of birds are represented, led by the hoopoe.

It would seem that Fāriḍ al-dīn practiced medicine, but no medical writings of his are known.

[7] I referred to him in vol. 1, 713.

Text—Critical edition of the Tadhkirat al-awliyā' by R. A. Nicholson (London 1905–1907).

Pandnāma, edited and translated into French by Silvestre de Sacy (Paris 1819).

Manṭiq al-ṭayr, edited by J. H. Garcin de Tassy (Paris 1857), and translated into French by the same (Paris 1863); English translation, Bird-parliament, by Edward Fitzgerald in his Letters, etc. (vol. 2, 431–482, 1889). Reprinted by Nathan Haskell Dole: Salāmān and Absāl (190 p., Boston 1899).

Collected works, Kullīyāt. Lithographic edition, Lucknow 1877 (or 1872).

Criticism—The best account was given by Mīrzā Muḥammad ibn 'Abd al-Wahhāb al-Qazwīnī, as introduction to Nicholson's edition (vol. 1, 1905; in Persian).

J. H. Garcin de Tassy: La poésie philosophique et religieuse chez les Persans d'après le Mantic uttaïr (Paris 1856; 4th ed., 76 p., Paris 1864; introduction to his translation). E. G. Browne: Literary history of Persia (vol. 2, 506–515, 1906). Encyclopaedia of Islām (vol. 1, 513, 1911; short unsigned note containing nothing new).

MUḤAMMAD AL-'AWFĪ

Nūr al-dīn Muḥammad al-'Awfī. The nisba is derived from the name of one of his ancestors, 'Abd al-Raḥmān ibn 'Awf, one of the Companions of the Prophet. Persian man of letters who flourished in Khurāsān and Transoxiana, especially in Bukhārā, and later in India. He flourished some time after 1206, at the court of Nāṣir al-dīn Qubācha, ruler of Sind. When the latter lost his life and kingdom in 1228, Muḥammad passed into the service of the conqueror, Shams al-dīn Altamish (Iltutmish), sulṭān of Dehlī (Hindūstān) from 1210 to 1235.

He wrote two important works in Persian: (1) Lubāb al-albāb, a history of some three hundred Persian poets, dedicated to Qubācha's wazīr, thus composed c. 1206–1228; (2) an enormous collection of anecdotes, entitled Jawâmi' al-ḥikāyāt wa lawāmi' al-riwāyāt, dedicated to Altamish, thus completed before 1235. The first work is of capital importance for the early history of Persian literature; the second contains information of all kinds; e.g., cosmographical and zoological.

Text—The Lubāb al-albāb has been edited by Edward G. Browne and Mīrzā Muḥammad ibn 'Abd al-Wahhāb al-Qazwīnī (2 vols., London 1903–1906).

The second work is unpublished.

Criticism—E. G. Browne: Literary history of Persia (vol. 2, 477–479, and by index, 1906). J. Stephenson: The zoological section of the Nuzhatu-l-qulūb (Isis, 11, 297–299, zoological extracts quoted). Muḥammad Niẓamu'l-dīn: Introduction to the Jawāmi'ul-ḥikāyāt (339 p., Gibb Memorial, London 1929; very elaborate study; J. R. A. S., 1930, 665–669).

X. SYRIAC

SOLOMON OF AL-BAṢRA

Mār Shĕlēmōn. Syriac encyclopaedist. Born in Khilāṭ (or Akhlāṭ) on lake Vān, Armenia. He was the Nestorian metropolitan of Pĕrath dĕ-Maishān (i.e., al-Baṣra) in 1222. His main work is a volume of analecta, partly theological, partly historical, entitled Kĕthābhā dhĕ-dhebbōrīthā (Book of the bee). He also wrote prayers, discourses (mēmrōnē), a treatise on the figure of the heavens and of the earth (lost), and another on the calendar. The Book of the bee was dedicated to his friend, Narsai, bishop of Khōnī Shābhōr (i.e., al-Bawāzīj, on the Lesser Zāb).

Text—Edition of the Book of the bee by Ernest A. Wallis Budge, with an English translation (350 p., Oxford 1886).

Latin translation by J. M. Schönfelder: Liber apis. Syr. arabicumque textum latine vertit (Bamberg, 1866).

Criticism—William Wright: Syriac literature (282, 1894). Heinrich Selzer: Julius Sextus Africanus (vol. 2 (2), 458–465, 1898). Rubens Duval: Littérature syriaque (3d ed., 82, 280, 402, 1907). Anton Baumstark: Syrische Literatur (309, 1922).

JACOB BAR SHAKKŌ

Also called 'Īsā bar Mark, of Barṭallā near Mūṣul. Syriac philosopher and encyclopaedist; Jacobite theologian (the Jacobite Church is one of the monophysitic churches). He was a monk at the neighboring monastery of Mār Matthew, of which he became bishop under the name of Severus. He died in 1241. He was educated by the grammarian, John bar Zō'bī, at the monastery of Bēth Qūqā in Ḥĕdhaiyabh, and by Kamāl al-dīn Mūsā ibn Yūnus at Mūṣul. His main work is an elementary encyclopaedia in two books, the Dialogues, dealing with grammar, logic, philosophy, physics and physiology, mathematics, music, metaphysics and theology. His mathematics are derived from Nicomachos and the neo-Pythagorean writings available in Arabic. In 1231 he wrote the Book of treasures, a theological treatise in four parts, of which the fourth on the creation of the universe, is largely devoted to cosmology and geography. Jacob was essentially a theologian; his scientific interest was subordinated to a theological purpose; he was very uncritical.

Text—Many extracts of the Dialogues in A. Baumstark: Aristoteles bei den Syrern vom V.-VIII. Jahrh. (Leipzig 1900). Extracts on grammar (accentuation) have been edited by Adalbert Merx in his Historia artis grammaticae apud Syros (Leipzig 1889). See also Abbé Paulin Martin: De la métrique chez les Syriens (Leipzig 1879). Julius Ruska: Das Quadrivium aus Severus bar Schakkū's Buch der Dialoge (Leipzig 1896, Syriac and German with commentary).

Criticism—Assemani: Bibliotheca orientalis (vol. 2, 237–240). Wm. Wright: Syriac literature (260–263, 1894). F. Nau: Notice sur le Livre des trésors de Jacques de Bartela, évêque de Tagrit (Journal asiatique, vol. 7, 286–331, 1896; analysis of the scientific part with many extracts and their translations). J. Ruska: Studien zu Severus' Buch der Dialoge (Z. für Assyriologie, vol. 12, 8–41, 145–161, 1897). R. Duval: Littérature syriaque (405–406, 1907). Anton Baumstark: Geschichte der syrischen Literatur (311–312, 1922).

XI. HISPANO-JEWISH

JUDAH BEN SOLOMON HA-KOHEN

Also called: Ibn Matqah. Jewish mathematician, astronomer, and philosopher of Toledo; born c. 1219. In 1237 he was already in mathematical correspondence with Frederick II's "Philosopher" (Theodore of Antioch is probably meant). In 1247 he attended the imperial court in Toscana. About that time he compiled an encyclopaedical treatise in Arabic, or began its compilation, and later translated it into Hebrew under the title Midrash ha-ḥokmah (The search for wisdom). The most complete Hebrew text contains two parts dealing respectively with: (part 1) Aristotelian logic, physics and metaphysics (as transmitted by Ibn Rushd), and Biblical commentaries; (part 2) mathematics and other subjects. The mathematical section contains: extracts from Euclid Bks I-VI and XI-XIII, followed by the above-mentioned correspondence presumably with Theodore of Antioch; an adaptation of the Almagest with references to Jābir ibn Aflaḥ; an adaptation of al-Biṭrūjī; an astrological introduction which is an adaptation of Ptolemy's Quadripartitum.

Text—The astrological introduction was published in Warsaw, 1886.

Criticism—Moritz Steinschneider: Die hebraeischen Übersetzungen des Mittelalters (1–4, 164, 507, 858, 1893); Die Mathematik bei den Juden (Bibliotheca mathematica, 110–111, 1896); Die arabische Litteratur der Juden (162, 1902). Max Seligsohn: Jewish Encyclopaedia (vol. 6, 537, 1904).

AL-ḤARIZI

Judah ben Solomon al-Ḥarizi (The name al-Hofni or ben Hofni seems to be due to a mistake). Hispano-Jewish poet, philosopher, theologian, physician, and translator from Arabic into Hebrew (c. 1170–bef. 1235).

Born in Spain, perhaps in Granada or in Toledo, studied theology, philosophy, medicine; about 1190 he traveled to southern France and remained a long time in Marseilles, then returned to his country; in 1216 he went back to southern France, thence to Egypt, Palestine[8] and Syria; in 1218 he was in Jerusalem, and in 1220 in Damascus; finally, being in Baṣra, he decided to return to Spain, which he reached c. 1230; he died before 1235.

He translated many works from Arabic into Hebrew, notably the following:

(1) A pseudo-Galenic treatise on the soul, c. 1200, Sefer ha-nefesh.

(2) Ḥunain ibn Isḥāq: Sayings of the philosophers (lost in Arabic?). Musre-hapilosofim. This was one of his last works.

(3) 'Alī ibn Riḍwān: Iggeret ha-mussar (Letter on education). Ethical treatise ascribed to Aristotle. Translated by al-Ḥarizi at the request of Ezra ben Judah ben Nathanael of Beaucaire.

(4) Al-Ḥarīrī: Maqāmāt. Maḥberot ithiel. Only a part of the first maqāma, and the twenty-six following maqāmāt are preserved. It is partly translation, partly adaptation. After having completed this work, al-Ḥarizi resolved to compose an original one of the same kind; see no. 9 below.

(5–7) Maimonides. (5) Partial translation of the Kitāb al-sirāj, Maimonides' commentary on the Mishnah. This was one of al-Ḥarizi's earliest works (c. 1194–1197). He seems to have translated only the general introduction, and the first five massektoth of the first seder.

(6) Dalālat al-ḥā'irīn, Moreh nebukim. This translation was made after his first return from Provence, before his departure for the East. It is more fluent than the translation completed shortly before by Samuel ibn Tibbon (1204). He added to it a glossary of technical terms, and a table of contents. It was unfavorably criticized by contemporaries, and was finally superseded by Samuel's translation, yet it played an important part in the transmission of Maimonidean philosophy, because it was the basis of the early anonymous Latin translation, which was used by many Latin theologians, and whose revision by Agostino Giustiniani was printed in Paris, 1520. It was also the basis of the Castilian version by Pedro of Toledo.[9]

[8] After 1199, when Jerusalem fell again into Muslim hands, the Jews were allowed to live there.

[9] I have not been able to identify this Pedro of Toledo. Could it be the prelate Pedro Gómez Barroso who died at Avignon in 1345?

(7) Ma'amar teḥiyyot ha-metim. Essay on resurrection. It would seem that this was first translated from Arabic into Hebrew by Samuel ibn Tibbon, then from Hebrew into Arabic by Joseph ben Joel, finally from Arabic into Hebrew by al-Ḥarizi.

(8) Sheshet Benveniste (second half of the twelfth century): Segulah le-harayon, a gynaecological treatise.

His main original works were:

(9) Taḥkemoni (The wise one; see II Samuel 23:8). This was his most important production, the one from which his fame is derived. It is a desultory composition in verse and rhyming prose composed toward the end of his life on the model of al-Ḥarīrī's Maqāmāt. It is divided into fifty maqāmāt and contains much information of value for the study of contemporary Jewish culture. It was very popular, as is witnessed by the number of MSS., printed editions, and partial translations into Latin, English, French, German, and Magyar.

(10) Refu'at ha-gewiyah (Healing of the body), a poem on diet.

Text—The numbers refer to those given above to each work.

(1) Sefer ha-nefesh. First edition in the Liqquṭe ha-pardes, i.e., the gleanings from the Pardes of Solomon ben Isaac, edited by Samuel of Bamberg (Venice 1519). New edition with introduction and notes by Adolph Jellinek (Leipzig 1852).

(2) Musre ha-pilosofim. First edition, Riva di Trento 1562. New edition by Abraham Loewenthal (70 p., Francfort a.M., 1896). German translation by same: Ḥunains Sinnsprüche der Philosophen nach der hebr. Übers. von Charisi (Berlin 1896).

Carl Heinrich Cornill: Das Buch der weisen Philosophen nach dem Aethiopischen untersucht (59 p., Leipzig 1875). C. Brockelmann: Arabische Litteratur (vol. 1, 206, 1898).

(3) Iggeret ha-mussar. First edition, Riva di Trento 1559. New edition in Isaac Benjacob: Debarim 'attiqim (vol. 1, Leipzig 1844).

(4) Maḥberot ithiel. Extracts in Silvestre de Sacy's Arabic edition (Paris 1822). Edition by Thomas Chenery (London 1872).

(5) Maimonides' commentary on Mishnah, I. (Naples 1492; etc.). See my note on Maimonides.

(6) Moreh nebukim. Part I edited by Löb Schlossberg with notes by Simon Scheyer (London 1851). Parts II and III with notes by Solomon Munk (London 1876–1879).

(9) Taḥkemoni. First complete edition, Constantinople 1578. Later editions, Amsterdam 1729; by Mendel Emanuel Stern, vocalized (Vienna 1854); by Paul de Lagarde (Göttingen 1883); by A. Kaminka (Warsaw 1899). Many partial editions and translations.

(10) Refu'at ha-gewiyah. In the Liqquṭe ha-pardes (Venice 1519). See no. 1. Again, Ferrara 1552. Edited by Ḥayyim Samuel Levi of Janina in Ha-Maggid (vol. 9, 1865).

Criticism—Frederick de Sola Mendes: Jewish Encyclopaedia (vol. 1, 390–392, 1901); carelessly written but with abundant references. M. Steinschneider: Arabische Literatur der Juden (159, 1902). H. Brody: Encyclopaedia judaica (vol. 5, 312–318, 1930).

For Abraham Ibn Ḥasdai, Solomon Ibn Ayyub, Samuel Ibn Tibbon, and Jacob Anaṭoli, see the chapter above devoted to translators from Arabic into Hebrew.

JUDAH IBN 'ABBAS

Judah ben Samuel ibn 'Abbas. Spanish Jew, who composed at the age of twenty about the middle of the thirteenth century, in Hebrew, an ethical and religious treatise called Yair netib or Shebeṭ Yehudah. A section of it (no. 15) explains the ordinary course of Hispano-Jewish studies in those days. First, the Bible and Talmud, then reading of ethical works, then scientific studies in the following order: medicine, mathematics, logic, astronomy, physics; finally, metaphysics. For each branch of knowledge the main authorities are quoted. A similar work had been composed a little earlier by Joseph ibn 'Aqnīn (second half of the twelfth century). Another work of Judah ibn 'Abbas, almost entirely lost, was entitled Minḥat Yehudah or Meqor ḥayyim (source of life).

Text—M. Güdemann: Das Jüdische Unterrichtswesen (vol. 1, 147, Wien 1873). Text and translation of section 15.

Criticism—M. Steinschneider: Hebraeische Übersetzungen (35-36, 1893). Israel Abrahams: Jewish life in the Middle Ages (365, 1896). Very short article by Hartwig Hirschfeld in Jewish Encyclopaedia (vol. 1, 37, 1901). Encyclopaedia judaica (vol. 1, 175, 1928).

AZRIEL BEN MENAHEM

'Azri'el ben Menaḥem ben Solomon, nicknamed "The Saint." (One Ezra ben Menahem was supposed to be his brother; it is almost certain that both names, Azriel and Ezra, represent one single person). Born at Gerona, Catalonia, in 1160; traveled in South France, where he was the pupil of Isaac the Blind, and in Spain, then returned to Gerona, where he founded a school; he died in 1238. He was the founder, or at any rate one of the founders, of the speculative Qabbala, a mystical doctrine derived from the neo-Platonism transmitted by Ibn Gabirol and others. To reconcile the idea of creation with the Aristotelian view that the universe cannot proceed from nothing, he elaborated a very complicated theory of emanation. There never was an absolute creation, but a gradual transformation of potentiality into reality, of indefiniteness into definiteness. The transformation occurred through ten intermediaries, the Ten Sefirot: the first three forming the world of thought, the next three the world of soul; the last four the material world.

The word sefirah (pl. sefirot) means originally number, category; but Qabbalists gave it new significations, such as sphere (σφαῖρα) or light.

Azriel's ideas were elaborated and systematized in a number of other works during the thirteenth century, some of them ascribed to definite authors with whom we shall deal at the proper time, others anonymous. Among the latter might be quoted the Ma'areket ha-'elohut and the Sefer ha-temunah (Book of form). The Temunah contains the earliest account of the theory of double emanation, which remained afterwards an essential feature of the Qabbala. This theory made it possible, for example, to solve the problem of evil. The Sefirot exist in two forms, positive and negative. The positive emanations represent the divine tendencies toward perfection; the negative represent the opposite tendencies.

It is not possible, nor is it worthwhile, here to consider all the ramifications and elaborations of these ideas, nor to enter into the endless discussions to which they have given birth. It will suffice to quote by way of illustration, and because it is interesting from the anatomical point of view, the correspondence which was soon established between the ten sefirot and different parts of the body: (1) head, (2) brain, (3) heart, (4) and (5) right and left arm, (6) chest, (7) and (8) right and left leg, (9) sexual organs, (10) complete body.

Text—Azriel's commentary on the Ten sefirot, entitled Ezrat Adonai, was edited by Nahman Abraham Goldberg (Berlin 1850). Other commentaries of his, ascribed to Naḥmanides (said to have been his pupil), were published under the latter's name in Mantua, 1719, and Altona, 1764.

The Ma'areket ha-'elohut, ascribed to one Pharez or Perez (ben Isaac?), was printed at Ferrara, 1557. New edition by Immanuel ben Jekuthiel (Mantua 1558).

A Sefer ha-temunah, ascribed to Neḥunya ben ha-Qanah or Neḥunya ha-gadol (a tanna of the first and second centuries!) was published at Korzec, in 1784.

Criticism—I. Broydé: Jewish Encyclopaedia (vol. 2, 373, 1903). See also Broydé's article sefirot, (ibidem, vol. 11, 154–155, 1905).

ASHER BEN DAVID

Asher ben David ben Abraham ben David of Posquières. Languedocian Qabbalist, who flourished in the first half of the thirteenth century. He was a grandson of Abraham ben David of Posquières, who died in 1198 and he was one of the disciples of his uncle, Isaac the Blind. He was in touch with Meir ben Simon of Narbonne, who approved himself, c. 1240, a resolute opponent of the Qabbala. His views are very similar to those of Azriel ben Menahem; this is not surprising, since both were disciples of Isaac the Blind. One of these views, however, is original; that is, his comparison of the ten sefirot with the ten spheres of Greek cosmology. He wrote a cosmological commentary (Ma'aseh bereshit) and various other Qabbalistic treatises.

Philipp Bloch: Jewish encyclopaedia (vol. 2, 181, 1902). G. Scholem: Encyclopaedia judaica (vol. 3, 439, 1929).

IBN LAṬĪF

Isaac ben Abraham Ibn Laṭīf. Hispano-Jewish physician and Qabbalist; born probably in Toledo; died in Jerusalem, c. 1290. He tried to put Qabbalistic doctrines on a scientific basis! His main work out of many, the Sha'ar ha-shamayim (Gate of heavens) was written c. 1244; it contains by way of introduction a brief history of Jewish science down to Maimonides. He dedicated to Todros Abulafia (a great patron of Qabbalists, born 1234; died at Seville after 1298) another treatise and a letter from Jerusalem, Iggeret ha-teshubah, containing thirty-nine scientific questions and answers.

Text—The Sha'ar ha-shamayim was published by Adolf Jellinek in Ha-shaḥar. Twenty-six of the thirty-nine scientific questions contained in the Iggeret ha-teshubah have been edited by Senior Sachs in the Teḥiyyah (vol. 2, 50, Berlin 1857).

Criticism—Philipp Bloch: Jewish Encyclopaedia (vol. 6, 536, 1904). For Todros Abulafia, see ibidem (vol. 1, 143, 1901).

XII. GERMANO-JEWISH

JUDAH HA-ḤASID

Judah the Pious. Judah ben Samuel ben Qalonymos ha-Ḥasid (the pious). Judaeo-German mystic and moralist. Born in Spires; about 1195 he moved to

Ratisbon, where he founded a yeshibah; he died in 1217. He introduced mystical tendencies into German Jewry. He edited the travel notes of Pethahiah ben Jacob second half of the twelfth century). An astrological treatise, Gemaṭriot,[10] is ascribed to him. His main work is the Sefer ha-ḥasidim (Book of the pious), which is a popular account of theology and ethics; it is a valuable source for the study of the Jewish culture of his time. It is largely a compilation, which Judah edited and revised more than once, and is somewhat confused. It has been ascribed also, but without sufficient reason, to a contemporary, bearing sometimes the same name, Judah ha-Ḥasid; i.e., Judah ben Isaac or Judah Sir Leon of Paris (French tosafist, born in Paris, 1166; died there, 1224). It is also said, and this is more plausible, that it was revised and increased by Judah ben Samuel's most famous disciple, Eleazar of Worms. Whoever the author (or authors), the Sefer ha-ḥasidim is a good mirror of Jewish ethics in Germany about the thirteenth century.

Text—Sefer ha-ḥasidim. First edition, Bologna, 1538. Many other editions: Basle 1580; Cracow 1581; Sulzbach 1685; Francfort a.M., 1712; etc. Editions by Ḥayim Joseph David Azulai (Leghorn 1794), and by Jacob Reifmann (Prag. 1860). Extract in B. Halper: Post-Biblical Hebrew literature (Philadelphia 1911, with English translation).

Criticism—Max Schloessinger: Jewish Encyclopaedia (vol. 7, 356–358, 1904).

ELEAZAR OF WORMS

Eleazar ben Judah ben Qalonymos. Eleazar ha-Roqeaḥ (meaning Eleazar the Perfumer, after his book). Judaeo-German Talmudist, Qabbalist, and moralist. Born probably at Mayence c. 1176; in 1196 his wife and three children were murdered by Crusaders; he flourished in Worms, and died there in 1238. Disciple of Judah ha-Hasid. He wrote a large number of ethical and Qabbalistic treatises, of which the best known is the Sefer ha-roqeaḥ (Book of the perfumer), dealing with ethics. He continued his master's work, and the two of them are largely responsible for the introduction of Qabbalistic and other mystical doctrines among the German Jews.

Text—Sefer ha-roqeaḥ. First edition, Fano 1505. Many other editions: Cremona 1557; Hanau 1630. Short extract with translation in B. Halper: Post-Biblical Hebrew literature (Philadelphia 1921).

Criticism—Isaac Broydé: Jewish Encyclopaedia (vol. 5, 100–101, 1903).

XIII. SAMARITAN

SADAQA BEN MUNAJA

See medical chapter below.

XIV. MONGOL AND CHINESE

CHINGIZ KHĀN

Mongol conqueror and lawgiver (1155–1227). One of the greatest conquerors of all times. Founder of the Mongol empire, part of which was later continued by the Yüan dynasty. He was born in 1155, on the right bank of the Onon in the district of Dülün-Buldaq; he was originally called Timūchīn, and was the son of

[10] Word derived from γεωμετρία.

Yisūkāi-Bahādur (d. 1167); he was a Tatar of the tribes living between the Black Tatars and the Wild Tatars (the name Mongol or Mughūl to designate these peoples appeared only about the middle of the thirteenth century). Timūchīn obtained very gradually a predominant position among those tribes; he was helped by Muslim urtaq (Turkish, middleman) or traders, Ja'far Khuja, Ḥasan, and Dānishmand Ḥājib, and it was possibly to such men that he owed the inspiration of his later and greater efforts. By the year 1206 he had conquered the greater half of Mongolia; it was then that he summoned the first parliament (qurultai) and assumed imperial power under the name Chingiz Khān (the word Chingiz is spelled in many ways; e.g., Changez, Genghis; the second i of Chingiz is long or short; the first and third consonants of the Persian spelling are the specifically Persian letters which I represent by ch and g[11]). His capital was Qaraqorum, on the Orkhon. It is not necessary to tell the history of his campaigns outside of Mongolia; he conquered successively the Tangut (Kingdom of Hsia), the Chin dynasty of Northern China (not completely), the kingdom of the Gurkhān of the Qarā-Khitai, the territories of the Shāhs of Khwārizm (Persia and Transoxiana). This last conquest was of immense significance, for it integrated Chinese and Muslim culture to an extent hitherto unparalleled. Chingiz himself went as far westward as Bukhārā, and southward as the Indus near Peshāwar. His empire finally extended from Armenia to Korea. He died in 1227, not far from Tsin-chou in Kansu; his body was taken to Mongolia and buried in the mountain of Burkhān-Khaldūn (some pseudo-relics of his are revered to this day in Ordos, on the river Jamkhak).

He was a military genius comparable to Alexander, a great organizer, a stern disciplinarian, and gave his peoples a new code of laws. He never knew any language but his own, Mongol; in 1206 he became acquainted with the use of seals and the art of writing and he introduced the Uighūr alphabet; in 1219 or later, he introduced the Chinese script; later still he employed Persian secretaries. The main cultural influences to which he was submitted were the Muslim (Persian) and Chinese. In spite of his barbarity and ruthlessness he was sensitive to culture and showed some toleration of other faiths. He had contacts not only with Buddhism, but also with Islām, Christianity, and Taoism. While he was sojourning in the Hindū-Kush, c. 1223, he called to his court the Taoist sage, Ch'iu^1 Ch'ang^2-ch'un^1 (2313, 450, 2854), and received some teachings from him. His educational reforms were carried out by Yeh-lü Ch'u-ts'ai, who bears the same relation to him as Alcuin to Charlemagne.

The Chinese call him T'ai^4 Tsu^3 (10573, 11826), a name generally given to the first emperor of a dynasty, though the Yüan dynasty did not really begin until 1271. He was succeeded by his son Ogotāy (1227–41), called in Chinese, T'ai^4 Tsung^1 (10573, 11976). The famous Khubilāy Khān (1257–1294), whom the Chinese call Shih^4 Tsu^3 (9969, 11826), was one of his grandsons.

Ogotāy extended considerably the Mongol empire. It was under his rule that Mongol hordes, led by his nephew Bātū, invaded Russia and Hungary (1238–1241). They entered Moscow and Novgorod, burned Cracow, and besieged Pest. Ogotāy's death in 1241 relieved the pressure, and in the same year the Mongols were defeated at the battle of Wahlstatt, near Liegnitz (Silesia). This stopped their western advance, but they remained in Russia until 1480—a fact which helps one to understand later vicissitudes of Russia's development.

[11] Vol. 1, p. 50.

Sources—Mongolian: The earliest Mongolian source, the Altyn debter (Golden book), is lost and known only indirectly through the Yüan shih and through Rashīd al-dīn. Another contemporary Mongolian source originally written in Uighūr script is known through a Chinese transcription and version, the Yüan[2] chao[1] mi[4*] shih[3] (13744, 478, 7835, 9893) (Secret history of the Yüan dynasty). It was translated into Russian by the archimandrite Palladius Katharov: Trudy Rossijskoi dukhovnoi missii v Pekinie (vol. 4, 3–258, table, 1866). A much later Mongolian work, the Chung taishi (Khadun toghuji), compiled about the middle of the seventeenth century by Ssanang Setzen, was translated into Russian by the Archimandrite Hyacinth. Partial translation from Russian into German by Isaac Jacob Schmidt: Geschichte der Ost-Mongolen . . . verfasst von Ssanang Ssetsen Chungtaidschi (St. Petersburg 1829).

Chinese: The T'ung chien kang mu, for which see my notes on Chu Hsi (second half of the twelfth century) and Khubilāy Khān (second half of the thirteenth century).

The Mongolian annals, Yüan shih. French translation by Antoine Gaubil: Histoire de Gentchiscan et de toute la dynastie des Mongous (Paris 1739).

The Hsi yu chi of Ch'iu Ch'ang-ch'un (see geographical chapter below).

Account by Meng-hung translated into Russian by V. Vasiliev in Trudy vostochnogo otdel. archeol. obshch. (vol. 4).

The Hsin[1] Yüan[2] shih[3] (4574, 13744, 9893). New annals of the Yüan dynasty, recently compiled by Ko[1] shao[4]-min[2] (6039, 9773, 7926), style name Shao[3]-chan[1] (9746, 276) sumptuously published at the expense of the ex-President, Hsü[2] Shih[4]-ch'ang[1] (4748, 9969, 427), contains abundant information (in contrast with the old Yüan shih, from which but little knowledge was obtainable).

Arabic: See my notes on Ibn al-Athīr (first half of the thirteenth century), and al-Juwainī (second half of the thirteenth century).

Persian: See my note on Rashīd al-dīn (first half of the fourteenth century). This is the most valuable single source.

General studies on the Mongols—Mouradga d'Ohsson: Histoire des Mongols (vol. 1, The Hague 1834). Sir Henry Hoyle Howorth: History of the Mongols (3 vols., London 1876–1888; vol. 4, index, 1927; Isis, 11, 501). Léon Cahun: Introduction à l'histoire de l'Asie: Turcs et Mongols (Paris 1896). René Grousset: Histoire de l'Extrême-orient (403–493, 1929; Isis, 14, 437–441).

Studies mainly devoted to Chingiz Khān—Petis de la Croix: Histoire du grand Genghizcan (Paris 1710; derived from Arabic and Persian sources). Wilhelm Barthold: Die Entstehung des Reiches Tchinghiz-chans (St. Petersburg 1896); Turkestan im Zeitalter des Mongoleneinfalls (St. Petersburg 1900); Encyclopaedia of Islām (vol. 1, 856–862, 1912). Rudolf Stübe: Tschingizchan, seine Staatsbildung und seine Persönlichkeit (Neue Jahrbücher für das klassische Altertum, vol. 21, 532–541, 1908). F. E. A. Krause: Cingis Han. Die Geschichte seines Lebens nach der chinesischen Reichsannalen (112 p., autograph, 2 pl., Heidelberg 1922). B. J. Vladimirtsov: Chingīz Khān (176 p., Leningrad 1922; in Russian; making use of many sources, including the Armenian and Georgian which have been generally neglected); Englished by D. S. Mirsky (184 p., London 1930). Harold Lamb: Genghis Khan. The emperor of all men (270 p., 12 pl., New York 1927); semi-popular but well informed.

Paul Pelliot: Les systèmes d'écriture en usage chez les anciens Mongols (Asia major, vol. 2, 284–289, 1925).

TS'AI CH'ÊN

See mathematical chapter below.

CHAPTER XXXIII

MATHEMATICS AND ASTRONOMY

(First Half of Thirteenth Century)

I. LATIN AND VERNACULAR

FIBONACCI

Leonardo of Pisa, or Pisano. Leonardo Fibonacci. (The last word, meaning son of Bonaccio, should not be taken literally. That is, one of his ancestors, but not necessarily his father, was called Bonaccio. Cf. the Arabic names beginning with Ibn, and the modern names Johnson, MacMurrich, etc.). Italian mathematician, born c. 1170; died after 1240. His father was the head of the Pisan factory in Bugia on the Barbary Coast; Leonardo was there brought into touch with the East; he was taught by a Muslim master; later he traveled about the Mediterranean Sea, studying the arithmetical means used by the merchants of many countries.

Fibonacci was the greatest Christian mathematician of the Middle Ages, and the mathematical renaissance in the West may be dated from him. His most important and largest work (if not the most original), the Liber abaci (or abbaci) appeared in 1202 (revised edition, 1228). It was the first complete and systematic explanation of the Hindu numerals by a Christian writer; also, naturally, the first complete exposition of Hindu and Muslim arithmetic, but Leonardo gave more rigorous demonstrations than the Muslims. He had a good knowledge not only of Muslim, but also of Greek mathematics (Euclid, Archimedes, Heron, Diophantos). It is probable that this knowledge was largely derived from Latin translations.

He called the unknown quantity, its square, and the constant, respectively radix (also res and causa), census, numerus; and in one case at least represented numbers by letters to increase the generality of his proof. Casting out of nines (with proof), of sevens, and of elevens. Approximative extraction of quadratic and cubic roots. First use of the recurrent series[1] 1,2,3,5,8,13, ... (each term being equal to the sum of the two preceding ones) in a problem on the number of offspring of a pair of rabbits. Formerly called series of Lamé, it is now properly called series of Fibonacci. This series and others developed in a similar way (e.g., 1/2, 1/3, 2/5, 3/8, 5/13, ...) find many applications in the geometrical structure of living organisms.[2] To determine whether n is prime or not, one can restrict one's attention to divisors $\leqslant \sqrt{n}$. There is an infinity of perfect numbers of the form $\frac{1}{2}2^n\,(2^n - 1)$, wherein $(2^n - 1)$ is prime. (This rule is incorrect, but it holds for the first eight perfect numbers.)

The other great work of Fibonacci, the Practica geometriae, was written in 1220.

[1] Liber abaci, Boncompagni's edition (p. 283).

[2] F. M. Jaeger: Lectures on the principle of symmetry (Cambridge 1917; 2nd ed., 1920; Isis, 4, 32). L. Blaringhem: Les transformations brusques des êtres vivants (333, Paris 1911).

It was apparently based on the lost book of Euclid, περὶ διαιρέσεων (on the divisions of figures), and also on Heron's Metrica. It contains various geometrical and arithmetical problems, notably an extension of the Pythagorean proposition to solid geometry and the rule to calculate the volume of a pyramid frustum. Fibonacci used algebra to solve geometrical problems (this was a great novelty in Christendom).

Two other works, both dating from 1225, the Flos (Flos super solutionibus quarundam questionum ad numerum et ad geometriam uel ad utrumque pertinentium), and the Liber quadratorum, are much smaller but more original. In the Flos we find a number of indeterminate problems of the first and the second degrees solved in integers. The importance of this will be better appreciated if one realizes that Fibonacci was the only Diophantist of note before Bachet de Méziriac (1581–1638), and it would seem that some at least of his solutions were not derived from Diophantos. We find in the same book a remarkable value of the only (real) root of $x^3 + 2x^2 + 10x = 20$, i.e., $x = 1°22' 7'' 42^{iii} 33^{iv} 4^{v} 40^{vi}$ (error, c. $1\frac{1}{2}^{vi}$)—this value may have been determined by means of the regula falsi; a negative solution interpreted as a debt; solution of a system of five linear equations with five unknown quantities. The Liber quadratorum contains also many excellent things: solution of $x^2 + y^2 = z^2$ in integers, derived from $\Sigma_1^n (2n - 1) = n^2$; theorems derived from the identity

$$(a^2 + b^2)(c^2 + d^2) = (ac + bd)^2 + (bc - ad)^2 = (ad + bc)^2 + (ac - bd)^2;$$

to find three squares x^2_1, x^2_2, x^2_3, and a number (congruum) y such that

$$x^2_1 - y = x^2_2 \qquad x^2_1 + y = x^2_3;$$

affirmation that no square can be a congruent number, i.e., $x^2 + y^2$ and $x^2 - y^2$ are not both squares (this implies that the area of a rational right triangle is never a square, and that the difference of two biquadrates is not a square); ingenious proof of $\Sigma_1^n n^2 = \frac{n(n + 1)(2n + 1)}{6}$.

Aside from their purely mathematical interest, which is considerable, Fibonacci's works are also of cultural interest, for the many practical problems included in them contain information on weights and measures, economic conditions of his time, etc.

Though Fibonacci's mathematical initiation was probably due to his father's commercial activity, it is misleading to consider him the founder of a school of commercial arithmetic. His work was not commercial but highly theoretical, and he can hardly be said to have founded a school; his was a lonely personality. The Liber abaci of 1202 marks the beginning of the new (European, Christian) mathematics, an original development of Greek and Muslim mathematics.

Text—Partial editions of the Liber abaci and the Practica geometriae were given for the first time by Guglielmo Libri in his Histoire des sciences mathématiques en Italie (vol. 2, Paris 1838). Prince Baldassarre Boncompagni published the smaller writings of Leonardo (the two I have quoted plus a letter to Theodorus, philosopher to the emperor Frederick II, which is included in the Flos) for the first time in: Tre scritti inediti di Leonardo Pisano (Firenze 1854; 2d ed., 1856), then later a monumental edition of all of Leonardo's writings: Scritti di Leonardo Pisano (2 large vols., Roma 1857–1862). The first volume contains the Liber abbaci (459 p. without notes); the second, the Practica geometriae (224 p.) and the opuscoli (p. 227–283), also without any note, introduction, or index.

General criticism—B. Boncompagni: Della vita e delle opere di Leonardo Pisano (Ann. acc. pontif. de' Nuovi Lincei, vol. 5, 5–91, 208–246, 1851–1852); Intorno ad alcune opere di Leonardo Pisano (417 p., Roma 1854). J. Giesing: Leben und

Schriften Leonardos (Progr., 35 p., Döbeln 1886). M. Lazzarini: Leonardo, le sue opere e la sua famiglia (Boll. di bibliogr. e storia delle scienze mat., vol. 6, 98–102, 1903; vol. 7, 1–7, 1904). G. Eneström: Über zwei angebliche mathematischen Schulen im christlichen Mittelalter (Bibliotheca mathematica, vol. 7, 252–262, 1907). Gino Loria has given an excellent summary of Leonardo's life and works in Gli scienziati italiani (vol. 1, 4–12, 1921, with bibliography); Leonardo et le matematiche nel secolo di Dante (Periodico di matem., 4, 131–134, 1924). Ettore Bortolotti: Leonardo ed il rinascimento delle scienze matematiche in Occidente (Periodico di matematiche, 4, 134–139, 1924). Gino Loria: Storia delle matematiche (vol. 1, 379–405, Torino 1929; Isis 13, 228).

Special criticism—B. Boncompagni: Glossarium ex libro abbaci (18 p., Roma 1855). Francesco Bonaini: Memoria unica sincrona di Leonardo (14 p., Pisa 1858). V. A. Le Besgue: Notes sur les opuscules de Léonard (Bull. di bibliografia e di storia d. sci. mat., vol. 9, 583–594, 1876). Edouard Lucas: Recherches sur plusieurs ouvrages de Léonard et sur diverses questions d'arithmétique supérieure (ibidem, vol. 10, 129–176, 239–293, 1877). P. Gram: Restitution du calcul de Léonard sur l'équation $x^2 + 2x^2 + 10x = 20$ (Bull. de l'Académie de Danemark, 18–28, 1893). Hermann Weissenborn: Die Berechnung des Kreisumfanges bei Archimedes und Leonardo (Berliner Studien für class. Philologie, vol. 14, 32 p., Berlin 1894). G. Eneström: Sur un traité d'algèbre du moyen âge en langue hébraique (Bibliotheca mathematica, vol. 2, 152, 1901; Über Summierung der Reihe von Kubikzahlen im christlichen Mittelalter (ibidem, vol. 3, 243, 1902; Leonardo does not deal with the sum of cubic numbers); Woher hat Leonardo seine Kenntnisse der Elementa des Euklides entnommen? (ibidem, vol. 5, 414, 1905; rejecting the hypothesis of a direct knowledge of the Greek text). G. Wertheim: Die Numeri congrui und congruentes (Bibliotheca mathematica, vol. 3, 144, 1902). Raymond Clare Archibald: Euclid's book on Divisions of figures with a restoration based on Woepcke's text and on the Practica geometriae of Leonardo Pisano (96 p., Cambridge 1915). R. B. McClenon: Leonardo and his Liber quadratorum (American mathematical monthly, vol. 26, 1–8, 1919; Isis, vol. 3, 456). Leonard Eugene Dickson: History of the theory of numbers (vol. 1, Divisibility and primality, 5, 337, 347, 393, 1919; Isis, 3, 446–448; vol. 2, Diophantine analysis, 59, 77, 105, 166–167, 226, 402, 419, 460–462, 509, 527, 615, 689, 1920; Isis, 4, 107–108). Quido Vetter: Nota alla risoluzione dell' equazione cubica di Leonardo Pisano (Atti d. R. Accad., 63, 296–299, Torino 1928); note concerning the solution of a cubic equation in Leonardo's Flos (Casopsis pro Pestovani matematiky a fysiky, vol. 58, 1–3, Prague 1928; in Czech; Isis, 13, 159).

JORDANUS NEMORARIUS

Jordanus de Nemore, also called Jordanus Saxo (or de Saxonia), Jordanus Teutonicus. German mathematician and physicist. Born in the second half of the twelfth century, probably in Westphalia; was professed in the Dominican order in Paris, 1220, and became its second general in 1222 (1222 to 1237); during Clean Lent he preached in alternate years in Paris and Bologna; he died at sea on the homeward journey from the Holy Land in 1237.

N. B.—The dates quoted by me are based on the assumption that the mathematician, Jordanus Nemorarius, and the Dominican, Jordanus Saxo, are the same person; they refer to the Dominican. This identity is very probable but not absolutely certain. It is denied by Duhem who would place the mathematician Nemorarius in the twelfth century.

Jordanus Nemorarius was the founder of the mediaeval (Christian) school of mechanics, and was second only to Fibonacci as a mathematician.

His mechanical ideas, explained in the Elementa super demonstrationem ponderis, were an original development of those ascribed to Aristotle, the two main novelties being: (1) the notion of gravitas secundum situm (component of gravity along the trajectory); (2) the axiom of Jordanus (so named by Duhem); i.e., that which can lift a certain weight up to a certain height, can also lift a weight k times heavier to a height k times smaller.

Another mechanical treatise, De ratione ponderis (or De ponderositate), contains the fundamental notion of statical moment and its application to the study of the angular lever and of the inclined plane. However, its authenticity is not certain. Duhem ascribes it to a later—thirteenth century—author, whom he calls "the Forerunner of Leonardo." (Such denomination is to be deprecated, for one should not name a person in function of the unknown future). Whether Nemorarius composed it himself or not, it is a development of his Elementa, and is obviously a product of his school. That school discovered the germ of the principle of virtual displacements. The whole tradition leading to this principle may thus be summarized as follows: Aristotle, Nemorarius, Forerunner of Leonardo (or Nemorarius?), Leonardo da Vinci, Descartes, John Bernoulli (1717).

Nemorarius wrote two arithmetical treatises, Demonstratio de algorismo and Arithmetica decem libris demonstrata. In great contrast with Fibonacci's arithmetic, Nemorarius' work shows no trace of Muslim influence, but continues the tradition of Nicomachos and Boetius. In the Arithmetica letters are constantly used instead of figures for the sake of generality. Nemorarius was not interested in reckoning; his purpose was to give a deductive account of arithmetical knowledge. His main concern was the theory of numbers. He showed (Arithmetica, VI, 26) that $x(x+1)$ is neither a square nor a cube ($x \neq 0, -1$); that every multiple of a perfect or abundant number is abundant, and every divisor of a perfect number is deficient (ibidem, VII, 55-56); he tried to prove (VII, 57) the erroneous statement that all abundant numbers are even.

His Tractatus de numeris datis (or de lineis datis), in four books, is a treatise on algebra; it contains algebraic rules and a number of problems leading to linear and quadratic equations. The "numerus datus" is the given number occurring in a problem (numerus datus est cuius quantita nota est).

Finally he composed two geometrical treatises, the De triangulis, in four books, dealing with the usual problems, the determination of the center of gravity, etc.; and the Planisphaerium, a treatise on mathematical astronomy, which contains the first general demonstration of the fundamental property of stereographic projection—i.e., that circles are projected as circles (Ptolemy had proved it only in special cases).

Various other works are ascribed to him, notably the De speculis and the Algorithmus demonstratus. The former is probably, and the latter certainly apocryphal (see my note on Gernardus, below).

Under Jordanus' leadership, the Dominican Order increased considerably. Four new provinces (Denmark, Poland, Greece, and Palestine) were added to the eight older ones. Two Dominican chairs were established at the University of Paris (1229, 1231). Many distinguished men were attracted into the order; e.g., Hugh of Saint Cher, Raymond of Peñafort, Albert the Great, Vincent of Beauvais.

General studies—M. Cantor and Stanonik: Allgemeine deutsche Biographie (vol. 14, 501-504, 1881). Stanonik's article deals with Nemorarius' activity as a

Dominican and with his theological and religious writings. The most elaborate accounts are those of M. Cantor: Geschichte der Mathematik (vol. 2, 2nd ed., 53-86, 1899); and P. Duhem: Origines de la statique (vol. 1, 98-155, 1905). Lynn Thorndike: Vatican Latin MSS. (Isis, 13, 79, 1929).

Mechanics—For the relation between the Nemorarius writings as preserved in the MSS. and the De ponderibus propositiones XIII et earumdem demonstrationes, edited by Peter Bienewitz (Petrus Apianus) in Nürnberg, 1533, see Duhem.

P. Duhem: Origines de la statique (vol. 1, 98-155, 1905, Nemorarius and his school; 354-355, Nemorarius and R. Bacon; 356-358, axiom of Jordanus; vol. 2, 318, 1906). Philip E. B. Jourdain: Supplement to the 3rd English ed. of Mach's Mechanics (Chicago 1915).

"The Forerunner of Leonardo"—The liber Jordanis de ratione ponderis was edited by N. Tartaglia and published after the latter's death: Jordani opusculum de ponderositate Nicolai Tartaleae studio correctum novisque figuris auctum (Venice 1565). Tartaglia's corrections are negligible.

For the analysis of this text, see Duhem; Origines de la statique (vol. 1, 134-147, 192, 1905; vol. 2, 318-323, 1906).

Arithmetic—Arithmetica decem libris demonstrata. First edition by Jacques Lefèvre d'Etaples, Paris 1496. This same volume contains a commentary, a treatise on music, and an epitome of Boetius' arithmetic, all three by Lefèvre; and an account of the game rithmimachia,[3] by Lefèvre, or by John Shirwood, bishop of Durham (d. 1494). Lefèvre's commentary on Nemorarius was very popular at the University of Paris. The volume was many times reprinted in Paris (1503, 1507, 1510, 1514). The edition of 1514 is practically identical with that of 1496.

G. Eneström: Über die Demonstratio Jordani de algoritmo (Bibliotheca mathematica, vol. 7, 24-37, 1906); Über eine dem Nemorarius zugeschriebene kurze Algorismusschrift (ibidem, vol. 8, 135-152, 1908); Über die Arithmetica des Nemorarius (ibidem, vol. 9, 175, 1908); Das Bruchrechnen des Nemorarius (ibidem, vol. 14, 41-54, 1914). For the Algorismus demonstratus, see below, the note dealing with Gernardus.

David E. Smith: Rara arithmetica (1908, 62, 82).

Algebra—The De numeris datis to which this section is devoted is not purely algebraic, but we may call it algebra for the sake of brevity. It was first edited by H. Treutlein: Z. für Math. und Physik (vol. 24, Supp., 127-166, 1879) with introduction. Better edition by Max Curtze (ibidem, vol. 36, 1891, hist. Abt.).

M. Curtze: Kommentar zu dem Tractatus de numeris datis (Progr., 20 p., Thorn 1890); further commentary with the edition of the text (1891). R. Daublensky von Sterneck: Zur Vervollständigung der Ausgaben der Schrift de numeris datis (Monatshefte für Mathematik, vol. 7, 165-179, 1896). G. Wertheim: Über die Lösung einiger Aufgaben in de numeris datis (Bibliotheca mathematica, vol. 1, 417-420, 1900).

Geometry—The Geometria vel de triangulis libri IV was edited by Max Curtze in the Mitt. des Coppernicusvereins (vol. 6, 65 p., 5 pl., Thorn 1887).

P. Duhem: Un ouvrage perdu cité par Jordanus de Nemore, le Philotechnes (Bibliotheca mathematica, vol. 5, 321-325, 1905); A propos du φιλοτέχνης (Archiv für Geschichte der Naturwissenschaften, vol. 1, 380-384, 1909). Duhem claims that the book of geometry twice quoted in the Elementa Jordani under the name of filotegni is the De triangulis. G. Eneström: Über den ursprünglichen Titel der geometrischen Schrift des Nemorarius (Bibliotheca mathematica, vol. 13, 83-84, 1912). H. Bosmans: Le Philotechnes (Revue des questions scientifiques, 12 p., janvier, 1923). Apropos of a fourteenth century MS. of that work in the Library of Bruges, confirming Duhem's hypothesis; Isis, 5, 499; 12, 93).

[3] About which see my vol. 1 (757, 763).

Astronomy—The Planisphaerium was printed together with Ptolemy's Planisphaerium (Venice 1558). This is probably identical with the Demonstratio astrolabii et planisphaerii, mentioned by Joh. Fried. Weidler: Historia astronomiae (Wittenberg, 276, 1741), which was published together with Theon of Alexandria's commentary on Aratos (Basel 1507, 1536, 1558).

GERNARDUS

Magister Gernardus. Unknown author of an arithmetical treatise entitled Algorithmus (or algorismus) demonstratus, which was one of the best known works of its kind in the Middle Ages. There are many MSS. of it ranging from the thirteenth to the sixteenth centuries. These MSS. are anonymous except one ascribing the treatise to Magister Gernardus. The name Gernardus has thus no more signification to us than the phrase "the author of the Algorismus demonstratus." The treatise belongs to the thirteenth century but we cannot guarantee that it was composed in the first half of it. Our main reason for placing Gernardus here is his affinity with Jordanus Nemorarius. Indeed his Algorismus was ascribed to Nemorarius; it was probably derived from the latter's arithmetical writings. Its popularity is illustrated by the fact that Regiomontanus made himself a copy of it (kept in Vienna); on account of that copy, the treatise was foolishly ascribed to Regiomontanus.

The Algorismus demonstratus is a Boetian arithmetic of about 20,000 words divided into two parts dealing respectively with integers and with fractions (Algorismus de integris, Algorismus de minutiis). Letters are used in the demonstrations instead of numerals, and there are many references to Euclid. An appendix on proportions contains the eighteen combinations of the regula catta.

Incipit: Digitus est omnis numerus minor decem. Explicit: Haec sunt quae de minutiis scienda, ideo colligenda putaui.

Text—First edition by Joh. Schöner (1477–1547), anonymously published under the title Algorithmus demonstratus (Nuremberg 1534). This edition was derived from a copy made by J. Vögelin c. 1525. Title page in D. E. Smith: Rara arithmetica (179, 1908). Critical edition, including comparisons with the Demonstratio Jordani and the Opus numerorum of Nemorarius, by Gustaf Eneström: Algorismus de integris (Bibliotheca mathematica, vol. 13, 289–332, 1913); Algorismus de minutiis (ibidem, vol. 14, 99–149, 1914).

Criticism—G. Eneström: Ist Nemorarius Verfasser der Schrift Algorithmus? (Bibliotheca mathematica, vol. 5, 9–14, 1904). P. Duhem: Sur l'algorithmus (ibidem, vol. 6, 9–15, 1905; would consider Gernardus a contemporary of Campanus). L. C. Karpinski: Nemorarius and John of Halifax (American mathematical monthly, vol. 17, 108–113, 1910). Suzan Rose Benedict: Comparative study of early treatises introducing into Europe the Hindu art of reckoning (Thesis, University of Michigan, 1914). G. Eneström: Über die Geschichte der Stammbrüche im Mittelalter (Bibliotheca mathematica, vol. 14, 269–270, 1914).

VILLEDIEU

Alexandre de Villedieu. Alexander de Villa Dei. French Franciscan; mathematician and grammarian. Born in Villedieu, Normandy; he was a canon of the church of St. André, at Avranches, at the time of his death c. 1240. He wrote didactic poems on arithmetic, Carmen de algorismo (284 hexameters), on the compotus and on grammar, Doctrinale puerorum. The Carmen and even more the

Doctrinale were immensely popular, as is witnessed by the number of MSS., translations, and commentaries.

The Carmen contributed considerably to the diffusion of Hindu numerals. It explains fundamental operations with integers, very much like the Liber algorismi translated by John of Seville (first half of the twelfth century). It is the first Latin text wherein the number of operations is definitely given, and also the first wherein zero is considered one of the numerals—that is, it speaks of ten numerals, not of nine plus a zero, as is done by earlier writers. It was translated into English, French, and Icelandic.

The Doctrinale was largely based on Donatus (first half of the fourth century) and on Priscianus (first half of the sixth century). It was in the Doctrinale that Aldo Manuzio (second half of the fifteenth century) studied the rudiments of Hebrew; being dissatisfied with that wretched account, he then prepared his own grammar (1501).

Text—The Carmen de algorismo is included in J. O. Halliwell: Rara arithmetica (74, 1839). Partial French translation of the thirteenth century edited by Charles Henry in Boncompagni's Bullettino (vol. 15, 53–70, 1882), and by Victor Mortet in Bibliotheca Mathematica (vol. 9, 55–64, 1908). For an Icelandic edition, see my note on Haukr Erlendsson (first half of the fourteenth century). A fragment of an English commentary of the fourteenth century MS. was edited by David Eugene Smith: An ancient English algorism (Archiv für Geschichte der Naturwissenschaften, vol. 1, 301–309, 1909; dating from c. 1300; Egerton MS. no. 2622, British Museum).

The Massa compoti of Alexander de Villa Dei, edited by Robert Steele (Opera hactenus inedita Rogeri Baconi, fasc. 6, 268–289, Oxford 1926). This text is followed by a note on the mediaeval division of time (p. 290–297).

The Doctrinale puerorum was first printed before 1470. For the almost innumerable incunabula editions, see Gesamtkatalog der Wiegendrucke (vol. 1, 470–671, 1925). Critical edition with introduction and notes by Dietrich Reichling, 521 p. (Monumenta Germaniae paedagogica, 12, Berlin 1893).

Criticism—Charles Thurot: De Alexandri de Villa Dei Doctrinali ejusque fortuna (Thesis, 68 p., Paris 1850); Notices et extraits de divers MSS. latins pour servir à l'histoire des doctrines grammaticales au Moyen Age (Notices et extraits, vol. 22 (2), 592 p., 1868). Suzan Rose Benedict: Comparative study of the early treatises introducing into Europe the Hindu art of reckoning (1914).

SACROBOSCO

Joannes de Sacro Bosco (Sacro Busto); John of Halifax or Holywood (Holyfax, Holywalde). English mathematician and astronomer; born probably at Halifax in Yorkshire; he is said to have studied in Oxford, and to have settled in Paris c. 1230; he spent the remainder of his life in Paris, where he died about the middle of the century. He wrote elementary treatises on astronomy, arithmetic, and the calendar, which were immensely popular for centuries.

The astronomy, Tractatus de sphaera, or Sphaera mundi (c. 1233) was slavishly derived from al-Farghānī and al-Battānī. It is divided into four chapters: (1) terrestrial globe; (2) great and small circles; (3) rising and setting of stars; (4) orbits and movements of the planets. Its popularity is proved by the number of manuscripts, commentaries, printed editions, and translations. It was translated into Hebrew by the Provençal, Solomon Abigdor, in 1399, and there are a number of Hebrew commentaries on it. The first printed (Latin) edition (Ferrara 1472) was the second astronomical book to be printed. At least twenty-five editions appeared within the fifteenth century, and a great many more continued to be published for school use until the middle of the seventeenth century, not only in Latin, but also in Italian, French, German, and Spanish. Among the many commentators may be quoted Michael Scot, Cecco d'Ascoli, Pierre d'Ailly, Regiomontanus, Jacques Lefèvre, Melanchthon, Clavius.

The arithmetic, Algorismus vulgaris (or Tractatus de arte numerandi), is entirely different from Nemorarius' Arithmetica and from the Algorithmus demonstratus (ascribed to Nemorarius). These treatises are theoretical and philosophical; Sacrobosco's is a practical account of reckoning. It is very well arranged, each operation being dealt with completely in a separate chapter: numeratio, additio, subtractio, mediatio, duplatio, multiplicatio, divisio, progressio, preambulum ad radicum extractionem, extractio radicum in cubicis. The Algorismus was exceedingly popular and contributed powerfully to the diffusion of the Hindu numerals. Sacrobosco did not call these numerals Arabic, but he spoke twice of the "Arabs" as the inventors of algorism. Hence the common belief expressed by the phrase "Arabic numerals."[4] The practical methods explained by him remained unchanged until the time of Prosdocimo de' Beldomandi (first half of the fifteenth century).

Finally, Sacrobosco composed c. 1232 (1235, 1244) a treatise on the calendar, De anni ratione or De computo ecclesiastico. This compotus was translated into Icelandic before the end of the thirteenth century.

Text—(1) *Sphaera*: First edition (24 p., 4to, Ferrara 1472). The edition of 1498 is sometimes dated by error 1468. Houzeau and Lancaster quote a great many editions (Bibliographie de l'astronomie, vol. 1, part 1, 506–510, 1887). The Sphaericum opusculum printed by Ratdolt in Venice, 1485, was the first printed book to include diagrams (printed) in colors. Editions for school use appeared in Wittenberg as late as 1629, and in Leiden as late as 1656!

Italian versions by Mauro (Venice 1537, 1550); by A. Brucioli (Venice 1543), by Dante de Renaldi (Florence 1571, 1579), by Pifferi (Siena 1604). French editions (Paris 1546, 1570, 1584). German translation by C. Heinfogel (Nuremberg 1516, 1519; Strassburg 1533). Spanish translations (Seville 1545, Madrid 1650).

Abigdor's Hebrew translation was printed together with the astronomy of Abraham bar Ḥiyya (Offenbach 1720). For the editions of Hebrew commentaries, see M. Steinschneider: Hebraeische Übersetzungen (642–647, 1893).

(2) *Algorismus*: The Algorismus was first printed together with the Compotus manualis of Anianus, in Strassburg, 1488. Many later editions are enumerated by D. E. Smith: Rara arithmetica (31–33, 1908). The latest quoted by him are those of Wittenberg (1550, 1568) and Antwerp (c. 1558, 1559). The Algorismus and the Sphaera were printed together on several occasions. Modern edition of the Algorismus by James Orchard Halliwell: Rara arithmetica (London 1839; also 1–26, 1841). Better edition by Maximilian Curtze: Petri Philomeni de Dacia in Algorismum vulgarem Johannis de Sacrobosco commentarius. Una cum algorismo ipso edidit et praefatus est (112 p., Copenhagen 1897).

(3) *Compotus*: The Compotus was first published, together with the Sphaera, by Philip Melanchthon (Wittenberg 1545; Melanchthon's preface dated 1538). This was reprinted in 1550. Libellus de anni ratione seu, ut vocatur vulgo, Computus ecclesiasticus (Antwerp 1547, Paris 1550, Venice 1564; etc.).

[4] Later still the numerals were sometimes called "Jewish;" for example, in the Fifteenth century French algorism edited by E. G. R. Waters (Isis, vol. 12, 195, 211, 1929). Yet the "Arabic" label has prevailed to this day.

Icelandic version of the Compotus in the Codex Arnemagneanus, no. 1812; see N. Beckman and Kr. Kålund: Alfraeði islenzk (2. Rímtol, 257, 1915).

Criticism—C. L. Kingsford: Dictionary of national biography (vol. 27, 217, 1891). On the editions of the Algorismus, see G. Eneström: Bibliotheca mathematica (63, 1894); P. Riccardi (ibidem, 73–78); Max. Curtze (ibidem, 36–37, 1895). G. Eneström: Sur les neuf "limites" mentionnées dans l'Algorismus (ibidem, 97—102, 1897); Année de la mort de Sacrobosco, 1256? (ibidem, 32, 1899); Année de la mort de Sacrobosco (Intermédiaire des mathématiciens, vol. 7, 268; answer by P. Tannery, ibidem, vol. 8, 263–65, reprinted in Mémoires, vol. 10, 393–395). L. C. Karpinski: Jordanus Nemorarius and John of Halifax (American mathematical monthly, vol. 17, 108–113, 1910). David Eugene Smith and Louis Charles Karpinski: The Hindu-Arabic numerals (Boston, 135, 1911). Suzan Rose Benedict: Comparative study of early treatises introducing into Europe the Hindu art of reckoning (Thesis, University of Michigan, 1914). P. Duhem: Système du monde (vol. 3, 238–240, 1915). Henri Bosmans: Sur l'auteur d'un traité d'algorisme contenu dans le MS. D. 372 de la bibliothèque reconstituée de l'Université de Louvain (Annales de la Soc. scientif. de Bruxelles, 458–462, déc. 1925; Isis, 8, 741). Lynn Thorndike: Vatican Latin MSS. (Isis, 13, 88, 1929).

For Robert Grosseteste, see philosophical chapter; for William of Lunis, the chapter on translators from the Arabic into Latin; for John of Garland, the philological chapter.

ANONYMOUS ARITHMETICAL TREATISES

Hanover Latin algorism

A treatise, which was one of the MSS. in Leibniz's possession and is now in the Library of Hanover. It explains the fundamental operations with integers. It contains about 3000 words.

Incipit: Quis titulus huius artis. Quid in ea doceatur . . . Explicit: . . . sic tamen ut minor auferri non possit a majore secundum artem minor cyfram proponens et negocium.

Edited by Karl Immanuel Gerhardt (Programm, Salzwedel 1853).

Salem Latin algorism

A treatise which was formerly in the Salem cloister on the Lake of Constance (Bodensee) and is now in the University Library of Heidelberg. It contains about 4000 words and explains the fundamental operations with integers. The author was apparently acquainted with Villedieu's Carmen de algorismo or with Sacrobosco's Algorismus vulgaris, but he was primarily a theologian and took pains to indicate the mystical signification of the seven operations.

Incipit: Omnis sapientia sive scientia a Domino Deo . . . Explicit: . . . qui nos extrahere et abstrahere dignetur ab hoc saeculo nequam et perducere in vitam aeternam, qui vivit et regnat.

Edited by Moritz Cantor: Über einen Codex des Klosters Salem (Zeitschrift für Mathematik und Physik, vol. 10, 1–16, 1865).

Oxford French algorism

One of the earliest algorisms in any vernacular is now preserved in the Bodleian Library of Oxford. It does not follow any of the known treatises, but there are points of contact with Sacrobosco's Algorismus and with the Salem algorism above-mentioned. It is written in French verse. There are in all 512 (519) lines. It contains two rules for the learning of the multiplication table between 5-times-5 and 10-times-10 which are not found together in any of the early treatises:

$$a.b = 10[a - (10 - b)] + (10 - a)(10 - b)$$
$$d^2 = 10[d - (10 - d)] + (10 - d)^2$$

Incipit: Li dui clerc qui ont translaté . . . Explicit: Se a droit ta raïz as traite.

E. G. R. Waters: A thirteenth century algorism (Isis, 11, 45–84, 1928). Diplomatic edition with English version, notes, glossary, and facsimiles of two pages.

For Michael Scot and John of London, see philosophical chapter above.

WILLIAM THE ENGLISHMAN

English physician and astronomer who flourished in Marseilles c. 1231. He is often called Marsiliensis or Massiliensis, without a Christian name, or simply with the abbreviation W. or Willel. He wrote a book on medical astrology, Astrologia de urina non visa, and an abridgment of the Almagest, also called Astrologia, wherein he laid special stress on the principles underlying the construction of astronomical tables. With regard to the size of the solar system, he was the first Latin writer to give an account of the Greek ideas which al-Farghānī (first half of the ninth century) had transmitted to Muslim astronomers. His main writings were devoted to the explanation of the work of al-Zarqālī (second half of the eleventh century), Compositio tabulae quae saphea dicitur sive astrolabium Arzachelis, Tabula de stellis fixis secundum Azarchelem (completed in 1231 after six years work), Scripta super Canones Arzachelis. He thus continued the task begun by another Marseillais, Raymond of Marseilles in 1140. We may say that it is through Marseilles, and later through Montpellier, that the Toledan Tables became known in Christian Europe.

As an interpreter of al-Zarqālī he was necessarily acquainted with the false notion of the trepidation of the equinoxes. He also referred to the new theories of al-Biṭrūjī (second half of the twelfth century).

Text—Opus astrolabii, partly published in Louis Amélie Sédillot: Mémoire sur les instruments astronomiques des Arabes (p. 185–190, 1841). The rest was edited by P. Tannery: Le traité de l'astrolabe universel ou Saphea d'Arzachel par Guillaume l'Anglais (Notices et extraits, vol. 35 (2), 1897; Mémoires, vol. 5, 190–197, 1922).

Criticism—P. Duhem: Système du monde (vol. 3, 287–291, 1915). P. Tannery: Mémoires (vol. 5, by index, 1922). R. T. Gunther: Early science in Oxford (vol. 2, 200, 1923; apropos of saphaea).

The Englishman William, who translated "The very great secret of Catenus, King of the Persians, concerning the virtue of the eagle" from Arabic into Latin, seems to be another person. M. Steinschneider: Europäische Übersetzungen (80, 1904). Lynn Thorndike: History of magic (vol. 2, 93, 487, 1923, quoting other Williams, who may be identical or not).

LONDON TABLES

These tables were compiled c. 1232 by an unknown astronomer, for the position of London which was given as 57° West of Arim and 51° North. They continued the tradition represented by the Marseilles Tables compiled c. 1140 by Raymond of Marseilles. They extend from 1232 (hence the dating) to 1540, the years being arranged in eleven groups (anni collecti) of twenty-eight.

There is an introduction dealing with such subjects as the four elements, motion of heavy and light bodies, the ether or quintessence, the nine spheres, the fixed stars, planetary motion.

Text—Latin MS. 7272, Bibliothèque nationale, Paris.
Criticism—P. Duhem: Système du monde (vol. 3, 231–238, 1915).

The astrological treatises written by Salio of Padua, Leopold of Austria, and Henrik Harpestraeng are dealt with in other parts of this volume. For John of Vicenza, see the religious chapter, above.

II. WESTERN MUSLIM

AL-BŪNĪ

See philosophical chapter above.

AL-ḤASAN AL-MARRĀKUSHĪ

Abū 'Alī al-Ḥasan ibn 'Alī ibn 'Umar al-Marrākushī. Also called Abū-l-Ḥasan 'Alī. Moroccan astronomer, mathematician, and geographer, who flourished in Morocco until c. 1262. He wrote various astronomical treatises: Talkhīṣ al-a'māl fī ru'yat al-hilāl (on the occupations at the apparition of the new moon), Ālāt al-taqwīm (on the calendar), on the influence of planetary conjunctions and eclipses. The first two are apparently lost; the authorship of the third is probable but not certain. The first treatise was probably theological at least in part; the third, astrological. His main work is his Jāmi' al-mabādī wa-l-ghāyāt (The uniter of the beginnings and ends; i.e., principles and results), probably completed in 1229–1230. This is a very good compilation of practical knowledge on astronomical instruments and methods, trigonometry, and gnomonics. He was well acquainted with the mathematical and astronomical works of al-Khwārizmī, al-Farghānī, al-Battānī, Abū-l-Wafā', al-Bīrūnī, Ibn Sīnā, al-Zarqālī, and Jābir ibn Aflaḥ. For example, al-Ḥasan shared al-Zarqālī's belief that the obliquity of the ecliptic oscillates between 23° 33′ and 23° 53′, a belief which tallied with the notion of the trepidation of the equinoxes.

He mentioned not only the sine and versed sine (sahm, arrow), but also what he called complementary sine (jaib tamām), $\sin(90° - \alpha) = \cos\alpha$, and exceeding sine (jaib faḍl), $\sin(\alpha - 90°) = -\cos\alpha$. He gave a table of sines for each half degree, also tables of versed sines and arc sines (this last one he called the table of al-Khwārizmī). To facilitate the use of gnomons he added a table of arc cotangents. The second part of the Jāmi' was devoted to the explanation of graphical methods of solving astronomical problems. These methods were essentially derived from Ptolemy's analemma, but the construction of planispheres, astrolabes, quadrants, and the needs of gnomonics had considerably increased their importance. Thus in al-Ḥasan's work they are very developed. It is probable that little of that was due to his own invention, but his work was the most elaborate treatise on trigonometry, gnomonics, and related questions in the Muslim West. The part dealing with gnomonics contained studies of dials traced on horizontal, cylindrical, conical, and other surfaces, for every latitude. We find in it the notion of equal or equinoctial hours, but this notion was not generally accepted, and temporary hours continued to be used for a considerable time.

The Jāmi' also includes a catalogue of 240 stars for the year 622 (1225–1226), and the latitudes and longitudes of 135 places, the observations having been made by himself in thirty-four of them. Value of the precession of the equinoxes 54″ per year.

Text—The Jāmi' was translated into French by J. J. Sédillot and published by his son, L. A. Sédillot: Traité des instruments astronomiques des Arabes composé par Aboul-Hassan Ali de Maroc (2 vols., 700 p., Paris 1834–1835; supplement, 1844). An unpublished chapter was edited by Carra de Vaux: L'astrolabe linéaire ou bâton d'Et-Tousi (Journal asiatique (9), vol. 5, 464–516, 1895). See my note on al-Muẓaffar al-Ṭūsī, below.

Criticism—J. B. J. Delambre: Histoire de l'astronomie du moyen âge (185–190, 515–545, Paris 1819; full discussion of the gnomonics). L. A. Sédillot: Mémoire sur les instruments astronomiques des Arabes (Paris 1841). J. T. Reinaud: Géographie d'Aboulféda (vol. 1, introduction, 136–138, 1848). H. Suter: Die Mathematiker und Astronomen der Araber (144–145, 1900). A. von Braunmühl: Geschichte der Trigonometrie (vol. 1, 83–86, 1900). Hugo Seemann and Th. Mittelberger: Das kugelförmige Astrolab nach den Mitteilungen von Alfons X von Kastilien (44–46, Erlangen 1925; Isis, 8, 743). H. P. J. Renaud: Aperçu sur la géographie scientifique des Arabes (Bulletin de l'Enseignement public du Maroc, 14 p., Paris 1927; Isis 15, 212). Peter Schmalzl: Zur Geschichte des Quadranten bei den Arabern (115–126, München 1929; Isis 15, 462).

IBN BADR

Abū 'Abdallāh Muḥammad ibn 'Umar ibn Muḥammad, called Ibn Badr. (In Spanish, Abenbéder). Flourished in Seville at an unknown time, probably in the thirteenth century. Hispano-Muslim mathematician. He composed a compendium (ikhtiṣār) of algebra, including a theoretical part and a collection of problems or numerical examples. The subjects touched upon include quadratic equations, surds, multiplication of polynomials, arithmetical theory of proportion, linear Diophantine equations, etc. One Abū Kāmil is quoted, who may be the Egyptian mathematician Shujā' ibn Aslam. A commentary on Ibn Badr's Ikhtiṣār was written in verse by one Muḥammad ibn al-Qāsim al-Gharnāṭī in 1311–1312.

Text—Compendio de álgebra de Abenbéder. Texto árabe, traducción y estudio por José A. Sánchez Pérez (241 p., Madrid 1916; Isis, 4, 509).

Criticism—H. Suter: Die Mathematiker und Astronomen der Araber (197, 1900; only 4 lines).

III. EASTERN MUSLIM

AL-MUẒAFFAR AL-ṬŪSĪ

al-Muẓaffar ibn Muḥammad ibn al-Muẓaffar Sharaf al-dīn al-Ṭūsī. Muslim mathematician and astronomer, of Ṭūs in Khurāsān; died c. 1213. He is quoted as teacher of Mūsā ibn Yūnus Kamāl al-dīn, which would imply that he flourished in Baghdād or Mūṣul.

He wrote (1) a treatise on the astrolabe (al-musaṭṭah); (2) a paper discussing the sub-division of a square into four parts under certain conditions; (3) a treatise on algebra. No. 2 was composed in 1209–1210, for the prince Shams al-dīn, in Hamadān. No. 3 is known only through a commentary (talkhīṣ) by an unknown author.

al-Muẓaffar al Ṭūsī was the inventor of the linear astrolabe (al-asṭurlāb al-khaṭṭay) called Ṭūsī's staff. As the plane astrolabe is essentially the projection of a sphere upon a plane, the linear one represents the projection of that plane upon a straight line. Strings were attached to it to measure angles. Ṭūsī's staff should not be confused with the so-called Jacob's staff or cross-staff. It should be noted also that Ṭūsī's staff was named after al-Muẓaffar and not after Nāṣir al-dīn al-Ṭūsī (as Sedillot believed).

Ibn Khallikān (vol. 3, 470, 1858). Louis Sédillot: Matériaux pour servir à l'étude comparée (vol. 1, 1845). H. Suter: Zur Geschichte des Jakobsstabes (Bibliotheca mathematica, 13–18, 1895; ibidem, 13–15, 1896); Die Mathematiker und Astronomen der Araber (134, 1900). Carra de Vaux: L'astrolabe linéaire ou bâton d'Et-Tousi (Journal asiatique, vol. 5, 464–516, 1895). Containing a text by al-Ḥasan al-Marrākushī describing the instrument; with French translation.

KAMĀL AL-DĪN IBN YŪNUS

See philosophical chapter above.

QAIṢAR IBN ABĪ-L-QĀSIM

Qaiṣar ibn Abī-l-Qāsim ibn 'Abd-al-Ghanī ibn Musāfir, 'Alam al-dīn, al-Ḥanafī (Qaiṣar is the Latin Caesar, probably derived through the Greek καῖσαρ). Egyptian mathematician, astronomer, and engineer. Born at Aṣfūn in Upper Egypt in 1178–1179 (or 1168–1169); died at Damascus in 1251. He studied in Egypt and Syria, and finally in Mūṣul, under Kamāl al-dīn Ibn Yūnus, who taught him music and other sciences. He then returned to Syria and entered the service of al-Muẓaffar II Taqī al-dīn Maḥmūd (ruler of Ḥamāh from 1229 to 1244). He constructed for the latter water-mills (nā'ūra) on the Orontes, and fortifications.

In 1225–1226 he made a celestial globe. That globe was kept until 1809 in the cabinet of cardinal Borgia at Velletri; it is now in the Museo Nazionale of Naples. It is composed of two brass hemispheres, upon four supporting feet, with horizon and meridian circles, and bears a Kūfic inscription quoting the author's name and the date 622. It is the earliest but one of the Arabic celestial globes extant.

He wrote a treatise on Euclid's postulates and dedicated it to Nāṣir al-dīn al-Ṭūsī.

With regard to the water-mills or water-wheels, such contrivances were very ancient; they go back to Hellenistic times (see the Pneumatics of Philon of Byzantium). Of course improvements of many kinds were gradually invented. We don't know whether Qaiṣar introduced original improvements; e.g., whether he was the real inventor of the type of water-wheels which can still be seen on the Orontes and are one of the glories of Ḥamāh. It has been claimed that water-wheels were brought back to Europe by the Crusaders. Some water-wheels must have existed in Europe before this time (cf. e.g., Gregory of Tours), but it is probable that the Crusaders saw more of them and better ones in the East and brought back home that improved type or at least a clearer conception of their usefulness. Moreover the enormous economic expansion which took place in Western Europe in the twelfth and thirteenth centuries must have brought into being a great number of water-wheels, whether of the Western or of the Eastern type. (Water-wheels of an oriental type may still be seen in Franconia near Bayreuth).[5] For the early history of water-wheels, see F. M. Feldhaus: Die Technik (1300–1301, 1914, unterschlägiges Wasserrad). Water-wheels were apparently known in China, for we hear of their introduction from China into Tibet in the first half of the seventh century (vol. 1, 467).

Ibn Khallikān (de Slane, vol. 3, 471–473, 1868). Giuseppe Simone Assemani: Globus coelestis cufico-arabicus Veliterni Musei Borgiani (Patavii 1790). L. Ideler: Untersuchungen über den Ursprung der Sternnamen (Berlin 1809). H. Suter: Mathematiker (143, 1900; 175, 1902). Edward Luther Stephenson: Terrestrial and celestial globes (vol. 1, 29, New Haven 1921; Isis, 4, 549). See my note on Early Arabic celestial globes, below.

IBN AL-LUBŪDĪ

Abū Zakarīyā Yaḥyā (or Aḥmad) ibn Muḥammad ibn 'Abdān, al-Ṣāḥib Najm al-dīn Ibn al-Lubūdī. Syrian physician, mathematician, astronomer, and philosopher. Born in Ḥalab, 1210–1211; died after 1267. Educated in Damascus, where he studied medicine under 'Abd al-raḥīm ibn 'Alī Muhadhdhab al-dīn (Ibn) al-Dakhwār (born in Damascus, 1169–1170; died 1230; teacher of Ibn abī Uṣaibi'a). He entered the service of al-Manṣūr Ibrāhīm (ruler of Ḥimṣ, 1239–1245) and became his wazīr (hence the title Ṣāḥib). After al-Manṣūr's death, he entered the service of al-Ṣāliḥ Najm al-dīn Ayyūb (ruler of Egypt, 1240–1249), who appointed him government inspector in Alexandria. Later he returned to Syria, where he occupied a similar post.

He wrote a number of medical works: treatises on rheumatism, on Hippocrates' aphorisms, on the questions of Ḥunain ibn Isḥāq. Only two have been preserved, both dedicated to al-Manṣūr, thus anterior to 1245: (1) collection of discussions relative to fifty physiological and medical questions (these discussions are merely theoretical, not experimental); (2) commentary on the generalities (Kullīyāt) of Ibn Sīnā's Qānūn.

His mathematical writings include: an extract from Euclid; explanation of Euclid's postulate; an arithmetical textbook; a treatise dealing with the essential points of Euclid and of the middle books[6]; a treatise on algebra; an essay on magic squares dedicated to al-Manṣūr; on the art of (astrological) judgments. He also compiled tables: (1) al-zāhir (the brilliant), extracted from the tables of the Shāh by Ḥabash al-Ḥāsib (first half of the ninth century); (2) al-muqarrab (the approximate), based on observations.

Ibn abī Uṣaibi'a (A. Müller's edition, vol. 2, 185, 1884). F. Wüstenfeld: Arabische Aerzte (120, 1840). L. Leclerc: Médecine arabe (vol. 2, 160–161, 1876). H. Suter: Mathematiker (146, 1900).

IV. SYRIAC

For Solomon of al-Baṣra and Jacob bar Shakkō, see philosophical chapter, above.

[5] According to M. Sobernheim: Encyclopaedia of Islām (vol. 2, 240, 1915).

[6] For the middle books, see my note on Nāṣir al-dīn al-Ṭūsī (second half of the thirteenth century).

V. WESTERN JEWISH

AARON BEN MESHULLAM

Aaron ben Meshullam ben Jacob of Lunel (not a Kohen). Died in 1210. One of the younger sons of the Meshullam praised by Benjamin of Tudela; disciple of Abraham ben David of Posquières. Ardent Maimonidean. In 1206 he wrote in Hebrew a treatise devoted to a comparison of the Christian and Jewish calendars; it was partly derived from non-Jewish sources.

E. Renan: Rabbins français (448, 511, 518, 733, 1877). Michael Friedländer: Jewish Encyclopaedia (vol. 1, 18, 1901). J. Freimann: Encyclopaedia judaica (vol. 1, 67, 1928).

For Judah ha-Ḥasid and Judah ben Solomon ha-Kohen, see the philosophical chapter above; for Jacob Anaṭoli, see translators from Arabic into Hebrew.

VI. HINDU

CAṄGADEVA

Hindu mathematician. Grandson of Bhāskara (first half of the twelfth century). In 1205–1206, he founded a school for the study of the Siddhāntaśiromaṇi. It is probable that his interest was astrological rather than mathematical. At any rate this was apparently the last mathematical effort of mediaeval India.

M. Winternitz: Geschichte der indischen Litteratur (vol. 3, 564, 1922). A. Berriedale Keith: History of Sanskrit literature (Oxford, 524, 1928).

VII. CHINESE

For Yeh-lü Ch'u-ts'ai's calendar, see the chapter on education, above.

TS'AI CH'ÊN

Ts'ai^{4} Ch'ên^{2} (11519, 649). Born in Chien^{4}-yang^{2} (1592, 12883), Fuhkien, 1167; died in 1230. Styled Chiu^{3}-fêng^{1} (2263, 3564). In 1437 his tablet was placed in the Confucian temple. Chinese philosopher, historian, mathematician. Disciple of Chu Hsi. His commentary on the Book of History (Shu Ching; see vol. 1, p. 67) is a standard textbook in China. It contains a description of a decimal number system (the Chinese decimal system goes back at least to the time of Sun Tzŭ, see vol. 1, 321; for the introduction of the zero into China, see my note on Ch'in Chiu-shao, below). Another work of his, the Hung^{2} fan^{4} huang^{2} chi^{2*} nei^{4} p'ien^{1} (5252, 3429, 5106, 859, 8177, 9220), based on the so-called Writing of Lo, deals with number mysticism.

Text—The Library of Congress has two editions of T'sai Ch'ên's commentary on the Shu Ching under the title, Shu^{1} Ching^{2} chi^{2*} ch'uan^{2} (10024, 2122, 906, 2740), each in five vols. and 6 chüan.

Criticism—A. Wylie: Notes on Chinese Literature (3, 85, 1902). H. A. Giles: Chinese biographical dictionary (747, 1898). D. E. Smith and Y. Mikami: History of Japanese mathematics (20, 1914).

CH'IN CHIU-SHAO

Ch'in^{2} Chiu^{3}-shao^{2} (2093, 2263, 9778). Flourished at Chien^{4}-k'ang^{1} (1592, 5908) Fu in 1244; during the Pao^{3} Yu^{4} (8720, 13438) era—1253 to 1258—he was in the service of the Sung government on the banks of the Yangtze kiang. He later became governor of Ch'iung^{2}-chou^{1} (2376, 2444), and then of Mei^{2}-chou^{1} (7705, 2444), where he died. Chinese mathematician. One of the greatest mathematicians of his race, of his time, and indeed of all times. He wrote in 1247 his main work called "the Nine Sections of Mathematics" Shu^{4}-shu^{1} chiu^{3}-chang^{1} (10075, 10024, 2263, 390), or Shu^{4}-hsüeh^{2*} (4839) chiu-chang. It was so called because it was divided into nine sections (resolution of indeterminate problems; chronological calculations; land mensuration; trigonometry; state service; imposts, fortifications; military arithmetic; barter), and not to imitate the Chiu-chang suan-shu (for which see my note on Chang T'sang, first half of the second century B.C.). Both works, it is true, are divided into nine sections, but those sections do not correspond. It is probable that the words Chiu-chang were not part of the original title of Ch'in's work. He wrote also a less important work called General rules on arithmetic Shu^{4} shu^{4*} ta^{4} lüeh^{4*} (10075, 10053, 10470, 7564). The Nine Sections contain eighty-one problems involving indeterminate analysis and higher equations. These problems, some of which are very difficult, are distributed according to their species (not according to the methods of solving them) into eighteen books or chapters.

The method consists essentially in the application of the use of computing rods to algebra. It is called t'ien^{1} yüan^{2} shu^{1} (11208, 13744, 10024), meaning the method of the celestial element (in Japanese tengenjutsu), or li^{4*} t'ien^{1} yüan^{2} i^{1*} (6954, 11208, 13744, 5342), meaning the setting up of the celestial monad (i.e., the unknown quantity). See my note on I-hsing, first half of the eighth century. Red and black rods are used respectively to represent positive and negative quantities (or, in writing, red and black ink). See my note on Liu Hui (second half of third century). The unknown quantity is represented by a unit or monad, the zero by a little circle, like ours. This Chinese zero may have come directly from India with Buddhism (see vol. 1, 444, 450, 513) or it may have been imported later by Muslims. Numbers are written in accordance with the principle of local value; this being a natural consequence of the use of the suan^{4}-p'an^{2} (10378, 8620), or counting board, which can be traced back to the time of Hsün Yüeh (second half of the second century) and is probably much older still. Numerical expressions are all written horizontally. Ch'in arranged his equations in such manner that the absolute term would be negative; this is equivalent to Thomas Harriot's practice (1631)[7] of writing them so that the absolute term would stand alone in one member. Ch'in invented a method of solving numerical equations of any degree and applied it, e.g., to an equation of the tenth degree. This method is called ling^{2} lung^{2} k'ai^{1} fang^{1} (7205, 7491, 5794, 3435), which might be translated, the harmoniously alternating evolution. It is substantially identical to the Ruffini-Horner procedure (discovered by Paolo Ruffini c. 1805, and by William George Horner in 1819). Ch'in's method of indeterminate analysis, ta^{4}-yen^{3} shu^{4*} (10470, 13113, 10053), was similar to the Hindu method called kuṭṭaka (pulverizer or multiplier).[8]

[7] Thomas Harriot died in 1621, but his Artis analyticae praxis appeared only in 1631 (Isis, 11, 316).

[8] This word is translated "pulverizer" by Colebrooke, but according to a letter kindly addressed to me by my Harvard colleague, Walter Eugene Clark (July 1, 1929), the translation "multiplier" is more accurate.

Text—The Library of Congress has the Shu-shu chiu-chang in vols. 43–48 of the I^2 chia^4 t'ang^2 ts'ung^1 shu^1 (5353, 1143, 10760, 12039, 10024). This edition was printed in 1842.

By way of addition to my note on Chang Ts'ang (in vol. 1, 183), I may mention that the Library of Congress has the Chiu chang suan shu in the following three editions: Ssŭ^4 pu^4 ts'ung^1 k'an^1 (10291, 9484, 12039, 5861) vols. 390–392; Wu^3 ying^1 tien^4 chü^1 chên^1 pan^3 ts'ung^1 shu^1 (12744, 13308, 11202, 3060, 599, 8588, 12039, 10024) vols. 246–249; Suan^4 ching^1 shih^{2*} shu^1 (10378, 2122, 9959, 10024), vols. 2–4.

A critical study of Ch'in Chiu-shao's text was published in 1842 by Sung^4 Ching^3-ch'ang^1 (10462, 2143, 427), entitled Shu^4-shu^1 chiu^3-chang^1 cha^{2*} chi^4 (10075, 10024, 2263, 390, 127, 923). The Library of Congress has a copy of this work in the I^2 chia^4 t'ang^2 ts'ung^1 shu^1 (5353, 1143, 10760, 12039, 10024), vols. 49–50, 1842.

Criticism—A. Wylie: Chinese literature (116, 1902). Yoshio Mikami: Development of mathematics in China and Japan (63–78, 1912). David Eugene Smith and Y. Mikami: Japanese mathematics (chapter 4, 1914). L. Van Hée: La notation algébrique en Chine (Revue des questions scientifiques, Oct., 1913); Le zéro en Chine (T'oung Pao, vol. 15, 182–184, 1914). L. Gauchet: Note sur la généralisation de l'extraction de la racine carrée chez les anciens auteurs chinois (T'oung Pao, vol. 15, 531–550, 1914). This paper deals mainly with problems of the Chiu^3-chang^1 suan^4-shu^{4*} (2263, 390, 10378, 10053) by Chang^1 Ts'ang^1 (416, 11596), for which see vol. 1, 183, but it is valuable for a better understanding of the t'ien yüan shu. L. Wieger: La Chine (449, 489, 502, 1920).

LI YEH

Li^3 Yeh^3 (6884, 12990) or Li^3 Chih^4 (6884, 1845). Li was his family name; Yeh, a personal name. "Style" name, Jên^2-ch'ing^1 (5627, 2198); "nom de plume," Ching^4-chai^1 (2144, 234). Chinese mathematician; one of the greatest of his time and of his race. Born at Luan^2-ch'êng^2 (7458, 763), under Chin rule;[9] c. 1178, governor of Chün^1-chou^1 (3294, 2444) until 1232; some time after the overthrow of the Chin monarchy by Kublai Khān in 1260, he was sent for by the latter, but does not appear to have been in his service. He became a member of the Han^4-lin^2 (3828, 7157) Academy in 1265, however, but died soon after at the age of eighty-seven.

He wrote his main work in 1248; it is called the Sea-mirror of the circle measurements, Ts'ê^{4*}-yüan^2 hai^3-ching^4 (11698, 13734, 3767, 2170). In 1259 he wrote another work called Exercises and applications improving the ancient methods, I^{2*}-ku^3 yen^3-tuan^4 (5485, 6188, 13130, 12140), containing sixty-four problems on quadrilaterals and circles, with their solutions. Both works are largely algebraical.

However, Ch'in's interest was arithmetical rather than algebraical. His main purpose was to obtain the numerical roots of equations. Li Yeh, on the other hand, was more interested in the equations themselves, their form and construction. He was essentially an algebraist.

The Sea-mirror does not deal with the quadrature of the circle, but with what might be called trigonometrical measurements. It is divided into twelve books or chapters and contains 170 problems.

Li used the method of celestial element, t'ien^1 yüan^2 (11208, 13744), but in a manner different from Ch'in's. As Ch'in and Li lived far apart from one another

[9] The Chins or Kins, who ruled over a great part of N. China from 1115 to 1260, were a Tartar tribe (the Nü-Chên Tartars), sometimes called "the Golden Horde." They were inveterate enemies of the contemporary Chinese dynasty of the Southern Sung (1127 to 1280).

and under hostile governments, and could not possibly have influenced one another, their use of the t'ien-yüan and of the same symbol for zero suggests a common origin. The zero may have been introduced into China many centuries before; the t'ien yüan also may be a vestige of an old tradition. Instead of using red and black colors to designate positive and negative quantities, as Ch'in did, Li differentiated the latter by drawing diagonal strokes across them. Ch'in's method was clear but inconvenient in the case of writing and even more of printing. Li Yeh's method was generally adopted in China and Japan.

Text—The Sea-mirror was republished by Wang^{2} Tê^{2*}-yüan^{2} (12493, 10845, 13713) in 1287. The Library of Congress has a copy of it in vols. 153–156 of the Chih^{1} pu^{1*} tsu^{2*} chai^{1} ts'ung^{1} shu^{1} (1783, 9456, 11840, 234, 12039, 10024); and in the Bibliotheca mathematica sinensis, Pai^{2} fu^{2} t'ang^{2} suan^{4} hsüeh^{2*} ts'ung^{1} shu^{1} (8556, 3617, 10760, 10378, 4338, 12039, 10024), vols. 21–24, 1875.

The I-ku yen-tuan was edited in 1797 by Li^{3} Jui^{4} (6884, 5727), who died in 1818. A new edition of it, prepared by Ting^{1} Ch'ü^{3}-chung^{1} (11253, 3118, 2877) was included in the Pai^{2}-fu^{2} t'ang^{2} suan^{4} hsüeh^{2*} ts'ung^{1} shu^{1}. We owe an abbreviated translation into French together with the corresponding text, to Father L. Vanhée: Li-Yé (T'oung Pao, vol. 14, 537–568, 1913).

The Library of Congress has the I ku yen-tuan in vols. 162–163 of the Chih^{1} pu^{1*} tsu^{2*} chai^{1} ts'ung^{1} shu^{1}; and in vols. 25–26 of the Pai^{2} fu^{2} t'ang^{2} suan^{4} hsüeh^{2*} ts'ung^{1} shu^{1}. It also has a copy of the Pai-fu, in thirty-six volumes.

Criticism—A. Wylie: Notes on Chinese literature (116, Shanghai 1902). Yoshio Mikami: Development of mathematics in China (79–84, 1913).

The standard Chinese Biographical Dictionary, Chung^{1} kuo^{2*} jên^{2} ming^{2} ta^{4} tz'ŭ^{2} tien^{3} (2875, 6609, 5624, 7940, 10470, 12402, 11177) (Shanghai 1921; Isis, 5, 446–447) adduces considerable evidence to prove that this mathematician's name was in reality Li^{3} Chih^{4} (6884, 1845) and not Li^{3} Yeh^{3} (12990). The stone tablet which lists this man's name as a Han-lin graduate of the Chin period makes it read Li Chih.

CHAPTER XXXIV

PHYSICS AND MUSIC

(First Half of Thirteenth Century)

I. MECHANICAL REBIRTH IN THE WEST

For Jordanus Nemorarius and the "Forerunner of Leonardo," see the mathematical chapter; for Michael Scot, see the philosophical chapter.

GERARD OF BRUSSELS

Unknown Flemish mechanician who flourished probably in the thirteenth century. He wrote a treatise De motu wherein he tried to solve the difficulties which were to be removed later by the introduction of the notion of angular rotation. It begins in the Euclidean style with eight propositions, of which the first is "Quae magis removentur a centro magis moventur et quae minus, minus." The eighth defines the speed of a radius (or of a part of it) as the speed of the middle point. In 1328 Bradwardine referred to this treatise under the title De proportionalitate motuum et magnitudinum.

This Gerard was probably a Fleming, because he is called in the MSS. Gerardus de Brussel (not Bruxella or Bruxellis). He may be identical with one Ricardus de Usellis (Uccle? near Brussels) or de Vercellys. One cannot help thinking also of the mysterious mathematician, Magister Gernardus, dealt with above.

P. Duhem: Etudes sur Léonard de Vinci (vol. 3, 292–294, 1913). G. Eneström: Sur l'auteur d'un traité De motu auquel Bradwardin a fait allusion en 1328 (Archivio di storia della scienza, vol. 2, 133–136, 1921).

II. METEOROLOGY AND OPTICS

For the translations of the Meteorologica, see the note on the Aristotelian tradition in the section on translations from the Greek. For Alfred of Sareshel's commentary on it, see the translators from Arabic into Latin.

For Robert Grosseteste, see the philosophical chapter.

III. COMPASS

FURTHER HISTORY OF THE COMPASS

The early history of the compass is extremely obscure, which is not surprising if one considers that the first pilots who had the wit to make use of a magnetic needle to direct their course had no reason to publish their discovery, and on the contrary had every inducement to keep and transmit it as a trade secret. In my earlier discussion of the subject (vol. 1, 764) I concluded that while the Chinese were probably the first to discover the directive property of the magnetic needle, they failed to apply it to any rational purpose. The first practical use of the magnetic needle was credited by the Chinese themselves to foreigners, who were in all probability Muslims. Indeed maritime trade between the Far East on the one hand, and India, Persia, Arabia, and Africa on the other was a Muslim monopoly.

This great discovery was made probably toward the end of the eleventh century if not before. Considering its origin, it is curious that the earliest references to it outside of China, are found not in Arabic or Persian writings, but in French and Latin ones. Indeed we read them in the works of the Englishman, Alexander Neckam (d. 1217), who does not speak of the compass as of a novelty, and of the Frenchmen, Guiot of Provins (c. 1205) and James of Vitry (c. 1219). The last named describes it as having come from India. The encyclopaedia of Thomas of Cantimpré contains an account of a compass of the floating type.

The earliest Muslim references are somewhat later, as follows:

(1) In the Jawāmi' al-ḥikāyāt, a collection of anecdotes compiled in Persian, c. 1228–1235, by Muḥammad al-'Awfī. Al-'Awfī speaks of a sailor finding his way by means of a fish rubbed with a magnet.

(2) In the Kanz al-tijār, a lapidary written by Bailak al-Qabajaqī in 1282–1283, the author describes the use of a floating compass witnessed by himself in 1242–1243.

(3) In Al-Bayān al-maghrib, a history of Muslim Spain and Africa, composed by Ibn al-'Idhārī toward the end of the thirteenth century, a passage relative to the year 853–854 mentions a qaramīṭ, or lodestone (calamita); it is not sure that a compass is meant.

It has been suggested that knowledge of that Muslim invention reached northern Europe along the Russian trade routes more quickly than through southern Europe. There is nothing to substantiate that theory. The navigations of the Norsemen were more dangerous, but not impossible, without a compass. However essential such an instrument may seem to us to cross the oceans, as long as it was not available people did without it. Even so, large deserts were crossed for centuries and are crossed to this day without other means of direction than the friendly stars.

It would seem that the Muslims attached more importance to the southern end of the needle than to the northern one as we do. This may be owing to the Chinese origin, or to the fact that for many Muslims—those of Syria and Asia Minor—the southern end pointed roughly towards Mecca. That is, the southern end gave the general direction of the qibla. In fact, on early Turkish rhomb-cards the south is called either al-janūb or al-qibla.

To return to the West, it would seem that whether they invented the compass or not, Italian sailors were among the first to use it, and such use led necessarily to gradual improvements. In some mysterious way, the sailors of Amalfi (on the gulf of Salerno) received special credit for this, and finally a legend crystallized according to which the compass (or bússola) was invented by one Flavio Gioja of Amalfi in 1302. Whatever this Flavio Gioja did or not we do not know, but it is certain that the compass had been invented and used long before that year, and that it had already been improved or modified in various ways. The first technical description of a compass was given by Peter the Stranger in 1269.

Criticism—See the notes devoted to the authors mentioned and to the early portolani (second half of the thirteenth century). E. Wiedemann: Maghnaṭīs (Encyclopaedia of Islām, vol. 3, 105–106, 1928).

The main work on the history of the compass is that of Albert Schück: Der Kompass (3 vols. folio, Hamburg 1911–1918; Isis, 4, 438). See also A. Schück: Erwähnung eines Vorgängers des Kompasses in Deutschland um die Mitte des 13. Jahrhunderts (Mitt. zur Geschichte des Medizin, vol. 13, 333–343, 1914). Apropos of an allusion to the compass and its nautical use in the German poetic paraphrase of the Pater noster by Heinrich von Krolewiz (Kröllwitz on the Saale near Halle) between 1252 and 1255. Ge. Chr. Fr. Lisch: Heinrich's von Krolewiz ûz Missen Vater Unser (212 p., Quedlinburg 1839). Francis H. Butler and S. P. Thompson: Compass (Encyclopaedia Britannica, vol. 6, 175–177, 1929).

To the references given (vol. 1, 764) with regard to the Chinese sources may be added Herbert A. Giles: The mariner's compass (Adversaria sinica, no. 4, 107–115; no. 7, 219–222, Shanghai, 1906–1909). Léopold de Saussure: L'origine de la rose des vents et l'invention de la boussole (Archives des sciences physiques et naturelles, vol. 5, 68 p., Geneva 1923; Isis, 6, 208). In defense of the Chinese invention of the nautical use of the compass; different windroses were devised by Chinese and Muslims. A. C. Moule: The Chinese south-pointing carriage (T'oung pao, vol. 23, 83–97, 2 diagrams, 1924; Isis, 7, 259; that device was not a magnetic compass). Masukichi Hashimoto: Origin of the compass (Memoirs of the research department of the Toyo bunko, no. 1, 69–92, Tokyo 1926; Isis 14, 525). Largely based on Chinese sources which are quoted; claims that the Chinese had some knowledge of the deviation of the compass before the end of the twelfth century. Jitsuzō Kuwabara: Of P'u Shou-kêng (Memoirs of the research department of the Toyo bunko, no. 2, Tokyo 1928; J. R. A. S., 207, 1930).

IV. REINTRODUCTION OF HOT BATHS

ḤAMMĀMĀT

One of the results of the Crusades was the reintroduction of public bathing places in Europe, on the Muslim pattern. I say reintroduction, because the technique of bathing (cold and hot) had been carried very far by the Romans, and elaborate bathing places (balneae, balineae, thermae) obtained in all their important cities. However, that practice was discouraged by the Christians and disappeared entirely in the West during the disintegration of the Roman empire.

It is probable that in spite of Christian prejudices against it, this old tradition was never entirely discontinued in the eastern empire. At any rate the Muslim peoples developed a new form of bathing, the hot steam-bath or ḥammām (from the Arabic root ḥamm, to heat). Arabic literature is full of references to it; see, e.g., the Alf laila wa-laila.

Crusaders experienced these comforts in the East and introduced them into their own countries. In the first half of the thirteenth century ḥammāmāt were available in the main cities of western Europe. Their diffusion was helped by the fear of leprosy which reached its climax in that century.

For an account of ḥammāmāt see almost any description of Muslim countries, for example, Edward William Lane: Account of the manners and customs of the modern Egyptians (1835; often reprinted; chapter 16, in vol. 2). Cl. Huart: Encyclopaedia of Islām (vol. 2, 253, 1915).

V. PHYSICS IN EASTERN CALIPHATE

IBN AL-SĀ'ĀTĪ

Riḍwān ibn Muḥammad ibn 'Alī, Fakhr al-dīn Ibn al-Sā'ātī. Muslim mechanician and physician. Born in Damascus; he flourished there and entered the service of the Ayyūbid princes al-Fā'iz Ibrāhīm and al-Mu'aẓẓam 'Īsā, sons of al-'Ādil Sayf al-dīn (Saphadin, ruler of Egypt and Damascus, until 1218; al-Mu'aẓẓam ruled Damascus from 1218 to 1227); he died at Damascus c. 1223–1233.

He wrote a commentary on Ibn Sīnā's Qānūn and a supplement to the latter's treatise on gripes.

Between 1146 and 1169 his father, Muḥammad ibn 'Alī ibn Rustam al-Khurāsānī al-Sā'ātī (i.e., the clockmaker), had constructed the clock placed in the Bāb Jairūn of Damascus (often called Bāb sā'ā, door of the clock, on its account); he remained in charge of it until his death c. 1184-1185. That clock was seen and described by many travelers: Ibn Jubair, 1184; Qazwīnī; Ibn Baṭūṭa; etc. Riḍwān repaired and improved it, and in 1203 he wrote a book to explain its construction and use. Next to the contemporary treatise composed by al-Jazarī (see below), this is the most important source on early Muslim clocks. The earliest Arabic reference to a clock is found in the Kitāb al-ḥayawān of al-Jāḥiẓ (second half of the ninth century).

Text—E. Wiedemann and Fritz Hauser: Über die Uhren im Bereich der islamischen Kultur (Nova acta academiae naturae curiosorum, vol. 100, Halle 1915). Contains (p. 176-266) an abbreviated translation of Ibn al-Sā'ātī's work (Isis, 4, 619; 5, 217).

Criticism—Ibn abī Uṣaibi'a (Müller's edition, vol. 2, 183, 1884). L. Leclerc: Médecine arabe (vol. 2, 159, 1876). C. Brockelmann: Arabische Litteratur (vol. 1, 473, 1898). H. Suter: Die Mathematiker und Astronomen der Araber (136, 1900; 174, 1902); Encyclopaedia of Islām (vol. 2, 413, 1918). E. Wiedemann: Beiträge zur Geschichte der Naturwissenschaften (Sitzungsberichte der physikalisch medicinischen Sozietät, vols. 37-38, Erlangen 1905-1906).

AL-JAZARĪ

Abū-l-'Izz Ismā'īl ibn al-Razzāz (son of the rice-merchant), Badī' al-zamān al-Jazarī. Muslim mechanician. He flourished from 1181-1182 to 1205-1206 under the Urtuqid rulers of the Diyār Bakr, the northernmost district of al-Jazīrah; their capital was Āmid, on the upper course of the Tigris.

He completed at Āmid, probably in 1205-1206, for the Urtuqid Nāṣir al-dīn Maḥmūd (ruled from 1200 to 1222), a treatise on the knowledge of geometrical (mechanical) contrivances, Kitāb fī ma'rifat al-ḥiyal al-handasīya, dealing chiefly with hydraulic apparatus (clepsydras, fountains, etc.). This is the best Arabic work for the study of the Muslim applications of Hellenistic mechanics. It represents the climax of that Muslim tradition which began with the Banū Mūsā (first half of the ninth century). It is of course far more interesting from the technical than from the purely scientific point of view.

It is divided into six parts or kinds (nau'), of which the first and most important deals with various types of clepsydras indicating either equal or temporal hours. Muslims divided the day into twenty-four equal hours (al-sā'a al-mustawīya), or else into two parts, day and night, each of which was then subdivided into twelve "temporal" hours of varying length according to the season. The word temporal is a translation of the Arabic zamānīya. Unequal hours of the second kind were used in Christian Europe—e.g., in Italy—until as late as the middle of the eighteenth century (see Mémoires de Jacques Casanova, edition Flammarion, vol. 2, 121).

Text—Al-Jazarī's treatise has been translated into German, with commentaries, by Eilhard Wiedemann, as follows:

Nau' 1. Über die Uhren im Bereich der islamischen Kultur (Nova Acta, vol. 100, 1915; with Fritz Hauser; the translation covers p. 58 to 166; Isis, 4, 619; 5, 217).

Nau' 2. Über die Konstruktion von Gefässen und Gestalten die bei Trinkgelagen passende Verwendung finden (Der Islam, vol. 8, 55–93, 1918; Isis, 3, 478).

Nau' 3. Über die Konstruktion der Krüge und Tassen zum Aderlassen und zur Waschung (Archiv für Geschichte der Medizin, vol. 11, 22–43, 1918; Isis, 3, 324).

Nau' 4. Über die Konstruktion der Springbrunnen in Teichen die ihre Gestalt wechseln und über die immerwährenden Flöten. Partly published in the Ber. der Wetterauischen Ges. (1908); partly in the Amari Festschrift (1909).

Nau' 5. Über die Konstruktion der Instrumente die Wasser aus Wassermassen, die nicht tief sind, und aus einem fliessenden Fluss emporheben (Beiträge zur Geschichte der Technik, vol. 8, 121–154, 1918).

Nau' 6. Über die Konstruktion verschiedener Gegenstände, die ein ander nicht ähnlich sind. (a). Über die Herstellung eines Türe . . . in Āmid (Der Islam, vol. 11, 213–251, 1921). (b). Über ein Instrument mit dem man einen Kreis durch drei Punkte auf einer Kugeloberfläche oder Ebene zeichnen kann (Z. für Vermessungswesen, H. 22 u. 23, 1910). (c). Über ein Schloss mit 12 Buchstaben zum Verschliessen eines Kastens (Der Islam, vol. 11, 213–251, 1921). (d). Über vier Riegel auf dem Rücken einer Türe (ibidem). (e). Über eine Kahnuhr (Nova Acta, vol. 100, 165–166, 1915).

Criticism—Carra de Vaux: Note sur les mécaniques de Bédi ez-Zaman el-Djazari et sur un appareil d'hydraulique attribué à Apollonius de Perge (Congrès d'histoire de Paris, 5e section, 112–120, 1900). H. Suter: Mathematiker (137, 226, 1900). E. Wiedemann: Beiträge 3 (Sitzungsberichte, Erlangen, vol. 37, 259–262, 1905); also in the memoir already quoted (Nova Acta, vol. 100, 1915; Isis, 4, 619; 5, 217); Über die Abbildung eines Affenführers und seiner Affen (Der Islam, vol. 13, 107–108, 1923).

There are scattered in many European and American collections a number of so-called "automata miniatures," all of which were probably taken from a Constantinople MS. (Hagia Sophia, 3606) of al-Jazarī's Kitāb fī ma'rifat al-ḥiyal al-handasīya. That manuscript was completed in 1354, probably in Egypt; of course the illustrations represent an older tradition, but those known to us date from 1354. A. C. Coomaraswamy: Early Arabic and Persian paintings (Museum of Fine arts Bulletin, 49–52, Boston 1922; Isis, 6, 149); The treatise of al-Jazarī on Automata. Leaves from a MS. of the Kitāb fi ma'arifat (21 p., 8 pl., Boston 1924; Isis, 7, 191). K. A. C. Creswell: Yearbook of oriental art and culture (33–40, London 1925). Rudolf M. Riefstahl: The date and provenance of the automata miniatures (The art bulletin, vol. 11, 206–215, 11 figs., New York 1929; Isis, 13, 427).

QAIṢAR IBN ABĪ-L-QĀSIM

See mathematical chapter above.

VI. MUSLIM MUSIC

For 'Abd al-Laṭīf and Ibn Sab'īn, see the philosophical chapter; for Qaiṣar ibn abī-l-Qāsim, see the mathematical chapter.

MUḤAMMAD AL-SHALĀḤĪ

Muḥammad al-Shalāḥī (or Shalājī) of Seville. Hispano-Muslim writer on music. He dedicated a treatise on music in 1221–1222 to the Almohade, Abū Ya'qūb Yūsuf II al-Mustanṣir (1214–1223). This treatise, entitled Kitāb al-imtā' wal-intifā' fī mas'alat samā' al-simā', does not really concern us, but is quoted to clear up misunderstandings and to illustrate an important type of Muslim musical literature. In fact, it is more theological than musical. It is essentially a collection of quotations from the ḥadīth for and against music: is it lawful or not for a Muslim to listen to music? Which instruments are allowable and which are not? Etc. Incidentally it gives some very brief information on various instruments (no real descriptions of them).

Michael Casiri: Bibliotheca arabico-hispana Escurialensis (vol. 1, 527, 1760). Julian Ribera: La musica de las Cantigas (Madrid 1922). Jules Rouanet: La musique arabe (Lavignac's Encyclopédie de la musique, vol. 5, 2743, 1922).

Information relative to this note was kindly given to me by Miguel Asín of Madrid, and by Henry George Farmer of Glasgow. The latter is planning to include this treatise in his corpus of Arabic musical texts (Isis, 9, 560). For a brief discussion of the theological arguments involved, see H. G. Farmer: History of Arabian music to the thirteenth century (22–36, 194, London 1929; Isis, 13, 375).

Farmer quotes (p. 196) a work, similar to the one I have dealt with, composed about the same time by another Sevilian, Aḥmad ibn Muḥammad al-Ishbilī (d. 1253): Kitāb al-samā' wa aḥkāmuhu (Listening to music and its ordinances). For other works of the same kind, published somewhat later, see ibidem (p. 195).

VII. MUSIC IN WESTERN CHRISTENDOM

For Franco of Cologne, see Book II; for John of Garland, see the philological chapter below.

SUMER IS ICUMEN IN

Though this early composition belongs to the history of music rather than to this survey, I quote it as the best proof that by that time western music had come of age.

It was written before 1240, and was probably performed in the Benedictine abbey of Reading, in Berkshire. The English words are a Wessex dialect. According to Rev. Dom Anselm Hughes, it is preeminent in six directions, for "(i) it is the oldest known canon; (ii) it is the oldest known harmonised music which is frequently performed and enjoyed by singers and listeners to-day; (iii) it is the oldest known 6-part composition; (iv) it is one of the oldest known spcimens of the use of what is now the major mode; (v) it is the oldest known specimen of ground-bass; (vi) it is the oldest known manuscript in which both secular and sacred words are written to the music." The scribe (author?) is supposed to have been John of Fornsete (there are two places called Forncett in Norfolk).

Text and criticism—This composition has very often been reprinted in facsimile and otherwise. See for instance Oxford History of music (vol. 1, 333, 1901). Jamieson Boyd Hurry: Sumer is icumen in (16 p., pl., Reading 1913; 2d ed., 53 pl., 1 pl., London 1914).

Anselm Hughes (O. S. B.): Grove's Dictionary of music (3d ed., vol. 5, 191, 1928; facsimile in frontispiece).

CHAPTER XXXV

CHEMISTRY

(First Half of Thirteenth Century)

I. WESTERN EUROPE

See notes on Alfred of Sareshel, and on the Aristotelian tradition, in the chapter on translators; on Michael Scot, in the philosophical chapter; on John of Garland, in the philological chapter; on Hugh and Theodoric Borgognoni, in the medical chapter.

II. EASTERN ISLĀM

AL-JAWBARĪ

'Abd al-Raḥīm (or Raḥmān) ibn 'Umar al-Dimashqī al-Jawbarī, Zain al-dīn. Born in Jawbar, near Damascus. He traveled considerably in the lands of the eastern caliphate, going as far as India. In 1216–1217 he was in Ḥarrān; in 1219–1220 in Qūniya (Iconium); later he flourished at the court of Urtuqid sulṭān of Āmid and Ḥiṣn Kaifā, Rukn al-dīn Mūdūd (ruled from 1222 to 1231). He dedicated to the latter his Kitāb al-mukhtār fī kashf al-asrār wa hatk al-astār (Revelation of secrets and tearing off of veils), wherein he exposed the frauds and deceptions of money-changers, quacks and alchemists, "the people of al-kīmiyā who know three hundred ways of making dupes." This is very valuable for the history of Muslim alchemy and technology, as well as for the history of Muslim manners and superstitions.

Text—The text was first printed in Damascus, 1885; then in Stambul; in Cairo, 1898–1899, c. 1908. Extracts have been edited (in Arabic) by L. Cheikho in al-Mashriq (vol. 12, passim, 1909). Analyzed by E. Wiedemann in Mit. zur Gesch. der Medizin (vol. 9, 386–390, 1910).

E. Wiedemann has published many extracts in German with commentary, unfortunately scattered in various places: Über Wagen bei den Arabern (Beiträge, 4, Sitzungsb. der phys. med. Soz., vol. 37, 388–391, Erlangen 1905); Zur Alchemie bei den Arabern (Journal für praktische Chemie, vol. 76, 82–86, 1907); Über das Goldmachen und die Verfälschung der Perlen (Beiträge zur Kenntnis des Orients, vol. 5, 77–96, 1907); Über das Färben der Tiere und Menschen (Mit. zur Gesch. der Medizin, vol. 9, 476–480, 1910); Einiges aus al-Gaubārī (Beiträge, 23; Sitzungsber. der phys. med. Soz., vol. 42, 311–322, 1910); Über Charlatane bei den Muslimen (Beiträge, 26, numbered erroneously 25; ibidem, vol. 43, 206–232, 1911).

Criticism—C. Brockelmann: Arabische Litteratur (vol. 1, 497, 1898); Encyclopaedia of Islām (vol. 1, 1026, 1913). Carra de Vaux: Penseurs de l'Islām (vol. 2, 385, 1921).

For 'Abd al-Laṭīf, see the philosophical chapter; for 'Umar ibn al-'Adīm, the historical one.

III. INDIA

ŚĀRṄGADHARA

See medical chapter.

IV. JAPAN

KATŌ SHUNKEI

Katō Shirōzaemon Kagemasa. Born in Seto, district of Kasugai, province of Owari. Japanese potter who went to China in 1223 with Dōgen;[1] after remaining there five years, he brought back to Japan the art of making "faïence," i.e. glazed earthenware (setomono) as distinguished on the one hand from unglazed ware and on the other from porcelain. (Porcelain was introduced only after 1510, by Shonzui, at Arita, in Hizen). He founded the great faïence industry of Seto, which was directed for seven centuries by the Katō family.

E. Papinot: Historical dictionary (264, 1909). F. Brinkley: History of the Japanese people (374, 451, 1915).

[1] About whom see my note on Japanese Buddhism in the first half of the thirteenth century.

CHAPTER XXXVI

GEOGRAPHY

(First Half of Thirteenth Century)

I. ENGLISH

GERVASE OF CANTERBURY

See historical chapter.

GERVASE OF TILBURY

English scholar. Born at Tilbury, in Essex; seems to have been brought up in Rome or at any rate to have spent part of his childhood in Italy; he studied and taught law in Bologna; in 1177 he was in Venice; later returned to England; he was for a time in the service of William II the Good (king of the Sicilies, 1166–1189), in 1190–1191 he was in Salerno. Otto IV (emperor, 1209–1218) made him marshal of the kingdom of Arles. It is possible that he returned to England after Otto's death. The date and place of his death are unknown.

He wrote c. 1211 for Otto IV, the Otia imperialia, a sort of geographical and historical olla-podrida, of little intrinsic value, but wherein some curious bits of information may occasionally be gleaned; e.g , a reference to "salamander skin" or asbestos (also referred to by Marco Polo). The Otia, also called Liber de mirabilibus mundi, or Solatium imperatoris, or Descriptio totius orbis, is divided into three parts (decisiones): (1) commentary on Genesis; (2) geography and history; topography of Rome; (3) marvels.

Text—First almost complete edition by G. W. Leibniz: Scriptores rerum brunsvicensium (3 vols., Hanover 1707–1711; vol. 1, 881–1004; vol. 2, 754–784). Third part edited by F. Liebrecht (296 p., Hanover 1856). Extracts in Joseph Stevenson's edition of Ralph of Coggeshall's chronicle (Rolls series, 1875).

Criticism—R. Röhricht: Bibliotheca geographica Palaestinae (45, 1890). William Hunt: Dictionary of national biography (vol. 21, 241–242, 1890). A. Potthast: Bibliotheca historica (507, 1896). C. R. Beazley: Dawn of modern geography (vol. 2, 216, 1901; vol. 3, 77, 1906). Charles Gross: Sources of English history (390, 1915). J. K. Wright: Geographical lore (1925).

BARTHOLOMEW THE ENGLISHMAN

See philosophical chapter.

II. SCANDINAVIAN

For Saxo Grammaticus, see the historical chapter; for the Konungs skuggsjá, see the philosophical chapter.

RAFN SVEINBJÖRNSSON

Icelandic chieftain, traveler and physician. Born in Iceland about 1170. He traveled to Norway before 1202 and then visited England, France and Spain;

in 1203 he went again to Norway and then returned to Iceland for good. He became a prominent chieftain in Western Iceland; a quarrel with a neighboring chieftain ended in his own defeat and surrender; he was beheaded on March 4, 1213. He is said to have performed the stone operation according to the so-called Celsus method.

Text—A saga of Rafn was written shortly after his death. It was edited together with the Sturlunga saga by G. Vigfússon (Oxford 1878), and in Biskupa sögur, I (Copenhagen 1858).

Criticism—For this saga see Finnur Jónsson: Den oldnorske og oldislandske Litteraturs Historie (second ed., volume 2, 552–555, Copenhagen 1923).

L. Faye: Rafn Sveinbjörnsson's Liv og Virksomhed (Kristiania 1878). G. Rasch: Medicinalhistoriske Skitser (Magasin for norsk Laegevidenskab, 108, 1880). E. Gurlt: Geschichte der Chirurgie (vol. 2, 239, 1898). Fr. Grön: Altnordische Heilkunde (Janus, 266, 1908).

SCANDINAVIAN EXPEDITIONS TO THE WHITE SEA

In all probability the region of the White Sea including the lower course of the Dvina was already known to Northmen at the end of the ninth century. The sagas tell us of many expeditions to Bjarmeland, the territory south of the White Sea; e.g., those of Eric Blood-Axe c. 920, of his son Harold Gråfeld c. 965, of Thore Hund and others c. 1026, and of Håkon Magnusson c. 1090. Unfortunately we have little if any definite information about these early voyages, but with regard to two later ones we are on safer ground.

In the year 1217—i.e., in Håkon Håkonsson's time—the following went to Bjarmeland: Ogmund of Spånheim from Hardanger, Svein Sigurdsson from Sogn, Andres of Sjomaeling from Nordmör, all on one ship; and Helge Bograngsson and his men from Hálogaland on another. Svein and Andres went home with their ship the same year. Ogmund traveled southward across Russia to Suzdal, then to the Black Sea and to the Holy Land; he returned to Norway many years later. Helge and his men remained in Bjarmeland and were killed by the natives.

A fleet of four ships was sent in 1222 to avenge Helge's death. It was headed by Andres Skjaldarbrand and Ivar Utvik, and accomplished its purpose, but on the homeward journey Ivar's ship was lost in a whirlpool and its crew perished, save Ivar and one other.

C. R. Beazley: Dawn of modern geography (vol. 2, 1901). Fridtjof Nansen: In northern mists (vol. 2, 135–140, 1911).

III. CHRISTIAN PILGRIMS

WOLFGER VON ELLENBRECHTSKIRCHEN

Last scion of a noble Bavarian family. Bishop of Passau from 1191 to 1204, then patriarch of Aquilèia (at the northern end of the Adriatic sea) to the time of his death in 1218. German churchman, diplomat, and traveler. He pilgrimed to the Holy Land, via Sicily, in 1195–1198. He traveled extensively in the Danubian region and in Italy. The terse account of his travel expenditures, written in Latin before 1209, contains interesting information.

Text—Reiserechnungen. Edited by Ign. Vinc. Zingerle with glossary, index and introduction (120 p., Heilbronn 1877).

Criticism—F. von Krones: Allgemeine deutsche Biographie (vol. 44, 124–126, 1898). A. Potthast: Bibliotheca historica (1120, 1898).

WILBRAND OF OLDENBURG

Wilbrand or Willebrand, Graf of Oldenburg-Wildeshausen. Provost in Zütphen, later canon in Hildesheim; bishop of Paderborn, 1225; bishop of Utrecht from 1228 to his death in 1233 (not 1234). In 1211 he traveled to the Holy Land. Jerusalem was then in Muslim hands. Wilbrand's journey was apparently less a pilgrimage than a reconnaissance. He visited Leo I, king of Armenia (1196–1219), whose help might be expected in their common struggle against the Saracens, and traveled to Cyprus with Hermann of Salza (grandmaster of the Teutonic Knights from 1211 to 1239). His last years in the Utrecht see were largely devoted to the struggle against the Friesians.

Text—J. C. M. Laurent: Reise nach Palästina und Kleinasien (Latin and German, with notes, 77 p. Hamburg 1859); Peregrinatores medii aevi quatuor (Leipzig 1864; 162–190, 1873).
Criticism—R. Röhricht: Bibliotheca geographica Palaestinae (46, 1890). A. Potthast: Bibliotheca historica (1116, 1896). Heyd: Allgemeine deutsche Biographie (vol. 42, 474–476, 1897). J. C. van Slee: ibidem (vol. 43, 260, 1898).

ST. SABBAS OF SERVIA

St. Sabbas (or Sabas, Sava). (I call him Sabbas of Servia to distinguish him from St. Sabbas of Palestine, who died in 531 in very old age, the founder of the laura bearing his name—Mar Sava—in the wilderness of Judah). He was born in the second half of the twelfth century, and died at Tirnova, Bulgaria, in 1237. He was the son of Stephen Nemanya, who was the real founder of the kingdom of Servia (1217). He became a monk at Mt. Athos, and was the first independent archbishop of Servia, 1219. He may thus be considered the founder of the national Servian church. Toward the end of his life (c. 1225) he undertook a pilgrimage to the Holy Land, visiting Egypt and Sinai. He died at Tirnova on his way back to his see. He wrote an account of his journey in Servian.

Text—Sabbas' account was edited by the archimandrite Leonid in Servian and in an old Slavonic translation (Publication no. 5 of the Russian Palestinian Society, 68 p., Petersburg 1884).
Criticism—Henri Thiers: Nouvelle biographie générale (vol. 42, 962, 1863). K. Krumbacher: Byzantinische Litteratur (1059, 1095, 1897). R. Röhricht: Bibliotheca geographica Palaestinae (48, 1890). C. R. Beazley: Dawn of modern geography (vol. 2, 215, 1901).

OTHER CHRISTIAN PILGRIMS TO THE HOLY LAND

To the accounts of pilgrimages dealt with in this chapter may be added in the briefest manner the three following, of which two are anonymous and the third is ascribed to one Thietmar, who cannot be identified. I quote them in chronological order:

(1) One anonymous pilgrim of Soissons (Aisne)—the Anonymus Suessionensis—wrote c. 1205–1207 in Latin, an account of Jerusalem and of the transfer of relics from Constantinople thither.

Alexandre Eusèbe Poquet: Rituale Suessionense (264–270, Laon 1856). Paul Riant: Exuviae sacrae Constantinopolitanae (vol. 1, 1–9, Geneva 1877).

(2) Thietmar (Thietmarus magister). He wrote a Peregrinatio, c. 1217.

Edited by J. C. M. Laurent (84 p., Hamburg 1857). A fourteenth century text derived from this one had been edited before by the Baron St. Genois: Voyages faits en Terre Sainte par Thetmar en 1217 . . . (Mémoires de l'académie belge, 26, 19–58, 1851); and by Titus Tobler: Magistri Thetmari Iter ad terram sanctam (76 p., St. Gall 1851).

(3) Pelerinaiges por aler en Jherusalem (c. 1231).

Melchior de Vogüé: Les églises de la Terre Sainte (444–451, Paris 1860). Henri Michelant and Gaston Raynaud: Itinéraires à Jérusalem (229–236, 1882).

R. Röhricht: Bibliotheca geographica Palaestinae (47, 51, 1890). A. Potthast: Bibliotheca historica (102, 908, 1062, 1060, 1896).

For the pilgrimage of Ogmund of Spånheim, see my note on Scandinavian expeditions to the White Sea.

For the French description of Jerusalem "L'estat de la cité de Jherusalem," see my note on the chronicler Ernoul.

IV. CHRISTIAN TRAVELERS TO THE MONGOL EMPIRE

PIAN DEL CÀRPINE

Giovanni del Pian del Càrpine. Joannes de Plano Càrpini. Often called Càrpini. Italian Franciscan, diplomatist, missionary; first European explorer of the Mongol empire. Born near Perugia c. 1182 (for he was one of the companions of St. Francis of Assisi, born in 1182); towards the end of his life he was archbishop of Antivari; he died in 1252.

Having been placed by Innocent IV (1243–1254) at the head of a diplomatic mission to the Mongols, he left Lyon on April 16, 1245, crossed Europe, Russia, and a large part of Asia, reached the Mongolian capital, Qaraqorum (on the Orkhon, south of lake Baikal), and was back in Lyon in 1247. He had been accompanied successively by two other Franciscans: Stephen of Bohemia left with him from Lyon and went with him as far as Russia; Benedict the Pole joined him in Breslau to act as interpreter.

His Latin relation of this immense journey, Historia Mongolorum quos nos Tartaros appellamus (or Liber Tartarorum), is remarkably impersonal, clear, accurate, matter-of-fact. It is one of the two most important books of its kind before Marco Polo's, the other being the somewhat later one of Rubruquis. It contains an account of Tartar manners and history, which is excellent, and indeed unsurpassed in mediaeval times. Fra Giovanni was not a linguist like Rubruquis, yet he had obtained some knowledge of Slavonic. His account was supplemented with a shorter one by his companion Benedict.

Innocent IV had intrusted to Fra Giovanni a letter addressed to the Great Khān. Fra Giovanni brought back an answer from the Great Khān, Kuyuk, which was discovered in 1920 in the Vatican archives. "This letter written in the Persian and Uighūr languages, sealed with a Mongol seal of Chinese style that had been cut by a Russian seal cutter [Cosmas] and sent by an Italian monk to the Pope is a typical example of the cosmopolitan character of the Mongol empire bridging the gap between the Far East and the West."[1]

Innocent's decision to appeal to the Mongols for help against the Saracens was partly prompted by the tenacious belief in Prester John (see my note, second half of the twelfth century). His decision was reached in 1244 and it was ratified the following year by the Council of Lyon. The mission was first entrusted to the Franciscan, Lawrence of Portugal, but we know nothing of that first effort; it is possible that Lawrence never started.

Text—An abridgment of Càrpini's history was included in Vincent of Beauvais' Speculum historiale. Parts of the original text were printed in Hakluyt's Principal Navigations (vol. 1, 1–117, London 1598). Later partial edition by Pierre Bergeron (Paris 1634).

First complete edition by D'Avezac: Relation des Mongols ou Tartares (383 p., Paris 1838; Recueil de voyages de la Société de géographie, 4). This contained also the first edition of the narrative by Benedict the Pole. English translation by William Woodville Rockhill: The journey of William of Rubruck with two accounts of the earlier journey of John of Pian de Carpine (360 p., Hakluyt Society, London 1900; with abundant notes, bibliography, and index). C. Raymond Beazley: The texts and versions of John de Plano Carpini and William de Rubruquis as printed for the first time by Hakluyt in 1598 together with some shorter pieces (Hakluyt society, 365 p., London 1903). Girolamo Gobulovich: Biblioteca bio-bibliografica della Terra Santa et dell'Oriente francescano (vol. 1, 190–213, 1906). Giorgio Pullé: Historia Mongolorum (Studi italiani di filologia indoiranica, 9, Firenze 1913); Viaggio a' Tartari di frate Giovanni da Pian del Carpine (340 p., 12 pl., Milano 1929; Isis 13, 159).

Criticism—Galsang Gombojew: Randbemerkungen zu Carpine (Mélanges asiatiques de l'Académie des sciences de St. Pétersbourg, vol. 2, 650–666, 1856). Francesco Liverani: Fra Giovanni nel contado di Magione (Perugia 1876). C. R. Beazley: Dawn of modern geography (vol. 2, 279–317, 375–381, 1901); on a hitherto unexamined MS. of Carpini (Geographical Journal, 3 p., December, 1902); article in Encyclopaedia Britannica (1911, with Sir Henry Yule). Joseph de Ghellinck: Les Franciscains en Chine aux XIIIe-XIVe siècles (Xaveriana, nos. 42, 40 p., Louvain 1927).

The original letter from the Grand Khān to the Pope was discovered in 1920 in the Vatican archives by Father Cyril Karalevskyi; it was identified, and published by Paul Pelliot: Les Mongols et la papauté (Revue de l'Orient chrétien, vol. 3, 3–30, 1923).

ASCELIN

Or Anselm (?). Dominican of Lombardy. Traveler and diplomat. He was sent by pope Innocent IV on a diplomatic mission to the Mongols of Persia. The mission included three other Dominicans: Simon of Saint Quentin, Alberic, and Alexander; and two more joined it in Tiflis, Andrew of Longjumeau, and Guichard (Guicciardi, Guiscard) of Cremona. In August 1247 they reached the camp of the Mongol chief, Baijū, at Kars in Armenia (or Gurjīstān, Georgia). They behaved very arrogantly and were badly treated. They returned home in or before 1250. The account of their journey has far less interest than that of the Franciscan mission led shortly before by Pian del Càrpine.

[1] T. F. Carter: Invention of printing (1925, 121; Isis 8, 361).

Text—This journey is known incompletely through the account communicated by Simon of Saint-Quentin to Vincent of Beauvais, who published it in his Speculum historiale. French translation in Pierre Bergeron (d. 1637): Relation des voyages de Tartarie (Paris 1634; often reprinted).

Criticism—C. R. Beazley: Dawn of modern geography (vol. 2, 277, 318, 1901). Henri Cordier: Histoire de la Chine (vol. 2, 392-394, 1920). P. Pelliot: Les Mongols et la Papauté (Revue de l'art chrétien, vols. 23 sq., 1923 sq.).

ANDREW OF LONGJUMEAU

Alias Lonjumeau, Lonciumel, etc. (Longjumeau is the name of a town in Seine-et-Oise, half way between Versailles and Corbeil). French Dominican who accompanied Ascelin in a mission to the western Mongols in 1247. In 1248 St. Louis, being then in Cyprus, sent him on a new mission to the Mongol general Ilchīkadāy, commanding in Persia, who had offered the French king an alliance against the Muslims, and to the Great Khān, Kuyuk. Andrew, together with the Mongol envoy David and others, traveled probably via Lesser Armenia, across Anatolia and Georgia, then south of the Caspian, and by way of Khiva (Khwārizm), Talas and Chimkent; they finally reached Kuyuk's Horde on the Imil. They were badly received, but returned in 1251 to St. Louis with a fantastic report, exaggerating the Christian tendencies of the Mongols. In Talas they saw German prisoners.

C. R. Beazley: Dawn of modern geography (vol. 2, 277-278, 317-320, 1901). P. Pelliot: Les Mongols et la Papauté (Revue de l'orient chrétien, vols. 23 sq., 1923 sq.).

V. EASTERN MUSLIM

YĀQŪT

Abū 'Abdallāh Yāqūt ibn 'Abdallāh Shihāb al-dīn al-Ḥamāwī al-Baghdādī. Muslim traveler and one of the greatest Muslim geographers. Born in Rūm (Asia minor) of Greek parents, c.1179; died at Ḥalab in 1229.

He had been enslaved in youth and had then received the name Yāqūt, meaning jacinth, a precious stone (names of precious things were often given to slaves—e.g., Lūlū, pearl; Kāfūr, camphor); it is said that he later changed this name Yāqūt into Ya'qūb. He was called al-Ḥamāwī because the merchant who had bought him in Baghdād, who caused him to be educated, and who later (1199-1200) enfranchised him, was himself of Ḥamā. He engaged in various trades and traveled extensively from Syria and Egypt in the West to Marw in the East, meeting with many adventures and suffering many hardships.

His main work was a geographical dictionary, the Mu'jam al-buldān. He conceived the plan of it in 1218-1219 while he was enjoying himself in the rich libraries of Marw; he completed the first draft at Mūṣul in 1224, and began the final redaction at Ḥalab in 1228. The Mu'jam al-buldān is one of the most important works of Arabic literature. It is a storehouse of information not simply on geography, but also on history, ethnography, and natural history. It is preceded by an introduction dealing with mathematical, physical, and political geography, the size of the earth, the seven climates, etc. The dictionary proper is arranged in alphabetical order. The astronomical coordinates of places are given. The orthography and vocalization of proper names are carefully established. There are abundant historical notes, biographical sketches of learned men, grammatical discussions, etc.

Yāqūt wrote various other works, notably a very elaborate dictionary of literati, Kitāb irshād al-arīb ilā ma'rifat al-adīb; and a lexicon of places bearing the same names, Kitāb al-mushtarik waḍ'ā wal-mukhtalif (or muftariq) saq'ā.

Text—Ferd. Wüstenfeld: Jācūts geographisches Wörterbuch (6 vols., Leipzig 1866-1873; Arabic edition with most valuable index). C. Barbier de Meynard: Dictionnaire géographique, historique et littéraire de la Perse et des contrées adjacentes extrait du Mo'djem el-bouldan de Jaqout et complété à l'aide de documents arabes et persans pour la plupart inédits (Paris 1871).

A summary of this geographical dictionary entitled Marāṣid al-iṭṭilā' 'alā asmā' al-amkina wal-biqā', was compiled by Abū-l-Faḍā'il 'Abd al-Mu'min ibn 'Abd-al-Ḥaqq Ṣafī al-dīn, who died in 1338-1339. It was edited by T. G. J. Juynboll (6 vols., Leyden 1850-1864). This Marāṣid (observatories) is important because it contains valuable corrections of first hand authority for places in the region around Baghdād. G. Le Strange: Lands of the Eastern Caliphate (15, 1905).

The Mushtarik was edited by F. Wüstenfeld (Göttingen 1846).

The biographical dictionary is being published by David Samuel Margoliouth in the Gibb Memorial Series (vol. 1 appeared in 1907; vol. 7 in 1926).

Criticism—Ibn Khallikān: de Slane's translation (vol. 4, 9-24, 1871).

J. T. Reinaud: Géographie d'Aboulféda (vol. 1, 129-135, 1848). Ferd. Wüstenfeld: Der Reisende Jācūt als Schriftsteller und Gelehrter (13 p., Göttingen 1865); Geschichtschreiber (111, 1881). Friedrich Justus Heer: Die historischen und geographischen Quellen in Jāqūt's geographischen Wörterbuch (Diss., Strassburg 1898). C. Brockelmann: Arabische Litteratur (vol. 1, 479-481, 1898). E. Wiedemann: Biographie von al-Baihaqī nach Jāqūt (Beitr. 28, Sitzungsber. Erlangen, vol. 44, 113-117, 1912). Carra de Vaux: Penseurs de l'Islam (vol. 2, 14-19, 189, 1921). Ernst Honigmann: Die sieben Klimata und die πόλεις ἐπίσημοι (Heidelberg 1929; Isis, 14, 270-276).

'ABD AL-LAṬĪF

See philosophical chapter above.

VI. WESTERN MUSLIM

For al-Ḥasan al-Marrākushī, see mathematical chapter; for Ibn al-Baiṭār, see the medical chapter.

VII. WESTERN JEWISH

SAMUEL BEN SAMSON

Rabbi Samuel bar Simson. Jewish pilgrim. In 1210 he accompanied rabbi Jonathan ben David ha-Kohen of Lunel (Maimonides' famous correspondent), and two other rabbis, to the Holy Land. He traveled as far as Mūṣul, then returned to Palestine on his way back to Europe. He wrote an account of his journey describing mainly the sepulchers of the Saints which he had visited. This was done in the shape of a long letter, the purpose of which was to increase Jewish interest in the Holy Land and stimulate pilgrimages. This account was authenticated by a firman of Jean de Brienne, king of Jerusalem, who seems to have been anxious to attract Jewish settlers. In fact some three hundred Jews left England and France in 1211 to go and settle in the Holy Land, where they were welcomed by King Jean (according to the Shebeṭ Yehudah of Ibn Verga, q.v., second half of the fifteenth century).

Text—French translation with notes by Eliacin Carmoly: Itinéraires de la Terre Sainte (115–167, Bruxelles, 1847). Hebrew text in J. D. Eisenstein: Ozar massaoth. A collection of itineraries by Jewish travelers to Palestine, Syria, etc. (New York 1926; Isis, 11, 147–149).

Criticism—R. Röhricht: Bibliotheca geographica Palaestinae (45, 1890). Samuel Krauss: L'émigration de 300 rabbins en Palestine en l'an 1211 (Revue des études juives, vol. 82, 333–352, 1926). E. N. Adler: Note sur l'émigration en Palestine de 1211 (ibidem, vol. 85, 70–71, 1928).

JACOB ANAṬOLI

See translators from Arabic into Hebrew.

VIII. SYRIAC

JACOB BAR SHAKKŌ

See philosophical chapter.

IX. CHINESE

CHINESE GEOGRAPHICAL DOCUMENTS OF THE FIRST HALF OF THE THIRTEENTH CENTURY

The first volume of Emil Vasilievich Bretschneider's Mediaeval Researches from Eastern Asiatic sources (London 1888, reprinted in 1910) contains English extracts from various Chinese texts dealing with the geography of China and Central Asia in the thirteenth century. The second part of this first volume is devoted mainly to a comparison of western and eastern accounts of the Mongol invasions (1219–1242). It deals also with the Chinese knowledge of the Muslims in the Middle Ages.

Out of the five Chinese itineraries, three belong to the first half of the century.

(1) The Hsi[1] yu[2] lu[4] (4031, 13423, 7386), account of a journey to the West by the great Mongol educator, Yeh[1]-lü[4] Ch'u[3]-ts'ai[2] (12974, 7548, 2662, 11496), already dealt with. This describes Chingiz Khān's expedition into Persia in 1219.

(2) The Pei[3] shih[3] chi[4] (8771, 9896, 923), notes on an embassy to the North, by Wu[1]-ku[3]-sun[1] Chung[4]-tuan[1] (12721, 6188, 10431, 2876, 12138), dated 1220–1221. By "embassy to the north" is meant an embassy to the Mongol court, but as Chingiz Khān was then traveling westward, the envoy of the Chin[1] (2032) emperor traveled also to the west. The text of this narrative forms chapter fourteen of the Kuei[1] ch'ien[2] chih[4] (6419, 1739, 1918), a book composed by Liu[2] Ch'i[2] (7270, 1089) in 1295. But Liu Ch'i was not the real author of the Pei shih chi.

(3) The Hsi[1] yu[2] chi[4] (4031, 13423, 923) by Ch'iu[1] Ch'ang[2]-ch'un[1] (2313, 450, 2854), dated 1221–1224. See below.

Text—The Library of Congress has the Kuei ch'ien chih in vols. 36–38 of the Chih[1] pu[1*] tsu[2*] chai[1] ts'ung[1] shu[1] (1783, 9456, 11840, 234, 12039, 10024); in vols. 84–85 of the Hsüeh[2*] hai[3] lei[4] p'ien[1] (4839, 3767, 6853, 9220); and in vols. 311–314 of the Wu[3] ying[1] tien[4] chü[1] chên[1] pan[3] ts'ung[1] shu[1] (12744, 13308, 11202, 3060, 599, 8588, 12039, 10024).

CH'IU CH'ANG-CH'UN

Ch'iu[1] Ch'ang[2]-ch'un[1] (2313, 450, 2854), Chinese traveler. Taoist monk of great repute at the courts of the Chin and the Sung. Born at Hsi[1]-hsia[2] (4127, 4201),

Têng[1]-chou[1] fu[3] (10858, 2444, 3682), Shantung, in 1148; died at Peking, 1227. His family name was Ch'iu; his personal name Ch'u[3]-chi[1] (2660, 786); hence he is often called Ch'iu Ch'u-chi. In 1221–1224, he made a long journey from his home to Peking, and then through Central Asia to Persia and the Indian frontier, and back, by order of the Mongol emperor, Chingiz Khān. An account of this journey, the Hsi[1] yu[2] chi[4] (4031, 13423, 923), was written by one of his disciples, Li[3] Chih[4]-ch'ang[2] (6884, 1918, 440), and published by another, Sun[1] Hsi[2]* (10431, 4157) in 1228. It includes excellent descriptions of the lands and people of Central Asia, and its geographical value is relatively great.

The Hsi yu chi should not be confused with another work bearing the same title (or more correctly Hou[4] (4025) hsi yu chi—the later Hsi yu chi), a fantastic novel based on the travels of Hsüan Tsang; nor with Hsüan Tsang's own account, the title of which is almost alike, Hsi[1] yü[4]* chi[4] (4031, 13662, 923).

Text—The Chinese text is included in vol. 116 of the Tao[4] ts'ang[4] chi[4]* yao[4] (10780, 11601, 943, 12889), a large collection of Taoist writings. Also in vol. 6 of the collection called Lien[2] yün[1] i[2] ts'ung[1] shu[1] (7109, 13824, almost like 5417, 12039, 10024), Peking, 1848. Both of these editions have prefaces by Sun[1] Hsi[2]* (10431, 4157); both are available in the Library of Congress.

A complete translation into Russian was given by the archimandrite Palladius (Records of the Peking ecclesiastical mission, vol. 4, 1866). Poor and abridged version into French by Guillaume Pauthier (1867). English translations with commentary by E. Bretschneider: Mediaeval researches (vol. 1, 35–108, 1888). This translation is not complete but contains all the essentials relating to history and geography. Ch'iu's numerous poems have been omitted. On the other hand, Bretschneider has added the two interesting letters exchanged between Ch'iu and Chingiz Khān in 1219–1220. Arthur Waley: The travels of an alchemist (174 p., London 1931).

The best edition of the novel known as the Hsi yu chi is the newly annotated one by Dr. Hu[2] Shih[4]* (4930, 10000) and published by the Shanghai Ya[4] tung[1] t'u[2] shu[1] kuan[3] (12810, 12248, 12128, 10024, 6353) in 1928. This edition is in the Library of Congress. This work was translated into English by Timothy Richard: A mission to Heaven (410 p., Shanghai 1913). Richard thought that certain terms of that work revealed Christian (Nestorian) influences; he believed that the author had been converted to Nestorian Christianity, and he gave an allegoric interpretation of his book in that light, considering it as the Pilgrim's Progress of Nestorianism. This theory is unproved and unsound. The Hou hsi yu chi is simply a Taoist satire on Hsüang Tsang's Buddhist account.

Helen M. Hayes: The Buddhist Pilgrim's progress. From the Shi yeu ki, The records of the journey to the Western paradise, by Wu Ch'eng-en (105 p., London 1930?, not seen). See also my note on Hsüan Tsang (vol. 1, 477–478).

The full title of Hsüan Tsang's account is Ta[4] t'ang[2] hsi[1] yü[4]* chi[4] (10470, 10767, 4031, 13662, 923). The Library of Congress has at least the following editions: sŭ[4] pu[4] ts'ung[1] k'an[1] (10291, 9484, 12039, 5861), vols. 301–304; Shou[3] shan[1] ko[2]* s'ung[1] shu[1] (10012, 9663, 6037, 12039, 10024), vols. 43–44; Mo[4]* hai[3] chin[1] hu[2] 8022, 3767, 2032, 4954), vols. 69–71.

Criticism—H. A. Giles: Biographical dictionary (158, 1898). Encyclopaedia inica (109, 241, 1917).

CHAO JU-KUA

Chao[4] Ju[3]-kua[4] (498, 5666, 6295). Born in the imperial family; flourished at h'üan[2]-chou[1] (3187, 2444), Fuhkien, in the first half of the thirteenth century. hinese geographer. Inspector of maritime trade in the great port of Ch'üan chou (i.e., the Zayton of Marco Polo) in Fuhkien. He compiled c. 1225 a treatise entitled Chu^{1} fan^{2} chih^{4} (2571, 3392, 1918), meaning Description of barbarian peoples (or Records of foreign nations), containing valuable ethnographic and commercial information on the peoples known to the Chinese and Muslim sea-traders of his day. It is based largely on personal inquiries but also on previous authorities, chiefly the Ling^{3}-wai^{4}-tai^{4}-ta^{2*} (7220, 12442, 10547, 10479) written c. 1178 by Ch'ou^{1} Ch'ü^{4}-fei^{1} (2450, 3068, 3459). It is divided into two parts, the first of which deals with countries (forty-six chapters: Tongking, Annam, Java, the Arabs, Sicily, etc., the second with products (forty-three chapters: camphor, frankincense, myrrh, dragon's blood, etc.).

The date of the Chu fan chih given above, c.1225, is in accordance with Pelliot's interpretation. But according to Hirth and Rockhill the compilation was made somewhat later, between 1242 and 1258.

Text and translations—The Chinese text was not printed until 1783 when Li^{3} T'iao^{2}-yüan^{2} (6884, 11102, 13744) included it in his collection known as the Han^{2} hai^{3} (3809, 3767), vol. 42. Another edition, practically identical, was included in 1805 by Chang^{1} Hai^{3}-p'êng^{2} (416, 3767, 8885) in his collection entitled Hsüeh^{2*}-ching^{1}-t'ao^{3}-yüan^{2} (4839, 2163, 10838, 13700).

Friedrich Hirth and W. W. Rockhill: Chau Ju-kua; his work on the Chinese and Arab trade in the twelfth and thirteenth centuries (298 p., Imperial Academy of Sciences, St. Petersburg, 1911 (1912). Excellent translation, with notes, map, and elaborate English and Chinese indexes).

The Library of Congress has both ts'ung shu mentioned above, the Han hai and the Hsüeh-ching-t'ao-yüan. It also has a copy of the Ling-wai-tai-ta in vols. 130–132 of the Chih^{1} pu^{1*} tsu^{2*} chai^{1} ts'ung^{1} shu^{1} (1783, 9456, 11840, 234, 12039, 10024).

Criticism—H. A. Giles: Biographical dictionary (66, 1898). Extensive reviews of Hirth and Rockhill's translation by P. Pelliot (T'oung Pao, vol. 13, 1912, 446–481, 1912); by Eduard Schaer (Archiv für Geschichte der Naturwissenschaften, vol. 6, 329–337, 1913); by O. Franke (Ostasiatische Zeitschrift, vol. 2, 98–99, 1913); by A. Vissière (Journal Asiatique, vol. 3, 196–202, 1914); by G. Vacca (Rivista degli studi orientali, vol. 6, 209–214, 1913).

For Ch'üan-chou, see Encyclopaedia sinica (114, 1917).

CHAPTER XXXVII

NATURAL HISTORY

(First Half of Thirteenth Century)

I. LATIN

For Alfred of Sareshel and Peter Gallego, see translators from Arabic into Latin; for Michael Scot, Bartholomew the Englishman, Arnold the Saxon, and Thomas of Cantimpré, see philosophical chapter.

II. VERNACULAR

For the Konungs skuggsjá and other encyclopaedic treatises, see the philosophical chapter; for Henrik Harpestraeng, see the medical chapter.

WALTER OF HENLEY

English "chivaler," later Dominican, who flourished about the middle of the thirteenth century. He served as bailiff, probably for Canterbury. He wrote about the middle of the century a book on husbandry in French, entitled Hosebondrie. It was soon translated into Latin and English, one English version being wrongly ascribed to Grosseteste. It remained the leading book on the subject in England until the appearance of Sir Anthony Fitzherbert's Husbandrie (1523). It contains a reference to the practice of marling; i.e., fertilizing with marl (Pliny, marga; a kind of earth containing clay mixed with calcium carbonate).

Text—Henley's Husbandry, together with an anonymous Husbandry, Seneschaucie and Robert Grosseteste's Rules. Edited by Elizabeth Lamond, glossary and translations by the same; introduction by W. Cunningham (Royal Historical Society, 215 p., London 1890). The Seneschaucie explains the duties of the different officers and servants of a manor.

One of the English versions was printed by Wynkyn de Worde: Boke of Husbandry, whiche Mayster Groshede, sometyme Bysshop of Lincoln, made and translated it out of Frensshe into Englysshe (Unique copy in Cambridge Library).

A similar French text of the thirteenth century, entitled Enseignements agricoles, has been published by Louis Lacour in the Bibliothèque de l'Ecole des Chartes (4e série, vol. 2, 123–141, 367–381, 1856).

Criticism—Dictionary of National Biography (vol. 25, 420, 1891).

WALTON

An Irishman called Walton is said to have invented, about the middle of the thirteenth century, the remarkable system of mussel-culture which is still practiced in the Anse de l'Aiguillon near La Rochelle. I suspect that there is some error about the date. An investigation of this subject in the local archives is very desirable.

George Sarton: Walton, a mediaeval aquiculturist (Isis, 6, 306–310, 1924).

III. FALCONRY

TREATISES ON FALCONRY

The Ars venandi of the emperor Frederick II is by far the most important work of its kind (see my note on him, above), but the deep interest taken by noblemen in that sport is evidenced by the appearance about the same time of many other treatises.

As in the case of Frederick himself, much of that knowledge was of Muslim origin. At least two oriental treatises must have been known to Frederick: the first, an Arabic work by one Moamyn (see my note on Theodore of Antioch); the other, a Persian treatise ascribed to one Yatrib (Ghatrif, Tarif?), in seventy-five chapters; it dealt mainly with the sparrow-hawk. Frederick's natural son, Enzio (born c.1220, king of Sardinia, prisoner in Bologna from 1249 to his death in 1272), patronized Daniel of Cremona, who translated these two treatises from Latin into French. Frederick's own treatise was translated into French before the end of the century.

I may still mention the Provençal poem "Romans dels auzels cassadors" by Deudes de Prades (near Rodez, Aveyron) or Daude de Pradas (beg. of the thirteenth century), and a curious Catalan tract entitled "Lo libre dell nudriment he de la cura dels ocels los quals sepertãye ha cassa." The Catalan text purports to be a translation of a letter addressed to a certain king Ptolemy of Egypt by Aquila Symmachus and Theodotio. This text is referred to in the De falconibus of Albert the Great, but is now represented only by this Catalan version. It deals with the different kinds of hawks used by falconers, their diseases and treatment.

Which of these treatises was the first to be written in any vernacular? It is difficult to answer such a question. Considering that the noble huntsmen, then as now, were not scholars, it is probable that vernacular treatises had been prepared very early for their convenience. It is thus possible that the treatises I have mentioned were preceded by others.

With regard to the Catalan treatise, see my note on the physician, Theodoric Borgognoni.

Text—The Catalian text was published by Nicolas Rigaltius (Rigault), librarian to Louis XIII, Epistola Aquilae Symmachi et Theodotionis ad Ptolemaeum regem Aegypti de re accipitraria catalanica lingua, in his collection entitled Ierakosophion, Rei accipitrariae scriptores (Paris 1612; earlier edition, Basle 1578?)

Criticism—James Edmund Harting: Bibliotheca accipitraria (317 p., 26 pl., London 1891). C. H. Haskins: Studies in mediaeval science (chapter 14, 299-326, 1924); The Latin literature of sport (Speculum, vol. 2, 235-252, 1927). Gunnar Tilander: Etude sur les traductions en vieux français du traité de fauconnerie de Frederic II (Z. für romanische Philologie, vol. 46, 211-290, 1926).

THEODORE OF ANTIOCH

According to Abūl-l-Faraj, Theodore was a Jacobite Christian, who studied ancient learning in Greek and Syriac in Antioch, and later Arabic learning in Mūṣul under Kamāl al-dīn ibn Yūnus. He entered the service of Frederick II sometime before 1236, and cast the emperor's horoscope at Padua in 1239. He acted as his Arabic secretary in 1239-1240; and remained in the imperial service until his own death not long before November 1250. He may be identical with the Theodore of Antioch mentioned in the Romance of Sidrach (q.v.).

He extracted a regimen for the emperor from the Sirr al-asrār (vol. 1, 556, 1927), and translated for him Moamyn's treatise on the care of falcons and dogs, from Arabic into Latin, De scientia venandi per aves. This translation was corrected by the emperor at the siege of Faenza (1240-1241). It is divided into five books: (1) generalities, classification of birds of prey; (2 and 3) their diseases and how to cure them; (4 and 5) dogs. This treatise enjoyed some popularity. It was translated from Latin into French by Daniel of Cremona for Frederick's son Enzio.

Finally this Theodore submitted mathematical questions to Fibonacci, and was a mathematical correspondent of Judah ben Salomon ha-Kohen (in 1237).

I have not been able to identify the Arabic author Moamyn, mentioned above. He is also called Moamus, Mohamin.

Text—Epistola Theodori philosophi ad imperatorem Fridericum edited by Karl Sudhoff: Ein diätetischer Brief an Kaiser Friedrich II (Archiv für Geschichte der Medizin, 9, 1-9, 1915).

Criticism—J. E. Harting: Bibliotheca accipitraria (1891); Moamus is quoted on p. 66, 72, 181, 205). M. Steinschneider: Europäische Übersetzungen (79, 1904). H. Suter: Beiträge zu den Beziehungen Kaiser Friedrichs II. zu zeitgenössischen Gelehrten des Ostens und Westens (Abhdl. zur Geschichte der Naturwissenschaften, Heft 4, 1-8, Erlangen 1922). C. H. Haskins: Studies in mediaeval science (chiefly p. 246-248, 318-319, 1924). Paul Kraenner: Falkenheilkunde (76 p., Berlin 1925; not seen).

IV. EASTERN MUSLIM

For 'Abd al-Laṭīf, Farīḍ al-dīn 'Aṭṭār, Muḥammad al 'Awfī, see the philosophical chapter above.

IBN AL-ṢŪRĪ

Manṣūr (or Abū Manṣūr) ibn abī Faḍl ibn 'Alī Rashīd al-dīn Ibn al-Ṣūrī. One of the most original of Muslim botanists. Born at Ṣūr (Tyre) in 1177-1778; studied medicine in Damascus under 'Abd al-Laṭīf; was attached to a hospital in Jerusalem; served under the Ayyūbid, al-Mu'aẓẓam, and after the latter's death in 1227, under his successor, al-Nāṣir, who appointed him chief of physicians; he finally established himself in Damascus, where he died c. 1242.

He wrote for al-Mu'aẓẓam (ruler of Damascus from 1218 to 1227) a treatise on simple medicines (al-adwiya al mufrada), wherein he discussed the views explained by one of his colleagues, Taj al-dīn al-Bulghārī, in a similar treatise.

He was especially distinguished as a botanist. According to Ibn abī Uṣaibi'a, who herborized with him in the country surrounding Damascus, Ibn al-Ṣūrī traveled extensively and explored the Lebanon range to discover and collect plants. He was accompanied by an artist whose business it was to represent them in color as completely as possible at different stages of their growth. This is, I believe, the earliest definite instance of such illustrations in Arabic literature, but they are unfortunately lost. He was well acquainted with the writings of Dioscorides, Galen, and al-Ghāfiqī (second half of the twelfth century). Strangely enough, Ibn al-Baiṭār does not mention him.

Criticism—Ibn abī Uṣaibi'a (Müller's edition, 1884, vol. 2, 216-219; this is an exceptionally long article). Ḥājī Khalīfa (Fluegel's edition, vol. 1, no. 361, p. 227). For Taj al-dīn al Bulghārī, see ibidem (vol. 6, no. 12624, p. 34).

F. Wüstenfeld: Arabische Aerzte (129, 1840). L. Leclerc: Médecine arabe (vol. 2, 171–173, 1876). Carra de Vaux: Penseurs de l'Islam (vol. 2, 290, 1921).

AL-TĪFĀSHĪ

Abū-l-'Abbās Aḥmad ibn Yūsuf Shihāb al-dīn al-Tīfāshī. Muslim mineralogist who flourished in Egypt and died in 1253–1254.

He wrote, c. 1242, a book on precious stones entitled Kitāb azhār al-afkār fī jawāhir al-aḥjār (Flowers of thoughts on precious stones) divided into twenty-five chapters (one introductory and twenty-four devoted each to a separate stone). For each stone he examines successively the origin, the places where it is found, the qualities, the special properties and applications, the commercial value.

Another work of the same kind, entitled Maṭāli' al-budūr fī manāzil al-surūr (Risings of the full moon over the abodes of joy), is ascribed to him, but also to a later writer of Berber origin, 'Alī ibn 'Abdallāh 'Alā' al-dīn al-Bahā'ī al-Ghuzūlī al-Dimashqī, who died in 1412–1413. It deals with jewels and their proper use, and is divided into fifty chapters.

One of the best known Arabic books on erotics, the Nuzhat al-albāb fī mā lā yūjad fī kitāb, was composed by him, and two other books of the same kind are ascribed to him (Rujū' al-shaikh ilā ṣibāh fī-l-qūwa 'alā-l-bāh; Risāla fī mā yaḥtāj ilaihi al-rijāl wal-nisā' fī 'sti'māl al-bāh mimmā yaḍurr wa-yanfa'). He was apparently well acquainted with the anterior Arabic literature on this popular subject.

Text—A specimen of the Azhār was published by S. F. Ravius (Utrecht 1784). The whole text with Italian translation was edited by count Antonio Raineri[1] (1780–1839): Fior di pensieri sulle pietre preziose di Ahmed Teifascite (Florence 1818). This text is less complete, however, than that contained in the Paris MSS. used by Clément-Mullet. Reprinted by order of count Camillo Raineri Biscia (144 p., Bologna 1906), with a biography of count Antonio (see J. Ruska in Mitt. zur Gesch. der Medizin, vol. 6, 426–428).

Criticism—Ḥājī Khalīfa (vol. 5, 598). Clément-Mullet: Essai sur la minéralogie arabe (Journal asiatique, vol. 11, 5–81, 109–253, 502–522, 1868). Almost exclusively based on al-Tīfāshī. L. Leclerc: Médecine arabe, (vol. 2, 237–239, 1876). Moritz Steinschneider: Arabische Lapidarien (Z. der deutschen morgenländischen Gesellschaft, vol. 49, 244–278, 1895, p. 254–256). C. Brockelmann: Arabische Litteratur (vol. 1, 495, 1898; vol. 2, 55, 1902). Eilhard Wiedemann: Über die Eigenschaften des Jāqūt, Hyazinthes (Sitzungsber. der phys. med. Soz., vol. 52, 220, Erlangen 1922; apropos of the Maṭāli' al-budūr). Julius Ruska: Tabula smaragdina (151–155, Heidelberg 1926); Encyclopaedia of Islām (vol. 4, 751, 1929). J. E. Sarkis: Dictionnaire de bibliographie arabe (651, Cairo 1928).

V. WESTERN MUSLIM

ABŪ-L-'ABBĀS AL-NABĀTĪ

Abū-l-'Abbās Aḥmad ibn Muḥammad ibn Mufarraj, often called al-Nabātī (the botanist) or Ibn al-Rūmiya (son of the Greek or Christian woman), also al-Ḥāfiẓ (he who knows the Qur'ān and ḥadīth by rote). Hispano-Muslim botanist; according to Muslim traditions one of the greatest botanists among them. Born in Seville in 1165–1166 or 1171–1172; died in Spain, probably in Seville, c. 1239–1140.

[1] Family name, Biscia.

His knowledge of plants was primarily derived from his direct study of them, and he seems to have been interested in them for their own sake, not simply for medical purposes. He made many botanical excursions in Spain and across the Strait; then c. 1217 he traveled eastwards, in North Africa, Egypt and further on, to complete his botanical investigations and perform the Pilgrimage. The Ayyūbid sulṭān, al-'Ādil Sayf al-dīn (1199–1218), tried to retain him in Cairo, but al-Nabātī remained only long enough to collect the ingredients necessary for the king's treacle, and he then proceeded to Syria and 'Irāq, where he learned to know many plants which do not grow in the West. He finally returned to Spain (via Sicily?).

He wrote an account of his journey, Kitāb al-riḥla. Judging by the extracts that have come down to us, it dealt primarily with his observations of plants, many of which were new; e.g., those relative to plants growing along the shores of the Red Sea. Two other books are ascribed to him: Explanation of the names of simples in Dioscorides, and Treatise on the composition of drugs.

His works are known only through the abundant quotations of his famous disciple, Ibn al-Baiṭār.

Criticism—Ibn abī Uṣaibi'a (Müller's edition, vol. 2, 81, 1884). Hājī Khalīfa (Flügel's edition, vol. 5, no. 10130, 86, 1850).

F. Wüstenfeld: Arabische Aerzte (118, 1840). Ernst H. F. Meyer: Geschichte der Botanik (vol. 3, 233–236, 1856). L. Leclerc: Médecine arabe (vol. 2, 244, 1876).

IBN AL-BAIṬĀR

See medical chapter.

VI. HINDU

For Śārṅgadhara and Narahari, see medical chapter.

VII. CHINESE

CHAO JU-KUA

See geographical chapter.

CH'ÊN JÊN-YÜ

Ch'ên[2] Jên[2]-yü[4]* (658, 5627, 13630). Flourished c. 1245. Chinese botanist. He wrote in 1245 a treatise on mushrooms, Chün[4] p'u[3] (3298, 9515), dealing with eleven species obtainable at T'ai[2] chou[1] (10583, 2444), Chehkiang. The purpose was agricultural rather than scientific. An antidote is given at the end.

Text—The Library of Congress has the Chün p'u in vol. 122 of the Mo[4]* hai[3] chin[1] hu[2] (8022, 3767, 2032, 4954); in vol. 106 of the Shuo[1]* fu[1] (9598, 3650); and in vol. 8 of the Chu[1] ts'ung[1] pieh[2]* lu[4]* (2549, 12039, 9155, 7386).

Criticism—A. Wylie: Chinese literature (152, 1902).

CHIA SSŬ-TAO

Chia[3] Ssŭ[4]-tao[4] (1181, 10289, 10780). Chinese minister of State, and general, who lived in the first half of the thirteenth century and was one of the cricket fanciers famous in history. He wrote the earliest treatise on crickets, Ts'u[4]* chih^{1*} ching^{1} (11870, 1812, 2122), which contains much information on the subject. Indeed by that time the Chinese were already very familiar with crickets, and had developed considerable lore on their rearing, training and medical care. The keeping of crickets in cages to enjoy their chirping goes back at least to the T'ang; the sport of cricket fights was developed under the Sung. A new edition of Chia's treatise with additional matter, was prepared by Chou^{1} Li^{3}-ching^{4} (2450, 6952, 2131) of the Ming; it is in this form that it has come down to us, being still the most elaborate and authoritative work on the subject.

Another Ming author, Liu^{2} T'ung^{2} (7270, 12270), wrote Records of crickets, Ts'u^{4*} chih^{1*} chih^{4} (11870, 1812, 1918), and a treatise bearing this same title was also written by Yüan^{2} Hung^{2} Tao^{4} (13739, 5275, 10780) who flourished during the Wan Li period (1573–1620). Finally, as I may have no other occasion to speak of this, I shall still mention the treatise on crickets, Ts'u^{4*} chih^{1*} p'u^{3} (9515), written by Fang^{1} Hsü^{4*} (3435, 4760) of the Manchu dynasty. The Mirror of flowers, Hua^{1} ching^{4} (5002, 2170), written by Ch'ên^{2} Fu^{2}-yao^{2} (658, 3613, 12916) in 1688, also contains several sections on crickets.

The Chinese knew that the chirping was caused by the motion of the wings. Of the many species of crickets distinguished and used by them, females are kept only of one, the black tree cricket (Homoeogryllus japonicus), which they call Golden Bell, chin^{1}-chung^{1}-êrh^{2} (2032, 2893, 3333), because they say this is the only species for which the presence of females is necessary to induce the male chirping.

Text—The following editions are available in the Library of Congress:

The Ts'u chih ching by Chia Ssŭ-tao, in vol. 34 of the I^{2} mên^{2} kuang^{3} tu^{2*} (5397, 7751, 6397, 12064).

The Ts'u chih chih by Liu T'ung, in a separate undated edition.

The Ts'u chih chih by Yüan Hung Tao, in vol. 158 of the Shuo^{1*} fu^{1} (9598, 3650).

The Hua ching, printed in 1783, in 3 vols. and six chüan. The Library of Congress also has the Pi^{4} chuan^{2} hua^{1} ching^{4} (8932[2], 2703, 5002, 2170) in four volumes and six chüan.

Criticism—Berthold Laufer: Insect musicians and cricket champions of China (27 p., 12 pl., Field Museum, Chicago 1927; Isis, 10, 510–511).

[2] I give Giles's transcription of 8932, pi^{4}, but it is more commonly pronounced mi^{4}.

CHAPTER XXXVIII

MEDICINE

(First Half of Thirteenth Century)

I. TRANSLATORS FROM ARABIC INTO LATIN

For Theodore of Antioch, see chapter on natural history; for Philip of Tripolis and Stephen of Saragossa, see chapter on translators.

II. ITALIAN

ADAM OF CREMONA

"Cantor ecclesiae." He composed for the emperor Frederick II a treatise on the hygiene of a crusading army or of a large body of pilgrims: Regimen iter agentium vel peregrinantium. This was probably written before the time appointed for the crusade which the emperor had planned to undertake in August, 1227, but had to abandon because of the occurrence of a plague. It is an elaborate treatise in three books: the first dealing with diet and sleep, camping, exercising, delousing, bathing, bloodletting and cupping, sea sickness, etc.; the second, with fatigue and rest, the care of feet; the third, with the religious purpose of a crusade, i.e. with the soldier's morale; the first book is by far the longest (86 p. out of 96).

Text—Fritz Hönger: Ärztliche Verhaltungsmassregeln auf dem Heerzug ins Heilige Land für Kaiser Friedrich II, geschrieben von Adam v. Cremona (Diss., 120 p., Leipzig 1913; with dietetic and medical glossary).
Criticism—Karl Sudhoff: Ärztliche Regimina für Land- und Seereisen aus dem 15. Jahrhundert (Archiv für Geschichte der Medizin, vol. 4, 263–281, 1911).

ROLAND OF PARMA

Rolandus Parmensis. Sometimes called Rolando Capelluti or Capezzuti. He may have belonged to the Capelluti family of Parma, yet it is better to avoid calling him so lest he be confused with the physician of that name who flourished in the second half of the fifteenth century.

Italian surgeon, disciple of Roger of Salerno. He flourished in Parma and Bologna about the beginning of the thirteenth century. He wrote the so-called Chirurgia rolandina, which is an elaboration of Roger's Practica chirurgiae. It is more than a mere commentary and shows deeper traces of Arabic influence.

An extensive commentary on both Roger's Practica and the Rolandina was composed, probably in France, in the second half of the thirteenth century, by four masters. It is entitled Glossulae quatuor magistrorum super chirurgiam Rogerii et Rolandi. The Arabic tendencies are even more strongly marked in this commentary than in the Rolandina.

The Rolandina was translated into Hebrew at least once. One Hebrew text is entitled Sefer ha-ḥabburot ve ha-nega'im (Book of ulcers and plagues); another, Rolandina.

Text—The Rolandina was published in the Collectio chirurgica veneta (third edition; Venice 1499; and following editions).

Giovanni Carbonelli: La Chirurgia di Rolando da Parma detto dei Capezzuti. Riproduzione del Codice latino n. 1382 della Bibliotheca Casanatense, Roma. Volgarizzamento e note (24 p., 56 pl. facsimile in color, Roma 1927).

Glossulae quatuor magistrorum edited by S. De Renzi: Collectio salernitana (vol. 2, 497–724, 1853).

Criticism—M. Steinschneider: Hebraeische Übersetzungen (830, 1893). E. Gurlt: Geschichte der Chirurgie (vol. 1, 702–720, 1898). Waldemar Linge: Die Bologneser Roger Glosse des Rolando Capelluti (Diss., 33 p., Leipzig 1919). Analysis of the Rolandina and comparison with the surgery of Roger (Isis, 4, 585). Oskar Schwind: Zahnärztliches bei den italienischen Chirurgen des 13. Jahrhunderts und bei Guy de Chauliac (Diss., 50 p., Leipzig 1924). Davide Giordano: Sulla posizione inversa in chirurgia (Riv. di storia d. scienze, 16, 189–192, 1925). Showing that Rolando recommended the use in certain cases of the declive position, a practice which is thus much older than is generally believed (Isis, 8, 742).

JOANNES JAMATUS

Also Jamaticus, Jammarius, Jamerius. Italian surgeon who flourished in South Italy about the same time as Roland of Parma, probably c. 1230–1252 (Sudhoff). He wrote a surgical compendium in nine books, based on Roger's work with which it has much in common, but also on personal observations.

Text—P. Pansier: Cyrurgia Johannis Jamarii (Janus, vol. 8, 304–309, 359–362, 426–431, 1903). Edition of book IX only—i.e., the antidotarium—from Oxford and Paris MSS. First complete edition by Jul. Leopold Pagel: Chirurgia Jamati (98 p., Berlin 1909).

Criticism—F. Arthur Saland: Die Chirurgie des Jamerius nach den Fragmenten des Guy de Chauliac (Diss., Berlin 1895). E. Gurlt: Geschichte der Chirurgie (vol. 1, 720, 1898). M. Neuburger: Geschichte der Medizin (vol. 2, 308, 1911). K. Sudhoff: Beiträge zur Geschichte der Medizin (vol. 2, 391–394, 1918; Joannis Jamati Chirurgia quae dicitur thesaurus secretorum).

HUGH BORGOGNONI

Ugo da Lucca. Hugh of Lucca (in Tuscany). Italian physician and surgeon. Born in the third quarter of the twelfth century, flourished in Bologna in 1214 and following years; in 1219 he accompanied the Bolognese Crusaders to Syria and Egypt and attended the siege of Damietta conducted by Jean de Brienne; he died c. 1252–1258, probably in Bologna, in very old age.

He may be called the founder of the surgical school of Bologna (c. 1214). Various simplifications in the treatment of luxations, fractures, and wounds are ascribed to him, also the sublimation of arsenic.

Three of his four sons were physicians, but only one of them, Theodoric, became famous (i.e., assuming that Theodoric was his son, which is uncertain). It is difficult if not impossible to say exactly which improvements were invented by Hugo, and which by this son Theodoric.

THEODORIC BORGOGNONI

Teodorico Borgognoni, Theodoricus Cerviensis. Italian physician. Son and disciple of Hugh Borgognoni. Born at Lucca in 1205; died at Bologna on Christmas eve, 1298.

He assumed the Dominican habit; was penitentiary to Innocent IV (pope from 1243 to 1254); bishop of Bitonto (Bari delle Puglie) from 1262 to 1266, during which time he resided in Lucca; and bishop of Cervia (near Ravenna) from 1266 to 1298, with residence in Bologna.

His treatises, De sublimatione arsenici, de aluminibus et salibus, are lost.

A treatise of his on horse medicine, Practica equorum (Liber de medela equorum; Mulomedicina) exists in Latin, Italian, and Catalan. A treatise on falconry is extant in Catalan.

His main work is a treatise on surgery (Cyrurgia), which he composed while he was penitentiary to Innocent IV, thus possibly before the middle of the century. He prepared a new edition when bishop of Bitonto (1262–1266) and dedicated it to Andreas, bishop of Valencia (bishop from 1248 to 1279). This circumstance may explain the existence of an excellent Catalan translation (and of the other Catalan translations of his works). There are also translations into Spanish, Italian, French, English, German, and at least one into Hebrew. One Hebrew text seems to have been translated from the Spanish (or Catalan?).

He developed his father's method for the treatment of wounds without festering, dressing them preferably with wine. He suggested improvements in the use of the spongia soporifera to induce a state of narcosis; the use itself can be traced to a much earlier date, at least to the ninth century and possibly to Hellenistic times.[1] He made a careful use of mercury salts in various skin diseases, and observed the resultant salivation.

Some doubts have been raised with regard to the relationship between Theodoric and Hugh. It is certain that the surgeon Theodoric was a disciple of Hugh, but less so that he was his son and a Borgognoni. One critic (L. Karl) has gone so far as to suggest that Theodoric was not an Italian, but a Catalan. This is unproved; the existence of Catalan texts of his works can be explained otherwise.

Text—Theodoric's Cyrurgia was published together with those of Guy of Chauliac and others (Venice 1498). Later editions: Venice 1499, 1500, 1513, 1519. Ars chirurgica, Venice 1546.

Antoine Thomas: Traduction provençale abrégée de la Mulomedicina de Teodorico Borgognoni, suivie de recettes pour le vin (Romania, vol. 40, 353–370, 1911).

The Catalan treatise De cura accipitrum was edited by Nicholas Rigault: Rei accipitrariae scriptores (vol. 2, 185–200, Paris 1612). Rigault's collection not being available to me, I had no means of checking this, and of finding out whether or not this Catalan treatise is different from the Epistolae Aquilae Symmachi et Theodotionis mentioned above in the section on falconry.

Criticism—M. Steinschneider: Hebraeische Übersetzungen (832, 1893). E. Gurlt: Geschichte der Chirurgie (vol. 1, 740–753, 1898). Eugen Perrenon: Die Chirurgie des Hugo von Lucca nach den Mitteilungen bei Theodoric (Diss., Berlin, 1899). L. Moulé: Histoire de la médicine vétérinaire (Deuxième période, deuxième partie, 31, Paris 1900). Alberto Vedrani: Gli scienziati italiani (vol. I, 1923, 312–320). A. Deffarge: Histoire critique des anesthésiques anciens et en particulier des éponges somnifères à base de drogues végétales (Thesis, Toulouse 1928; not seen). Louis Karl: La chirurgie, le traitement des chevaux et des oiseaux (en latin et en catalan) par Théodoric le Catalan (Revue des bibliothèques, 18 p., Paris 1928); Theodoric der Catalane, Theodoricus von Cervia und Theodorus von Kalabrien (Archivum romanicum, vol. 12, 482–499, 1928); Théodoric et sa chirurgie (Bull. de la Société française d'histoire de la médecine, vol. 23, 140–183, 1929). Davide

[1] Karl Sudhoff in Archiv für Geschichte der Medizin (vol. 13, 127, 1921).

Giordano: Sulla patria e sulla chirurgia di frate Teodorico (Rivista di storia delle scienze mediche, anno 21, 3–22, 1930); Ancora sulla identità di Teodorico (o Tederico) autore della Chirurgia "filia principis" con Teodorico figlio di Ugone, vescovo di Cervia, e prima di Bitonto (ibidem, anno 21, 133–137, 1930).

For the medical regulations promulgated by Frederick II, see the note devoted to him at the beginning of the philosophical chapter, above.

III. FRENCH

AGILINUS

Gualterus Agilinus (or Agulinus, Aquilinus). Walter Agilinus. Gauthier Agilon (?). Salernitan physician who flourished probably about the middle of the thirteenth century and was probably a Frenchman. He was influenced by Giles of Corbeil (second half of the twelfth century). His main works are a Summa medicinalis which is a complete special pathology and therapeutics based on uroscopy, and a Compendium urinarum which appears to be simply an elaboration of earlier writings on the subject.

He also wrote Liber pulsuum; Glossulae super versus Aegidii (lost); De febribus; Summa or Practica; De dosi medicinarum. Two treatises ascribed to him were translated into Hebrew. The Peraḥ ha-refuah (Flower of medicine) and the Ma'amar ba-eresim (Treatise on poisons). The second, dealing with four kinds of poisons, was translated by Jacob ben Joseph ha-Levi (c. 1297–1301).

Text—Paul Diepgen: Gualteri Agiloni Summa medicinalis erstmalig ediert mit einer vergleichender Betrachtung älterer medizinischen Kompendien des Mittelalters (Studien zur Geschichte der Medizin, 232 p., Leipzig 1911; excellent edition).

Julius Pfeffer: Das Compendium urinarum des Gualterus Agulinus (Diss., Berlin 1891).

Criticism—Emile Littré: Histoire littérarie de la France (vol. 21, 411–415, 1847). Salvatore de Renzi: Storia documentata della scuola di Salerno (2. ed., 421–423, 1857). M. Steinschneider: Hebraeische Übersetzungen (800, 1893). F. Hartmann: Die Litteratur von Früh- und Hochsalerno (37–38, 1919).

WILLIAM OF CONGENIS

William of Congeinna (Conienniis, Congenie?) also called Burgensis. Unknown physician who flourished after Roger of Salerno and before Yperman—probably about the middle of the thirteenth century in southern France. He was a master of Montpellier. (The places to which the names Congenis and Burgensis refer cannot be identified; Burgensis is of course extremely vague; there is a place called Congianus in north-eastern Sardinia).

He wrote a Latin treatise on surgery in five books. The first two books and the first part of the third are directly derived from Roger's Practica; the rest is more original but unimportant. William's treatise was translated into Hebrew.

Text—Julius Pagel: Die Chirurgie des Wilhelm von Congeinna. Fragment eines Collegienheftes nach einer Handschrift der Erfurter Amploniana (86 p., Berlin 1891). Karl Sudhoff: Beiträge zur Geschichte der Chirurgie im Mittelalter (vol. 2, 297–384, 1918; Domini et magistri Willehelmi de Congenis, Burgensis zu Montpellier, Scriptum cirurgiae, sowie dazugehörige Notulae cirurgiae eines Schülers).

Criticism—M. Steinschneider: Hebraeische Übersetzungen (801, 1893). E. Gurlt: Geschichte der Chirurgie (vol. 1, 722, 1898). K. Sudhoff: Gedanken über die Ausbildung chirurgischer Operateure an den Hochschulen im 13. Jahrhundert (Mitt. zur Geschichte der Medizin, vol. 17, 294–295, 1918). R. Ganszynieč: Zur Chirurgie des Wilhelm de Congenis (Archiv für Geschichte der Medizin, 13, 166–170, 1921).

IV. SPANISH

STEPHEN OF SARAGOSSA

See translators from Arabic into Latin.

V. ENGLISH

RICHARD OF WENDOVER

Richard the Englishman. Ricardus Anglicus; Ricardus Parisiensis. Flourished in Paris; died in London in 1252. English physician, anatomist (?), alchemist (?). Physician to pope Gregory IX from 1227 to the latter's death in 1241. After 1241 he flourished in Paris; and later still in London, where he was for a time canon of St. Paul's.

Author of many medical writings, notably the Micrologus, a brief medical encyclopaedia based on the Greek and Arabic knowledge available in Latin translations. The Practica, the Anatomia, and some of the other writings ascribed to him, were probably parts of the Micrologus.

The ascription of the Anatomia to him is not absolutely certain. This so-called Anatomia Ricardi Anglici has been identified with the De anatomia vivorum, ascribed to Galen and included in many early editions of Galen. Whoever the author, it was written c. 1210–1240, probably c. 1225. It is largely based on the translation of Ibn Sīnā's Qānūn by Gerard of Cremona of which it includes many passages copied verbatim. Much space is devoted to explaining the differences between Aristotle and Galen as to the origin of the veins and the relative importance of the heart in comparison with the brain and the liver; the conclusion is in Aristotle's favor. This text should not be confused with the Anatomia Ricardi Salernitani, which is a little earlier (see my note on Richard of Salerno, second half of twelfth century).

An alchemical treatise, Correctorium alchymiae, is also ascribed to him.

Text—The Anatomia Ricardi Anglici was edited by Robert von Töply (Vienna 1902). Töply believed himself to be the first editor of this text, not realizing that it had been printed many times before under the title De anatomia vivorum among Galen's works. English translation, partly based on the consideration of a new MS. (Chartres, middle or second half of the thirteenth century) by George W. Corner: Anatomical texts of the earlier Middle Ages (Washington 1927; Isis, 9, 452–456). K. Sudhoff: Der Micrologus-Text der Anatomia (Archiv für Geschichte der Medizin, 19, 209–239, 1927; Isis, 11, 174).

Hermann Seyfert: Die Flebotomia Richardi Anglici (Diss., 15 p., Leipzig 1924; text without notes).

Correctorium alchymiae. Strassburg 1581; again 1596.

Criticism—E. Littré: Richard médecin (Histoire littéraire de la France, vol. 21, 383–393, Paris 1847). S. de Renzi: Collectio salernitana (vol. 3, 345, 1854; vol. 4, 608, 1856). C. L. Kingsford: Dictionary of national biography (vol. 48, 201–202, 1896). John Ferguson: Bibliotheca chemica (vol. 2, 270–272, 1906). K. Sudhoff: Der Wiener Cod. lat. 1634 und die Anatomia Ricardi Anglici (Archiv für Geschichte der Medizin, vol. 8, 71, 1914). H. H. Beusing: Leben und Werke des Richardus Anglicus und seine Schrift Signa (Diss., Leipzig 1922).

GILBERT THE ENGLISHMAN

Gilbertus Anglicus. English physician, who was chancellor of Montpellier in 1250. He wrote a number of medical treatises, of which by far the most important was his Compendium medicinae (also called Lilium or Laurea medicinae). It is a good compilation of Salernitan and Arabic medicine, comprehensive and up-to-date. It is divided into seven books: (1) fevers; (2) diseases of the head, hair, and nerves; (3) of the eyes and face; (4) of the external members; (5 and 6) internal diseases; (7) genito-urinary diseases, gout, cancer, skin diseases, poisons, etc. It closes with two very interesting chapters on the hygiene of travel, suggesting that Gilbert must have been a seasoned traveler. It contains some interesting nosological descriptions; e.g., leprosy, variola, rubeola. Gilbert was the first to recognize the contagious nature of smallpox; he emphasized the importance of the surgical treatment of cancer; he advised travelers to use distilled water, and sea-travelers to eat fruit. The surgical part (fifty chapters) of the Compendium follows closely the Chirurgia of Roger of Salerno, but not the Rolandina. It must be added that the Compendium contains also a good number of magical and irrational recipes.

The Compendium, or at any rate extracts from it, was translated into Hebrew, Qiẓẓur ha-refuah, by Judah ben Solomon Nathan (1362).

If one accepts, as I have done, the identity of Gilbert with the Chancellor of Montpellier of 1250, his activity is dated. But this identity is not entirely proved. The authenticity of one of the minor writings, a collection of recipes entitled "Experimenta magistri Gilliberti cancellarii montepessulani," is doubtful. However, internal evidence leads to a similar date. For Gilbert quotes Richard of Wendover and Ibn Rushd; he follows Roger's Practica, but not the Rolandina; on the other hand he is often quoted in the Thesaurus pauperum of Peter of Spain. It is thus practically certain that the Compendium was composed about the middle of the thirteenth century, and rather before the middle than after. The fact that Gilbert was called the Englishman proves that he lived outside of England.

Text—First edition, corrected by Michael of Capella: Compendium medicinae Gilberti Anglici tam morborum universalium quam particularium non tantum medicis sed et cyrurgicis utilissimum (Lyon 1510).

Second edition. Laurea anglicana seu compendium totius medicinae (Geneva 1508).

P. Pansier: Experimenta magistri Gilliberti, cancellari montispessulani. Publiés d'après le MS. de la Bibliothèque nationale de Paris avec introduction historique (Janus, vol. 8, 20–25, 65–69, 141–147, 1903). Pansier says that these Experimenta are certainly from another author than the Compendium.

Criticism—Emile Littré: Histoire littéraire de la France (vol. 21, 393–403, 1847). C. L. Kingsford: Dictionary of national biography (vol. 21, 318, 1890). M. Steinschneider: Hebraeische Übersetzungen (798, 1893). E. Gurlt: Geschichte der Chirurgie (vol. 2, 148–157, 1898). M. Neuburger: Geschichte der Medizin (vol. 2, 369, 1911). Henry E. Handerson: Gilbertus Anglicus (77 p., Cleveland 1918; Isis, 3, 325). Martin Seidemann: Zahnärztliches in den Werken des Gilbertus Anglicus (Diss., 22 p., Leipzig 1922; Isis, 5, 501). Lynn Thorndike: History of magic (vol. 2, 477–487, 1923).

For Alfred of Sareshel, see translators from Arabic into Latin; for Michael Scot and Robert Grosseteste, see philosophical chapter; for William the Englishman, see mathematical chapter.

VI. WELSH

The mediaeval medicine of Wales is represented by a series of texts called Meddygon Myddvai; i.e., The physicians of Myddvai (Myddveu or Myddfai, not far from Llandeilo, in Carmarthenshire). The earliest of these texts is traditionally supposed to have been written about the middle of the thirteenth century by one Rhiwallon, the most famous leech of his time, and the earliest of a long series who succeeded one another from father to son, in Myddfai, down to the eighteenth century.

The scientific value of these texts is very small, but they are most interesting from the ethnographic point of view.

Text—The physicians of Myddvai, Meddygon Myddfai, or The medical practice of the celebrated Rhiwallon and his sons, of Myddvai, in Caermarthenshire, physicians to Rhys Gryg, Lord of Dynevor and Ystrad Towy, about the middle of the thirteenth century. From ancient MSS. in the libraries of Jesus College, Oxford, Llanover, and Tonn; with an English translation; and the legend of the Lady of Llyn y Van. Translated by John Pughe, and edited by John Williams ab Ithel. Published for the Welsh MSS. Society (500 p., Llandovery 1861). Celtic text with English translation; the edition and translation being equally careless. Brief note on weights and measures.

P. Diverres: Le plus ancien texte des Meddygon Myddveu (315 p., Paris 1913). Better text with a French translation, a long historical and philological introduction, a glossary of plant names (p. 165–222), elaborate bibliography, and index.

New edition in preparation by the Wellcome Historical medical museum, announced in a pamphlet issued by that museum (14 p., 18 fig., London 1928).

VII. GERMAN

We have but very few documents on contemporary German medicine. These documents are generally more interesting from the folkloric and philologic than from the purely scientific point of view.

I can quote only two memoirs, and as neither was available to me, I am not quite sure that they belong to this period.

C. Külz and (Frau) Trosse-Külz: Das Breslauer Arzneibuch (c. 190 p., Dresden 1905). A dispensatory in Middle-High German taken from a MS. (R 291) in the Stadtbibliothek of Breslau. The MS. dates from the thirteenth or fourteenth century. See Mitteilungen zur Geschichte der Medizin (vol. 3, 484, 1904; vol. 13, 560–564, 1914).

Hermann Fischer: Mittelhochdeutsche Receptare aus bayerischen Klöstern und ihre Heilpflanzen (Mitt. der bayer. botan. Gesell., vol. 4, 69–75, 1926); Mittelalterliche Pflanzenkunde (München, 1929; Isis, 15, 367).

VIII. SCANDINAVIAN

RAFN SVEINBJÖRNSSON

See geographical chapter.

HENRIK HARPESTRAENG

"Medicus et canonicus Roschildensis;" physician to Eric IV Waldemarssön (king of Denmark from 1241 to 1250); born c. 1164; died in 1244; buried at Roskilde, Denmark. The earliest Scandinavian writer of note on natural history and medicine. He has been identified with Henricus Dacus, or Henricus de Dacia[2] and Henri de Danemarche, and seems to have stayed at Orléans and perhaps at Salerno. His works are: (1) a tract about laxative remedies (in Latin); (2) astrological papers and prognostications (among these are rules for bloodletting, written for King Eric); (3) herbal; (4) papers on hygiene, diagnosis and surgery; (5) perhaps a medical tract, from head to foot, of the Salernitan type.

Certain lapidaries and cookery books have been arbitrarily ascribed to him. His sources are al-Rāzī, Ibn Sīnā, Macer Floridus, Constantine the African, Copho, and Nicholas of Salerno. The lapidary (edited by Molbech and later by Kristensen) is derived from Marbode.

Text—I. *Icelandic*: (1) A fragmentary Laekningabók, derived from Macer, edited from Codex Arnamagnaeanus 655 by Konrad Gislason: Fire og fyrretyve for en stor Deel forhen utrykte Pröver af oldnordisk Sprog og Litteratur (Copenhagen 1860). German translation of this text by F. Grön in Pharmacia (nos. 19–20, 1906).

(2) Medical treatise containing several incantations and magic formulas partly written in runes. The fragment edited by Gislason is included in it, and it also contains eighteen chapters of Harpestraeng's Simplicia. K. Kålund: Den islandske laegebog Codex Arnamagnaeanus 434 a in 12° (Kgl. d. Vid. Selsk. Skr., 6. R., hist. og filos. Afd., 6, 4; Copenhagen 1907).

(3) Codex Arnamagnaeanus 194, in 8°, written in 1387, contains extracts from articles on seven simples from Harpestraeng's Herbarium. Edited by K. Kålund in Alfraeði Islenzk (vol. 1, 1908).

(4) A text found in Dublin has been edited by Henning Larsen but is as yet unpublished; see my note on Thorleif Björnsson (second half of the fifteenth century).

II. *Swedish:* Seven MSS.; edited in G. E. Klemming: Läke- och Orteböcker från Sveriges medeltid (Stockholm, 1883–1886). The first of these is a medical treatise describing diseases a capite ad calcem. The other texts are partly derived from Pliny and Bartholomaeus Anglicus.

III. *Norwegian:* Marius Haegstad: Gamalnorsk fragment av H. Harpestreng (Vid. Selsk. Skrifter, hist. Kl., Kristiania 1906).

IV. *Danish:* C. Molbech: H. Harpestraeng's Danske Laegebok (Copenhagen 1826; contains two herbals and a lapidary). Marius Kristensen: Harpestraeng Gamle danske Urteböger, Stenböger og Kogeböger (Copenhagen 1908; including also other Scandinavian works of the same kind).

V. *Latin:* Henricus Dacus: De simplicibus laxativis udgivet for förste gang af J. W. S. Johnsson (98 p., Copenhagen 1914; with abundant commentary in Danish; Isis, 4, 137). French translation by Johnsson in Janus (vol. 22, 27–55, 61–114, 1917).

VI. *Medical anonymous works of the same time or somewhat later*—V. Såby: Det Arnamagnaeanske håndskrift 187 in 8° indeholdende en dansk Laegebog (Copenhagen 1886). Poul Hauberg: En middelalderlig dansk Laegebog (102 p., Copenhagen 1927; Isis, 10, 128). Marius Haegstad: Eit Stykke av ei austlandsk Laekjebok fraa 14 Hundradaaret A.M. 673 a (Kristiania 1913; Norwegian texts).

[2] In this and other Scandinavian names the word Dacia does not refer of course to the Roman province, situated north and later south of the Danube. At some later time Dacia came to mean Denmark, but later still this term was used to designate the ecclesiastical province extending over the three Scandinavian Kingdoms. This final extension may be somewhat dated by the fact that the Dominicans and Franciscans reached Denmark respectively in 1221 and 1222. Thus after Roman times, but before 1221, Dacia meant Denmark; after 1222, Dacia may mean Denmark or Scandinavia. (J. W. S. Johnsson, Janus, vol. 22, 29, 1917).

Criticism—Max Höfler: Zur altgermanischen Heilkunde (Janus, vol. 8, passim, 1903). Fredrik Grön: Altnordische Heilkunde (Janus, vols. 12 and 13, passim, 1907, 1908). Ernest Wickersheimer: Maitre Henri de Danemark, médecin à Orléans sous le règne de Philippe-Auguste (Bull. soc. franç. hist. méd., vol. 14, 243–245, 1920). J. W. S. Johnsson: H. Harpestraeng (Isis, 4, 13–16, 1921; summary with bibliography). T. Reichhorn-Kjennerud: En oversigt over og karakteristik av de gamle nordiske laegeböker (Tidsskrift for den norske Laegeforening, nos. 8–10, 1924). Poul Hauberg: Salernoskolen og dens Indflydelse paa dansk medicinsk Literatur (Archiv for Pharmaci og Chemi, 1928; Isis, 12, 400).

This note was kindly revised by Henning Larsen of Iowa City, and twice by the late J. W. S. Johnsson of Copenhagen.

IX. EASTERN MUSLIM

For Ibn al-Sā'ātī, see chapter on physics; for 'Abd al-Laṭīf, see the philosophical chapter; for Ibn al-Ṣūrī, the chapter on natural history; for Ibnal- Lubūdī, the mathematical chapter; for Ibn al-Qifṭī and Ibn abī Uṣaibi'a, the historical chapter.

NAJĪB AL-DĪN AL-SAMARQANDĪ

Abū Ḥāmid Muḥammad ibn 'Alī ibn 'Umar, Najīb al-dīn al-Samarqandī. Muslim physician who was born or flourished at Samarqand, and was killed by the Tartars during the sack of Herāt in 1222–1223. (His older contemporary, Fakhr al-dīn al-Rāzī, had died, also in Herāt, in 1210.)

He wrote various medical works in Arabic. The most important, entitled Kitāb al-asbāb wal-'alāmāt—i.e., Causes and symptoms (of diseases)—enjoyed some popularity. There are many MSS. of it. It was known also through a commentary completed in Samarqand, 1423–1424, by Ulugh Beg's physician, Nafīs ibn 'Iwaḍ al-Kirmānī, the Sharḥ (or Mamzūj) al-asbāb wal-'alāmāt. This commentary was itself the nucleus of the Persian treatise Ṭibb-i-Akbarī (Medicine of Akbar) completed in 1700–1701 by Muḥammad Arzānī, son of Mīr Ḥājī Muḥammad Muqīm. That is, Muḥammad Arzānī added to his translation of Nafīs's Sharḥ many extracts from other Arabic medical works.

Text—Nafīs' Sharḥ was edited by Mauluwī 'Abd al-Majīd (Calcutta 1836).

There are many printed and lithographed editions of the Ṭibb-i-Akbar. Calcutta 1830, 1832; a third Calcutta edition without date; Bombay 1847–1848; Delhi 1848–1849; Bombay 1858–1859; Teheran 1858–1859; Bombay 1862–1863; Lucknow 1872–1873; etc.

Criticism—Ibn abī Uṣaibi'a (Müller's edition, vol. 2, 31, 1884).

F. Wüstenfeld: Arabische Aerzte (119, 1840). L. Leclerc: Médecine arabe (vol. 2, 127, 291, 1876). C. Brockelmann: Arabische Litteratur (vol. 1, 490, 1898; vol. 2, 213, 1902). Adolf Fonahn: Zur Quellenkunde der persischen Medizin (24–26, 1910; analysis of the Ṭibb-i-Akbarī).

IBN ṬARKHĀN

Abū Isḥāq Ibrāhīm ibn Muḥammad ibn Ṭarkhān (ibn) al-Suwaidī al-Anṣārī al-Dimishqī, 'Izz al-dīn. Syrian physician and philosopher. Born in 1203–1204; flourished in Damascus; died in 1291–1292.

His main work is a very large treatise on medicine, arranged a capite ad calcem, entitled Tadhkirat al-hādiya (Memorial of direction). It is also called Tadhkirat ibn Ṭarkhān and Tadhkirat al-Suwaidī. For each drug the opinions of many doctors are quoted verbatim, also sometimes the results of personal observations. It is said in one of the MSS.) that Ibn Ṭarkhān used the writings of more than four hundred physicians. It is certain that he quotes a great many of them, Westerners as well as Easterners (e.g., he often quotes Ibn Rushd, though the latter was far less known in the East than in the Maghrib).

Two abbreviated editions were prepared in the sixteenth century; the one by the Cairene Ṣūfī, 'Abd al-Wahhāb ibn Aḥmad al-Sha'rānī, who died in 1565-1566; the other by the Turkish doctor Badr al-dīn Muḥammad ibn Muḥammad al-Qauṣūnī, who flourished under Sulaymān I (ruled from 1520 to 1566). Al-Qauṣānī suppressed all the references for the sake of brevity.

Another treatise of Ibn Ṭarkhān, the Kitāb al-bāhir fī-l-jawāhir, deals with the substances (οὐσία).

Text—Al-Shar'ānī's Mukhtaṣar tadkhirat al-Suwaidī fī-l-ṭibb was printed in Cairo, 1862.

Criticism—Ḥājī Khalīfa (vol. 2, nos. 1618, 2783, 2810, 2857). Ibn abī Uṣaibi'a (Müller's edition, vol. 2, 177, 266, 1884).

F. Wüstenfeld: Arabische Aerzte (147, 1840). L. Leclerc: Médecine arabe (vol. 2, 199–202, 1876). C. Brockelmann: Arabische Litteratur (vol. 1, 493, 1898; for the two abbreviators, see vol. 2, 335, 447, 1902).

MESUË THE THIRD

Pseudo-Mesuë II[3]. Unknown Arabic surgeon who flourished probably in the first half of the thirteenth century. I give him this non-Arabic name to emphasize our ignorance of his personality, and to distinguish him clearly from two other Mesuë: Ibn Māsawaih or Mesuë Major (first half of the ninth century), and Māsawaih al-Mārdīnī or Mesuë Junior (first half of the eleventh century), both Christians. He composed a treatise on surgery which was translated into Latin by Ferrarius (Faraj ibn Salīm, second half of the thirteenth century), and into Hebrew by Jacob ben Joseph ha-Levi in 1297. The Arabic text is lost and it has been claimed that it never existed; i.e., that the original work, though derived from Arabic sources, was not written in Arabic. It is of course difficult to distinguish, even with regard to the vocabulary, between a treatise directly translated from the Arabic and one derived from such translations.

The "Cyrurgia Joannis Mesuë" is divided into five books: (1) De anathomia et primo de anathomia membrorum consimilium (bones, cartilage, vessels, nerves, etc.); (2) De anathomia membrorum officialium (separate parts and organs; in reality this book contains a list of simple medicines); (3) De curis omnium aegritudinum a causa antecedente provenientium cum medicinis et cauteriis et instrumentorum formis; (4) De cura omnium morborum a causa primitiva in subjecto medicinae a capite usque ad pedes provenientium et de algebra[4] et quibusdam accidentibus alicui aegrotantium provenientibus et de venis ad flebotomandum expositis et ventosis et sanguissugis; (5) Antidotarium. The first two chapters of book (1) deal with generalities: the eight qualities which a surgeon must possess; definitions of surgery.

[3] For pseudo Mesuë I, see my note on Māsawaih al-Mārdīnī (vol. 1, 728), or the note on Samuel ben Jacob of Capua in this volume.

[4] Al-jabr, reduction (e.g., of a dislocation). From the mathematical meaning of the same Arabic word came our mathematical term, algebra.

Text—Julius Leopold Pagel: Die angebliche Chirurgie des Joh. Mesuë jun. nach einer Hds. der Pariser Nationalbibliothek zum ersten Male, theils herausgegeben, theils analysiert nebst einem Nachtrag zur Chirurgie des Heinrich von Mondeville (146 p., Berlin 1893). This contains the German translation of the first three books only; translations of book 4 were published in Berlin theses by Frederick Alexander Sternberg (51 p., 1893), and Walther Schnelle (34 p., 1895); and of book 5, by Hans Brockelmann (38 p., 1895).

Criticism—M. Steinschneider: Hebraeische Übersetzungen (721, 1893). E. Gurlt: Geschichte der Chirurgie (vol. 1, 663–669, 1898; long analysis of the surgical part).

X. WESTERN MUSLIM

IBN AL-BAIṬĀR

Abū Muḥammad 'Abdallāh ibn Aḥmad ibn al-Baiṭār Diyā' al-dīn al-Mālaqī. (Ibn al Baiṭār means son of the horse doctor or farrier). Hispano-Muslim botanist and pharmacist; the greatest of Islām and of the Middle Ages. He was born in or near Malaga towards the end of the twelfth century, and died in Damascus in 1248. He was a pupil of Abū-l-'Abbās al-Nabātī, with whom he collected plants around Seville; about 1219 he left Spain and traveled in North Africa eastward; in 1220 he was in Bugia, later he passed through Constantine, Tunis, Tripoli, Barca; it is possible that he sailed from that neighborhood to avoid crossing the Libyan desert; in 1224 he was near Adalia on the south coast of Asia Minor. Later he entered the service of the Ayyūbid sulṭān of Egypt, al-Kāmil, being appointed chief herbalist, Ra'īs 'alā sā'iri-l-'ashshābīn; in 1237 al-Kāmil became also sulṭān of Damascus, and Ibn al-Baiṭār went thither with him. After al-Kāmil's death in 1238, Ibn al-Baiṭār went for a time to Cairo, but not long afterwards he returned to Damascus where he remained until the end of his days in the service of al-Ṣāliḥ (sulṭān of Egypt and Damascus from 1240 to 1249). Outside of the places already mentioned, it would seem that he herborized also in Arabia, Syria, Palestine, and as far east as Mūṣul; at any rate he knew plants growing in those localities.

His main work is a collection of simples, Kitāb al-jāmi' fī-l-adwiya al-mufrada, which is the foremost Arabic and mediaeval treatise of its kind, the greatest from the time of Dioscorides to the middle of the sixteenth century. It is not only a very methodical and critical compilation, but it contains also a good number of personal observations. It does not deal only with simples or drugs, but also with various species of food. Leaving out duplications, some 1400 different items are considered, of which about 300 (including some 200 plants) were novelties. Practically the whole of Dioscorides' and of Galen's knowledge on the subject was incorporated in the Jāmi', but many other authors were quoted, some 150 in all, among whom were twenty Greeks. It may be recalled that since the middle of the tenth century Dioscorides had been very diligently studied in Muslim Spain (e.g., see my notes on Ḥasdai ibn Shaprut, Ibn Juljul, and Ibn al-Wāfid, in vol. 1, 680, 682, 728). The Arabic writers most frequently quoted are al-Rāzī and Ibn Sīnā.

Ibn al-Baiṭār paid considerable attention to the synonyms of plant names, and quoted names not only in Arabic and Greek, but sometimes also in the Latin and Arabic dialects of Spain, in Persian and Berber.

His second great work, in point of importance and of time, was the Kitāb al-mughnī fī-l-adwiya al-mufrada, which might be considered almost a reversion of the first one. It deals largely with the same simples and vegetables, but instead of being arranged in their own alphabetical order as in the Jāmi', the new order is therapeutical. The Mughnī is divided into twenty chapters: (1) simples for head diseases; (2) for ear diseases; (3) for eye diseases; . . . . (17) cosmetics; (18) simples against fevers; (19) antidotes; (20) most common drugs. The point of view of the Mughnī is thus entirely different; that of materia medica instead of natural history. The authorities vary somewhat too; for example, Abū-l-Qāsim is more often quoted in the Mughnī than in the Jāmi'.

It would seem that Ibn al-Baiṭār derived a considerable part of his materia medica from al-Idrīsī, and even more so from al-Ghāfiqī, but I have no means of measuring the extent of his borrowings from these two sources until they have been published.[5]

Ibn al-Baiṭār's two great works were dedicated to al-Ṣāliḥ; they were thus completed during the fifth decade of the thirteenth century, the Jāmi' first, then the Mughnī. Ibn abī Uṣaibi'a was a disciple of Ibn al-Baiṭār and herborized with him around Damascus.

The influence exerted by Ibn al-Baiṭār's Kitāb al-jāmi' was not at all commensurate with its real importance. The fact is, it appeared too late. Thus it remained practically untranslated until the nineteenth century. Andrea Alpago (second half of the fifteenth century) made use of it to enrich his glossary of Ibn Sīnā's Qānūn (vol. 1, 711). The article on lemons which he translated was not an original piece but an extract from Ibn Jamī' (second half of the twelfth century) which Ibn al-Baiṭār had embodied in his own work. Guillaume Postel (1510–1581) was perhaps the first western orientalist to pay sufficient attention to Ibn al-Baiṭār. He was followed by a few others in the seventeenth and eighteenth centuries, yet the first complete translation in any western language was available only in 1842 (see below).

Text—First edition entitled Kitāb al-jāmi' li-mufradāt al-adwiya wal-aghdhiya (4 vols., 4°, Būlāq, 1874–1875). An abbreviated translation into French by Antoine Galland (1646–1715) has remained unpublished. Partial Latin translation by Fr. R. Dietz: Elenchus materiae medicae Ibn Beitharis (Leipzig 1833; only first two letters). German translation by J. v. Sontheimer: Grosse Zusammenstellung über die Kräfte der bekannten einfachen Heil- und Nahrungsmittel (2 vols., Stuttgart 1840–1842; complete but very imperfect). French translation by Lucien Leclerc: Traité des simples (Notices et extraits, vol. 23, 1877; vols. 25–26, 1883).

The Mughnī is still unpublished.

Criticism—Ibn abī Uṣaibi'a (Müller's edition, vol. 2, 133, 1884). Joseph Elian Sarkis: Dictionnaire de bibliographie arabe (p. 49, Le Caire 1928).

Fr. Wüstenfeld: Arabische Aerzte (130–131, 1840). E. Meyer: Geschichte der Botanik (vol. 3, 227–234, 1856; contains inaccuracies derived from Sontheimer's bad translation). L. Leclerc: Etudes historiques et philologiques sur Ebn Beithār (Journal asiatique, vol. 19, 433–461, 1862); Médecine arabe (vol. 2, 225–237, 1876; including a list of Muslim additions to materia medica). E. Sickenberger: Les plantes égyptiennes d'Ibn al-Baiṭār (Bull. de l'Institut égyptien, Cairo 1890). C. Brockelmann: Arabische Litteratur (vol. 1, 492, 1898). René Basset: Les noms berbères des plantes dans le traité des simples d'Ibn el Beïṭār (Giornale della soc. asiatica italiana, vol. 12, 53–66, 1899). J. Ruska: Encyclopaedia of Islām (vol. 2, 366, 1916).

[5] Max Meyerhof is preparing editions of them. In a private communication to me (May 30, 1930) he went so far as to call Ibn al-Baiṭār a plagiarist, with special reference to those two sources.

XI. WESTERN JEWISH

For al-Ḥarizī, see the philosophical chapter; for Samuel ibn Tibbon, see the section on translators from Arabic into Hebrew.

ABRAHAM OF ARAGON

Jewish oculist who flourished c. 1253. The Jews having become involved in the persecutions against the Albigenses were subjected to various new restrictions; for example, the Council held at Béziers in 1246 forbade them to practice medicine among the Christians. Abraham is here quoted to illustrate this prohibition and its evasion. In 1253 he was asked to treat Alphonse, count of Poitou and Toulouse, St. Louis' brother; he refused in compliance with the council's decree, but was finally obliged to accept.

H. Graetz: History of the Jews (vol. 3, 583, 1894). Fritz Kahn: Encyclopaedia judaica (vol. 1, 418, 1928).

P. Pansier: Anonymi Tractatus de egritudinibus oculorum etc. (Collectio ophtalmologica veterum auctorum, fasc. 6, 104, Paris, 1908). Pansier quotes the text of a letter dated Lunel 1253 proving that it was in that year that Abraham was appealed to (Trésor des chartes de Toulouse, 1253 sac II, no. 94). Had I known that date earlier I would have placed Abraham in the second half of the thirteenth century. As long as it was unknown to me, I dated the event tentatively, c. 1246.

XII. EGYPTIAN JEWISH

AL-AS'AD AL-MAḤALLĪ

Ya'qūb ibn Isḥāq As'ad al-dīn al-Maḥallī al-Yahūdī. Born in al-Maḥallah, between Cairo and Damietta. Egyptian Jewish physician highly praised by Ibn abī Uṣaibi'a. In the autumn of 1201 he went to Damascus and remained there a certain time disputing with local physicians, chiefly with the Samaritan Ṣadaqa ben Munaja' (see below). He returned to Cairo and died there. He wrote various medical works in Arabic: Maqālah fī qawanīn al-ṭabāyib (Discourse on the principles of medicine); Kitāb al-nazh (Book of purity), medical questions addressed to Ṣadaqa ben Munaja', etc.

Ibn abī Uṣaibi'a in A. Müller's edition (vol. 2, 118, 1882). I. Broydé: Jewish Encyclopaedia (vol. 2, 161, 1902). M. Steinschneider: Arabische Literatur der Juden (225, 1902).

DAVID BEN SOLOMON

Abū-l-Faḍl Dā'ūd ibn Sulaimān ibn abī-l-Bayān al-Isrā'īlī Sadīd al-dīn (?). Egyptian Qaraite, born c. 1161–1170; died in Cairo, being more than 80 years old. One of the leading Egyptian physicians of his time. Disciple of Ibn Jamī' (second half of the twelfth century), and of the Cairene oculist, Abū-l-Faḍā'il Ibn al-Nāqid (d. 1188–1189). Physician to the Ayyūbid sulṭān, al-'Ādil Sayf al-dīn Abū Bakr (r. 1199–1218); chief professor at the hospital al-Nāṣirī in Cairo. He was still teaching there in 1236–1237 when Ibn abī Uṣaibi'a was his pupil; at any rate Ibn abī Uṣaibi'a praises him in such a detailed way as to suggest this relationship to him. He composed in Arabic an antidotary entitled Al-dastūr al-māristānī (The hospital's canon). Ibn abī Uṣaibi'a studied the Dastūr with the author and helped him to correct it. Al-Kūhīn al-'Aṭṭār (second half of the thirteenth century) speaks of it as the best book of its kind. David also wrote a commentary on Galen's treatise on causes and symptoms.

The Dastūr has also been ascribed to another Cairene Qaraite, Ibn al-Mudawwar (second half of the twelfth century). On the other hand, the latter's Risālat al-mujarrabāt has been credited to David ben Solomon.

The main source is Ibn abī Uṣaibi'a in Müller's edition (vol. 2, 118, 1882). F. Wüstenfeld: Arabische Aerzte (128, 1840). C. Brockelmann: Arabische Litteratur (vol. 1, 491, 1898). M. Steinschneider: Arabische Literatur der Juden (195–196, 1902). M. Seligsohn: Jewish Encyclopaedia (vol. 5, 324, 1903). I. Markon: Encyclopaedia judaica (vol. 5, 865, 1930).

XIII. SAMARITAN

ṢADAQA BEN MUNAJA'

Ṣadaqa ben Abū-l-Faraj Munaja' ben Ṣadaqa al-Sāmirī al-Dimishqī, al-ḥakīm. Samaritan physician and theologian. Physician to al-Ashraf, Ayyūbid king of Mesopotamia from 1210 to 1230, or (and) to al-'Ādil (Saphadin), Ayyūbid king of Damascus from 1196, and of Egypt from 1199, to 1218. He died in Ḥarrān, in 1223–1224. He wrote in Arabic a commentary on the Torah, theological and medical treatises.

The medical treatises are: (1) Ta'līq fī-l-ṭibb (medical notes), dealing with diseases and their symptoms ('alāma); (2) Sharḥ fuṣūl Buqrāṭ (commentary on Hippocrates' Aphorisms), unfinished; (3) Maqāla fī asmā' al-adwiya (on the names of simples); (4) answers to medical questions asked by his Jewish contemporary, al-As'ad al-Maḥallī.

His main philosophical and theological works are the Kitāb fī-l-nafs wal-rūḥ (Soul and spirit), the Kitāb al-kanz fī-l-fauz (Treasure in success, on the unity of God), the Kitāb al-i'tiqād (on faith, dealing with dogmatics).

As Ṣadaqa was one of the most famous Samaritan authors, his people have ascribed various other treatises to him, but these ascriptions are doubtful. Ibn abī Uṣaibi'a spoke very highly of him.

Ḥājī Khalīfa (Fluegel; vol. 2, 463; 4, 438; 5, 165, 257). Ibn abī Uṣaibi'a (Müller; vol. 2, 230).

Eliakim Carmoly: History of Jewish physicians (Baltimore, 64, c. 1844). M. Steinschneider: Mose b. Zedaqa, Imran b. Ṣadaka und Mose Dar'i (Jüdische Zeitschrift für Wissenschaft und Leben, vol. 9, 172–183, 1869; reprinted in Gesammelte Schriften, vol. 1, 523–535, 1925); Arabische Literatur der Juden (331, 1902). Isaac Broydé: Jewish Encyclopaedia (vol. 10, 630, 1905). Moses Gaster: Samaritan literature (7, 12, 1925).

ABŪ-L-ḤASAN BEN GHAZĀL

Abū-l-Ḥasan ben Ghazāl ben abī Sa'īd. Samaritan scholar established in Damascus, executed in 1250–1251. He embraced Islām and became wazīr, being named Amīn al-dawla. He had collected an immense library, containing no less than ten thousand volumes. His disciple, Ibn abī Uṣaibi'a, dedicated to him his famous history of physicians. Abū-l-Ḥasan wrote in Arabic a treatise entitled Al-nahj al-wāḍiḥ fī-l-ṭibb (Plain introduction into medicine). This treatise is lost. It was divided into five books: (1) physical questions and affections of bodies; (2) simple remedies; (3) compound remedies; (4) hygienic rules and cure of external disorders; (5) internal disorders and their cure.

Ḥājī Khalīfa (vol. 6, no. 14121, 410). M. Steinschneider: Arabische Literatur der Juden (323, 1902). Moses Gaster: The Samaritan literature (8, 1925).

XIV. HINDU

ŚĀRṄGADHARA

Hindu physician who lived at an unknown time after the Muslim conquest, but not later than the thirteenth century, because there exists a commentary on his work by Vopadeva who flourished during the last third of the century. His work, called after him Śārṅgadharasaṃhitā, is one of the oldest Sanskrit works of its kind dealing with the calcination of mercury and other mercurial and metallic preparations (rasa, rasendra) and their therapeutic use. There are also references to opium (ahiphena) and bertram root (akarākarabha), i.e., pellitory of Spain, used as an irritant and sialagogue (or some other plant having similar properties: sneezewort, feverfew, yarrow, etc.).

It is divided into three parts as follows: (1) weights and measures, properties of drugs, influence of the seasons, diagnosis and prognosis, action of drugs, anatomy and physiology, embryology, varieties and subvarieties of diseases; (2) decoctions, infusions, pastes, powders, pills, electuaries, butters, gold dust and other metallic dusts, mercurial preparations; (3) ordinary therapeutic methods; e.g., fattening substances, sudorifics. In the paragraph on diagnosis there is an elaborate analysis of the pulse (nāḍīparīkshā). His classification of diseases is far more detailed than those of his predecessors.

The popularity of this saṃhitā is attested by the existence of many manuscripts and of many native editions and translations into Hindu vernaculars.

The main quality of Śārṅgadhara's work was its emphasis upon the chemical side of materia medica. In this respect it may be considered an anticipation of the iatro-chemical reforms which were heralded in the center of Europe many centuries later by Paracelsus. But even as early as Śārṅgadhara's time this was not a novelty in India. The study of rasa can be traced back many centuries before his time, though the uncertainties of Hindu chronology do not allow us to prove its existence in pre-Islāmic times. Thus the question of India's priority in this matter is very doubtful. Remember that Dioscorides knew many chemical preparations, including mercury. The Chinese alchemist, Ko Hung (first half of the fourth century), was familiar with cinnabar, and in all probability that substance had already been used during the Han dynasty, if not before, for the making of red ink. Cinnabar occurs in the natural state in China, but not in India. (See vol. 1; e.g., 258, 316, 355, 369).

The iatro-chemist, Śārṅgadhara, should not be confused with the poet bearing the same name who compiled in 1363 one of the best known anthologies of Sanskrit poetry, the Śārṅgadharapaddhati (i.e., S.'s guide).

Text—Critical edition by Prabhuram Jivanram (Bombay 1891).

Criticism—Julius Jolly: Medizin (Grundriss der indo-arabischen Philologie, vol. 3, part 10, p. 4, 7, 1901). Praphulla Chandra Ray: History of Hindu chemistry (2 vols., Calcutta; vol. 1, 2d ed., 1903; vol. 2, 1909; new edition, 2 vols., Calcutta 1925; Isis, 3, 68–73; 9, 555). M. Winternitz: Geschichte der indischen Litteratur (vol. 3, 157, 551, 1922). H. E. Stapleton, R. F. Azo, M. Hidāyat Ḥusain:

Chemistry in 'Irāq and Persia in the tenth century (p. 402, Calcutta 1927; Isis, 11, 133). A. Berriedale Keith: History of Sanskrit literature (511, Oxford 1928). Deals with the medical use of mercury (raseśvara) but not with Śaṅgadhara. Johann Almkvist: Über die Anwendung des Quecksilbers bei den alten Arabern (Festschrift Max Neuburger gewidmet, 5–15, Wien 1928; Isis, 13, 220).

NARAHARI

Kashmirian physician and grammarian who composed between 1235 and 1250 a dictionary of materia medica called Rājanighaṇṭu (or Nighaṇṭurāja or Abhidhānacūḍāmaṇi).

Text—Published in Benares, 1883, also in the Ānandāśrama Sanskrit Series (vol. 33, Poona). Edition of the chapter dealing with minerals and translation by Richard von Garbe: Die indische Mineralien (Leipzig 1882).

Criticism—According to Theodor Zachariae: Die indische Wörterbücher, Kośa (39, Strassburg 1897), the Rājanighaṇṭu is a much later work, later than 1374. M. Winternitz: Indische Litteratur (vol. 3, 554, 1922). A. Berriedale Keith: History of Sanskrit literature (512, Oxford 1928).

XV. CHINESE

CH'ÊN TZŬ-MING

Ch'ên[2] Tzŭ[4]-ming[2] (658, 12365, 7946). Chinese physician, who flourished under the Sung, c. 1237. He wrote in that year a treatise on women's diseases, entitled Fu[4]-jên[2] ta[4]-ch'üan[2] liang[2]-fang[1] (3749, 5624, 10470, 3176, 7017, 3435), divided into eight sections and 260 articles. Each article is devoted to a special ailment and is concluded with a prescription. Another treatise of his Wai[4] k'o[1] ching[1] yao[4] (12442, 6089, 2133, 12889), deals with the most important points in the character and cure of external troubles.

Text—Revised edition by Hsieh[1]* Chi[3] (4371, 921) of the Ming dynasty, containing a number of new cases.

Criticism—A. Wylie: Chinese literature (98, 103, 1902). L. Wieger: La Chine (424, 492, 1920). F. Huebotter: Guide (63, Kumamoto 1924; Isis, 7, 259).

SUNG TZ'Ŭ

Sung[4] Tz'ŭ[2] (10462, 12406). Chinese physician and commissioner of justice, who flourished during the period Shun Yu (1241–1253) of the rule of Li Tsung, of the Southern Sung dynasty. He composed, partly on the basis of earlier works, a treatise on forensic medicine, entitled Instructions to coroners, Hsi[3]-yüan[1] lu[4]* (4146, 13729, 7386), which reveals considerable knowledge and acumen. Revised editions of this work are still used today by the high Chinese officials acting as coroners.

It should be noted that European works of a similar kind appeared only three centuries later; to wit, the criminal codes of Bamberg (1507), Brandenburg (1516) and of the emperor Charles V (1532).

Text—The Library of Congress has four editions of the Hsi yüan lu, as follows: Hsi yüan lu chi[2]* chêng[4] (906, 726) printed with charts in 5 vols. and 6 chüan in 1822; the Hsi yüan lu chi chêng hui[4] tsuan[3] (5215, 11889) printed with charts in 1826 in 2 vols. and 5 chüan; the Hsi yüan lu hsiang[2] i[4] (4279, 5454) printed in 1890 with charts in 6 vols. and 4 chüan with an appendix in two additional vols.; and the Hsi yüan lu ko[1] chüeh[2]* (6046, 3225) printed in 1879 in one volume.

Herbert A. Giles: The Hsi yüan lu (Proceedings of the R. Soc. of Med., vol. 17, historical section, 59–107, 1924; Isis, 8, 541). This is the translation of an edition of which the preface is dated Huai-pei, 1843. It is divided into four books as follows: Book I, 16 chapters, detailed examination of a dead body, special rules for women to determine virginity, pregnancy, etc., examination of bones, dropping blood (to establish consanguinity!), examination of ground, etc., containing curious anatomical charts; Book II, 12 chapters, wounds of various kinds, suicides, murders passed off as suicides, drowning, burning, scalding; Book III, 6 chapters, miscellaneous remarks on suspicious appearances, various wounds, accidental poisoning, all kinds of poisons; Book IV, methods of restoring life, antidotes.

Criticism—Alex. Wylie: Notes on Chinese literature (93, 1902). B. Scheube: Puschmann's Geschichte der Medizin (vol. 1, 34, 1902).

CH'ÊN JÊN-YÜ

See chapter on natural history.

CHAPTER XXXIX

HISTORIOGRAPHY

(First Half of Thirteenth Century)

I. FRENCH

VILLEHARDOUIN

Geoffroi de Villehardouin. One of the greatest French chroniclers. Born probably at Villehardouin, near Troyes, Champagne, c. 1150; marshal of Rumania after 1204; still living in 1212, died not long afterwards. He was one of the organizers and one of the most distinguished participants of the Fourth Crusade, and composed an account of it and of the early years (1204–1207) of the Latin Empire of Constantinople. He dictated it in French after 1207. "La conquête de Constantinople" is one of the masterpieces of early French literature, and indeed of the European literature of that time. We do not trust the author's sincerity as completely as was done before, for we realize that he could not be an independent witness of the political events which he describes. However, his account is an impressive proof of the superiority of the Byzantine culture to the Latin culture of those days. Villehardouin was no sentimentalist or romanticist but a grim realist; feudal honor was the whole of his morality; his account is brief and matter of fact like that of a business man. It was continued by Henry of Valenciennes.

To appreciate Villehardouin's effort, one must remember that the Fourth Crusade (1202–1204) had been organized by Innocent III primarily against Egypt, which was rightly considered the mainstay of Muslim power. Yet the result of the Crusade was the conquest and sack of Constantinople, and the foundation of the short-lived Latin Empire (1204–1261). How can one account for such an extraordinary deviation of purpose? Villehardouin explained it as an accidental development; others—like Ernoul, Robert of Clari, Innocent III himself—as a natural result of Venetian betrayal. The treason of Venice cannot be positively proved, but it is clear that for Venice the Crusade was mainly a matter of business, and that it was against its interests to destroy the Egyptian power. On the other hand, the hatred between Latins and Greeks had been increasing for centuries. The organizers of the Crusade were not as innocent as Villehardouin (one of them) would have it, nor as criminal as others have claimed.

Text—An edition of Villehardouin's chronicle was being prepared c. 1573 by order of the Venetian Senate, but was not published. The first edition, by Blaise de Vigenère, was dedicated to the Seigniory of Venice (Paris 1585). The MS.which Venice had planned to publish c. 1573 was used for the second edition (Lyon 1601). Reprinted with learned commentary by Charles Ducange: Histoire de l'empire de Constantinople sous les empereurs français (vol. 1, Paris 1657). Later editions by Dom M. J. J. Brial in Recueil des historiens des Gaules et de la France (vol. 18, 1822); by J. A. C. Buchon (Paris 1828). Critical editions by Natalis de Wailly (Paris 1871); by Emile Bouchet (2 vols., Paris 1892).

Latin translation by Paolo Ramusio (Venice 1604). Italian version of the Latin text by Ramusio's son (1604). English translation by Sir Frank Marzials (Everyman's library, 1908).

Criticism—Sainte Beuve: Causeries du lundi (vol. 9). Potthast (1094, 1896). Auguste Molinier: Sources de l'histoire de France (vol. 3, 38–41, 1903).

ROBERT DE CLARI

Robert of Clari or Clary, i.e., Cléry-les-Pernois, near Amiens, in Picardy. A poor knight who took part in the Fourth Crusade together with his brother, Aleaume, both of them following Hugh of Amiens. He returned to Picardy probably in 1205, and died after 1216. He gave, c. 1216, in French (Picard dialect) an account of the conquest of Constantinople, which is of great value because he was a candid, if uneducated and unintelligent, witness. It enables us to understand the point of view of the average crusader, while Villehardouin's narrative reflected the opinions of the leaders. It contains some very interesting information on the topography and treasures of Constantinople. One of the relics stolen by Robert in the imperial chapel is still preserved in the abbatial church of Corbie, to which he had presented it. It is possible that his account was dictated by him in that very monastery.

Text—First edition by Paul Riant: Li estoires de chiaus qui conquisent Constantinople (87 p., Paris 1868; reprinted, Genève 1871). Second edition by Karl Hopf: Chroniques gréco-romaines (1-85, Berlin 1873). New edition by Philippe Lauer (Classiques français du Moyen âge, 40, 148 p., Paris 1924, with notes and glossary).

Criticism—Potthast (975, 1896). Auguste Molinier: Sources de l'histoire de France (vol. 3, 42, 1903). For later bibliography see Lauer's edition.

JAMES OF VITRY

Jacques de Vitry. Jacobus de Vitriaco. Born at Argenteuil, near Versailles, or Vitry-le-Francois, or Vitry-sur-Seine, c. 1178; died in 1240. French chronicler. Augustinian monk, curate of Oignies near Namur (Belgium), bishop of Acre, 1216; returned to Oignies in 1226; cardinal-bishop of Tusculum, 1229, and confident of pope Gregory IX (1227–1241); patriarch of Jerusalem, buried in Oignies. His main work is a history of the Holy Land from the Hegira down to 1218, Historia Orientalis, composed c. 1219–1226. It is largely based on that of William of Tyre (second half of the twelfth century), but James was a witness of many of the later events described by him, or could obtain first-hand information about them. His work is valuable for the study of culture; e.g., it contains one of the earliest European accounts of the use of the compass.

Text—Historia orientalis (seu Hierosolymitana) in 3 books. Books I–II edited by Franc. Moschus (Douai 1597); Book III (1211–1218) by Jac. Gretser (Ingolstadt 1608). Books I and III in Jac. Bongars: Gesta Dei per Francos (vol. 1, 1047–1145, 1611). Other text of Book III edited by Edm. Martène: Thesaurus novus anecdotorum (vol. 3, 268–287, 1717). This book III is apocryphal.

French translation in Fr. P. G. Guizot: Collection des mémoires (vol. 22, 1–390, 1825).

Partial English translation by Aubrey Stewart: The history of Jerusalem, 1180 (Palestine Pilgrims' Text Society, no. 31, London 1896).

Criticism—Julius Klaproth: Lettre à A. de Humboldt sur l'invention de la boussole (14, 44, Paris 1834). Daunou: Histoire littéraire de la France (vol. 18,

209–246, 1835). Ernst H. F. Meyer: Geschichte der Botanik (vol. 4, 110–113, 1857). Gustav Zacher: Die Historia Orientalis (Diss., 43 p., Königsberg i. Pr., 1885). A. Potthast: Bibliotheca historica (633–634, 1896). C. R. Beazley: Dawn of modern geography (vol. 2, 212–214, 1901). Auguste Molinier: Sources de l'histoire de France (vol. 3, 49, 1903). Philipp Funk: Jacob von Vitry (194 p., Leipzig 1909). Goswin Frenke: Die Exempla des Jacob von Vitry, ein Beitrag zur Geschichte der Erzählungsliteratur des Mittelalters (München 1914).

ERNOUL

French chronicler who flourished in Syria in the first half of the thirteenth century. He wrote in French a chronicle, Estoires d'oultremer et de la naissance de Sallehadin, which contains an independent and very elaborate account of the third and fourth Crusades.

It appears in the MSS. in the form of a continuation to the Livre d'Eracles (i.e., the emperor Heraclius, mentioned in the first sentence), or Livre du conquest, a French translation (by one Hugh Plagon?) of Books I–XXII of William of Tyre. Ernoul's continuation extends to 1228 (or 1231). It was for a time wrongly ascribed to Bernard the Treasurer, treasurer of the abbey of Corbie. It would seem that Bernard was simply Ernoul's editor or abbreviator.

Ernoul's chronicle was partly translated into Latin by Francesco Pipino, Dominican of Bologna, who died after 1325. It was continued by unknown authors to 1261 and to 1275.

It contains an account of Palestine which is interesting though far less accurate than another French description, L'estat de la citez de Jherusalem, sometimes erroneously ascribed to Ernoul. The author of La citez describes also the ordinary pilgrim roads from Acre, Haifa, and Caesarea to the Holy City, and from Jerusalem to the Jordan, to Samaria and Galilee, the distances being very accurately indicated.

Text—The Livre du conquest was published in the Recueil des historiens des croisades (Hist. occid., vol. 1, 1841–1842), and by P. Paris, (2 vols., Paris 1879–1880).

Pipino's Latin translation of Ernoul's continuation was published in L. A. Muratori: Rerum italicarum scriptores (vol. 9, 587–752, Milano 1725).

The French text appeared a few years later in Edm. Martène: Veterum scriptorum amplissima collectio (vol. 5, 583–752, Paris 1729). New edition by Louis de Mas-Latrie: Chronique d'Ernouf et de Bernard le Trésorier (Société de l'histoire de France, Paris 1871).

For the continuations, see Recueil des historiens des croisades (Hist. occid., vol. 2, 483–639, 1859).

La citez de Iherusalem. See Mas-Latrie's edition (188–210, 1871). Titus Tobler: Descriptiones Terrae sanctae (197–224, Leipzig 1874). Henri Michelant and Gaston Raynaud: Itinéraires à Jérusalem (1882). Englished by Claude Reignier Conder: The city of Jerusalem (Palestine Pilgrim's Text Society, no. 8, 70 p., 2 maps, London 1888; followed by an English translation of Ernoul's account of Palestine).

Criticism—Petit-Radel: Histoire litéraire de la France (vol. 18, 414–430, 1835). Paulin Paris (ibidem, vol. 21, 679–685, 1847). R. Röhricht: Bibliotheca geographica Palaestinae (50, 1890). C. R. Beazley: Dawn of modern geography (vol. 2, 208–212, 1901). Auguste Molinier: Sources de l'histoire de France (vol. 3, 29–30, 1903).

WILLIAM OF TUDELA

Guillem de Tudèle. Guilelmus Tudelensis. Brought up in Tudela, Spanish Navarra; moved to Montauban c. 1198, and remained there until 1210. Later canon in St. Antonin near Montauban. He began in Montauban, 1210, a chronicle in verse (2770 lines) of the crusade against the Albigenses, dealing with the events of the years 1207 to 1213. He died presumably in this year, or his work was otherwise interrupted. He was a conscientious chronicler. He tried to write in French, with the result that his language is a barbaric mixture of langue d'oc and langue d'oïl.

This poem was followed by another, much longer (c. 7000 lines) dealing with the events of the years 1213–1219. This second poem is written in langue d'oc by an unknown author. The tendencies of both poems are as different as their languages; Guillaume is writing from the crusader's point of view, though with some impartiality; on the contrary, the anonymous poet does not hide his deep sympathy for the Count of Toulouse and the oppressed peoples of the south. Apropos of this it is well to bear in mind that the aim of the Crusade was not exclusively religious; a leader like the cruel Simon of Montfort, earl of Leicester (c. 1165–1218) was concerned at least as much with political as with religious motives: he aimed to dispossess the Counts of Toulouse and Foix and other southern lords.

Text—First edition with French translation, by Claude Charles Fauriel: Histoire de la croisade contre les hérétiques albigeois (Collection de documents inédits sur l'histoire de France, 872 p., Paris 1837). Critical edition of both texts by Paul Meyer: La Chanson de la croisade contre les Albigeois (Société de l'histoire de France; 2 vols., Paris 1875–1879; vol. 1 contains the text and vocabulary; vol. 2 the French translation, index, and a long introduction, 120 p.).

Jean Audiau: La Chanson de la croisade contre les Albigeois. Principaux épisodes (Poèmes et récits de la vieille France, 5, 172 p., Paris 1924; French translation of select fragments).

Criticism—Introduction to Meyer's edition (1879). Rudolph Diehl: Guillem Anelier von Toulouse, der Dichter des zweiten Theils der Albigenserchronik (Diss., 41 p., Marburg 1885). Potthast (215, 601, 1896). Auguste Molinier: Sources de l'histoire de France (vol. 3, 64–66, 1903). Karl Heisig: Studien zur Chanson de la croisade contre les Albigeois (Diss., 35 p., Breslau 1926).

PETER OF VAUX CERNAY

Petrus Sarnensis sive Vallis Sarnaii. French chronicler. He entered the Cistercian monastery of Vaux de Cernay near Chevreuse (Seine-et-Oise), of which his uncle Gui was the abbot. In 1202 they both joined the Fourth Crusade in Venice. About 1210–1211, they were in southern France; Gui became bishop of Carcassonne in 1212. Peter took part in the crusade against the Albigenses and wrote on account of it, from 1203 to 1218, in Latin. This account is valuable in spite of its fanaticism; it is mainly centered upon Simon de Montfort, and Peter's partiality for him is so obvious and so childish that it does not matter much. For example, he reports acts of cruelty and treachery of his hero which a more intelligent writer would have preferred to hide.

Text—Historia Albigensium, et sacri belli in eos anno 1209 suscepti, duce et principe Simone a Monte-forti. (First edition, 354 p., Troyes 1615). Second Latin edition with French translation (Troyes 1617), etc. Migne's Latin patrology (vol. 213, 543–712). Aubert, Carru and others: Premier fragment d'une édition critique, chapitres 1 à 38 (Cinquièmes mélanges d'histoire du moyen âge, edited by Achille Luchaire, 1–75, 1908).

French translation in Guizot's Collection des mémoires (vol. 14, 1–344); including many additional documents).

Criticism—Paul Meyer: La Chanson de la croisade contre les Albigeois (vol. 2, p. viii–xiii, 1879). Potthast (922, 1896). Auguste Molinier: Sources de l'histoire de France (vol. 3, 63–64, 1903).

RIGORD

French official chronicler (regis Francorum cronographus). Born in Bas-Languedoc; i.e., in the neighbourhood of Alais or Nîmes; he practiced the medical profession in southern France until c. 1183–1186; monk in Argenteuil, then, 1189, in Saint-Denis; royal physician; died c. 1209. He wrote a chronicle of the reign of Philip II (king of France from 1180 to 1223) down to 1206 (or 1208). This chronicle, the Gesta Philippi Augusti,[1] is carefully written, with some show of independence. The first edition was completed in 1196, the second c. 1200, etc. It is largely based on official letters and documents. His work was continued by William the Breton, and translated into French in the Grandes chroniques de Saint-Denis.

Text—First edition by Peter Pithou: Historiae Francorum (Francfort 1596). Modern edition by H. Francois Delaborde: Oeuvres de Rigord et de Guillaume le Breton (vol. 1, 1–167, Paris 1882).

French translation in the editions of the Grandes Chroniques (Paris 1477, etc.), and in Guizot's Collection (vol. 11).

Criticism—August Potthast: Bibliotheca historica (973, 1896). Auguste Molinier: Sources de l'histoire de France (vol. 3, 3, 1903; for the Grandes Chroniques, see ibidem, 97–101).

WILLIAM THE BRETON

Guillaume le Breton, Guilelmus Brito (or Armoricus). French official chronicler. Born in the diocese of Saint-Pol-de-Léon, between 1159 and 1169; educated in Mantes and Paris, canon of Saint-Pol and Senlis; flourished at the court of Philip Augustus; died after 1224. He wrote a Latin chronicle of the reign of Philip Augustus, Gesta Philippi regis, continuing Rigord to 1220; a new edition largely based on William's notes was completed in 1227 or later. A French translation of the section dealing with the years 1208–1223 was inserted in the Grandes Chroniques. The author was well informed and in many cases an eye-witness; e.g., he attended the battle of Bouvines (1214) and gave a vivid account of it; but he was biased. He also wrote a Latin poem devoted to the same subject, the Philippis, in ten books, composed 1214–1217; new edition in twelve books completed in 1224. This poem was translated into French within the century.

Text—First edition of the Gesta by Andrew Duchesne: Historiae Francorum scriptores (vol. 5, 68–93, 1649). Critical edition by H. François Delaborde: Oeuvres de Rigord et de Guillaume le Breton (vol. 1, 1882).

First edition of the Philippis by P. Pithou (Francfort 1596). Better edition by Duchesne (vol. 5, 93–259, 1649). Critical edition by Delaborde (vol. 2, 1–385, 1885).

[1] Rigord was the first to call that king Augustus.

French translation of both works in Guizot's collection (vols. 11 and 12).
Criticism—Potthast (552, 1896). Molinier (vol. 3, 3, 1903).

MOUSKET

Philip Mousket (Mouskès, Mousquet). French chronicler, who belonged to a prominent family of Tournai, Hainaut (Belgium), and died c. 1244. (He is not to be confused with Philip Mus or Musche, of Ghent, who was bishop of Tournai in 1274 and died in 1283). He wrote a chronicle of the kings of France in French verse from the Trojan war to 1242 (more than 31000 lines). From the year 1180 on, it contains original material, and from 1225 on, it becomes a first hand authority.

Text—Baron de Reiffenberg: Chronique de Philippe Mouskes (2 vols., Bruxelles 1836–1838; supplement, 1845).

Criticism—Histoire littéraire de la France (vol. 19, 861–872; vol. 21, 698–702). Potthast (797, 1896). H. Pirenne: Biographie nationale de Belgique (vol. 15, 329–332, 1899). A. Molinier: Sources de l'histoire de France (vol. 3, 92, 1903).

II. SPANISH

RODRIGO JIMÉNEZ DE RADA

Rodrigo Jiménez de Rada, Rodericus Ximenes (or Simonis) Toletanus. Spanish historian. Born in Rada (or in Puente la Reina?) c. 1170–1180; died in Rodano, 1247. Studied philosophy and law in Bologna, and theology in Paris (he was there in 1201). Archbishop of Toledo, 1208. He knew Arabic. His main work is a history of Spain, from Adam to 1243; i.e., it is a universal history focused upon Spain; the first general history of that country. He also compiled a history of the Muslims, etc. His works are of special interest for the study of the penetration of Muslim culture into Spain; the author was very well placed in Toledo to obtain information on that subject. He was one of the creators of the cathedral of Toledo.

Text—Chronica Hispaniae (or De rebus Hispaniae) ab origine prima ad a. D. 1243, in 9 books. First edition, Granada 1545. Rob. Bel: Rerum Hispanicarum scriptores aliquot (vol. 1, Francfort 1579). Andrew Schott: Hispania illustrata (vol. 2, 25–148, Francfort 1603).

Translated into Catalan in 1266 by Pedro Ribera de Perpeja.

Translated into Castilian and continued by Gonzalo de Hinojosa, bishop of Burgos from 1313 to 1327, and later by an anonymous writer, down to 1451. Edited in the Colección de documentos inéditos para la historia de España (vol. 105, Madrid 1893).

Historia Arabum a Mahomede usque ad Almoadum. Andr. Schott: Hispania illustrata (vol. 2, 162–186, 1603). Better edition by Jac. Golius: Elmacini Historia Saracenica (Leiden 1625).

Historia Ostrogothorum, Hunnorum, Vandalorum ac Suevorum, etc., 453–555. First edition, Granada 1545. Later editions by Bel and Schott together with the Chronica Hispaniae.

Historia Romanorum to 1150. And. Schott: Hispania illustrata (vol. 2, 186–195).

Criticism—Potthast: Bibliotheca historica (979, 1896). Enrique de Aguilera y Gamboa: Discursos (R. Academia de historia, Madrid 1908). Javier Gorosterratzu: Don Rodrigo Jiménez, gran estadista, escritor y prelado (Pamplona 1925). Enciclopedia universal ilustrada (vol. 28, 2790–2791, Barcelona 1926, with photograph of Jiménez' mummy, preserved in the monastery of Santa Maria de Huerta). M. Asín: Islām and the Divine Comedy (249, 1926).

III. ITALIAN

PIAN DEL CÀRPINE

See geographical chapter.

IV. ENGLISH

GERVASE OF TILBURY

See geographical chapter.

GERVASE OF CANTERBURY

Gervasius Cantuariensis or Dorobernensis. English chronicler and topographer. Monk at Christ Church, Canterbury, where he professed in 1163, was sacristan in 1193, and died after 1210. He began his historical work in 1188 and wrote the following:

(1) A Chronica of England from 1135 to 1199, with brief account of the years 1100-1135.

(2) Another chronicle of England, Gesta regum, from Brutus to 1210. Valuable for John 's rule. Continuation to 1328.

(3) History of Canterbury from the arrival of St. Augustine, 596, to 1205.

(4) Description of England, shire by shire, entitled Mappa mundi.

Gervase's chronicles are especially valuable for the last twenty years. He was strongly biased against the Plantagenets.

Text—Two of these works (nos. 1, 3) were edited by Rog. Twysden: Historiae anglicanae scriptores decem (London 1652). Critical edition of all the historical works by William Stubbs (Rolls series, 2 vols., London, 1879-1880).

English translation of no. 3 in Joseph Stevenson: Church historians of England (vol. 5, 1858).

Criticism—R. L. Poole: Dictionary of national biography (vol. 21, 239-240, 1890). Potthast (506, 1896). Charles Gross: Sources and literature of English history (348, London 1915).

ROGER OF WENDOVER

English chronicler. Born probably at Wendover, Buckinghamshire; possibly a relative of the physician, Richard of Wendover. Monk at St. Albans, later for a time prior at Belvoir, Leicestershire, a cell of St. Albans; he returned to St. Albans c. 1131, and in all probability became its historiographer and the head of its scriptorium; he died in 1236. He compiled a general chronicle, dealing with the continent as well as with England, entitled Flores historiarum, from the creation to 1235. As the title indicates, it is largely a collection of extracts from other works, yet from the year 1154 on, it contains some original material, and from 1202 on, it is a first-hand authority. Even in this last part, Roger remains a mere chronicler, an honest one, yet he never becomes a historian like Matthew Paris, who revised his work and continued it to 1259. It has been shown that Roger used as a nucleus for his own collection, an earlier one, extending to 1188, compiled by John of Cella, abbot of St. Albans (1195-1214).

For the sake of curiosity I may add that the Flores historiarum contain the first account of the legend of Lady Godiva riding naked through Coventry (Warwickshire) to obtain the release of the "villa" from a heavy bondage of toll. Lady Godiva was a benefactress and founder of monasteries who flourished c. 1040–1080.

Text—First edition by Henry Octavius Coxe (English historical society, 4 vols., London 1841–1844; additional volume, 1849). New edition by Henry G. Hewlett (Rolls series, 3 vols., London 1886–1889).

Englished by J. A. Giles: Flowers of history (Bohn Library, London 1849).

Criticism—Potthast (981, 1896). William Hunt: Dictionary of national biography (vol. 60, 250–252, 1899). Charles Gross: Sources and literature of English history (396, London 1915).

For Lady Godiva see Alexander Gordon: Dictionary of national biography (vol. 22, 36–38, 1890). K. Häfele: Die Godivasage (Heidelberg 1929).

V. SCANDINAVIAN

SAXO GRAMMATICUS

Danish historian. Born in Seeland, Denmark, flourished in Denmark in the second half of the twelfth century; died c. 1206. At the request of his master, Archbishop Absalom, he began, c. 1185, the compilation of a Danish history (Gesta Danorum; Historia danica) which was not completed until the beginning of the thirteenth century. It deals with the whole history from the mythical origins to his own time. It is based on national tales and poems. Though very crude as a historical work, it is one of the most important sources for the study of Danish origins, and as a record of early Danish literature it is invaluable. It was a popular book during the Middle Ages.

The Gesta contains observations relative to the glaciers of Iceland, including the earliest mention of the motion of glaciers. Earliest reference to barrows (prehistoric graves, Hünengräber).

Text—Editio princeps by Christiern Pedersen (Paris 1514). Often reprinted (Basel 1534; Francfort 1576; etc.). Modern edition by Alfred Holder (812 p., Strassburg 1886).

English translation by Oliver Elton and Frederick York Powell (Folklore society; 562 p., London 1894); Viking edition (1905). German translation by Hermann Jantzen (552 p., Berlin 1900); by Paul Herrmann with commentary (2 vols., Leipzig 1901–1922).

Criticism—Axel Olrik: Kilderne til Sakses oldhistorie (2 vols., Copenhagen 1892–1894). Potthast (999–1001, 1896). Léon Pineau: Saxo quid et quo modo ad Gesta Danorum conficienda, ex carminibus patrio sermone traditis hauserit (Thesis, Paris 1901). Axel Olrik: Danmarks Heltedigtning (2 vols., Copenhagen 1903–1910). Paul Schätzlein: Saxo in der deutschen Dichtung vom Ausgange des Mittelalters bis zum Verfall der Romantik (Diss., 54 p., Münster 1913). J. K. Wright: Geographical lore (219, 1924). On the glaciers, based on Thorvaldur Thoroddsen: Geschichte der isländischen Geographie (vol. 1, 1897). Albert Mennung: Über die Vorstufen der prähistorischen Wissenschaft (Veröff.d. Ges. für Vorgeschichte und Heimatkunde d. Kreises Calbe, 1, 53 p., Schönebeck a. Elbe, 1925).

SNORRI STURLUSON

Born in one of the western fjords of Iceland in 1179; flourished in Norway and Iceland, speaker of the law (i.e., president of the Icelandic republic) in 1215–1218 and again in 1222–1231; slain at Reykjaholt, Iceland, in 1241. One of the greatest mediaeval historians. He first wrote a separate saga of St. Olaf (King of Norway from 1016 to 1029, and its patron saint); then added to it the lives of the earlier kings of Norway and of those who succeeded St. Olaf down to 1177; the whole work has been called from its initial words Heimskringla (The round world, orbis terrarum). It is based partly on old poems contemporary with the events, partly on old chronicles (e.g., see my note on Ari Fróði þorgilsson, first half of the twelfth century), and partly on oral tradition. Snorri composed poems, of which the most famous is the Háttatal, written in honor of King Hákon of Norway and his father-in-law, Duke Skúli. He is also the author of the prose or younger Edda, named after him Edda Snorra Sturlusonar.

The last part of this Edda is a treatise on prosody, the earliest of its kind in Icelandic, including the poem Háttatal mentioned above. The title Háttatal, meaning list of meters, is given both to the whole treatise and to the poem. Indeed this poem illustrates in its 102 stanzas as many different metres. Some MSS. of the prose Edda also contain four treatises on grammar, but it is now generally agreed that none of them was composed by Snorri Sturluson; see my note on Ólafr Thorðarson (first half of the thirteenth century).

Text of Heimskringla—Danish edition by Peder Claussøn (Copenhagen 1683). Icelandic, Danish, Latin editions by Johann Peringskiöld (2 vols., Stockholm 1697), and by G. Schøning and others (6 vols., Copenhagen 1777–1826). Icelandic edition by Carl Rikard Unger (880 p., Christiania 1863–1868); by Finnur Jónsson (4 vols., Copenhagen 1893–1901).

German translation by Ferdinand Wachter (2 vols., Leipzig 1835–1836); by Gottlieb Mohnike (vol. 1, Stralsund 1837; not continued); by F. Niedner (Thule, 2. Reihe, 14–16, Jena 1922–1923).

English translation by Samuel Laing (3 vols., London 1844). Laing's translation has been often reprinted. A part of it is now included in Everyman's Library. Another translation by William Morris and Eiríkr Magnússon (4 vols., London 1893–1905).

French translation by Georges Sautreau: Saga des rois de Norvège; Saga de Saint Olav, 1015–1030. (304 p., Paris 1930; Isis, 15, 408).

Text of Edda Snorra Sturlusonar—Icelandic, Danish, Latin edition by Peder Hansen Resen (376 p., Copenhagen 1665). Icelandic, Latin and Swedish edition by Johann Görannson (134 p., Upsala 1746). Icelandic and Latin edition (sumptibus legati Arnamagnaeani, 3 vols. in 4, Copenhagen 1848–1887). Icelandic edition by Finnur Jónsson (249 p., Copenhagen 1900; reprinted in 1926, 248 p.; also in Reykjavík, 1907, 436 p.) Codex Wormianus. Edited for the Arnamagnaean foundation by F. Jónsson (132 p., Copenhagen 1924).

English translation by George Webbe Dasent (Stockholm 1842); by I. A. Blackwell in the Edda Saemundar of the Norroena Society (London 1906); by Arthur Gilchrist Boucheur (American Scandinavian Foundation, 288 p., New York, 1916).

German translation: Die jüngere Edda mit dem sogenannten ersten grammatischen Traktat, by F. Niedner and G. Neckel (Thule, 2. Reihe, Bd. 20, Jena 1925).

Criticism—Abraham Cronholm: De Snorronis Sturlonidis historia (53 p., Lund 1841). Gustav Storm: Snorre Sturlassöns Historieskrivning (293 p., Copenhagen 1873). Potthast (1024–1026, 1896). A. Bley: Eigla-Studien (Ghent 1909). Halldór Hermannsson: Bibliography of the Sagas of the kings of Norway and related sagas and tales (Islandica, vol. 3, 75 p., Ithaca, N. Y., 1910); Bibliography of the Eddas (Islandica, vol. 13, 95 p., Ithaca 1920). Gustav Neckel: Reallexikon der germanischen Altertumskunde (vol. 4, 195–198, 1918–1919). Sigurður Nordal: Snorri Sturluson (274 p., in Icelandic, Reykjavik 1920; by far the best study).

VI. GERMAN

For Arnold of Lübeck, see under Helmold (second half of the twelfth century); for Eike of Repgow, see legal chapter below.

VII. OTHER LATIN

VINCENT OF CRACOW

Wincenty Kadlubek. Vincentius Cracoviensis. Born in Galicia in 1160; studied in France and Italy; provost of Sandomir, professor in Cracow, 1189; bishop of Cracow, 1208; he resigned in 1218 to assume the Cistercian habit in the Jendrzejow monastery in Galicia; he died there in 1223. Canonized in 1764. He wrote a history of Poland, Historia polonica, down to 1203, which is one of the most important sources on the subject. For the earlier period it is largely based on the Chronicae Polonorum (to 1113), formerly ascribed to one Martinus Gallus. The greatest part is written in the form of a dialogue.

Text—First edition, Dobromil 1612 (very imperfect). Later editions: Leipzig 1712; Warsaw 1824. Critical edition by Alexander Przeździecki (Cracow 1862; with Polish translation). By Adolph Mułkowski (Cracow 1864). By Wydał August Bielowski: Monumenta Poloniae historica (vol. 2, Lwów 1872).
Criticism—W. Wattenbach: Deutschlands Geschichtsquellen (6th ed., vol. 2, 358, 1894). Potthast (243, 1096–1097, 1896).

HENRY OF LATVIA

Henricus Lettus or de Lettis, Henry the Lett. He was probably of northern German origin, but followed Albert, Bishop of Riga, in 1203, and became priest in Papendorf, near Wolmar, in Livonia (Latvia). He took part in the movement to Christianize the peoples settled south of the Gulf of Finland and north of the river Düna; he also took part (on the German side) in the fight between Germans and Danes for supremacy in that country. In 1215 he attended the Fourth Lateran council in Rome; in 1225, he inspected Livonia with the papal legate, and in the following year be began missionary work in Esthonia. In 1225–1227 he wrote a history of Livonia from 1186 to 1227, which is of great importance not only because he was a witness of many events or could obtain direct information about them, but also because it contains much material of cultural interest.

Text—First but incomplete edition by Johann Daniel Gruber: Origines Livoniae sacrae et civilis (Latin and German; Francfort 1740). Better edition with German translation in A. Hansen: Scriptores rerum Livonicarum (vol. 1, 50–311, Riga 1846; reprinted separately, Riga 1857). Edition by Wilh. Arndt in Monum. Germ. hist. (23, 241–332).
Eduard Pabst: Livländische Chronik (380 p., Reval 1867; German translation based partly on MS. study).
Criticism—H. Hildebrand: Allgemeine deutsche Biographie (vol. 11, 637–639, 1880). W. Wattenbach: Deutschlands Geschichtsquellen (6th ed., vol. 2, 359, 1894). Potthast (583–584, 1896).

VIII. BYZANTINE

NICETAS ACOMINATOS

Νικήτας 'Ακομινάτος. Byzantine annalist and theologian. Born about the middle of the twelfth century at Chonae in Phrygia, hence his name Choniates. (Chonae is the ancient Colossae made famous by St. Paul's Epistle to its inhabitants). He flourished at the courts of Constantinople and, after 1204, of Nicaea; died between 1210 and 1220.

His main work is a history of the years 1180 to 1206, in twenty-one books, including an account of the conquest of Constantinople in 1204. This work is largely based on first-hand information; its remarkable objectivity can be checked by referring to western historians; e.g., to Villehardouin. He also wrote a short description of the statues destroyed by the Latins in 1204 in Constantinople. This is of special interest because the Byzantine scholars paid no attention to ancient art; it is almost unique in Byzantine literature.

His main theological work is the Treasure of orthodoxy, Θησαυρὸς ὀρθοδοξίας, written c. 1204–1210, at Nicaea, in twenty-seven books. It is valuable for the history of Christian heresies in the twelfth century.

Text—History. First edition by Hieronymus Wolf (Basle 1557; with Latin translation). Edition by Im. Bekker in the Bonn corpus (vol. 22, 990 p., 1835; together with the description of the statues); both reprinted in Migne's Greek Patrology (vols. 139 and 140).

Latin translation by Hieronymus Wolf, above-mentioned (Basle 1557). Often reprinted.

Italian translation by Joseppe Horologgi (Venice 1562).

French translation by Louis Cousin (Paris 1685).

French translation of the Description of statues in J. A. C. Buchon: Collection des chroniques nationales françaises (vol. 3, 1828).

Treasure. No complete edition. For partial editions, see Krumbacher (p. 92).

Criticism—Potthast (848, 785, 1896). K. Krumbacher: Byzantinische Literatur (91–93, 281–286, 1897). Ida Carlton Thallon: Michael Akominatos (Vassar mediaeval studies, 275–314, 1923; Isis, 6, 149). Michael, Nicetas' brother, was archbishop of Athens in 1204; he died c. 1220. Νικόλαος Βέης: 'Ελευθερουδακὴ ἐγκυκλοπαιδικὸν λεξικόν (vol. 1, 637, 1927).

IX. ARMENIAN

JOHN VANAGAN

John Vanagan; i.e., the monk. Armenian theologian and historian. Born c. 1280; educated in the famous monastery of Kadig (?) in Great Armenia; enslaved by the Mongols; after having recovered his freedom he founded the monastery of Khoranashat (of many tabernacles) in Kartman, Udi, near the upper Cyrus river (Nahr al-Kur), and died there in 1251. His many theological and religious writings do not concern us, but he wrote in Khoranashat a chronicle which contained an account of the Mongol invasion of 1236. He formed many disciples, through whom some fragments of his works have come down to us.

C. F. Neumann: Geschichte der armenischen Literatur (184–185, 1836).

X. SYRIAC

SOLOMON OF AL-BAṢRA

See philosophical chapter above.

XI. HISPANO-JEWISH

IBN LAṬĪF

See philosophical chapter.

XII. WESTERN MUSLIM

IBN ḤAMMĀD

Abū 'Abdallāh Muḥammad ibn 'Alī ibn Ḥammād. Maugrabin chronicler. Born at Bū-Hamra c. 1150; studied at the Qala'a of the Banū Ḥammād nearby, then in Bougie and other places; was qāḍī in Algesiras and Salé, and died in 1230. He wrote a chronicle of Bougie (Bijāya), and in 1220 a brief account of the Fāṭimid rule in Africa (909–1171), Akhbār mulūk Banī 'Ubaid wa sīratuhum. In spite of its brevity that account is valuable because it is one of the earliest and contains first-hand references to local conditions.

Text—First complete edition, by N. Vonderheyden: Histoire des rois 'obaïdides (Publications de la Faculté des lettres d'Alger, 3e série, fasc. 2; 164 p., Paris 1927; Arabic text with French translation; Isis, 13, 159).
Criticism—René Basset: Encyclopaedia of Islām (vol. 2, 383, 1916). Short note superseded by Vonderheyden's introduction to his edition.

'ABD AL-WĀḤID AL-MARRĀKUSHĪ

Abū Muḥammad 'Abd al-Wāḥid ibn 'Alī al-Tamīmī al-Marrākushī, Muḥyī al-dīn. Born at Marrākush in 1185; studied there, in Fez, and after 1208 in Spain; in 1217 he went to Egypt, where he seems to have spent the rest of his life; he died in or after 1224. He wrote, in 1224, a history of the Muwaḥḥid dynasty, preceded by a summary of Spanish history from the Muslim conquest to 1087 (Kitāb al-mu'jib fī talkhīṣ akhbār ahl al-Maghrib). It is uncritical and exceedingly biased in favor of the Almohades.

Text—Edition by R. P. A. Dozy: The history of the Almohades (Leiden 1847; again, 1881). French translation by Edmond Fagnan (Revue africaine, vols. 36 and 37, passim; separate edition, 332 p., Alger 1893).
Criticism—F. Wüstenfeld: Geschichtschreiber der Araber (109, 1881). C. Brockelmann: Arabische Litteratur (vol. 1, 322, 1898). E. Lévi-Provençal: Documents inédits d'histoire almohade (440 p., Paris 1928, p. iii; Isis, 13, 221).

IBN 'ARABĪ

See philosophical chapter.

IBN AL-ABBĀR

Abū 'Abdallāh Muḥammad ibn 'Abdallāh ibn Abī Bakr Ibn al-Abbār al-Quḍā'ī. Hispano-Muslim historian. Born at Valencia in 1199; after the conquest of Valencia by the Christians in 1238, he went to Tunis and was secretary to the salāṭīn of Tunis; he was murdered in Tunis, 1260. He composed many works, of which the two most important were a continuation (takmila) to the Kitāb al-ṣila of Ibn Bashkuwāl (first half of the twelfth century)—i.e., a history of the learned men of Spain; and another compilation of the same kind, the Kitāb al-ḥulla al-siyarā'.

Text—Kitāb al-takmila li kitāb al-ṣila, edited by Francisco Codera y Zaidín (Biblioteca arabico-hispana, vols. 5 and 6, Madrid 1887–1889). Angel González Palencia and M. Alarcón: Apéndice a la edición Codera de la Tecmila (Miscelánea de estudios y textos árabes, Madrid 1915). A. Bel et M. ben Cheneb: La préface d'Ibn el-Abbār à sa Takmila (Revue africaine, nos. 296–297, p. 306–335, Algiers 1913); Arabic text with French translation (Isis, 13, 427).

A part of the Ḥulla was edited by R. P. A. Dozy: Notices sur quelques MSS. arabes (Leiden 1847–1851); another part by Marcus Joseph Müller: Beiträge zur Geschichte der westlichen Araber (München 1866–1878).

Al-mu'jam fī aṣhāb al-qāḍī al-imām Abī 'Alī al-Ṣadafī (index of the disciples of this Spanish traditionalist, born c. 1052, died 1120), edited by F. Codera (Biblioteca arabico-hispana, vol. 4, Madrid 1886).

Criticism—F. Wüstenfeld: Geschichtschreiber der Araber (p. 128–129, 1881). C. Brockelmann: Arabische Litteratur (vol. 1, 340, 1898). Francisco Pons Boigues: Ensayo bio-bibliográfico sobre los historiadores arábigo-españoles (291–296, 1898). Moh. ben Cheneb: Encyclopaedia of Islām (2, 352, 1916).

XIII. EASTERN MUSLIM

For Yāqūt, see geographical chapter; for 'Abd al-Laṭīf, see philosophical chapter.

IBN AL-ATHĪR

Abū-l-Ḥasan 'Alī ibn Muḥammad 'Izz al-dīn Ibn al-Athīr al-Shaibānī (of the tribe of Shaibān) al-Jazīrī. The second and most distinguished of three brothers, all of whom won fame as authors and scholars. He was born in 1160 at Jazīrah ibn 'Umar in Jazīrah (Mesopotamia); he moved to Mūṣul in 1180 when his father was appointed governor of that city; he had many occasions of going to Baghdād and of traveling in Syria and Arabia to accomplish the Pilgrimage or on diplomatic missions for the rulers of Mūṣul, but the best part of his life was spent in that city where he died in 1233.

One of the greatest chroniclers of mediaeval times. His main work is a universal chronicle down to 1231 called the Kāmil (Kitāb al-kāmil fī-l-ta'rīkh, the perfect book of chronicles). The earlier part of it, down to c. 915, is essentially an elaboration of the Kitāb akhbār al-rusūl wal-mulūk of al-Ṭabarī (first half of the tenth century). A continuation of the Kāmil was composed by Maḥmūd ibn Salmān ibn Fahd al-Ḥalabī (d. 1325).

In 1211–1212, he wrote a history of the Atābeg rulers of Mūṣul (1127 to 1211). He also compiled an alphabetic dictionary of the contemporaries of the Prophet, Kitāb usd al-ghāba fī ma'rifat al-ṣaḥāba, and an abridgment of the Kitāb al-ansāb of al-Sam'ānī (second half of the twelfth century), called the Lubāb (Kitāb al-lubāb mukhtaṣar al-ansāb lil-Sam'ānī).

Text—Edition of the Kāmil by C. J. Tornberg: Ibn el-Athiri Chronicon quod perfectissimum inscribitur (14 vols., Leyde 1851–1876; vols. 13–14 contain the indexes). Būlāq edition in 12 vols. (1873–1886, without index). Carl Johan

Tornberg: Berättelse om Arabernas eröfning af Spanien (Arabic and Swedish, Lund 1851). Extracts edited in Arabic and French, in the Recueil des historiens des Croisades (vols. 1 and 2, 1872–1887). Annales du Maghreb et de l'Espagne traduites par E. Fagnan (664 p., Alger 1898).

Historia dynastiae Atabegidarum Mosulae principum. Extracts published by de Guignes in the Notices et extraites (vol. 1, 542–578, 1787). Complete edition in the Recueil des historiens des Croisades (vol. 2, part 2, 394 p., Paris 1876; with French translation).

Usd al-ghāba (5 vols., Cairo 1883–1884).

Medulla (i.e., abridgment of al-Sam'ānī's work). Specimen el Lobābi edited by F. Wüstenfeld (Göttingen 1835).

Criticism—Ibn Khallikān (de Slane's translation, vol. 2, 288–290, 1843). Ibn Khallikān met Ibn al-Athīr in Ḥalab, 1229. Joseph Elian Sarkis: Dictionnaire de bibliographie arabe (36–38, Cairo 1928).

F. Wüstenfeld: Die Geschichtschreiber der Araber (Göttingen, 113, 1881). C. Brockelmann: Das Verhältnis von Ibn al-Athīrs Kāmil zu Ṭabarīs Akhbar (Diss. 58 p., Strassburg 1890); Arabische Litteratur (vol. 1, 345, 1898); Encyclopaedia of Islām (vol. 2, 365, 1916).

Sir William Muir's Caliphate (1883) was largely derived from Ibn al-Athīr. See new and revised edition by T. H. Weir (Edinburgh 1915; Isis, 3, 352).

IBN ABĪ-L-DAM

Abū Isḥāq Ibrāhīm ibn 'Abdallāh ibn 'Abd al-Mun'im ibn abī-l-Dam al-Hamdānī al-Ḥamāwī, Shihāb al-dīn. Born at Ḥamāt in 1187–1188, where he flourished, and where he died in 1244–1245. Shāfi'ite qāḍī; historian. He wrote a history (Ta'rīkh) of the Prophet and of the Caliphs down to 1231. He dedicated to the Ayyūbid prince of Mesopotamia, al-Muẓaffar Ghāzī (ruled from 1230 to 1244–1245), an elaborate history of Islām, in six volumes (Al-ta'rīkh al-Muẓaffarī).

Text—Extracts of the last named work, relative to Sicily, were translated into Italian by Agostino Inveges (1595–1677): Annali della felice città di Palermo (vol. 2, 659, Palermo 1650). Latin translation of the same extracts in Joh. Bapt. Carusius: Bibliotheca historica regni Siciliae (vol. 1, 19–23, Panormi, 1723); again in L. A. Muratori: Rerum italicarum scriptores (vol. 1, part 2, 251) and in Rosario Gregorio: Rerum Arabicarum quae ad historiam Siculam spectant (53–68, Panormi 1790).

Criticism—F. Wüstenfeld: Geschichtschreiber der Araber (122, 1881). C. Brockelmann: Arabische Litteratur (vol. 1, 346, 1898).

'UMAR IBN AL-'ADĪM

Kamāl al-dīn Abū-l-Qāsim 'Umar ibn Aḥmad . . . ibn abī Jarāda ibn al-'Adīm al-'Uqailī al-Ḥalabī al-Ḥanafī. (The Banū Jarāda of the tribe of 'Uqail had emigrated from Baṣra to Syria in the first half of the ninth century). Muslim-Syrian historian. Born in Ḥalab (Aleppo) in 1192; studied in Jerusalem, Damascus, in the 'Irāq and the Ḥijāz; was appointed professor in a madrasa of Aleppo in 1219–1220, later qāḍī and wazīr to the Ayyūbid rulers of Aleppo, al-'Azīz and al-Nāṣir; he fled with the latter to Egypt when the Mongols captured the city in 1260. Hūlāgū appointed him chief qāḍī of Syria, but Ibn al-'Adīm died in Cairo, 1262, before he could reach his new post.

He wrote an enormous history of Aleppo; that is, a collection of biographies of the famous men of Aleppo, arranged alphabetically, Bughyat al-ṭālib fī ta'rīkh

Ḥalab (The gratification of one's desires with regard to the history of Aleppo); it would seem that that work was never completed in a fair copy. He wrote an abridgment of it arranged chronologically down to 1243–1244 (Zubdat al-ḥalab fī ta'rīkh Ḥalab, Cream of the milk of the history of Aleppo[2]). He composed a guide for the making of perfumes, Kitāb al-wuṣlat (or wasīlat) ilā-l-ḥabīb fī waṣf al-ṭaiyibāt wal-ṭibb.

The Bughyat was continued down to 1439–1440 by 'Alī ibn Muḥammad ibn Khaṭīb al-Nāṣirīya (d. 1439–1440), and by Muḥammad Ibn al-Shiḥna al-Ḥalabī (d. 1485).

Text—G. W. Freytag: Selecta ex historia Halebi (Arabic and Latin; Paris 1819); Regnum Saahdal daulae in oppido Halebi (Bonn 1820). E. Blochet: L'histoire d'Alep de Kamāladdīn (Revue de l'Orient latin, 1896 to 1899; French translation).

Criticism—F. Wüstenfeld: Geschichtschreiber der Araber (130–131, 1881). C. Brockelmann: Arabische Litteratur (vol. 1, 332, 1898); Encyclopaedia of Islām (vol. 2, 703, 1924). Ign. Kratschkovsky: Angebliche Autographe des Kamāl al-dīn in Leningrad (Der Islam, 15, 334, 1926). Joseph Elian Sarkis: Dictionnaire de bibliographie arabe (171, Cairo 1928).

IBN AL-QIFṬĪ

Abū-l-Ḥasan 'Alī ibn Yūsuf, Jamāl al-dīn al-Shaibānī Ibn al-Qifṭī. Egyptian historian. Born in Qifṭ (Coptos) in Upper Egypt, 1172–1173; flourished in Cairo until c. 1187, then in Jerusalem until c. 1202, finally in Aleppo, where he spent the rest of his life. He was many times wazīr to the Ayyūbid rulers of Aleppo, the last time from 1236 to his death in 1248.

He was extremely learned, and was perhaps the greatest bibliophile of Islām, among a great many others. His library was valued after his death at 60000 dinars. He was a patron of scholars; e.g., of Yāqūt.

The most important of his works has come down to us in abbreviated form, the others are almost completely lost. The Kitāb ikhbār al-'ulamā' bi-akhbār al-ḥukamā' (Information given to the learned on the history of the wise) is known through the summary made in 1249–1250 by Muḥammad ibn 'Alī al-Zawzanī, the Kitāb al-muntakhabāt al-multaqaṭāt min kitāb ta'rīkh al-ḥukamā', generally called Ta'rīkh al-ḥukamā'. It is a collection of 414 very unequal biographies of ancient and Muslim physicians, men of science, and philosophers. It is an important source for the history of Muslim science; it contains hardly any new information on Greek science, but shows what the Muslims knew and thought of it.

The Bibliotheca philosophorum so often quoted by Miguel Casiri in his Bibliotheca arabico-hispana escurialensis (Madrid 1760–1770) has been identified with the Ta'rīkh al-ḥukamā'. This identification has much decreased the interest of Casiri's work.

Text—The Tar'īkh al-ḥukamā was edited on the basis of August Müller's investigations by Julius Lippert (518 p., Berlin 1903). Reviewed from the mathematical point of view by H. Suter in Bibliotheca mathematica (vol. 4, 293–302, 1903).

Biographies of Greek mathematicians have been translated by Eilhard Wiedemann in his Beiträgen (nos. 3 and 5, Sitzungsber. der physik. mediz. Societät, Erlangen, vol. 37, 247–255, 441–448, 1905). A full English translation with notes is much needed.

[2] The word ḥalab means Aleppo, and also milk.

Criticism—L. Leclerc: Médecine arabe (vol. 2, 193–198, 1876). A Müller: Das arabische Verzeichnis der aristotelischen Schriften (Morgenl. Forsch., 1–32, Leipzig 1875); Über das sogenannte Ta'rīkh al-ḥukamā' (Actes du 8ᵉ congrès des orientalistes, Leiden, 15–36, 1891). F. Wüstenfeld: Geschichtschreiber der Araber (124, 1881). C. Brockelmann: Arabische Litteratur (vol. 1, 325, 1898). H. Suter: Die Mathematiker und Astronomen der Araber (143, 1900). E. Mittwoch: Encyclopaedia of Islām (vol. 2, 398, 1918).

IBN ABĪ UṢAIBI'A

Muwaffak al-dīn Abū-l-'Abbās Aḥmad ibn al-Qāsim Ibn abī Uṣaibi'a al-Sa'dī al-Khazrajī. Muslim-Syrian physician and historian of medicine. Born in Damascus 1203–1204 in a medical family (his father was an oculist); he studied in Damascus and later walked the hospital al-Nāṣirī in Cairo; in 1236–1237, he obtained a post in the opthalmologic department of that hospital, but soon afterwards entered the service of an amīr in Ṣarkhad near Damascus; he died in Ṣarkhad in 1270. He had herborized with Ibn al-Baiṭār, had been in correspondence with 'Abd al-Laṭīf, and had known personally a great many physicians.

He compiled a collection of medical observations which is lost. His main work was historical, the Kitāb 'uyūn al-anbā' fī ṭabaqāt al-aṭibba' (Sources of information on the classes of physicians). It is a series of bio-bibliographies of the most eminent physicians from the earliest times to his own. It was composed at Ṣarkhad c. 1242, but revised at a later date. It is our main source for the history of Muslim medicine; it deals with about 400 Muslim or Arabic physicians, but it deals also with others. It is divided into fifteen chapters: (1) Origins of medicine; (2) Early physicians; (3) Greek physicians beginning with Asclepios (Asqlībiyūs); (4) Hippocrates and his contemporaries; (5) Galen and his time; (6) Physicians of Alexandria; (7) Physicians of the Prophet's time; (8) Syrian physicians under the early 'Abbāsid caliphs; (9) The translators and their patrons; (10 to 15) the last six chapters deal with the physicians respectively of 'Irāq, Persia, India, Maghrib and Spain, Egypt, Syria.

Not less than six chapters deal with pre-Islāmic medicine. It is seldom that his data relative to Greek physicians are at once new and true, yet his account is very valuable for the understanding of Muslim science. It helps us to realize what the Arabic speaking people knew and thought of Greek medicine. Though Ibn abī Uṣaibi'a's work is primarily a history of physicians, its interest is not by any means restricted to medicine. Most of the Muslim physicians were not simply physicians; many were mathematicians, physicists, astronomers, philosophers, or men of encyclopaedic type. Thus the 'Uyūn al-anbā' is a source for the history of Muslim science in general; for example, the historian of mathematics must often refer to it.

Text—The 'Uyūn al-anbā' was edited by Imru-l-Qais Ibn al-Ṭaḥḥān (2 vols., Cairo 1882; with incomplete index). The same text (apparently the same sheets) was republished by August Müller with 162 additional pages including a German preface, lists of corrections and variants and a complete index (2 vols., Königsberg, 1884).

An English translation with critical notes would be very desirable.

Criticism—F. Wüstenfeld: Arabische Aerzte (132–144, 1840; containing a list of the Syriac and Muslim physicians dealt with; Wüstenfeld's own notices were largely derived from Ibn Abī Uṣaibi'a); Geschichtschreiber der Araber (133, 1881).

L. Leclerc: Médecine arabe (vol. 2, 187–193, 1876). August Müller: Ueber Ibn Abi Oçeibi'a und seine Geschichte der Aerzte. Congrès des Orientalistes de Leide (vol. 2, 259–280, 1884); Text und Sprachgebrauch von Ibn abī Uṣeibi'a's Geschichte (Sitzungsber. der bayer. Akad. d. Wiss., phil. Kl., 1884, 853–977, Müchen, 1885). C. Brockelmann: Arabische Litteratur (vol. 1, 325, 1898). J. E. Sarkis: Dictionnaire de bibliographie arabe (27, Le Caire 1928).

I have very often referred to Müller's text in the preparation of my work, but not always; in some cases I have depended on other scholars who had already made use of it.

XIV. PERSIAN

AL-BUNDĀRĪ

al-Fatḥ ibn 'Alī ibn al-Fatḥ al-Iṣfahānī, Qawām al-dīn, flourished c. 1226. Muslim historian. He composed in 1226 an abridgment of the history of the Saljūq rule by 'Imād al-dīn al-Iṣfahānī (second half of the twelfth century); it is said that he also abridged the latter's Kitāb al-barq al-Sha'mī. He translated Firdawsī's Shāhnāma into Arabic for al-Mu'aẓẓam, Ayyūbid ruler of Damascus who ruled from 1218 to 1227.

Text—Abridgment of the Nuṣrat al-fatra, entitled Zubdat al-nuṣrat wa nukhbat al-'uṣra, edited by M. Th. Houtsma: Recueil des textes relatifs à l'histoire des Seldjoucides (vol. 2, Leiden 1889).

Criticism—F. Wüstenfeld: Geschichtschreiber der Araber (112, 1881). C. Brockelmann: Arabische Litteratur (vol. 1, 321, 1898). Encyclopaedia of Islām (vol. 1, 743, 1912).

J. E. Sarkis: Dictionnaire de bibliographie arabe (591, 1928).

AL-NASAWĪ

Muḥammad ibn Aḥmad ibn 'Alī, Shihāb al-dīn al-Nasawī. Born in the district of Nasā (or Nisā), Khurāsān; he became secretary to Jalāl al-dīn Mangbarti (Shāh of Khwārizm, 1220–1231) after the latter's defeat by the Mongols on the Indus in 1221–1222, and remained with him until that sulṭān's murder in a Kurdish village in 1231; he himself died in or after 1241. He completed in 1241–1242, a biography of his patron, the Sīrat al-sulṭān Jalāl al-dīn. He wrote it in Arabic, but one can feel that he thought in Persian. This work is of great value because it is the record of an immediate witness who is apparently sincere and who tries to explain the tragic events which he describes.

Text—Arabic text with French translation by O. Houdas in the Publ. de l'Ecole des langues orientales vivantes (vols. 9–10, Paris 1891–1895).

Criticism—F. Wüstenfeld: Geschichtschreiber der Araber (121, 1881). C. Brockelmann: Arabische Litteratur (vol. 1, 319, 1898). E. G. Browne: Persian literature (vol. 2, 449, 473, 1906).

MUḤAMMAD AL'AWFĪ

See philosophical chapter.

XV. CHINESE

For Ts'ai Ch'ên, see mathematical chapter; for Yeh-lü Ch'u ts'ai, see chapter on education.

YEH LUNG-LI

Yeh^{4*} Lung^{2}-li^{3} (12997, 7504, 6949). Chinese historian. Born at Chia^{1}-hsing^{1} (1158, 4611), Chehkiang; graduated as chin shih in 1247. He wrote the history of the Kitan Tartars (907–1125), Ch'i^{4}-tan^{1} kuo^{2*}-chih^{4} (1053, 10618, 6609, 1918), and probably also that of the Chin Tartars, Ta^{4}-chin^{1} kuo^{2*}-chih^{4} (10470, 2032, 6609, 1918). It is claimed in the preface of the second history that it was completed in 1234 by a Chinese official of Tartar origin, Yü^{2}-wên^{2} Mou^{4}-chao^{1} (13540, 12633, 8043, 473); it seems more probable, however, that Yeh Lung-li was the real author.

H. A. Giles: Biographical dictionary (933, 962, 1898). L. Wieger: La Chine (224, 318, 500, 523, 1920).

XVI. JAPANESE

KAMO CHŌMEI

Japanese writer. Born near Kyōto c. 1154; died c. 1225. He was for a time director (yoriudo) of the poetical department (uta-dokoro) of the imperial palace. Later he retired into a Buddhist monastery on (mount) Ōhara-yama, near Kyōto, assumed the religious name Ren-in, and wrote there, in 1212, a little book entitled Hōjō-ki, wherein he describes among other things the great fire of Kyōto in 1177, the cyclone of 1180, the famine of 1181, the long series of earthquakes of 1185, and by contrast the peace of his hermitage. Hōjō means ten feet square, the size of his hut. The title of this book might thus be translated "Annals of ten feet square." (Cf. the Voyage autour de ma chambre by Xavier de Maistre, 1795). He wrote various other works, but this one is the most famous, one of the classics of Japanese literature. He has sometimes been called the Japanese Wordsworth, or the Japanese Thoreau.

W. G. Aston: Littérature japonaise (140–150, 1902, including translation of long extracts). Minakata Kumagusu and Frederick Victor Dickins: A Japanese Thoreau of the twelfth century (Journal R. Asiatic Soc., 237–264, 1905; complete English translation with many notes). Michel Revon: Anthologie de la littérature japonaise (245–266, Paris 1910; including French translation). A. L. Sadler: The Ten foot square hut and Tales of the Heike (284 p., Sydney 1929; new English translation).

CHAPTER XL

LAW AND SOCIOLOGY

(First Half of Thirteenth Century)

I. ITALIAN

DEVELOPMENT OF CANON LAW

This brief survey of the juridical and sociological endeavors of the thirteenth century may properly begin with a few words on the development of the Canon Law, the international law of Christendom.

Its organization may be ascribed to the Italian Gratian (first half of the twelfth century), who in 1139 compiled the Decretum, the first part of the Corpus juris canonici. The Decretum was still informed with Roman law, but the development of Canon Law was essentially a gradual emancipation from the older law. This appeared already in the Summa Magistri Rolandi of Alexander III (pope 1159–1181) and became clearer as time went on. That evolution was naturally accelerated by the growing misunderstandings between Popes and Emperors.

The second part of the Corpus juris canonici, the Liber extra or Quinque libri decretalium, was published by Gregory IX (pope from 1227 to 1241) in 1234, a little more than a century after the Decretum. It was compiled by the Catalan Dominican, Raymond of Peñafort, whose task was simply one of codification, for by that time the new collections of decretals had been growing for almost half of a century.

The anti-Roman tendencies of the Curia are sufficiently illustrated by the fact that in 1219 Honorius III prohibited the teaching of Roman law at the University of Paris, and forbade priests to study it.

However, Roman Law was being spread all over western Christendom by the students of Bologna. At the beginning of the century the University of Orleans was a new center for its diffusion. Finally there was an increasing demand for legists (i.e., doctors in Roman law or in both laws) in the royal courts; they were equally needed to resist the papal chancery, to stabilize government institutions, to organize the expanding bureaucracy, to frustrate centrifugal tendencies, to favor by all means, fair or foul, national integration.

The growth of this new profession was especially conspicuous in France. In England, Roman Law was forbidden in favor of the Common Law, yet the development of the latter was not and could not be entirely independent of the former.

The growth of political theory was hastened considerably by the conflict between the imperial and papal ideas of sovereignty, by the struggle between both Laws, the lay and the ecclesiastical.

The best general study of these questions was given by Sir Robert Warrand Carlyle and Alexander James Carlyle: A history of mediaeval political theory in the West (5 vols., 1903–1928). Vol. 5 is a systematic account of political theory in the thirteenth century (Isis, 12, 357).

AZO

Azo Portius (or Azzo, Azone, Azzoleno). Italian civilian. Born at Bologna about the middle of the twelfth century; flourished at Bologna; died c. 1230. He was the main pupil of John Bassianus, became professor of law at Bologna, and was one of the most important of the glossators. His most famous pupil was Accorso. His own authority is attested by the old saying: "Chi non ha Azo non vada a Palazzo." Bracton (second half of the thirteenth century) was much influenced by him. His main work was his summary of Roman law entitled Summa codicis et institutionum.

Text—Summa super Codice et Institutis. First edition, Speyer 1482 (324 leaves). Later editions: Pavia 1484; Venice 1489, 1498, 1499, Etc. Gesamtkatalog der Wiegendrucke (vol. 3, 255-259, 1928). Some 30 editions from 1482 to 1610.

Quaestiones, first edition by Ernst Landsberg (Freiburg i. B., 1888).

Criticism—Paul Vinogradoff: Roman law in mediaeval Europe (47-49, 1909). R. W. and A. J. Carlyle: History of mediaeval political theory (vol. 2, 1909). C. P. Sherman: Roman law (vol. 1, 205, Boston 1917).

HUGOLINUS

Hugolinus glossator. Ugolino. Italian jurist. Born in Bologna in the twelfth century; died soon after 1233. Teacher of civil law in Bologna. He compiled many law books, notably a Summa digestorum, previously ascribed to others. The titles of the following works need no explanation: Glossae; Diversitates seu dissensiones dominorum; Distinctiones; Quaestiones.

Text—The Summa digestorum is appended to the editions of Azo's Summa, except the first. Summa super usibus feudorum in Scripta anecdota glossatorum (vol. I-III, Bologna 1888-1901); also edition by John Baptist Palmieri (Bibliotheca juridica medii aevi, vol. 2, 1892).

Criticism—R. W. and A. J. Carlyle: History of mediaeval political theory (vol. 2, 1909).

ACCORSO

Francesco Accorsi. Franciscus Accursius. Born at Bagnolo, Tuscany, or in Florence, 1182; pupil of Azo; practiced law in Florence, later, c. 1220, in Bologna, where he died in 1260. He was the most famous of the glossatores (the commentators on Roman law), and the one who had the greatest share in the renaissance of legal studies; the fame of the school of Bologna was largely due to his immense activity. His main work is a methodical compilation of all the commentaries on Roman law, the Glossa ordinaria or Glossa magistralis (vulg., Chiosa grande; Chiosa continua; Great gloss), which remained the final authority until the time of Bartolo (second half of the fourteenth century), whose reforms it prepared. The authority of the Glossa is witnessed by the old maxim "Quidquid non agnoscit Glossa, non agnoscit curia."

Three of his sons became distinguished lawyers. The eldest, Francesco II (born at Bologna in 1225, died there in 1293), was also professor of law in Bologna, and later for a few years, c. 1275, in Oxford; later still he was the diplomatic representative of Edward I (1272-1307) in Rome. The second son, Cervotto, was professor of law in Pavia and Bologna; the third, Guglielmo, was attached to the Roman court.

Text—There are many sixteenth century editions of the Glossa, Corpus juris civilis. At least three editions in 5 vols. folio: Lyon 1556–1558, Paris 1576, Venice 1584. At least three editions in 6 vols. folio: Lyon 1589, 1612, 1618. The best of these editions is said to be that of Denis Godefroy the Elder (1549–1629), Lyon 1589.

There are no incunabula editions of the elder Francesco, but there are three of the younger. Casus longi super digesto novo (Basel c. 1489–1497; Lyon c. 1500). Casus in terminis super Codice (Strassburg c. 1485). Gesamtkatalog der Wiegendrucke (vol. 1, 77–78, 1925).

Criticism—See the books on mediaeval law (Savigny), and on mediaeval education (Rashdall, vol. 1, 1895). P. Vinogradoff: Roman law in mediaeval Europe (47–49, London, 1909). R. W. and A. J. Carlyle: History of mediaeval political theory (vol. 2, 1909). John Edwin Sandys: History of classical scholarship (vol. 1^3, 604–605, 1921).

ODOFREDUS

Italian jurist. Born and studied in Bologna. He practiced his profession in France and southern Italy; returned to Bologna c. 1228 to teach law; spent there the greatest part of his life, and died there in 1265. Many commentaries on Roman law were published under his name, being probably the notes of his students.

According to him, the pope's authority was supreme in spiritual things, the emperor's in material ones.

Nouvelle biographie générale (vol. 38, 485, 1862). Nino Tamassia: Odofredo (Atti d. R. deput. di storia patria, Romagna, vol. 11, 183; 12, 330, 1894–1895). C. H. Haskins: The renaissance of the twelfth century (203, 1927). R. W. and A. J. Carlyle: History of mediaeval political theory (vol. 2, 1909; vol. 5, 1928).

FREDERICK II

See philosophical chapter.

PETER OF VINEA

Petrus de Vinea (or Vineis). Pietro della Vigna, Pier delle Vigne. Born in Capua. Chancellor, protonotary and ambassador of the emperor Frederick II. Having fallen into disgrace, he ended his life in San Miniato, 1249. His Letters are historical material of the first order for the study of Frederick's rule and time, but they are not historical works. Peter is mentioned here because he is said to be the real author of Frederick's Sicilian code of 1231.

Text—First edition of the Epistolae, Hagenau, 1529. More complete yet very imperfect edition by Simon Schard: Epistolarum quibus res Friderici II gestae describuntur libri VI (Basel 1566). Alphonse Huillard-Bréholles: Vie et correspondance de Pierre de la Vigne. Avec une étude sur le mouvement réformiste au 13e siècle (462 p., Paris 1865).

Criticism—Potthast (918, 1896).

INNOCENT IV

Sinibaldo Fieschi dei Conti di Lavagna. Born in Genoa. Elected pope in Anagni, 1243; died in Naples, 1254. During his papacy most of his energy was devoted to his merciless struggle with Frederick II. He convoked the Council of

Lyon (1245), which excommunicated and deposed the emperor; later he preached a crusade against him. He is mentioned here because of his remarkable activity as a jurist before 1243. He wrote Apparatus super decretales; De potestate ecclesiastica et juridictione imperii, etc. He claimed that all power, temporal as well as spiritual, originates with the pope. He is said to have been the first to speak of a corporation as a persona ficta—and also the first pope to give a red hat to the cardinals!

Text—B. Hauréau: Quelques lettres d'Innocent IV, extraites des MSS. de la Bibliothèque nationale (94 p., Paris 1874). Elie Berger: Les registres d'Innocent IV publiés ou analysés d'après les MSS. originaux du Vatican et de la Bibliothèque nationale (4 vols., Paris 1884–1920).

Criticism—Otto von Gierke: Die Staats- und Korporationslehre des Altertums und des Mittelalters (279, Berlin 1881). Hans Weber: Der Kampf zwischen Innocent IV und Friedrich II bis zur Flucht des Papstes nach Lyon (93 p., Berlin 1900). August Folz: Friedrich II und Innocent IV, ihr Kampf in den Jahren 1244 und 1245 (158 p., Strassburg 1905). Ludwig Dehio: Innocent IV und England (Diss., 94 p., Berlin 1913). Werner Meyer: Ludwig IX von Frankreich und Innocent IV in den Jahren 1244–47 (Diss.; Marburg 1915). R. W. and A. J. Carlyle: History of mediaeval political theory in the West (vol. 5, 1928; Isis, 12, 357).

II. SPANISH

PETER GALLEGO

See translators from the Arabic.

III. ENGLISH

MAGNA CARTA

The longest and most important charter granted by the Norman kings to their barons (not to the people!) was the Magna Carta granted by king John at Runnimede, near Windsor, in June 1215. It was an eleboration of the accession charter of Henry I (1100) and contained little that was absolutely new. It was less a grant of new privileges than a restoration of lost liberties, namely those guaranteed by the laws of Edward the Confessor in 1070 (Edward died in 1066, but his "laws" are supposed to have been drawn up in 1070), and by the charter of Henry I already mentioned. Besides king John did all he could to destroy it—for example, he caused Innocent III (pope from 1198 to 1216) to publish a bull in August 1215 declaring the Magna Carta null and void and to excommunicate the barons—but fortunately he died in October of the following year. Though less important than many scholars until relatively recent times had imagined it to be, the Magna Carta is one of the great landmarks in the development not simply of the English government but of constitutional practice in general.

Text—There are four authentic copies of the Magna Carta bearing John's seal, two at the British Museum and two others in the cathedrals of Lincoln and Salisbury. The Lincoln copy is considered the best. The first printed edition (of an inferior text, however) appeared in 1499. First edition of the original text by William Blackstone: The Great Charter and the Charter of the Forest (162 p., Oxford 1759). Photozincographed facsimile with English translation (Southampton 1867). There are various other facsimile copies or engravings.

Criticism—William Stubbs: Select charters (Oxford 1870; 9 ed., 1913). William Sharp McKechnie: Magna Carta (626 p., Glasgow 1905; 2 ed. revised, 547 p., 1914). Arthur William Holland: Encyclopaedia Britannica (11th ed., 8 cols., 1911); contains a summary of the 63 articles of the Charter, one by one. Henry Elliot Malden: Magna Carta commemoration essays (341 p., R. Historical Soc., London 1917). Containing essays by Lord Bryce, W. S. McKechnie, P. Vinogradoff, Rafael Altamira, etc. Faith Thompson: The first century of Magna Carta: why it persisted as a document (133 p., Minneapolis 1925). Léon Leclère: La Grande charte de 1215 est-elle une illusion? (Mélanges Henri Pirenne, vol. 1, 279-290, Bruxelles 1926).

WILLIAM OF DROGHEDA

Drogheda is the name of a place in Leinster, Ireland, some thirty miles north of Dublin; Drogheda is a Celtic name; it stands for droicheadatha, bridge at the ford. William of Drogheda was a lecturer on canon law in Oxford. He died in 1245. He wrote for his pupils, c. 1239, a treatise on canon law, Summa aurea, which enjoyed a long popularity, even in Bologna. It is interesting because of many references to Roman law. This suggests that the teaching of Roman law was not entirely discontinued in England in spite of royal efforts to suppress it (see my note on Vacarius, second half of the twelfth century).

Frederic William Maitland: William of Drogheda and the universal ordinary (English historical review, vol. 12, 625-658, 1897; including extracts from the Summa); Roman canon law (107, 1898). Albert Frederick Pollard: Dictionary of national biography (vol. 61, 370, 1900). Paul Vinogradoff: Roman law in mediaeval Europe (85, 1909).

IV. GERMAN

EIKE OF REPGOW

Eike von Repgow (or Repkow). German jurist, the earliest known to us. Sheriff of Reppichau in Anhalt; flourished c. 1230. He compiled the largest and most important code of mediaeval Germany, the Sachsenspiegel. He wrote it first in Latin, then translated it into Low-German before 1235. This code was exceedingly popular and its success retarded to some extent the progress of Roman law in German countries; it was soon translated into High-German, Dutch, and Polish, and was freely imitated.

Later German codes were essentially based on the Sachsenspiegel, the two most important being the Deutschenspiegel (or Spiegel deutscher Leute), and the Schwabenspiegel. Both, as their titles indicate, had a more ambitious scope; the latter was adapted to the needs of South Germany; the former to those of the Empire. The Schwabenspiegel (c. 1259, c. 1273-1282) included the substance of the Sachsenspiegel, but it contained also fragments of Roman, Canon and Imperial law.

A world chronicle, the Sächsische Weltchronik, written in Low-German—the earliest historical work of its scope in German prose—was previously ascribed to Eike. It extends to the year 1225 (1230, 1235, 1248 in later editions). It also enjoyed considerable popularity, as is shown by the number of MSS. and continuations. It was soon translated into Latin, and that translation was long thought to be the original text.

Text—Sachsenspiegel. First edition of Landrecht, Basel 1474; and of Lehnrecht, Augsburg 1482. Many other early editions. Modern edition by C. Gustav Homeyer: Landrecht (Berlin 1827; 3rd ed., 1861); Lehnrecht (2 vols., Berlin 1842–1844). School edition of Landrecht by Julius Weiske (Leipzig 1840; 8th ed., by R. Hildebrand, Leipzig 1905). Baron de Geer von Jutphaas: De Saksenspiegel in Nederland ('s Gravenhage 1888). Karl von Amira: Die Dresdener Bilderhandschrift (facsimile, Leipzig 1902).

A Dutch translation of the Landrecht appeared in print before the German text (Gouda 1472). Latin and Polish translations appeared respectively in Cracow, 1506, and Cracow, 1559.

Julius Ficker: Der Spiegel deutscher Leute. Textabdruck der Innsbrucker Handschrift (242 p., Innsbruck 1859).

Sächsische Weltchronik. A large part was edited by Joh. Georg Eccard: Corpus historicorum medii aevi (vol. 1, 1315–1412, Leipzig 1723). Hans Ferdinand Massmann: Das Zeitbuch des Eike von Repgow, in ursprünglicher niederdeutscher Sprache und in früher lateinischer Übersetzung (763 p., Stuttgart 1857). Ludwig Weiland: Die sächsische Weltchronik in verschiedenen Rezensionen (bis 1225, 1230, 1235, 1248) und mit zahlreichen auch süddeutschen Fortsetzungen (Mon. Germ. hist., Deutsche Chroniken, vol. 2, 65–258, 1877).

Latin translation, Historia imperatorum ad a. 1235, first published by Joa. Burch. Mencken: Scriptores rerum germanicarum (vol. 3, 63–128, Leipzig 1730). Reprinted by H. F. Massmann (Stuttgart 1857).

Criticism—Potthast (992, 1109, 1896). G. C. Lee: Historical jurisprudence (406–409, New York 1900). E. J. H. Steffenhagen: Die Entwicklung der Landrechtsglosse des Sachsenspiegels (Wiener Ak., phil. Kl., vols. 98, 100, 101, 106, 110, 111, 113, 114, 167, 1881–1911). Paul Vinogradoff: Roman law in mediaeval Europe (109–113, 1909). Hermann Ballschmiede: Die Sächsische Weltchronik (Diss., Berlin 1914?). R. W. and A. J. Carlyle: History of mediaeval political theory in the West (vol. 3, 1915; vol. 5, 1928).

V. ICELANDIC

KONUNGS SKUGGSJÁ

See philosophical chapter.

VI. HISPANO-JEWISH

AL-ḤARIZĪ

See philosophical chapter.

VII. EGYPTO-MUSLIM

IBN AL-ḤĀJIB

See philological chapter.

VIII. CHINESE

For Chingiz Khān, see philosophical chapter; for Sung Tz'ŭ, the medical.

IX. JAPANESE

JAPANESE LAW

In 1232, during the regency of Hōjō Yasutoki (born 1183–died 1242), a new code of law was promulgated. This Hōjō Yasutoki was the third Kamakura Shikken (i.e., first minister of the Shōgun of Kamakura) out of nine; from 1200 to 1333 the head of the Hōjō family was the actual ruler of Japan under that title. This code for the use of samurai was divided into fifty-one brief articles; it was called Jōei-shikimoku, after the name of the nengō (period) Jōei (or Tei-ei) of its promulgation, 1232–1233; it was drawn by Miyoshi Yasutsura and Hokkyō Enzen under the guidance of the Shōgunal government. It was not meant to supersede the Daihō-ryōritsu (first half of the eighth century), but to complete it and to take into account an entirely different political situation, feudalism as opposed to absolute monarchy.

While the Daihō was written exclusively in Chinese characters, the Jōei-shikimoku was largely written by means of the Japanese syllabary (vol. 1, 519).

Text—John Carey Hall: Japanese feudal law. The institutes of judicature being a translation of Go seibai shikimoku, the magisterial code of the Hōjō power-holders (Transactions of the Asiatic Society of Japan, vol. 34, 1–44, 1906).

Criticism—E. Papinot: Historical and geographical dictionary of Japan (164, 233, 1909). James Murdoch: History of Japan (vol. 1, 462 sq., 1910). F. Brinkley: History of the Japanese people (348–350, 1915).

CHAPTER XLI

PHILOLOGY

(First Half of Thirteenth Century)

I. LATIN

EBERHARD OF BETHUNE

Everard, Evrard, etc. Eberhardus Bethuniensis. Flemish grammarian and poet. He hailed from Bethune in Flanders (not Bethune in Artois) and flourished at the end of the twelfth century and the beginning of the thirteenth. His main work is a Latin grammar, called Graecismus, because of a chapter on derivations from the Greek. It was written in Latin verse (2200 lines), probably in 1214. It enjoyed some popularity: Erasmus used it as a primer; Rabelais mentions it.

He also wrote the Anti-haereses in twenty-eight chapters, against heretics, chiefly the Waldensians, and the Labyrinthus (in 3000 Latin verses) dealing with Latin grammar and poetry and the misery of teachers. The third and last part of the Labyrinthus contains estimates of some thirty popular Latin poets of ancient and mediaeval times (Horace not included).

Text—The Graecismus was printed in Lyon, 1483 (?), 1490; Paris 1487, etc. much used as a schoolbook during the sixteenth century.

Critical edition by John Wrobel (Corpus grammaticorum medii aevi, 1, 342 p., Breslau 1887).

Anti-haereses edited, together with two other writings of the same kind, by Jacob Gretser: Trias scriptorum adversus Waldensium sectam (Ingolstadt 1614). Reprinted in other anti-Waldensian collections, 1654, 1677, 1734.

Criticism—Alphonse Wauters: Biographie nationale (vol. 6, 747–751, Bruxelles 1878). J. E. Sandys: History of classical scholarship (vol. 1^3, 1921).

GARLAND

John of Garland, Joannes de Garlandia, Garlandius, etc. This name is derived from the "clos de Garlande" which formed one of the oldest parts of the University of Paris.[1] He was born in England c. 1195, and studied in Oxford c. 1210–1213, under John of London. He moved to France c. 1217 and became deeply Frenchified. He flourished in Paris, except for a few years spent in Toulouse (1229–1232) at the University which had been founded there in 1229 to consecrate the victory over the Albigenses and establish a bulwark against that heresy. He was probably still living in 1272.

Latin humanist and poet, grammarian, lexicographer, moralist. He had some knowledge of Greek. His best known work is the De triumphis ecclesie, a long epic poem celebrating the victory of the Church over the Albigenses; it has some historical value. His main ethical work was the Morale scolarium, which he

[1] The "rue Galande" near St. Julien le Pauvre and St. Séverin is still a witness to that old clos de Garlande.

composed in 1241 in order to reform the morals of the Parisian students and incidentally their Latin. It is a valuable source for the study of college life.

He wrote many grammatical works, glossaries, lists of synonyms, etc. The most interesting perhaps is the Dictionarius (c. 1220, before 1229) a list of common things composed on the model of the De utensilibus of Alexander Neckam (second half of the twelfth century). This represents the first use of the word dictionary. His main grammatical treatise was the Compendium grammatice (c. 1234, before 1249); he wrote about the same time a summary of it entitled Clavis compendii.

Garland's grammatical activity is of great cultural importance. He was one of the first "speculative" grammarians or "modistae," whose teaching superseded in Paris the fossilized teaching based on Donatus (first half of the fourth century) and Priscian (first half of the sixth century). The modistae were so called because they were specially interested in the connection between words and ideas (significatio), and wrote many books entitled De modis significandi. They inaugurated a new philosophical study of language; such kind of study had been carried on by Greek philosophers, especially by the Stoics, but had since fallen into oblivion (vol. 1, 137, 181).

Treatises on compotus and on music may have been composed by him, or they may have been ascribed to him through confusion with another Garland, or Gerland, who flourished in Besançon in the second half of the eleventh century (vol. 1, 758). The treatise on music contains a full treatment of mensural music, introduced into Christian Europe in the first half of the eleventh century (vol. 1, 542, 628, 703), and deals with the ochetus (īqā'āt), meaning truncation.

He was probably the author of a medical treatise (Memoriale) which is lost.

The Compendium alchemiae sometimes ascribed to him is certainly apocryphal. According to Hauréau, this Compendium was written by one Martin Ortolan or Lortholain (second half of the fourteenth century).

Text—Dictionarius. First edition by H. Géraud: Paris sous Philippe le Bel (580–612, Paris 1837). Later editions by baron Kelvyn de Lettenhove (Annales de la Société d'Emulation, vol. 8, 160–176, 219–220, Bruges 1850); by Thomas Wright: Volume of vocabularies (120–138, London 1857); by Aug. Scheler: Trois Traités de lexicographie latine du XIIe et du XIIIe siècles (Jahrbuch für romanische und englische Litteratur, 6, 43–49, 142–162, 287–321, 370–379, 1865).

De triumphis ecclesiae libri octo, edited by Thomas Wright (Roxburghe Club, London 1856).

Compendium grammatice. Still unpublished. The Compendium totius grammatices, without date or place (Deventer 1489) is another work. The Clavis is also unpublished.

The Morale scolarium was edited by Louis John Paetow (Memoirs of the University of California, vol. 4, no. 2, p. 65–273, pl. 11–14, Berkeley 1927). This excellent critical edition is accompanied by an English paraphrase and an elaborate discussion of Garland's life and works. My note has been almost entirely rewritten on the basis of Paetow's work (Isis, 10, 126).

The Compendium alchemiae was printed for the first time with other alchemical writings in a collection called "de alchemia" (Nürnberg 1541; reprinted in Berne 1545). It was printed again in an edition claiming to be the first, in Bale 1560. Again in Bale 1571, etc. The edition of 1560 is the first bearing Garland's name (Joannes Garlandius); it is very different from the earlier editions.

Criticism—A. Scheler: La lexicographie latine des XIIe et XIIIe siècles (Paris 1875). Barthélemy Hauréau: Notice sur les oeuvres authentiques et supposées de Jean de Garlande (80 p., Paris 1877). C. L. Kingsford: Dictionary of national biography (vol. 20, 436–439, 1889). John Ferguson: Bibliotheca chemica (vol. 1, 18, 419–422, 1906; article Hortolanus containing a long discussion of the Compendium; vol. 2, 157). J. E. Sandys: History of classical scholarship (vol. 1^3, 549, 1921). Henry George Farmer: The Arabian influence on musical theory (Journal R. Asiatic Soc., 61–80, 1925; Isis, 8, 508–511). Julius Ruska: Tabula smaragdina (195–203, Heidelberg 1926; apropos of the apocryphal Compendium alchemiae). M. de Wulf: Mediaeval philosophy (vol. 1, 93, 1926). A. Hughes-Hughes: Grove's Dictionary of music (3d ed., vol. 2, 351, 1927). Louis John Paetow: The crusading ardor of John of Garland (The Crusades, essays presented to Dana C. Munro, 207–222, 1928). C. H. Haskins: Studies in mediaeval culture (mainly chapter 3, Manuals for students, 72–91, Oxford 1929; Isis, 14, 434).

VILLEDIEU

See mathematical chapter.

ALBERTANO OF BRESCIA

Albertano Giudice da Brescia. Albertanus Causidicus Brixiensis. Albertanus de Albertanis. Albertanus de Ora S. Agathae. Judge in Brescia. Podestà of Gavardo, near Salò (Brescia). He wrote three didactic treatises on morality and language which have some importance because of their extraordinary popularity. The first, De amore et dilectione Dei, was written by him in 1238 in the prison of Cremona where he had been thrown by Frederick II. The second, De arte loquendi et tacendi, dates from 1245; the third, Liber consolationis et consilii, from 1246 (or 1248).

These treatises were translated into many vernaculars. Judging by the number of incunabula of the Latin text and of the Dutch translation, the second, Ars loquendi, was especially popular. It was translated into Icelandic. The third, Liber consolationis, was successful in another way; it was put into French under the title of Livre de Mélibée et de dame Prudence; an English version, The tale of Melibeus, was included in Chaucer's Canterbury Tales. The treatises were translated into Italian by Andrea da Grosseto in 1268, and again at Pistoia in 1278 by Soffredi del Grathia.

Text—De arte loquendi et tacendi. First known edition: Basel c. 1474 (10 leaves). Later editions, Strassburg c. 1476; Cologne c. 1482; Toulouse c. 1484; Antwerp 1484, 1485; Louvain 1485; Antwerp 1486; Paris 1486; Cologne 1486; Antwerp 1487; Cologne 1487; Lyon 1487, c. 1488; Toulouse c. 1488; Memmingen 1489; Cologne 1489; Deventer 1490; Leipzig 1490; Angoulême c. 1491; Paris c. 1491; Cologne 1491; Leipzig 1491; Deventer 1491; Ingolstadt c. 1492; Leipzig 1492; Antwerp c. 1493–1498; Lyon c. 1493; Augsburg c. 1494; Leipzig 1495; Cologne c. 1496; Cologne 1497; etc. Appendix to the Italian translation of Thor Sundby's study on Brunetto Latini (p. 476–506, Florence 1884).

Dutch translation, Die konste om te leren spreken ende swighen, Haarlem c. 1484; Delft c. 1486; 's Hertogenbosch c. 1488; Gouda c. 1489; Delft c. 1493–97; Deventer 1496.

Liber consolationis et consilii, ex quo hausta est fabula gallica de Melibeo et Prudentia, quam anglice redditam et The tale of Melibe inscriptam Galfridus Chaucer inter Canterbury Tales recepit. Edited by Thor Sundby (160 p., Chaucer Society, London 1873).

Bastiano de Rossi (called l'Inferigno): Sull' amor di Dio e del prossimo, sulla consolazione e sui consigle e sulle sei maniere del parlare (Florence 1610). Later editions, Mantua 1737; Brescia 1824.

Volgarizzamento inedito fatta nel 1268 da Andrea da Grosseto. Edited by Francesco Solmi (Bologna 1873). Volgarizzamonto dei tratti morali di Albertano da Soffredi del Grazia, 1278. Edited by Sebastiano Ciampi (Florence 1832). Soffredi's version was also edited by Gustav Rolin (176 p., Leipzig 1898).

Icelandic version of the Ars loquendi et tacendi, c. xxvi moralium dogmatis. Edited by Thor Sundby (350 p., Copenhagen 1869).

Criticism—John Knight Bostock: Albertanus Brixiensis in Germany, being an account of the Middle High German translations from the didactic treatises (123 p., Oxford 1924). Gesamtkatalog der Wiegendrucke (vol. 1, 244-258, 1925).

OTHER GRAMMARIANS

Brief references to two other grammarians must suffice.

Thomas of Capua, cardinal, who died in 1239, wrote an Ars dictandi, of which a critical edition has been recently published by Emmy Heller.

Emmy Heller: Ars dictandi (Sitzungsber. der Heidelberger Akademie, philos. Klasse, 1928-1929, 4, 60 p., Heidelberg 1929). On earlier "dictators" see Charles Homer Haskins: The early artes dictandi in Italy (Studies in mediaeval culture, 170-192, Oxford 1929; Isis, 14, 435).

Walter of Ascoli, author of an etymological dictionary entitled Dedignomium, Summa derivationum, or Speculum artis grammatice. Master Walter came from Bologna to teach grammar at Naples; he had begun his Dedignomium in Bologna before 1229, and completed it in Naples.

C. H. Haskins: Magister Gualterius Esculanus (Mélanges offerts à Ferdinand Lot, 245-257, Paris 1925; Isis, 14, 477, 518).

II. FRENCH

Read summary on p. 530, and refer by index to the authors quoted.

III. ITALIAN

Read summary on p. 531, and note on Frederick II in philosophical chapter.

IV. SCANDINAVIAN

THÓRÐARSON

Ólafr Thórðarson, nicknamed Hvítaskáld, the white poet. Nephew of Snorri Sturluson and brother of Sturla Thórðarson, the historian. Born c. 1210, died in 1259. Icelandic poet and grammarian. He spent many years abroad at the courts of Norway and Denmark. The Prose Edda (for which see my note on Snorri Sturluson) contains in some MSS. four grammatical treatises, the third of which was composed by Ólafr Thórðarson. This treatise includes fragments of an older work on runes by Thóroddr Rúnameistari (Thorod the Rune-master) who flourished at the beginning of the twelfth century. The fourth treatise is a continuation of Thórðarson's work by another writer, possibly the abbot Bergr Sokkason, who died in 1345.

The first two treatises are anonymous. The first cannot be earlier than c. 1130-1140 and is probably not later than 1170-1180. The second was composed c. 1250 by a man who had some knowledge of music.

Text—The four treatises were published with Latin translations in vol. 2 of the Arnamagnaean edition of Snorri Sturluson's Edda (Copenhagen 1852). Icelandic text with Danish notes and introduction in Islands grammatiske Litteratur i Middelalderen. Udgivet for Samfund til udgivelse af gammel nordisk Litteratur (2 vols., Copenhagen, 1881–1886; nos. 1 and 2 edited by Finnur Jónsson and Verner Dahlerup; nos. 3 and 4 by Björn Magnússon Ólsen). Separate edition of no. 3 by Finnur Jónsson (1927).

V. GREEK

See notes on John Basingstoke among the translators, and on Robert Grosseteste in the philosophical chapter.

VI. ARMENIAN

ARISTACES THE GRAMMARIAN

Armenian grammarian. He originated in Great Armenia, and flourished c. 1211. He was a pupil of Gregory of Sgevrha (Sgevrha was a famous monastery not far from Lampron in Cilicia). Aristaces composed an Armenian dictionary and a treatise on the art of writing.

C. F. Neumann: Geschichte der armenischen Litteratur (182, 1836).

VII. HEBREW

See notes on Abraham ben Azriel in the religious chapter; on Samuel ibn Tibbon and Jacob Anaṭoli in the chapter on translators; on Robert Grosseteste in the philosophical chapter.

JOSEPH BEN SAMSON

Joseph, son of rabbi Samson, otherwise unknown, wrote in 1240 (not 1241) for rabbi Samuel a Hebrew-French glossary to a great part of the Old Testament. It gives the Hebrew words, their French equivalents in Hebrew character (la'azim),[2] and eventually Hebrew synonyms and glosses. Many of those la'azim are apparently borrowed from Rashi (second half of the eleventh century). The words are in general vocalized with great care and precision. The French dialect is Bourguignon.

I am quoting this glossary as the best specimen of a group of writings which were the natural by-products of linguistic studies. They extend over a period of five centuries, from the end of the tenth to the end of the fifteenth century. These works are most useful to determine the pronunciation of contemporary Hebrew and French. They illustrate the interpenetration of both languages. The Jews were more inclined to use a lay vernacular than Latin, which was the vehicle of another faith. Some other glossaries were prepared by Latin scholars studying Hebrew; they were written in Roman script.

From the French point of view the earliest of these glossaries are the most important, being almost the only documents enabling us to determine the pronunciation of the new language. The earliest collection of la'azim is that contained in the Talmud commentaries of Gershon of Metz, who flourished at Mayence, and died in 1028 (130 la'azim). The most important after that is Rashi's (c. 2000 la'azim).[3] But by far the most extensive is the glossary to which the present note is devoted.

[2] La'az means foreign language or word (chiefly Greek).

[3] Vol. 1, 752.

Compare with early Arabic glossaries (vol. 1, 782).

Text—Mayer Lambert and Louis Brandin: Glossaire hébreu-français du XIIIe siècle. Recueil de mots hébreux bibliques avec traduction française. Manuscrit de la Bibliothèque nationale, fonds hébreu, no. 302 (312 p., Paris 1905).
Louis Brandin: Les glosses françaises (loazim) de Gershom de Metz (Revue des études juives, vol. 42, 48–75, 237–252; vol. 43, 72–100, 1901).
Criticism—Samuel Berger: Quam notitiam linguae hebraicae habuerint Christiani medii aevi temporibus in Gallia (Paris 1893). Arsène Darmesteter and David Simon Blondheim: Les gloses françaises dans les commentaires talmudiques de Rashi. Tome 1. Texte des gloses (288 p., Bibliothèque de l'Ecole des chartes, 254; Paris 1929; OLZ, 238–240, 1931; DLZ, 390–391, 1931).

TANḤŪM YERUSHALMI

Tanḥūm ben Joseph Yerushalmi. Jewish grammarian and theologian who flourished in Jerusalem or in another city of the Near East in the thirteenth century. He was called by later writers with pardonable exaggeration "the Ibn Ezra of the East"; indeed, he was the last great Jewish scholar of the orient. He wrote in Arabic various Biblical commentaries, collected under the title Kitāb al-ījāz wal-bayān (Concise exposition), with a general introduction (Kulliyat) dealing with Hebrew grammar and some earlier grammarians. He quoted many commentators, from Saadia Gaon to Abraham ibn Ezra. He compiled a dictionary entitled Al-murshid al-kāfī (The sufficient guide), wherein are listed in alphabetical order the words of Maimonides' Mishneh Torah, and a great many others found in the Mishnah, with references to earlier lexicographers, chiefly to Nathan ben Jehiel (second half of the eleventh century).

Text—There is no complete edition of the Ījāz, but many special commentaries have been published, for which see the Jewish Encyclopaedia.
Wilhelm Bacher: Aus dem Wörterbuche Tanchum Jerushalmi's. Nebst einem Anhange über den sprachlichen Charakter des Maimūni'schen Mischne tora (Jahresbericht der Landes-Rabbinerschule in Budapest für 1902–1903; reprint, Strassburg 1903).
Criticism—M. Steinschneider: Arabische Literatur der Juden (234–236, 1902). Isaac Broydé: Jewish Encyclopaedia (vol. 12, 43, 1906).

VIII. ARABIC

See notes on Yāqūt in the geographical chapter, and on Ibn al-Baiṭār in the medical chapter.

IBN AL-ḤAJIB

Abū 'Amr 'Uthmān ibn 'Umar Ibn al-Ḥājib, Jamāl al-dīn. Born in Fanā, Upper Egypt in 1175; his father was a Kurdish chamberlain (ḥājib). Ibn al-Ḥājib studied in Cairo, taught law in Damascus, then settled in Cairo; he died in Alexandria in 1249. Mālikī theologian and grammarian. He wrote many treatises on grammar, prosody, and law.

His most important grammatical work was a short Arabic grammar called Al-kāfiya (The sufficient); another, still shorter, was called Al-shāfiya (The satisfactory). Both obtained, especially the first, an immense popularity. His treatise on prosody, Kitāb al-maqṣad al-jalīl fī 'ilm al-Khalīl (Great purpose with regard to the art of Khalīl; i.e., Khalīl ibn Aḥmad, the reputed founder of Arabic prosody, see vol. 1, 541), was also much appreciated; at least five commentaries were devoted to it.

His two books on Mālikī law were almost equally successful, chiefly in the Maghrib; he was the first to harmonize the teachings of the Mālikī theologians of Egypt and of the West. The larger one is entitled Muntahā al-su'āl wal-āmāl (The end of asking and hoping); the shorter, Mukhtaṣar al-muntahā (or Mukhtaṣar al-uṣūlī).

Text—Al-kāfiya. Printed in Rome, 1591. Many oriental editions.

Al-shāfiya. Printed in Calcutta in 1805, Constantinople in 1850, etc. Extracts edited by F. Buhl, with Danish commentary (Leipzig 1878).

Criticism—Ibn Khallikān: Slane's translation (vol. 2, 193–195, 1843). Ibn Khaldūn: Prolégomènes (vol. 3, 20–21, 34, 274, 312). C. Brockelmann: Arabische Litteratur (vol. 1, 303–306, 1898). Moh. ben Cheneb: Encyclopaedia of Islām (vol. 2, 381, 1916).

AL-SAKKĀKĪ

Abū Bakr Yūsuf ibn abī Bakr ibn Muḥammad Sirāj al-dīn al-Khwārizmī. Born in Khwārizm in 1160; he began life making locks, knives, etc., hence the name Sakkākī; he was a Ḥanīfite. He died near Almāligh (on the Ilih) in 1228–1229. Turkish man of letters who wrote in Arabic and Turkish (?). His best known work among many was a treatise on rhetoric, which was the most elaborate Arabic treatise on the subject up to his time. This work, entitled Kitāb miftāḥ al-'ulūm, is divided into three parts, dealing respectively with phonology and morphology, grammar, and rhetoric ('ilm al-ṣarf, 'ilm al-naḥw, 'ilm al-ma'ānī wal-bayān). The third part includes some prosody and practical logic (istidlāl).

The Miftāḥ al-'ulūm was the subject of many commentaries and summaries. It was almost entirely superseded by one of these, the Talkhīṣ al-miftāḥ, by Muḥammad ibn 'Abd al-Raḥmān al-Qazwīnī (1267–1338), which itself became the subject of many more commentaries. In this indirect manner the Miftāḥ al-'ulūm has influenced Arabic letters and thought almost until the present day. Al-Sakkākī is quoted here for the same reason that Quintilian was quoted in my first volume.

Ḥājī Khalīfa: Lexicon (vol. 6, 15, 1852). C. Brockelmann: Arabische Litteratur (vol. 1, 294–296, 1898; calls him Abū Ya'qūb?; vol. 2, 22, 1902). F. Krenkow: Encyclopaedia of Islām (vol. 4, 80, 1925).

IX. SANSKRIT

See note on Narahari, in the medical chapter.

X. CHINESE

See note on Chingiz Khān, in the philosophical chapter.

XI. JAPANESE

See note on Japanese law.

APPENDIX TO BOOK III

(First Half of Thirteenth Century)

The following notes were added at the last moment, when it was no longer possible to insert them at their proper places or to take them into account in the general survey of scientific thought in the first half of the thirteenth century. Fortunately, none but one would have materially affected my conclusions, and their complete omission would not have mattered much. The exception is the Egyptian eye-doctor, Aḥmad ibn 'Uthmān al-Qaisī, who flourished in the fifth decade of the century and who was certainly a physician of note.

Peter of Beauvais wrote a bestiary and a geography in French. These productions are so crude that they would hardly deserve mention but for the fact that they help us to realize the sad predicament of the French people who could not read Latin.

The Persian, Aḥmad ibn al-Khalīl, composed an Arabic treatise on the soul, and a collection of anecdotes relative to the seven branches of knowledge.

Ismā'īl ibn Ibrāhīm of Mārdīn, in Mesopotamia, wrote treatises on arithmetic and algebra.

An Arabic treatise on hygiene is ascribed to the Alexandrian Jew al-Barqamānī. The importance of that treatise, which is not great, is still further decreased by our ignorance of its exact date. We only know that it is posterior to Maimonides, and have placed it tentatively in this period.

Finally Sibṭ Ibn al-Jauzī, an 'Irāqian man of letters of Turkish origin, composed historical accounts and a treatise for the general guidance of a princely education.

PETER OF BEAUVAIS

French writer who hailed probably from the Île de France or from Normandy. He was in Beauvais in 1212. He wrote in French verse the lives of three saints, a "mappemonde," etc.; and in prose a bestiary, etc. The bestiary, that is, a translation of the Physiologus, was composed for Philip of Dreux, bishop of Beauvais (1175–1217); the "mappemonde" for Robert of Dreux (d. 1218). The "mappemonde" was derived from Solinus (second half of the third century), and to a lesser extent from the Imago mundi of Honorius Inclusus. Peter apparently thought that he was the first to offer the fruits of Solinus' learning to French readers, but he was mistaken, for a French version of it had been made by Simon of Boulogne for the count of Guise, Baldwin II (d. 1206). Simon's version is lost.

Peter's works are exceedingly mediocre, but his Bestiary and his Mappemonde are witnesses of the kind of knowledge available to French readers in the first quarter of the thirteenth century. And it should be noted that, for all their mediocrity, his works were appreciated. For example, the Bestiaire was read until the fifteenth century. However, it was one of the last French "moralized" bestiaries; two others were composed at about the same time by the Norman trouvères William the Clerk and Gervase of (the diocese of) Bayeux.

Text—The Bestiaire was edited by Charles Cahier: Mélanges d'archéologie (vols. 2 to 4, Paris 1851–1856).

Extracts from the Mappemonde edited by Paul Meyer in Notices et extraits vol. 33, part 1, p. 35–37, 1890).

Criticism—Paul Meyer: Histoire littéraire de la France (vol. 34, 381–388, 1914). This is a part of his memoir on French bestiaries (vol. 34, 362–390), wherein the best information on William the Clerk and Gervase of Bayeux will also be found. Ch. V. Langlois: La connaissance de la nature et du monde au Moyen âge (La vie en France au Moyen âge, vol. 3, 122–134, 1927). Analysis of the Mappemonde with brief extracts.

AḤMAD IBN AL-KHALĪL

Abū-l-'Abbās Aḥmad ibn al-Khalīl ibn Sa'āda, al-Khuwayyī, Shams al-dīn. Muslim philosopher, physician, and Shāfi'ī theologian.

Born in 1187–1188; he began very early the study of law and medicine; after the birth of his son he traveled to Baghdād to sit at the feet of Ibn Hubal; later he studied under 'Alā al-dīn al-Tā'ūsī (?) in Hamadān, and of Fakhr al-dīn al-Rāzī, presumably in Herāt. According to his own testimony he studied the following books: the Masā'il of Ḥunain ibn Isḥāq, the Murshid of al-Rāzī (i.e., the Fuṣūl fī-l-ṭibb), the Dhakhīra of Thābit ibn Qurra,[1] the Qānūn of Ibn Sīnā. He became chief justice (qāḍī al-quḍāt) in Damascus, and died there in 1239–1240.

He wrote the Janābī' al-'ulūm (Aqālīm al-ta'ālīm fī-l-funūn al-sab'a), anecdotes relative to the seven main branches of knowledge, to wit, tafsīr, ḥadīth, fiqh, adab, medicine, geometry and arithmetic; and a treatise on the soul, entitled Kitāb al-safīnat al-nūḥiyya fi-l-sakīnat al-rūḥiyya. The latter begins with a collection of opinions on the soul given in the following order: physicians, philosophers, wise men, mystics, ordinary people. Then a classification of souls, those of plants being the lowest; means of purifying the soul; personal conclusions containing autobiographical details.

Text—Al-safīnat al-nūḥiyya (34 p., Ḥalab 1929; J. R. A. S., 483–485, 1930).
Criticism—C. Brockelmann: Arabische Litteratur (vol. 1, 508, 1898).

ISMĀ'ĪL IBN IBRĀHĪM AL-MĀRIDĪNĪ

Abū-l-Ṭāhir Ismā'īl ibn Ibrāhīm ibn Ghāzī al-Numairī al-Ḥanafī, Shams al-dīn, al-Māridīnī (i.e., of Māridīn, or Mārdīn, near Naṣībīn, in Jazīrah). Often called Ibn Fallūs. Muslim (Mesopotamian) mathematician. Born in 1194; died in 1239–1240 or 1252.

He wrote three mathematical treatises: (1) Kitāb i'dād al-asrār fī asrār al-a'dād (Preparation of the secrets, or the secrets of numbers). Arithmetic. After the letter of Nicomachos to Pythagoras (?). Written during the Pilgrimage.

(2) Kitāb irshād al-ḥussāb fī-l-maftūḥ min 'ilm al-ḥisāb. Composed in Mecca. Arithmetic.

(3) Niṣāb al-ḥabr fī-l-ḥisāb al-jabr. Also written in Mecca. Algebra.

Criticism—C. Brockelmann: Arabische Litteratur (vol. 1, 472, 1898). H. Suter: Mathematiker und Astronomen der Araber (143, 1900).

[1] That is, the work but recently edited by G. Sobhy (Cairo 1928; Isis, 13, 364–365), and analyzed by Max Meyerhof in Isis (vol. 14, 55–76, 1930).

AḤMAD IBN 'UTHMĀN AL-QAISĪ

Qāḍī Fatḥ al-dīn Abū-l-'Abbās Aḥmad ibn 'Uthmān al-Qaisī. Egyptian oculist who flourished in Cairo during the rule of the Ayyūbid sulṭān al-Ṣāliḥ (1240–1249).

His father, Qāḍī Jamāl al-dīn Abū 'Amr 'Uthmān, had been also a prominent physician; born at Damascus, he followed al-Malik al-'Azīz when the latter became governor of Egypt; after the death of al-'Azīz (1198) he remained in Egypt; he was physician to the Ayyūbid al-Kāmil (1218–1238).

To return to Aḥmad, he was called prince of the Egyptian doctors (rais al-aṭibbā bi-diyār al-miṣrīya). Under al-Ṣāliḥ's rule he wrote a treatise on eye diseases, entitled Kitāb natījat al-fikar fī-'ilāj 'amrāḍ al-baṣar (Result of the thinking on the treatment of the troubles of vision). It is a summary divided anatomically into fourteen chapters, the affections of various parts being considered in the following order: (1) conjunctiva; (2) cornea; (3) aqueous humor of the anterior and posterior chambers [floating specks or "mouches volantes" were anciently ascribed to unclean particles or opacities in the aqueous humor]; (4) uvea (iris and ciliary body); (5) albuminoid humor (aqueous of to-day); (6) arachnoid; (7) lens; (8) vitreous body; (9) retina; (10) choroid and sclerotic; (11) optic nerve (hemeralopia, nyctalopia); (12) muscles of the eyeball; (13) eyelids; (14) canthi and lacrimal glands. A final chapter (15) deals with the weakness of sight, and hygiene.

Aḥmad al-Qaisī does not quote his sources. He is not mentioned by Ibn abī Uṣaibi'a, which is not very surprising as the 'Uyūn al-anbā' was composed c. 1242; he is quoted by Ṣalāḥ al-dīn ibn Yūsuf (after 1296).

L. Leclerc: Médecine arabe (vol. 2, 219, 1876). Julius Hirschberg, J. Lippert and E. Mittwoch: Die arabischen Lehrbücher der Augenheilkunde (Abhdl. der preussischen Akademia, 91, 1905). N. Kahil: Une ophtalmologie arabe par un praticien du Caire du XIIIe siècle (p. 241–260, Congrès de médecine du Caire, December 1928). Analysis of the Natījat al-fikar, and translation of the part explaining the operation of the cataract in chapter 3 (Isis, 15, 406).

AL-BARQAMĀNĪ

Japheth (?) Ibn abī-l-Ḥasan al-Barqamānī al-Isrā'īlī al-Iskandarī (of Alexandria). Perhaps one should read Turkomānī,[2] for the nisba Barqamānī cannot be explained. The other names are almost equally uncertain.

Jewish—perhaps Qaraite— physician who flourished in Alexandria some time after Maimonides. He wrote in Arabic a treatise on hygiene, entitled Al-Maqāla al-muḥsiniyya bi-ḥifẓ al-ṣaḥḥa al-badaniyya (Beneficent discourse on the preservation of bodily health), divided into ten chapters.

Criticism—M. Steinschneider: Die Handschriften-Verzeichnisse der k. Bibliothek zu Berlin (vol. 2, 102–104, 1897). Analysis of the MS. written in Hebrew script (there is another MS. in Arabic script in Oxford). An extract is given on p. 157.

M. Steinschneider: Arabische Literatur der Juden (no. 172, p. 233, 1902). G. A. Kohut: Jewish Encyclopaedia (vol. 3, 68, 1902). Irene Chanoch: Encyclopaedia judaica (vol. 4, 211, 1929).

Ḥājjī Khalīfa mentions a treatise having almost a similar title. Al-maqāla al-muḥsiniyya fī tadbīr al-saḥḥa al-badaniyya (vol. 6, no. 12696, 182) but he gives nothing but the title; no author's name.

[2] In the Arabic script the syllables *bar* and *tur* could very easily be confused, but not the syllables *qa* and *ko*.

YŪSUF IBN QIZ-UGHLI

Abū-l-Muẓaffar Yūsuf ibn Qiz-ughli ibn 'Abdallāh, Shams al-dīn. Muslim ('Irāqian) historian (1186–1257).

He is often called Sibṭ Ibn al-Jauzī. His father was a Turkish slave of Yaḥyā ibn Muḥammad Ibn Hubaira (d. 1165), wazīr to the caliphs al-Muqtafī and al-Mustanjid. Qiz-ughli was emancipated and educated by his master the wazīr, and he married the daughter of the famous Ibn al-Jauzī (d. 1201). Their son, Yūsuf, was born in Baghdād in 1186–1187, and was educated by his maternal grandfather, Ibn al-Jauzī. After having completed his studies in Baghdād, he traveled for a while, then settled down in Damascus, where he preached and taught Ḥanafī law, and where he died in 1257.

He compiled (1) a general history from the creation to 1256, the Kitāb mir'āt al-zamān fī ta'rīkh al-a'yān. This was a very large work of which there are no complete MSS., and which has been only incompletely transmitted to us. He wrote also:

(2) Tadhkirat khawāṣṣ al-umma bi-dhikr khaṣā'iṣ al-a'imma (History of the caliph 'Alī, his family, and the twelve a'imma[3]).

(3) Kitāb al-jalīs al-ṣāliḥ wal-anīs al-nāṣiḥ (The honest companion and the sincere friend), written for the education of the Ayyūbid al-Ashraf Mūsā, governor of Damascus (1237). It would be interesting to compare this text with the many Latin treatises composed in the thirteenth century with a similar purpose (Regimen principum, Eruditio regum, etc.).

(4) Kanz al-mulūk fī kaifīyat al-sulūk. Collection of anecdotes.

Text—Extracts from the Mir'āt al-zamān were edited by C. A. C. Barbier de Meynard, and translated into French (Recueil des historiens des croisades, historiens orientaux, vol. 3, Paris 1872). A MS. of that work belonging to Yale University was reproduced in facsimile by James Richard Jewett, with introduction (544 p., Chicago 1907). Extracts from the Mir'āt al-zamān, relative to Damascus, are included in Ḥamzah ibn Asad Ibn al-Qalānisī: History of Damascus, in Arabic, edited by H. F. Amedroz (Beyrut 1908).

Criticism—F. Wüstenfeld: Geschichtschreiber der Araber (no. 340, 126, 1881). C. Brockelmann: Arabische Litteratur (vol. 1, 347, 1898). Includes a brief summary of the Jalīs ṣāliḥ.

[3] Plural of imām.

BOOK FOUR

The Time of Roger Bacon, Jacob ben Maḥir ibn Tibbon, and Quṭb al-dīn al Shīrāzī

(Second Half of Thirteenth Century)

Contemplatio humana secundum statum praesentis vitae non potest esse absque phantasmatibus . . . Sed tamen intellectualis cognitio non sistit in ipsis phantasmatibus sed in eis contemplatur puritatem intelligibilis veritatis.

—*St. Thomas Aquinas*

(Summa theologiae, Secunda secundae, Quaestio 180, art. 5
Opera iussu Leonis XIII P.M. edita, tomus x, p. 429, Romae 1899)

CHAPTER XLII

SURVEY OF SCIENCE AND INTELLECTUAL PROGRESS IN THE SECOND HALF OF THE THIRTEENTH CENTURY

I. INTRODUCTION

The equality between Christians, Jews, and Muslims which characterized the twelfth century was disrupted in the thirteenth century. The contributions of Israel and especially of Islām were still considerable, but the hegemony of Christendom—that is, western Christendom, western culture—which was already clear by the middle of the thirteenth century, was absolutely indisputable by the end of it. During the second half of the thirteenth century Muslims were still the world leaders in at least two fields, mathematics (trigonometry) and ophthalmology, and perhaps in a third one, chemistry. The Jews were almost everywhere reduced to secondary importance. Some of the works which they continued to produce in abundance were still of value, but only for other Jews; they almost ceased to have an international significance. This will be proved repeatedly. One of the best witnesses of the new state of things is the existence of a growing number of translations from Latin into Hebrew. The Jews themselves, that is, those who paid any attention to the intellectual activities of the Gentile world, were beginning to be aware of that unpleasant situation. For example, one of the greatest of them, Jacob ben Maḥir ibn Tibbon, declared in the preface of his Hebrew translation of Euclid that he had undertaken it to disarm the Christian criticism that the Jews were foreign to scientific studies.

The period under review marked the triumph of Aristotelianism in many forms. Nowhere was that triumph more complete than in Western Christendom in the form of Thomist philosophy. It is not surprising that Roman catholics like to think of the thirteenth century as the greatest of centuries, for St. Thomas' triumph over Ibn Rushd was indeed a magnificent symbol of the hegemony of his people, of his race, of his creed, of Latindom against the rest of the world. This Aristotelian triumph was so complete that the more optimistic people might have thought it final—indeed for a certain group of men Thomism is almost final—but that was only an appearance. Even on purely scientific issues, Aristotelianism was already defeated before the end of the century by Ptolemaism and Galenism. And it should be noted that those who speak of the thirteenth century as the greatest, admit by so doing that the climax was followed by an anticlimax.

The relative inferiority of the Jews was not surprising considering their political and social disabilities and the recurrent persecutions of which they were the victims. The astounding thing is not that the Jews did so little, but that they did so much.

I propose to call this period "The time of Roger Bacon, of Jacob ben Maḥir ibn Tibbon, and of Quṭb al-dīn al-Shīrāzī." This requires some explanation.

Instead of choosing Bacon as the flag-bearer of Christendom and Latindom, one might have thought of St. Thomas or Albert the Great. However great St.

Thomas' philosophical importance, his scientific importance was negligible. Moreover, he died before the middle of the period and hence cannot represent more than half of it. Albert died a little later, in 1280. Bacon lived at least until 1292, that is, almost until the end of the century. Moreover, Bacon has infinite titles to our gratitude. These will be set forth by and by; it will suffice at present to recall him as one of the founders of the experimental method, and thus one of the heralds of modern science and modern life. It is one of the amusing paradoxes of history, that such a prophetic part should have been played not by a systematic Dominican, but by a gentle brother of St. Francis (not so gentle, if the truth be told), not by an Aristotelian but by a Platonist! This illustrates once more the necessity of paying full attention to mediaeval Platonism. The historian of science might be tempted to neglect it in favor of the more scientific Aristotelianism, but the fact is, these two great lines of thought were constantly interwoven like the woof and warp of a fabric. One cannot neglect one more than the other. Platonists and Aristotelians were incompletely right; they did not even cover the truth between them, for there was something else, which might be called the Archimedian spirit, slowly growing throughout the ages, which would finally lead to the development of the experimental methods and of mathematical physics. Mankind was still far away from that goal at the time with which we are now dealing, yet was coming nearer to it by occasional little steps. One of these little steps was made by Friar Bacon. A very little step to be sure, but the smallest step in the right direction is worth more than a million in any other.

Bacon's selection is also somewhat paradoxical in another way: the leading country of Christendom was then, as we shall prove below, Italy, considerably ahead of all others; then Spain, then France, and England came far behind. And yet an Englishman was our main hero. This may serve to exemplify once more the unpredictability of genius. A country may be backward in a thousand ways, as England was, and yet be the cradle of one or two men of outstanding intelligence and merit (I do not mean rulers or generals, but scientists or philosophers), and its secret history is then suddenly lifted up to a much higher level. The birth of a Dante in Florence, 1265, seems natural enough to us looking from a distance, and what it would mean to Italy and to the world in the following century will be explained in volume III. The birth of a Bacon in that remote island, England, was far less natural, or let us say, more miraculous, but the consequences of that inconspicuous event would not be less remarkable.

No explanation is needed with regard to Jacob ben Maḥir. He was undoubtedly the greatest man of science in Israel, and he lived throughout the period, dying only at the beginning of the fourteenth century.

It would have been tempting to choose Nāṣir al-dīn al-Ṭūsī as the representative of Islām, rather than Quṭb al-dīn, for he was a greater man, but he was ruled out for purely chronological reasons. He died in the same year, 1274, as St. Thomas and St. Bonaventure, and thus covered less than half of the period.

It is out of the question for me to attempt to outline the historical background of my own story. The reader can easily refer to one of many textbooks on mediaeval history if his memory needs refreshing. But it will be easier for him to find his bearings, even without the necessity of referring to other books, if I mention a few of the cardinal events.

In 1250 the Crusaders were defeated at al-Manṣūra in Lower Egypt, and their retreating army was captured together with its leader, St. Louis. Twenty years later St. Louis led a new crusade, but he died of the plague off Tunis. Thus did the sixth and seventh crusades utterly fail, and thus ended almost two centuries of reckless, glorious, sordid, and futile adventure. In spite of his defeats, St. Louis was a great king, indeed the noblest king of Christendom.

The death of Frederick II in the same year, 1250, started a period of confusion in the German Empire. (Great interregnum, 1256–1291). In 1256 two princes were elected to the German throne, one of whom was Alfonso el Sabio—who showed very little wisdom in those affairs.

The main Asiatic event was the fall of Baghdād in 1258 and the sudden ending of the Caliphate. The sack of the City of Peace was atrocious and the loss to Islām incalculable,[1] and yet it was not by any means a death blow to Arabic culture. For one thing, the Mongol rulers proved themselves to be great in peace as well as in war. Their toleration and the very terror which they inspired helped to maintain throughout Asia a remarkable security. It was that Pax Mongolica which made possible the amazing trans-Asiatic journeys of so many Christian, Muslim, and Chinese travelers. At no time—until very recently—were the relations between Cathay and Western Europe more frequent, and on the whole more secure than then. Another proof of Mongolian interest in science was the development of the scientific institutes of Marāgha and Khānbaliq.

In 1261 the Franks were driven out of Constantinople, and the Palaeologoi ascended the Roman throne. In the same year Bela IV, king of Hungary, succeeded in repelling a second Mongol invasion.

In 1266 Manfred's death put a dramatic end to the development of Sicilian poetry, but this was somewhat compensated by the birth in 1265 of Dante Alighieri, who would eventually carry another Italian dialect, the Tuscan, to the very highest level and help to make of it by and by one of the world's greatest languages.

French unity was promoted in 1271 by the lapse of the domains of Toulouse to the French crown. On the other hand, French control of Sicily was brutally stopped by the Sicilian Vespers in Palermo, 1282. Charles of Anjou was driven out of the country, but continued to rule in Naples, calling himself king of Sicily. The crown of Sicily proper was given to the king of Aragon.[2]

Finally the protracted war between Genoa and Venice ended badly for the latter. In 1298 the Venetian fleet was defeated by the Genoese off Curzola, an island of the Dalmatian coast. This was not by any means a fatal event for Venice, whose prodigious development continued for centuries, but I mention it because among the prisoners taken by the Genoese were the Doge and Marco Polo! It was during his Genoese captivity that the latter dictated the account of his extraordinary adventures.

The kings of France after St. Louis' death in 1270 were Philip III the Bold, and Philip IV the Fair. The kings of England: Henry III to 1272, then Edward I. The kings of Leon and Castile: Alfonso X the Wise to 1284, then Sancho IV, Ferdinand IV. The kings of Aragon: James the Conqueror to 1276, then Peter III (who obtained the Sicilian crown in 1282), Alfonso III, and James II the Just. The popes from Innocent IV to Boniface VIII were too many—no less than fourteen—to be named, but we shall come across some of them many times.

[1] See e.g., Ibn al-Ṭiqṭaqī's account which I shall discuss in Vol. III, because it was not completed until 1301–1302. Extracts of it are quoted by E. G. Browne: Literary history of Persia (vol. 2, 463, 1906).

[2] Hence the phrase "the two Sicilies." They were reunited under the kings of Spain from 1503 to 1806.

II. RELIGIOUS BACKGROUND

1. *Christendom*—As we shall see further on, this age was a golden age of Christian theology, but theology and religion are two very different things and we are dealing here mainly with the latter. The religious life of Christendom had the same general characteristics in the second half of the century as in the first. To be sure such immense events as the foundation of the Franciscan and Dominican orders were not duplicated. Other orders were established; for example the Celestines, c. 1260, by Peter of Morrone (pope Celestine V in 1294); but however successful, they added nothing essentially new to the Christian communities. By this time the various modalities of cenobitic life had already been tried, and the later religious orders, with very few exceptions, were not real innovations; they simply expressed the renewed fervor of their founders. As opposed to theology, which needs systematic formulation, true religion thrives best in freedom. It must be constantly refreshed, and so to say recreated by the minds and hearts of new men. Hence the everlasting struggles all over the world between theologians on the one side, who want definite creeds, finality and stability, and fervent men on the other, who crave neither words nor systems, but solace and love, a burning and living faith.

An interesting example of this struggle was given in the period under consideration by the nonconformists who preached the Eternal Evangel of Joachim of Floris. Their religious and social radicalism was condemned by the Church in 1255, but not suppressed. To stop the rebellion of those passionate hearts it would have been necessary to cure the unspeakable evils of the time, and this was beyond the power of any church. The fact is, social and spiritual conditions were terrible, the lot of the poorer people (i.e., of the great majority) was exceedingly miserable, person l security was very low, there was no hope for man but what the church could give him, and if the priests disappointed him, his own soul must create a new faith or share his body's starvation. A more striking revolt even was that of the Battuti, whole bands of half-naked men who crossed the towns scourging themselves by way of penitence, self-debasement, and edification. Their exaltation was as contagious as a disease, and their bands increased in numbers not only in Italy but in many other countries, spreading ecstasy, dissatisfaction and terror everywhere. The fervor of the Italian Battuti manifested itself also in poetical form, and we owe to its inspiration one of the greatest poets of the Middle Ages, Jacopone da Todi. I wish that the scholars who magnify every evil of our own days and idealize the past beyond recognition, would bear in mind these pathetic and frightful processions of Battuti. A spiritual revolt of such magnitude, and characterized by such frenzy, can only be explained by the intolerability of social circumstances.

Besides the inevitable strife between orthodoxy and heterodoxy, there was also considerable strife within the Church itself. The secular clergy could not help taking umbrage at the growing popularity of the friars and at their ambition to become the real leaders of Christendom. In fact the friars became the leaders; the magnificent theological structure was completed within the century almost entirely by their efforts. Their very activity intensified other causes of friction, to which I have alluded in the preceding book, namely, the rivalry between Franciscans and Dominicans. That rivalry is a standing feature of the intellectual pattern; we shall come across it repeatedly.

In spite of the fact that conditions were very far from perfect at home and that Christian ideals were realized only in exceptional cases, the Church was feeling so strong that it opened a new era of missionary activity abroad. This was another result of the existence of religious orders; a surplus energy was thus released which must be spent in one way or another. To be sure, the Gray and Black Friars would have found more than enough work to keep them busy in their own countries, but they dreamed of greater exploits. Immense territories were waiting to be conquered for Christ's sake. The protracted struggle with Islām gave a new scope to missionary endeavour and also to the diplomatic calculations of the Roman Curia. The Muslim dominions were only a small part of Asia. If it were possible to win the innumerable people of the Far East to the Christian faith, the Muslim could be attacked from both sides; they would be placed between the hammer and the anvil. A beautiful dream. . . . Under the combined influence of pure missionary zeal and of diplomatic enterprise the Roman church finally followed the paths which had been blazed more than eight centuries before by Nestorian heretics. The first Catholic missions in India and China were established by the Salernitan Franciscan, John of Monte Corvino, in 1291 and 1293.

The Roman church asserted its triumph in still another way. The culmination of the century (which was also in many respects, though people did not know it then, a culmination of Romanism) was celebrated by the institution of the Jubilee Year. In 1300 Boniface VIII invited the whole Christian world to come "ad limina apostolorum" and thus to obtain remission of penance and even of sin. His appeal, touching the very heart of an anxious world, met with more success than could have been hoped for by the most optimistic. Pilgrims reached Rome from every country and left a wealth of gifts behind them. The Jubilee Year became a new instrument of Roman politics, an instrument of such efficacy that the Curia could not resist the temptation of abusing it and of helping thus to prepare the great schism of the Reformation.

Christian education was continued with admirable zeal in the schools and in the universities, and for the unlettered who formed the vast majority of the population there was provided the concrete and silent teaching of the cathedrals: the cathedrals themselves, miracles wrought in stone, and their encyclopaedic decoration. Therefore, the history of Christian art is an essential part of the history of thought.

To complete this sketch of Christian effort, I should speak of a number of individuals who were the living symbols of it. Out of many, with whom I shall deal in the following chapters, I select three, Villanova, Lull, and Ricoldo di Monte Croce, two Catalans and one Tuscan; the first a free lance, the second a Franciscan tertiary, the third a Dominican.

Arnold of Villanova, the Valencian, was one of the most singular personalities of mediaeval times. An alchemist, prophet, and social reformer, his restless spirit led him into all sorts of adventures. Joachimite ideals found a ready soil in his mind. He was almost instinctively anti-Thomist and his religious feelings took naturally an anti-clerical bent. It is not surprising that he got into trouble with the Inquisition; it is more surprising that he escaped from its clutches so easily. Arnold is a good specimen of the spiritual rebel.

The two others were more orthodox though in very different ways. Ramon Lull, the great Majorcan, was a genuine apostle who defended his mother the Holy Church to his last breath. He died a martyr of his faith. The main business of his life was to convert the infidels, especially the Jews and Muslims, and he was so sure of the absolute superiority of his creed that he was confident all that was needed to convert unbelievers was to explain it well enough. Yet he had a good knowledge of the Jewish and Muslim religions, and was remarkably tolerant.

Much of his time was devoted to the writing of apologetical books and religious romances; one of these, the "Book of the lover and the beloved" has become one of the best known of its kind in the world literature. Like Arnold, though in a very different style, Ramon was a scientist. He was one of the first to insist that missionary activities must be established on a solid basis of knowledge. In particular, missionaries to the Muslims should be as deeply versed in the Arabic language and lore as possible. He was the first to understand and explain clearly and forcibly the needs which were not fully answered until more than three centuries later by the Congregation of propaganda.

I have indicated many times the difference, not to say the opposition, between Franciscan and Dominican ideals. The complexity and extreme individuality of Ramon's mind is well illustrated by the fact that he never developed an exclusive sympathy for one of these orders, but turned now toward the one, now toward the other; it is true, when he was at least sixty years of age he became a Franciscan tertiary, but that was not the last of his oscillations, for later he spent some time in a Dominican monastery, and when he died it was found that he had made bequests to both orders. He was too great a man to be imprisoned in the meshes of such petty jealousies, but if his heart could not choose between them, they knew better. His was undoubtedly a Franciscan rather than a Dominican spirit. Moreover he was one of the first upholders of the Immaculate Conception of Our Lady, an incipient dogma which the Dominicans resisted to the limit. A mind as free as his could not remain entirely clear of heresy, or more exactly of the suspicion of it: the main persecutor of his memory was naturally enough a Dominican inquisitor.

The third personage, the Florentine Dominican Ricoldo of Monte Croce, is quoted for a very different reason. He had traveled as far east as Tabrīz and obtained a good knowledge of the Muslim faith and manners. He wrote a refutation of the Qur'ān and of Islām which had an extraordinary fortune: it was translated into Greek, then from Greek into Latin, finally from Latin into German by none other than Martin Luther!

These three men—Arnold, Ramon, and Ricoldo—have this in common, that they were intensely religious, intensely devoted to their faith. Arnold showed his devotion by his Quixotic efforts to purify the Church; Ramon and Ricoldo proved theirs by their missionary zeal.

2. *Israel*—The internal history of Israel is even more closely bound up with theology and philosophy than that of Christendom and we shall have occasion to consider it more fully in Chapter XLVI. But its external history, that is, the history of its relations with Christendom, must be considered now. There is not much to add to what I said in Book III. The stream of persecution once started could not be stopped. Evil begets evil, and so on indefinitely, until it be destroyed by a miracle of charity, and such a miracle can hardly be expected.

In Spain, a vigorous anti-Jewish propaganda was carried on by the Dominicans, notably by Raymond of Peñafort and Raymond Martin. In 1263 they obliged the great Jewish doctor, Moses ben Naḥman, to defend his faith in a public disputation at Barcelona, against their brother the Jewish renegade Pablo Christiani. Pablo seems to have had the worst of it, but this only added fuel to the fire, and the persecution was renewed with increased vigor. Once more the Talmud was scrutinized and attacked, and this touched the Jewish community on its most sensitive spot.

In England things were hardly better. The aloofness of the Jews and the financial success of some of them excited the hatred and covetousness of their Christian neighbors. More and more vexations were piled upon them, and the hostile feelings which they inspired accumulated throughout the thirteenth century, gathering more and more intensity. The Spanish method of persuasion was tried in 1280 when they were obliged to attend Dominican sermons, but this could only make matters worse. The almost inevitable climax occurred in 1290: Edward I ordered all the Jews to leave England before All Saints Day, their immovable property being confiscated to the crown's profit. Sixteen years later the Jews were expelled from France.

3. *Islām*—What little I have to say of the religious evolution of Islām will be more conveniently inserted in my chapter on philosophy. Christian anti-Muslim activities have been dealt with above.

4. *Hinduism*—Buddhism, which might have favored the natural expansion of Hindu genius, was entirely suppressed in India proper and replaced by a number of sects, Vishnuite and Śivaite, which however different, were almost equally unfavorable to the growth of scientific ideas. Vishnuism was perhaps a little less unfavorable, yet it was dominated by a fantastic mythology and irrational concepts which were incompatible with scientific research except in the fields of medicine, astrology, and alchemy, and this only to a very small extent. This helps to explain the relative sterility of Hindu science in spite of its glorious beginnings.

5. *Buddhism*—Thanks to the influence of the great Yüan emperor Kublai Khān, Mongolia was converted to Buddhism. Unfortunately the Buddhism which struck the emperor's fancy was the debased Tantric kind which had thriven so remarkably in the highlands of Tibet. Kublai ordered the translation of the Kanjur from Tibetan into Mongolian.

Mongolian Lamaism penetrated China proper to some extent, and helped to debase Chinese Buddhism and to sterilize Chinese thought. Fortunately it remained foreign to the great majority of Chinese people, and thus its blighting influence was restricted.

In the meanwhile the Buddhist evolution continued in Japan on a much higher plane. Two great sects were established within this period. The Nichiren-shū, so called after Nichiren who founded it in 1253; and the Ji-shū, organized by Ippen Shōnin twenty-two years later. There is a remarkable parallelism between these two sects on the one hand, and the two founded in the preceding period on the other. The Ji-shū, even as the Shin-shū, was deeply Amidaist; both were doctrines of salvation by faith. On the contrary, the Nichiren-shū was as deeply opposed to Amidaism as the Zen-shū, though in a very different way. It distinguished itself from all other sects by its aggressiveness and intolerance; in spite of this (or perhaps because of it) it won a considerable number of adherents. This parallel evolution illustrates the persistence of strong opposite needs in the Japanese soul, and the relative maturity of their minds. By this time Japan was already emancipated in some respects at least, from her old foster mother China.

Summary

The outstanding fact was the glorification of Roman Christianity, which was evidenced by a number of splendid cathedrals, by the immense success of the Jubilee Year, and for the learned, by the magnificent effort of great theologians. Yet this was only one aspect of reality, the bright side of it; there was also a dark one, very dark, which all these material and intellectual splendors could not remove.

The Joachimites and Battuti gave utterance, loudly and dramatically, to the deep spiritual unrest of western Christianity.

Anti-Muslim and anti-Jewish propaganda increased in vigor and spread farther. The Jews were driven out of England in 1290, and out of France in 1306.

The Hindu and Chinese civilizations were debased respectively by the extravagances of Hinduism, and by the introduction of Lamaism into the Mongol empire.

In the meanwhile Buddhist thought flourished and became more and more differentiated in Japan, and its continued development proved the spiritual maturity of the Japanese and their gradual emancipation from China.

III. THE TRANSLATORS

1. *From Greek into Latin*—It is fitting to begin our account of translators, this time, with the Christian Hellenists, for their activity marks a new epoch. For the preceding period we could but mention one important translation from the Greek, the Nicomachean Ethics, by the great teacher of the Oxford Franciscans, Robert Grosseteste (c. 1241). The situation is now very different, suggesting that the sluices are finally opened which will allow Greek knowledge to flow directly into Latin channels. This change was largely due to one single man, William of Moerbeke.

Before speaking of him we must say a few words of at least one other, Bartholomew of Messina, who flourished at the court of Manfred, king of Sicily. Bartholomew translated Aristotle's Magna moralia and Problems, a number of pseudo-Aristotelian writings, and Hierocles' treatise on the veterinary art. Other pseudo-Aristotelian opuscula were translated for Manfred by unknown scholars.

To return to William of Moerbeke, he was a Flemish Dominican, chaplain to many popes, and a friend of St. Thomas. Writings of Hippocrates, Aristotle, Archimedes, Hero, Galen, Alexander of Aphrodisias, Proclos, and Simplicios were translated by him, or earlier translations were corrected by him with reference to the Greek text. The most important of these translations were Archimedes' Hydrostatics, Aristotle's Zoölogy, and Aristotle's Politics. This last one was made in 1260 at St. Thomas' request.

2. *From Arabic into Latin*—The group of translators from Arabic is so large that we shall begin by considering the translators into Latin, then those into Spanish and Portuguese, who form a natural group. The reader will bear in mind that the difference between these two groups is but small, except from the purely Hispanic point of view. The essential to us is the fact that a large number of writings was now transferred from the mysterious Arabic vehicle into the Latin one; whether the new vehicle was mediaeval Latin, Spanish, or Portuguese is a matter of detail.

The Latin-writing translators are themselves so numerous that it is expedient to divide them into four smaller groups as follows: (a) Italians in Italy; (b) group of Montpellier (c) Sicilian group; (d) Spanish group.

(a) Italians in Italy. The first of these is the Neapolitan, William of Lunis, who was already dealt with in the previous book because we do not know whether he belongs to the first or the second half of the century. He translated Ibn Rushd's commentaries on the Organon, and an Arabic treatise on algebra. Bonacosa, a Jew, translated Ibn Rushd's Kullīyāt fī-l-ṭibb (a medical treatise) in Padua, 1255. Giovanni Campano of Novara, chaplain to Urban IV, translated Euclid's Elements, or rather revised the earlier translation by Adelard of Bath and discussed it. John of Brescia belongs rather to our second group.

(b) Group of Montpellier. John of Brescia collaborated with Jacob ben Mahir in the translation of al-Zarqālī's treatise on the astrolabe (1263). Robert the Englishman was familiar with Arabic astronomy, but was not himself a translator; no definite translation can be ascribed to him; he may easily have obtained his Arabic knowledge from Jacob ben Maḥir or another member of the group. We are on safer ground with Armengaud son of Blaise, who was at Montpellier c. 1290 (he also spent some time in Spain and in Rome). He translated a Galenic treatise, the pseudo-Galenic Economy, medical treatises by Ibn Sīnā and Maimonides, and Jacob ben Maḥir's treatise on the quadrant. The last named translation was made from the Hebrew, and it is quite possible that other translations were also made by him from the Hebrew or with the help of Hebrew versions.

We touch here a very delicate point. It is often very difficult to say whether a text was translated from the Arabic or the Hebrew. The presence of Hebraisms or Arabisms in the Latin text would not be in itself conclusive, for the Hebraisms might come from an Arabic treatise, and vice versa the Arabisms from a Hebrew one. The two civilizations had developed for centuries so close together, and the two languages have so many points of contact, that each could easily be contaminated by the other. Moreover, there was an abundance of Arabic texts in Hebrew, or in Hebrew script, and it is quite conceivable that some southern Jews could not always remember in which of both languages they had read this or that work.

We might also attach to this group the Catalan, Ramon Lull, for he spent some of the best years of his life in Montpellier.

(c) Sicilian Group. Manfred approved himself a true son of his father, the great emperor Frederick II, in his patronage of learning. A number of translators were gathered around him at the Sicilian court. I have already referred to a few of them, Bartholomew of Messina and others unknown, in the section dealing with translations from the Greek. Another was Hermann the German, who translated for him from the Arabic Aristotelian commentaries by al-Fārābī and Ibn Rushd.

After Benevento (1266), the Hohenstaufen patronage was worthily continued by Manfred's conqueror, Charles of Anjou. As the activity of the translators had nothing to do with politics, we can imagine that they simply continued their work at the Sicilian court irrespective of its stewardship. Two Jews distinguished themselves in Charles' service, translating medical works. Moses of Palermo translated the pseudo-Hippocratic treatise on veterinary medicine. Faraj ben Salīm (Faragut) was bold enough to tackle the Kitāb al-ḥāwī of al-Rāzī, the largest encyclopaedia of Greco-Arabic medicine; he completed his version of it in 1279. And this was not all: he also translated a pseudo-Galenic treatise, and two others by Ibn Jazla and Mesuë the Third (?).

(d) Spanish Group. The Galician, Peter Gallego, translated an Arabic summary of the Aristotelian zoology, and the Economy ascribed to Galen. Hermann the German flourished many years in Toledo before entering the Angevin service; in fact most of his work seems to have been done in that city.

Though I do not propose to discuss it in this volume, a passing reference may be made here to the Philosophia of Virgil of Cordova, said to have been translated from Arabic into Latin, in Toledo, 1290. This is a very enigmatic work full of contradictions.[3] Its scientific value is negligible, but whether the treatise or translation be genuine or not, it is a witness of the Toledan and Arabic prestige.

[3] H. G. Farmer: Virgilius Cordubensis (Journal R. Asiatic Soc., 599–603, 1929; Isis, 13, 429).

To this Spanish group we may attach two great Catalan scholars, two of the greatest men of their time: Arnold of Villanova and Ramon Lull. Arnold translated from the Arabic a number of treatises by Galen, al-Kindī, Qusṭā ibn Lūqā, Ibn Sīnā, Abū-l-'Alā' Zuhr, and Abū-l-Ṣalt. These were all medical works; even Qusṭā's treatise De ligaturis, though magical in spirit, did really belong to the medical literature of those days. It should be noted that this represented but a very small and incidental part of his activity. Lull was not actually a translator but he must be mentioned here because of his lifelong efforts to promote Arabic studies. He was himself an extraordinary Arabic scholar; witness the fact that he wrote some of his own books in Arabic!

Considering all of these translators together, the most striking feature is the cosmopolitanism of their company. Some of them hailed from Italy or Spain, others from France, England, Germany; some were Christians, others Jews. This reminds us of the cosmopolitanism of the scholars who a few centuries before had translated much of the same literature from Greek into Arabic. It confirms the incipient hegemony of Latin culture, even as the many Jews and Christians who helped to enrich the Arabic literature bore unconsciously testimony to the leadership of Islām.

3. *From Arabic into Spanish and Portuguese*—Impressive as it is, the company of translators from the Arabic which we have thus far reviewed represents only a part of the immense movement of transfusion which was then taking place, for the Arabic knowledge was not only poured out into Latin vessels, but into many others, Spanish, Portuguese, Hebrew, Syriac, Armenian, Persian, etc. A novelty of this period is the appearance of a vast number of translations into the new Hispanic vernaculars, whose maturity was thus corroborated.

The activity of the school of translators which was publishing Arabic knowledge in Spanish was particularly intense, and that is hardly surprising since their leader was the very king of Castile and León, Alfonso X el Sabio. Alfonso was not simply a patron, but a worker, and his interest in learning was not only genuine but ardent. In fact he was too much of a scholar to be a good king. His father, San Fernando, had already begun this work, but with moderation; Alfonso threw himself into it with amazing zeal and perseverance. He ordered the translation into Castilian of the fables of Kalīla wa Dimna, of the Sirr al-asrār, of the Qur'ān, and above all of a whole series of astronomical and physical treatises. Indeed he was especially interested in astronomy, and organized a school of translators whose main business it was to make the astronomical works of the ancients and the Muslims available in Castilian. I shall come back to this in the astronomical and physical chapters. In the meanwhile it may be remarked that Alfonso's work in this direction was so comprehensive and successful that he deserves to be called the father of Spanish science.

The translations were not made by the king himself but under his direction. His main collaborators were Jews: Judah ben Moses ha-Kohen, Samuel ha-Levi Abulafia, Isaac ibn Sid ha-Ḥazzan, Abraham Alfaquin of Toledo; but there were working with him also a few Christians: Guillen Arremon Daspa and John Daspa, John of Messina, John of Cremona, Fernando of Toledo, one Bernardo. Some of the Spanish versions were eventually Latinized or Italianized by other Christians, but that is another story.

The magnificent effort of the Alphonsine school was repeated on a humbler scale toward the end of the century by the great Portuguese king, Dinis the Liberal.

A number of translations into Portuguese were made under his orders, but it is not clear to me whether they were made from the Arabic or from the Castilian.

4. *From Arabic into Hebrew*—Thus far we have been dealing with the transmission of Arabic knowledge to Western Christendom. We shall now consider its parallel transmission to Israel. The number of translators is again so great that we must subdivide it into three smaller groups: (a) Spanish; (b) Provençal; (c) Italian. Naturally enough no Eastern Jews were involved; this was essentially a western affair.

(a) Spanish Group. (I take Spanish here in a broad sense, it refers to the whole peninsula.) Solomon Ibn Ayyub of Granada translated a theological treatise by Maimonides, two grammatical ones by Ibn Janāḥ, a medical one by Ibn Sīnā, and one of Ibn Rushd's commentaries on Aristotelian physics. Shem-ṭob ben Isaac of Tortosa translated Ibn Rushd's middle commentary on the De anima, and two of the greatest medical works of Arabic literature, the Kitāb al-taṣrīf of Abū-l-Qāsim al-Zahrāwī (1258) and the Kitāb al-Manṣūrī of al-Rāzī (1264). Late in life he began a new Hebrew version of the Hippocratic aphorisms (so popular in the Semitic world); this version is of special value because it includes otherwise unknown glosses by Palladios the Iatrosophist. Zereḥiah Gracian of Barcelona translated several Aristotelian treatises, the De causis, commentaries by Themistios, al-Fārābī, and Ibn Rushd; medical treatises by Galen, Ibn Sīnā, Maimonides. Shem-ṭob Ibn Falaquera translated long extracts from the Yanbū' al-ḥayāt of Ibn Gabirol and was first to see that work in its true perspective. His other writings were largely derived from Arabic sources without being translations; however his treatise De'ot ha-filusufim is almost a translation of some of Ibn Rushd's commentaries. In 1292 or later, Isaac Albalag translated the first two parts of the Maqāṣid al-falāsifa of al-Ghazzālī, a book which deeply influenced Jewish philosophy. Finally Abraham ben Shem-ṭob of Tortosa, better known as a translator from Hebrew (or Arabic?) into Latin, may be the author of the Hebrew version of the pseudo-Galenic De plantis.

(b) Provençal Group. (Provençal is taken broadly, as referring to Languedoc as well as to Provence proper.) However imposing the Spanish group, the Provençal, though much smaller, is even more so. Moreover, the most prominent of the Spaniards, Shem-ṭob ben Isaac, spent part of his life in Montpellier and Marseilles. His translation of the Taṣrīf was completed in the latter city. It is probable that the work on which his fame is based was done almost entirely in southern France.

I have already spoken of the illustrious Tibbonid family in Book III. Its fame was still increased during the second half of the thirteenth century, for the two greatest translators of that period were members of it: Moses ibn Tibbon and Jacob ben Maḥir; Moses was the son of Samuel ibn Tibbon and Jacob a maternal grandson of the same; both were probably born in Marseilles.

Moses' translations are too numerous to be quoted. They include many of Ibn Rushd's commentaries, and other Aristotelian commentaries; three theological and philosophical works by Maimonides; Euclid's Elements, and other mathematical and astronomical treatises by Geminos, Theodosios of Bithynia, Jābir ibn Aflaḥ, al-Biṭrūjī, etc.; Aristotle's Problems; medical works by Ibn Sīnā, Ibn al-Jazzār, Ḥunain ibn Isḥāq, al-Rāzī, Maimonides—in short a whole library of Greco-Arabic science.

Moses' nephew, Jacob ben Maḥir, though almost equally great as a translator, was even more famous as an original astronomer. The authors translated by him include Autolycos, Euclid, Menelaos, Qusṭā ibn Lūqā, Ibn al-Haitham, Ibn al-Ṣaffār, al-Zarqālī, al-Ghazzālī, Jābir ibn Aflaḥ, Ibn Rushd!

Finally Jacob ibn Abbassi translated a part of the Kitāb al-sirāj of Maimonides. Strangely enough, while many Spaniards emigrated across the Pyrenees, this Languedocian (he hailed from Béziers) moved to Huesca, in northern Aragon, and it is there that his translation was made. I might have counted him in the Spanish group.

(c) Italian Group. The greatest of these was Nathan ha-Me'ati, who flourished in Rome. He was called the Italian Tibbonid, which proves at once the prestige of that name and his own fame. Leaving out works of uncertain authorship, he translated medical works by Hippocrates, Galen, Ibn Sīnā, 'Ammar ibn 'Alī, and Maimonides. His work as a translator was continued by his son and by his grandson, Solomon and Samuel.

The Spaniard, Zeraḥiah Gracian, came to Rome c. 1277, and seems to have spent there the rest of his life; hence we might count him among the Italians. It is interesting to note that while in Rome he translated the first two books of Ibn Sīnā's Qānūn; and that at about the same time (1279) Nathan ha-Me'ati completed his translation of it, also in Rome.

Aḥiṭub ben Isaac of Palermo translated Maimonides' logic; and Samuel ben Jacob of Capua, the treatise on purgatives and emetics of Māsawaih al-Māridīnī (Mesuë junior or pseudo-Mesuë I). Speaking of this pseudo-Mesuë reminds us of the other pseudo-Mesuë, the mysterious author of a surgical textbook. That textbook was translated into Latin by Faraj ibn Salīm, and a little later (1297) into Hebrew by Jacob ben Joseph ha-Levi, otherwise unknown.

This ends our account of translations into Hebrew: it is not necessary to insist upon the immensity of the task which was accomplished, but it may be briefly pointed out that practically all of these texts (excepting of course the specifically Jewish ones) had already been available to Latin readers for some time when they appeared in Hebrew.

5. *From Arabic into Persian*—It is said that Nāṣir al-dīn al-Ṭūsī prepared translations of Greek scientific texts from Arabic into Persian. This is plausible but unproved. Of course Nāṣir al-dīn might easily have done that, but there was no real need of it. Every Persian Muslim had to know Arabic to read the Qur'ān; it was if anything easier for them to read scientific writings in the same language. A Persian translation of an Arabic text was as unnecessary to a Persian scholar of that time, as a French one of a Latin text to a French scholar. In fact the chances are that in both cases genuine scholars would have put such translations aside even if they had been available, and would have found the original texts not only more trustworthy but more readable as well. On the other hand, even as French scientific writings were derived from Latin ones, if not slavishly translated, Persian scientific writings were largely if not entirely copied from Arabic ones. The difference between a translation and a self-styled original work is often but superficial; or to put it otherwise, the translation is derived from a single work, while the "original" work is derived from many.

6. *From Arabic into Syriac*—Similar remarks would apply to Syriac. The greatest Syriac scientist, Abū-l-Faraj, translated or elaborated a number of Arabic writings into his own language. For example, he began a translation of the Qānūn.

The case of Syriac is particularly curious. For much of the Greek knowledge had reached the Arabic speaking people only after having passed through Syriac intermediaries. Now that same knowledge was retranslated from Arabic into Syriac. And this is not all. Some of Abū-l-Faraj's books were eventually retranslated into Arabic! This final step may be interpreted in two ways—as a proof of his fame, or of the gradual debasement of Arabic scholarship.

7. *From Arabic (or Persian) into Armenian*—The translation of an Arabic (or Persian?) astronomical treatise is ascribed to Mekhitar of Ānī. Other writings might easily have been derived from Greek or Latin sources, as Armenian doctors were in touch, some of them with Greek theologians, others—far more numerous—with the priests and missionaries of the Latin kingdom of Lesser Armenia, or of neighboring countries such as Cyprus. In fact I do not know of any contemporary translations of scientific writings of any kind from Latin or Greek into Armenian.

8. *From Hebrew into Latin and Romance languages*—The occurrence of translations from Hebrew into Latin, and, as we shall see below, of others from Latin into Hebrew, is one of the most interesting events of this time. The number of translators from the Hebrew is sufficient to warrant their subdivision into three groups: (a) Spanish; (b) Italian; (c) Anglo-French.

(a) Spanish Group. Alfonso el Sabio is chiefly known for his translations from the Arabic, but he also ordered the translation of some Talmudic and Qabbalistic writings. His interest in Hebrew literature was natural enough considering that his best collaborators were Jews. It is said that he wanted a new translation of the Old Testament to be made into Spanish. Certain it is that Hermann the German translated the Psalter into that language. His translation was made from the Vulgate but with reference to the Hebrew original. This was the earliest attempt to connect a vernacular translation directly with the fountain head. Whether Hermann was inspired by King Alfonso I do not know, but that would have been likely enough. Hermann was bishop of Astorga in León from 1266 to his death in 1272; he must have been in touch with the king of León. The translation of Abraham ben Shem-ṭob of Tortosa quoted in another section as made from the Arabic, may have been made from the Hebrew. It is exceedingly difficult to decide such questions.

(b) Italian Group. King Manfred was very genuinely interested in Arabic and Hebrew learning. The famous Book of the apple (Sefer ha-tappuaḥ), a pseudo-Aristotelian dialogue lost in Arabic, was translated into Latin under Manfred's direction; the translation is even sometimes ascribed to himself.

The greatest translator from Hebrew into Latin was a converted Jew who called himself John of Capua. He translated two medical treatises (one of Maimonides', and the Taisīr of Ibn Zuhr), and the fables of Kalīla wa Dimna. The last of these translations, entitled Directorium vitae humanae, was of course of no scientific value, but its cultural importance was very great. A good deal of Eastern folklore reached the West through this Latin translation of the Hebrew Kalīla. The Directorium was in its turn translated more or less freely into many vernaculars.

The popularity of Ibn Zuhr's Taisīr is proved by the fact that the translation by John of Capua was followed a few years later by another one, also from the Hebrew, prepared by Paravicius, of Padua (?) helped by a Jew named Jacob. This translation was inferior to John's, yet it was eventually printed, while John's was not.

(c) Anglo-French Group. The last chief rabbi of England before the expulsion, Hagin Deulacres, was possibly identical with "Hagin the Jew" who translated Ibn Ezra's astrological treatises into French in 1273, in Henry Bate's house in Malines; Bate retranslated them into Latin. The translations ascribed to Armengaud son of Blaise were possibly made from the Hebrew; this was certainly the case for the treatise on the quadrant by Jacob ben Maḥir, translated by Armengaud in Montpellier, 1299, with the author's help, and for Ibn Sīnā's medical poem.

9. *From Latin into Italian, French, and Dutch*—The translations to be dealt with in this section are less important for the history of science than for the history of thought and the history of language. No European scholar needed vernacular translations, but there was a growing public of noblemen, burghers, and gentlewomen who knew no Latin, or read it too haltingly to enjoy it. Naturally it was not the more scientific books which were thus translated but others having a wider appeal. For example, the Education of princes, by Giles of Rome, was very promptly Italianized and Frenchified. A number of translations into French were made, presumably after 1280, by John of Meung: the letters of Abaelard and Heloise, the marvels of Ireland as told by Gerald the Welshman, above all, Boetius' Consolation. This last named work was exceedingly popular in France, at least a dozen translations or paraphrases being published within a century and a half. John's was neither the first nor the last of these. The Consolation was the first great work of antiquity to be fully translated into French, and its many versions contributed not a little to the fixation of the philosophical terminology in that language.

Among other translations we might still quote those of the Secretum secretorum, a work second in popularity only to the Consolation, no less than eight French or Anglo-Norman versions of it appearing within the thirteenth and fourteenth centuries. Two date from the second half of the thirteenth century, the one by Peter of Abernon (alias Peter Peckham), the other by the Dominican, Jofroi (Geoffrey) of Waterford (d. 1300) and Servais Copale.[4]

The only contemporary philosophical works to appear in French were a few of Lull's, and this was probably due to the author's own initiative. The De gentili et tribus sapientibus, the De doctrina puerili, Blanquerna, and the Arbor philosophiae amoris, were eventually translated. With regard to the last of these works we know that Ramon Lull, who was an indefatigable propagandist, had it Frenchified for Jeanne of Navarre, Philippe le Bel's queen (1284–1305) toward the end of the century.

There was also a need of medical works in the vernacular for, then even as now, a large class of physicians had no heads for scholarship (one can be a very good physician without being a scholar). The Régime du corps which Aldobrandin of Siena wrote in 1256 for Beatrice of Savoy was largely translated from Latin versions of Arabic works. For example, the fourth quarter of it is almost a verbatim translation of a part of the Kitāb al-Manṣūrī of al-Rāzī. On the other hand, the Florentine physician, Taddeo Alderotti, realized the importance of obtaining direct versions of the Greek medical classics and he encouraged their preparation. This same Taddeo translated Aristotle's Ethics from Latin into Italian.

Another class of readers to whom translations were welcome were the soldiers and sportsmen, whose scholarly abilities have always been very limited. Thus John of Meung translated Vegetius' De re militari into French. Daniel of Cremona translated Arabic and Persian treatises on falconry from Latin into French for Enzio, one of the emperor Frederick's natural sons. The emperor's own treatise was also Frenchified before the end of the century.

[4] See my vol. 1, 556, adding the following reference. Ch. V. Langlois: La connaissance de la nature et du monde (2d ed.; La vie en France au Moyen âge, vol. 3, 71–121, 1927). Largely devoted to Brother Geoffrey's translation.

Many Dutch translations from the Latin and the French were prepared by Jacob van Maerlant, the educator of the Netherlands. The texts he translated from the French, most of them tales of chivalry, do not concern us, but later in life, as he realized that Latin was the vehicle of knowledge, he undertook to make as much as possible of that knowledge available to his people. He translated a lapidary, a book of dreams, the Secreta secretorum, the De natura rerum of Thomas of Cantimpré, the Historia scolastica of Peter the Eater, the Speculum historiale of Vincent of Beauvais. It is significant that his attention was largely drawn to the contemporary Latin literature, not to the ancient.

10. *From Latin into Hebrew*—David Caslari of Narbonne translated Galenic treatises from Latin into Hebrew; Solomon ben Moses of Melgueil, an Aristotelian commentary by Ibn Sīnā, a part of Ibn Rushd's metaphysics, and the Circa instans of Platearius; Hillel ben Samuel of Verona, the Liber de causis, 'Alī ibn Riḍwān's commentary on the Tegni, and the Chirurgia magna of Bruno the Lombard.

This list is not very long but it is unusually interesting; it proves the growing prestige of Latin writings and the growing ignorance of Arabic among the Jews. Many other Latin writings of this time (chiefly medical ones) were also translated into Hebrew, but somewhat later—in the fourteenth and fifteenth centuries—and thus these translations need not be considered at this place.

11. *From Latin into Greek*—Still more remarkable is the appearance of a few translations from Latin into Greek. Manuel Holobolos prepared a Greek version of the logical and dialectical treatises of Boetius—old Greek knowledge diluted and adulterated returning to its original source! Maximos Planudes translated some works of Cato the Censor, Ovid, Cicero, Caesar, Donatus, Augustine, Boetius, and possibly St. Thomas. The translation by one Petros Theoctonicos of an alchemical treatise ascribed to Albert the Great may also belong to this period.

12. *From Chinese and Tibetan into Mongolian*—In 1282 Kublai Khān ordered the translation into Mongolian of the Chinese annals of Ssŭ-ma Kuang as revised by Chu Hsi. He had become a fervent Lamaist and wished to open the great treasure of Buddhist knowledge, the Kanjur, to his people. The Kanjur is the Tibetan equivalent of the Chinese Tripiṭaka; it is not a book but a whole collection of books. Kublai appointed an academy of twenty-nine Tibetan, Uighūr, Chinese, and Hindu scholars to investigate that collection and to compare the Tibetan texts with the Sanskrit and Chinese. The translation of the Kanjur into Mongolian was only completed after Kublai's death, c. 1310.

These translations into Mongolian are a good example of cultural sidetracking. I have often remarked that human progress is not by any means a simple development; the path which man followed from one discovery to another was not necessarily the shortest—sometimes it was short, sometimes not so short, sometimes labyrinthine. Then very often great efforts were made which led nowhere, and a portion of mankind found itself in a blind alley. The gigantic labor involved in the translations of Chinese and Tibetan collections into Mongolian was largely wasted. Of course it was of use to a number of Mongols but it produced no new developments of any importance, not even in Mongolia. To make my meaning clearer, compare these Mongolian translations with the Arabic. The latter were a necessary channel, one of the main channels which human thought had to follow in order to reach its goal, while the former remained sterile. Of course it is easy for us to see that for we can contemplate the whole evolution from a great distance, as it were from the cabin of an airship, but it was impossible for the contemporaries to be aware of it. Kublai Khān and his collaborators who were bold enough to undertake these enormous translations and to create the Mongolian literature deserve as much praise as those kindred souls of theirs who built up the Arabic, Hebrew, or Latin literatures by similar means. They were sidetracked, but this was beyond their ken; their failure was not dishonorable, nor does it affect in any way the greatness of their endeavor.

Summary

Aristotelian tradition in the second half of the thirteenth century—The preceding section may be considered a digression, for these Mongolian translations remained practically without influence. As far as the rest of the world, that is, mankind in general, was concerned the existence or non-existence of these translations was indifferent. We may thus leave that section out of our summary, and turn to the others.

I shall not attempt to make as complete a summary as I did for the first half of the thirteenth century, for this would be far too long. Moreover it will be better to consider the scientific translations in the following chapters together with the original works relative to the same branches of science. But by way of example we may examine the progress of the Aristotelian tradition. The main result of such a survey is to bring out the growing intricacy of cultural exchanges. A whole series of languages was involved: Greek, Arabic, Hebrew, Persian, Syriac, Latin, Spanish, Catalan, French, etc. Moreover, thus far translations had taken place only in one direction, from Greek into Arabic, or from Greek into Latin, and hardly ever in the opposite one. Now two civilizations, two languages, were competing, Latin and Hebrew, and the exchanges between them took place in both directions. As we now know, the Latin culture finally triumphed, but this was not yet by any means certain at the time of which I am speaking, in spite of the hegemony of the Christians and the political abjection of the Jews. Moreover there was even some competition between the Greek and Latin cultures, and the spectacle of Latin works translated into Greek was at first sight almost as amazing as that of water running uphill.

The progress of Aristotelianism involved an advance in lay knowledge and hence a theological reaction; that reaction created naturally another reaction and the more advanced Aristotelians took spontaneously, or were driven to take, an anticlerical attitude. The spiritual unrest, referred to in the chapter on religion, caused the Church to be very nervous and sensitive. Hence a series of anti-Aristotelian measures, which were gradually mollified when the dangers were better understood and circumscribed and when Christian doctors had completed their harmonization of the Aristotelian with the theological doctrines. By the end of the century the fight against Aristotelianism was replaced by a fight, more restricted but more intense, against the extreme left of the movement—Averroism. A similar contest took place at the same time in Israel, except that in this case the scapegoat was not so much Ibn Rushd as Maimonides. We shall have occasions to come back to this in our philosophical survey; for the present it suffices to make our readers realize the growing complexity and intensity of intellectual life in the second half of the thirteenth century.

IV. EDUCATION

1. *Christendom*—More universities were created, no longer novelties to be sure, though each was still a great and far-reaching novelty in its own surroundings. Each of these universities was at least potentially a new focus of learning and culture.

Three new universities appeared in Spain: Valladolid, about the middle of the thirteenth century; Seville, 1254, with special reference to Arabic studies; Lerida, 1300. One more in Portugal: Lisbon, 1290, moved eighteen years later to Coimbra.

The earliest Oxford and Cambridge colleges date from this same period, not counting the Franciscan and Dominican houses which go back to the first half of the century. The earliest Oxford colleges were Balliol, Merton, and University; these were soon followed by the earliest Cambridge college, Peterhouse, the only one of the thirteenth century.

A similar foundation was made in Paris, 1257, by Robert of Sorbon—the house of learning named after him. A friend of Robert, the poet Richard of Fournival, bequeathed to the Sorbonne his own collection of books, some three hundred in number, thus establishing the earliest public library of Paris.

So much for colleges. Another aspect of Christian education is afforded by some of the contemporary treatises. For example, Gilbert of Tournay wrote the Rudimenta doctrinae christianae, of which the third part deals with the psychology and methods of teaching, and for Saint Louis he composed in 1259 an ethical treatise, Eruditio regum et principum. We have many other books of the same kind. Great scholars were often invited to educate royal princes, and some such writings were the natural by-products of their tutoring. Vincent of Beauvais wrote the De eruditione filiorum regalium for St. Louis' wife, and addressed his Tractatus consolatorius de morte amici to the king himself when the latter lost one of his children. It is a complete treatise on education; one of its chapters even deals with physical education, which was not unknown in mediaeval times as many people imagine. In fact, there was a great need of physical training among gentlemen, not only for the chase but also for the war which recurred every year with the good season. Saint Thomas began a treatise De regimine principum for the king of Cyprus; he left it unfinished but it was completed by his disciple, Ptolemy of Lucques. However this is a very different work from those previously mentioned as it is far more concerned with political training and method than with general education.

Finally there is a French text traditionally ascribed to St. Louis himself, "Les enseingnemenz que monseigneur Saint Loys fist à son ainzné fils Phelippe" (and other similar texts written by the same king for his daughter and his other children). Most of the pictures which represent the king dying show him in the act of delivering to his heir the "Enseignements" which he was said to have written with his own hand. Whether the king was the real author or not, these texts have come down to us and are excellent witnesses of the contemporary point of view on the subject.[5] They are much to the credit of St. Louis, who was undoubtedly the noblest king and one of the noblest men of that age.

[5] The critical study of these French texts and their Latin versions and paraphrases is full of difficulties. Paul Viollet: Note sur le véritable texte des instructions de Saint Louis à sa fille Isabelle et à son fils Philippe le Hardi (Bibliothèque de l'Ecole des chartes, vol. 5, 129–148, 1869). H. François Delaborde: Le texte primitif des Enseignements de Saint Louis à son fils.

The greatest "educator" of the time was probably Albert the Great. Much of his energy was devoted to the study of educational problems and to the organization of teaching. In 1259 he was engaged at Valenciennes in drawing up a plan of studies for the Dominican Order; in this he was helped by St. Thomas and by Peter of Tarentaise.

Martino da Fano, who taught law in Arezzo and Modena, wrote a little book explaining to the students how to learn and to behave.

Alfonso el Sabio completed the incorporation of the University of Salamanca in 1254, and in the same year established the Latin and Arabic college of Seville. We may conceive the group of translators and astronomers organized by him as forming what would be called today a research institute. A title of his famous code (Las siete partidas) defines universities and explains their duties, privileges and administration.

Even as Alfonso was to a large extent the educator of Spain, the noble Dinis was the educator of Portugal. He was the founder of the university of Coimbra, but his interest in the intellectual welfare of his subjects took many other fòrms. Nor was it necessary to be a king to acquit oneself of such a mission, for Jacob of Maerlant, who was nothing but a clerk, was also in the fullest sense the educator of all the Dutch speaking people.

I have kept for the end the man who was perhaps, among so many teachers of divers kinds, the one who was most completely devoted, body and soul, to his self-appointed task. I am thinking of Ramon Lull, the Majorcan. All of his virtues and of his errors proceed from his overpowering desire to enlighten his fellowmen. He was a born teacher and propagandist. Many of his works were pedagogical in their purpose, but three of them deserve special mention; the Book of chivalry, the Puerile doctrine, and the Book of first and second intention. It is probable that they were originally written in Catalan; they exist in Catalan and in Latin, and the first in sundry other languages for it enjoyed considerable popularity.

2. *Islām*—There is not much to be said about Muslim schools which I have not said before; but one school of Spain should arrest our attention, not because it was typical (it was rather the opposite) but because it illustrates very well the cultural amalgamation which was taking place in that country.[6] Under the patronage of Alfonso el Sabio, who was then governor of the newly reconquered province of Murcia, a school was built for Muḥammad al-Riqūṭī. This Muḥammad, about whom we know but too little, must have been a remarkable teacher. He gathered around him students of the three races, and four languages—Arabic, Hebrew, Latin, and Spanish—were being used.

3. *China and Mongolia*—It is hardly necessary to insist upon the immense educational task accomplished by Kublai Khān. In a sense everything was to be done for his Mongolian subjects, and he did the most difficult part, the beginning. To be sure a great effort had already been made by Chingiz Khān, and by the latter's minister, Yeh-lü Ch'u-ts'ai, but it would seem that Yeh-lü had tried to educate his people in Chinese and naturally he had not been able to reach them, except a very few. Kublai Khān realized the need of an education in their own language, of a Mongolian literature.

(Bibliothèque de l'Ecole des chartes, vol. 73, 73-100, 237-262, 4 figs., 490-504, 1912). Text, commentary, and discussion with Paul Viollet. Ch. V. Langlois: La vie spirituelle (La vie en France au Moyen âge, vol. 4, 23-46, 1928).

[6] Isis, 10, 67-68; 15, 183-187.

In the meanwhile another educator, of the more conventional type, Wang Ying-lin, was slowly compiling his new encyclopaedia, the Sea of jade (Yü hai). The most popular textbook of China, the so-called Three character classic (San tzŭ ching) is traditionally ascribed to him.

4. *Japan*—A school and a library of Chinese and Japanese books were founded c. 1270, not far from Yokohama, by Hōjō Sanetoki. The library was gradually increased by his successors, members like himself of the illustrious Hōjō family, until about the middle of the fourteenth century.

V. PHILOSOPHIC AND CULTURAL BACKGROUND

1. *Eastern Islām*—Since the glorious days of Ibn Ṭufail and Ibn Rushd, Western Islām had been declining steadily, and in the second half of the thirteenth century it could not boast a single philosopher of importance. It is true the ṣūfī Ibn Sab'īn, who answered some of the emperor Frederick's questions, lived until 1269, but he belongs rather to the first half of the century. Thus all of the Muslims dealt with in this section were easterners.

To begin with, there were at least half a dozen logicians, mathematicians—encyclopaedists in the best sense of the term. Al-Mufaḍḍal ibn 'Umar al-Abharī wrote a summary of Porphyry's Isagoge, and a general treatise on science and philosophy, the Hidāyat al-ḥikma (Guide to wisdom) which was the subject of many commentaries. Treatises of the same kind were composed by 'Alī ibn 'Umar al-Kātibī. A textbook on logic was dedicated by Muḥammad ibn Sālim Ibn Wāṣil to King Manfred, but after his return to Syria, he changed its title, that is, its dedication.

The following three were primarily mathematicians. Nāṣir al-dīn al-Ṭūsī was one of the greatest scientists of the Middle Ages, and his mind was truly encyclopaedic. He wrote treatises on logic, the classification of knowledge, metaphysics, the limits of understanding, theology, and ethics. The so-called Nāṣirian ethics (Akhlāq-i-Nāṣirī) was one of the most popular works of its kind in Islām. Originally written in Persian, it was soon translated into Arabic, and was often published, elaborated, and glossed upon; its popularity has continued until our own time. Muslim ethics, as represented by this work and others of the same class, was essentially a development of Aristotelian and Platonic thought. Muḥammad ibn Ashraf al-Samarqandī was a lesser mathematician and a lesser man, but he wrote logical treatises and a dialectical one which was immensely successful. Quṭb al-dīn al-Shīrāzī was almost as great a scientist as Nāṣir al-dīn (we shall come back to both of them many times), but he did not devote as much attention to generalities and philosophical questions except toward the end of his life when he became more and more of a ṣūfī. He wrote two encyclopaedic and philosophical treatises, and commentaries on the ḥadīth and the Qur'ān. These three mathematicians were Persian-writing Persians, but they also wrote in Arabic.

We must now consider two men of a very different type. Encyclopaedists too, but on a much lower level, the level of Pliny and al-Mas'ūdī. Such men compiled more or less intelligently all the superficial knowledge available in their days, without serious effort to penetrate deeper into it or to integrate it into a single system. It is significant that the elder and greater of the two, Zakarīyā ibn Muḥammad al-Qazwīnī, has sometimes been called the Muslim Pliny. Al-Qazwīnī published two large compilations, an encyclopaedia of natural history and a geography, containing an immense amount of information. However superficial, these books must be taken into account because of their influence. In fact if we want to measure contemporary knowledge, we cannot do better than to consult them. The deeper and more learned publications of such scientists as Nāṣir al-dīn and Quṭb al-dīn could only be appreciated by a very small élite. On the contrary, al-Qazwīnī's represented the average knowledge of the educated man, that is, not the knowledge which these men had, but that which was available to them, which they could really understand, and of which they readily availed themselves. The other cosmographer, Muḥammad ibn Ibrāhīm al-Waṭwāṭ, was much less known and less important.

The majority of Muslim doctors were interested primarily in theology and in the traditions of their faith. Their interest in philosophy was but secondary. To give a complete list of these theologians would be useless, but I have selected three of them by way of illustration.

Yaḥyā ibn Sharaf al-Nawawī, who flourished mainly in Damascus, wrote a popular textbook on Shāfi'ite law, and many other theological and religious books. Al-Baiḍāwī was another Shāfi'ite doctor who lived in Persia. He was the author of a commentary on the Qur'ān, which Sunnite Muslims hold in respect almost as if it were a holy book. The third of these theologians, Muḥammad ibn Muḥammad al-Tabrīzī, is named here because of his commentary on the twenty-five propositions summarizing Aristotelian philosophy, which are included in Maimonides' Guide of the perplexed. That commentary, though very valuable, is lost in Arabic; we know it only through Hebrew versions. It is a good example of an Arabic work, which the historian of Muslim philosophy may possibly neglect, but which exerted a definite influence on Jewish philosophers.

It would take us too far out of our field to deal with the purely literary productions, but a few exceptions may be made. One is the Ṭaif al-khayāl (Ghosts of the imagination) by Muḥammad ibn Dāniyāl, the only extant specimen of the dramatic poetry of mediaeval Islām. It contains curious descriptions of contemporary types.

One may discuss the propriety of including this Muḥammad ibn Dāniyāl in my survey, but I am sure all will agree that it would be essentially incomplete if the two greatest poets of the time were left out. These two poets can be fully appreciated only by Persian readers, yet they belong to the world literature. The elder, Sa'dī, is one of the greatest lyrical poets of all times, and his influence was felt not only in the East but all over the West; in the West it was especially great in the second half of the eighteenth century. Jalāl al-dīn al-Rūmī, though much less known outside of Persia and of the East, is more important from the philosophical point of view. He was the greatest Ṣūfī poet of Persia, the greatest writing in Persian, even as the Egyptian Ibn al-Fāriḍ was the greatest Ṣūfī poet writing in Arabic. Incidentally he founded one of the main monastic orders of Islām, the order of Mawlawīs, or whirling dervishes. A history of science in the thirteenth century which did not refer to Sa'dī and Jalāl al-dīn would scandalize humanistic readers as much as a history of Roman science forgetting Lucretius, or a history of science in the fourteenth century making no mention of Dante.

2. *Eastern Jews and Samaritans*—As opposed to Islām, which was going down in the West but holding its own in the East, Israel became less and less important in the East while growing stronger in the West. Let us consider the weaker, the eastern side, of Israel first.

I could only find three men worth mentioning, none of whom was a fully orthodox Jew. Indeed the first embraced Islām, the second was a Samaritan, and the third a Qaraite! (The third was the only one writing in Hebrew.)

The first, Ibn Kammūna, was an Egyptian logician, physician, and alchemist, who wrote many philosophical and scientific treatises in Arabic. He composed a commentary on the Elucidations of Yaḥya al-Suhrawardī. This Yaḥya had been, a century before, the introducer of the illuministic philosophy (ḥikmat al-ishrāq) into the East. It is interesting to find a Jew taking up that kind of mysticism, so different from the mysticism of his own people. But then Ibn Kammūna was an Egyptian Jew to begin with, and he was finally converted to Islām. Soon after his Islamization he wrote a book wherein he compared the three great religions of Western Asia and Europe. (We have a whole collection of such books written by Jews, Christians, and Muslims. A synoptic study of them would be very desirable. The best on the Christian side were Ramon Lull's).

The second, Muwaffaq al-dīn, a Samaritan of Damascus, was better known as a physician, but he wrote a philosophical and theological introduction. Like all the Samaritans of that time he wrote in Arabic.

The third, Aaron ben Joseph, was a Qaraite of Crimean origin who flourished in Constantinople. His commentary on the Torah, the Mibḥar, is one of the outstanding books of Qaraite literature.

3. *Western Jews*—As opposed to their Eastern brethren, the Western Jews are so numerous and a few of them so important that we must break the whole group into smaller ones. I shall consider five sub-groups: (a) Spanish; (b) Catalan; (c) Provençal; (d) Italian; (e) German. This geographical classification is the most expedient, but the reader must bear in mind that it is not absolute. Individuals often passed from one group to another, this being especially true with regard to the first three between which the exchanges were numerous.

(a) Spanish Jews. A brief reference to the translators Solomon ibn Ayyub and Jacob ibn Abbassi will suffice. Solomon came from Granada, and Jacob from Huesca, but both were finally established in Béziers. They translated some of Maimonides' works; Solomon, the Kitāb al-farā'iḍ, and Jacob, a part of the Kitāb al-sirāj. Jacob was well acquainted with Greek philosophy but was too orthodox to have much confidence in it.

Shem-ṭob Ibn Falaquera was more of a philosopher, a disciple and defender of Maimonides and Ibn Rushd, making gallant efforts to harmonize their Aristotelianism with the Jewish dogmas. His translation of the Yanbū' al-ḥayāt of Ibn Gabirol exerted some influence on later philosophers. He wrote a number of philosophical treatises, largely derived from Arabic sources, yet independent. Isaac Albalag's translation of al-Gazzālī's Maqāṣid al-falāsifa was also very influential. His own attitude was unusual; he was an Aristotelian and an Averroist, but opposed to al-Ghazzālī and to Maimonides, whose errors, according to him, were due to their imperfect knowledge of Aristotle. The majority of orthodox Jews opposed Maimonides because of his Aristotelianism; Isaac opposed him rather because of his lack of Aristotelianism.

In contrast to these, we may still mention Isaac Aboab, not a philosopher but a popular Talmudist. His Menorat ha-maor is philosophically insignificant, but it helped to shape the thoughts of many men and women and to diffuse Talmudic lore.

And finally we have a whole group of Qabbalists continuing the tradition of Isaac the Blind and his pupils, Azriel ben Menahem and Asher ben David. Indeed the climax of that tradition may be said to have taken place in this time, for the greatest book, the bible, of the Qabbala, the Book of splendor (Sefer ha-zohar) was very probably compiled by Moses ben Shem-ṭob of Leon who died in 1305. Like other bibles, the Zohar is extremely complex: it contains elements of all kinds and all ages down to its own and even later interpolations, but the dominating note is mystical. It is an esoterical commentary on the Torah which exerted a very deep influence not only on the more mystical of the Jews, the Qabbalists and the Ḥasidim, but—it is no exaggeration to say—on the whole of Israel. Its immense success was due to the fact that it afforded a means of escape to the many Jews whose souls could not be satisfied either by the fundamentalism of the orthodox rabbis, or by the excessive intellectualism of the Averroists and the Maimonideans. This integration of all the mystical fancies of the Jews into a single book completed the organization of Qabbalism. The Zohar soon attained a position of authority second only to that of the Holy Torah itself. In fact, from the extreme Qabbalistic point of view, the Torah could not be properly understood without the Zohar, and was thus of much less worth without it. The success of Qabbalism was magnified by the very miseries which the Jews had to bear with, for when life is hard beyond endurance one is more tempted to indulge in visions and the more irrational these are the better. The Zohar was a source of good and evil; it was the fountain head of much generosity and wisdom, but also of considerable nonsense and madness, of all the extravagant dreams of the Ghetto.

It is not our business to judge the Zohar and the Qabbala, but simply to account for their appearance and influence as well as we can. Whether good or evil, the importance of the Zohar can hardly be exaggerated because the souls of so many men were molded by it. Its indirect influence on science was almost entirely bad, for it encouraged irrational thoughts and superstitions, and discouraged the use of the humbler and safer means of finding and testing the truth. The mediocrity of Jewish science is largely due to the abject enthralment of Jewish minds to canonic writings; in that respect the Zohar did but complete the task begun by the Bible and the Talmud.

Moses of Leon was not the only Qabbalist of that age. There were quite a few others, notably Abraham Abulafia of Saragossa who tried to make Pope Nicholas III see the obvious truth of Qabbalism! His was an errant and adventurous life. His main disciple was the Castilian, Joseph ben Abraham Giqatilia, or Joseph Ba'al ha-nissim (the miracle worker). Still another was Todros Abulafia of Seville.

(b) Catalan Jews. The Jews of Catalonia were not far behind their brethren of Spain. In fact two of them were truly great personalities.

Moses ben Naḥman (or Naḥmanides) is perhaps best known because of his public disputation on Christianity and Judaism with the apostate Pablo Christiani (Barcelona, 1263). That disputation, arranged by the Dominicans as a part of their anti-Jewish propaganda, could but end in one way, a further condemnation of the Talmud and of Israel. Moses himself was exiled; he finally settled in the Holy Land, where he composed his main work, a very conservative commentary on the Torah, and where he died c. 1270.

Solomon ben Adret was another venerable leader of the rabbis. We may say that Moses and Solomon represented the moderate portion of Judaism, the center of it, if we consider the Maimonideans and other "philosophers" as forming the left wing, and the Qabbalists as a sort of right wing. Solomon's thoughts are best revealed in the abundant responsa written by him in answer to the questions which reached "the Rabbi of Spain" from every corner of Israel. He was responsible for the translation of Maimonides' commentary on the Mishnah from Arabic into Hebrew. He defended Israel with equal vigor against the enemies from without, Muslims and Christians, and those from within, rationalists and Qabbalists. Under his direction the rabbis of Barcelona went so far in 1305 as to excommunicate the young men who studied philosophy and science without professional necessity (physicians were allowed to make such studies). In their fear of philosophy and lay knowledge, the defenders of Jewish orthodoxy were certainly behind their Christian contemporaries. We shall see[7] that the teaching of the whole Aristotelian corpus was already permitted at the university of Paris by 1255. To be sure after that date there were still persecutions of Averroism, especially of the more radical forms of it, but the Roman Church had made its peace with Aristotle. This difference of attitude is doubly symptomatic of the intellectual progress which the Christian orthodoxy had made, and which the Jewish orthodoxy had somehow failed to make.

Aaron ha-Levi was a much humbler man, comparable to his Spanish contemporary Isaac Aboab. His Book of consecration, explaining the precepts of Mosaic law, enjoyed a very long popularity.

Two of the philosophical translators were also Catalans; Shem-ṭob ben Isaac of Tortosa, and Zereḥiah Gracian of Barcelona. They translated Aristotelian and other philosophical texts. Such men belonged necessarily to the left wing of Israel, for it is they who introduced into it the teachings which their rabbis considered so full of danger. Their activity implied a strong belief in the value of knowledge, and in the insufficiency of dogmas and theological and Talmudic commentaries.

(c) Provençal Jews. (Provençal here refers to Languedoc as well as to Provence.) As opposed to the Spanish and Catalan Jews, the Provençal were all of them liberal, which shows that our geographical classification goes below the surface.

Two of them were encyclopaedists of the philosophical type. Levi ben Abraham ben Ḥayyim, leader of liberal Judaism in southern France, compiled two scientific encyclopaedias, the one in Hebrew verse, the other in prose; Gershon ben Solomon, very probably the father of the more famous Levi ben Gershon, wrote a third work of the same kind. The occurrence within the last quarter of the thirteenth century of three works answering broadly the same purpose—to provide a body of scientific information—proves that there was a demand for such information among the Jews of Provence and Languedoc. Both men are sometimes spoken of as Catalan, which is not surprising considering the very close relations between Catalonia and southern France. In fact both were connected with Roussillon, which was a sort of transition between the two countries. Its main city, Perpignan —where Gershon is said to have died—was the capital of the whole kingdom of Majorca as long as the latter existed. Leaving political considerations aside, there was a great difference between the spiritual atmosphere of Perpignan and that of Barcelona. In my third volume I shall have to deal with a third man of this kind, Jedaiah ben Abraham Bedersi, whose most popular work was completed only in the fourteenth century. Yet long before the end of the thirteenth century he had already written his Book of paradise, an ethical treatise of which the fourth part is

[7] See my note on Aristotelian tradition in the second half of the thirteenth century, at the end of the chapter on translations.

a summary of scientific knowledge. Needless to say, all of these men were ardent Maimonideans.

Two great philosophical translators hailed from the same country: Moses ben Tibbon and Jacob ben Maḥir. It is not necessary to descant upon them; their names speak loud enough. Thanks to these giants, abundant treasures of Greco-Arabic knowledge were revealed to the Hebrew reading world. A third translator, Solomon ben Moses of Melgueil, though much less important, must be quoted because he translated Aristotelian commentaries into Hebrew, not from Arabic but from Latin! This illustrates strikingly the counter currents which were already playing.

(d) Italian Jews. Zeraḥiah Gracian, the translator from Arabic into Hebrew, referred to in the Catalan section above, might be counted among the Italians for he spent the end of his life in Rome and did there at least a part of his work. Aḥiṭub ben Isaac of Palermo translated Maimonides' logic, fought Qabbalism, and composed an ethical poem.

Hillel ben Samuel of Verona suggested that the growing conflict between Maimonideans and anti-Maimonideans, which was bidding fair to divide western Israel, should be submitted for arbitration to a council of eastern rabbis. He was himself a staunch Maimonidean. His Tagmule ha-nefesh (Benefits of the soul) is a collection of opinions of Greek, Muslim, Jewish,—and Christian—sages. He was a translator from Latin into Hebrew and one of the first Jews to have a direct knowledge of Latin scholastic literature. Another symptom of changing times!

Isaiah ben Elijah of Trani, and Benjamin 'Anav of Rome, were distinguished Talmudists; Jehiel 'Anav of Rome was a copyist of Hebrew manuscripts and the author of an ethical treatise. He too showed traces of Latin influence.

This Italian group is small but original. It occupies so to say an intermediate position between the rationalists and the fundamentalists, and also—and this is even more interesting—between the Latin and the Arabic worlds.

(e) German Jews. The main Talmudic authority of Germany was Meir ben Baruch of Rothenburg in Bavaria, often called Ma'or ha-golah (The light of the exile).

Abraham ben Alexander of Cologne, a disciple of the German Qabbalist, Eleazar of Worms, went to live in Spain. He wrote a treatise wherein German and Spanish Qabbalism are curiously combined. A much younger man, Asher ben Jehiel, who had sat at the feet of Meir ben Baruch, was also driven out of his country and after long peregrinations finally established himself in Toledo. Like his master he was a pure Talmudist opposed to any deviation from the accepted traditions. He threw the weight of his learning and authority on the side of fundamentalism, and under the cumulative influence of Naḥmanides, Solomon ben Adret and his own, Spanish Jewry became more and more bigoted. I am running a little ahead of my story in speaking of this, for Asher died only in 1327 and remained in Germany until the end of the thirteenth century. The account of his life in Spain thus belongs to the fourteenth century, but after all he did but complete the work begun by Naḥmanides and Solomon ben Adret.

Summary of Jewish efforts—The activity of the Jews interested in philosophy, or opposed to it (which is but another way of being interested), was so considerable and so varied that we must stop a moment to survey it in a different way.

It is not necessary to speak again individually of the translators, though they were the real pioneers of progress along the main road. Let us mention only once more the two greatest ones, two members of the illustrious Tibbonid family, Moses ibn Tibbon and Jacob ben Maḥir. And also two pioneers of a different kind, Solomon ben Moses of Melgueil, and Hillel ben Samuel of Verona, who began the exploitation of Latin literature.

Besides the translators, the main body was made up of Talmudists. Exclusive of the Qaraite, Aaron ben Joseph, I counted at least nine distinguished Talmudists: Isaac Aboab, Moses ben Naḥman, Solomon ben Adret, Aaron ha-Levi, Isaiah ben Elijah, Jehiel and Benjamin 'Anav, Meir ben Baruch, and Asher ben Jehiel. These are of course the least interesting from our point of view; they did not care for science; we cannot care very much for them.

Then there were a number of mystics. Illuminism was represented by the Egyptian, Ibn Kammūna. In the west all the mystical tendencies were swallowed up in the Qabbala, and the home of that movement was Spain. The foremost mequbbalim were Moses ben Shem-ṭob of Leon, Abraham and Todros Abulafia, and Joseph Giqatilia. And to these we must add Abraham ben Alexander who wove together the threads of German and Spanish Qabbalism.

We now come to what might be called "the philosophical party," "the philosophers"—with almost the same implications as in the eighteenth century, relatively speaking. Certain it is that their opponents considered them "radicals," or "liberals," or "Bolsheviki," and they were all that if we bear in mind that the radicals of one century might easily be mistaken for the conservatives of the next one. Leaving out the Samaritan, Muwaffaq al-dīn, the most distinguished philosophers were Shem-ṭob ibn Falaquera, Isaac Albalag, Levi ben Abraham ben Ḥayyim, Gershon ben Solomon, and Jedaiah ben Abraham Bedersi.

Most of these philosophers were disciples of Maimonides and of Ibn Rushd in various proportions, even as the Talmudists were anti-Maimonidean almost to a man. This requires qualification. To begin with, the Maimonidean strife which threatened to disrupt European Jewry was restricted to his philosophical writings. There was some discussion also about his rabbinical authority, about his theological and Talmudic works, but not half as venomous. In fact the translation of his commentary on the Mishnah was promoted by that arch-conservative, Solomon ben Adret. All of the translators belonged almost of necessity to the philosophical rebellion, except perhaps Jacob ibn Abbassi, who translated a part of that commentary. In the second place one could be Averroistic without being Maimonidean; that is, one could oppose Maimonides from other grounds than conservatism; this was the case of Isaac Albalag.

In short, the leaders of Israel were engaged in a three-cornered fight involving Talmudism, Greco-Arabic philosophy, and Qabbalism: this implied three major conflicts and a great many secondary ones. It could easily be shown that these conflicts, representing fundamental tendencies of the human mind, are still continuing to-day in various forms. It would have been a thousand pities if one of the three parties had completely overcome the two others, even had it been the philosophical one which triumphed ultimately, for the human mind would have been much poorer. Many of the questions which were then raised needed centuries to be cleared, and some are not solved yet.

4. *Western Christendom*—The Jewish activity of this age was far greater than the Muslim, yet it was itself very small as compared with the Christian. Indeed this age witnessed the apotheosis of Christian philosophy; it was one of the great climaxes in the philosophical evolution of mankind. We shall divide the Christian

philosophers into seven national or geographical groups (a) Spain; (b) Italy; (c) France; (d) Central Europe; (e) the Low Countries; (f) the British Isles; (g) Scandinavia.

(a) Spain. (Meaning the whole peninsula.) The Spanish group was not very large but it contains at least three personalities of the first magnitude.

Peter of Spain, the Portuguese physician who sat in St. Peter's chair for less than a year (1276–1277) under the name of John XXI, was one of the leading logicians and psychologists of his time. His Summulae logicales was a compendium of logic —of the whole of it, that is, the older and newer Aristotelian knowledge, and the mediocre additions made to it by "modern" philosophers (logica modernorum). It was one of the most popular schoolbooks of the Middle Ages, its popularity being due as usual not to any transcendent merit, but on the contrary to its practical nature and to its conveniently low level, not too far out of the reach of the majority of readers. There are a great many manuscripts, editions, and elaborations of it, commentaries and translations into Greek and into Hebrew. He was also the author of a treatise on psychology, which was far more ambitious and remained almost unknown. It includes a history of Greek and Arabic psychology. Peter was a moderate, or rather a timid, Aristotelian who developed gradually Augustinian tendencies. It was during his pontificate that the bishop of Paris was ordered to investigate and to check the philosophical and theological "errors" which were then propagated among the students.

Of Alfonso the Wise I have already spoken. His activity was far more important from the mathematical and astronomical point of view than from the philosophical, yet it was impossible to do as much as he did without modifying perceptibly the "Weltanschauung" of the intellectual élite among his subjects.

Let us now pass to Aragon and Catalonia. The Dominican, Raymond Martin, distinguished himself mainly by his controversies against the Jews. He was the main organizer of anti-Jewish propaganda in Spain; he caused Hebrew writings to be examined and censored, and reached the conclusion that the Talmud was not entirely bad and need not be burned completely! His best known work was the "Dagger of faith," a dagger pointed against the hearts of Jews and Muslims; many parts of it have been identified with passages of St. Thomas' Summa contra gentiles. It is not yet quite clear who was the original writer and who the borrower. St. Peter Paschal was also a specialist in Christian apologetics, but he was better acquainted with Islām than with Israel. Indeed his knowledge of Muslim theology and of Arabic literature was very extensive; he may have been one of the channels through which Arabic lore reached Dante.

And we now come to the two greatest men of contemporary Spain—or more exactly of Catalonia; two men who were among the most arresting personalities of the Middle Ages: Arnold of Villanova and Ramon Lull. Both are excellent illustrations of the passage of power from Islām to Christendom, from the Arabic to the Latin world, for they had themselves one foot in each. Both, but especially the second, were deeply steeped in Arabic lore and letters.

They had that much in common, but little else. Arnold was an encyclopaedist, a social reformer, a visionary. Most of his time was devoted to medicine, astrology, and alchemy, but he dabbled in psychology, and every kind of magic attracted him. He was an anticlerical theologian, dominated by Joachimite and apocalyptic ideas.

Ramon on the contrary was very orthodox, and though he had an intimate knowledge of the Muslim and Jewish faiths, he was so profoundly convinced of the superiority of his own, and on the other hand he had such confidence in the efficacy of logical methods, that he spent part of his life dreaming of the possibility of converting unbelievers by purely intellectual efforts. Nor did he simply dream; he was full of energy and anxious to transform his dreams into realities. He wrote a large number of treatises in many languages, but chiefly in Catalan, explaining his ars magna, the great logical art, which would enable one to correlate all knowledge into a single system of irresistible simplicity and persuasion; at its worst this was nonsense, at its best, a crude anticipation of the mathematical logic of our own days. He did not restrict himself to theories, but applied his method to as many branches of science as he could. He was a true encyclopaedist, not satisfied to juxtapose items of knowledge as the above-mentioned Muslim and Jewish writers were doing; he must correlate them in every possible way, bind them together by innumerable links, integrate them into a single scheme. He had an unquenchable thirst for unity—an intellectual unity which his faithful heart could not distinguish from the religious unity symbolized by Christ. Under the influence of theological "tours de force," such as the identification of Trinity with Unity, and of Qabbalistic ideas, which were even more marvelous, it is not surprising considering his faith and his excessive logical bent that his mind developed in the extraordinary way it did. He remains unique in the history of philosophy—the model of extreme realism, the archetype of logical extravagance.

The Averroistic tendencies of the Parisian scholars are well known to us through their condemnation by Stephen Tempier (1277); that Stephen did not succeed in checking them is proved by the fact that when Ramon Lull stayed in Paris in 1297, then again in 1309-1311, they angered him so that he was roused to indite a whole series of anti-Averroistic elucubrations.

Ramon Lull was not simply orthodox, but passionately so, yet he was so Quixotic and peculiar that he was involuntarily pointing the way to various heterodoxies. As is usually the case, his followers were inspired by his aberrations rather than by his fundamental doctrines, and there grew up after his death a Lullian school or Lullian philosophy (Lullism) which came dangerously near to heresy and excited violent controversies. As usual also, Lull's thought was enriched with various accretions for which he was in no way responsible.

The striking notes in Ramon's personality were his gentleness and forbearance; he was a true brother of St. Francis. He was perhaps just as restless as Arnold of Villanova, but what an abyss between them! Ramon's was the restlessness of love, Arnold's the restlessness of defiance; Ramon's spirit was apostolic, Arnold's was refractory. Both deserve our admiration, but it is as difficult to love the latter as it is easy to love the former.

(b) Italy. Under King Manfred's patronage philosophical works were translated from Greek and Hebrew into Latin. Aristotle's Magna moralia, the Problems, and other pseudo-Aristotelian treatises, were translated from the Greek by Bartholomew of Messina; the Book of the apple was translated from the Hebrew, some said by the king himself.

The greatest Christian philosopher of the age, the very champion of Christendom, St. Thomas Aquinas, hailed also from southern Italy. He was born in Campania and received his first education in Monte Cassino and Naples. The task accomplished by him was the study of Aristotelian philosophy (his friend, William of Moerbeke, helped him to obtain excellent texts) and its harmonization with the

Christian dogmas. That is, his purpose was very similar to that of many of the Muslim and Jewish philosophers who came before him. To be sure, those had tried to harmonize Aristotelianism with other dogmas, but in many cases there was no disagreement between them. For example, they all believed in a creation ex nihilo, and not in an eternal world. In fact, St. Thomas made considerable use of the writings of Muslim philosophers, chiefly al-Ghazzālī and Ibn Rushd, and of Jewish ones, chiefly Ibn Gabirol and Maimonides. His attitude was essentially one of moderation, comparable to al-Ghazzālī's, between the extreme Aristotelianism or Averroism on the one hand and the extreme anti-Aristotelianism or Scotism on the other. In the famous altar-piece painted by Francesco Traini for Santa Catarina, Pisa (c. 1341–1346), St. Thomas is represented triumphing over heresy and especially over Ibn Rushd prostrated at his feet. Now that picture is right to a certain extent. St. Thomas' philosophy was a triumph over Averroism, but not so much more so than al-Ghazzālī's, as far as principles were concerned. The completeness of his triumph was due not only to his genius, but also to the political supremacy of Christendom over Islām. The hour of Western Europe, of Latindom, had finally struck. St. Thomas' Summa was the political philosophy of the conquerors. This is not said at all in disparagement of St. Thomas, who was by general consent a magnificent expositor. It is not surprising that he became the mouthpiece of triumphant Christianity, for the vigor, grasp, and clearness of his mind have seldom been equalled. Yet the fact remains that he was not the conqueror, but the conqueror's mouthpiece. The conqueror was Western Christendom. It was a remarkable coincidence that at the very hour of its own glory the Church found such an ideal exponent of its thought. However, the perfection of that agreement was not realized at once, and was not generally accepted until after a protracted struggle. Thomism was an adaptation of Aristotelianism within the dogmatic limits of Christianity; its triumph was thus indirectly a triumph for Aristotelianism, welcome enough to the Peripatetics, but equally unwelcome to their adversaries. It satisfied the minds of the Dominicans, not only because St. Thomas was one of them, but because they were instinctively Aristotelians; it grated upon the hearts of the gentler Franciscans, not because St. Thomas belonged to the other Order, not at all, but because they were instinctively Platonists. However, the church militant realized, as soon as its need of him arose, that St. Thomas had considerably strengthened its structure. Centuries later, when it had to weather the terrible crisis of the Reformation, it realized its need and St. Thomas' strength even more acutely. During the council of Trent the Summa theologica was kept upon the altar together with the Bible. A whole series of encyclics have consecrated St. Thomas' victory, and his philosophy may be said to be the official philosophy of the Roman Catholic Church. It is remarkable enough that a philosopher of the second half of the thirteenth century should be the guide of a great part of Western Christendom to this day, but such is the fact, and the historian of science must bear it in mind.

Another Italian—a Tuscan—St. Bonaventure, represented the other pole of thought. He was a Franciscan and became one of the generals of his order; he was naturally a Platonist and a mystic. It is the St. Thomases who have built the church, who have built everything in the world, yet this does not mean either that the mystics were unwanted or that they ever lacked a following. The St. Thomases and the St. Bonaventures are like the Marthas and Marys of philosophy. Our minds may prefer the former, and our hearts the latter, but if we be endowed at once with good brains and loving hearts we are very embarrassed to choose between them. And why should we?

St. Bonaventure and St. Thomas died in the same year, 1274, at about the same age, the former being a little over fifty, the latter a little below. We might compare with them and place in their company, if not on the same level, a much younger man, Giles of Rome. Giles really belongs to the following generation; as he was born some twenty years later and lived twenty years longer, he survived them by more than forty years. Yet the best of his work was done before the end of the thirteenth century. He was neither a Dominican nor a Franciscan, but an Augustinian hermit; an ardent if eclectic Thomist, fighting like his master for the middle doctrine against the overbold Averroists on the one side, and against the timid anti-Thomists on the other. He composed many Aristotelian commentaries and a classification of knowledge, which was the last original contribution of its kind in mediaeval times.

We may now pass to a group of men who, from the philosophical point of view at least, were far less important.

First, two encyclopaedists of that popular type with which we are already familiar: Ser Brunetto Latini, a Florentine, wrote his main work, Li livres dou tresor, in French (c. 1266). A little later (c. 1282) another Tuscan, Ristoro d'Arezzo, wrote an encyclopaedic treatise in Italian, Della composizione del mondo colle sue cagioni. It should be noted that Brunetto wrote in Italian, as well as in French; he composed in the former language a short encyclopaedic poem, the Tesoretto, and translated Cicero's Rhetoric into it. Both writers, but especially Brunetto, had derived a substantial part of their knowledge from Arabic sources. That knowledge it must be admitted was mediocre and largely out of date, yet the Arabic part of it was on the whole the best. Brunetto had visited the courts of Toledo and Seville as an ambassador from Florence. He was Dante's teacher or guide and may have been the instrument, or one of the instruments, of Dante's familiarity with Muslim lore.

The astrologer, Bartholomew of Parma, was the author of the most elaborate treatise on geomancy of that age (a poor distinction), and of a Philosophia Boetii derived from the περὶ διδάξεων of William of Conches. Finally Taddeo Alderotti and Peter of Abano applied the methods of scholastic philosophy to the teaching of medicine. Taddeo was at once a physician, a philosopher and a humanist. He introduced the Aristotelian ethics to Italian readers. With Peter we shall deal more fully in volume 3, for his main works, the Conciliator and the Lucidator, date only from the beginning of the fourteenth century.

Compare the philosophical contributions of Italy during the second half of the thirteenth century with those of the first half of the same century. The contrast is enormous. Frederick II was obliged to surround himself with foreigners—Greeks, Muslims, Jews, or Christians hailing from distant countries, like Michael Scot. After 1250 the situation is reversed. Some of the leading teachers of the day were Italians and they were called to teach beyond the Alps. St. Bonaventure, Giles of Rome, and Brunetto Latini lived in France. St. Thomas has remained to this day one of the great world teachers.

(c) France. The French situation was less brilliant than the Italian in spite of the fact that the University of Paris was undoubtedly the main philosophical center of Christendom. That university was exceedingly cosmopolitan, and not only many of the students but many of the teachers were foreigners.

The most notable Frenchman was Vincent of Beauvais, not properly a philosopher, but an encyclopaedist. The encyclopaedic knowledge accumulated by him in his Speculum maius was not of a very high quality, nor even up-to-date, but its immensity was very impressive. His position as tutor and librarian to the royal family gave him an extraordinary opportunity of reaching and using abundant sources, and he improved it to the limit. The Speculum remained for centuries the equivalent of our modern encyclopaedias; the first printed edition of it, a set of seven enormous folio volumes, was by far the largest incunabula.

While the gigantic size of Vincent's work had some advantages— it exerted a sort of mass action—it also had a great disadvantage in that it restricted its circulation. Very few institutions could afford to own a copy of it; very few individuals had enough intellectual curiosity to need such an instrument and sufficient mental training to use it. Therefore the Speculum failed to answer the encyclopaedic purpose except for a very small élite. The rank and file of educated people and even of scholars needed humbler works better adapted to their needs. For though very few had enough curiosity for a Speculum, there is no doubt that the intellectual curiosity of the clerks and even of the people was constantly increasing.

We know that their curiosity was increasing, because more and more books were published to gratify it. From the supply we may to some extent deduce the demand. The outstanding example of a popular encyclopaedia was John of Meung's continuation of the Romance of the Rose. Not less remarkable than its contents was its tone. John of Meung was not writing for lords and ladies, as his predecessor William of Lorris, but for burghers like himself, practical people who wanted facts rather than fancies. Needless to say, John wrote in French.

Other types of philosophical activity were represented by the following scholars. Robert of Sorbon, the founder of the Sorbonne, wrote a few treatises on ethical and theological subjects. The Franciscan mechanician, Peter Olivi, discussed a number of philosophical problems in the form of "questions" and commentaries on the Books of Sentences. Olivi was an original and well informed thinker, inclined to radicalism. He was opposed to Thomism but also to some extent to neo-Platonism. His disciple, Peter de Trabibus, was also anti-Thomist. Armengaud, son of Blaise, who flourished at Montpellier, translated the pseudo-Galenic Economy from the Arabic. This was what might be called a domestic encyclopaedia, dealing not only with domestic economy as we understand it, but as well with the hygiene of body and soul. Peter of Auvergne, bishop of Clermont, wrote Aristotelian commentaries in the Thomist vein.

This Peter was the only distinguished Thomist among the contemporaries of his own nationality. To be sure, Vincent of Beauvais was acquainted with some of St. Thomas' writings, but he was not in any sense a Thomist. The third part of his Speculum quadruplex, the Speculum morale, was an abridgment of St. Thomas' Summa, but it was not composed by Vincent, nor in the latter's lifetime; it dates only from the first quarter of the fourteenth century and its author is unknown.

(d) Central Europe. Even as the cultural life of France was dominated by Vincent of Beauvais, the gigantic personality of Albert the Great was by far the most conspicuous among the Germans. My comparison with Vincent is perhaps not entirely fair to Albert. They had much in common: they belonged to the same order, that of the Friar Preachers, and were excellent symbols of it; both had a passion for encyclopaedic knowledge, yet Albert was by far the better philosopher and the greater scientist. Or let us say more simply that Albert was a real philosopher and a genuine scientist, while Vincent was neither the one nor the other.

Hence Albert's learning, if not vaster than Vincent's, was deeper. Much of Vincent's knowledge had accumulated by sheer juxtaposition; Albert's was the result of a process of gradual intussusception and organic synthesis. But this must not be exaggerated; it is only by contrast with Vincent that Albert looks like a philosopher. In fact he was too eclectic, too eager for fresh information on every subject; in a sense he was more of a scientist than of a philosopher. He wrote a whole series of Aristotelian commentaries wherein he inserted a fair amount of new facts; he was one of the main instruments for the diffusion of the Greco-Arabic knowlege which had been made recently available to Latin readers.

There is but little to say of his German contemporaries. Hermann the German, who flourished in Spain and southern Italy, translated some of al-Fārābī's and Ibn Rushd's commentaries from Arabic into Latin. Ulrich of Strassburg wrote commentaries on Aristotelian and pseudo-Aristotelian writings. His scientific knowledge was derived from his master, Albert, and so was his philosophy, with perhaps increased leanings toward neo-Platonism.

I have already mentioned two Dominicans, Albert and Ulrich. A third, Theodoric of Freiberg, belongs rather to the following century, for his main work—on optics, one of the most important physical works of the Middle Ages—was only completed after 1304. Yet he must be named, for his life covered almost the whole of the period now under consideration. These German Dominicans were remarkably akin in their philosophic eclecticism; they managed to combine St. Thomas' dogmatism with varying doses of neo-Platonism.

Theodoric calls to mind another optician, the Silesian Witelo. Whether this Witelo must be called a Pole or a Thuringian may be of great concern to German or Polish nationalists, but is relatively indifferent to others. He resided for many years in Paris and Italy, but finally returned to his country where he did his main work and spent the balance of his life. He was influenced by William of Moerbeke, whose philosophical views he shared. These were also largely impregnated with neo-Platonism.

The main characteristic of German philosophy was its inherent mysticism. It is typical enough that even the Dominicans and Thomists among them, even the most scientifically minded, were more or less fascinated by neo-Platonic conceits.

(e) Low Countries. Though the Low Countries did not produce any giant comparable to St. Thomas, Albert the Great, Roger Bacon, or even Vincent of Beauvais, they could boast a number of personalities remarkable alike for their merit and their great diversity.

To begin with, there were two neo-Platonists: the Flemish Dominican, William of Moerbeke, who seems to have been the main inspirer of that movement—we might almost call it a neo-Platonic revival; and Henry Bate of Malines, whose Speculum divinorum et quorundam naturalium was an encyclopaedia of Aristotelian knowledge strongly tinged with neo-Platonism.

One of the leaders of the Averroistic radicals in Paris was Siger of Brabant, whose brilliant and tumultuous career was brutally cut short by murder in Umbria. The condemnation pronounced by the bishop of Paris in 1277 was chiefly directed against him and Boetius of Denmark. The main adviser of the bishop in that circumstance was another Belgian, Henry of Ghent. Siger and Henry were engaged in the same activity, the interpretation of the new Aristotle, but while the former enjoyed pointing out the incompatibilities between reason and faith, the latter would explain the difficulties away in the name of orthodoxy. The former was a troublemaker, the other an adept in theological legerdemain.

Then we have two Thomists, the Dominican Giles of Lessines, and Godfrey of Fontaines. Giles wrote a treatise in defense of St. Thomas' theory of unity of substantial form. Godfrey was a member of the Sorbonne, more independent in his thinking than the Dominicans; like Giles of Rome, he did not hesitate to protest against the anti-Thomist tendencies of the bishop of Paris.

Finally, a great popular encyclopaedist, Jacob of Maerlant, who did for the Dutch-speaking people what John of Meung was doing for the French-speaking ones, and considerably more. He translated into Flemish, among other things, the natural history of Thomas of Cantimpré, the Historia scolastica of Peter the Eater, and the Speculum historiale of Vincent of Beauvais. His general attitude was very similar to that of John of Meung—contempt of chivalresque romance and lies, love of prosaic truth.

(f) The British Isles. The distinction achieved by the British school of philosophers in the twelfth century and in the first half of the thirteenth continued, and reached a magnificent climax in this and the following periods with Roger Bacon and later with William of Occam. While the glory of Italian, French, and German philosophy was largely bound up with that of the Dominican Order, it was almost entirely to the Franciscans that England owed its own philosophical fame.

This does not mean that the English Dominicans did not count at all, but they were comparatively of little importance. It is interesting to recall that it was an Irishman, Petrus de Hibernia, who was St. Thomas' teacher "in naturalibus" at the University of Naples c. 1241; it is also interesting to know that this Peter had Averroistic leanings. Perhaps his teaching helped St. Thomas to crystallize his own thoughts in the opposite direction? The only distinguished English Dominican of this time was Robert Kilwardby. It is typical enough of British singularity that this Dominican assumed an anti-Thomist attitude. While he was archbishop of Canterbury he took pains to obtain the condemnation of sundry Thomist ideas by the University of Oxford. He wrote various philosophical commentaries, a treatise on the unity of forms, and another on the subdivision of knowledge. This last named one was superior to the one written a little later by Giles of Rome under Thomist influence.

All of the other men were Franciscans. The very founder of the Oxford Franciscan school, Adam Marsh, lived until about 1257; and the greatest Franciscan teacher of the first generation, Robert Grosseteste, did also witness the beginning of this period for he died only in 1253.

Thomas of York wrote a metaphysical treatise which is of historical significance because it was anterior to St. Thomas' Aristotelian commentaries, and was in fact the earliest original Latin synthesis posterior to the Latin assimilation of Muslim and Jewish philosophy. John Peckham, who succeeded Robert Kilwardby in the see of Canterbury—the first Franciscan archbishop following the first Dominican[8] —is more famous as an optician than as a philosopher. He wrote many commentaries and theological treatises, and took up the cudgels for the mendicant orders against their enemies, whose mouthpiece was William of Saint Amour. He included the Dominicans in his defense, and at the beginning of his career showed some generosity to St. Thomas; yet he was gradually drawn into the Thomist controversy and when he became archbishop continued Kilwardby's anti-Thomist policy. St. Thomas had made great efforts to follow the middle path between

[8] Their immediate predecessor, Boniface of Savoy (Bonifacius de Sabaudia), archbishop from 1240 to 1270, was a Carthusian.

fundamentalism on the one side and radicalism on the other. But one man's middle path will not answer for another. What the Thomists considered moderation was already a kind of unwarranted radicalism in the eyes of such men as Kilwardby and Peckham and they tried to break a new middle path between the older scholasticism on the right and Thomism on the left.

The manifesto of Franciscan opposition to Thomism, Correctorium fratris Thomae, was written by William de la Mare of Oxford, and at the Franciscan chapter held at Strassburg in 1282 the brethren were warned not to read St. Thomas' Summa, if they must read it at all, without William's explanation. Needless to say, William's Correctorium, or Corruptorium as the Dominicans preferred to call it, did not remain unchallenged; it was but the beginning of a long polemic between the two orders.

William of Ware's commentaries are interesting because of their dependence on the Moreh ha-nebukim of Maimonides. This may serve to illustrate the complexities of contemporary Aristotelianism, and enable us to appreciate the endless misunderstandings to which the conflicting Aristotelian traditions could not but lead. Another curious case was that of Richard of Middleton—presumably English—whose eclecticism was extended to the point of including a modicum of Thomism. Probably Richard meant also to find the "middle path." His name, Ricardus de Media Villa, was peradventure a misreading of Media via?

And thus do we finally reach the two outstanding men of the group, Roger Bacon and Duns Scot, both brothers in St. Francis, otherwise as unlike as possible.

It would not seem necessary to say much of the former, for he is one of the best known mediaeval personalities, one of the very few with whom educated people are more or less familiar in spite of the "darkness" of his times. Unfortunately the popular conception of him is, if not altogether legendary, incorrect in many respects. For example, he is often thought of as a martyr. Now it is quite possible that he was punished in his old age for the independence and indiscipline of his views and the causticity of his remarks (bear in mind that he was not a free man but a common soldier in the Franciscan army), but this is not proved, and his disappearance after 1278 would admit of other explanations. On the other hand, an extraordinary opportunity was opened to him in 1266 when he was invited by Clement IV to prepare a complete statement of his views. Could a better proof be given of the prestige which was then already attached to him? Was any other philosopher ever honored in the same way? As opposed to Lull, Bacon's interest and confidence in logic were mediocre, but he shared his Catalan brother's belief in the necessity and possibility of converting heathens by peaceful means. This may seem a small matter to modern readers, but it required more imagination and charity in Lull's and Bacon's time than we can conceive to-day, and indeed these two were almost alone among their contemporaries to combine religious zeal with so much gentleness. Mind you, it is far more difficult to be tolerant when one is absolutely convinced of the superiority of one's own faith, as they certainly were.

Bacon was a Platonist and an anti-Thomist, and yet as genuine an encyclopaedist as his Dominican rivals. He was of course far less systematic, but his passion for unified knowledge was equal to theirs. He realized the need of getting at the facts and of reading the fundamental texts in the original languages; he was one of the first to vindicate the experimental spirit and to appreciate the practical utility of knowledge. This must seem very strange in our days, when the majority of people cannot be persuaded to obtain any knowledge unless its immediate usefulness is shown to them. We must make continuous efforts to persuade them that much knowledge which does not pay and perhaps never will, is yet worth having. In the Middle Ages, it would have been more necessary to prove that knowledge had material as well as spiritual utility. Bacon was one of the first to see that.

As compared with St. Thomas, Bacon was hardly a philosopher, but he was a seer, which is much rarer and perhaps better. He had no very definite philosophy, but a method, and rightly or wrongly, modern scientists feel more strongly attracted to him than to any other mediaeval thinker. They are conscious of a certain kinship with him. He was groping for the very method which they have been exploiting ever since with such prodigious fortune. It is possible that they idealize him. Bacon's spirit was a curious mixture of experimentalism with fundamentalism, of scientific positivism with mysticism. Like his own personality, it was full of mystery, and invited misunderstandings and legends. Thus did it happen that Bacon became to the scientifically minded a symbol of the best mediaeval thought, so to say the mediaeval prophet of modern science, and at the same time, to the unthinking people, a wonderworker, a rationalist, a reformer and a martyr!

The realism and mysticism of the Franciscan school were developed beyond measure by Duns Scotus, in revolt against the growing Aristotelianism and matter-of-factness of the age. Among the Muslim and Jewish philosophers, Duns was especially influenced by Ibn Gabirol, whose tendencies were magnified by him and even more so by his pupils. His main work, the Opus oxoniense, seems to have been completed only in the first years of the following century, and at any rate the full force of the reaction launched by him was hardly felt before that century; but we must deal with him right now and bear in mind that the seeds of Scotism were sown at the very time when Bacon was nursing the experimental spirit, and the Dominicans were establishing the dogmatic theology of St. Thomas. Duns Scot became the standard bearer of the Franciscan opposition to Thomism, of the waxing impatience with Aristotelianism and intellectualism. The law of the equality of action and reaction is just as true in the spiritual as in the material world. One of the results of the Scotist revolt was to increase the reaction against theology and thus to prepare the liberation of philosophical and scientific thought from ecclesiastical bondage.

(g) Scandinavia—The only Scandinavian worth mentioning was Boetius of Dacia, who was, together with Siger of Brabant, one of the leaders of Averroism in Paris. It is curious that these two radicals, the leaders of the extreme left in the great French University, were both of them foreigners, the one a Belgian, the other a Dane. They were promptly suppressed and disappeared mysteriously: Siger was assassinated in Orvieto; about Boetius we know nothing definite. According to Peckham, he came to a miserable end in Italy (but this may be due to a confusion with Siger); it is possible that he took refuge and found oblivion in the Dominican order.[9]

Summary of Christian work in the West—The amount of work accomplished by Christians in western Europe was at once so enormous and so diversified that, lest our readers be confused, we must summarize it and indicate the main drifts.

For the sake of clearing the ground, let us first refer to the Aristotelian translations which were continued and completed. I have already dealt with them sufficiently. Some other translations which now became available to Latin readers

[9] He is mentioned in a catalogue of Dominican writers of the thirteenth century. See Pierre Mandonnet: Siger de Brabant (Les philosophes belges, vol. 6, 228, 1911).

should be briefly mentioned. Proclos' writings were translated directly from the Greek by William of Moerbeke. The Aristotelian tradition was unfortunately contaminated by a number of spurious works, and as always the adulterated goods tended to attract more attention than the purer ones. Thus the Sirr al-asrār found a new circle of readers in Spanish, and the Sefer ha-tappuaḥ was translated from the Hebrew into Latin. The stories of Kalīla wa Dimna were translated at once from the Arabic and from the Hebrew.

To return to Aristotle, the teaching of the whole Aristotelian corpus was finally permitted by the Paris faculty soon after the middle of the century. In this respect western Christendom was far ahead, as a body, of Islām and even of Israel, and perhaps nothing shows more clearly the change which had taken place in the relative position of the three faiths than this, the official reception of Aristotle by Christendom, in contrast with its continued rejection by the more conservative Jewish and Muslim theologians.

This does not mean that the fight about Aristotle came to an end, far from it, but it took a different nature. The boundary between conservatism and liberalism was definitely moved toward the left. The anti-Aristotelians were now divided into two groups, a very large one opposing the extreme Aristotelians or Averroists, and a much smaller one whose antagonism to Peripateticism was so strong that they could not even stand it in the Christian garb of Thomism.

The leaders of the Averroistic radicals were Siger of Brabant and Boetius of Dacia, and their main opponents among many, Stephen Tempier, Thomas Aquinas, and Ramon Lull. In fact, everybody was against them. That struggle was so unequal —at least in the thirteenth century—that it lacks interest.

Thomism did not attain its full strength until the following century. To be sure as early as 1278 it was already the official doctrine of the Dominican Order, but the opposition then was intense and not by any means restricted to Franciscan rivalry. I would say that Thomism did not come of age, as far as its influence was concerned, until the council of Vienne in 1311–1312, when St. Thomas was significantly called "doctor communis."

Among the earliest defenders of St. Thomas I would quote Peter of Auvergne, Giles of Lessines, Godfrey of Fontaines, and perhaps Henry of Ghent (three Belgians out of four!). I say perhaps, because Henry was very conservative, too conservative in fact to be partisan to a new doctrine, even if that doctrine happened to be, as it was, a triumph of moderation. On the whole it would be better to place him within the group of eclectic philosophers, timid Aristotelians with Augustinian tendencies, who observed a kind of benevolent neutrality between St. Thomas and his adversaries. This was a much larger group, and withal more distinguished, than that of the open Thomists. I would count among them Peter of Spain, Giles of Rome, Ulrich of Strassburg, Theodoric of Freiberg, Witelo, William of Moerbeke, Henry Bate, Richard of Middleton, even Roger Bacon. At first sight the success of Thomism seems to have been very slow in coming, but on reflection one realizes that it was, all considered, as rapid as it could be. Such a doctrine appealed more strongly to the more conservative, that is, to the more timid; we could hardly expect it to be received with wild cheers. Moderation is a beautiful thing but it is difficult to grow enthusiastic about it. The final victory of Thomism was partly due to the fact that it was accepted rather slowly, with diffidence, and without enthusiasm. Thanks to that tardiness, the triumph, when it finally came, excited less jealousy and was even taken for granted.

If we leave out of account the lukewarm adherents of whom I have just spoken, the group of Thomists was certainly far less considerable than that of their frank adversaries. They had against them to begin with a splendid body of Franciscan Platonists: St. Bonaventure, Thomas of York, John Peckham, William de la Mare, William of Ware, Duns Scot! Then many others, like Peter Olivi and Peter de Trabibus, Stephen Tempier, and even the Dominican, Robert Kilwardby. Is it not clear that Thomism would have been hopelessly defeated but for its cautious friends who appeared gradually as the storm abated?

Though the three-cornered fight between the Averroists, Thomists, and old-fashioned scholastics was the main contest of the age, there were many other intellectual streams which we shall now briefly consider. There were occultists like Arnold of Villanova, Ramon Lull, Bartholomew of Parma, and Bacon; logicians, like Peter of Spain and Lull; psychologists, like Peter of Spain again and St. Thomas; medical scholastics, like Taddeo Alderotti and Peter of Abano; encyclopaedists, like Ristoro d'Arezzo, Brunetto Latini, Lull, John of Meung, Jacob of Maerlant, Vincent of Beauvais, Albert the Great, and Roger Bacon. This last group is particularly impressive, and it is significant of changing times, of growing democracy, that the majority of them did not write in Latin but in their own vernaculars—Italian, French, Catalan, and Dutch. We need not insist upon them now for we shall have to come back to them many times.

A group even more impressive was formed by what might be called the "experimentalists," the men who were beginning to conceive, however vaguely, the method and the spirit of experimental science: Arnold of Villanova, Lull, Peter of Spain, Peter Olivi, Peter the Stranger, Villard of Honnecourt, John Peckham, Albert the Great, Roger Bacon, and many others. For example, every great physician was intuitively an experimentalist, and at this age of mankind their intuitions were becoming more explicit. This movement was too slow and too imperceptible to attract attention; it is only now that we are able to realize its importance retrospectively. It is paradoxical enough that the main exponent of that new method, the main prophet of modern science, was not an Aristotelian but a Platonist, not a Dominican or a layman, but a brother of St. Francis, Roger Bacon! These are the surprises of history, the spice of life!

Some of these remarks would apply as well to the non-Christian philosophers. For example, the experimental spirit was showing signs of growth in Islām. In any case we must not think of Christendom as separated from the East. On the contrary, its final hegemony was largely due to its dependence upon eastern sources. Christendom was seeing further than Islām, for the simple reason that it was standing on its shoulders. St. Thomas was leaning on Ibn Sīnā, Ibn Rushd, Maimonides, al-Ghazzālī; Duns Scot on Ibn Gabirol; Lull on al-Ghazzālī and perhaps on Ibn 'Arabī; Siger and Boetius on Ibn Rushd; William of Ware on Maimonides, etc. This is so true that the story of Averroism, Avicennism, Avicebronism, or Maimonidism, cannot be told completely without reference to Christendom. These stories are not simply chapters of the Muslim or Jewish past, but of the whole human past.

The connection between East and West was established also in another—opposite—way. Muslims, Christians, and Jews were keenly aware of the differences between their faiths and philosophies, and some of them devoted the best of their time and energy to the explanation of those differences and of their own superiority. Thus we have a vast apologetic literature written by Muslims like Ibn Kammūna, by Jews like Solomon ben Adret, but chiefly by Christians—for they were and have remained the foremost propagandists—like Raymond Martin, St. Peter Paschal, Ramon Lull, and Ricoldo di Monte Croce. These writings are not simply of religious but of philosophical interest because they truly reveal the "Weltanschauung" of the authors. A comparative study of them would be well worth undertaking.

5. *Eastern Christendom*—Though the total contributions of the eastern Christians were insignificant as compared with those of their western brethren, we shall divide them into three groups: (a) Greeks; (b) Syrians; (c) Armenians. In a way the subdivision is more natural and more needed than in the case of Western Christendom, because these subgroups represent totally different cultures, separated from one another by their language as well as by their political and ecclesiastical institutions.

(a) Greeks. Theodoros II Lascaris, emperor of Nicaea until his premature death in 1258, was a distinguished humanist and much might have been expected from him had he been permitted to live longer. He wrote treatises on the unity of nature and on Christian theology. He explains the unity of nature by the ancient theory of the four elements out of which everything is made.

Nicephoros Blemmydes, who had frequented the court of Nicaea but had already withdrawn from it into a monastery before Theodoros' accession, wrote various textbooks, one of them on logic. He was an encyclopaedist, but on a very humble scale.

The Byzantine writers of whom I shall speak presently were all[10] associated with the Palaeologoi who occupied the throne of Constantinople after the fall of the Latin empire in 1261. Manuel Holobolos, secretary to the first Palaeologos, Michael VIII, was a logician; he wrote a commentary on the first book of the Prior Analytics and distinguished himself by translating Boetius' logical treatises into Greek! Just think of that! Aristotelian logic, one of the immortal creations of the Greek genius, was now retransmitted to the Greek speaking people after having been filtered through the mind of a decadent Roman! This does not mean that the Greek text was not available to them, but rather that it was intellectually beyond their reach. Paraphrases of it and of other Aristotelian treatises were composed at about this time by one Sophonias, otherwise unknown.

The two leading humanists and scholars were Georgios Pachymeres and Maximos Planudes. Pachymeres wrote, among many other books, a summary of Aristotelian philosophy and a manual dealing with the four branches of the quadrivium. His main work, a chronicle of contemporary events, was full of the theological discussions which were then dominating and sterilizing Byzantine thought.

The study of Latin philosophy begun by Holobolos was continued, with more vigor and efficiency, by Planudes. He introduced to the Greek world Cato the Censor, Ovid, Cicero, Caesar, Donatus, Augustine, and Boetius' Consolation. He may possibly be the author or co-author of a Greek version of St. Thomas' Summa. What better proof could one ask for of the growing prestige of the Latin culture? The Latin-speaking people upon whom the Greeks had looked down—not so long ago—with so much contempt were now considered as equals. I hasten to add that the Greeks who felt that way were but very few in number. The great majority were far too bitter against the Roman church and the Latin people to judge them with any indulgence or equity, let alone to want to read their books or submit

[10] Except perhaps Sophonias, about whom we know almost nothing.

themselves to their evil influence in any way. Planudes' interest in Latindom was exceptional; it was due to the fact that he had been the ambassador of Andronicos II in Venice and had thus learned to know and appreciate western achievements. Nevertheless it was very significant; we may think of it as an opening wedge preparing greater events in the future. To most scholars Planudes is best known as the compiler of Greek anthologies, but from a higher point of view his decanting Latin thought into Greek vessels was far more weighty.

(b) Syrians. The parallel development of two Syriac literatures, the one Monophysitic, the other Nestorian, continued in this period, which was practically the last one. There were still a few Syriac writers in the following century, but they were insignificant. The two Syriac authors with whom we shall deal presently were truly the last to be of any scientific or philosophical importance, and by a strange turn of fate one of them was by far the greatest Syriac writer of all times.

Abū-l-Faraj, a Jacobite priest who reached the dignity of mafriān, was not only a great Syriac writer, but one of the outstanding personalities of the Middle Ages. If a great man could save a language, certainly Syriac would have been preserved, thanks to the genius of this son of a Jew, who surpassed all the Syrians in the use of their own language. To be sure literary genius lends dignity to a language and gives to it a kind of immortality, but it cannot affect the social and economic circumstances which are the only causes of popularity. No amount of individual genius could give life to a language which is dying. The most lively of the Syrians were speaking Arabic, which has continued to be their main language to this day. Before long it was necessary to translate some of Abū-l-Faraj's works into Arabic to make them available to his own people! He was a scientist as well as a philosopher and a theologian, and his abundant writings constitute a sort of encyclopaedia of Syriac knowledge. In that respect they are very useful to us, for after having consulted them we can say with some confidence, the Jacobite Syrians knew this; they did not know that. Abū-l-Faraj composed many theological treatises. His philosophical works were essentially paraphrases of the Aristotelian corpus available to him in Arabic.

His Nestorian contemporary, 'Abhd-īshō' bar Běrīkhā, was somewhat younger; he had hardly been appointed bishop of Sinjār when Abū-l-Faraj died (1286); he himself died only in 1318. 'Abhd-īshō' was a much smaller man than Abū-l-Faraj, but his relation to the Nestorian community was very similar to the latter's relation to the Jacobites. He was their spiritual purveyor; his main business, of course—just as in Abū-l-Faraj's case—was to provide them with sound theological doctrine and ecclesiastical information, but he also tried to convey to them the secrets of Greek philosophy, that is, as much of them as was safe for them to know. The Nestorians were not more able to hold to their sacred language (except for purely liturgical purposes) than the Monophysites, and some of 'Abhd-īshō''s writings had soon to be translated into Arabic. In fact he translated one of them himself.

The very fact that Syriac literature came to an end soon afterwards, diminishes its value considerably for the historian of civilization who is not especially interested in the Syrians for themselves, because it means that the Syriac road led nowhere and was simply a blind alley. In a briefer survey it might almost be disregarded.

(c) Armenians. John of Erzinjān was a theologian and grammarian, but hardly a philosopher. He may be mentioned here as a symbol of the philosophical indifference of his people.

6. *China*—The master of Chinese destinies at that time was Kublai Khān. He ruled from 1260 on, founded the Yüan dynasty in 1271, and remained at the post of supreme command until the end of his days in 1294. He was a benevolent and, relatively speaking, an enlightened despot, who did all that was humanly possible to lift his people to a higher level. He was helped by advisers of various races, for example by the Lama Phagspa, and by the Nestorian 'Īsā the Mongol.

The leading philosophers and scholars were Ma Tuan-lin and Wang Ying-lin. The former compiled a large encyclopaedia, the Wên hsien t'ung k'ao; the latter compiled a smaller one, the Yu hai (Sea of jade).

Summary

Out of that mass of personalities and that complicated web of circumstances, two great facts or groups of facts emerge above all the others: the growth of Qabbalism in Israel, and of Thomism in Christendom, a triumph of intellectual extravagance on the one side, and of moderation on the other.

To be sure, Qabbalism was not the only activity of the Jews; witness the many great names above-mentioned; but it was the dominating one, the one which unfortunately left the deepest mark on the contemporary and following generations. Nor was Thomism the only or the main stream of Christian thought, but again when we look from a great distance, we realize that if it was not yet the largest stream it certainly led to it.

Another characteristic of the age was its encyclopaedic curiosity. Under the influence of Aristotelianism on the one side, and of growing literacy and democracy on the other, a number of encyclopaedic writers were busy trying to satisfy the philosophic and scientific hunger of a larger and larger public. This movement was especially conspicuous in western Christendom which was then borne upon an exceptionally high tide of prosperity. Think of Vincent of Beauvais, Albert the Great, Brunetto Latini, John of Meung, Jacob of Marlant, Roger Bacon. The extension of the public is measured by the number of vernaculars which were gradually replacing the Latin idiom of the learned. But similar tendencies were perceptible everywhere; witness the publication of encyclopaedic treatises in Arabic, Hebrew, Persian, Greek, Syriac and Chinese.

The main nursery of the future was now undoubtedly Latin Christendom, and we saw being planted in it the seeds of Averroism, of Scotism, of Thomism, and above all of experimental philosophy.

VI. MATHEMATICS AND ASTRONOMY

1. *Western Christendom*—(a) Diffusion of Hindu numerals. The use of these numerals extended gradually but very slowly. They were forbidden in Florence and Padua, and this implies that some people at least were trying to make use of them.

This is but indirect evidence. In this particular case we happen to be far better informed with regard to the Greek world, for the two leading Byzantine mathematicians, Pachymeres and Planudes, wrote treatises explaining the use of these numerals. The greatest arithmetician of the West, Ibn al-Bannā', employed them constantly in his Talkhīṣ, but as he was a Muslim this is less surprising.

To return to western Christendom the best proof of its backwardness in this respect is the fact that the Alphonsine tables, completed c. 1272, contained probably none but Roman numerals. This can only be inferred, for the original manuscript is lost, but the probability almost amounts to certainty. I would suggest the following explanation: the Arabic and Jewish mathematicians engaged in the compilation of these tables were of course familiar with the ghubār numerals, but these numerals were associated with the Arabic script, were in fact an intrinsic part of it, and were almost naturally dropped by them, together with that script, as soon as they began to write in Latin or in Spanish. The passage from ghubār to Roman numerals was a part of the process of translation, and was not stranger to them than the rest of it.

(b) Mathematical translators. Without entering into many details on the subject, it is clear that the mathematical activity of western Christendom was still largely dependent upon outside stimulation. It still needed a constant admixture of foreign leaven. The same was true of Israel. In fact the labor of pouring out the contents of Arabic mathematics into European minds was largely accomplished by the combined efforts of Jews and Christians. For example, John of Brescia worked with Jacob ben Maḥir to translate al-Zarqālī's treatise on the astrolabe, from the Arabic, and Armengaud son of Blaise collaborated with the same Jacob to translate the latter's treatise on the quadrant, from the Hebrew; the astrological writings of Ibn Ezra were translated from the Hebrew by Hagin and Henry Bate. It must be noticed that in two of these cases out of three, Arabic mathematics reached Latindom only after having passed through Hebrew channels.

However, the outstanding example of Judeo-Christian collaboration in this field occurred under the patronage of the king of Castile and León, Alfonso X the Wise. His chief translators were Jews, but a few Christians were working with them. They were often paired together for this or that piece of work; e.g., Judah ben Moses with John Daspa; which suggests that they were working according to the old eastern method—a preliminary version by a dragoman, who knows best the language of the original, is finished and written up by a Christian scholar who knows best the new language. It is not necessary to insist upon the size of the task accomplished by Alfonso's school of translators. Unfortunately much of their attention was attached to writings which were either of secondary importance, or positively evil because of their astrological tendencies. The truth of this is proved by the sterility of their immense effort. Alfonso did not succeed in creating a single original astronomer.

(c) Spain. Alfonso's interest in astronomy was not restricted to translations. This, he wisely realized, was the first step, the means, not the end. The crying need of every astrologer was for better tables than the Toledan ones compiled by al-Zarqālī in the second half of the eleventh century. New tables were prepared under the king's patronage and under the direction of Judah ben Moses and Isaac ibn Sid for the coordinates of Toledo and the year 1272. The Alphonsine tables became known in Paris only by 1292. Their influence was hardly felt before the fourteenth century. When thirteenth century astronomers speak of the Toledan tables they always mean the old ones.

Ramon Lull, without being an astronomer, was interested in that science as he was in every other. He wrote astronomical and mathematical treatises which show clearly enough that he had no real grasp of the subject.

(d) Italy. Many Italians were interested in astronomy or astrology; but I know of but one genuine mathematician, John Campano of Novara, he who elaborated Adelard's translation of Euclid's Elements. The earliest printed edition of Euclid (Venice 1482) was a reproduction of Campano's text. He was not a mean mathematician. His Euclid contains a few interesting remarks on continuous quantities, the irrationality of the (golden) section, the angles of stellated polygons.

Astronomy was a very popular subject. Every philosopher and even every theologian was obliged to have some understanding of it, if only to be able to discuss the cosmological views of Genesis. On the other hand medicine was tied up with astrology; thus every physician needed a modicum of astronomical knowledge.

St. Thomas introduced into the Latin world the astronomical views of Simplicios translated by his friend William of Moerbeke. St. Bonaventure upheld Aristotelian and Averroistic astronomy against the Ptolemaic. However, Peripatetics were put more and more on the defensive as Ptolemaism grew in favor among astronomers. Gerard of Sabbioneta, Campano, John of Sicily, and Giles of Rome wrote treatises wherein the Ptolemaic theory was explained. Unfortunately under the influence of Robert Grosseteste that theory generally included the erroneous conception of the trepidation of the equinoxes. For example, that conception was accepted by Campano and Giles of Rome; but John of Sicily, in his criticism of the Toledan tables, rejected it. Campano described various astronomical instruments, one of which, called after him, was much used by Parisian astronomers.

As we might expect, much attention was paid to astrology, and to related superstitions such as geomancy. We have a treatise on the latter subject by Gerard of Sabbioneta; and another, the most popular, by Bartholomew of Parma. The most famous astrologer of that age was Guido Bonatti; his Liber astronomicus was an uncompromising defense of the art of which he was himself a very successful practitioner. When we read that book or the story of his adventurous life, we cannot help wondering whether such a man could be at once intelligent and honest. It is impossible to answer such a question offhand, and it is probable that no investigation, however searching, could enable us to solve it. Moreover there are many degrees in intellectual honesty, especially for people whose thought is largely irrational. It is quite possible for such people to say things which are flagrantly absurd or contradictory without being dishonest or stupid. One thing is certain, Bonatti and other professional astrologers were not by any means disinterested. Discussions on Ptolemaism versus Aristotelianism, or on the reality of the trepidation of the equinoxes, were financially unprofitable, but the astrological business was a paying one; it required considerable psychological skill and involved serious risks, but the clever adept could earn riches and power which would have remained otherwise inaccessible to him. To return to Bonatti, Dante and Pico della Mirandola were agreed in condemning and despising him.

In his popular encyclopaedia, Ristoro d'Arezzo remarked that the scintillation of the stars originates in the observer's eyes.

(e) France. The Ptolemaic movement was even stronger in France than in Italy. Of course there was some opposition to it in Aristotelian and Dominican circles, but all of the distinguished French astronomers were neatly Ptolemaic. For example, Vincent of Beauvais had taken trouble to review the controversy; he was well acquainted with Alpetragian ideas but concluded in favor of Ptolemy. Bernard of Trilia reached the same conclusion, but he did not succeed in shaking off the false idea of trepidation. While the astronomical views of Vincent of Beauvais and of Bernard of Trilia were more or less influenced by Albert the Great, the two astronomers of whom I shall speak presently, Bernard of Verdun and William of Saint Cloud, may be said to have belonged to the school of Bacon. In a sense Bacon's influence was hardly better than Albert's, for he was never able to decide clearly between Ptolemy and al-Biṭrūjī, and he introduced into the discussion the strange ideas of Ibn al-Haitham and Muḥammad ibn Aḥmad al-Kharaqī; but his theoretical indecision was richly compensated by his experimental bent. Bernard of Verdun restudied the whole question and decided unequivocally against al-Biṭrūjī, rejecting the whole of the latter's theory including the trepidation. William of Saint Cloud was less of a theorist, but more of an observer. In 1290 he redetermined experimentally the obliquity of the ecliptic; his determination being the only mediaeval one in Christian Europe. He compiled planetary tables and calendars. He may be called the founder of the astronomical school of Paris (see vol. 3), which was perhaps the best fruit of Baconian influence in France.

There was no organized Alpetragian opposition in that country, but an anonymous treatise of that time must be mentioned because it went back not only to Aristotle but to Heraclides of Pontos. It was written in French by an unknown astrologer for Baldwin II of Courtenay, the last effective ruler of the Latin empire of Constantinople. It is a good specimen of backwardness such as is bound to occur in every period. There are a few stragglers behind each army. This unknown astrologer was a belated disciple of the school of Chartres.

A treatise on the astrolabe was composed by Peter the Stranger, the famous author of a letter on the magnet. The earliest compotus to appear in print (Paris 1483), ascribed to one Anianus, was probably edited about this time. Another compotus was naturally included in the great treatise on liturgy, the Rationale divinorum officiorum, written about 1286 by William Durand.

Pure mathematics were completely neglected. France could not even boast a Campano. In fact, I am unable to mention a single mathematician of this time. We are given a glimpse of practical geometry in the notebook of Villard de Honnecourt, and of elementary arithmetic in two French algorisms. In both of these, six operations are dealt with, duplication and mediation being considered different from multiplication and division.

(f) England. There was less astronomical discussion among the English. The neo-Platonist, Robert the Englishman, who lived in France, had Alpetragian and Averroistic tendencies but was chiefly known because of his treatise on the quadrant invented or modified by him. That treatise enjoyed some popularity, witness Greek and Hebrew versions; but the instrument itself was soon superseded by another devised by a contemporary, Jacob ben Mahir, whom he probably met in Montpellier.

The other Englishmen were all of them Franciscans. To begin with, there was Bacon who, like his master Grosseteste, remained undecided between the Ptolemaists and the Aristotelians. This is not surprising, for there was much in al-Biṭrūjī and in Ibn Rushd to attract him, and yet he was essentially a Platonist. He continued vigorously Grosseteste's effort to reform the calendar. Then John Peckham, primarily concerned with meteorology and optics, whose astronomical views were similar to Bacon's. A curious case was that of William of Ware who derived his astronomical knowledge from Maimonides' Moreh nebukim: this was a slightly different form of anti-Ptolemaism. Finally in great contrast with the preceding ones, there was Richard of Middleton who assumed a Ptolemaic attitude. The final vindication of Ptolemaism even among these Franciscans, Baconians, and Platonists, is very striking. In this respect Richard of Middleton was the English (?) counterpart of Bernard of Verdun. Together with the revival of experimental astronomy, this new attitude represents a turning point. Not so much an achievement as a promise.

The only mathematician was Bacon and he was not much of one, but he was fully aware of the transcendental value of mathematics in the Platonic sense, and also of its practical value. We may see in him a prophet of mathematical physics as well as of experimental science; very vague to be sure, but if a prophet were not vague he would be something else—not a seer but a doer. Bacon was a true prophet; he did very little but he saw very far.

(g) Flanders. William of Moerbeke had a strong if indirect share in the scientific progress of his time, through his translations from the Greek and his friendship with St. Thomas. He translated the commentaries on Aristotelian astronomy by Simplicios, and on the meteorology by Alexander of Aphrodisias.

Under William's stimulation Henry Bate of Malines wrote a treatise on the astrolabe which was primarily an astrological textbook. With the help of Hagin the Jew he translated Ibn Ezra's astrological treatises into Latin. He composed an encyclopaedia, which included an astronomical summary of anti-Ptolemaic tendency. He was first and last an astrologer, but made astronomical observations and compiled new tables for his native city.

(h) Other Countries. There remain to be considered four students of astronomy who represented four different countries: the German, Albert the Great; the Pole, Witelo; the Austrian, Leopold; the Scandinavian, Peter of Dacia.

Albert the Great was a very poor mathematician, and hardly better as an astronomer. Like all of his brother philosophers and encyclopaedists, he had been obliged to investigate the Alpetragian controversy. In fact he helped to diffuse the Alpetragian theory in a distorted shape, but he finally came back to the Ptolemaic point of view; and this shows that he was relatively unbiassed.

Witelo had been influenced by William of Moerbeke whom he met at Viterbo in 1269. He was especially interested in meteorology and optics; he was not an astronomer but was led to consider problems of physical astronomy and terrestrial physics.

Leopold of Austria composed an astronomical treatise the purpose of which was primarily astrological. He was a poor theorist without any definite theories of his own, but it would be better on the whole to put him in the Ptolemaic group. His treatise contains a good account of astrological meteorology. It was soon translated into French.

Peter of Dacia was not only the single representative of Scandinavia but one of the rare mathematicians of his age. This may be explained by the fact that his activity was the repercussion of that which had taken place in western Europe earlier in the century, but that explanation would be incomplete. To be sure much of what he did was simply a matter of transmission of earlier knowledge—e.g., of Sacrobosco; yet he developed new ideas on geometrical continuity and on the extraction of cubic roots.

2. *Eastern Christendom*—Our account of Eastern Christendom, short as it is, must be divided into three sections: (a) Greeks; (b) Syrians; (c) Armenians.

(a) Greeks. Nicephoros Blemmydes composed geographical treatises in one of which he discussed the spherical shape and size of the earth, and the climates. Georgios Pachymeres and Maximos Planudes had both studied Diophantos: Georgios' Tetrabiblon contains a paraphrase of Diophantos' first book as well as extracts from Euclid and Nicomachos; Maximos wrote a commentary on books I and II. Both writers were acquainted with Hindu numerals, but strangely enough they used numerals of different types which would suggest that their sources were different. Planudes was by far the best Byzantine mathematician of his time.

The contrast between Latin and Greek mathematics is considerable; it illustrates the paucity, not to say the lack, of contacts between the two main branches of Christendom.

(b) Syrians. With the partial exception of Blemmydes, these Greeks were mathematicians; their great Syrian contemporary, Abū-l-Faraj, was more of an astronomer. In fact he was the author of the only astronomical treatise of any importance in the Syriac language; it is a summary of the Almagest. We know that Abū-l-Faraj had lectured in Marāgha on Euclid and on Ptolemy; his "Ascent of the mind" was probably the written form of his lectures on the Almagest. He took special pains to prove the immobility of the earth. His Nestorian contemporary, 'Abhd-īshō' bar Bĕrīkhā, composed a poem on the calendar.

(c) Armenians. Astronomical treatises were composed in Armenian prose and verse by John of Erzinjān. Another was translated from the Persian (or Arabic?) by one Mekhitar of Ānī, whose personality is not well established.

3. *Israel*—This section might be entitled western Israel, for not a single eastern Jew is referred to in it.

The best part of Jewish activity was devoted to translations into Hebrew, of which there was a growing need as fewer and fewer scholars among them were able to read the Arabic texts. The two foremost translators, Moses ibn Tibbon and Jacob ben Maḥir, produced between them a whole corpus of Greek and Arabic mathematics and astronomy. They translated Autolycos, Euclid, Geminos, Theodosios, Menelaos, Qusṭā ibn Lūqā's treatise on the celestial sphere, Ibn al-Haitham's astronomy, treatises on the astrolabe by Ibn al-Ṣaffār and al-Zarqālī, Jābir ibn Aflaḥ's and al-Biṭrūjī's astronomy, the arithmetic and algebra of Muḥammad ibn Ḥaṣṣār. This activity was enormously superior to that of the Latin translators, but we must bear in mind that the need of Latin versions was considerably smaller. Most of the works I have just mentioned were already available in Latin; many of them had been translated by Gerard of Cremona or other twelfth century translators and hence Latin people had had plenty of time to assimilate them. The feverish pouring out of that treasure of knowledge into Hebrew was tremendously important from the Jewish point of view, but from a purely human angle it was almost superfluous. By this time the totality of that knowledge had already been transmitted to western Europe and was a part of the main scientific stream.

Jacob ben Maḥir was not only a translator, but an original astronomer. Indeed if we were to judge by the testimonies of scientific men of the sixteenth century down to Kepler, he was one of the most famous astronomers of mediaeval times. That fame seems to have been somewhat exaggerated but we have to take it into account. He compiled new astronomical tables for Montpellier; and invented and described a new instrument, the quadrans novus, which promptly superseded the quadrans vetus of Robert the Englishman. Jacob's quadrans was apparently far more elaborate than Robert's; it was a kind of universal instrument to be used like an astrolabe. Jacob's description of it was immensely popular.

While Moses' and Jacob's translations were refreshing the scientific atmosphere, two authors were publishing encyclopaedic treatises which included astronomical summaries. The third part of Gershon ben Solomon's Gate of heaven is an explanation of the astronomical views of al-Farghānī, Ibn Sīnā, and Ibn Rushd; Levi ben Abraham ben Ḥayyim derived his astronomical knowledge mostly from Ibn Ezra, which amounts to saying that it was largely astrological.

The Roman maḥzor (prayerbook for the holidays) contains calendrical rules drawn by Benjamin 'Anav.

4. *Western Islām*—While the scientific life of Israel was more and more westernized, that of Islām on the contrary was easternized. Two mathematicians dealt with in Book III may still belong to the present period: al-Ḥasan al-Marrākushī who died only about 1262 (though his main work was done thirty-two years earlier), and Ibn Badr whose real time is undetermined. Muḥyī al-dīn al-Maghribī, who will be dealt with in the following section because he was attached to the Marāgha observatory, was of western origin as his name plainly indicates. As far as we know, his career was entirely in the East.

The only western mathematician who flourished in the west in the third quarter of the thirteenth century was the Moroccan, Ibn al-Bannā'. He was a very prolific writer who published a whole collection of mathematical and astronomical treatises. The most popular of these was his Talkhīṣ, an arithmetical textbook, which was the subject of at least six Arabic commentaries. It is a good textbook containing many interesting features but no real novelties. Ibn al-Bannā' may not be very brilliant—he was a regular textbook maker—but there was nobody comparable to him in Christendom.

5. *Eastern Islām*—It must be admitted that our survey thus far has not revealed much mathematical or astronomical genius: Campano, William of St. Cloud, Planudes, Jacob ben Maḥir, Ibn al-Bannā', that is about all and it is not very much. But when we pass to the eastern caliphate the situation changes completely.

Of course, the caliphate was now a thing of the past. The last caliph, al-Musta'ṣim, was put to death by the Mongols in 1258, but the caliphate had become politically negligible long before that time, about the middle of the twelfth century. By eastern caliphate, I simply mean the lands of Islām around the eastern Mediterranean Sea and beyond, chiefly the territories of the Baḥrī Mamlūks (Egypt and Syria), of the Saljūqs of Rūm, and of the Īlkhāns of Persia. These, and especially the last named country, Persia, were now the leading centers of mathematical and astronomical progress. (When I do not mention the nationality of a man in this section, the reader may infer that he was a Persian.)

The encyclopaedist, al-Abharī, a pupil of Kamāl al-dīn Ibn Yūnus, compiled astronomical tables and wrote various astronomical and astrological treatises. Other tables and more treatises were composed by the Syrian, Ibn al-Lubūdī, already dealt with in Book III, but who lived at least until 1267. Needless to say, al-Qazwīnī's cosmography contains a summary of astronomical geography. Muḥammad ibn abī Bakr al-Fārisī wrote a general treatise on astronomy and a more special one wherein he explained the difficulties in the making of tables.

We now come to the greatest mathematician of the age, Nāṣir al-dīn al-Ṭūsī, one of the greatest of mediaeval times. He edited a large series of mathematical writings, the Kitāb al-mutawassiṭāt or middle books corresponding to the "Little astronomy" of the Greeks plus a few Arabic classics. It was a collection of Greek and Arabic classics which one had to study, outside of the Elements and the Almagest, to become an accomplished mathematician. Parts of the Mutawissiṭāt were simply versions, others were elaborations or commentaries. Nāṣir al-dīn discussed the postulates of Euclid, and his discussion of the fifth postulate was taken up later by Girolamo Saccheri (1733). In other words, the history of non-Euclidean geometry can be traced back through Saccheri to one of Nāṣir al-dīn's own writings. His greatest work was the Shakl al-qaṭṭā', which was the first independent textbook of trigonometry, plane and spherical, the climax of a long Greek-Hindu-Arabic tradition. Some spherical problems were solved by implicit consideration of polar triangles. This treatise was almost equivalent to the Latin treatise composed by Regiomontanus two centuries later.

Nāṣir al-dīn's astronomical activity was even greater. His Tadhkira, a general textbook on theoretical astronomy, was exceedingly popular. It was a summary of the Almagest with many criticisms and restrictions suggested by Thābit ibn Qurra, Ibn al-Haitham, and others. The author succeeded in showing the insufficiency of the Ptolemaic theory, but his own attempts at improvement were far too complicated to be satisfactory. The fact remains that it was such books as this one which gradually prepared the astronomical reformation of the sixteenth century. In 1259 the Īl-khān Hūlāgū gave him the means to construct an observatory—we might call it an institute for scientific research—with a rich library, at Marāgha in Adharbāyjān. Under Nāṣir al-dīn's direction, Marāgha became the outstanding astronomical center of the time and one of the leading scientific centers of the world (unfortunately its leadership did not survive its founder very long). A number of mathematicians, astronomers, and instrument makers gathered around him. They came not only from the neighboring countries, but also from distant ones such as the Caucacus, or Morocco in the Far West; and not only from the Dār al-Islām, but from Christian Syria (Abū-l-Faraj), and even from China. The main task of the Marāgha astronomers was the compilation of new tables, the Zīj īlkhānī, completed c. 1272. These tables included new observations, but not many, for otherwise their compilation would have taken considerably more time, and the Īl-khān was too impatient. They were immensely popular in the East, even as far as Cathay. A part of these tables was devoted to the comparative chronology of eastern nations.

Two of Nāṣir al-dīn's regular collaborators deserve special mention. Al-'Urḍī of Damascus was apparently the mechanician and instrument maker of the staff; a treatise describing the Marāgha instruments was probably composed by him; the celestial globe which he constructed gives us a good pretext to discuss the early Muslim globes and illustrated astronomical MSS. in Arabic and Persian. The other, Muḥyī al-dīn, the Maugrabin, was more of a mathematician; he continued his chief's trigonometrical studies and editions of the classics, and published a study on Chinese and Uighūr chronology and many astrological treatises.

Two other members of the Marāgha circle may be quoted. The one, 'Alī ibn 'Umar al-Kātibī, compiled encyclopaedic works, one of which contains an elaborate discussion of the daily rotation of the earth. 'Alī concluded against the reality of that rotation. The other, Quṭb al-dīn al-Shīrāzī, became eventually more famous as a physicist, but he was also a full-fledged mathematician and astronomer. His Nihāyat was a sort of commentary on Nāṣir al-dīn's Tadhkira. It contains a discussion on the question whether the earth is at rest or not, concluding like 'Alī in favor of the first alternative. The fact that two great scientists found it necessary to discuss that question suggests that the second alternative was considered by a few bolder spirits. The conclusion reached by 'Alī ibn 'Umar and Quṭb al-dīn was not surprising. At that stage of astronomical progress their attitude was probably the wisest; it was Ptolemaism mitigated by many reservations. It is always a good deal easier to see the defects of a theory than to propound a new and better one. The leading astronomers of the thirteenth century, whether Christian or Muslim, realized the many imperfections of the Almagest, but it would take them and their descendants two centuries and a half of effort to remove them in a satisfactory manner.

One more mathematician, Muḥammad ibn Ashraf al-Samarqandī, though himself a Persian, was apparently not connected with the Marāgha institute. He was primarily a logician, but wrote a commentary on Euclid, and a stellar calendar, the latter in Persian.

6. *China*—Chinese mathematics was second in importance only to the Eastern Muslim. Before dealing with the distinguished mathematicians of this period, it is well to recall that of the two leaders of the preceding period, one at least and possibly both continued their work in the second half of the thirteenth century. Li Yeh died in very old age after 1265. His main work appeared in 1248, but the other one only in 1259. Ch'in Chiu-shao was still living in 1258, but his mathematical activity was possibly completed before the middle of the century.

Kublai Khān was too great an administrator not to realize the need of mathematicians and astronomers, and it is typical of the cultural mixture organized by him that his scientific assistants were drawn from many nations. 'Īsā the Mongol (in Chinese, Ai-hsieh) was a Nestorian, who was followed in the Yüan service by his four sons, also Nestorians. In 1263 Kublai appointed him the head of the astronomical board. In 1267 a new calendar was devised for Kublai Khān by the Persian, Jamāl al-dīn (Cha-ma-li-ting); Jamāl al-dīn introduced new astronomical instruments. Finally we have the Chinese Hsü Hêng, who wrote a treatise on the calendar and became eventually president of the astronomical board; and Kuo Shou-ching, who was ordered to prepare a new calendar in 1276. Kuo's calendar remained in force throughout the Yüan dynasty.

This Kuo deserves to be dealt with at greater length. He was not simply a calendar maker, but a genuine astronomer. He made astronomical observations and wrote various astronomical treatises. Two of the instruments used by him (dated 1279) are still extant in Pei-ping. It has been suggested that Kuo was the one who introduced Arabic spherical trigonometry into China. That hypothesis is plausible but not proved, and the strange graduation of his instruments—not the Arabic, but another sui generis and very awkward—is an argument against it.

The main Chinese mathematician of this period was Yang Hui, who was a remarkable arithmetician and algebraist. It is curious that he seems to have been independent of his older contemporaries, Li Yeh and Ch'in Chiu-shao, because he does not speak of their famous method, the method of the celestial element (t'ien yüan shu). We must still say a few words of Chu Shih-chieh, though he belongs rather to the following period. His most important work, the Precious mirror of the four elements, appeared only in 1303, but four years earlier he had published his Introduction to mathematical studies, which was itself a treatise of unusual distinction. In fact there was nothing comparable to it in 1299 outside of China. It gave the rules of signs for algebraical addition and multiplication. Moreover it was the main vehicle for the transportation of Chinese algebra into Japan. Apparently Chu was continuing the tradition of Li Yeh and Ch'in Chiu-shao, though he did not mention them.

Summary

As we are specially concerned with mathematical progress, we shall devote but little attention in this summary to astrology, and none at all to superstitions and regressions. Nor is it necessary to insist upon the translations, beyond recalling to the reader's mind the unusual importance of the translations from Arabic into Hebrew, and of the new Arabic edition of the Kitāb al-mutawassiṭāt prepared by Nāṣir al-dīn and his colleagues at the Marāgha observatory.

Let us now consider in turn the various branches and aspects, first, of mathematics, then of astronomy.

The best general appreciation of mathematics was due to Roger Bacon, who combined in a very remarkable way strong Platonic aspirations with a very utilitarian spirit. He could appreciate at once the mystical and the practical value of numbers. Ramon Lull came but second and was far behind, but he was a true ancestor of the mathematical logicians of to-day, and abundant if somewhat vague anticipations of their extravagances can be found in many of his writings.

Arithmetic—For the best arithmetical work in Latin Christendom we have to address ourselves, strange to say, to a Scandinavian, Peter of Dacia. To be sure, Peter studied in Paris, but he returned to Copenhagen. The leading arithmeticians were two Greeks, Georgios Pachymeres and Maximos Planudes, and a Moor, Ibn al-Bannā'. The latter was the most prolific and popular writer on the subject. The three of them used Hindu numerals or explained their use.

Algebra—The outstanding fact is the study of Diophantos by Pachymeres and Planudes. The Diophantine tradition was never entirely lost in the Greek and Arabic East.

The work of Chinese mathematicians is difficult to classify and to appreciate; it was not geometrical, but a combination of algebra and arithmetic, very different from our western productions. Its interest is due partly to its relative excellence, and partly to its singularity. Four great mathematicians flourished in China at various times during the second half of the thirteenth century: Li Yeh, Ch'in Chiu-shao, Yang Hui, Chu Shih-chieh. The latter was the main connecting link with Japan.

Geometry—Western work in geometry was on a low level: Campano was reediting Euclid, Peter of Dacia and Georgios Pachymeres did a little geometrical thinking. But in Persia, Nāṣir al-dīn al-Ṭūsī was making a new and thorough study of many of the masterpieces of Greek and Arabic mathematics, and in this he was ably followed by one of his assistants, Muḥyī al-dīn al-Maghribī. Nāṣir al-dīn reinvestigated Euclid's postulates.

Trigonometry—The finest mathematical work of that period was the Shakl al-qaṭṭā' of Nāṣir al-dīn, the earliest independent treatise on trigonometry. It is curious that one of the most important works of the preceding period, the Jāmi' of al-Ḥasan al-Marrākushī, was also devoted to trigonometry, though in a very different vein (an elaborate technical comparison of the Shakl al-qaṭṭā' with the Jāmi' is much to be desired). The outstanding trigonometrical achievements of the first and second half of the thirteenth century were due respectively to a Maugrabin and to a Persian. Strangely enough, Nāṣir al-dīn's trigonometrical research was continued by another Maugrabin, one of his Marāgha assistants, Muḥyī al-dīn al-Maghribī.

Arabic trigonometry was probably introduced into China about this time if not before. There were various Muslim advisers and experts at the Mongol court, and the astronomers among them could not introduce their astronomical knowledge without its trigonometric foundations. However, such an introduction could only be completed by a Chinese—e.g., Kuo Shou-ching; but this is a moot question which will require considerable additional investigation to be solved, if it can be solved at all.

By way of transition to astronomy, let us first consider the subjects of compotus and chronology.

Compotus—Under the stimulation of Robert Grosseteste much attention was paid to the reform of the calendar by Roger Bacon. It is not too much to say that the Gregorian reform was largely prepared by these two men.

The earliest calendar to appear in printed form, the one ascribed to Anianus, was probably produced about this time. The Rationale of William Durand contained naturally a discussion of the compotus.

Kublai Khān made serious efforts to reform the Chinese calendar. For this purpose he secured the cooperation of Nestorian, Persian, and Chinese astronomers.

Chronology—The cosmopolitanism of the Īlkhānic culture of Persia (1256–1349) is illustrated by the chronological investigations of the Marāgha astronomers. The first book of the Zīj īlkhānī is devoted to Chinese, Greek, Arabic and Persian chronology. Muḥyī al-dīn al-Maghribī wrote a special treatise on the Chinese and Uighūr calendars. Such undertakings were made necessary and at the same time easier by the constant relations between these peoples. There were probably Chinese astronomers in Marāgha; there were certainly Persian ones in Khānbaliq (Pei-ping).

Ptolemaic versus Alpetragian Astronomy—The main issue of the time was the validity of Ptolemaic theories. As observations accumulated, the difficulties inherent in those theories had multiplied and their validity had been called into question. The main challenge had been made by the Spanish astronomer al-Biṭrūjī in the second half of the twelfth century and had attracted considerable attention. That revolt was, curiously enough, a part of the Aristotelian revival. It tended to substitute a modification of the Aristotelian system of homocentric spheres for the Ptolemaic eccentrics and epicycles. Albert the Great contributed much to the diffusion of Alpetragian ideas in Latindom, but he also contributed to their ultimate defeat because his account of them was oversimplified. However there was a good deal of truth in them; the purely critical or negative part was incontrovertible; the positive part was less satisfactory. Ptolemaism could not resist indefinitely the stress of growing knowledge; its defects were transparent, but anyone who tried to replace Ptolemaic makeshifts with Alpetragian ones was finally disappointed. Hence the Alpetragian opposition remained weak and ineffective. Albert the Great himself finally concluded in Ptolemy's favor.

The anti-Ptolemaic movement was partly Franciscan and neo-Platonic—for example, with St. Bonaventure and Robert the Englishman; or Maimonidean, with William of Ware; or independent.

By the middle of the thirteenth century the anti-Ptolemaic opposition had spent itself in the vain effort of finding something less imperfect than what the Almagest had to offer. Most of the astronomers and philosophers of this time, East and West, were Ptolemaists, which does not mean that they did not recognize the weaknesses of their system. They were Ptolemaists faute de mieux and the boldest were not afraid of saying so. Roger Bacon, like his teacher, Grosseteste, did not commit himself one way or another. The leading defenders of the Almagest were Bernard of Verdun and Richard of Middleton, two Franciscans, and the final victory of Ptolemaism was largely due to them. Their leadership was easy for most of the astronomers were eager to walk in the same direction: Vincent of Beauvais, Bernard of Trilia, Gerard of Sabbioneta, Campano, John of Sicily, Giles of Rome; these were all Ptolemaists. In the East similar conclusions had been reached; Abū-l-Faraj, Nāṣir al-dīn al-Ṭūsī, Quṭb al-dīn al-Shīrāzī, remained substantially Ptolemaists though they were not sparing in their criticisms.

The Trepidation of the Equinoxes—The Ptolemaic controversy was complicated by another one dealing with the reality of the trepidation of the equinoxes. That wrong theory according to which the precession is not continuously progressive, but that an oscillation (or trepidation) around the average position is added to it,[10a] was first suggested by Theon of Alexandria, but its real introducer was Thābit ibn Qurra (second half of the ninth century). In spite of al-Battānī's opposition to it and Ibn Yūnus' disregard of it, it found growing favor during the following centuries. Al-Zarqālī accepted it, and so did al-Biṭrūjī. Observe that this discussion cut across the Ptolemaic one. Most astronomers rejected Alpetragianism, but believed in trepidation which was an essential part of it, and not a part of the purer Ptolemaic doctrine. While he sat on the fence with regard to the major issue, Grosseteste gave his assent to the hypothesis of trepidation; he was in fact the first non-Muslim writer to speak of it. It is probable that Grosseteste's influence was responsible for the wide acceptance of that wrong theory in Latindom. Campano, Giles of Rome, Bernard of Trilia, the authors of the Alphonsine Tables, had no hesitations about it. The only Ptolemaists to make a clear stand against it were Bernard of Verdun and John of Sicily, and they deserve special praise for it.

Complexity of Astronomical Thought—For the special benefit of the many historians and philosophers who still think of the Middle Ages as a period of homogeneous darkness and unrelieved monotony and indulge in glib generalities about it, we might pause a moment to examine the great complexity of thought in the second half of the thirteenth century. For the sake of simplification this is restricted to astronomy and to Latindom. The main issue was Ptolemaism versus several kinds of opposition, but it implied secondary ones like Thābitism, and larger ones like Aristotelianism vs. Averroism on the one hand, and vs. Platonism, Avicebronism, Scotism on the other; finally it was variously interwoven with the polemics relative to the religious orders, and with the jealousies between Franciscans and Dominicans. Hence an almost unlimited amount of possibilities (apply combinatorial analysis to all these independent alternatives which might be associated in many ways!). One might be a Franciscan Ptolemaist anti-Thābitian like Bernard of Verdun, or else a Franciscan Alpetragian like St. Bonaventure, or else a Dominican Ptolemaist and Thābitian, like Bernard of Trilia, etc.

The Ptolemaic victory was in the last analysis a paradoxical triumph over Aristotelianism in spite of the fact that Thomism was then consecrating the latter's supremacy in Christendom. It was also a victory over scholasticism, but this was something too subtle to be realized at once. Indeed the crucial issue was not yet attracting much attention, yet it was secretly growing all the time—that was the issue between scholasticism and experimentalism. Though the majority of

[10a] It would be very misleading to consider the trepidation as an anticipation of the nutations, for the latter could never have been detected without the observational and computational means of a much later time.

Latin astronomers were mere theorists, some were devoting more and more time to observations; e.g., this William of Saint Cloud, who has been called with some justification the founder of the astronomical school of Paris. The main inspiration of observational astronomy came directly or indirectly from Bacon. The experimental tendencies were at first rather vague and almost subconscious. Their outward symptoms were the growing importance attached to instruments and the compilation of tables. I shall come back to this presently.

Is the Earth at rest, or not?—Before dealing with the tables, we must return for a moment to the East where an additional topic of discussion was grafted upon the Ptolemaic controversy. At least three Eastern astronomers—two Muslims, 'Alī ibn 'Umar al-Kātibī and Quṭb al-dīn al-Shīrāzī, and one Syrian, Abū-l-Faraj—took special pains to prove that the earth was at rest and did not move in any way. I have already pointed out that considering the facts at their disposal their conclusion was rational enough. But it is remarkable that the same question was hardly discussed in the West. This affords an additional proof of eastern superiority.

The fact that great scholars found it necessary to prove the fixity of the earth implies that they themselves and others had considered the alternative. Many people may have thought that the earth was moving, but they did not know that it was. To believe such a thing would have been in itself of little importance; the true scientific achievement was to change that belief into conviction, and that was to be the work of a later time. In the meanwhile the eastern discussion of the question was superior to the western ignorance of it. The fact that Copernicus' work was not done earlier remains difficult to explain; this tardiness may serve to illustrate the capricious and enigmatical nature of scientific advance.

Tables and Spheres. Astronomy versus Astrology—To return to observations, their results were naturally embodied in astronomical tables of which quite a few belong to this period.

It is a striking coincidence that by far the most important of these tables were completed about the same year, 1272, the Alphonsine Tables in Toledo, and the Īlkhānic ones in Marāgha. They were almost equally influential, but as the latter appeared at a time when western science was already in the ascendant their own influence was restricted to Asia. The Alphonsine Tables dominated Christian and Jewish astronomy for many centuries, the Zīj īlkhānī conquered the Muslim and the Far East.

It will suffice to mention a few other tables in chronological order.

About 1281. Henry Bate. Malines tables.

1292. William of Saint Cloud. Paris tables.

1300. Jacob ben Maḥir. Montpellier tables.

In the East we have the Zīj shāmil of al-Abharī and the Zīj zāhir and Zīj muqarrab of Ibn al-Lubūdī.

Besides these tables, eastern astronomers made drawings of the constellations and constructed celestial spheres. Some four or five Arabic globes anterior to the fourteenth century are still extant. No Chinese globes of that time have come down to us, but we have two remarkable instruments dated 1279, used by Kuo Shou-ching. Sundry astronomical instruments were constructed for the Marāgha observatory by al-'Urḍī, and described probably by himself, but they have not come down to us.

Much of the experimental effort of which these tables and instruments are eloquent witnesses was astrological in its purpose rather than purely astronomical, and we must never lose sight of that in our judgment of astrology. The purpose of astrology was irrational, from our privileged point of view, but the means were scientific enough, and in that respect astrology was the mother of astronomy even as alchemy was the mother of chemistry. Even to-day much foolish work is accomplished with the help of the most elaborate and the soundest technicalities, and it may always happen that such work, however sterile as far as its own purpose is concerned, leads to genuine improvements in this or that technique.

Most tables were compiled not to answer astronomical needs, but to facilitate the drawing of horoscopes. Some of the best experimental work was done by astrologers. Astronomical progress was incidental, but not less real on that account. It should be noted that the line between science and superstition was not drawn exactly where we would draw it, and that much astrological work was truly scientific from the point of view of the age. Yet the line was drawn, and there was mixed with what we might call legitimate astrology enough superstition of the rankest sort and concomitant imposture to disgust honest astrologers. It should be noted also that the terms astronomy and astrology were not used then as we use them now; in fact their present meanings were often interchanged. It is by mere chance that the term astrology[11] has come to denote a system of superstitions, while biology, geology, on the one hand, and astronomy, taxonomy, on the other, represent regular branches of science.

The greatest virtue of experimental work lies in this, that the value of its results depends only on the concrete experimental methods which have been used to obtain them, and are independent of the guiding theories. A good observation does not any more lose its value because it was made for a silly reason, than a bad one increases its own because the observer had a wise purpose. Thus astrologers were gradually collecting the very materials upon which astronomical science would eventually be built.

Increasing speed of Astronomical Progress—The emphasis on observations led to the construction of better instruments, and vice versa better instruments helped to produce better observations. An additional consequence was that the acceleration of research which is one of the main characteristics of modern science (at once wonderful and frightening) began to make itself felt. A remarkable example is that of the instrument invented in Montpellier about 1276 by Robert the Englishman. Some fourteen years later a more elaborate and better instrument was devised in the same town by Jacob ben Maḥir, and it superseded the other so completely that they were called respectively quadrans novus and quadrans vetus. The interval between the two inventions was very small indeed, comparable to that which we often observe in our own days.

Main Mathematicians and Astronomers—Considering again this period from a purely human point of view, and leaving out the men who belong more completely to the two adjoining periods, the thirteen outstanding personalities were Campano, Bernard of Verdun, William of Saint Cloud, Planudes, Abū-l-Faraj, Jacob ben Maḥir, Ibn al-Bannā', Nāṣir al-dīn al-Ṭūsī, al'Urdī, Muḥyī al-dīn al-Maghribī, Quṭb al-dīn al-Shīrāzī, Kuo Shou-ching, Yang Hui. That is, three Latins, one

[11] The Greek term for what we now call astrology was ἀστρομαντεία (astromancy, cf. geomancy) already used by Diodoros of Sicily (second half of the first century B.C.). On the mediaeval use of astrologia vs. astronomia, see, e.g., my notes on Bernard of Verdun and Leopold of Austria.

Greek, one Syrian, one Jew, five Muslims, two Chinese. The superiority of the orientals was overwhelming, and if it were possible to give weights to each unit it would be even magnified for the Muslims were undoubtedly the greatest of them all, especially such men as Nāṣir al-dīn and Quṭb al-dīn who would have cut mighty figures in any surroundings. As far as the West was concerned this was a period of regression, but the new advance of the East was but accidental and temporary, a kind of swan song, foretelling the end, while the western quietness was only (we know it now) a period of preparation, the trough of a wave the crest of which would soon follow.

VII. PHYSICS, TECHNOLOGY AND MUSIC

On account of the great variety of physical problems it will be best to divide our survey as follows: 1. Optics; 2. Weights and measures; 3. Magnetism; 4. Mechanics, technology, engineering; 5. Music.

1. *Optics*—We begin with optics because it is the subject which attracted most attention. There is a strong probability that spectacles (occhiali) were invented toward the end of this period in northern Italy. It is equally probable that these earlier glasses were very imperfect, and this would explain the slowness of their diffusion. This is not a matter like the Hindu numerals which were almost perfect from the moment of their creation (and yet how slow their own spread!); there was a long way between the idea of spectacles and a realization of sufficient value to satisfy very complex and divergent needs. To be sure, there was a marked increase in the sale of spectacles in the sixteenth century and even more so in the seventeenth and eighteenth centuries, yet the extensive use of them is very recent. For example we could not well understand Goethe's strong prejudices against people wearing glasses, if those people had been as common in his day (including women and children) as they are to-day.[12]

Though the reality of that invention is plausible enough (at least in the West), it was technically premature. Optical knowledge and technique were utterly insufficient for the solution of the problems involved. Some of these problems could not even be formulated, nor conceived in any way. However, many students were pondering on the nature of vision, on perspective, and on many other subjects naturally or artificially related to these. As I explained above, the heterogeneous science of perspective and meteorology was one of the most popular in mediaeval times, East and West.

A great stimulus to optical investigation had been given in the first half of the eleventh century by the Egyptian physicist, Ibn al-Haitham, whose works became known to Christians and Jews in the twelfth and thirteenth centuries. One of the latter, Joseph ibn 'Aqnīn, spoke of Ibn al-Haitham's Optics as a greater work than those of Euclid and of King Ptolemy.[13] Witelo composed, c. 1270–1278, a new treatise on the subject which was largely derived from Ibn al-Haitham's work, but contained a few novelties; e.g., a theory of the rainbow implying refraction as well as reflection of light, yet inferior to the contemporary explanations by Muslim scientists. It included also interesting observations on the psychology of vision. The value of Witelo's work is much impaired if one realizes how much of it was of Arabic provenience, but his followers did not realize this and admired him far

[12] For Goethe's prejudices see Johann Peter Eckermann: Gespräche mit Goethe in den letzten Jahren seines Lebens (ed. H. H. Houben, 592, 731, 759, Leipzig 1925).

[13] Amusing confusion with the author of the Almagest.

beyond his deserts. An undertaking very similar to Witelo's was accomplished at about the same time by the English Franciscan, John Peckham. His sources were very much the same as Witelo's, the main one being Ibn al-Haitham, and hence it is not surprising to find similarities in both works (e.g., mention of camera obscura); the surprising thing is that the similarities were not greater. It speaks volumes for the relative excellence of Witelo's and Peckham's treatises, or, let us say, for the relative mediocrity of later ones, that their popularity extended into the seventeenth century. The persistency of Witelo's fame is proved by the title of Kepler's earliest great work (Ad Vitellionem paralipomena, 1604). As to Peckham, his Perspectiva communis was reprinted as late as 1627!

When I spoke of an English Franciscan a moment ago, the reader must have thought that I was going to introduce Roger Bacon. In fact, Bacon was a great optician, the greatest of Christendom, and Peckham's exact contemporary; they were of about the same age and died probably in the same year, 1292. They must have influenced one another. Bacon was by far the most original, but his optical work was far less popular. Their fund of knowledge was very much the same, Ibn al-Haitham being the main origin of it, but Bacon made experiments with mirrors and lenses and anticipated vaguely great discoveries: that is, he was first to think of the combination of lenses which was to lead a few centuries later to the creation of those revolutionary instruments, the microscope and the telescope. He did not make these discoveries, but he came near to them and might possibly have made them. Moreover, he reflected upon the nature of light and concluded, against Grosseteste, that its transmission, however swift, could not be instantaneous; here again one may read between his lines an adumbration of the wave theory, but it is better not to do that. Bacon's optical writings were not taken as seriously as Peckham's and Witelo's, but they stimulated Leonard Digges' practical mind three centuries later.

After having introduced these three worthies—Bacon, Witelo and Peckham—we may dispose more rapidly of the others. Peter the Stranger, the famous magnetician of whom more anon, had planned to compose a treatise on mirrors. William of Moerbeke, who was Witelo's inspirer, translated Hero's work on the same subject (Catoptrics) from the Greek into Latin, thinking it was Ptolemy's. Giles of Rome discussed the nature of light and of color in the best scholastic manner. Still another contemporary was Theodoric of Freiberg, but his most important work, including the earliest satisfactory explanation of the rainbow, in Latin, appeared only in the first decade of the following century.

So much for the Latin West. Let us now fly to Persia where similar investigations were being carried out by Nāṣir al-dīn al-Ṭūsī and his pupil Quṭb al-dīn al-Shīrāzī. Nāṣir al-dīn prepared a recension of Euclid's optics and discussed various optical questions. How are colors affected by heat and cold, wetness and dryness? Where do the light rays originate? How can one account for optical illusions? Quṭb al-dīn indulged in speculations of the same kind—a physicist with a sufficient philosophical bent could hardly avoid it—but his main achievement, one of the greatest in the history of mediaeval physics, was his explanation of the rainbow, an explanation essentially equivalent to that of Descartes. This was contained in Quṭb al-dīn's astronomical treatise, Nihāyat al-idrāk, of which I do not know the exact date. As he died only in 1311 it might possibly belong to the fourteenth century, but this is hardly probable for he was born in 1236. We may assume that his main work was done some time before the end of the thirteenth century. Theodoric of Freiberg was about fourteen years younger, and his explanation of the rainbow, similar to Quṭb al-dīn's, dates from c. 1304–1310. There is a very high probability that Quṭb al-dīn was the first; the two discoveries were certainly independent.

Looking back on the optical work of the second half of the thirteenth century, we are struck first by its cosmopolitanism, second, by its homogeneity. For out of the nine scientists mentioned in this account, two hailed from England, two from Persia, one each from France, Flanders, Germany, Poland, and Italy. The homogeneity of their thoughts is more striking because of the wide distribution of their bodies, yet it is easy enough to explain it. Whether they flourished in England or in far distant Persia they had all drunk at the same source—the Kitāb al-manāẓir (or Taḥrīr al-munāẓara) of Ibn al-Haitham. Nor was the latter's influence stopped in the thirteenth century and superseded by that of Witelo, Peckham, or Quṭb al-dīn. It continued to be felt directly, East and West. Quṭb al-dīn's main pupil, Kamāl al-dīn al-Fārisī, wrote a valuable commentary on the Kitāb al-manāzir, and the Latin translation of Ibn al-Haitham was printed together with Witelo's treatise as late as 1572.

2. *Weights and measures*—This is of archaeological rather than of physical interest. Nor is there much to be said.

Moses ibn Tibbon wrote a treatise explaining the weights and measures mentioned in the Bible and the Talmud. Incidentally this same Moses translated Aristotle's Problems from Arabic into Hebrew.

Of a more practical nature was chapter twenty-two of al-Kūhīn al-'Aṭṭār's pharmaceutical handbook. This is quoted by way of illustration: students of ancient weights should always consult the treatises on materia medica.

3. *Magnetism*—The outstanding physical treatise of this period was the one written by the Picard crusader, Peter the Stranger, outside of the walls of Lucera in 1269. Peter's Letter on the magnet was a summary of the magnetic knowledge then available, to which he himself had added considerably by his own experiments. Much attention was naturally devoted to compasses of various kinds, one of them very elaborate. Peter's Letter was the most remarkable example of experimental research in mediaeval times. We find in it the first suggestion of terrestrial magnetism.

4. *Mechanics, Technology, Engineering*—The subject of mechanics attracted almost as much attention as optics, but its study was apparently less fruitful. That is, it was less fruitful as far as immediate and practical results were concerned, and this is what we would expect considering the peculiarly elusive nature of mechanical concepts. A strange subject it is, which stretches from the most abstract and impalpable ideas down to the most concrete appliances. We shall begin our account on the most abstract side and proceed downwards.

The deepest thinker on mechanical problems was Roger Bacon, who had received a strong impulsion in that direction from Grosseteste and had also benefited by investigations made by other contemporaries of his, chiefly Peter the Stranger. Bacon and Olivi seem to have been the only ones of their generation to be reached by the astounding wave of knowledge due to the school of Nemorarius. Jordanus Nemorarius himself died in 1237, Robert Grosseteste in 1253; the treatise De ratione ponderis explaining the notion of statical moment may date only from the second half or end of the thirteenth century. However, Bacon's thoughts did not dwell so much on statics as on dynamics. He was pondering on the nature of force, especially on force or action at a distance. Curiously enough, these thoughts, earnest as they were, were partly astrological. For among the forces or actions considered by him were light and gravity, but also astrological influences, the reality of which were beyond doubt. How were these astrological influences transmitted across the open spaces? How were these distant causalities propagated? It was very remarkable to ask such questions, and we must not blame him for failing to solve them. He concluded logically enough in favor of the Aristotelian idea of the impossibility of a vacuum.[14] For how could any action be transmitted across nothingness? He also concluded that if there is no vacuum a plurality of worlds becomes inconceivable.

Another Franciscan, but hailing from southern France, Peter Olivi of Sérignan continued the elaboration of the concept of impetus which was to lead later to the concept of inertia. His own contribution may seem small to the non-historical physicist, but historians who realize the immense travail which was needed to pass from the crude intuitions of Philoponos and Simplicios to the more definite ideas of Galileo and Newton, will honor his memory.

In the meanwhile Persian philosophers were approaching the same problem from a different angle. 'Alī ibn 'Umar al-Kātibī of Qazwīn was discussing the rotation of the earth. If it did rotate, could a flying bird keep up with it? He answered yes, because the atmosphere might be turning together with the earth and drag the bird. Yet he concluded against the possibility of such a rotation, because there are but two kinds of natural motions, rectilinear and circular, and sublunar motions are of the first kind. Quṭb al-dīn of Shīrāz argued in the same vein. These shrewd minds were stupidly deadlocked because of an Aristotelian prejudice the power of which was not broken until the time of Galileo and Kepler.

Still another approach was that of engineers trying to improve their machines. The dream of perpetual motion was beginning to engross their imagination. We find proofs of it in the album of Villard de Honnecourt—architect, mechanician, naturalist, a humble forerunner of Leonardo da Vinci—and in Peter the Stranger's treatise. Peter tried to create a perpetual motion by means of magnets!

Let us pass to hydrostatics and hydraulics. In the very year when Peter wrote his famous Epistola (1269), William of Moerbeke translated Archimedes' treatise on floating bodies from Greek into Latin. This is especially important because the Greek text is lost. Some hydraulic work was done by al-'Urḍī in Damascus. This was before his departure for Marāgha c. 1259, and may even have occurred before the middle of the century. Arabic hydraulics was but a mediocre continuation of the Archimedian and Hellenistic.

Muslim astronomers had devised some nice instruments for the measurement of time. Among the Arabic works translated by order of King Alfonso was an anonymous one on the construction and use of the candle clock. This particular work was translated by Samuel ha-Levi.

Some paper money, ch'ao[4] (514), was printed in Chinese and Arabic in 1294, at Tabrīz, which is by the way the only place in Islām where there is an early record of blockprinting. That method was of Chinese origin.[15] We have a contemporary

[14] I regret to say that the earlier history of that fundamental question was not sufficiently developed in my volume 1, however many hints will be found in it. The idea of vacuum was introduced by the Atomists; its main defender in early mediaeval times was Philoponos, later al-Bāqilānī. On the other hand, the Ikhwān al-ṣafā' were in this respect representatives of the Aristotelian tradition, which was later continued by Adelard of Bath, and by Bacon.

[15] Vol. 1, 451, 512, 633. Some Egyptian blockprints are possibly earlier than the Tabrīz

account of it by the great Persian historian, Faḍl Allāh Rashīd al-dīn, who lived in Tabrīz (see vol. 3). Rashīd al-dīn must have known of the issue of paper money in 1294, but does not speak of it.

Speaking of China, by far the largest engineering undertaking of that time was completed during Kublai Khān's rule—the Grand Canal which connected his capital Khānbaliq with the old Sung capital Hang-chow, a distance of about twelve hundred miles. The part built by Kublai Khān, the northern part, from the Yellow River to Khānbaliq, was 500 miles long.[16]

And we now come to what one would be tempted to call the lowest form of engineering—military engineering, the art of hurting and killing one's fellowmen. However, that would be taking a sentimental and erroneous view of the matter. Without going to the extreme attitude of military historians like General Rathgen who proclaims that "Die Waffe ist der Ausgangspunkt aller Kultur,"[17] we must reconcile ourselves to the fact that from the boomerang down to the airplane many human inventions have been due to war or immeasurably developed by it. At any rate we must explain human progress as it occurred, and war played a large part in it, most of the time retrogressive, but sometimes in the right direction.

Al-Ḥasan al-Rammāḥ wrote two Arabic treatises on horsemanship and the art of war. As the titles suggest, much attention was paid to the use of horses. This is not surprising. Al-Ḥasan was a Syrian who was naturally well acquainted with the old Arabic traditions of spirited raids (ghazū). Yet as we shall see presently, his work dealt also with what we now call chemical warfare. Other tactics were introduced by the Mongols, and some improvements in military technique may possibly be ascribed to their immoderate lust for power. In his conquest of Persia and 'Irāq, Hūlāgū Khān is said to have employed a thousand Chinese engineers; on the other hand, we know that Kublai Khān engaged Persian technicians, such as A-lao-wa-ting and I-ssŭ-ma-yin, and the sons of these men, Ma-ho-sha and Ya-ku, remained in the Mongol service. These Persian engineers constructed ballistic engines, such as mangonels—not cannons.

5. *Music*—By this time the theory and practice of music was sufficiently advanced in Christian Europe to continue its development without additional reference to Muslim examples. We may thus just as well begin our account in the West.

The Galician poems composed by King Alfonso were meant to be sung. Their melodies have been preserved and their collection is one of the greatest treasures of mediaeval music. One of the best sources on contemporary music, as practised by the Franciscans, is the Latin chronicle of Fra Salimbene of Parma.

The theory of music was explained by Georgios Pachymeres in his treatise on the quadrivium.

Musical treatises were composed by Nāṣir al-dīn al-Ṭūsī, and by Quṭb al-dīn al-Shīrāzī. However, the main theorist of this time, and one of the most famous in Islām to this day, was Ṣafī al-dīn 'Abd al-Mu'min al-Baghdādī. Ṣafī al-dīn witnessed the last days of the eastern caliphate, and after the fall of Baghdād (1258)

---

ones, but this is not proved, and there is no record of them, only the undated prints. They must date from the period 900 to 1350, mostly from the latter part of it. Thomas Francis Carter: The invention of printing in China (128, 130, 137, New York 1925; Isis, 8, 361–373).

[16] For the sake of comparison, consider the following distances (i.e., the shortest traveling distances): Boston to St. Louis, 1217 miles; London to Madrid, or to Rome, 1183 miles; Brussels to Berlin, 505 miles; Philadelphia to Cleveland, 487 miles; San Francisco to Los Angeles, 475 miles.

[17] Bernhard Rathgen: Das Geschütz im Mittelalter (127, Berlin 1928; Isis, 13, 125–127).

entered the Mongol service. He was one of the founders of the "systematist" school. The invention of various instruments was ascribed to Nāṣir al-dīn (flute) and to Ṣafī al-dīn (archlute, psaltery).

Summary

The outstanding achievements were the following:

(1) Peter the Stranger's magnetic experiments described by him in 1269.

(2) First accurate theory of the rainbow by Quṭb al-dīn al-Shīrāzī, to be rediscovered independently by Theodoric of Freiberg.

(3) Bacon's experiments and prophecies. In general, prophecies would not be taken into account, but Bacon's were too many to be discarded.

(4) Invention of spectacles in North Italy.

(5) Restatements of Ibn al-Haitham's optics by Witelo and John Peckham. Though their treatises were not intrinsically of great importance, they continued to dominate optical teaching and thinking throughout the end of the Middle Ages and the Renaissance until the beginning of modern times.

(6) Discussion of optical principles by Bacon, Nāṣir al-dīn al-Ṭūsī, and Quṭb al-dīn.

(7) Bacon's discussion of force, action at a distance, vacuum, plurality of worlds.

(8) Discussion of impetus by Peter Olivi.

(9) Further theorization of music by Ṣafī al-dīn.

Of the nine leaders, three came from France—Villard de Honnecourt, Peter the Stranger, and Peter Olivi; two from England—John Peckham and Roger Bacon; one from Poland—Witelo; two from Persia—Nāṣir al-dīn and Quṭb al-dīn; one from 'Irāq—Ṣafī al-dīn.

VIII. CHEMISTRY

The account of chemical progress in the second half of the thirteenth century is divided into five parts: 1. Gunpowder and pyrotechnics; 2. Glass industry; 3. Colors and pigments. Limning; 4. Strong and medicinal waters; 5. Alchemical theory and practice.

1. *Gunpowder and Pyrotechnics*—It is impossible to say when and where gunpowder was invented, but it is probable that the invention was made in the Latin world or perhaps in Syria in the second half of the thirteenth century. The possibility of a Chinese invention is not excluded but is unproved. The discovery hinged on the isolation and purification of potassium nitrate. It was necessary to distinguish that kind of saltpeter from others which were of no use for this special purpose, and to free it sufficiently from the impurities which jeopardized its usefulness. Moreover, it was not enough to discover gunpowder, but to apply its explosive force to the propulsion of missiles. That application—the invention of fire-arms—was the most important step, but it was not made before the second quarter of the fourteenth century. The invention of gunpowder, or more correctly of fire-arms, is often quoted as an example of revolutionary invention, but this is very misleading. The earlier fire-arms were so crude that their efficacy was very small. They were gradually improved, and many of these improvements were as revolutionary as the basal invention, if not more so. Thus that invention was not one great revolution, but a long series of smaller revolutions; like almost anything else, it reduces itself to a slow and gradual evolution. To illustrate its

slowness and the relative inefficiency of early fire-arms, it may suffice to recall that as late as 1775–1776—that is, almost five centuries later—Benjamin Franklin, who was an exceedingly practical man, being unable to obtain enough gunpowder for the army, seriously proposed to return to the use of bows and arrows![18]

Two of the early authors of pyrotechnic recipes deserve separate mention: Marc the Greek, and al-Ḥasan al-Rammāḥ. The former is unknown except as the author of a Liber ignium which dates probably from this period. It includes a collection of recipes of all ages, one of the latest being a recipe for gunpowder. This may be the earliest recipe of its kind (Bacon's is certainly apocryphal). Al-Ḥasan al-Rammāḥ was probably a Syrian; he died in 1294. He wrote treatises on the art of war in general, but they include pyrotechnic recipes, notably methods of preparing and purifying saltpeter.

2. *Glass Industry*—That ancient art received a great impetus because the use of glass, at once for vessels and for windows, became far more common. The main center of fabrication and distribution was now Venice. We are not aware of any definite improvement which can be ascribed to the glassmakers of Venice or Murano, at any rate at this time, but the existence of such a flourishing industry must have influenced the development of chemistry. As always, the influence was much diminished by trade secrecy, yet it must be taken into account.

3. *Colors and Pigments. Limning*—The traditions relative to painting and limning which we followed in the Mappae clavicula, Heraclius, Theophile the Priest, etc. were continued in the Liber de coloribus faciendis of Peter of Saint Omer, and in other anonymous treatises. The subject was of interest to a growing public of scribes, limners, painters, dyers and other craftsmen.

These needs were not restricted to the Christian world. Beautifully illuminated MSS. were produced by Muslims and Jews. I do not know contemporary treatises on the subject in Arabic, but we have two treatises written by Abraham ben Judah ibn Ḥayyim. One, finished at Loulé, Portugal, 1262 (?), is in Portuguese written in Hebrew script.

4. *Strong and Medicinal Waters*—For another source of chemical ideas we may consult the medical treatises explaining the preparation and virtues of healing waters. A good example is the Tractatus mirabilis aquarum of Peter of Spain, dealing with twelve marvelous "waters," including alcohol, the elixir of life, and other menstrua. There are many such treatises ascribed to Theodoric Borgognoni, Albert the Great, Arnold of Villanova, Ramon Lull; but most of them are anonymous, or attributed to mythological authors, such as Hermes.[19] Moreover such "waters" are dealt with in medical MSS. or incidentally in other MSS.; e.g., in the Liber ignium of Marc the Greek.

5. *Alchemical Theory and Practice*—We now come to the most important group, the one dealing with chemical generalities and methods. I have disposed before of the other treatises because they were more concrete, and humbler in their scope. Their scarcity and relative mediocrity must not surprise us, because we could hardly expect many chemical discoveries to be promptly divulged. In the case of technical applications for example, we must bear in mind that the craftsmen were not learned men; they were either illiterate, or their literacy was too shallow to make writing easy or tempting.

[18] Sydney George Fisher: The true Benjamin Franklin (266, Philadelphia 1898). Quoting Franklin's reasons in his own words.

[19] For a number of examples see D. W. Singer: Catalogue of Latin and vernacular alchemical MSS. in Great Britain (section XX, p. 639–685, Brussels 1930; Isis, 12, 168; 15, 299).

However, the learned men were not lacking in curiosity. Their attention had been focused on chemical problems by Aristotle's Meteorology, and the Kitāb al-shifā' of Ibn Sīnā, works which were now available to the Latin as well as to the Arabic readers. Every philosopher had to face the alchemical challenge and to make a stand with regard to it. The Latin doctors were obviously embarrassed, and many of them sat on the fence. On the one hand, they had read Latin versions or elaborations of Ibn Sīnā and of other Arabic treatises on alchemy; on the other hand, some of the statements made by the more radical alchemists were too blatant and the conduct of these men savored but too often of quackery. Where was the truth? They felt that there must be some of it in alchemy, together with abundant lies, but it was difficult to depart the good from the evil.

Let us consider more closely the attitude of a few of the leaders. Vincent of Beauvais' ideas were largely derived from the De aluminibus et salibus of al-Rāzī translated by Gerard of Cremona; he believed in the possibility of transmutation, but not unreservedly; his hesitations were probably due to Ibn Sīnā's influence. The chemical knowledge of Albert the Great was more concrete and detailed than Vincent's, but his general position was somewhat similar. He qualified his acceptance of alchemy by adding that transmuted gold was different from real gold! One of the alchemical treatises ascribed to Albert, the Semita recta, was translated into Greek by one Petros Theoctonicos (unless this be a corruption of Albert's own name?). That treatise is more radical than, for example, the Libellus de alchimia: the author of the Semita recta, whoever he be, declares that the differences between metals are only accidental, and hence that transmutation is possible, and he proceeds to describe instruments and methods. Roger Bacon was deeply concerned with alchemy, and he even sent a treatise on the subject to Clement IV. He was opposed to the theory of the essential unity of matter, as explained for example in the Semita recta, and made a prudent distinction between good and bad alchemy.

It should be noted that it requires some boldness to summarize these alchemical opinions, because authentic writings are very few and apocryphal ones very numerous. For practically none of these texts have the MSS. been studied critically, and their vicissitudes investigated. Hence all this is said under correction: "Albert's conclusions are such if the Libellus de alchimia is genuine," etc. To illustrate, a large number of alchemical writings bear the names of Arnold of Villanova and Ramon Lull, but most of them are probably apocryphal. We are not so sure about Arnold, who was a restless and unbalanced spirit anyhow. The main treatise ascribed to him, the Thesaurus thesaurorum, was very popular. With Ramon we are on much safer ground. No alchemical writings are mentioned in the contemporary lists of his works. Moreover in his authentic works (e.g., in Felix) he expressed very neatly his disbelief in alchemy. His sayings on the subject remind us sometimes of the condemnation of alchemical imposture found in the Arabic writings of al-Jawbarī and 'Abd al-Laṭīf. After his death the Lullian school exaggerated every tendency of his toward the occult, and in spite of his aversion for them, it favored alchemical dreams. Thus it came to pass that some eighty alchemical treatises were gradually ascribed to him.

To be sure, this large apocryphal literature—it includes treatises attributed to Lull, Villanova, Duns Scot, Alfonso X, Albert the Great, etc.—would deserve to be studied; but the value of many of these writings is considerably reduced for the historian by the impossibility of dating them. At any rate apocryphal writings are generally posterior to their alleged authors; it is probable that most of that literature is not anterior to the fourteenth century and thus that it lies outside the scope of this volume. With regard to the treatises ascribed to Lull, it has been proved that some of them were composed by a converted Jew, Raimundo de Tárrega (d. 1371).

There is a group of writings which we must now consider with special attention, the Latin treatises ascribed to Geber. They are not posterior to the thirteenth century, for there are two MSS. of the end of that century. The largest and most important of these writings is the Summa perfectionis, which is an elaborate treatise on theoretical and practical alchemy. It is certainly derived from Arabic sources, but the real nature of that derivation is not yet understood. It will only be possible to solve such questions when a corpus of the early alchemical literature in Arabic is finally established.[20] In the meanwhile, the pseudo-Geber treatises enable us to measure the extent of alchemical knowledge in Latindom toward the end of the thirteenth century, and to realize its Arabic origin. Much of that knowledge was experimental, and we are given a definite idea of the methods and instruments employed to obtain it.

Though Arabic alchemy dates back at least to the second half of the ninth century, it was still very vigorous at the end of the thirteenth, and continued to be so for another century at least. Abū-l-Qāsim Muḥammad ibn Aḥmad, a famous alchemist of 'Irāq, flourished probably at this time, if not earlier. Indeed his main work, the "Knowledge acquired concerning the cultivation of gold," was the subject of a long commentary by al-Jildakī, who died in 1342. It defends without hesitation and qualification the alchemical teachings concerning the essential unity of metals and the possibility of their transmutation. In another book Abū-l-Qāsim al-'Irāqī set forth the social aspect of alchemy, the obligation of secrecy. That obligation was a real godsend for the alchemists for it enabled them to justify the lack of intelligibility of their explanations! The reader who failed to understand dared not complain for his failure proved nothing but his own unworthiness.

To sum up, such treatises as the Summa perfectionis and Abū-l-Qāsim's are excellent accounts of the advanced and radical teachings of the alchemists; while all the writings which can be legitimately ascribed to the Latin philosophers—Vincent of Beauvais, Albert the Great, Bacon, Lull, etc.—represented rather a compromising point of view which was, all considered, a wise one. The extravagant claims of the alchemists and their quackish manners could not be countenanced, and yet were they not groping for some knowledge of essential value? They might fail eventually to discover the philosopher's stone, but maybe they would find something better?

Alchemical research was not restricted to Latindom and to Islām, but it was there that it flourished best. The seeds of alchemy, which had come from Hellenistic Egypt, had found their most favorable soil in the Arabic speaking countries, and had continued their growth for centuries under the patronage of Muslim princes.

[20] Since the publication of my vol. 1 (1927), the study of Arabic writings ascribed to Jābir (Geber) has progressed in a very remarkable way. That progress may easily be followed in the Critical bibliographies of Isis (no. 19 and ff. in vol. 8 and ff.), mainly in the sections devoted to the second half of the eighth century and to Islām. The most recent investigations by Paul Kraus lead to the conclusion that these writings were composed under Ismā'īlī influence sometime before the Epistles of the Brethren of Purity (second half of the tenth century). Paul Kraus: Dschābir ibn Ḥajjān und die Ismā'īlijja (Dritter Jahresbericht des Forschungs-Instituts für Geschichte der Naturwissenschaften, 23–42, Berlin 1930; Isis, 15, 399); Studien zu Jābir ibn Ḥayyān (Isis, 15, 7–30, 1931).

The time had now come for those vigorous seedlings to be transplanted and to start a new life in Western Europe. A work like the Summa perfectionis might be considered the first monument of Latin alchemy, itself the ancestor of our modern chemistry.

It is hardly necessary to speak of the alchemical efforts which were made in other countries. It will suffice to say that we have alchemical treatises written in Greek by Nicephoros Blemmydes, and in Syriac by the Nestorian 'Abhd-īshō' bar Bĕrīkhā; there is also one by the Egyptian Jew, Ibn Kammūna, but it was written in Arabic and should be studied together with the other Arabic treatises.

Summary

Thanks to the arts, chemical knowledge was slowly but gradually increasing. The makers of colors and dyes, of glass and ceramics, of cosmetics and medicinal waters, of fireworks and maybe of gunpowder, improved little by little their craftsmanship. Each generation added a few recipes to the stock of older ones collected from everywhere. Unfortunately most of the recipes were trade secrets and remained unpublished. These craftsmen as a rule were interested only in the recipes, and were not concerned in the theories which might be back of them. A recipe worked or it did not work, and that was the end of it.

For theories—that is, for science proper—we have to go to the alchemists and to the philosophers who were more or less interested in alchemical research. The alchemical theory hardly developed, but it was now conquering the Latin world. Thus the Latin alchemists were guided by provisional hypotheses, and this enabled them to accumulate an increasing amount of experimental technique and knowledge and to reduce their results to a semblance of order. By the end of this period western alchemy was well on its way.

IX. GEOGRAPHY

For the history of geography it is expedient to return to our racial subdivision. We shall deal successively with: (1) Western Christians; (2) Eastern Christians; (3) Western Jews; (4) Western Muslims; (5) Eastern Muslims; (6) Chinese.

1. *Western Christians*—Let us begin with the maps, each of which is a neat synthesis of geographical knowledge. To be sure they never represent the latest stage of that knowledge, for there is always a delay—and in mediaeval times that delay might be very long—between the discovery of new lands and the cartographical record of it. It is clear, for example, that the explorations to be dealt with presently could hardly be recorded by the map makers of this period. Thus if we had to tell the history of the discovery of any single country, we would explain first when and how the discovery was made, then when it was described, when it was mapped.

The most progressive cartography was that of the portolani, created to meet the urgent needs of seafaring men. There is much discussion as to where the earliest portolani appeared. At any rate the "normal portolano" was almost certainly a Mediterranean production; it had already reached a high stage of development in the last third of the thirteenth century. The importance of these portolani can hardly be exaggerated. As opposed to the monastic maps of the theologians and the Ptolemaic maps of the cabinet geographers, they were primarily derived from direct observations. Unfortunately these observations were not astronomical but purely empirical, the relative positions of places being determined by dead reckoning. However, crude observations are better than blind tradition, and these observations were not made once for all but on the contrary submitted to frequent verification. This fact is proved by the gradual improvement of the portolani during the following century. Their chief merit is that they introduced the spirit of direct observation into cartography.

Most of the portolani that have come down to us are western, but there are a few Muslim ones (none of the thirteenth century). There is no doubt that the Arabic navigators who were the masters of the eastern seas from the ninth century to the end of the fifteenth had also some kind of sea charts, but no early one has yet come down to us. The existence and use of such charts, East and West, in the second half of the thirteenth century, if not before, is confirmed by references to them in the Arbor scientiae of Ramon Lull, in the memoirs of Marco Polo, and in the lives of Saint Louis and Arghūn, the Īl-khān of Persia.

Naturally portolani could not supersede the earlier maps at once. To begin with, they were a little too onesided for general use. Sailors were interested only in the coasts, hardly in the hinterland which was the main concern of the land-lubbers, that is, of the great majority of men. Hence portolani could not satisfy the ordinary geographical needs. No wonder that monastic maps continued not only to be used but also to be constructed. Three typical maps of this time may be quoted: the small Psalter map of the British Museum, the larger Hereford map, and the immense Ebstorf map. These maps are very different with regard to particulars, but the general conception is the same in all three: the universe is in the shape of a wheel, of which Jerusalem is the hub, and the ocean the rim.

Interesting maps were compiled by the great English chronicler, Matthew Paris. These maps are excellent examples of the scholarly cartography continuing and improving the Ptolemaic tradition. Paris' knowledge was not experimental in the same way as that of the portolan designers, but it was derived from written or spoken itineraries. Its lack of geographical precision was largely due to the fact that travelers on land do not attempt to determine their position as accurately as sailors, and do not even have to determine it themselves; they can depend on the inhabitants to tell them where they are and to guide them to the next stage of their journey. Paris' map of England is the earliest known detailed map of that country.

A map of the world showing the coordinates of the principal places was drawn by Bacon to accompany the Opus majus which he sent to the Pope. That map is unfortunately lost but we know his geographical ideas from the Opus itself. He took pains to be well informed; for example, he made use of the traveling account of his contemporary, William of Rubruquis, while Vincent of Beauvais and even fourteenth century writers were ignorant of it. He impressed upon the Pope the value of geographical research. He believed in the habitability of the southern hemisphere and suggested the possibility of reaching India by sailing westward from Europe. That suggestion was indirectly known to Columbus.

Albert the Great paid less attention to geography than did Bacon, but he wrote a treatise on weather and climates.

We have a number of accounts of pilgrimages to the Holy Land, some twenty-eight in Latin, eight in French, one in German. It is not worthwhile to consider them separately, except the one written by the German Dominican, Burchard of Mount Sion, which includes one of the best mediaeval descriptions of Palestine.

By far the most remarkable geographical events of this age were the immense journeys from western Europe to the Mongolian court, and vice versa. One such journey would have been striking enough, but we know many men who accomplished the same feat and there must be others whose names have not come down to us. The causes of these journeys were complex: missionary activities of Franciscans and Dominicans, commercial enterprise of Venice and Genoa, desire on the part of popes and Christian princes to find allies in the Far East against the Muslim terror. Whatever the motives, the scientific results were of considerable importance. The increase in our geographical knowledge of Asia was perhaps greater in this period than in any other before the nineteenth century.

All of these travelers to the Far East were Italians, except William of Rubruquis, who was a Fleming. He was sent unofficially by St. Louis to the Mongolian court in 1253, traveled overland all the way from Crimea to Qaraqorum and returned in 1255. His account was far more elaborate than Carpini's, though less well written; it is full of geographical and ethnographical information.

As far as we know, the Genoese, Buscarello de' Ghizolfi, did not go beyond the Īl-khānate of Persia; however he did not simply reach the court of the Īl-khān, Arghūn, but was employed by him and sent back as his envoy to the western powers. He returned to Persia in 1291 together with Geoffrey of Langele, who represented the king of England. The letter which Arghūn wrote to Philip le Bel, king of France, in 1289, and entrusted to Buscarello, is preserved to this day in the national archives of France; it is one of the most curious diplomatic documents in existence. It is a long roll written in Mongolian, Uighūr script, with a Chinese seal affixed to it.

With John of Montecorvino, like Rubruquis a Franciscan, we pass from the realm of diplomacy to that of religion. Friar John founded, c. 1291, a mission in the Madras region, this being the earliest Catholic mission in India, with the legendary exception of the one ascribed in the same region to St. Thomas the Apostle. Then he proceeded to Cathay by sea and founded a new mission in Cambaluc. His task was very difficult because his opponents were not simply Mongols and Chinese, but Muslims and worst of all, Nestorian Christians, who had been established in China for centuries. John's mission was again the first Catholic one in that country, and he was the first archbishop of Cambaluc. Thus he was the first missionary of Rome both in India and in China. He wrote an admirable description of India, especially of the Coromandel coast which he knew best.

And we now come to the Polo family, the two elder ones, Niccolò and Maffeo, and the younger Marco, Niccolò's son. As their exploits, especially Marco's, have captured the imaginations of men, they are among the best known personalities of mediaeval times. The Poli were not missionaries of the kingdom to come, but of the commercial power of Venice; they were not diplomats, or more exactly their diplomacy was restricted to trade. The elder Marco, Marco Polo's uncle, had built up a business in Constantinople and Crimea, and this served as a basis of operation to his younger brothers, Niccolò and Maffeo, when they extended their trade to other parts of the Mongolian dominions. They finally reached the court of Kublai Khān and the latter sent them back as his envoys to the pope. In 1271 Niccolò and Maffeo, accompanied by their son and nephew Marco, left Venice and retraced their steps towards Mongolia. They crossed Asia overland, reaching Kublai's capital in 1275. In 1292 they returned home, most of the return voyage being made by sea. During his long stay in Cathay young Marco made long journeys across the country in various directions on imperial errands and was even for a while governor of a great city! When they reached Venice in 1295 they brought back with them such wonderful tales that their countrymen were at first incredulous. Marco dictated a long account of his travels, which is the most fascinating work of its kind in mediaeval times. Strange as much of his news seemed, its general truthfulness has been amply confirmed by archaeological and literary evidence. The fact that he was a merchant, not a missionary or diplomat, gave him a keener sense of realities and of values.

We must mention one more missionary, this time a Dominican, Ricoldo di Monte Croce, though his travels are insignificant compared with those already mentioned. He did not go further east than Tabrīz, but he spent many years in 'Irāq and wrote a valuable description of the various communities (Mongolians, Muslims, Nestorians, etc.) he had come across.

The six great men I have dealt with were only the leaders and the more conspicuous examples of many more who were then traveling along the highroads and along the byways of Asia. We have indirect evidence of the presence of many other Europeans: not to speak of the Nestorians who had had time to become true Asiatics, though without abandoning their faith, remember the "Ethiopians" who came to visit John of Montecorvino in Cambaluc, and that impious Lombard surgeon who gave him so much pain. Remember also the Caucasian guards (A su) of Kublai Khān. And how did Montecorvino's letters reach Italy? They were relayed throughout the whole length of Asia by Franciscan and Dominican missionaries.

And yet such was the spiritual and commercial activity of Latin Christendom, that the tremendous events I have outlined did not even suffice to satisfy it. While the Rubruquis, the Montecorvini, the Poli, were plodding eastwards dreaming of gold and jewels, or of the fabulous power of Prester John, or of the innumerable souls to be redeemed in the name of Jesus Christ, other adventurers and heroes were making other dreams, not less bold nor less fertile. Would it not be possible to reach the legendary isles of the Ocean, to find a way around Africa to the wealth of India and Cathay? Under the influence of these dreams began the series of navigations which was to lead two centuries later to the discovery of a New World.

I say began—perhaps I ought to have said began anew, for the first beginning had been made in ancient times; the second, according to al-Mas'ūdī and al-Idrīsī, by Muslim sailors; and thus the attempts made by Genoese sailors were only the third series. But never mind which series it was; each of these beginnings was a true beginning, for there remained nothing of the earlier ones to encourage them in their enterprise but stories too vague to give them the slightest hold. The first of these Genoese was Lanzarote Malocello who rediscovered the Fortunate Islands (the northern Canaries) c. 1270–1275, and tried to colonize them but failed. Then some fifteen years later Ugolino and Vadino Vivaldo—if one may believe the tradition—set out from Genoa in two galleys to discover the seaway round Africa to India. Franciscans sailed with them, and thus religion was mixed up with trade. All hands were lost. Some time later a younger scion of the same family, Sorleone Vivaldo, tried to find them, and in the course of his travels reached what is now Italian Somaliland, that is, the eastern coast of Africa. This implies that he had so much faith in his people that he assumed they had accomplished at least a part of their purpose.

Finally, Lull's religious romance, Blanquerna, (c. 1283) contains an account of the earliest European journey to the Sūdān.

The Venetians and Genoese were not the only rivals in the international competition for foreign and colonial markets. They were simply the leaders of the Mediterranean trade. In the meanwhile the strength of northern merchants was steadily growing. The commercial towns of the Baltic and North Seas realized the need of cooperation, and thus was prepared the creation of the Hanseatic League. The history of that League did not really begin before the second half of the fourteenth century, but its origins can be traced back to the thirteenth century. This concerns economic history rather than the history of geography, yet it must be taken into account if we wish to visualize the commercial and political background of geographical discoveries.

2. *Eastern Christians*—As compared with the immense achievements of the Latins, those of Eastern Christians were of little moment. Let us consider in succession the Greeks, Syrians, and Armenians.

(a) Greeks. Nicephoros Blemmydes wrote a geographical summary largely derived from the poem composed almost twelve centuries earlier by Dionysios Periegetes, and a treatise on the spherical shape of the earth and its zones. One of the anthologies compiled by Maximos Planudes was made up of historical and geographical extracts.

(b) Syrians. The Syriac chronicle of Abū-l-Faraj included a map of the climates, which was said to be the best example of Syriac cartography. We cannot appreciate it as it is lost, but it was in all probability a reflection of Muslim knowledge, and its qualities were due to Arabic rather than to purely Syriac influences.[21] A far more interesting Syriac document is the translation of Bar Sauma's Persian diary of his journey from China to the West. The original text is lost and we know this most remarkable story only through the Syriac translation. I shall come back to it in the Chinese section below.

(c) Armenians. The geography of Armenia ascribed to Vardan the Great is certainly apocryphal but nevertheless very valuable, one of our best sources for the study of the topography of mediaeval Armenia. The real author was probably one of Vardan's disciples.

Even as the western potentates were sending one emissary after another to the Great Khān with the hope of obtaining his help against the dreaded Saracens, even so the head of the Latin kingdom of Armenia was impelled to do the same. Indeed his predicament was far worse than that of the European kings, and but for the protection afforded to him by his mountainous boundaries his little kingdom would have been in the direst peril. Hayton the Elder, the third sovereign of the New Armenia to bear the title of king, sent his brother Sempad to the Great Khān Kuyuk in 1246, and a few years later, after Mangū's accession, he himself went all the way to Mongolia and back, thus repeating the exploits of the Latin missionaries. An astounding feat for a king! Unfortunately the account, which was written in Armenian by his secretary, Cyriacus of Gandzak, is tantalizingly short.

3. *Western Jews*—Israel has never been rich in travelers and explorers, and her pilgrims have been far less numerous than the Muslim or Christian and less anxious to bequeath to posterity an account of their journeys. The only one of this period worth mentioning was the Rabbi Jacob sent by the Jewish community of Paris to the eastern synagogues to obtain their financial help. The account of his mission includes a list of sacred places visited by him in the Holy Land. He may be the author of an anonymous Hebrew itinerary from Paris to Acre.

[21] Isis, 9, 460.

4. *Western Muslims*—The reader may have noticed that thus far I have not yet spoken of a single geographical treatise, with the exception of the one which formed a part of Bacon's Opus majus. For such treatises we have to turn to Islām. A very remarkable one was composed by the Maugrabin, 'Alī ibn Mūsā Ibn Sa'īd. Of course it was largely derived from Ptolemy and al-Idrīsī, but it contained novelties, for example many coordinates not given by the latter. He had some knowledge of the Senegal River, and of the northern countries of Europe, including Iceland. He had traveled extensively throughout the Dār al-islām and had met the Īl-khān Hūlāgū in Persia. His work was much used, and later corrected, by Abū-l-Fidā' in the following period.

Two distinguished Muslim pilgrims hailed from western Islām: Muḥammad al-'Abdarī from Valencia, and Muḥammad ibn Rushaid from Ceuta. In those days Moorish pilgrims preferred to travel overland all along the African coast, because this was entirely an Islāmic road. Thanks to the immense activity of Venetian and Genoese navigators, not to speak of others, the Mediterranean Sea was becoming more and more of a Christian Sea; it was dangerous for Muslim craft to cross it lengthwise. And perhaps also the overland road (with a possible break from Tunis to Egypt, this part being often done by water to avoid the hardships of the desert) was more congenial to the pilgrims, each of whom, whether learned or not, acquired sooner or later the reckless spirit of a tramp, who is not afraid of the length of a journey but would lengthen it if he could and thus increase his own happiness. God's own tramps! Could anything be more pleasant than walking day after day, seeing strange people and countries, stopping here or there for a week or a month or a year, then resuming one's journey, and all the while acquiring merit and escaping the tracasserie, and tedium, and responsibility of home life! Al-'Abdarī wrote a very valuable account of his long journey, and from Ibn Rushaid we have two precious itineraries, the one dealing with Spain, the other with Africa.

5. *Eastern Muslims*—While Ibn Sa'īd al-Maghribī was writing his geographical treatise, various other treatises of similar or larger scope were being composed in the East.

Nāṣir al-dīn translated into Persian the Suwar al-aqālīm of al-Balkhī, adding remarks of his own and maps. His astronomical tables included naturally geographical data. A part of his Tadhkira dealt with the explanation of the earth's shape and size, and contained an account of the seas, sea-winds, etc. The Nihāya of his disciple, Quṭb al-dīn, dealt with similar subjects—geodesy, seas, climes, etc. When Arghūn had sent Buscarello de' Ghizolfi to Europe in 1289, he was shown the latter's progress on a map by Quṭb al-dīn.

Nāṣir al-dīn and Quṭb al-dīn were primarily mathematical geographers, but not exclusively so; witness their interest in seas and winds, etc. The two following geographers, al-Qazwīnī and al-Waṭwāṭ, were of the encyclopaedic or cosmographic type. Al-Qazwīnī, sometimes called the Persian Pliny, wrote an immense cosmography which contains much material of geographical interest, and also a geography proper, that is, a description of the world, clime by clime. This is very systematic: for each clime the separate cities, countries, mountains, islands, etc. are arranged in alphabetical order. It is a collection of seven geographical dictionaries, one for each clime. Al-Qazwīnī's cosmography and geography were immensely popular in the East, as is shown by the number of MSS. (including many illuminated ones), elaborations, commentaries, and translations into Persian, Turkish, and Mongolian. Al-Waṭwāṭ was to al-Qazwīnī as a bat is to an eagle, yet his encyclopaedia of natural history and geography deserves mention.

I have kept the best for the end. Al-Qazwīnī's work was immense, to be sure, but we are less impressed by it than by the achievements of the great historian al-Juwainī. The latter traveled twice from Persia to Mongolia and back, and later continued his peregrinations in the wake of his master, Hūlāgū. To be secretary to such a man as Hūlāgū was not exactly a sedentary occupation. However for many years he was governor of Baghdād. It is very interesting to compare his account of Qaraqorum with the contemporary one by William of Rubruquis.

6. *Chinese*—Any account of Chinese endeavors in this period must always begin with a reference to Kublai Khān, who was a partner, and of necessity the biggest one, in every great undertaking. Under his orders the Yellow River was explored up to its sources in the Kokonor region, and missions were sent to South India, East Africa, and Madagascar. We have already seen that Marco Polo was also sent by him on long errands. These took Marco as far west as Yünnan and Tibet, and as far south as Burma and Cochin-China.

Besides the explorers employed by Kublai, at least four other men distinguished themselves greatly, and raised the record of Chinese traveling of that time almost as high as the Latin one.

First there was Ch'ang Tê who was sent by Mangū Khān to Hūlāgū in 1259, and thus traveled from Qaraqorum to 'Irāq. Then Yeh-lü Hsi-liang, who explored Central Asia in 1260–1263. The third was Chou Ta-kuan, who went on a mission to Cambodia in 1296 and described that marvelous group of temples, Angkor-Vat, which remained practically unknown from the time of Chou's visit to 1861. He gave a very good account of Cambodian customs. Finally, the Nestorian priest, Bar Sauma, traveled all the way from Pei-ping to Western Asia and then to Italy and other European countries, then returned to Baghdād, where he died in 1293. Bar Sauma was the earliest identified Chinese to reach western Europe.

Chinese work in mathematical geography was far less important. However it is recorded that Kuo Schou-ching, Kublai's astronomer, sent assistants into various parts of China to determine geographical coordinates.

Summary

This was indeed a golden age from the geographer's point of view. Let us see briefly how much was accomplished, leaving out of the picture the secondary or retrogressive activities.

The earliest normal portolani date from this time and they inaugurated a new period in the development of cartography. Matthew Paris' maps were memorable in spite of their crudity. Many other maps were mentioned—e.g., apropos of Bacon, Abū-l-Faraj, Quṭb al-dīn—but as they have failed to reach us we have no means of appreciating their value.

The only geographical theorist in the West was Bacon, and in this field he proved himself once more a prophet. For other works on theoretical and mathematical geography we have to go to Muslims or Chinese: Ibn Sa'īd al-Maghribī, Nāṣir al-dīn al-Ṭūsī, Quṭb al-dīn al-Shīrāzī, Kuo Shou-ching. The immense cosmographical work of al-Qazwīnī is one of the outstanding monuments of mediaeval learning.

The two most valuable studies of local geography were the Armenian topography ascribed to Vardan the Great, and the account of Cambodia published at the end of the century by Chou Ta-kuan.

The most significant achievements of the age were in the line of exploration and travel. The long journeys made by Christian and Jewish pilgrims to reach the Holy Land hardly deserve to be recalled; the trans-African journeys to Mecca of Muḥammad al-'Abdarī and Muḥammad ibn Rushaid are more interesting, yet commonplace. The new expeditions into the Atlantic, along the West African coast and the East African coast and into the Sūdān, were anticipations and promises rather than durable accomplishments.

The great events were the trans-Asiatic journeys; one is amazed by each of them, and even more by their frequency. Just realize that within half a century the innumerable risks of such long journeys were faced and successfully overcome by no less than thirteen persons, not counting the many less known or anonymous ones who traveled in their wake or independently. Listen to this roll call: William of Rubruquis, Buscarello de' Ghizolfi, John of Montecorvino, Niccolò, Maffeo and Marco Polo, Ricoldo di Monte Croce, Hayton the Elder and his brother Sempad, al-Juwainī, Ch'ang Tê, Yeh-lü Hsi-liang, Bar Sauma. What a magnificent array of men!

As compared with the previous period, during which Italy could boast but a single hero of travel, or geographer—Giovanni Pian del Càrpine—she now set out a whole company of them: Buscarello de' Ghizolfi, Montecorvino, the three Poli, Ricoldo di Monte Croce, to whom might be added perhaps Lanzarote Malocello and the brothers Vivaldi—nine outstanding men. Three times more than all the rest of Europe put together: the two Englishmen, Matthew Paris and Bacon, and the Fleming, William of Rubruquis.

So much for Europe. Among Eastern Christians there were three great Armenians, Hayton the Elder, his brother Sempad, and Vardan (or rather the unknown author of the Armenian geography); and one Nestorian, Bar Sauma. Perhaps we ought to have counted also Bar Sauma's fellow traveler, Marcos Bainiel, who became patriarch in 1281 under the name of Yaballaha III.

Thus, in all, sixteen or seventeen Christians. We dealt also with seven Muslims, three from the West: Ibn Sa'īd, Muḥammad al-'Abdarī, and Muḥammad ibn Rushaid; and four from the East: Nāṣir al-dīn, Quṭb al-dīn, al-Qazwīnī, al-Juwainī. Finally four Chinese: Kuo Shou-ching, Chou Ta-kuan, Ch'ang Tê, and Yeh-lü Hsi-liang. Truly a golden age!

X. NATURAL HISTORY

It is difficult to classify the men dealt with in this chapter, for the simple reason that none of them, except perhaps the Chinese, were true naturalists. They were most of them philosophers, encyclopaedists, geographers, translators, physicians, almost anything, but not naturalists. And yet when one tries to measure the progress of natural history at this time one is surprised to find a not inconsiderable quantity of materials of great value and diversity. For if naturalists were rare and far between, almost every philosopher or physician was obliged to ask himself and to answer as well as he could a whole series of questions which belong to the field of natural history. Hence this is a strange drama, involving many actors, some of them great ones, but great in another way, and not especially concerned in this action. Many actors, but no leading ones.

1. *Western Christendom*—The album of the French architect, Villard de Honnecourt, contains various sketches of animals (molluscs, crustacea, insects, birds, porcupine, lion) and of artistic anatomy, and on the last leaf a recipe to preserve the natural colors of flowers kept in a herbarium.

The wild asses of Central Asia and the great mountain sheep, incorrectly called ovis poli, were first mentioned (in a western language at least) by William of Rubruquis. The book of Marco Polo is full of interesting items: mentions of coal and its use, asbestos, tutty, mountain rhubarb, rice and rice wine, indigo, ginger, Georgian goshawks, fat-tailed sheep, humped oxen, etc. Polo is a good illustration of my initial statement. Of course you could not call him a naturalist; his active and agile mind was not bent that way; and yet thanks to him our knowledge of the natural history of Asia was enriched and improved at many points. Other travel accounts would perhaps yield additional little bits of information, not much however, for the singularities and "marvels" which attracted the attention were always the same, and the average traveler was so dull, so impervious to the spirit of observation, that he preferred to recite them secondhand rather than to try to observe them himself, even when the verification was easy. As to the observation of inconspicuous plants and animals, nobody was ready for them save perhaps a few obstinate herbalists searching for new remedies.

Should we mention at all the Bestiaire d'amour of Richard de Fournival? It is a bestiary, but we doubt whether the zoologist will find any grist in it for his own mill.

Peter of Spain wrote a long commentary on Aristotelian zoology based on Michael Scot's Latin version. It was more scholastic than zoological and was soon superseded by the far better commentary prepared by Albert the Great.

The Speculum naturale of Vincent of Beauvais was a vast encyclopaedia of natural history containing abundant extracts from a great number of writings. It gives us on the whole a good idea of the average knowledge available to the clerks, who were not specialized scientists, about the middle of the century. Much space was devoted to plants and animals, and his description of fishes was better than Albert's. His geology was indirectly derived from Ibn Sīnā.

Of all the Christians, the one who came nearest to being a true naturalist was Albert the Great. There was the stuff of a naturalist in him, and he might have become one, and a great one, if his interests had not been of encyclopaedic scope and his energy endlessly dispersed. He made genuine attempts to see things himself; for example, he visited laboratories and mines. His geological views were Avicennian. He discussed erosion, the formation of mountains, the movements of the sea (he noticed the sea's withdrawal from Bruges), volcanic explosions, the presence of fossil shells in rocks. The botanical part of his work was particularly remarkable. We find in it rudiments of botanical geography, notes on the morphology of seeds, on the relationship between galls and insects, etc. The zoological part was in the form of an elaborate commentary on Michael Scot's version, but of twenty-six books the last seven were more original and contained the results of observations made by himself or communicated to him by the observers. Many animals were here described for the first time. Albert had some crude notions of what we would call to-day comparative animal psychology. He did not hesitate to reject many of the fables which made up the bulk of the mediaeval bestiaries. On the whole he was a good observer, but a weak theorist easily subdued by his authorities, especially Aristotle and Ibn Sīnā.

As a naturalist Bacon was far behind Albert and even Vincent. It is true he wrote questions on the Aristotelian De plantis, and had planned to include an account of plants and animals in his Compendium philosophiae. Yet he was too much of a Platonist and of a mathematical physicist to take a real interest in natural history, that is (as it was then), nothing but description, with hardly the possibility of classification and generalization.

The Clavis sanationis of Simon of Genoa, an immense dictionary of materia medica, is our main source for the study of thirteenth century botany, in spite of the fact that the author's interest was linguistic and medical rather than botanical.

A separate group might be made of the men who promoted husbandry. This would include, to begin with, encyclopaedists like Vincent and Albert. However, Vincent's main views on the subject are not in the Speculum naturale, but in the Speculum doctrinale, that extraordinary hotchpotch which is itself the best illustration of the shallowness of his mind. As to Albert, his zoological treatise contains information on hunting and fishing, including even an account of whaling and walrus hunting. Much else of interest to husbandmen, at any rate to those who were sufficiently literate to refer to books—e.g., the abbots of rich monasteries and great stewards—could be found in Vincent's Specula and Albert's Aristotelian commentaries. Then one would have to speak also of a king like Dinis the Liberal, who considered it an essential part of his sacred trust to develop the economic resources of his country, foster agriculture in every way, improve the methods of cultivation, and plant new forests.

As to the authors of books on husbandry, two of the greatest in mediaeval Europe flourished in this period; Walter of Henley and Peter of Crescenzi. We do not know exactly when the former flourished—"about the middle of the thirteenth century," do we put it? Was his French "Hosebondrie" written before the middle or after it? It is impossible to say. We have placed him arbitrarily in the preceding period, but he belonged perhaps more completely to this one? With regard to Peter of Crescenzi we have no such doubts. He was undoubtedly a man of the thirteenth century, and he lived throughout the second half of it, yet like his illustrious forerunner, Cato the Censor, he composed his great work only in old age: the Liber cultus ruris was not completed until c. 1305. We shall deal with it in volume 3, but the reader must bear in mind that this is somewhat arbitrary, for the work as well as the man was to a large extent a product of the thirteenth century.

Another group is that of the writers on falconry. Some of the treatises dealt with in Book III belong to the present period. Manfred prepared a revision of the De arte venandi cum avibus of his father, the emperor Frederick II, and it was that revision which was finally printed. Two treatises of Arabic origin were translated from Latin into French by Daniel of Cremona for another of Frederick's natural sons, the poor Enzio. The apocryphal letter addressed to Ptolemy, king of Egypt, was inserted in the Speculum naturale of Vincent of Beauvais. We have already dealt with a Catalan version of the same text. A part of book twenty-three of Albert's zoology was devoted to the subject, and the special interest attached to it is proved by the existence of a separate Renaissance edition of it, De falconibus, asturibus et accipitribus (Augsburg 1596–1598). Another contemporary treatise is the one ascribed to Dancus, king of Armenia, which has come down to us in a French version dated 1284. That French text may be the original one, or else the treatise was first written in Latin; but in any case, it cannot be much anterior to the last quarter of the thirteenth century. The history of falconry is continued in the following section.

2. *Greeks*—There is but one Greek to be considered, Demetrios Pepagomenos, physician to Michael Palaeologos; but he was a man of some distinction. He wrote a treatise on falconry which was the most elaborate of the age and independent

of the somewhat earlier work of Frederick II. It includes helminthological observations. There are other Greek treatises on the subject dating presumably from the same time. Demetrios may be the author of a book on dogs.

3. *Western Israel*—Judah ben Moses, one of the translators employed by King Alphonso, translated from Arabic into Spanish a lapidary dealing with 360 stones, divided between the twelve signs of the zodiac.

Ibn Rushd's commentary on Aristotelian zoology was translated from Arabic into Hebrew by Jacob ben Maḥir, the task being completed in 1302.

The first part of the Sha'ar ha-shamayim of Gershon ben Solomon is a summary of natural history.

4. *Islām*—Considerable information is naturally contained in the cosmographies of al-Qazwīnī and al-Waṭwāṭ.

A Persian lapidary is ascribed to Nāṣir al-dīn al-Ṭūsī. Another lapidary was composed in 1282 for an Egyptian sulṭān by Bailak al-Qabajaqī. It includes among other things a description of a kind of floating compass and of its use by sailors. Orientals have always been extremely fond of precious stones, and such lapidaries explaining their occult qualities were much appreciated; there is a whole series of them in Arabic (also in Persian, Turkish, and other oriental languages). Needless to say their scientific value is very small. The naturalist can hardly derive any knowledge from them beyond a list of stones.

Another type of book appealing to Muslims was the one wherein traditions concerning horses were collected. A good specimen of it was composed by the Egyptian traditionalist, 'Abd al-Mu'min al-Dimyāṭī. It would disappoint the naturalist in search of information on Arabian horses. Indeed the point of view is not scientific, but legal and religious.

The two itineraries of Muḥammad ibn Rushaid contain a few facts relative to the natural history of Spain and Africa.

There are a number of Muslim MSS. (Arabic and Persian) which include miniatures representing animals and plants. A study of these miniatures from our point of view has not yet been made; however it is doubtful whether it would lead to any important results. The interest of these miniatures is chiefly artistic; some of them (and I have seen a good many) are beautiful indeed—more beautiful than convincing.

5. *China*—In 1256 a large botanical encyclopaedia was completed by Ch'ên Ching-i. It is largely made up of extracts from earlier writings. It is essentially different from western works on the same subject because of the abundant literary and historical references which it contains, and also because of the importance attached to flowers. In fact the first half of it is entirely devoted to flowers, the second half to fruits, herbs, trees, husbandry—including of course sericulture—vegetables, etc. For each plant the prose description is followed by a poetical one. This mixture of art and poetry with the most practical information is typically Chinese. We pass back and forth from reality to dream.

In 1273 the Nung sang chi yao, a treatise on agriculture and sericulture, was compiled by order of Kublai Khān. That treatise was often reedited with new additions; for example, c. 1314, by Lu Ming-shan, under the title Nung sang i shih ts'o yao.

Twenty-six years later (in 1299) Li K'an published a separate treatise on the bamboo which has remained a standard book in Chinese literature. The purpose was purely artistic, yet it may interest botanists.

A treatise on birds, Ch'in ching, has come down to us in an edition of the end of the Sung dynasty. The elements of it can be traced back to much earlier times, but this edition remains the earliest tangible book on the subject.

6. *Japan*—The veterinary doctor Seia produced in 1267, with the aid of an artist, illustrations of seventeen plants used for horse ailments. In 1282 Koremune Tomotoshi completed an index to the Chinese pên ts'ao, that is, to the edition of it published in China in 1108, which remained the standard work on materia medica in Japan until the beginning of the seventeenth century.

Summary

Leaving out the encyclopaedias, as such, and unimportant items, the achievements of the time may be summarized as follows:

The geological views explained by Vincent of Beauvais and Albert the Great were simply restatements of those of Ibn Sīnā, but Albert added some observations of his own.

In mineralogy no progress was made; the Hebrew, Persian, and Arabic lapidaries were not scientific books in any sense.

The Asiatic fauna and flora were better known, thanks to the reports of western travelers, above all William of Rubruquis and Marco Polo.

The main botanical work in the West was that of Albert the Great. A remarkable botanical encyclopaedia was composed by Ch'ên Ching-i. Li K'an's treatise on bamboo was an artistic rather than a scientific achievement. Botanical dictionaries were compiled by Simon of Genoa and Koremune Tomotoshi. A treatise on husbandry and sericulture was published in 1273 by order of Kublai Khān.

The best students of zoology in the West were Vincent of Beauvais and Albert the Great. Ibn Rushd's commentary on Aristotelian zoology was translated from Arabic into Hebrew by Jacob ben Maḥir. A few French treatises on falconry belong to this period; namely, those translated by Daniel of Cremona, and the one ascribed to Dancus, king of Armenia. The most elaborate treatise on that subject was written in Greek by Demetrios Pepagomenos.

For the sake of curiosity we may recall three other contemporary treatises: a Greek one on dogs, an Arabic one on horses, a Chinese one on birds.

The outstanding personalities were Vincent of Beauvais, Albert the Great, Simon of Genoa, Demetrios Pepagomenos, Ch'ên Ching-i, Li K'an, Koremune Tomotoshi. Three Latins, one Greek, two Chinese, one Japanese.

XI. MEDICINE

The account of medical work is divided into the following parts: 1. Western Christians; 2. Eastern Christians; 3. Western Jews; 4. Eastern Jews and Samaritans; 5. Eastern Muslims (including Arabic speaking Christians); 6. Hindus; 7. Chinese; 8. Japanese.

1. *Western Christians*—The number of distinguished physicians was so great in Latindom that we have to subdivide that part into many smaller ones, as follows: (a) Italy; (b) France; (c) Spain; (d) England; (e) Flanders; (f) Central Europe; (g) Scandinavia. As we shall see presently, the first of these subdivisions was by far the most important; in fact it was more important than all the others put together.

(a) Italy. I have explained in Book III that by the beginning of the thirteenth century the school of Salerno had already lost its hegemony and that Frederick's efforts to revive it utterly failed. By the middle of the thirteenth century Salerno was already superseded by Bologna.

This does not mean that medical effort ceased in South Italy; indeed, this would be hardly conceivable. To clear the ground, let us speak first of the South Italians. Many of these were still devoting themselves to translations. (Some of them were Jews, but I place them here because the language they were translating into being Latin, their effort was a part of the Christian effort. Even so Christians writing in Arabic are generally considered by me together with the Muslims.) By far the most important of these translations was that of the Kitāb al-ḥāwī of al-Rāzī, the largest treasure of Greco-Arabic medicine, completed in 1279 by Faraj ben Salīm. Faraj translated also other medical treatises; e.g., the Taqwīm al-abdān of Ibn Jazla. Another great Arabic work, the Taisīr of Ibn Zuhr, as well as Maimonides' treatise on diet, was translated by John of Capua from the Hebrew.

Obviously these South Italians were much interested in veterinary medicine. Jordan Ruffo, who had been in Frederick's service, dedicated to the emperor's memory a treatise on the medical treatment of horses, partly derived from his own observations. This remained the main mediaeval work on the subject. Bartholomew of Messina, who flourished at Manfred's court, translated Hierocles' treatise from the Greek. We have also a treatise in Sicilian dialect by one Bartolommeo Spadafora of Messina. Are these two Bartholomews identical? Moses of Palermo, employed by Charles of Anjou, translated the pseudo-Hippocratic treatise from the Arabic. Finally there is the book written in Latin (or Greek?) by Boniface of Gerace (I shall come to him in the section on Greek medicine).

The greatest South Italian physician was Bruno da Longoburgo, a Calabrian educated in Salerno, but his life was spent and his fame obtained in the North. We shall come back to him presently.

One more Neapolitan may be quoted, John of Procida, though he was more famous as a politician and diplomat than as a physician. Yet a summary of medical practice is ascribed to him.

So much for the South. Let us now proceed to northern Italy, which was then—especially Bologna—the medical center of the Christian world.

Two translators were connected with Padua and Venice. Bonacosa, a Jew, translated the Kullīyāt of Ibn Rushd from the Arabic, in Padua, 1255. Paravicius translated the Taisīr of Ibn Zuhr from the Hebrew with the help of a Jew called Jacob, in Venice c. 1281. Though Paravicius' translation was not as good as the anterior one by John of Capua, it superseded it.

The most progressive branch of medicine was surgery. Under the stimulation of the Crusades and of continuous warfare the surgical school of Salerno had highly distinguished itself. At the beginning of the century the best Salernitan traditions had been taken to Bologna by Roland of Parma, and under the combined influence of Salerno and Bologna a new surgical school had been created by Hugh Borgognoni and his son Theodoric. Their effort was continued throughout the century; the father died before 1259 but the son lived until 1298. In the meanwhile another South Italian, Bruno da Longoburgo had established himself in Padua, where he completed, c. 1252, his Chirurgia magna. This work marked a new stage in the transmission of Arabic medicine to the West and its further elaboration in a new direction. Bruno's main authority was Abū-l-Qāsim, but he himself was full of experience. The Chirurgia magna was translated into Hebrew before the end of the century, and thus it influenced Jewish as well as Christian medicine.

Even greater than Bruno was William of Saliceto, who completed his Cyrurgia at Verona in 1275. The Cyrurgia was again a new stage in the history of surgery. It was more independent of the Arabic sources than Bruno's Chirurgia; at any rate it showed more independence. William also wrote a general treatise on medicine. His most illustrious pupil was Lanfranchi who practised in Milano until his banishment c. 1290, when he carried the Bolognese traditions to France. Lanfranchi's Chirurgia magna was dedicated in 1296 to Philip le Bel: it was full of novelties, genuine clinical cases well described.

The history of surgery is closely associated with that of anatomy, for the surgeon's anatomical knowledge must be far deeper than that of the ordinary physician. Whether this was due to the influence of a great surgeon who was also a great physician, like William of Saliceto, or to the influence of medical progress in general, at any rate we have proofs that human dissections were made in this period. The earlier Latin anatomies were based upon the dissection of pigs. Of course surgeons would obtain some direct knowledge of the human body in the very exercise of their art. Human dissections of the living and of the dead were prepared for them by the accidents of life. But outside of that there are some traces of formal dissection in the Cyrurgia of William of Saliceto. By the way, that great work may be said to contain the earliest account of topographical anatomy. Strangely enough another reason for the introduction of human dissections at this time was legal. Bologna was the greatest center of legal teaching in Christendom. It is not surprising that some teachers realized the legal value of post mortem evidence and took pains to obtain such evidence. Post mortems are referred to by Taddeo Alderotti, and by the chronicler Salimbene of Parma (1286); however, the earliest formal account of an autopsy which has come down to us—one made by Bartholomew of Varignana—dates only from 1302.

It is not true that the Catholic Church prohibited human dissections, but it very wisely surrounded them with restrictions. It is true however that the Church was strongly prejudiced against them, and this was natural enough. The same prejudices were felt with greater force by Muslims and Jews. They help to explain the low social status of surgeons on the one side, and the very slow progress of anatomical studies on the other. There are a number of anatomical discoveries which implied no special difficulties and would certainly have been made much earlier than they were if dissections had been more frequent, less frowned upon, less hurried.

Besides some chapters in the medical and surgical textbooks and the encyclopaedias, we have no anatomical treatise of this time, except one, ascribed to Giles of Rome. That treatise, largely derived from Ibn Rushd, would hardly deserve mention but for the fact that it is one of the very few which may have been known to Leonardo da Vinci.

Let us now consider physicians who were not surgeons. John of Parma composed a little medical handbook of no special importance. A general treatise on hygiene was written in French by Aldobrandin of Siena, for Beatrice, countess of Provence. It was very popular. Simon of Genoa, papal archiater, compiled a dictionary of materia medica which remained a standard work until the sixteenth century.

A new vein was opened by Taddeo Alderotti. Under the all-pervading influence of the legal school of Bologna, physicians attempted to express their views in the way which was considered proper by the learned jurists and theologians. Perhaps they were afraid of appearing to be ignorant themselves! How fast, or rather how slowly, that evolution took place, we do not know, but we are provided with excellent examples of the new style in the writings of Taddeo Alderotti of Florence. The remarkable thing is that these scholastic tendencies did not entirely pervert and sterilize Taddeo's thought. In fact his Consilia contain excellent clinical observations. Taddeo has the strange distinction of being at once the renovator of clinical literature in Christendom, and the first scholastic physician! He was very learned, somewhat of a humanist, and at the same time a wealthy practitioner.

The scholastic approach to medicine was carried a step further first by William Corvi, and then by Peter of Abano. William was nicknamed Aggregator, after the title of his main work which is a large collection of medical opinions on every kind of disease. The habit of writing consilia was growing, and many have been preserved under his name.

It is clear that the Italian school of medicine was very flourishing. Its influence was soon felt in other countries, especially in France which promptly became a secondary center of diffusion of Bolognese medicine. The main carriers of Italian medicine across the Alps were Aldobrandin of Siena, Lanfranchi of Milan, and William Corvi. The influence of the first named was natural enough, for his Régime du corps was written in French, and he was physician to a French princess, and later possibly to her son-in-law, St. Louis; he died in Champagne, 1287. Lanfranchi was exiled from Milan by the Visconti c. 1290; he practised in Lyon and other provincial cities, and finally in Paris where he seems to have given a really clinical teaching; he may be called the father of French surgery. William Corvi went to Avignon with his patron Clement V in 1309, and continued to reside for a while in Avignon, finally moving to Paris, where he died c. 1326. This has taken us into the fourteenth century, when Italian medicine was already well rooted in France and was producing fruits which were typically French.

To return to the thirteenth century, the influence of Bologna was not restricted to France. A curious example of its internationalism is given by that unnamed Lombard physician who gave so much pain to John of Montecorvino in Cambaluc![22]

(b) France. We have already crossed the Alps together with Aldobrandin, Lanfranchi, and Corvi. The new medical ideas which they introduced into France would eventually find there a rich soil for their further growth, but this took considerable time. Italy continued—even in the first half of the fourteenth century—to be the leading country. Few French physicians distinguished themselves in the second half of the thirteenth century; none reached the level of their Italian tutors.

It is possible that the Salernitan, Walter Agilinus, was still living in the latter half of this century. A medical summary in 456 chapters forms a part of the Speculum doctrinale of Vincent of Beauvais. A poem on venesection is ascribed to one John of Aquila, who was probably a French physician of this period. A commentary on the surgical treatises of Roger of Salerno and Roland of Parma, called Glossulae quatuor magistrorum, was possibly composed in France during the seventh decade. This question is full of difficulties. Did the "four masters" actually exist? Or if they did, is it not more likely that they were Salernitans of Roger's or Roland's own time, whose opinions were edited by the unknown author of these Glossulae?

[22] C. R. Beazley: Dawn of modern geography (vol. 3, 170, 1906).

The main French doctor, John of Saint Amand, hailed from Tournai in Hainaut; that is, he was what would be called to-day a Belgian. He composed two summaries of Greek and Arabic medicine and materia medica, the one in the form of a commentary on the antidotary of Nicholas of Salerno, whose popularity it shared, the other in the shape of a large compilation entitled Revocativum memoriae. He quoted many Greek and Arabic authorities, most of all, Galen and Ibn Sīnā.

We may still name two doctors of Montpellier, plus one Limousin, and one Parisian. The Montpelliérains were Peter of Capestang, who wrote a short regimen and was interested in the translation of Ibn Zuhr's Taisīr; and Armengaud son of Blaise, who translated from the Arabic (or from the Hebrew?) medical treatises of Galen, Ibn Sīnā, and Maimonides. Peter of Limoges wrote a Tractatus de oculo morali which, as the title suggests, deals primarily with ethics, yet includes a summary of ophthalmology. John Pitart, surgeon to Philip le Bel, is said to have founded the College of Saint Côme (a surgical training school) in Paris, in 1271. That is uncertain, but the school may date back to this period. I shall deal more fully with it and with Pitart in volume 3.

Most of that French medicine was out of date as compared with the Bolognese, and to know the latest discoveries the best that the French could do was to listen to the Italian exiles in their midst, especially Lanfranchi and Corvi.

(c) Spain. There are a number of Spanish treatises on farriery and veterinary medicine which may date from this time. The dating is made more plausible by the publication of various treatises of the same kind in Sicily, but it is unproved and requires further investigation.

The three main physicians of the Hispanic peninsula were not Spaniards proper; one of them was a Portuguese, the two others Catalans.

Peter of Spain, who sat in St. Peter's chair for eight months (1276–1277) under the name of John XXI, wrote many medical treatises, notably his Treasure of the poor, which was perhaps the most popular of medical books down to the Renaissance, and a treatise on eye-diseases. He had made a deep study of the Greco-Arabic knowledge available in Latin, witness his commentaries on Hippocrates, Galen, Theophilos Protospatharios, Hunain ibn Isḥāq, Isḥāq al-Isrā'īlī, Ibn al-Jazzār.

The medical publications of Arnold of Villanova were far more numerous than those of Peter of Spain (even if one makes allowance for the fact that many of them may be apocryphal), but none enjoyed much popularity, except of course his edition of the Regimen sanitatis. In my list of his writings, which is probably incomplete, I mention some forty-five medical treatises, plus four commentaries on Hippocrates and Galen, plus half a dozen translations from the Arabic—treatises of Galen, al-Kindī, Qusṭā ibn Lūqā, Ibn Sīnā, Abū-l-'Alā' Zuhr, Abū-l-Ṣalt.

There are also quite a few medical treatises bearing the name of Ramon Lull, but their authenticity is uncertain. Ramon was not a physician, but he may easily have thought that he was one, even as some librarians imagine that they know a subject because they happen to be familiar with the catalogue headings relative to it. Ramon's logical illusion was exactly of the same kind; he mistook the frame of knowledge for the reality of it, and unfortunately did not even realize that a good frame or classification cannot be constructed ahead of the knowledge which is going to fill it. The value of a classification depends on the extent and depth of the inductions on which it is based; a purely deductive classification, or one of which the experimental foundation is too slight, is almost worthless. Ramon's medical writings might be dismissed altogether if they did not represent a typical attitude which the historian must take into account.

(d) England. The only English writer on medicine was Bacon. His writings on the subject were not original, except the one dealing with the errors of physicians in which he defended once more the experimental point of view. To be sure this was not a medical treatise proper, but a methodological discussion. Another treatise of his, of no particular value, his mediocre book on how to delay the infirmities of old age, was plagiarized by Arnold of Villanova and enjoyed some popularity.

(e) Flanders. William of Moerbeke translated directly from the Greek into Latin two Hippocratic and Galenic treatises. Some anatomical and medical knowledge was published in Flemish by Jacob van Maerlant, notably in his translation of the De natura rerum of Thomas of Cantimpré.

(f) Central Europe. The commentary on Aristotelian zoology composed by Albert the Great contains an anatomical section very similar to the Anatomia vivorum ascribed to Richard of Wendover. The point to remember in this connection is that Albert's anatomy was largely a reversion to Aristotle's point of view against Galen's. But this strange Aristotelian revival was not to be any more successful in the field of medicine than in that of astronomy. Albert drew interesting comparisons between the anatomical structure of man and that of animals. Sundry medical writings are ascribed to him but their authenticity is uncertain.

There is a German translation, dating probably from this period, of the medical section of the De proprietatibus rerum of Bartholomew the Englishman. It should be noted that the German text published a century later by Conrad of Megenberg was derived mainly from the De natura rerum of Thomas of Cantimpré. Thomas' influence upon Germanic thought, through Maerlant and Megenberg, was much greater than Bartholomew's.

Nicholas of Poland, a Montpellier alumnus, was the author of a medical poem entitled Antipocras. The prose work, Experimenta, ascribed to him is probably apocryphal. Both works are on the same low level: a mixture of the crudest empiricism with all manner of superstition and quackery.

(g) Scandinavia. Peter of Dacia wrote various treatises on bloodletting, medical astrology, and hygiene. An anonymous Danish text of the same time, recently published (1927),[23] is of interest as showing a Scandinavian tradition derived from the Salernitan, and yet somewhat different from the one represented by Henrik Harpestraeng.

2. *Eastern Christians*—(a) Greeks. Boniface of Gerace, who flourished under Charles I of Anjou, composed a treatise on veterinary medicine; it is not known whether it was originally written in Greek or in Latin. I place him here on the first assumption. That assumption is plausible, for there were still Greek speaking people in Calabria at that time; the Latin name Boniface proves nothing, for we would expect Greek and Latin names to be mixed in such a region. I am personally inclined to think that Boniface wrote in Latin, but pending further investigations one assumption is as justified (or unjustified) as the other.

Nicholas Myrepsos compiled an extensive materia medica called Dynameron. It was an elaboration of the Salernitan antidotary, including 2656 recipes. An abridged Latin translation of it remained the standard pharmacopoeia in Paris

[23] Isis, vol. 10, 128.

down to the middle of the sixteenth century. Myrepsos had flourished at the Nicaean court, but he lived at least until 1277, and his Dynameron was only completed toward the end of his life.

Demetrios Pepagomenos, whose treatises on hawks and dogs have already been mentioned, was physician to Michael Palaeologos. He wrote a good book on gout, the essential nature of which was recognized by him. His treatises on hawks and dogs dealt also with the diseases of these animals. It may be remarked here, once for all, that every treatise on falconry or hunting contained a good amount of veterinary information. Trained falcons were very valuable animals, and they were liable to various accidents and ailments which their owners were anxious to remedy. For example, Demetrios' treatise includes remarkable helminthological observations.

A treaties on uroscopy is ascribed to Maximos Planudes.

(b) Syrians. Abū-l-Faraj is said to have translated medical treatises of Ḥunain ibn Isḥāq and al-Ghāfiqī into Syriac, to have begun a translation of Ibn Sīnā's Qānūn, and to have written commentaries on Hippocrates, Dioscorides, and Galen. None of these works have come down to us, but the ascription of some of them at least to Abū-l-Faraj is plausible enough. He was the greatest teacher of his people, the transmitter to them of Greek and Arabic knowledge, and the medical part of that knowledge was the one the transmission of which was most urgent.

3. *Western Jews*—At this time western Jews were busily translating Arabic works into Hebrew. Solomon ibn Ayyub translated Ibn Sīnā's medical poem. Shem-ṭob ben Isaac translated two of the greatest works of the Arabic medical literature, the Taṣrīf of Abū-l-Qāsim al-Zahrāwī in 1258, and the Manṣūrī of al-Rāzī in 1264. (Another Hebrew translation of the Taṣrīf was made at about the same time by Meshullam ben Jonah.) Three years later he began a version of Hippocrates' Aphorisms, including Palladios' commentary of which only a few fragments are known to us in Greek. Other Arabic medical works he copied in Hebrew script. Zeraḥiah Gracian translated writings of Galen and Maimonides, and the first two books of Ibn Sīnā's Qānūn. Moses ibn Tibbon translated writings of al-Rāzī, Ḥunain ibn Isḥāq, Ibn al-Jazzār, Ibn Sīnā, Maimonides; Nathan ha-Me'ati translated writings of Hippocrates, Galen, Ibn Sīnā, 'Ammar ibn 'Alī, Maimonides, etc. The most important of Nathan's translations was that of the whole Qānūn completed at Rome, 1279. Another translation of his, that of Galen's commentary on the Hippocratic treatise on airs, waters and places, was completed by his son Solomon in 1299. Samuel ben Jacob of Capua translated the treatise on purgatives and emetics of Māsawaih al-Māridīnī.

Most of the Arabic (or Greco-Arabic) works I have quoted were already available to Christian physicians in Latin. The superiority of Latin culture is illustrated by the fact that a contemporary Latin treatise was almost immediately translated into Hebrew; I refer to the Chirurgia magna of Bruno da Longoburgo translated into Hebrew by Hillel ben Samuel. A more extraordinary case was that of Solomon ben Moses of Melgueil, who translated from Latin into Hebrew not only the Circa instans of Platearius, but also some writings of Aristotle, Ibn Sīnā, and Ibn Rushd! Of course that was a real aberration, from which no conclusion can be drawn. In truth, the intellectual relations between Jews and Christians were very complex. Generally speaking the Christians were now a little ahead, because Arabic literature had become more completely available to them than it was to the non-Arabic reading Jews. Yet they had not yet exhausted the Arabic sources, and when they wanted to go back to these they still needed Jewish assistance. In other words it was always simpler for Jews to study the Arabic originals; even if they had forgotten their Arabic it was a good deal easier for them than for the Latins to learn or relearn it. Thus we are not too surprised to find Abraham ben Shem-ṭob translating treatises of Abū-l-Qāsim and Ibn Sarābī and possibly others from Arabic (or Hebrew?) into Latin.

These translators were so absorbed in their task that they had little time or inclination for more original work. However, Solomon ibn Ayyub wrote a treatise on haemorrhoids at Béziers, in 1265. Shem-ṭob's version of the Taṣrīf was rather free and he added a philosophical introduction to it. Abraham ben Shem-ṭob composed a medical summary. By far the most ambitious of these Hebrew medical works was the Ẓori ha-guf of Nathan ben Joel Falaquera, a large collection of medical aphorisms of Greco-Arabic origin. A small treatise on pathology was written by an unknown author who was perhaps his pupil.

4. *Eastern Jews and Samaritans*—There is the best of reasons for separating the Eastern Jews from the Western ones; that is, the separation between them was now more complete than ever, and almost comparable to the abyss separating the Greeks from the Latins. Not quite as great however, for with the exception of the Qaraites and of course of the Samaritans, there was not much religious difference between the Eastern and Western Jews. There was really no conflict between them, but they could not understand one another for they spoke and wrote different languages. The western Jews after having crossed the Pyrenees had become more and more westernized. Many of them spoke European vernaculars and understood Latin; yet they wrote in Hebrew. The Eastern Jews spoke and wrote in Arabic; Hebrew was for them simply a religious and liturgical language. But for the initial doxology, their Arabic writings are hardly distinguishable from those written by Muslims. I would have combined my account of them with that of the Muslims, even as I did for Arabic writing Christians, but for the fact that they were sufficiently numerous to form a separate group, and that the contrast between Western and Eastern Jews deserved to be brought out.

These Eastern Jews, most of them Egyptians, nay Cairenes, formed a fine group indeed. There was first al-Kūhīn al-'Aṭṭār, whose pharmacopoeia, the Minhāj, was a very popular book in the Arabic East, and still is. Ibn Kammūna, who embraced Islām later in life, wrote a treatise on eye diseases. Solomon Kohen, possibly a Qaraite, compiled a medical encyclopaedia. Ibn al-Bishr composed a medical poem. The first three were Egyptians; I do not know the nationality of the last one.

There was also a Samaritan, yclept Muwaffaq al-dīn, established with the rest of his coreligionists in Damascus, who wrote a commentary on the generalities of Ibn Sīnā's Qānūn.

5. *Muslims*—(All of these Muslims were Easterners; an Arabic speaking Christian is included among them.) The group of Muslim physicians of Syria and Egypt was even more remarkable than that of their Jewish colleagues.

The great medical treatise of Ibn Ṭarkhān, dealt with in Book III, may date only from this period, for the author lived until 1291. Ibn al-Quff composed books on hygiene and surgery, and wrote commentaries on the Hippocratic aphorisms and on the Qānūn of Ibn Sīnā. This Ibn al-Quff was a Christian, but it is clear that he did not attend upon his coreligionists only, for his surgery contains an elaborate treatment of circumcision. Ibn al-Nafīs, a pupil of Ibn Dakhwār of Damascus, became even more famous than his teacher. He wrote treatises on eye diseases and on diet, and commentaries on Hippocrates and Ibn Sīnā. His commentary on the Qānūn, Mūjiz al-qānūn, enjoyed a long popularity; witness the number of manuscripts, oriental editions, supercommentaries in Arabic and Persian, and translations into Hebrew and Turkish. Finally we have two very distinguished ophthalmologists, Khalīfa ibn abī-l-Maḥāsin and Ṣalāḥ al-dīn ibn Yūsuf. The treatises written by them remained without equivalent in the West almost until the nineteenth century. Manuscripts of Khalīfa's treatise are illustrated with remarkable schematic figures representing the brain, eyes, eye nerves, etc. That iconography was also far ahead of western achievements. To be sure these treatises on eye diseases were not very original; they marked the climax of the long development of Arabic oculistics, itself derived from Greek models; but both doctors, especially Khalīfa, were men of considerable clinical experience.

A great treatise on veterinary medicine was composed by Ibn al-Mundhir al-Baiṭār, but as it dates more probably from the beginning of the following century we shall postpone its discussion until the next volume.

All of these men were Egyptians or Syrians, which amounts to the same thing, for both countries were then united under the strong rule of the salāṭīn of the Baḥrī Mamlūk dynasty. A tangible proof of the medical interest of these rulers may still be seen in Cairo to-day; I am referring to the remains of the great hospital built by the sulṭān Qalā'ūn (1279–1290): The Bīmāristān al-Manṣūrī is the earliest Muslim hospital of which the building is still partly extant; it was a huge structure, including not only the hospital proper with all the necessary annexes and appurtenances, but also a school and mosque.

I found no traces of medical creative activity in other eastern countries, except in Persia. It is clear that Nāṣir al-dīn al-Ṭūsī had some medical knowledge. Was he not a great astrologer? And astrology was then the main part of scientific medicine; an expert astrologer might have the same confidence in himself which a young doctor of to-day would derive from a serious training in chemistry and physics. Quṭb al-dīn's interest in medicine was far deeper than his master's. This was largely due to his long stay in Egypt during Qalā'ūn's reign. He composed a commentary on the generalities of Ibn Sīnā's Qānūn, and various other medical treatises.

6. *Hindus*—The account of medical work in other regions of the East need not detain us very long. The iatrochemical treatise of Śārṅgadhara which I placed in the first half of the century may belong to the second half, but this is less probable because a commentary on it was already written by Vopadeva, who flourished in the seventh decade of that century. Two other Hindu physicians, Tīsaṭācārya and his son Candraṭa, were possibly contemporaries of Vopadeva. Tīsaṭa wrote a medical summary, and his son added a commentary to it. Finally the jurist Hemādri wrote a commentary on Vāgbhaṭa.

7. *Chinese*—Various medical works were composed by Li Kao in 1232 (?) and 1276. The Nestorian doctor, 'Isā the Mongol, who was employed by Kuyuk Khān and later by Kublai Khān, seems to have practiced medicine as well as astronomy.

8. *Japanese*—The veterinary surgeon Seia prepared with the collaboration of an artist a set of illustrations representing seventeen herbs recommended for the cure of horse complaints. Koremune Tomotoshi compiled an index to the Chinese pên ts'ao of 1108 which remained the standard one in Japan until the beginning of the seventeenth century.

Summary

In our final appraisement of the medical achievement of this period, we must bear in mind, for the sake of fairness, that medical progress as we are able to register it to-day, year after year, was entirely impossible and unthinkable until relatively recent times. The outstanding medical advances have been due to the gradual invasion of the medical art by outside sciences—chemistry, physics, bacteriology, etc. With some pardonable exaggeration one might say that medicine progressed by ceasing to be what it was and surrendering its territory to other disciplines absolutely different from its own. Without the marvelous instruments which modern physicists have given to mankind, such as high-power microscopes, polarimeters, spectroscopes, sensitive manometers and galvanometers, X-ray and radium tubes, etc., the physician was essentially an artist, not a scientist; his main props were his experience, and his common sense, his clinical intuition. To be sure, these have kept their full value to this day, and no manner of instrument will ever make up for the lack of wisdom. However, during the Middle Ages the physician had no help whatever but what he could find or hoped to find in books; no scientific guidance of any kind, except unfortunately a wrong one.

The reader has already guessed that I am now referring to astrology. Belief in the principles of astrology was universal. It would not have occurred to any mediaeval physician to question these principles any more than to a modern one to doubt the indications of a good thermometer. The only differences of opinion concerned the application of these principles, which varied a great deal according to the degree of wisdom and honesty, and the scientific education of each practitioner. The majority of them were probably too ignorant to have a real understanding of astrology; the chances are they did not broadcast the fact, but applied blindly the astrological rules published in many textbooks. In this they were not worse than the modern physicians who use their instruments in a purely empirical way without any real grasp of the methods involved. The point to remember is that the most scientific physicians, those who were looked up to by their humbler colleagues, were the main defenders of astrological medicine. This was the great tragedy of mediaeval medicine: not that its scientific armature was small, but that it was awry.

If we analyze all the circumstances, we realize that this could hardly be helped. The main result is that physicians were groping in the dark with no better guide than their own wisdom. But each of them, and chiefly the best of them, could not quench the hope that some other guidance would be found in the books of the ancients—those illustrious Greek and Arabic physicians whose authority had become legendary. Of course these hopes were continually disappointed but they resurrected each time like the phoenix out of their own ashes. This explains that, next to astrology, the foremost activity of many of the leaders consisted in translating the ancient books or writing commentaries and supercommentaries on them.

We have already dealt with a part of the astrological literature in the astronomical chapter. Let us now consider the "authorities," to the discussion of which so much energy was devoted.

A number of classics were translated: the Hippocratic Aphorisms from Arabic into Hebrew by Nathan ha-Me'ati and Shem-ṭob ben Isaac; the treatise on Airs, waters, and places, with Galen's commentary, by Nathan ha-Me'ati; the Prognosticon, from Greek into Latin by William of Moerbeke. Galenic and pseudo-Galenic writings were translated from Arabic into Latin by Arnold of Villanova, Faraj ben Salīm, Armengaud son of Blaise; from Arabic into Hebrew by Zeraḥiah Gracian; from Greek into Latin by Moerbeke. A large number of Muslim treatises were also translated, too many to quote them. It will suffice to mention the more notable: The Isagoge ad tegni of Ḥunain ibn Isḥāq was translated from Arabic into Hebrew by Moses ibn Tibbon. The Kitāb al-Manṣūrī of al-Rāzī was translated into Hebrew in 1264 by Shem-ṭob ben Isaac, and fifteen years later the gigantic Ḥāwī (Continens) became available to Latin readers thanks to Faraj ben Salīm. Another encyclopaedia of Muslim medicine, the Taṣrīf of Abū-l-Qāsim al-Zahrāwī, was translated into Hebrew at least twice, by Shem-ṭob ben Isaac in 1258, and by Meshullam ben Jonah; a third translation of it is ascribed to Nathan ha-Me'ati; finally a part was translated from Hebrew into Latin by Abraham ben Shem-ṭob. The first two books of Ibn Sīnā's Qānūn were put into Hebrew by Zeraḥiah Gracian, and the whole of it by Nathan ha-Me'ati (Rome 1279). Of course other books of the prince of physicians were translated, above all his popular Arjūzat (Cantica), but I shall only mention the De viribus cordis Latinized by Arnold of Villanova. A Hebrew version of the Kitāb al-aghdhiya of Ibn Zuhr is ascribed to Nathan ha-Me'ati; his magnum opus, the Taisīr, was translated from the Hebrew into Latin by John of Capua, then again by Paravicius.

So much for Muslim medicine. There were also many translations of the medical writings of Maimonides: from Arabic into Hebrew by Zeraḥiah Gracian, Nathan ha Me'ati, Moses ibn Tibbon; and from Hebrew into Latin by John of Capua and Armengaud son of Blaise.

I have already drawn the reader's attention to the fact that the translations into Hebrew were far more important than those into Latin, but that was simply due to the fact that many of these works had long been available to Latin readers. To visualize the whole situation we might liken the transmission of knowledge to streams of water running from higher places to lower ones. The Greek sources were at the top, then below the Arabic, much lower still the Latin and Hebrew. Now at this time the Latin level was already a little superior to the Hebrew one, so that additional streamlets were beginning to trickle from the former to the latter. For example, the Chirurgia magna of Bruno da Longoburgo was translated from Latin into Hebrew by Hillel ben Samuel.

To continue our metaphor, we might conceive lower levels still, represented by various European vernaculars. Secondary transmissions were now in full swing: veterinary books appeared in Italian and Spanish, Arabic knowledge was vulgarized into French by Aldobrandin of Siena; the encyclopaedia of Thomas of Cantimpré was put into Flemish by Jacob van Maerlant, and that of Bartholomew the Englishman into German by an unknown scholar; Danish versions were prepared by Peter of Dacia and others. To be sure these Italian, Spanish, French, Dutch, German, and Danish treatises were of a popular kind and were somewhat behind the times, but this was unavoidable. Their existence marked nevertheless a great progress in the diffusion of knowledge. The general ignorance and darkness were being gradually—very slowly but steadily—alleviated.

Thus far I have spoken only of translations. Similar efforts were made in the form of commentaries on Hippocrates, Galen, Ibn Sīnā and other Muslim authors, Maimonides, etc. Some of the commentaries were not more original than the translations, others on the contrary might be more original than the self-styled original treatises. One must never decide such matters a priori.

The immense importance attached to what might be called the literary aspect of medicine led naturally to the composition of bulky treatises wherein all the medical problems were reviewed, and as many authorities as possible quoted. Many treatises which remained standard books for centuries date from this very time. Here are a few of them, leaving naturally out of account the encyclopaedias on the one hand and the more special medical books on the other: The Tadhkirat al-hādiya of Ibn Ṭarkhān, the Régime du corps of Aldobrandin of Siena (1256), the Mūjiz al-qānūn of Ibn al-Nafīs, the Ẓori ha-guf of Nathan ben Joel Falaquera, the Thesaurus pauperum of Peter of Spain, the Revocativum memoriae of John of Saint Amand, the Aggregator of William Corvi, the Regimen sanitatis edited by Arnold of Villanova (1307). And to these might be added a series of textbooks on materia medica: the Minhāj of al-Kūhīn al-'Aṭṭar (1259), the Dynameron of Nicholas Myrepsos (c. 1280), the Honzō iroha shō of Koremune Tomotoshi (1282), the Synonyma medicinae of Simon of Genoa (c. 1290), the Expositio super antidotarium Nicolai of John of Saint Amand.

Another characteristic of the age was the more systematic application, under the influence of the law school of Bologna, of scholastic methods to medical teaching. The main exponents of this new scholastic medicine were Taddeo Alderotti and William Corvi, to be followed a little later just after the turn of the century by Peter of Abano. Under the influence of the Aristotelian organon a different form of the same dialectical tendency found expression and was carried almost to the point of absurdity in the writings of Ramon Lull.

Let us pass now to special branches of medicine. The one which progressed most during this period was surgery. A brilliant school developed in northern Italy: Hugh and Theodoric Borgognoni, Bruno da Longoburgo, William of Saliceto, Lanfranchi. The last named carried their methods across the Alps to Paris. The foundation of the Parisian school of surgeons, the Collège and Confrérie de Saint Côme (St. Cosmas' college and guild), may be dated back to about this time. At any rate Lanfranchi taught in Paris before the end of the century and his teaching was to some extent of a clinical nature.

The tradition of human dissection which had been lost since the days of the great school of Alexandria was revived in northern Italy during this period (if not before), and the anatomical renaissance of the fourteenth century was thus prepared. Mondino de' Luzzi, who will be fully discussed in volume 3, was a child of the thirteenth century; he was born in Bologna c. 1275, but his work belongs entirely to the following period. Inasmuch as we have denounced the evil influence of the law school of Bologna, we must point out also its good influence: it was partly thanks to it that post mortem autopsies were introduced, and the medical value of such autopsies cannot be exaggerated.

The branch of medicine next in importance was ophthalmology; but while surgical progress was exclusively due to Christians, and more specifically to northern Italians, ophthalmological progress was due almost exclusively to Syrian Muslims. To be sure treatises on eye diseases were written by other people; for example by Christians like Peter of Spain and Peter of Limoges, or by an Egyptian Jew, Ibn Kammūna; the old treatise of 'Ammar ibn 'Alī was translated into Hebrew by Nathan ha-Me'ati; but the really progressive and creative works were composed in Arabic by two Syrians. I am referring to the Kāfī fī-l-kuḥl of Khalīfa ibn abī-l-Maḥāsin (c. 1265), and to the Nūr al-'uyūn of Ṣalāḥ al-dīn ibn Yūsuf (in or after 1296). No work comparable to these was produced in western Europe until almost the nineteenth century.

Of treatises referring to special diseases I remember only two; a Hebrew one on haemorrhoids by Solomon ibn Ayyub (1265), and a Greek one on gout by Demetrios Pepagomenos.

Much attention was paid to the veterinary art; witness treatises in Latin, Italian, Spanish, Arabic, to which must be added a number of books on hunting and falconry in Latin, French, Catalan, Greek, and perhaps in other languages—for these books always contained some sections dealing with the ailments of falcons and other animals and with the means of curing them.

Though the achievements of the age with regard to new discoveries were small, such discoveries were being prepared by patient work. I have already given an example of this: the revival of human dissections was paving the way for a new anatomical advance. In a similar way the growing favor of clinical observations, such as had been recorded in the best Hippocratic writings, was making possible new medical progress in the future. Such observations were collected in the form of consilia by Taddeo Alderotti and William Corvi. Many were made by surgeons who were thus helping the improvement not only of their own art, but of the whole of medicine.

The most distinguished physicians were Faraj ben Salīm, Jordan Ruffo, Bruno da Longoburgo, William of Saliceto, Lanfranchi, Aldobrandin of Siena, Simon of Genoa, Taddeo Alderotti, William Corvi, John of Saint Amand, Nicholas Myrepsos, Peter of Spain, Arnold of Villanova, Bacon, Shem-ṭob ben Isaac, Zeraḥiah Gracian, Moses ibn Tibbon, Nathan ha-Me'ati, al-Kūhīn al-'Aṭṭār, Ibn al-Quff, Ibn al-Nafīs, Khalīfa ibn abī Maḥāsin, Ṣalāḥ al-dīn ibn Yūsuf, Quṭb al-dīn al-Shīrāzī, Koremune Tomotoshi. A fine array of men! Twenty-five of them: thirteen Christians, six Jews, five Muslims, one Japanese. Or to put it otherwise: ten Italians, five Syro-Egyptians, four Spaniards, two Frenchmen, and one each of the following countries: England, Byzantium, Persia, and Japan. The most striking fact is the immense preponderance of Italy (which would still be increased if the names were weighted); the next country in medical importance was the Mamlūk kingdom of Syria and Egypt. The main medical centers were Bologna and Cairo, then Damascus, Montpellier and Paris. The surgical and anatomical progress and the best consilia came from Bologna; ophthalmological progress from Damascus (or Cairo).

XII. HISTORIOGRAPHY

It is not necessary to give any but the briefest account of the historiography of this period, because the value of the many chronicles mentioned cannot be properly appreciated. Each one of them may be inestimable in its own field, but it is difficult to say for example, that this, Catalan, chronicle is more important than that other, Scandinavian. It will suffice to give the reader some idea of the efforts made by several countries to record past events.

1. *Western Christendom*—(a) Italy. The French "Livres dou tresor" of Brunetto Latini include a historical summary down to 1260 (1268). Rolandino of Padua wrote a Latin chronicle of Italian events from 1200 to 1260, dealing mainly with the infamous tyrant Ecelino III da Romano. Fra Salimbene composed a Latin chronicle dealing with the years 1167–1287, which is valuable for the history of Lombardy and of the Franciscan Order and contains an unusual amount of miscellaneous information. Who does not know the Golden Legend of James of Voragine? We owe the same writer a chronicle of Genoa from the dimmest begin-

nings to 1297. In spite of the fact that the Golden Legend is worthless from a purely scientific standpoint, a book which enjoyed such an immense popularity must be seriously considered in any appraisal of mediaeval thought.

Needless to say, the writings of Ricoldo di Monte Croce and other travelers to the East were also to some extent contributions to historiography. Please refer for them to the geographical section.

(b) Spain. The greatest historian of Castile and León was the king, Alfonso X el Sabio. The first national history of Spain was compiled by him or by his order in Castilian on the basis of Arabic and Latin sources. Other historical works are ascribed to him. His father-in-law, Jaime el Conquistador, king of Aragon, was the first Catalan chronicler; he was followed by a greater one, the mysterious Bernat Desclot.

(c) France. This is a sort of interlude in French historiography: the time of Villehardouin is past, that of Joinville has not yet come. For though Joinville was a man of the thirteenth century (he was seventy-six years old at the end of it), the writings which have immortalized his name date only from the fourteenth.

The most pretentious historical work of this period was the Speculum historiale of Vincent of Beauvais. This was a universal history with special emphasis on religious and ecclesiastical events, extending to the middle of the century.

William of Puylaurens wrote a Latin account of the Albigensian crusade, representing a moderate point of view. William of Nangis, monk of Saint Denis, wrote a series of official chronicles of France, mostly in Latin, a shorter one in French. His main work was a universal chronicle to the end of the century, which was thrice continued by others.

(d) England. One of the greatest Christian chroniclers was Matthew Paris, monk of St. Albans. I have already pointed out the value of his geographical studies. His Chronica magna (to 1259) was much broader than the local chronicles which it continued; it contains valuable information on many continental events. Thanks to his scientific curiosity, his writings are unusually rich in observations concerning meteorology and natural history.

Robert of Gloucester wrote in English a metrical chronicle of England to 1270, the earlier part largely derived from Geoffrey of Monmouth.

(e) Low Countries. Jacob of Maerlant composed a free translation of the Speculum historiale in Flemish verse (90000 lines!). He added to it various interpolations concerning the Low Countries.

A remarkable attempt to fix historical dates by reference to eclipses and other such phenomena was made by Giles of Lessines in his Concordia temporum. This is, as far as I know, the only treatise on chronology of this period; and in a sense it belongs already to the following period for it stops at the year of his death, 1304, but Giles was then about seventy-four years old.

(f) Germany. Hermann of Nieder-Altaich compiled annals dealing mainly with Bavaria, Austria, and Bohemia for the period 1137–1273.

Martin of Troppau, wrongly called Martin the Pole, compiled chronological tables of the popes and emperors which were immensely popular in spite of their mediocrity.

(g) Hungary. Simon of Kéza wrote a history of the Huns and the Magyars from Nimrod's time down to 1282.

(h) Scandinavia. Of all the historical writings of this age in Christendom, the most impressive are those of Sturla Thórdarson, a nephew of Snorri Sturluson.

He wrote in Icelandic the saga of his own illustrious family, and later the sagas of the Norwegian kings, Hákon Hákonarson and Magnús Hákonarson. Other sagas of about the same time—dealing, e.g., with Denmark or with the Orkney Islands—are equally remarkable, but we do not know the names of their authors. These are all excellently written with a matter-of-factness, a directness and terseness which are truly refreshing.

2. *Eastern Christendom*—(a) Byzantium. What a contrast between those rugged but beautiful sagas, and the rhetorical exercises of Theodoros II Lascaris. It is not simply a literary contrast, for it reflects the opposition of two types of civilization. The emperor wrote eulogies of Frederick II, of his father John Ducas Batatzes, of Georgios Acropolites, etc., and would probably have left us many more but for an untimely death.

The chronicle of Nicetas Acominatos was continued by Georgios Acropolites for the years 1204–1261—i.e., for the duration of the Latin empire—and by Georgios Pachymeres for the years 1261–1308. A good part of these chronicles is naturally devoted to the theological discussions which were engrossing and sterilizing Byzantine thought.

Nicephoros Blemmydes composed autobiographies, and the acts of foundation (*τυπικά*) of monasteries established by Michael Palaeologos contain also autobiographical and historical information.

Maximos Planudes wrote a biography of Ptolemy, put together an anthology of historical extracts, and translated into Greek Caesar's account of the Gallic war.

(b) Armenia. A whole series of Armenian chroniclers belong to this period. Cyriacus of Gandzak wrote a summary of Armenian history from the times of Gregory the Illuminator to his own. It includes accounts of the destruction of Ānī by the Mongols in 1239, and of king Hayton's journey to Mongolia. A schoolmate of Cyriacus, the monk Malachiah, wrote a chronicle of the Mongol invasions of Armenia down to 1272. Vardan the Great caused the Syriac chronicle of Michael the Elder to be translated into Armenian (he may have done a share of that translation himself), and he wrote a universal chronology, naturally centered on his country, down to c. 1270. Stephen Orbelian recorded the history of his own illustrious family, one of the oldest and most powerful of Armenia. It is in fact a fragmentary history of Armenia from Adam down to 1290. Stephen was a staunch defender of the Armenian church against Roman and Greek sympathizers. His attitude required considerable courage, for toward the end of the century under the pressure exerted by the kings of Armenia, the catholicos Gregory VII proclaimed his allegiance to the Roman church. Vahram of Edessa continued the rhymed chronicle of Nerses the Graceful down to 1289. Mekhitar of Aïri-vankh composed another Armenian chronicle down to the same year.

The most striking feature of the best of these Armenian chronicles is the variety of their sources. Their main stock was derived from Syriac chronicles for the general events, and from earlier Armenian chronicles for the local ones. But they derived additional information from Arabic, Persian, and even Mongolian documents.

(c) Syria. Abū-l-Faraj's main work was a Syriac chronicle including a universal history down to 1286 and an ecclesiastical history which is one of the outstanding sources for the study of oriental Christendom. He also wrote an Arabic abridgment of the lay history, which was far better known than the Syriac original. He derived his abundant information from Syriac, Arabic and Persian documents.

A complete survey of the Christian historiography of this period should include an account of the works of two Arabic-writing Christians with whom I shall deal presently in the Arabic section, Ibn al-Rāhib al-Qibṭī and Ibn al-'Amīd al-Makīn.

3. *Western Israel*—The Perush ha-Torah of Naḥmanides contains information on Palestinian archaeology (e.g., numismatics). Benjamin 'Anav's messages (sheliḥot) recite many facts concerning Jewish persecutions in France and Italy.

4. *Western Islām*—Ibn al-Abbār, who wrote biographies of the learned men of Spain, was dealt with in Book III, but he died only in 1260. Other biographies—western and eastern—were compiled by the traditionalist and traveler, Muḥammad ibn Rushaid.

Ibn Sa'īd al-Maghribī completed two chronicles begun by his father, the one dealing with the West, the other with the East. He also wrote a history of pre-Islāmic Arabia, but perhaps his most valuable historical data must be looked for in his geographical treatise; e.g., a reference to the thirty-six libraries which he had visited in Baghdād before the Mongol invasion.

Ibn al-'Idhārī al-Marrākushī wrote a history of Africa and Spain which contains the best account of the Umayyads of Cordova.

Muḥammad ibn Rushaid and Ibn al-'Idhārī were two Moroccans; the two others were Spaniards but both died outside of Spain, Ibn al-Abbār of Valencia in Tunis, Ibn Sa'īd of Granada in Damascus or Tunis.

5. *Eastern Islām*—(Excluding Persians but including Arabic-writing Christians.) Egypt and Syria formed then, under Mamlūk rule, but a single country; on the other hand, 'Irāq and Persia were a Mongolian province. It is thus expedient to make two groups of the Eastern Muslim historians: first, the Egyptians and Syrians writing in Arabic, including two Christians; second, the Persians writing in Persian. Each of these groups was more distinguished than any other of the same period; taken together their superiority was enormous.

We have already spoken of the annals of Aleppo compiled by 'Umar Ibn al-'Adīm (d. 1262). A similar work relative to Damascus was published by Abū Shāma, or, more exactly, Abū Shāma continued the immense history of that city begun by Ibn 'Asākir. The same author wrote a history of Nūr al-dīn and Ṣalāh al-dīn ("Saladin"), and added to it later a chronicle of posterior events down to 1266. Another account of Ayyūbid rule was given by Ibn Wāṣil, and was later continued down to 1295 by 'Alī ibn 'Abd al-Raḥmān.

The histories of Aleppo and Damascus above mentioned were largely made up, in the Muslim fashion, of biographies. I have drawn the reader's attention more than once to the Muslim predilection for biographical collections. One of the most valuable for our purpose was the 'Uyūn al-anbā' compiled by Ibn abī Uṣaibi'a c. 1242, but revised by him not long before his death in 1270. Another collection of greater interest to the general reader was the Wafayāt al-a'yān of Ibn Khallikān which dealt not simply with learned men, but distinguished people of every kind. To call Ibn Khallikān an Eastern Boswell is misleading, but his biographies are generally as entertaining as they are accurate, and the collection is unique of its kind. It was continued by two other writers of the fourteenth century, and has remained to this day the best known biographical dictionary of Islām.

We must still consider the two Christians, Ibn al-Rāhib and Ibn al-'Amīd. The propriety of attaching them to the Muslim group may be questioned. At any rate in spite of the fact that their religion singled them out, they were more closely connected with that group than with any other. Even so a modern Syrian living in New York will reflect the American atmosphere rather than that of his own people; that is, as soon as English becomes his habitual language. This is the main point; the two Christians of whom I am going to speak wrote exclusively in Arabic,[24] hence they were in many ways nearer to their Muslim neighbors than to other Eastern Christians (let alone the Western ones).

Ibn al-Rāhib al-Qibṭī wrote a chronicle of eastern history from Adam down to 1258, including an account of the seven ecumenical councils. Another eastern chronicle extending to about the same time (c. 1260) was composed by Ibn al-'Amīd al-Makīn. Its intrinsic value is great chiefly with regard to the many items relating to Eastern Christendom; its extrinsic value is even greater. Partly because of the author's religion, and partly by accident, this was one of the earliest Arabic chronicles to be known in the West, and thus it was the earliest vehicle of relatively accurate knowledge on Muslim affairs. A part of it at least was translated into Ethiopic.

6. *Persia*—The group of Persians is very small, but excellent. Minhāj-i-Sirāj wrote a general history of the Muslim dynasties of Asia down to 1260. He had considerable political experience and was a witness of many of the events described in the last chapters, or at least could obtain first-hand news about them. The last chapter of his work deals with the Mongol invasion.

A greater man, indeed one of the very greatest historians of this time, was al-Juwainī. He wrote annals of the world conqueror (Chingiz Khān), which constitute a history of the Mongols. As he was himself in the Mongol service, had accompanied Hūlāgū in the expedition against the Assassins, and had traveled twice to Mongolia, he was well placed to secure the best inside information. In fact, his work is the main Persian source on the Mongols.

The great theologian, al-Baiḍāwī, wrote a chronology of world history from the creation to 1275.

All these works were written in Persian, but naturally these learned Muslims could also write in Arabic. In fact, the most important works of al-Baiḍāwī—e.g., his famous commentary on the Qur'ān,—were written in that language. Al-Juwainī too would use it occasionally; in the sad autumn of his life, when he suffered one persecution after another, he wrote an Arabic epistle to his brothers. A more interesting case is that of the incomparable poet, Sa'dī, who wrote elegies in Persian and also in Arabic to express his grief over the destruction of the caliphate by the Mongols in 1258.

7. *China*—In 1282 the T'ung chien kang mu (that is, Ssŭ-ma Kuang's annals as revised by Chu Hsi) were translated into Mongolian by order of Kublai Khān.

An account of Hūlāgū's campaigns and of other Mongolian matters was written by Ch'ang Tê. It is of special value as it enables us to complete and check the statements made by European, Armenian and Muslim observers. Chou ta-kuan published in or soon after 1297 a memoir on Cambodian customs, which is very precious indeed, as it is practically our only literary source with regard to that great civilization which was then in its heyday.

Two interesting encyclopaedias date from this time: the one, by Chu Mu, was written in 1246 (?); I place it here because Chu Mu obtained his doctor's degree only in 1256. Which date is the correct one? If both are, then he probably revised later in life the work of his youth. One may write a poem when one is very

[24] The case of Abū-l-Faraj is somewhat different. He could and did occasionally write in Arabic, but his main language was Syriac, an essentially Christian language.

young, but it is more difficult to compile an encyclopaedia. The other was published by Hsieh Wei-hsin in 1257. Both works are essentially collections of quotations.

8. *Japan*—A Japanese chronicle of the period 1180 to 1266, the Azuma-kagami, was edited by an unknown author. I might have included it in the previous section for it was written in Chinese. This was a real retrogression, for at least three other kagami (or mirrors), though dating from the twelfth century, were already composed in Japanese.

Summary

The only kind of conclusion I would venture, and not without diffidence, is an enumeration of the leading historians: Alfonso X, Bernat Desclot, Vincent of Beauvais, Matthew Paris, Giles of Lessines, Sturla Thórdarson, Georgios Acropolites, Georgios Pachymeres, Vardan the Great, Abū-l-Faraj, Ibn al-'Idhārī, Ibn Khallikān, Ibn al-'Amīd al-Makīn, al-Juwainī, Chou Ta-kuan. This selection is somewhat arbitrary, and must be accepted only as a rough approximation. As it is it includes fifteen men: eleven Christians, three Muslims, and one Chinese. Or otherwise: three Hispano-Moroccans, three Syro-Egyptians, two Greeks, and one each of the following countries: France, England, the Netherlands, Scandinavia, Armenia, Persia, and China.

XIII. LAW AND SOCIOLOGY

1. *Italy*—Some of the great legists dealt with in the previous book were still flourishing in the second half of the century. Innocent IV died in 1254, Accorso in 1260, Odofredus in 1265. Another legist of the Bolognese school was Martino da Fano, a pupil of Azo, who wrote a little book of advice for law students. The legal activity of this period is a continuation of that of the preceding one, less brilliant but essentially identical, and the remarks which I made on p. 528 apply to it with little change.

The greatest sociologist and economist of the time, and indeed of the Middle Ages down to this time, was St. Thomas Aquinas. It may be recalled that Aristotle's Politics had been translated from the Greek into Latin by William of Moerbeke at his request. That was in 1260, an important landmark in the history of social philosophy. St. Thomas wrote a commentary on Aristotle's Politics and, as we shall see presently, was deeply and dangerously influenced by it. His views on the subject were also explained in the De regimine principum composed for the young king of Cyprus, and completed after his death by his disciple, Ptolemy of Lucques.

One does not know what to marvel at more in St. Thomas' politics, the prophetic views on government, or the very backward ones on slavery and commerce. The fact that such forwardness and backwardness coexisted in the same brain proves once more the relativity of genius. A man of genius, even one of St. Thomas' size, is after all human and imperfect. However far he may be able to see in one direction or in one sector, he is not necessarily more clear-sighted than his fellowmen with regard to the rest of life. However original he may be, and St. Thomas was very original, he is dependent upon many other men and unable to emancipate himself completely from the teachings to which he has been submitted.

St. Thomas declared that individuals are the only social realities and that the state exists for their good rather than the opposite; he was the apostle of a moderate form of democracy; he even advocated the extension of suffrage to all enlightened citizens. Sovereignty comes from God, but is vested in the people, who delegate it to their rulers and can take it away from them.

On the other hand, under the influence of Aristotle and of the Fathers of the Church, he found that slavery was justified. In this he had much less excuse than Aristotle, for slavery had decreased and changed considerably since the latter's time.[25] The glory that was Greece would have been unrealizable without slavery; in St. Thomas' time its complete suppression would not have jeopardized the existing culture nor caused much economic trouble. Except perhaps in Germany, for a tremendous increase of slavery had taken place during the Ottonian period (second half of the tenth century) when the Slavic populations of beyond the Elbe had been sold wholesale. With that great exception, slavery had dwindled away in western Europe until its nature had changed gradually. It had become almost entirely rural; the remaining slaves or serfs were attached to the glebe. In a purely religious sense the church made but little distinction between slaves and freemen; in the world-to-come that distinction would vanish absolutely, yet in the world-that-was slaves were slaves. The church lightened their misery, but made no attempt to suppress it. In fact it had many slaves of its own, and by a strange paradox these were among the very last to be freed; most emancipations occurred by virtue of the owner's testament, but the church did not die. I hasten to add, lest the reader be misled, that many emancipations, probably most of them, were due to religious influence. With regard to slavery, the church was always better than her own theories. Such was also the case for St. Thomas. He was as charitable as a man can be, yet even the fact that a slave has an immortal soul did not alter in his eyes the essential nature of slavery: a slave was a piece of property like any other, which could not be alienated without the owner's consent.

St. Thomas' attitude toward commerce is equally surprising and repellent to the modern mind. In spite of the tremendous increase in commercial activity which he was privileged to witness, and of the evident social and intellectual progress caused by it, he persisted in considering commerce as evil and vile, and in condemning absolutely the lending of money upon interest (or usury as it was called). If St. Thomas receives full praise for his wise views on society and government, he deserves as well full blame for his deep misunderstanding of business. Thanks to his immense authority, the church opposition to business, even of the most legitimate kind, continued, financial transactions were generally abandoned to Jews and the latter's obloquy was increased in proportion. To be sure in the commercial hubbub of the thirteenth century these fantastic views on commerce were often disregarded by merchants,[26] yet the amount of perverse inhibition which they caused can hardly be exaggerated.

These ideas on the ownership of serfs and money are strange enough, and it is especially shocking to hear them being set forth by the greatest of all Christian philosophers, the philosophical mouthpiece of the Roman church to this day. It

[25] Strictly speaking, it was no longer slavery in the ancient acceptation, but serfage or bondage. There are juridical distinctions between a slave and a serf, but in a broader sense serfs were slaves.

[26] There were of course more means than one of lending money without interest but not without profit. For popular views on the subject before St. Thomas' time, see Le livre des manières ascribed to Stephen of Fougères, bishop of Rennes (d. 1178). Ch. V. Langlois: La vie en France au Moyen âge d'après les moralistes du temps (2d. ed., 12, 16, Paris 1926).

is difficult enough to imagine how such ideas could ever be countenanced by such a wise man, chiefly the combination of them. For according to St. Thomas, the ownership of money was in a way more restricted than that of men. Slaves brought interest, for the children of slaves or serfs were themselves in bondage; money was not allowed to fructify. It was evil to make money work, but lawful to condemn men to lifelong servitude and labor, them and their children!

St. Thomas' De regimine principum was followed by various other books of the same kind. Giles of Rome wrote a treatise bearing the selfsame title, for the future king of France, Philip le Bel. Giles' treatise enjoyed considerable popularity and was eventually translated into French, Hebrew, Italian, Spanish, Catalan, English, Portuguese and Dutch. There are still two other contemporary works answering the same purpose but of unknown authorship: the De informatione principum and the De eruditione principum. In some other writings of his Giles of Rome applied Thomist philosophy to the defense of papal authority.

2. *France*—The Speculum doctrinale of Vincent of Beauvais contained among many other things a summary of the views on law and government which were generally accepted in western Europe about the middle of the century. These views were naturally anterior and inferior to those of St. Thomas. The latter's commentary on Aristotle's Politics was continued by Peter of Auvergne.

Other "mirrors" of the law were composed by William Durand: the Speculum judiciale dealing with Roman and canon law, and the Repertorium juris canonici, following the order of the Decretales. Of course, Durand's fame rests chiefly upon another compendium, the Rationale divinorum officiorum, devoted to the Catholic liturgy, the first non-Biblical work to appear in print (1459).

All of this represents the past, but besides the Roman and canon law there was a living law in constant process of evolution—that is, in each country the law which sanctioned its own changing customs. Some of the most valuable mediaeval attempts at codification were made in this very period. At least four of them may serve to illustrate the juridical genius of France. Stephen Boileau's Livre des métiers (c. 1268) was a collection of all the customs relative to the guilds and trades of Paris. Roman law as it was taught in the famous school of Orléans inspired the so-called Etablissements de Saint Louis and the Livre de justice et de plaid, but the main and most interesting part of these works was derived not from the Roman law but from the local one. The Etablissements was in fact a "coutumier" of Anjou, Maine, and Orléanais, but compiled by a man who was well acquainted with the Corpus juris. Another work, Conseil à un ami, by Peter of Fontaines, is far less interesting, because it is hardly more than a summary, and not a very clever one at that, of the Digest and Institutes. Of greater importance than all these was the Livre des coutumes et usages de Beauvoisins, which we owe to Philip of Beaumanoir (c. 1281). This is one of the outstanding monuments of mediaeval law. It was instrumental in the transformation of feudal into national law.

3. *Spain*—Alfonso X el Sabio ordered the compilation of a code called El fuero real, and later (c. 1262) another, a more important one, Las siete partidas, which became eventually the nucleus of the law of Spain and its immense colonies. A part of it dealt with the universities which were by this time one of the fundamental institutions of Christendom. Another part referred to alchemy, the practice of which was protected.

Though we are more interested in the study and codification of law than in its emergence (which belongs to political history), it is impossible not to mention in passing the Privilegio general which Peter III the Great[27] bestowed upon Aragon in 1283. This general privilege has sometimes been called the Magna Carta of Aragon, and rightly so, for it granted more substantial freedom to the citizens of that country than the Magna carta to the barons of England.

4. *Low Countries*—In the Italian section of this chapter I dealt with the treatises on political education composed by St. Thomas and others. One of these treatises, the Eruditio regum et principum, was written in 1259 by Guibert of Tournay for St. Louis; however, Guibert was more concerned with the purely moral, than with the political, education. St. Thomas' political work was made possible to a large extent by the translation of Aristotle's Politics completed at his request from the original Greek by his friend William of Moerbeke in the following year.

5. *England*—One of the greatest jurists of mediaeval times was Henry de Bracton who died in Exeter, 1268. Under the stimulus of the school of Bologna he made the first attempt to digest the English common law. His great treatise, De legibus et consuetudinibus Angliae, the influence of which upon English law could hardly be exaggerated, was twice abridged during the reign of Edward I (1272–1307), once in Latin, the "Fleta," and once in French, the "Britton."

Speaking of Edward I, who has sometimes been called the English Justinian, it is well to bear in mind that the theoretical efforts of legists like Bracton were paralleled by a remarkable development of constitutional law. Edward's legislation helped to overthrow feudal institutions and to improve the parliamentary system. A "model parliament" in which the three estates of the realm were fairly represented met in 1295.

6. *Central Europe*—The most important of the German codes inspired by the Sachsenspiegel was the Schwabenspiegel.

Martin the Pole compiled the Margarita decreti, which was an index to the Decretum and the Decretales.

Engelbert of Admont wrote a treatise on the education of princes.

7. *Eastern Islām*—The illustrious astronomer, Nāṣir al-dīn al-Ṭūsī, was the author of a Persian treatise on ethics, Akhlāq-i-Nāṣirī, which was very popular. Apropos of this I may mention that another work belonging to the same domain, the pseudo-Galenic treatise on economy (including morality), was translated a little later from the Arabic (or Hebrew?) into Latin by Armengaud son of Blaise.

Various important treatises on Muslim law date from this period: al-Nawawī composed a manual of Shāfi'ite law; Ja'far al-Ḥillī the most popular textbook of Shī'ite law; al-Nasafī compendia of Ḥanafite law.

8. *India*—Hemādri composed a collection of Hindu laws and customs, including many fragments from earlier works some of which are otherwise unknown.

Wagaru introduced the laws of India into Burma.

9. *China*—Kublai Khān ordered the compilation of a new criminal code, and his laws and statutes dealing with a great variety of subjects were collected.

Summary

By far the outstanding personality of the time was St. Thomas Aquinas. As compared with the other authors of treatises on morality and government, he is

[27] Born in 1236; king of Aragon from 1276 to his death in 1286. After the Sicilian Vespers in 1282, he was proclaimed king of Sicily; hence his nickname "the Great."

like a Brobdingnagian giant among pigmies. While Vincent of Beauvais succeeds only in giving us the average point of view of his time, St. Thomas introduces new ideas of extraordinary pregnancy. And yet great and prophetic as the latter was, his views on commerce and slavery were hopelessly antiquated and reactionary. In some respects St. Thomas was a forerunner of modern times; in others, future progress could only be possible by disregarding him completely.

At any rate St. Thomas was one of the first of the great publicists who applied all the resources of the scholastic method and all the wealth of information which had accumulated in Latin writings to the discussion of social and economic problems.

In the meanwhile the juridical organization of many countries was continued with increasing vigor. In some cases the laws were simply sanctioning feudal usages, in others they were preparing the transformation of feudal society into something entirely different, much broader in its scope and more democratic. Under the pressure of circumstances a new class of specialists was emerging and was rapidly developing: legists unconcerned with theology. One of their first tasks was to codify the laws in force and interpret them. Four works of that type were specially noteworthy: the Livres des coutumes de Beauvoisins of Philip of Beaumanoir in France, Las siete partidas of Alfonso X el Sabio in Spain, the De legibus Angliae of Henry of Bracton in England, and the Schwabenspiegel in Germany. Armed with such books as these, and of course with the imposing classics of the school of Bologna, the lawyers felt more and more independent and self-assured. The legal profession was coming of age. And not only that, but the legists felt that they were dealing not with impalpable dreams but with the most tangible realities, with realities of the utmost importance. The conduct of public affairs as it became more technical and they themselves more expert, was falling more and more into their hands. As opposed to the Jews and Muslims who never succeeded in dissociating the civil from the religious laws and hence made social progress practically impossible, the legists of western Europe realized that they were the main agents in the social transformation and reconstruction. They were not simply independent of the theologians, but looked down upon them even as Hagar upon her barren mistress.

XIV. PHILOLOGY

For a survey of philological progress the most natural subdivision is by languages, which is somewhat different from that by nationalities.

1. *Latin*—The foremost Latin grammarian of the century, John of Garland, was still living in 1272, but apparently his best work was done in the first half of the century.

A number of grammatical treatises belong to this period. The Speculum doctrinale of Vincent of Beauvais includes not only a grammar but a small dictionary (c. 3200 words). The philosophical study of grammar originated by John of Garland was continued; we have two treatises on "speculative" grammar composed by such different men as Boetius of Dacia and Duns Scot.[28] Both had obtained their inspiration in Paris. Robert Kilwardby, though he had also resided in that city, had apparently resisted the influence of the "modistae" and was still satisfied with Priscian.

[28] Assuming the Grammatica speculativa ascribed to him to be genuine. If it is not, the real author of that grammar is meant.

Roger Bacon had a deep interest in philology, and even in what we would call to-day comparative philology. Thanks to the remarkable catholicity of his mind, he was able to appreciate at once the theoretical interest of linguistic studies and the multiplicity of their applications. The third part of his Opus majus was entirely devoted to philological questions. His most important work was not concerned with Latin but with Greek and Hebrew. He denounced the imperfection of the Latin translations of Aristotle and the Scriptures, insisting upon the necessity of recovering St. Jerome's text, and setting forth how this could be done.

The most ambitious work of this time, as well as the most popular for centuries, was the Catholicon of John Balbi. This was a combination of grammar, prosody, rhetoric, etymology, but the main part was the dictionary, so much so that the Catholicon is generally thought of as if it were nothing but a dictionary.

Another great lexicographical work was the Synonyma medicinae composed by a fellow citizen of Balbi, Simon of Genoa. We might call it a dictionary of medicine or of materia medica; it includes Greek and Arabic terms as well as the Latin ones, but is essentially a work of Latin lexicography.

For the sake of curiosity, I may mention that we have a Hebrew version of the Theorica planetarum of Gerard of Sabbioneta to which is added a vocalized transcription of the Latin text in Hebrew script. This is of great interest for the study of mediaeval Latin phonetics; unfortunately that version is undated.

2. *French*—It is very remarkable that no attempt was yet made to systematize the French language, for that language was becoming very important, in fact the most important vernacular of Europe, and by far. We have seen above that out of about thirty-seven accounts of pilgrimages to the Holy Land of this time, about twenty-eight were in Latin, eight in French, one in German. This gives us an approximate idea of the relative importance of these languages. To be sure all the learned people in Latindom knew Latin, and thus it was natural enough to publish scientific and philosophical works in that language. By its means one could reach at once the learned people of every country. And yet French was already more than a national language. Three important works of this time were written in French by Italians: The Régime du corps by Aldobrandin of Siena (1256); Li livres dou tresor by Brunetto Latini (c. 1266); and last but not least the book of Marco Polo (1298). Ser Brunetto explained his choice in the preface of his work: "If anybody asks why this book is written in French, though we are from Italy, I shall answer, that this was done for two reasons: the first, because we are in France, and the other, that the French language is more delectable and more commonly used than all the other languages."

It is certain that no other vernacular had yet obtained any prestige comparable to that. And yet more valuable scientific works appeared in Spanish, and literary fruits of greater abundance or higher quality in Catalan, Italian, and Icelandic. To quote a single example, there was nothing in French of equal beauty to some of the Italian poems of Jacopone da Todi. But the prestige of a language does not depend on its beauty alone, nor even on its literary masterpieces; it is largely determined by political and social circumstances. France was then the leading kingdom of Christendom, and Paris its most famous city; hence the French language was more popular abroad than any other.

3. *Castilian, Portuguese, and Catalan*—Thanks to the enlightened patronage of a great king, Alfonso X el Sabio, a whole library of scientific and historical works

became available in Castilian. For a long time no European vernacular was equally rich in astronomical and astrological literature. King Alfonso was not only a scientist, he was also a great poet; but strangely enough his poems were written in a different dialect, Galician, closer to Portuguese than to Spanish. Thus Alfonso was one of the founders at once of Spanish prose and of Portuguese poetry. The king of Portugal, Dinis the Liberal, tried to do for his country what his grandfather Alfonso had done for Spain, but on a much humbler scale.

The third great language of the Hispanic peninsula, Catalan, was raised to a very high level by the genius of Ramon Lull. Some of his greatest works were written in Catalan, and this is the more remarkable because no original works of equal merit and nobility were then obtainable in any other European vernacular. For example, the Libre de contemplació en Deu, an enormous encyclopaedia of practical theology, the Libre del orde de cavayleria, the Doctrina pueril, the great religious and encyclopaedic romances, Blanquerna and Felix, etc.

4. *Icelandic*—Some of the masterpieces of Icelandic prose, the sagas of Sturla Thórdarson, date from this time. What is more remarkable, that language had already attained a higher degree of grammatical consciousness than the other vernaculars. This may possibly be accounted for by the fact that the Romance languages—the only rivals—were too close to Latin to feel the need of grammatical elaboration. However the fact is very curious. I have referred to the Icelandic grammatical treatises in Book III.

5. *Greek*—Roger Bacon fully realized the necessity of knowing Greek, a knowledge which was then exceedingly rare and weak in Latindom. He did not content himself with the explanation of that need, but took pains to satisfy it. He was the first Latin scholar to complete a Greek grammar.

In the meanwhile Byzantine humanism was pursuing its course with more continuity than distinction. Consider the works of a Maximos Planudes, for example. There was nothing very startling in them, just enough to keep the lamp of Greek letters burning. Maximos wrote among many others two grammatical treatises. His knowledge of Latin gave him a keener consciousness of his own language.

The reign of Andronicos II Palaeologos (1282–1328) seems to have witnessed a sort of humanistic revival. Besides Maximos Planudes who died in 1310, there flourished under that emperor at least two other great scholars: a pupil of Maximos, called Manuel Moschopulos, who composed a grammar and a dictionary and wrote commentaries on the classics of ancient Greece; and Thomas Magister, who compiled another dictionary and added more scholia to the ancient books. As we do not know exactly when Manuel and Thomas lived, I have placed them arbitrarily in the fourteenth century and I shall deal with them more elaborately in volume 3.

6. *Armenian*—Armenian grammars were written by Vardan the Great and by John of Erzinjān. The latter's work was modeled on the Greek grammar of Dionysios Thrax. John was also the compiler of a sort of super-grammar based on the writings of the earlier Armenian grammarians.

7. *Syriac*—At least three grammatical treatises were written by Abū-l-Faraj, who derived his information from the earlier Syriac grammars and from Arabic literature, especially from the work of al-Zamakhsharī.

8. *Hebrew*—Latin scholars showed perhaps a little more interest in Hebrew than in Greek, though this does not mean much. They had two reasons for studying

Hebrew: the first was the growing belief in the necessity of reading the Ancient Testament in the original in order to penetrate mysteries obscured by the translations; the second, at least equally strong, was the wish to convert the Jews. One of the leaders of the Hebrew movement in Christendom was Roger Bacon. He even began the composition of a Hebrew grammar, the first to be due to a Christian. He was a true forerunner of Reuchlin. He realized the need of obtaining a living knowledge of the language and that this need could only be satisfied with Jewish cooperation. In this he was again a forerunner, and we cannot help admiring his foresight in contrast with the backwardness of so many gentile instructors of to-day who can neither write nor speak the language which they are engaged in teaching!

Other Franciscans were trying to obtain at least a few glimpses of the sacred language for the same reasons as Bacon's, which were mainly religious and intellectual. In the meanwhile other monks of a more bellicose mood, Dominicans, wanted to know Hebrew in order to be able to trap the Jews so to say in their own burrows.

The Dominicans of Spain distinguished themselves above all others in this connection. Raymond of Peñafort, chief inquisitor of Aragon and Castile, organized the teaching of Hebrew in the Dominican schools to facilitate the anti-Jewish propaganda. In 1264 Jaime el Conquistador commissioned him, together with Raymond Martin, Arnold of Segarra, and Peter of Genoa (all of them Dominicans), to examine the Hebrew writings, especially the Talmud. They finally reported that the Talmud contained some good points and that it was not necessary to destroy it entirely. Raymond Martin wrote various books against the Jews, one of which, the Dagger of faith, was published by him in Hebrew as well as in Latin.

So much for the study of Hebrew by Gentiles. The Jews themselves were passionately interested in their own language; this was especially true at this time of the western Jews, many of whom were engaged in the task of translating Arabic writings. Indeed nothing sharpens linguistic consciousness like such an occupation which brings necessarily to the surface of each language innumerable subtleties. Moreover some of the books translated from the Arabic dealt with Hebrew grammar. Two treatises of Ibn Janāḥ, the greatest Hebrew philologist of the Middle Ages, were translated into Hebrew by Solomon ibn Ayyub in Béziers, 1254. Thus did the subjection of Hebrew to Arabic thought continue even with regard to the study of their own tongue!

As the date of Tanḥūm Yerushalmī is very uncertain, his Hebrew-Arabic dictionary to the Mishneh Torah may date from this time instead of from the earlier part of the century as I assumed. A Hebrew grammar was composed by the Qaraite, Aaron ben Joseph, who flourished in Crimea and Constantinople.

9. *Arabic*—We shall proceed for Arabic as for Hebrew. A fundamental distinction must be made between the study of that language by foreigners and by men who use it every day.

The Dominicans organized the study of Arabic as well as that of Hebrew and for the same reason. It was necessary to meet the infidel with his own weapons, to be able to turn them against himself so to say. Dominican seminaries for the study of Arabic existed in Tunis and Murcia before 1265. Such a seminary may have been the nucleus of the university established by Alfonso el Sabio in Seville, 1254. Indeed that university was different from all others in that it was meant to be to a large extent bilingual, Latin-Arabic. However nothing is known of its activity and perhaps it did not really materialize.

A Latin-Arabic vocabulary is ascribed to Raymond Martin. St. Peter Paschal had a native knowledge of Arabic of which he made full use in his Spanish treatise against Islām. The greatest Arabist of this time—and indeed of the Middle Ages—was Ramon Lull. Lull did not simply know Arabic but was able to speak and write it. In fact some of his own books, notably his immense Book of contemplation, were directly composed in Arabic or translated into it by himself. An Arabic college was founded at Miramar, 1276, at his request, by James II of Majorca and pope John XXI. (Other Arabic schools were eventually established at Valencia, 1281, and Xátiva, 1291.) In a petition to the council of Vienne (1311), he recommended the creation of oriental colleges in various cities, and the council actually decided to establish five of them, in Rome, Bologna, Paris, Oxford, and Salamanca. Considering his efforts for the improvement and diffusion of Arabic teaching and his own writings in that language, Ramon Lull might properly be called the founder of western orientalism.

Another Dominican whose proficiency in Arabic was noteworthy was Ricoldo di Monte Croce who is said to have preached in that language in Tabrīz (of course it is one thing to speak Arabic, and another to write it; I praised Lull so much because he was able to do both). Like Peter Paschal, Ricoldo capitalized his knowledge to write a treatise against Islām. That treatise was amazingly successful; witness its translation into Greek, then from Greek into Latin, and finally from Latin into German by Martin Luther!

The only western orientalist outside of Spain and Italy was Roger Bacon, but his knowledge of Arabic remained in a rudimentary stage. However he realized the importance of its study, and the affinity of Arabic with Chaldaean and Hebrew.

Let us pass now to the study of Arabic by Arabic speaking people. The famous theorist of music, Ṣafī al-dīn, wrote a treatise on prosody, rhyme and rhetoric. His interest in prosody was natural enough, for in Islām poetry and music were closely bound together. A poet did not recite his verses but chanted them. The same was true of the early poets of western Europe, and their melodies were probably influenced by Arabic models. This was certainly the case for the Cantigas de Santa Maria of Alfonso el Sabio, the melodies of which have been preserved.

By far the greatest philological work of this age was accomplished by the Egyptian Ibn Manẓūr; namely, his immense Arabic dictionary, Lisān al-'arab. To measure the importance of this it will suffice to realize that no other language, certainly no western one, had then—nor for many centuries—a dictionary at all comparable to the Lisān. To visualize how far ahead Arabic philology was of Latin philology it is enough to place side by side Balbi's wretched Catholicon and the imposing volumes of the Lisān.[29] A less superficial examination of both works does but deepen the gap between them. Indeed the Lisān is not simply a glossary, but a real thesaurus of the Arabic language, including a large number of examples with all the necessary vocalizations.

10. *Sanskrit*—Vopadeva wrote a Sanskrit grammar, differing in method and terminology from Pāṇini's, and a dictionary of Sanskrit roots.

11. *Chinese*—Tai T'ung was the author of a treatise on the six classes of characters. That is, Chinese characters are divided according to their etymology (pictorial, phonetic, etc.) into six classes which he discussed. The imperial academy

[29] Twenty quarto volumes, almost 9000 p., in the edition of Būlāq, 1883–1891. The copy available to me, bound in ten volumes, occupies twenty inches of shelfspace.

(Han-lin yüan), which was the main center of Chinese studies, was reorganized by Kublai Khān in 1287. Six years later the same ruler ordered the amalgamation of the academy with the government printing press. He had increased considerably the importance of that press by adding quantities of blocks to it. For example, after the conquest of the Southern Sung dynasty he caused many blocks to be moved from their capital to his.

12. *Mongolian*—Kublai was even more interested in Mongolian than in Chinese, which is natural enough since Mongolian was his own language. The imperial press was used to print books in Mongolian as well as in Chinese. He ordered the translation of the Kanjur, the great Tibetan canon, into Mongolian, but that gigantic task was only completed after his death. In all this his main adviser was the Lama Phagspa, who had devised for him a new Mongolian alphabet derived from the Tibetan and written vertically. (That Mongolian script was superseded less than a century later by another of Uighūr origin).

Some of the western visitors to Cathay obtained a good knowledge of Mongolian. This was certainly the case with Rubruquis, who by the way seems to have been an extraordinary linguist. He knew not only Mongolian but Arabic and other eastern languages whose differences and affinities he discussed; he described the various kinds of script used in the Far East. Another nimble polyglot was Marco Polo, who also made some observations on the four kinds of script employed by the Mongols. Finally John of Montecorvino translated the New Testament and Psalms into Mongolian.

13. *Japanese*—My only remark on Japanese philology is of a negative kind. The fact that the Azuma-kagami was written in Chinese, while earlier Japanese chronicles had already been published in Japanese, proves the strength of the Chinese hold on Japanese culture. Indeed Chinese remained the learned language in Japan, even as Latin in the West.

The two Mongol invasions of Japan in 1274 and 1281 do not seem to have affected that situation, in the first place because they failed utterly, and in the second place because the Chinese influence was too deeply seated to be submitted to political vicissitudes. The Japanese looked and will always look to their Chinese antiquities as we do to our own intellectual ancestry. Our gratitude to ancient Greece and our reverence for its glories are entirely independent of the present status of the Greek world and would not be a bit less if the latter ceased altogether to exist. In the same way the old China, to which Japan owes the bedrock of its own culture, is properly immortal; no matter what young China may do to it, it will always live in the hearts of the educated Japanese. I do not mean to imply that it may cease to exist in China itself—heaven forbid—but simply that whatever may happen in that distracted country, Chinese culture will continue to flourish in Japan, even as Greek culture in America.

Summary

The outstanding philological events of this period were, I would say, the following:

(1) Balbi's Catholicon.

(2) The continued hegemony of the French language among other European vernaculars. This was largely due to political circumstances, for publications of equal or greater merit appeared in Spanish, Catalan, and Icelandic.

(3) The beginning of western orientalism, witnessed by such personalities as Ramon Lull and Roger Bacon, and by the organization of Hebrew and Arabic seminaries.

(4) The Lisān al-'arab of Ibn Manẓūr.

(5) The development of Mongolian literature by means of translations from the Tibetan, Chinese, and Latin.

XV. CONCLUSION

I. OUTSTANDING SCIENTIFIC ACHIEVEMENTS

1. Many translations were made from the Greek and the Arabic into Hebrew, Latin, and various vernaculars. On the whole these translations were more important from the Jewish than from the Christian point of view. Indeed the majority of the texts translated, though hitherto unavailable in Hebrew, were already known in Latin.

2. Triumph of Latin Aristotelianism against the older scholasticism on the right, and against Averroism on the left. Yet on purely technical issues Aristotelianism was defeated, in astronomy by Ptolemaism, in anatomy by Galenism.

3. Improvement of education in Christendom; witness the continued growth of universities and the publication of many special treatises.

4. Establishment of Thomist philosophy which has remained to this day the official philosophy of the Roman Catholic Church.

5. Final elaboration of Qabbalism, assuming that the Zohar was compiled toward the end of the century. It may seem strange to speak of this as a scientific achievement; but it really was, considering the age and circumstances, and notwithstanding the fact that it was a movement in the wrong direction. Its influence on Jewish thought was immense, if largely evil.

6. Publication of many encyclopaedic treatises in Latin, French, Italian, Catalan, Dutch, Greek, Syriac, Arabic, Hebrew, Persian, Chinese, etc. Of course this concerns not the advance, but rather the diffusion of knowledge, which was considerably accelerated by the growth of trades, commerce, literacy, and democracy.

7.* Beginnings of experimental practice and philosophy by such men as Peter the Stranger, Peter Olivi, Peter of Spain, Villanova, Lull, Bacon, Albert the Great, etc.

8. Synthesis of natural philosophy by Bacon and Albert the Great.

9. Astronomical and mathematical work by Kuo Shou-ching and Yang Hui.

10. Revision of Greek mathematics and astronomy by Nāṣir al-dīn al-Ṭūsī and the school of Marāgha.

11.* Elaboration of trigonometry, as a separate branch of mathematics, in the Shakl al-qaṭṭā' of Nāṣir al-dīn.

12.* Triumph of Ptolemaic against Alpetragian astronomy in Islām and Christendom, but with an increased consciousness of its shortcomings. Slow progress of astronomical observations.

13.* Alphonsine and Īlkhānic tables, c. 1272.

14.* Peter the Stranger's magnetic experiments, 1269.

15.* First accurate theory of the rainbow by Quṭb al-dīn al-Shīrāzī.

16.* Invention of spectacles toward the end of the century in northern Italy.

17. Discussion of physical principles (force, action at a distance, vacuum, etc.) by Roger Bacon.
18. Discussion of impetus by Peter Olivi.
19.* Invention of gunpowder (?)
20. The development of Arabic alchemy continues; its main doctrines and methods are now well understood in Latindom.
21.* Earliest normal portolani in the West.
22. Al-Qazwīnī's geography and cosmography.
23.* Transasiatic journeys by William of Rubruquis, John of Montecorvino, the Poli, Hayton the Elder, al-Juwainī, Yeh-lü Hsi-liang, Bar Sauma, etc.
24.* Better knowledge in the West of Asiatic fauna, flora, and minerals.
25.* Botanical treatises by Albert the Great, Simon of Genoa, Ch'ên Ching-i, and Koremune Tomotoshi.
26.* Zoological treatises by Vincent of Beauvais, Albert the Great, Jacob ben Maḥir, and Demetrios Pepagomenos.
27. Latin translation by Faraj ben Salīm, 1279, of the largest Arabic medical encyclopaedia, the Continens of al-Rāzī. Other textbooks of Arabic and Jewish physicians are translated into Latin and into Hebrew.
28.* Progress of surgery in northern Italy by the Borgognoni, Bruno da Longoburgo, William of Saliceto, Lanfranchi.
29.* Beginning of human dissection in northern Italy preparing the anatomical revival of the fourteenth century.
30.* Development of ophthalmology by Khalīfa ibn abī-l-Maḥāsin and Ṣalāḥ al-dīn ibn Yūsuf.
31. Beginning of western orientalism (study of Hebrew and Arabic), the main leaders being Ramon Lull and Roger Bacon.
32. Publication of the Arabic thesaurus, Lisān al-'arab by Ibn Manẓūr.

Such a list is necessarily somewhat arbitrary, but the chances are that it is not grossly erroneous; that is, that I have not omitted any achievement of real importance, or included any worthless one. I have enumerated these achievements as they occurred to me, making no attempt to mention them in order of importance. As most of them are incomparable, it is impossible to say that this one is more important than that other. However I have marked with an asterisk those which are of a more technical nature and more obviously constructive; that is, the most interesting from the scientific point of view stricto sensu.

II. COMPARATIVE ACHIEVEMENTS OF VARIOUS GROUPS

For the sake of comparison we shall follow the same plan as before, beginning with Japan and traveling westward. The outstanding names are italicized throughout.

Japanese (6)

Religious founders (2): Nihiren, Ippen Shōnin
Educator (1): Hōjō Sanetoki
Naturalists or physicians (2): Seia, *Koremune Tomotoshi.*
Historian (1): The author of the Azuma-kagami (in Chinese)

Chinese (23)

(Including a few Mongols, Tibetans, Muslims and Christians. The names of the Muslims and Christians are marked respectively with one and two asterisks.)

Organizers, philosophers, educators (4): *Kublai Khān, Ma Tuan-lin, Wang Ying-lin,* Phagspa (Tibetan).

Mathematicians, astronomers (5): Hsü Hêng, 'Īsā the Mongol**, Cha-ma-li-ting*, *Kuo Shou-ching, Yang Hui.*

Technicians (2): A-lao-wa-ting*, I-ssŭ-ma-yin*.

Travelers (5): *Ch'ang Tê, Yeh-lü Hsi-liang, Chou Ta-kuan,* Yaballaha III**, *Bar Sauma***.

Naturalists (3): *Ch'ên Ching-i, Author of the Ch'in ching, Li K'an.*

Physician (1): Li Kao.

Historians (2): Chu Mu, Hsieh Wei-hsin.

Philologist (1): Tai T'ung.

Hindu (5)

Physicians (3): Vopadeva, Tīsaṭa, Candraṭa.

Legists (2): Hemādri, Wagaru (Burmese).

Muslims (41)

Eastern Muslims (34)

In this section two asterisks following a name mean "wrote exclusively (or almost exclusively) in Persian;" one means "wrote in Persian and Arabic." A few Christians (3) are included because they wrote in Arabic; their name is followed by the symbol "(Chr.)."

Philosophers, encyclopaedists (9): al-Abharī, *Jalāl al-dīn al-Rūmī**, 'Alī ibn 'Umar al-Kātibī, al-Qazwīnī, Sa'dī**, al-Baiḍāwī**, Muḥammad ibn Dāniyāl, al-Waṭwāṭ, Muḥammad al-Tabrīzī.

Mathematicians, astronomers (5): *Nāṣir al-dīn al-Ṭūsī*, al-'Urdī, Quṭb al-dīn al-Shīrāzī**, Muḥammad ibn Ashraf al-Samarqandī*, Muḥammad ibn abī Bakr al-Fārisī.

Theorist of music (1): *Ṣafī al-dīn.*

Chemists (2): *al-Ḥasan al-Rammāḥ, Abū-l-Qāsim al-'Irāqī,*

Naturalists (2): Bailak al-Qabajaqī, 'Abd al-Mu'min al-Dimyāṭī.

Physicians (4): *Khalīfa ibn abī-l-Maḥāsin, Ibn al-Quff* (*Chr.*), *Ibn al-Nafīs, Ṣalāḥ al-dīn ibn Yūsuf.*

Historians (7): Minhāj-i-Sirāj**, Abū Shāma, *Ibn al-'Amīd* (Chr.), *Ibn Khallikān,* Ibn al-Rāhib al-Qibṭī (Chr.), *al-Juwainī***, Ibn Wāṣil.

Legists (3): al-Nawawī, Ja'far al-Ḥillī, al-Nasafī.

Philologist (1): *Ibn Manẓūr.*

Out of these thirty-four men, four wrote exclusively or almost exclusively in Persian, thirty in Arabic. Out of the latter, four wrote sometimes in Persian. The Arabic language was by far the most important; however, among the four Persian-writing Persians were two of the greatest poets of all times, Jalāl al-dīn al-Rūmī, and Sa'dī.

How were these men geographically distributed? It is not easy to classify them as many moved from one country to another, but the following rough classification will be sufficient for our purpose. A middle group, the men of 'Irāq and Jazīrah (Mesopotamians), then all the Easterners (or "Persians"), and the Westerners (Syro-Egyptians).

Mesopotamians (4): Ja'far al-Ḥillī, *Ibn Khallikān, Abū-l-Qāsim al-'Irāqī, Ṣafī al-dīn.*

Persians (14): *al-Qazwīnī, 'Alī ibn 'Umar al-Kātibī,* al-Nasafī, al-Abharī, Muḥammad ibn abī Bakr al-Fārisī, Muḥammad al-Tabrīzī, *al-Baiḍāwī**, *Nāṣir al-dīn al-Ṭūsī**, *Quṭb al-dīn al-Shīrāzī**, Muḥammad ibn Ashraf al-Samarkandī*, Minhāj-i-Sirāj**, *Jalāl al-dīn al-Rūmī***, *Sa'dī***, *al-Juwainī***.

Syro-Egyptians (16): Abū Shāma, *Ibn Manẓūr,* al-Nawawī, *Ibn al-Nafīs, Khalīfa ibn abī-l-Maḥāsin,* Ibn Wāṣil, *Ṣalāḥ al-dīn ibn Yūsuf, al-Ḥasan al-Rammāḥ, al-'Urḍī,* Bailak al-Qabajaqī, 'Abd al-Mu'min al-Dimyāṭī, al-Waṭwāṭ, Muḥammad ibn Dāniyāl, and the three Christians, Ibn al-Rāhib al-Qibṭī, *Ibn al-Quff, Jirjīs al-Makīn.*

I put the Mesopotamians in a separate group because they were not completely identified with either of the two other groups, though they were closer to the Persian than to the Syrian. The two main groups are very well balanced, far better than in the first half of the century when the superiority of the Syro-Egyptians was more striking.

To these Eastern Muslims (Persian subgroup) might be added the three in the Mongol service mentioned in the Chinese section.

Western Muslims (7)

Educator (1): Muḥammad al-Riqūṭī.

Mathematicians (2): *Muḥyī al-dīn al-Maghribī, Ibn al-Bannā'.*

Travelers (3): *Ibn Sa'īd al-Maghribī,* al-'Abdarī, Muḥammad ibn Rushaid.

Historian (1): *Ibn al-'Idhārī.*

This group of Western Muslims was considerably smaller than the Eastern one, but it did not lack distinction. The origin of some of these Moors is not exactly known, but three at least were of Spanish birth: Ibn Sa'īd al-Maghribī hailed from Granada, al-'Abdarī from Valencia, and Muḥammad al-Riqūṭī from Murcia. Muḥammad ibn Rushaid was born in Ceuta. The three remaining ones were Moroccans or Spaniards; in fact the difference was inconsiderable.

Samaritan (1)

The physician Muwaffaq al-dīn.

Jews (47)

Eastern Jews (5)

Philosophers (2): Ibn Kammūna, Aaron ben Joseph.

Physicians (3): *Al-Kūhīn al-'Aṭṭār,* Ibn al-Bishr, Solomon Kohen.

All of these men flourished in Egypt and wrote in Arabic, except Aaron ben Joseph, a Qaraite of Crimean origin, who flourished in Constantinople and wrote in Hebrew.

Western Jews (42)

The center of Jewish intellectual life was now in the West, even as the center of Muslim life was more and more in the East.

Philosophers, theologians (18): Abraham ben Alexander, *Moses ben Naḥman*, Gershon ben Solomon, Jehiel 'Anav, *Shem-ṭob ibn Falaquera*, Abraham Abulafia, Meir ben Baruch, *Hillel ben Samuel*, Todros Abulafia, Joseph Giqaṭilia, *Moses of Leon*, *Solomon ben Adret*, Levi ben Abraham ben Ḥayyim, Asher ben Jehiel, Isaiah ben Elijah, Isaac Aboab, *Isaac Albalag*, Aaron ha-Levi.

Translators (19): It is expedient to divide the translators into two groups, those who translated into Hebrew, and those who translated into Latin or Spanish. Indeed the functions of these two groups were essentially different: the former were working for Israel, the latter for Christendom.

Translators into Hebrew (10): Solomon ibn Ayyub, *Shem-ṭob ben Isaac*, *Moses ibn Tibbon*, *Nathan ha-Me'ati*, *Zeraḥiah Gracian*, Jacob ibn Abbassi, *Jacob ben Maḥir*, Aḥiṭub ben Isaac, Samuel ben Jacob, Solomon ben Moses.

Translators into Latin and Spanish (9): *Isaac ibn Sid*, *Judah ben Moses*, Samuel ha-Levi, Abraham of Toledo, Bonacosa, *John of Capua*, Moses of Palermo, *Faraj ben Salīm*, Hagin Deulacres.

Author of a treatise on limning (1): Abraham ibn Ḥayyim (?).

Traveler (1): Jacob of Paris.

Physicians (2): Nathan Falaquera, Abraham ben Shem-ṭob.

Historian (1): Benjamin 'Anav.

The outstanding feature is the large number of translators, about half of whom used their linguistic advantages to foster the intellectual progress of their own people, while the others served as intermediaries to pour Arabic knowledge into alien vessels. With the necessary exception of the second kind of translators, and the possible one of Abraham ibn Ḥayyim, all of these Western Jews wrote in Hebrew.

Geographically these Jews can be classified as follows:

Spain (14): Abraham ibn Ḥayyim, Solomon ibn Ayyub, *Isaac ibn Sid*, *Judah ben Moses*, Samuel ha-Levi, Abraham of Toledo, *Shem-ṭob ibn Falaquera*, Abraham Abulafia, Todros Abulafia, Joseph Giqaṭilia, *Moses of Leon*, Nathan Falaquera, Isaac Aboab, *Isaac Albalag*.

Catalonia (6): *Shem-ṭob ben Isaac*, *Moses ben Naḥman*, *Zeraḥiah Gracian*, *Solomon ben Adret*, Abraham ben Shem-ṭob, Aaron ha-Levi.

Languedoc (2): Jacob ibn Abbassi, Solomon ben Moses.

Provence (4): *Moses ibn Tibbon*, Gershon ben Solomon, *Jacob ben Maḥir*, Levi ben Abraham ibn Ḥayyim.

Italy (11): Bonacosa, *John of Capua*, Moses of Palermo, *Faraj ben Salīm*, *Nathan ha-Me'ati*, Jehiel 'Anav, Benjamin 'Anav, *Hillel ben Samuel*, Samuel ben Jacob, Isaiah ben Elijah, Aḥiṭub ben Isaac.

Germany (3): Abraham ben Alexander, Meir ben Baruch, Asher ben Jehiel.

Northern France (1): Jacob of Paris.

England (1): Hagin Deulacres.

Christians (143)

Eastern Christians (22)

Greeks (12)

Philosophers, organizers (6): Theodoros II Lascaris, Nicephoros Blemmydes, Michael Palaeologos, *Georgios Pachymeres*, *Maximos Planudes*, Sophonias.

Translator (1): Manuel Holobolos.
Chemists (2): Petros Theoctonicos, Marc the Greek.
Physicians (2): *Nicholas Myrepsos, Demetrios Pepagomenos.*
Historian (1): *Georgios Acropolites.*

Syrians (2)

Jacobite: *Abū-l-Faraj.*
Nestorian: 'Abhd-īshō' bar Bĕrīkhā.

Armenians (8)

Mathematician (1): John of Erzinjān.
Travelers (2): *Hayton the Elder* and Sempad.
Historians (5): *Vardan the Great,* Cyriacus of Gandzak, Methitar of Aïri-vankh, Vahram of Edessa, Stephen Orbelian.

To these twenty-two Eastern Christians might be added six others mentioned respectively in the Chinese and Muslim sections (three in each).

Western Christians (121)

All wrote in Latin except the few whose names are followed by an asterisk; these did not write or they used a vernacular, as indicated between parentheses.

Educators (3): Gilbert of Tournay, Richard of Fournival* (Fr.), Robert of Sorbon.

Translators (9): *Alfonso el-Sabio** (Sp.), King Manfred of Sicily, Bartholomew of Messina, Hermann the German, John of Brescia, Paravicius, *William of Moerbeke,* Armengaud son of Blaise, King Dinis* (Port.).

Philosophers, Theologians (30): Thomas of York, Peter the Irishman, *Vincent of Beauvais,* William of Saint Amour, *St. Bonaventure, St. Thomas Aquinas, Peter of Spain,* Ulrich of Strassburg, Boetius of Dacia, Robert Kilwardby, *Albert the Great,* Ristoro d'Arezzo* (It.), Siger of Brabant, Raymond Martin, Richard Middleton, *Roger Bacon,* Henry of Ghent, *Brunetto Latini** (Fr. It.), William de la Mare, *Jacob van Maerlant** (Du.), Peter Paschal, Godfrey of Fontaines, *Giles of Lessines, John of Meung** (Fr.), *Duns Scot, Arnold Villanova, Ramon Lull** (Cat.) *Giles of Rome,* William of Ware, Peter of Trabibus.

Mathematicians, astronomers (16): Leopold of Austria, Gerard of Sabbioneta, the astrologer* (Fr.) to Baldwin II of Courtenay, Robert the Englishman, Guido Bonatti, John of Sicily, Bernard of Trilia, *Campanus, William of Saint Cloud,* Bartholomew of Parma, Henry Bate, Peter of Dacia, *Bernard of Verdun,* Anianus, the authors of two French algorisms* (Fr.).

Physicists (5): *Villard de Honnecourt** (Fr.), *Peter the Pilgrim, Witelo, John Peckham, Peter Olivi.*

Chemists (2): Peter of Saint Omer, *pseudo-Geber.*

Travelers (11): *William of Rubruquis,* Burchard of Mount Sion, Lanzarote Malocello*, Buscarello de' Ghizolfi*, Ugolino Vivaldo*, Vadino Vivaldo*, *Niccolò Polo*, Maffeo Polo*, Marco Polo** (Fr.), *Ricoldo di Monte Croce, John of Montecorvino.*

Naturalist (1): King "Dancus"* (Fr.?).

Physicians (20): John of Parma, *Bruno da Longoburgo,* Quattuor magistri, *Aldobrandin of Siena** (Fr.), Nicholas of Poland, *William of Saliceto,* John of Procida,

Simon of Genoa, *Taddeo Alderotti** (L., It.), *Lanfranchi*, Peter Capestang, *John of Saint Amand*, *William Corvi*, Boniface of Gerace, John Aquila, one or two authors of Spanish treatises on the veterinary art* (Sp.).

Historians (12): *Matthew Paris*, William of Puylaurens, Hermann of Nieder-Altaich, Rolandino, James the Conqueror* (Cat.), Martin of Troppau, *Sturla Thórdarson* (Icel.), *Bernard Desclot** (Cat.), Simon of Kéza, Salimbene, James of Voragine, William of Nangis.

Legists (11): Martino da Fano, author of the Schwabenspiegel* (Ge.), *Henry de Bracton*, Stephen Boileau* (Fr.), Peter of Fontaines* (Fr.), *William Durand*, *Philip Beaumanoir** (Fr.), Peter of Auvergne, *Ptolemy of Lucques*, author of the Livre de justice et de plaid* (Fr.), author of the Etablissements de Saint Louis* (Fr.).

Philologist (1): *Giovanni Balbi*.

How were these men distributed across Europe?

Italy (39): John of Parma, *Bruno da Longoburgo*, Martino da Fano, Gerard of Sabbioneta, King Manfred, Bartholomew of Messina, John of Brescia, *St. Bonaventure*, *St. Thomas Aquinas*, Lanzarote Malocello*, Rolandino, *William of Saliceto*, Paravicius, Ristoro d'Arezzo* (It.), *Aldobrandin of Siena** (Fr.), Guido Bonatti, Salimbene, John of Sicily, Buscarello de' Ghizolfi*, Ugolino Vivaldo*, Vadino Vivaldo*, *Camponus*, *Brunetto Latini** (Fr., It.), Bartholomew of Parma, *Giovanni Balbi*, James of Voragine, John of Procida, *Simon of Genoa*, *Taddeo Alderotti** (L., It.), *Lanfranchi*, *Niccolò Polo**, *Maffeo Polo**, *Marco Polo** (Fr.), *Giles of Rome*, *Ricoldo di Monte Croce*, *William Corvi*, *Ptolemy of Lucques*, *John of Montecorvino*, Boniface of Gerace.

France (27):

Languedoc (6): William of Puylaurens, Bernard of Trilia, *William Durand*, *Peter Olivi*, Armengaud son of Blaise, Peter Capestang.

Other parts of France than Languedoc and Provence (21): *Villard de Honnecourt** (Fr.), Richard de Fournival* (Fr.), *Vincent of Beauvais*, *Peter the Pilgrim*, astrologer* (Fr.) to Baldwin II, Stephen Boileau* (Fr.), William of Saint Amour, Robert of Sorbon, Peter of Fontaines* (Fr.), *Philip Beaumanoir** (Fr.), *William of Saint Cloud*, William of Nangis, Peter of Auvergne, *John of Meung** (Fr.), Peter of Trabibus (may have been a Languedocian like his master Olivi?), *Bernard of Verdun*, Peter of Saint Omer, the authors of the Livre de justice et de plaid* (Fr.), Etablissements de Saint Louis* (Fr.), and two algorisms* (Fr.).

Hispanic peninsula (11):

Spain and Portugal (7): *Peter of Spain*, *Alfonso el Sabio** (Sp.), Peter Paschal, *Arnold Villanova*, king Dinis* (Port.), one or two authors of treatises on the veterinary art* (Sp.).

Catalonia (4): James the Conqueror* (Cat.), *Bernard Desclot** (Cat.), Raymond Martin, *Ramon Lull** (Cat.).

British Isles (12): *Matthew Paris*, Thomas of York, Peter the Irishman, *Henry de Bracton*, Robert the Englishman, Robert Kilwardby, Richard Middleton, *John Peckham*, *Roger Bacon*, William de la Mare, *Duns Scot*, William of Ware

Low Countries (10): *William of Rubruquis*, Gilbert of Tournay, Siger of Brabant, *William of Moerbeke*, Henry of Ghent, *Jacob van Maerlant** (Du.), Godfrey of Fontaines, *Giles of Lessines*, Henry Bate, *John of Saint Amand*.

Germany (7): Leopold of Austria, author of the Schwabenspiegel* (Ge.), Hermann the German, Hermann of Nieder-Altaich, Burchard of Mount Sion, Ulrich of Strassburg, *Albert the Great.*

Silesia, Bohemia, Poland, Hungary (4): *Witelo,* Martin of Troppau, Simon of Kéza, Nicholas of Poland.

Scandinavia (3): Boetius of Dacia, *Sturla Thórdarson** (Icel.), Peter of Dacia.

Unknown or uncertain origin (8): John Aquila, Quattuor magistri, *pseudo-Geber,* King "Dancus*," Anianus.

Use of the European vernaculars

French (14): *Villard de Honnecourt,* Richard de Fournival, astrologer to Baldwin II, Stephen Boileau, Peter of Fontaines, *Philip Beaumanoir, John of Meung,* authors of the Livre de justice et de plaid, Etablissements de Saint Louis, and two algorisms. Plus the following Italians: *Aldobrandin of Siena, Brunetto Latini, Marco Polo.*

Italian (3): Ristoro d'Arezzo, *Brunetto Latini, Taddeo Alderotti.* Latini wrote primarily in French; Alderotti, in Latin.

Catalan (3): James the Conqueror, *Bernard Desclot, Ramon Lull.* Lull wrote also in Latin and Arabic, and probably in French.

Spanish (3): *Alfonso el Sabio,* one or two authors on the veterinary art.

Portuguese (1): King Dinis.

Dutch (1): *Jacob van Maerlant.*

German (1): Author of the Schwabenspiegel.

Icelandic (1): *Sturla Thórdarson.*

In all, 27 writers in the vernacular, or more exactly 26, as Latini was counted twice. The main facts are: (1) the overwhelming superiority of Latin over all the vernaculars, singly or jointly; (2) the superiority of the French vernacular over all others, singly or jointly. French was the only international vernacular.

Summary

Table I

The figures between brackets indicate the number of outstanding personalities (see section III below).

Far East	29	(13)	Japan	6	(1)
			China	23	(12)
India	5		India	5	
Muslims	41	(23)	Eastern Muslims	34	(19)
			Western Muslims	7	(4)
Samaritans	1		Samaritans	1	
Jews	47	(16)	Eastern Jews	5	(1)
			Western Jews	42	(15)
Christians	143	(55)	Eastern Christians	22	(8)
			Western Christians	121	(47)
Total	266	(107)		266	(107)

The Christian group was more important than all the others put together, 143 against 123 (or even 149 against 117; see below). This was almost entirely due to

Latindom which was now enjoying the intellectual hegemony of the world, and has kept it ever since, increasing its preponderance as centuries went by.

The two Christian groups may be subdivided as follows:

Table II

Eastern

Greeks	12	(5)
Syrians	2	(1)
Armenians	8	(2)
In China	3	(1)
In Islām	3	(2)
	28	(11)

Table III

Western

Italy	39	(19)
France	27	(9)
British Isles	12	(5)
Spain	11	(5)
Low Countries	10	(5)
Germany	7	(1)
Central Europe	4	(1)
Scandinavia	3	(1)
Uncertain	8	(1)
	121	(47)

The most remarkable fact is the supremacy of Italy, the second country in order of importance—France—being far behind, especially if the most distinguished men are considered or if the items are weighted. It is interesting to bring together these two facts: the supremacy of Italian genius, and the supremacy of the French language. This shows that the supremacy of a language is established mainly by political and economic circumstances. To be sure that language must have some literary prestige, but the prestige is insufficient to insure international success.

The relative importance of nations will appear more clearly if we rearrange the tables I, II, III, placing the separate groups in order of importance. I shall do this in two ways; for the Christians and Muslims who were employed by the Mongols, and the Christians who flourished in the Dar al-islām, may be considered either as members of their adopted group or of their natural one. Both hypotheses —which I shall call A and B—are defensible,[30] hence both classifications are justified and necessary. The differences between tables A and tables B concern only the Chinese, Muslims (Eastern Muslims; Syro-Egyptians), and the Christians (Eastern Christians).

Comparative Importance of Larger Groups

Table IV (A)

Christians	143	(55)
Jews and Sam.	48	(16)
Muslims	41	(23)
Chin., Jap.	29	(13)
Hindus	5	
	266	(107)

Table IV (B)

Christians	149	(58)
Jews and Sam.	48	(16)
Muslims	38	(21)
Chin., Jap.	26	(12)
Hindus	5	
	266	(107)

[30] Even so Jacques Loeb may be called a German scientist or an American one. Indeed he was both. He was a loyal American and exerted a deep influence on American biology; yet nothing can alter the facts of his birth, ancestry, and education. In the same way a Christian Egyptian speaking and writing in Arabic belonged at once to the Christian group and to his adopted one.

Comparative Importance of Smaller Groups

Table V (A)

W. Christians	121	(47)
W. Jews	42	(15)
E. Muslims	34	(19)
Chinese	23	(12)
E. Christians	22	(8)
W. Muslims	7	(4)
E. Jews, Sam.	6	(1)
Japanese	6	(1)
Hindus	5	
	266	(107)

Table V (B)

W. Christians	121	(47)
W. Jews	42	(15)
E. Muslims	31	(17)
E. Christians	28	(11)
Chinese	20	(11)
W. Muslims	7	(4)
E. Jews, Sam.	6	(1)
Japanese	6	(1)
Hindus	5	
	266	(107)

The main difference between the two tables V is that the ranks of Chinese and E. Christians are permuted. The three main groups (together almost three-quarters of the whole) are almost entirely unaffected.

The following auxiliary tables need no explanations.

VI Italy

Christians	39	(19)
Jews	11	(4)
	50	(23)

VII France

Christians	27	(9)
Jews	7	(2)
	34	(11)

VIII Spain and Morocco

Jews	20	(9)
Christians	11	(5)
Muslims	7	(4)
	38	(18)

IX Egypt, Syria

Muslims	13	(6)
Jews	4	(1)
Arabic Christians	3	(2)
Syriac Christians	2	(1)
Samaritans	1	
	23	(10)

X Germany and Central Europe

Christians	11	(2)
Jews	3	
	14	(2)

XI British Isles

Christians	12	(5)
Jews	1	
	13	(5)

XII Byzantium

Greeks	12	(5)
Qaraite	1	
	13	(5)

Finally, putting all these data together, we can arrange the various countries in the following order:

Table XIII

Order of Nations

Italy	50	(23)
Spain, Morocco	38	(18)
France	34	(11)
China	23	(12)
Egypt, Syria	23	(10)
Mesopotamia, Persia	18	(11)
Central Europe (many nations)	14	(2)
British Isles	13	(5)
Byzantium	13	(5)
Low Countries	10	(5)
Armenia	8	(2)
Japan	6	(1)
India	5	
Scandinavia	3	(1)
Unclassified (uncertain origin)	8	(1)
	266	(107)

This final table places beyond the possibility of doubt the intellectual supremacy of Italy in the second half of the thirteenth century. To be sure one must not take its data too literally, but the distance between Italy and the other countries is so great that its leadership is unmistakable. Another thing appears quite clearly: Italy, France and Spain were the leading countries of Europe even as the Mongol Empire, the Mamlūk kingdom of Syria and Egypt, and the Īlkhānate of Persia were the leading ones of Asia. The other countries trailed far behind.

The backwardness of England was partly due to its insularity: no Moors and but few Jews reached those distant islands, and in 1290 the few Jews who had managed to reach them were driven out. This did not mean simply a loss of Jewish genius, but a loss of stimulation for the English genius.

III. COMPARATIVE ACHIEVEMENTS OF VARIOUS GROUPS IF ONLY THE OUTSTANDING PERSONALITIES ARE CONSIDERED

Some idea of this question has already been given in the preceding tables wherein the figures between brackets show the number of outstanding personalities. Out of 266 personalities I have selected 107 which may be distributed as follows. It is clear that I must have been less severe in this selection than I was in Book III. This change of mood is not surprising considering that the two selections are separated by a long interval of time and thought. In order to make a comparison between the two books easier, I have made a new selection italicizing the most important names in each group, 64 in all.

The 107 (64) selected philosophers and scientists, quoted below, are classified according to their main interests. It is hardly necessary to recall that such a classification is arbitrary. Most of these men ought to appear in more than one group, some of them in many, but this would be confusing in other respects.

Translators (11, 7)

William of Moerbeke	Shem-ṭob ben Isaac
Alfonso el Sabio	Nathan ha-Me'ati
Isaac ibn Sid	*Moses ibn Tibbon*
Judah ben Moses	Zeraḥiah Gracian
Faraj ben Salīm	*Jacob ben Maḥir*
	John of Capua

Philosophers, Encyclopaedists, Organisers (31, 16)

Vincent of Beauvais	Georgios Pachymeres
St. Bonaventure	*Abū-l-Faraj*
St. Thomas Aquinas	*Moses ben Naḥman*
Peter of Spain	Shem-ṭob ibn Falaquera
Albert the Great	Hillel ben Samuel
Roger Bacon	*Moses of Leon*
Brunetto Latini	Solomon ben Adret
Maerlant	Isaac Albalag
Giles of Lessines	'Alī b. 'Umar al-Kātibī
John of Meung	*al-Qazwīnī*
Duns Scot	al-Baiḍāwī
Villanova	*Jalāl al-dīn al-Rūmī*
Ramon Lull	*Sa'dī*
Giles of Rome	*Kublai Khān*
Planudes	Ma Tuan-lin
	Wang Ying-lin

Mathematicians, Astronomers (10, 8)

Campanus	Muḥyī al-dīn al-Maghribī
William of St. Cloud	*al-'Urḍī*
Bernard of Verdun	*Quṭb al-dīn al-Shīrāzī*
Ibn al-Bannā'	*Yang Hui*
Nāṣir al-dīn al-Ṭūsī	*Kuo Shou-ching*

Physicists (6, 4)

Villard de Honnecourt	*John Peckham*
Peter the Pilgrim	*Peter Olivi*
Witelo	Ṣafī al-dīn

Chemists (3, 2)

pseudo-Geber	al-Ḥasan al-Rammāḥ
	Abū-l-Qāsim al-'Irāqī

Travelers (12, 7)

William of Rubruquis	Ibn Sa'īd al-Maghribī
Niccolò Polo	*Hayton the Elder*
Maffeo Polo	*Ch'ang Tê*
Marco Polo	Yeh-lü Hsi-liang
Ric. di Monte Croce	*Bar Sauma*
John of Montecorvino	*Chou Ta-kuan*

Naturalists (4, 2)

Ch'ên Ching-i	Li K'an
Author of Ch'in ching	*Koremune Tomotoshi*

Physicians (15, 10)

Bruno da Longoburgo	*Nicholaos Myrepsos*
William of Saliceto	Demetrios Pepagomenos
Aldobrandin of Siena	Ibn al-Quff
Simon of Genoa	*al-Kūhīn al-'Aṭṭār*
Taddeo Alderotti	*Khalīfa ibn abī-l-Maḥāsin*
Lanfranchi	Ibn al-Nafīs
John of Saint Amand	*Salāḥ al-dīn ibn Yūsuf*
William Corvi	

Historians (9, 5)

Matthew Paris	Vardan the Great
Sturla Thórdarson	*Jirjīs al-Makīn*
Bernard Desclot	Ibn al-'Idhārī
Georgios Acropolites	*Ibn Khallikān*
	al-Juwainī

Philologists (2, 1)

Giovanni Balbi	*Ibn Manẓūr*

Legists, Sociologists (4, 2)

Henry de Bracton	William Durand
Philip Beaumanoir	Ptolemy of Lucques

CHAPTER XLIII

RELIGIOUS BACKGROUND

(Second Half of Thirteenth Century)

I. CHRISTENDOM

THE ETERNAL EVANGEL

In my note on Joachim of Floris (second half of the twelfth century) I said that his views were not fully revealed until 1254 when the Franciscan brother, Gherardo da Borgo San Donnino, edited a collection of his writings with sundry additions, under the title Liber introductorius ad Evangelium aeternum. (The words "eternal evangel" are a reference to Revelation, 14:6, εὐαγγέλιος αἰώνιος, everlasting gospel.) The religious and social radicalism of that work was bound to provoke a reaction. Hugh of Saint Cher employed himself in obtaining its condemnation, and succeeded in 1255. However such aspirations are not suppressed by ecclesiastical decisions. Note that Joachimism was itself a reaction against the political and moral corruption of the age, and the apparent failure of the church to cure it.

FLAGELLANTS

It must be admitted that the political conditions were terrible and the moral abasement almost beyond belief, especially in Italy. Think for example of the devilish career of Ecelino III da Romano (1194–1259)—a Ghibelline leader, utterly depraved and cruel. How was such a man permitted to live more than sixty years? Yet there were many good people who were driven almost to madness by the consciousness of sin and the experience and fear of unspeakable crimes. No wonder that they sought relief and expression. They must at least unburden themselves. Thus it is not surprising that by the year 1260—Ecelino was dead then but many people believed that his evil spirit was still alive—a new form of religious enthusiasm made itself felt through the organisation of flagellant fraternities. The first notable group of flagellants appeared in Perugia in 1260, and their example was promptly imitated in Rome and other parts of Italy.

Needless to say, flagellation was not a novelty, not even religious flagellation. It had been practised by Egyptians, Jews, later by Christians. It was an obvious form of penance and self-humiliation. Yet in Christendom it remained rare and sporadic at least until the eleventh century. One of the first doctors to recommend this practice and to try to organize it was San Pietro Damiani (988–1072), cardinal bishop of Ostia. It did not become really popular until the thirteenth century, when the Dominicans and Franciscans gave their sanction to it and spread it everywhere.

Now the Flagellants (or Battuti) who appeared in 1260 went one step further and completed this strange evolution. Instead of being a secondary activity, flagellation became the very purpose of the new brotherhoods. Did it not afford the best means of protesting publicly against the sins and evils of the time? The favorite method of penance of the Friars had become a method of edification and salvation.

This new form of popular religion spread with the rapidity of a mental disease, not only in North Italy, but in France, Germany, Bohemia, the Netherlands. It appealed with special strength to all kinds of religious enthusiasts, and in its turn it stimulated the diffusion of heresy. The number of Flagellants and their frenzy grew to such proportions that when their half-naked troops appeared in the proximity of towns, the doors were shut against them. Every calamity would fan their enthusiasm, and there was no lack of calamities in those troubled days. The climax was brought about later by the Black Death. In some cases the zeal of the Flagellants caused anti-Jewish outbreaks; it was always a source of disturbance. No wonder that the burghers were afraid of them.

Ecclesiastical authorities were obliged to repress these extravagances. The Flagellants were formally condemned by Clement VI in his bull of 1349. (Clement VI was pope in Avignon from 1342 to 1352). Their case was discussed at the Council of Constance (1414-1418), when St. Vincent Ferrer defended them while John Gerson was their foremost accuser. Many flagellants were persecuted by the Inquisition. In spite of all that, the practice has continued to this day with more or less moderation.

To return to the early Italian epidemic, a strange by-product of it was the creation of a new form of poetry in the vernacular. The Battuti sang hymns or laude, some of which as we might expect were poetical creations of the first order, being thoroughly genuine and as fervent as one could wish. This aspect of their activity was so common that they were called not only Battuti or Disciplinati, but also Laudesi. The greatest of these poets, Jacopone da Todi, was one of the founders of Italian literature. He was born in 1228, imprisoned by Boniface VIII in 1298-1303, and died in 1306.

Jacques Boileau: Historia flagellantium, de recto et perverso flagrorum usu apud Christianos (374 p., Paris 1700). French translation (Amsterdam 1701). English adaptation with commentary by Jean Louis de Lolme: Memorials of human superstition (2d ed., 426 p., London 1784).

John Addington Symonds: Renaissance in Italy (stereotyped edition, vol. 1, 482; vol. 4, 243, etc.). Good summary by Paul D. Alphandéry: Encyclopaedia Britannica (vol. 10, 463, 1910). George Friedrich Collas: Geschichte des Flagellantismus unter besonderer Berücksichtigung der Religionsgebräuche, usw. (vol. 1, Berlin 1913; no more published).

Ecelino III da Romano—Pietro Gerardo: Vita e gesti d'Ezzelino Terzo da Romano (Venice 1543). Friedrich Stieve: Ezzelino von Romano (135 p., Leipzig 1909); Kleine Nachträge (Historische Vierteljahrschrift, vol. 16, 77-82, Leipzig 1913).

Jacopone da Todi—Laude. First edition, Florence 1490. Literal reproductions of that edition by Giovanni Ferri (Rome 1910; again, Bari 1915, 316 p.); by Giovanni Papini (Florence 1923).

Alessandro d'Ancona: Jacopone da Todi, il giullare di Dio (Todi 1914). Jules Pacheu: Jacopone de Todi, frère mineur de St. François, auteur présumé du Stabat mater (Paris 1914; with French versions of selected poems). Evelyn Underhill: Jacopone da Todi, poet and mystic (530 p., London 1919; selected poems Englished by Mrs. Theodore Beck). Carla Cadorna: Il cantore della povertà (Firenze 1923).

Paul Runge: Die Lieder und Melodien der Geissler des Jahres 1349 nach der Aufzeichnung Hugo's von Reutlingen. Nebst einer Abhandlung über die italienischen Geisslerlieder von Heinrich Schneegans und einem Beitrage zur Geschichte der deutschen und niederländischen Geissler von Heino Pfannenschmid (230 p., Leipzig 1900).

CONFLICTS BETWEEN REGULARS AND SECULARS

The immense success obtained by the Franciscans and Dominicans was bound to create jealousies. The secular clergy lost to them a substantial part of its moral influence. The conflicts were especially serious in the universities where seculars and regulars were teaching together and competing for the attention of students. I have told above the history of the chairs of Paris, the Dominicans conquering the first chair in 1229 and a second one in 1231, the Franciscans a third one, soon afterwards. The fact that the Dominicans obtained their first chair in the capacity of strike-breakers did not make matters more pleasant.

The leader of the secular opposition, William of St. Amour,[1] published in 1255 a pamphlet against the friars, entitled De periculis novissimorum temporum, which was answered by St. Thomas Aquinas and by Hugh of St. Cher, who obtained its condemnation. This was the beginning of a war of pamphlets in which some of the best writers of the time took part, William of St. Amour, Nicholas of Lisieux, Gerard of Abbeville defending the seculars, St. Thomas, St. Bonaventure, John Peckham, the regulars. The latter had finally the best of it. These quarrels would not concern us but for their favorable influence on the progress of philosophy. They put Franciscans and Dominicans on their mettle and stimulated many innovations. In fact the leading philosophers of the time were regulars.

M. De Wulf: History of mediaeval philosophy (vol. 1, 259–263, 1926).

CHRISTIAN PROPAGANDA IN BUDDHIST ASIA

The first Catholic missions were established by the Franciscan, John of Monte Corvino, in India in 1291, and in China two years later. John was the first Roman Catholic bishop of Peking, 1307. We shall speak of him more fully in the geographical section below.

Up to this time, Christianity had been represented in these remote parts only by Nestorians, some of whom had already established bishoprics as far as Marw and Herat before the end of the fifth century. See my notes on Nestorios (first half of the fifth century), on the Nestorian monument of 781, on the Nestorian translators, etc. (vol. 1, 381, 526, 587).

Paul Pelliot: Chrétiens d'Asie centrale et d'Extrême-Orient (T'oung Pao, vol. 15, 623–644, 1914).

THE GREAT JUBILEE OF 1300

The first jubilee year[2] was decreed by Boniface VIII in the bull "Antiquorum habet fidem" dated February 22, 1300. A plenary indulgence—that is, a remission of punishment and even of sin (a poena et a culpa)—was granted during that year to the pilgrims visiting certain churches in Rome and performing certain rites. The pope said that it was a popular tradition to consecrate centenary years in that

[1] Canon of Beauvais, 1247; rector of the University of Paris, died 1272.

[2] Not to be confused with the magnificent Jewish idea of year of jubilee or year of release (Leviticus, Chapter 25), the forty-ninth year, a sabbath of sabbatical years when property was redistributed and Jewish slaves manumitted.

way, but there is no evidence of a jubilee year before 1300. That jubilee was enormously successful. Large numbers of pilgrims came to Rome and made abundant offerings. An account of it was written by Giovanni Villani; Dante referred to it (Inf. XVIII, 29; Purg., II, 98).

So great was this success that Clement VI decreed in 1343 by the bull "Unigenitus Dei filius" that the next jubilee year would be celebrated in 1350, instead of 1400, and then the following jubilee years, every fiftieth year. Urban VI in 1389 reduced the interval to thirty-three years (length of Christ's life), and Paul II in 1470 to twenty-five years.

The material success of these jubilees and the abusive sale of indulgences which they encouraged became a source of corruption and put the church in jeopardy. It is not the place here to discuss the theory of indulgences as formulated by Alexander Hales and other doctors; but it is certain that the practice was equivocal to begin with, and that it was gradually perverted to the limit of endurance. It will suffice to recall that the scandals relative to the indulgence business were the main cause of Luther's revolt and of its extraordinary success.

At any rate, the year 1300 was a year of triumph for the church and for the pope.

Henry Charles Lea: History of auricular confession and indulgences in the Latin church (3 vols., Philadelphia 1896). Herbert Thurston (S. J.): The holy year of jubilee; an account of the history and ceremonial of the Roman jubilee (London 1900). Franz Beringer: Die Ablässe, ihr Wesen und Gebrauch (14th ed. by Josef Hilgers; 2 vols., Paderborn 1915–1916). Nikolaus Paulus: Geschichte des Ablasses im Mittelalter, vom Ursprunge bis zur Mitte des 14. Jahrhunderts (2 vols., Paderborn 1922–1923).

CHRISTIAN ART

It has been shown many times above that the development of art was intimately connected with the development of religion and of culture. By virtue of their decoration and of their own beauty, the churches were like unto Bibles. In the same way, the first municipal buildings were delivering messages of civism. The architects and other artists were inspired by the contemporary doctors, above all perhaps by Vincent of Beauvais. Vice versa in order to understand the intellectual background of the people of that time, we must learn to appreciate their artistic efforts. If anything ever deserved to be considered a "mirror" of a given society, it was this its creative power in the field of art.

The following list, restricted to a few of the main buildings of that time, will give a sufficient idea of its architectural activity. Though I had in mind primarily Christian edifices, I have added the names of a few others.

1260. Salisbury cathedral completed except the spire (1350)

1270. Fortifications of Carcassonne

About 1273. Cathedral of Upsala commenced

1280–1290. Main part of Strassburg cathedral

1280. "Angel choir" of Lincoln cathedral

1280. Cathedral of Orvieto commenced

1283. Carnarvon Castle

1284. Conway Castle. (Both castles built in Wales by Edward I)

1288. Cathedral of Amiens completed

1295. Belfry of Bruges commenced

1295 etc. Town hall of Siena

1298. Cathedral of Florence

(These data, taken from Beazley, have not been checked)

C. R. Beazley: Notebook of mediaeval history (Oxford 1917). Emile Mâle: L'art religieux du XIIIe siècle en France. Etude sur l'iconographie du moyen âge et sur ses sources d'inspiration (1st ed., Paris 1898; 4th ed. revised, 496 p., 190 ill., Paris, c. 1920; Englished in 1913). Louis Bréhier: L'art chrétien (456 p., 233 ill., Paris 1918; Isis, 4, 540-544).

For Arnold of Villanova and Ramon Lull see the philosophical chapter, and for Ricoldo di Monte Croce, the geographical one.

II. ISRAEL

ATTEMPTS TO CONVERT THE JEWS OF SPAIN

As soon as the Inquisition was established in Aragon (1233), it devoted a good part of its energy to the conversion of the Jews. Its management was entrusted to the Dominicans, Raymond of Peñafort being appointed chief inquisitor for Aragon and Castile by Gregory IX (pope from 1227 to 1241). Raymond arranged for the teaching of Hebrew in the seminaries in order to facilitate the anti-Jewish propaganda. In 1263 he organized a public disputation in Barcelona between the converted Jew, Pablo Christiani, and Moses ibn Naḥman. In 1264 he and Raymond Martin were commissioned to examine and censor the Talmud.

See my notes on Raymond of Peñafort, Raymond Martin, and Moses ibn Naḥman.

EXPULSION OF THE JEWS FROM ENGLAND

As far as we know, the first Jewish immigrants into England came with William the Conqueror. They were forbidden to hold land and to join guilds; on the other hand, Christians were forbidden to take interest; hence money lending became a Jewish speciality. Some of them grew very rich and powerful, and thus they were hated more and more and their situation became less and less tenable. The religious enthusiasm fanned by the Crusades was turned against them. For example, some five hundred Jews were massacred at York on March 16-17, 1190. Many of the survivors emigrated in 1211 to the Holy Land (see my note on Samuel ben Samson); others left the country in 1218 when Henry III ordered the Jews to wear a badge. After this, a whole series of vexatious measures were enacted against them, they were the victims of continual taxations and confiscations, and their lives and properties became more and more precarious. This situation came to a climax under Edward I (1272-1307). By that time money could be obtained by the king from Lombard bankers established in London and hence there was less need of the financial activity of the Jews. In 1280 they were obliged to attend sermons preached by Dominicans. Finally in 1290, they were ordered to leave England before All Saints Day. They were allowed to take their movables with them, but their immovable property escheated to the king. Some sixteen thousand Jews left England; most of them went to France, about one-tenth to Flanders.

This was the first general expulsion which befell the Jews; they were expelled from France in 1306, from Spain in 1492, from Lithuania in 1495, from Portugal in 1497. They were readmitted into England in 1655, under Cromwell.

Max L. Margolis and Alexander Marx: A history of the Jewish people (384–391, 1927).

III. HINDUISM

Buddhism had been entirely driven out of India proper, as a sort of alien and unassimilable religion, and India had reverted to Hinduism. The history of the hundreds of popular cults which are covered by that label "Hinduism" is hopelessly complicated and of no interest to us, except in so far as it helps us to understand the scientific sterility of India.

When I spoke of the Buddha (vol. 1, 68) I suggested that the religion or wisdom which he explained was not incompatible with scientific research. Indeed no religion is nearer to the religion of science than the pure original Buddhism. Unfortunately, the true scientific spirit of Buddhism was made barren by excessive otherworldliness, by the lack of curiosity. Considering the quick intelligence and the philosophical genius of the Hindu peoples, it is possible that if Buddhism had been permitted to develop among them, their scientific creations would have been more numerous and more important.

As a matter of fact, though Jainism was allowed to thrive in a humble way (and throve nowhere else), Buddhism was soon smothered by the numberless Vishnuite and Śivaite sects. In all these sects, the rational part of religion was reduced to its minimum; the mystical and fantastic elements predominated. Hence such cults must needs discourage any scientific effort.

One of the most important branches of Vishnuism, the Ramanujas, so-called after the philosopher, Rāmānuja (second half of the eleventh century), was split into two schools during the thirteenth century, the northern and the southern. The southern school "were the Augustinians or Calvinists of Vishnuism," believing that a man has no more part in his own salvation than a kitten which its mother seizes by the nape of its neck (cat-hold theory), while the northern school claimed that man can help his salvation even as a baby monkey hugs to its mother (monkey doctrine). Another branch of Vishnuism, the Madhvas, dates back also to the thirteenth century. They were strongly opposed to the Vedantic monism of Śaṅkara (first half of the ninth century).

I have quoted these contemporary examples to show that the Hindu theologians were trying to solve in their own way the same problems as their Christian or Jewish colleagues. How could it be otherwise? The fundamental problems are determined by nature, and the number of solutions is not unlimited.

But in the case of India, these theological discussions were divorced from life. Christian doctors were gradually obliged to come more closely into contact with real and tangible problems; Vishnuite scholasticism remained unchecked and unruled. Thus Christian philosophy was brought slowly within the experimental field and made fertile; on the contrary, Hinduism drifted wider apart and thus was doomed to idle reiteration and sterility.

For a summary of Hinduism see George Foot Moore: History of religions (vol. 1, 2d ed., 325–356, 1920). Sir Ch. N. E. Eliot: Hinduism and Buddhism (3 vols., London 1921; Isis, 5, 163). Helmuth von Glasenapp: Der Hinduismus (München, c. 1922); Brahma und Buddha (350 p., ill., Berlin, c. 1926).

IV. BUDDHISM

INTRODUCTION OF TIBETAN BUDDHISM INTO MONGOLIA

The debased kind of Tantric Buddhism which the Guru Padma-sambhava brought to Tibet about the middle of the eighth century throve remarkably well in that country (vol. 1, 525). The purely Tibetan vicissitudes of Lamaism do not concern us, but it is highly significant that it was this religion which Kublai Khān (Yüan emperor from 1260 to 1294) introduced into Mongolia. He caused the Kanjur (vol. 1, 467–469) to be studied by a company of scholars whose investigations led eventually (but only after his death) to its translation into Mongolian.

Mongolian Lamaism flowed back into China proper, thus originating a new Chinese-Buddhist tradition. This tradition was considerably inferior in every respect to the earlier ones. Being full of magical ideas, it naturally appealed to superstitious people, enriched itself with their own fancies, and thus increased its debasement and influence. There is very little left in Mongolian Lamaism of the higher Buddhist conceptions. The Chinese do not count it among their Buddhist schools or tsung, and indeed it has remained to this day a Mongolian rather than a Chinese religion.

Mrs. E. C. Couling: Encyclopaedia sinica (73–75, 284–285, 1917). G. Sarton: Introduction (vol. 1, 467–469, 525, 1927).

JAPANESE BUDDHISM

Out of four great Buddhist sects established in the thirteenth century, two—the Zen-shū and Shin-shū—belong to the first half of the century. Yet the founder of the main branch of the former, the Sōdō-shū, Dōgen, lived until 1253; and the founder of the Shin-shū, Shinran-Shōnin, died only in 1268.

The two last sects, the Nichiren-shū and the Ji-shū, were founded respectively in 1253 and 1275.

1. *Nichiren-shū* (1253)—Nichiren was born in 1222 in the Awa province and was educated in Shingon and Tendai monasteries. His original name was Zennichimaru, but he assumed the religious name Nichiren (lotus of the sun). He founded a new sect, the Nichiren-shū or Hokke-shū in 1253; in 1260 he published the Rissho ankoku-ron, a political and religious treatise including violent attacks on the other sects. He was exiled to Itō (in Izu) in 1261; in 1264 he was pardoned but having resumed his pugnacious activity he was condemned to death; later this sentence was commuted to a new exile in the island of Sado where he remained until 1272; he died at Ikegami (in Musashi) in 1282.

This new sect was a violent reaction against the others and especially against those of the Amidaist type (the so-called Pure Land sects). Yet it was itself very remote from early Buddhism, and its methods were reactionary, intolerant, and even brutal. It created deep enmities—it has sometimes been called the Ishmael of Buddhism—but also deep loyalties. It is essentially based on the Saddharma-puṇḍarīka-sūtra, or Lotus of the True Law, which the Japanese call Hokke-kyō (hence the other name of the sect, Hokke-shū) or Myōhō-renge-kyō. It is significant that this sect is the only one called by its founder's name. Nichiren Shōnin was indeed the most turbulent and fanatic of the Buddhist reformers. At least two temples were founded by him, Kuon-ji at Minobu (in Kai), in 1273, where his ashes are kept; and Sōchū-ji at Ikegami where he died; these temples are the principal seats of the Hokke-shū.

Gradually the Nichiren-shū was divided into nine branches or bumpa, five of which are extant to this day, being represented (c. 1917) by 5074 temples. Three branches date from the thirteenth century, two from the fourteenth, one from the fifteenth, and three from the sixteenth century.

For the Saddharmapuṇḍarīka-sūtra, see vol. 1, 447.

E. Papinot: Historical dictionary (438–440, 1909). Masaharu Anesaki: Nichiren (172 p., Harvard Press, 1916). August Karl Reischauer: Studies in Japanese Buddhism (1917). Kishio Satomi: Japanese civilization. Nichirenism and the Japanese national principles (252 p., London 1923; Isis, 7, 192).

2. *Ji-shū* (1275)—The Ji sect was founded in 1275 by Ippen. Ippen Shōnin was born in 1239; his original name was Ochi Michihide; he was educated in a Tendai monastery on Tokuchi-yama, Iyo, and studied also the doctrines of the Jōdo-shū and of the Nembutsu-shū. He traveled considerably throughout Japan to preach his own doctrine, and was nicknamed the traveling priest, Yugyō Shōnin. He died at the Shinkō-ji, Settsu, in 1289. He received in 1886 the posthumous title, Enshō Daishi.

The Ji sect was the last of the four Amida sects, the first three being the Nembutsu, Jōdo, and Shin. It lays special emphasis on itinerant preaching, according to the master's example. It was not very successful, and was represented c. 1917 only by 513 temples. The main seat is Fujisawa in Sagami. It is divided into thirteen branches.

E. Papinot: Historical dictionary (208, 231, 1909). A. K. Reischauer: Studies in Japanese Buddhism (128, New York 1917).

CHAPTER XLIV

THE TRANSLATORS

(Second Half of Thirteenth Century)

I. FROM GREEK INTO LATIN

BARTHOLOMEW OF MESSINA

Translator from Greek into Latin who flourished at the court of Manfred, king of Naples and Sicily from 1258 to 1266. He translated Aristotle's Magna moralia, the Problems, and other pseudo-Aristotelian treatises: De principiis, De mirabilibus auscultationibus, Physiognomonia, De signis. He also translated Hierocles' treatise on the veterinary art.

Various other pseudo-Aristotelian opuscula (De mundo, De eupragia, De inundatione Nili, De respiratione et exspiratione, De juventute et senectute, De causis mortis et vitae) were translated from Greek into Latin for King Manfred by unknown translators.

There is a treatise on the veterinary art in fifty chapters, Lu libru de la maniscalchia di li cavalli, written in Sicilian dialect by one Bartolommeo Spadafora of Messina. Is this a different work, or is it identical with Bartholomew's translation of Hierocles?

Bartholomew of Messina may possibly be identified—as Steinschneider suggests—with John of Messina, who was one of the translators employed by Alfonso X in 1276, but this does not seem probable. See my note on John of Sicily. It is more probable that Bartholomew of Messina (fl., Naples c. 1262), John of Messina (fl., Seville 1276), and John of Sicily (fl., Paris 1290) were three different personalities.

Léon Moulé: La médecine vétérinaire en Europe au moyen âge (41, Paris 1900). M. De Wulf: History of mediaeval philosophy (vol. 1, 242, 1926). For the anonymous translation of the De mundo see William Laughton Lorimer: The text tradition of pseudo-Aristotle De mundo together with an appendix containing the text of the mediaeval Latin versions (St. Andrew's University publications, Oxford 1924). This contains the anonymous translation made for King Manfred and another ascribed to Nicholas of Sicily, who may be identical with Niccolò da Reggio (q. v., first half of the fourteenth century).

WILLIAM OF MOERBEKE

Guilielmus Moerbecanus or Moerbekensis. Flemish Dominican. Neo-Platonic philosopher. Translator from Greek into Latin (c. 1215–c. 1286).

Born at Moerbeke near Grammont, East Flanders, c. 1215; penitentiary and chaplain to many popes; took part in the council of Lyon, 1273–1274; archbishop of Corinth from 1278 to his death not long after 1281 (c. 1286?). It is difficult to know how long he resided in Greece: he was there at least twice, before 1266, and in 1280–1281. From 1266 to 1278 he was most of the time in Viterbo and Orvieto.

He wrote a treatise on geomancy, De arte et scientia geomantiae. The following translations were made by him, or under his direction, some of them at the request of his friend St. Thomas Aquinas.

Hippocrates: Prognostics.

Aristotle: Rhetoric (1281), Politics (1260), History and generation of animals (1260), fourth book of Meteorology, Economics (?), eleventh book of Metaphysics. (Translations of other Aristotelian treatises were revised by him; e.g., the other books of the Meteorology and Metaphysics, and the De anima).

Archimedes: De iis quae in humido vehuntur (1269). The Greek text of it is lost.

Hero: Catoptrics. Ascribed by him to Ptolemy.

Galen: De alimentis (1277).

Alexander of Aphrodisias: Commentaries on the Meteorology (1260) and on the De sensu et sensibili.

Themistios: Commentary on the Prior analytics and the De anima.

Proclos: Theological introduction (Viterbo 1268). At St. Thomas' request.

Proclos: Commentaries on the Timaeos and the Parmenides. The latter deals only, in seven books, with the first hypothesis. The Latin text is more complete than the Greek text. Of these two commentaries the first at least was made at St. Thomas' request.

Philoponos (?): Commentary on the third book of the De anima (1268).

Simplicios: Commentaries on the De coelo et mundo (1271), and on the Categories (1266), etc.

His translations were to a large extent revisions of earlier translations, but with scrupulous reference to the Greek text. They were sharply criticized by Roger Bacon, but their literalness was not entirely disadvantageous, as it enables us eventually to reconstruct the Greek text.

The translation of Aristotle's Politics, made at St. Thomas' request in 1260, introduced a text which had been hitherto unknown to the Western Christians as well as to the Muslims; it marked the beginning of a new development of social philosophy in the Christian West. Moerbeke does not seem to have been much influenced by the purer Aristotelian doctrine which he helped so powerfully to transmit. He was apparently far more interested in neo-Platonism. For example, it was at his request that Witelo explained neo-Platonic metaphysics in the prologue to his Perspectiva. Curiously enough, in this Moerbeke was again inspired by St. Thomas. Indeed toward the end of his life, the latter became increasingly curious to know neo-Platonic views. Some of Moerbeke's versions of Proclos, perhaps all of them, were made at St. Thomas' invitation, and these versions originated a new wave of neo-Platonism, which would culminate in the fifteenth century in the work of Nicholas Cusanus.

Text—The translation of Archimedes was published in Tartaglia's Latin edition of 1543 as Tartaglia's own, but the plagiarism is entirely proved.

Aristoteles Politicorum libri octo cum vetusta translatione, edited by Franz Susemihl (Leipzig 1872).

Gunnar Rudberg: Textstudien zur Tiergeschichte des Aristoteles(Uppsala Universitets Årsskrift, 1908, 134 p.). Contains the text of the first book of the Historia animalium.

Leonhard Dittmeyer: Guilelmi Moerbekensis translatio commentationis Aristotelicae de generatione animalium. (Progr., 53 p. Dillingen a.D., 1915; Isis, 5, 215).

See also the notes devoted to the translated authors.

Criticism—A. G. Demanet: Biographie nationale belge (vol. 8, 467–469, 1885). J. L. Heiberg: Neue Studien zu Archimedes (Z. für Mathematik, vol. 34, Suppl.,

1889); Die von Wilhelm von Moerbeke benutzten Handschriften (ibidem, vol. 37, hist. Abt., 81, 1892). Martin Grabmann: Eine ungedruckte Verteidigungsschrift von Wilhelms von Moerbecke Übersetzung der Nikomachischen Ethik gegenüber dem Humanisten Lionardo Bruni (Abhd. aus dem Gebiete der Philosophie, Hertling Festschrift, Freiburg, 133–142, 1913). Sandys: History of classical scholarship (vol. 1^3, 585, 1921). Henri Bosmans: Guillaume de Moerbeke et le Traité des corps flottants d'Archimède (Revue des questions scientifiques, 5–23, avril 1922; Isis, 5, 215; 12, 94). M. De Wulf: History of mediaeval philosophy (vol. 1, 243–246; 2, 117, 1926). Martin Grabmann: Mittelalterliche lateinische Aristotelesübersetzungen und Aristoteleskommentare in Handschriften spanischer Bibliotheken (9–20, 45–46, München 1928; Isis, 13, 205). Raymond Klibansky: Ein Proklos-Fund und seine Bedeutung (Sitzungsberichte der Heidelberger Ak., Philos. Klasse, Jahrgang 1928–1929, 5; 41 p., 1929). Apropos of a Latin translation of Proclos' commentary upon Plato's Parmenides (Isis, 15, 203). Lynn Thorndike: Translation of Simplicios' commentary on the De coelo et mundo (Isis, 13, 61, 1929). A. Birkenmajer: Morbecana, i–ii (Philosophisches Jahrbuch der Görresgesellschaft, Fulda 1930; Isis, 15, 408). Martin Grabmann: Die Proklosübersetzungen des Wilhelm von Moerbeke und ihre Verwertung in der lateinischen Literatur des Mittelalters (Heisenberg Festschrift, Byzantinische Zeitschrift, vol. 30, 78–88, 1930).

II. FROM ARABIC INTO LATIN

BONACOSA

Bonacosa is possibly a translation of the Hebrew name Ṭobiyah (Tobiah). Unknown Jew, who translated Ibn Rushd's Kullīyāt from Arabic (or from Hebrew?) into Latin, Padua, 1255.

Text—This translation was anonymously printed in Venice, 1482. New edition together with Ibn Zuhr (Venice 1490), ascribed to Armengaud. Also with al-Rāzī and Serapion (Strassburg 1531).

Criticism—M. Steinschneider: Hebraeische Übersetzungen (672, 973, 1893); Europäische Übersetzungen aus dem Arabischen (8,1904).

JOHN OF BRESCIA

Giovanni da Brescia, Joannes Brixiensis (Brisciensis). Italian translator who worked with Jacob ben Maḥir at Montpellier in 1263 and helped him to translate into Latin al-Zarqālī's treatise on the astrolabe, Liber tabulae quae nominatur saphaea patris Isaac Arzachelis. Jacob translated from Arabic into the vernacular, John wrote the Latin equivalent.

M. Steinschneider: Hebraeische Übersetzungen (590, 1893); Europäische Übersetzungen (40, 1904).

ARMENGAUD SON OF BLAISE

Armengandus Blasii Monspeliensis (Hermengaldus, Armengab, Ermengard, Ermengaud, etc.), French physician and translator, who flourished at Montpellier, c. 1290; physician to Jayme II (king of Aragon from 1291 to 1327) and to Clement V (pope from 1305 to 1314); he died in or before 1313. His Latin translations were made from the Arabic or from the Hebrew, or at any rate with the help of Hebrew versions. He translated the following works:

1. Galen: *περὶ τῶν ἰδίων ἑκάστῳ παθῶν καὶ ἁμαρτημάτων τῆς διαγνώσεως*. From the Arabic translation made by Tūmā al-Ruhāwī (Thomas of Edessa), upon request

of Ḥunain ibn Isḥāq, who revised it, Kitāb kaifa yata'araf al-insān dhunūbhi wa 'uyūbhi (How man recognizes his sins and vices).

2. Pseudo-Galen: Yconomica (Economy). Economy is here taken in its literal sense, household management. It includes morality and hygiene as well as domestic economy. This text is really a Latin abridgment of the Arabic version of a Greek treatise ascribed to the Pythagorean Bryson (Βρύσων, or Βρύσσων), otherwise unknown. The Greek text is lost, except for a few lines preserved in the anthology of Joannes Stobaeos (second half of the fifth century), but there are Arabic and Hebrew versions or adaptations of it.

3. Ibn Sīnā: Al-arjūzat fī-l-ṭibb, together with Ibn Rushd's commentary upon it. Avicennae cantica (1280 or 1284). This is a famous medical poem. Arjūzat means simply a poem written in the meter rajz or rajaz, often used for didactic purposes. The word arjūzat was first translated articuli; a better translation is canticum or cantica. With regard to this text, there can be no doubt that Armengaud translated it from the Hebrew, not from the Arabic.

4. Maimonides: Maqāla fī-tadbīr al-ṣiḥḥa. R. Moses Aegyptius, De sanitate or De regimine sanitatis ad sultanum Babyloniae (1290).

5. Maimonides: Al-sumūm wal-mutaḥarriz, De venenis. This translation was made in 1307 for Clement V.

6. Jacob ben Maḥir: Treatise on the quadrant translated from the Hebrew into Latin, in Montpellier, 1299 by Jacob and Armengaud.

Ibn Rushd's Kullīyāt was not translated by Armengaud but by the Jew Bonacosa (see above).

Armengaud compiled a collection of recipes, De remediis, which was translated into Hebrew by Estori Farḥi (first half of the fourteenth century). The Latin text is lost; all the translations seem to be derived from the Hebrew version.

Text—Translatio Canticorum Avicennae cum commento Averrois, in the edition printed in Venice, 1484, as a sequel to the Qānūn. Reprinted, Venice 1492–1495. Revised by Andrea Alpago and included in his edition of Ibn Sīnā (Venice 1544; again 1582). Alpago says that his translation is a revision of that made by Gerard of Cremona. Also included in the Latin edition of Aristotle—Ibn Rushd (vol. 10, Venice 1552, 1574).

The Yconomica Galieni was reprinted in Plessner's memoir quoted below.

Criticism—Ernest Renan: Averroès (stereot. ed., 217, 1869). L. Leclerc: Médecine arabe (vol. 2, 467, 1876). F. Wüstenfeld: Übersetzungen arabischer Werke (96–98, 1877). E. Renan: Histoire littéraire de la France (vol. 28, 127–138, 1881). M. Steinschneider: Hebraeische Übersetzungen (608, 778, 1893); Europaeische Übersetzungen (6, 1904). Lynn Thorndike: History of magic (vol. 2, 205, 207, 845, 852, 938, 1923). G. Berstraesser: Ḥunain ibn Isḥāq (p. 48 of Arabic text, Leipzig 1928; Isis, 8, 685). Martin Plessner: Der Οἰκονομικός des Neupythagoreers Bryson und sein Einfluss auf die islamische Wissenschaft (310 p., Heidelberg 1928; Isis, 13, 529).

HERMANN THE GERMAN

Hermannus Alemannus (or Teutonicus, Germanicus). German translator from Arabic into Latin, probably with the help of Muslim dragomans. He flourished at Toledo in 1240, 1256; was in the service of Manfred (king of Naples from 1258 to 1266); died in 1272, being then bishop of Astorga (in León). He is said to have been a teacher of Bacon; at any rate, Bacon knew of his translations. He translated:

1. Ibn Rushd: Middle commentary on Aristotle's Ethics (Toledo 1240; not 1260).
2. Ibn Rushd: Middle commentary on Aristotle's Rhetoric (?) and Poetic (1256).
3. Summa quorundam Alexandrinorum, relative to the Ethics (1243–1244).
4. al-Fārābī: Commentary on the Rhetoric.

He also translated the Psalter into Castilian. This translation was made from the Vulgate but with reference to the Hebrew text. This was the earliest attempt to translate the Old Testament from Hebrew into a vernacular; it was followed by many others more important in the fourteenth and fifteenth centuries. See my note on Moses Arragel (first half of the fifteenth century).

Text—Hermann's translations of these Arabic commentaries are found in the early Latin editions of the Aristotelian texts commented upon. For example, in the Ethics of 1483, and in the Rhetoric of Venice, 1481, etc.

Criticism—F. Wüstenfeld: Übersetzungen arabischer Werke (91–96, 1877). M. Steinschneider: Die europäischen Übersetzungen (Wiener Sitzungsber., phil. Kl., vol. 149, 32, 1904). Sandys: History of classical scholarship (vol. 1, 569, 1921).

MOSES OF PALERMO

Moses Panormitanus. Judeo-Sicilian translator of medical works from Arabic into Latin. In 1277 Charles of Anjou (king of Naples and Sicily, 1266 to 1282), who continued the learned tradition of the Hohenstaufen, ordered him to study Latin "donec libri ipsi fuerint translati." Moses translated a pseudo-Hippocratic treatise on veterinary medicine, De curationibus infirmitatum aequorum.

Text—Trattati di mascalcia attribuiti ad Ippocrate tradotti dall' arabo in latino da maestro Moisè da Palermo, volgarizzati nel sec. XIII, edited by Pietro Delprato (Bologna 1865). Contains the Latin text and two early Italian versions together with an introduction.

Criticism—M. Steinschneider: Hebraeische Übersetzungen (985, 1893); Europäische Übersetzungen aus dem Arabischen (58, 1904). Léon Moulé: Histoire de la médecine vétérinaire en Europe au Moyen âge (24–25, Paris 1900). I. Broyde: Jewish Encyclopaedia (vol. 9, 92, 1905).

See my note on Boniface of Calabria.

FARAJ BEN SALĪM

Moses Farachi or Faragut (Fararius, Ferrarius?, Ferragius, Franchinus). Sicilian-Jewish physician and translator from Arabic into Latin. He was employed by Charles of Anjou to translate medical works and became one of the greatest translators of his time.

His main translation was that of the Kitāb al-ḥāwī (Continens) of al-Rāzī (second half of the ninth century). He completed it in 1279, together with a glossary. The Ḥāwī was the largest encyclopaedia of Greco-Arabic medicine, much larger than the more famous Qānūn of Ibn Sīnā. The long delay in its translation was probably due to its very size. The importance of this translation can hardly be exaggerated.

His other translations include:

2. Pseudo-Galenic De medicinis expertis, from the Arabic version by Ḥunain ibn Isḥāq. Greek text lost.
3. Ibn Jazla (second half of the eleventh century): Taqwīm al-abdān (c. 1280).

4. Mesuë the Third (first half of the thirteenth century): Treatise on surgery (if this was really translated from the Arabic).

A beautifully illustrated manuscript of the Continens was made in 1282 by order of Charles of Anjou. It is now in the Bibliothèque Nationale, Paris (five magnificent folios). It contains three portraits of the translator; these are in all probability the earliest portraits of a definite Jew. Faraj's translation was printed at Brescia, 1486, this being the largest and heaviest of all incunabula (22 lbs!).

Text—Continens. First edition, Brescia 1486. Includes the glossary and a dissertation entitled De expositionibus vocabulorum seu synonimorum simplicis medicine. Later editions: Venice 1500, 1506, 1509, 1542.

Tacuini aegritudinum et morborum fere omnium corporis humani cum curis eorunden Buhahylyha Byngezla auctore (Strassburg 1532).

De medicinis experimentatis, sive experimentatio medicinalis, e graeco sermone in arabicum a Johannicio et ex arabico in latinum a Magistro Franchino conversa. Opera Galeni (vol. 10, p. 561), edited by René Chartier (1572–1654).

Criticism—L. Leclerc: Médecine arabe (vol. 2, 464–467, 1876). F. Wüstenfeld: Übersetzungen arabischer Werke (107–110, 1877). M. Steinschneider: Hebraeische Übersetzungen (1893, 974); Europaeische Übersetzungen (14, 1904). I. Broyde: Jewish encyclopedia (vol. 5, 342, 1903). E. Wickersheimer: A note on the liber de medicinis expertis (Annals of medical history, vol. 4, 323–327, 1922; Isis, 5, 537).

Faraj's portrait of the Paris MS. is reproduced in Legacy of Israel (222, Oxford 1927).

For Giovanni Campano and Robert the Englishman, see the mathematical chapter; for Virgil of Cordova, the introductory one; for Arnold of Villanova and Ramon Lull, the philosophical one.

III. FROM ARABIC INTO SPANISH AND INTO PORTUGUESE

ALFONSO X EL SABIO

Alphonso X the Wise (El Sabio means the learned, the knower, rather than the wise), King of Castile and León from 1252 to his death at Seville, 1284.

His father, San Fernando (Ferdinand III the Saint, 1199–Seville 1252), had considerably increased the kingdom of Castile and León at the expense of the Muslims, conquering Cordova in 1236, then Seville, the kingdom of Murcia, Jaen (1246), and reducing the (Muslim) kingdom of Granada to a small territory on the southeastern coast of Spain. Before Ferdinand's death, Alfonso was governor of the newly conquered Murcia. He was naturally brought up in an intellectual atmosphere which was impregnated with Muslim and Jewish influences. While in Murcia, he ordered a school to be established for one Muḥammad al-Riqūṭī, who taught Christians, Muslims and Jews alike. He completed the incorporation of the University of Salamanca in 1254, and in the same year he established at Seville a Latin and Arabic college where Muslim physicians were the colleagues of Christian teachers.

He gathered around him a number of Jewish and Christian scholars to continue the great work undertaken by his father, the transmission of Muslim knowledge to Christendom, the translation of Arabic writings into Spanish. Ferdinand had patronized the compilation of the Libro de los doce sabios and of the Flores de filosofía. Alfonso ordered the translation into Castilian of the fables of Kalīla wa Dimna, of the Sirr al-asrār (Poridad de poridades), of the Qur'ān, of Talmudic and

Qabbalistic writings, and of a number of astronomical treatises. We shall deal more elaborately with the latter, but I must first offer a few general remarks.

The importance of Alfonso's activity as a promoter of translations and of scientific research can hardly be exaggerated. He might be called the founder of Spanish science; he was one of the greatest intermediaries between Arabic and European knowledge.

On the other hand it must be confessed that he showed but little ability as a king and statesman. The popular saying according to which he paid so much attention to celestial things that he lost his terrestrial crown is misleading, for he sacrificed the realities of his Spanish trust not so much to his scientific endeavors as to his imperial ambitions. He had some claim to the imperial throne, being a Hohenstaufen through his mother; in 1254 he was actually nominated by the German electors, and he spent an immense amount of money in the hope of transforming that nomination into a reality. He failed entirely and never set foot on German ground. In the meanwhile he had been led to establish extravagant tariffs, to debase the coinage of his realm, and in other ways to work scathe to his own people. He finally caused a rebellion against himself which developed into a civil war. In 1282 he was deposed by his son Sancho, and at the time of his death at Seville in 1284 he was not only defeated but disowned by his own subjects.

His main title to fame lies in the organization of what we might call an institute for the translation of astronomical works from Arabic into Spanish. These translations were not made by himself, but under his direction; witness the many prefaces which he wrote for them. In some cases the translations were published as such; in others they were used by members of his scientific staff and revised or elaborated in various ways. The following works were translated at his request (all the translations are into Spanish unless otherwise stated):

1. Ptolemy: Tetrabiblon together with commentary by 'Alī ibn Riḍwān translated into Spanish by an unknown translator, and from Spanish into Latin by Aegidius de Thebaldis.
2. al-Battānī: Canones, by Isaac ibn Sid.
3. Ibn abī-l-Rijāl: Kitāb al-bāri' fī aḥkām al-nujūm, an astrological treatise translated by Judah ben Moses in 1256. The Spanish text was Latinized by Aegidius de Thebaldis of Parma and Petrus de Regio and often printed.
4. Ibn al-Haitham: Fī-hai'at al-ālam. On the configuration of the world, by Abraham of Toledo. Abraham's version was Latinized under the title Liber de mundo et coelo, de motibus planetarum, etc.
5. A series of astronomical works which were edited together by Alfonso's order in 1276–1277 under the collective title Libros del saber de astronomia. The Libros del saber include plain translations from the Arabic, revised translations more or less distant from the original text, more or less original treatises derived by the translators from the Arabic writings, introductions by the translators and by the king himself. At least ten prefaces were written by the latter. It is clear that he was not a passive patron, but that his personal effort was quite considerable. This enormous work is primarily an encyclopaedic account of all astronomical instruments, explaining their construction and their uses, and giving many examples of observations and computations. It was meant to be so complete that other books would be unnecessary. It is composed of eleven parts, of which the first is a sort of astronomical introduction dealing with the stars, and the ten following are devoted to a series of instruments. We shall consider each part separately

(nos. 6 to 16). For the Spanish titles see below under *Text*. There is but one complete MS., preserved in Alcara de Henarez; but an incomplete Italian translation, made in 1341 by Gueruccius son of Cion Florentine, is in the Vatican.[1]

6. Four books on stars. Derived from the Kitāb al-kawākib al-thābita al-muṣawwar, by 'Abd al-Raḥmān al-Ṣūfī (second half of the tenth century), translated in 1256 by Judah ben Moses and Guillen Arremon Daspa (or d'Aspa), and from other Arabic treatises. The catalogue of stars was certainly based not upon Hipparchos and Ptolemy, but upon 'Abd al-Raḥmān, who was inspired by Menelaos of Alexandria. Al-Battānī's value of the precession (1° in 66 years) was used. The constellations are inverted as they would appear on a globe. The latitudes and longitudes of fourteen stars were observed in Toledo in 1260 by Alfonso's order. This Spanish text derived from various Arabic sources was edited in 1276 under Alfonso's direction, with the assistance of two Jews, Judah ben Moses and Samuel ha-Levi, and two Christians, John of Messina and John of Cremona.

7. Book on celestial globe. Revised translation of the Kitāb al-'amal bilkura al-fulkīya by Qusṭā ibn Lūqā (second half of the ninth century). The literal translation was made in 1259 by Judah ben Moses and John Daspa. The present elaboration was completed in 1277; the first four chapters are an introduction contributed by Alfonso's staff. A final chapter dealing with astrology was written by one "Xosse" (José).

8. Two books on armils. Essentially derived from al-Zarqālī (second half of the eleventh century), but elaborated by the translator, Isaac ibn Sid. The instrument described contained equatorial, ecliptical, and horizontal armils, and was thus universal; moreover it could be used also to solve mechanically various mathematical problems. Many examples are given, also auxiliary tables.

9. Two books on the spherical astrolabe. Composed by Isaac ibn Sid. The Arabic source is not determined. Treatises on the subject were written by al-Nairīzī and Qusṭā ibn Lūqā. Isaac may have used these, or others, without any attempt at direct translation. The spherical astrolabe was also a sort of universal instrument, making possible many kinds of observations and reductions.

10. Two books on the plane astrolabe. Source and translator unknown. References to Ptolemy in the text.

11. Book of atazir in two parts (this is probably the Arabic word tasyīr, referring to the course of the planets). Composed by Isaac ibn Sid. This instrument was a plane astrolabe with alidade, used mainly by astrologers to expedite computations.

12. Two books of the universal plate. The Arabic author was probably Abū-l-Ḥasan 'Alī ibn Khalaf ibn Ghālib al-Anṣārī, of Cordova, who flourished c. 1019 (H. Suter, 96, 214, 1900). According to Alfonso's preface this "lamina universal" was invented in Toledo by the author, and later improved by al-Zarqālī. Elaborate introduction by Isaac ibn Sid, who was probably the translator. The treatise ascribed to 'Alī ibn Khalaf is in the main a collection of problems of practical astronomy, divided into five parts: construction and use of the instrument, astronomical geography, sun, stars, moon.

13. Book of the ṣafīḥa. Translation of al-Zarqālī's treatise on this kind of astrolabe invented by him in two stages. The first type was dedicated to Yaḥyā al-Ma'mūn (king of Toledo, 1037–1074); the second to Muḥammad II al-Mu'tamid (king of Seville, 1068–1091). Al-Zarqālī's treatise was translated in 1255–1256 by

[1] Isis, 13, 93, 1929.

Fernando of Toledo; revised in Burgos, 1277, by Abraham of Toledo and one Bernaldo.

14. Two books on the plates of the seven planets (aequatoria). One was written by Ibn al-Samḥ (first half of the eleventh century), the other by al-Zarqālī, at Seville, c. 1081. These aequatoria were astrolabes or planispheres enabling one to determine promptly the position of a planet without computation.

15. Book of quadrants. Composed by Isaac ibn Sid in 1277. Arabic original, if any, unknown.

16. Five books on clocks: (a) stone dial; (b) waterclocks; (c) quicksilver clock; (d) candleclock; (e) clock of the palace of the hours (a fanciful conception of no importance). Four of these books were composed by Isaac ibn Sid, one (d) by Samuel ha-Levi. The sources are unknown, except for (c) wherein "Iran el filósofo" is quoted (this might be Heron?). These books on clocks complete the Libros del saber.

17. Libro de las cruces (Book of the crosses). Elaborate treatise on judicial astrology, divided into 65 chapters. The Arabic original was composed by one 'Ubaid Allāh. The translation was made in 1259 by Judah ben Moses and John Daspa.

18. Libro de las formas et de las imagines que son en los cielos et de las virtudes et de las obras que salen de ellas en los cuerpos que son de yuso de cielo, que mando componer de los libros de los philosophos antiguos . . . . D. Alphonso . . . . (1276–1279). Book of the forms and images which are in the heavens and of their virtues and power upon the terrestrial bodies, which was composed out of the writings of the ancient philosophers by order of D. Alfonso. This is an astrological collection divided, like the Libros del saber, into eleven parts. The first part is a lapidary De la propriedad de las pietras, dealing with 360 stones. It was translated from "Chaldaean" into Arabic by Abolays (Abū-l-'Aysh), and from Arabic into Spanish by Judah ben Moses. The authors of the following parts are (2) Timtim; (3) Pythagoras; (4) Yluz; (5) Belyenus (Apollonios?) and Yluz; (6) Pliny, Belyenus; (7) 'Uṭārid; probably 'Uṭārid ibn Muḥammad (first half of the ninth century; (8) Ragiel, probably Ibn abī-l-Rijāl (first half of the eleventh century); (9) Yāqūt; (10) 'Alī; (11) none named.

These translations of astronomical and astrological works prove Alfonso's deep interest in astronomy. But he gave another and even better proof of it, by ordering the compilation of new astronomical tables to replace the Toledan tables which had been edited by al-Zarqālī two centuries before in the same town. The so-called Alphonsine Tables were prepared under Alfonso's direction, in Toledo, by Judah ben Moses and Isaac ibn Sid, not in 1252 (as has often been repeated at least since the fifteenth century), but c. 1272. It is highly probable that the original tables (which are lost) were written in Spanish; it is equally probable that the numerals used were Roman rather than Arabic, for the tables included in the Libros del saber (e.g., in the treatise no. 8 above) contain only Roman numerals.

The original tables are lost, but the introduction has been preserved (Libro de las taulas Alfonsíes) and thus we have a definite idea of the nature of these tables, and can appreciate their differences from later ones.

The tables published by Rico y Sinobas (vol. 4, 1866) as fragments of the original Alphonsine Tables are probably fragments of an Almanach perpetuum giving ephemerides of planets for long intervals of years (e.g., Mercury for 46 years, Venus for 8, Mars for 79, Jupiter for 83, Saturn for 59). The tables for the Sun and Moon give the minutes and seconds, those for the planets only round degrees; latitudes are not considered. Whether this Almanach belongs to the Alphonsine school is uncertain; there is no reason to postulate it; the MSS. from which it was published are dated 1309 and 1396. Many such almanachs were computed in later times, the best known being the Bi'ur luḥot of Abraham Zacuto (1473), or rather its Latin translation.

To return to the Alphonsine Tables, they became known in Paris only by 1292. In their Spanish form they could hardly exert any influence outside of the peninsula. They owed their immense popularity to the Latin versions, especially to the elaboration prepared by John of Saxony (first half of the fourteenth century). The Latin Tabulae Alphonsii cannot represent the original text without modifications; e.g., they contain traces of antisemitism. The Latin tables were frequently printed in the fifteenth and sixteenth centuries. An edition appeared even as late as 1641, in Madrid, but this was a real aberration, for the Rudolphine Tables, computed by Kepler, had appeared in 1627.

They were translated into Hebrew by Moses ben Abraham of Nîmes in 1460; the existence of an earlier Hebrew translation by Qalonymos ben Qalonymos (first half of the fourteenth century) is very doubtful, or if a translation was made by one Qalonymos, this was probably a later member of the same family; e.g., the astronomer, David Qalonymos (fl. c. 1465).

There are a number of differences between the Spanish introduction to the Alphonsine Tables and the printed editions: the fundamental epochs are different (Jan. 0, 1252 in the MS; June 1, 1252, date of Alfonso's coronation, in the printed texts); the latitude of Toledo is quoted as 39° 54′ in the MS., 41° in the printed text; the longitudes and average motions are computed differently. The erroneous theory of the trepidation of the equinoxes is very much elaborated in the MS. and Latin editions, but not at all in the same way.

Considered as a whole, Alfonso's astronomy was not on a very high level. There was more good will and energy in his efforts, and those of his assistants, than outstanding intelligence. This Alphonsine astronomy was hardly superior to Ptolemy's.

A figure of the deferent of Mercury in the form of an ellipse with what looks like a Sun in the center in the second treatise on the plates of the seven planets (no. 14 in my list above; Madrid edition, vol. 3, 282, 1864) is purely accidental; it is not in any sense an anticipation of Kepler's discovery of the ellipticity of celestial orbits.

Alfonso's statement that if he had been consulted for the creation of the world it would have been far better arranged (or something to that effect), does not deserve to be seriously discussed; it was probably neither a blasphemy nor a criticism of Ptolemaic astronomy to which he was hardly equal, but simply an irresponsible sally.

King Alfonso combined the best points of the existing charters to compile El fuero real which became the charter of the unchartered districts. Later (c. 1260–1265) he compiled what may be called the earliest Spanish code, Las siete partidas (it is divided into seven parts; it is also called Libro de las partidas, Leyes de las partidas, or simply Las partidas). It was promulgated only at the Cortes at Alcalá, 1338; the history of its becoming gradually the code of Spain is as complicated as that of the Cortes or of Spanish unification; it need not be told here. Suffice it to say that it became eventually the main law of Spain and of its colonies. Its influence is illustrated by the fact that as late as 1819 Louisiana found it expedient to make a new compilation of the parts of Las siete partidas which were in force within its own boundaries, together with the Code Napoléon.

One title of the Siete partidas (part II, title XXXI) is of special interest to us. It refers to the universities and may be considered the earliest educational code of Europe. It contains the first authoritative definition of a "studium generale," and lays down some rules concerning its administration and the privileges of its members.

Alfonso compiled (or caused to be compiled) c. 1260–1268, the first national history of Spain in Spanish, Grande y general historia (down to 1252), derived from Arabic as well as from Latin sources. He may thus be called the father of Spanish historiography. He wrote other historical works: La gran conquista de ultramar; Historia sagrada, etc.

Alfonso's Siete partidas (1265) pays attention to alchemy, the practice of which is protected, though he considered its purpose unattainable. Two treatises on alchemy are ascribed to him, El candido and El libro del tesoro (or do these two titles represent the same work?). The Tesoro (1272) deals with the philosopher's stone in a mixture of prose and verse, much of which is unintelligible. It is almost certainly apocryphal. The Clavis majoris sapientiae de transmutatione metallica which the king ordered to be translated into Spanish is an account of cosmogonical evolution rather than of transmutation. See my note on "Artephius" (first half of the twelfth century).

Various other works are ascribed to him, notably on navigation and on chess, Iuegos diversos de axedrez.[2] He is said to have ordered the Old Testament to be translated into Spanish.

Finally Alfonso composed (or edited) a large number of poems; some 450, of which 426 are of a religious character, most of these being in honor of Our Lady (Cantigas de Santa Maria). Strangely enough, these poems were not written, as Alfonso's prose works, in Castilian, but in Galician, another dialect, more closely related to Portuguese than to modern Spanish, which was then spoken over a large territory as far as Navarre. Thus Alfonso is at once through his prose writings one of the fathers of Spanish literature, and through his verse one of the fathers of Portuguese literature.

Moreover these poems were meant to be sung, and their respective melodies have been preserved, their collection forming one of the greatest monuments of mediaeval music. In fact the text is inseparable from its melody, nor can the rhythm of the words be fully appreciated without it. The composers were deeply influenced by the Muslim singers (mughannī) and by the troubadours, yet they were very original, Spanish to the core.

Alfonso was also the founder of the Spanish scientific language and literature. The translations ordered by him required the building up of a new vocabulary. In this important respect his service to Spain was comparable to that of Alfred the Great, four centuries earlier, to England.

Text—Libros del saber—Libros del saber de astronomía del rey D. Alfonso X de Castilla. Copilados, anotados y comentados por D. Manuel Rico y Sinobas (5 vols. large folio, many plates and facsimiles, Madrid, 1863–1867; the last volume was not completed). As this fundamental publication is available only in the largest libraries (not more than 200 copies were printed), and as it is difficult to

[2] I.e., ajedrez.

handle it on account of its awkward size, I append a complete analysis of it. The numbers in front of each title correspond to the numbers given in the text above.

Vol. 1 (306 p., 1863). Editorial introduction dealing with Alfonso, the MSS. of the Libros del Saber, list of authors quoted in the Libros, etc. (92 p.).

6. Los IIII libros de la ochaua espera e de sus XLVIII figuras con sus estrellas: 1. De las estrellas y constelaciones boreales de la octava esfera; 2. De las estrellas y constelaciones zodiacales de la octava esfera; 3. De las estrellas y constelaciones meridionales de la octava esfera; 4. Del cuento de las estrellas y constelaciones de la octava esfera (p. 1–145).

7. Libro de la fayçon dell espera et de sus figuras et de sus huebras (Libro de la alcora, ó sea el globo celeste) (p. 153–208).

Vol. 2 (330 p., 1863). (8) Los dos libros de las armellas (p. 1–79).

9. Libros dell astrolabio redondo (p. 113–222). Preceded by an editorial introduction dealing with the Alphonsine astrolabes (p. 83–112).

10. Libros dell astrolabio llano (p. 225–292).

11. El libro dell ataçir (or atazir) (p. 295–309).

Vol. 3 (374 p., 1864). Editorial introduction (47 p.).

12. Libros de la lámina uniuersal (p. 1–132).

13. Libro de la açafeha (p. 135–237).

14. Libros de las laminas de los VII planetas (p. 241–284).

15. Libro del quadrante pora rectificar (Libros del cuadrante ó cuarto de círculo de corredera). (p. 287–316.)

Vol. 4 (278 p., 1866) (16). Los cinco libros de los relogios alfonsies. L. Libro del relogio de la piedra de la sombra; II. Libro del relogio dell agua; III. Libro del relogio dell argento uiuo; IV. Libro del relogio de las candelas; V. Libro del relogio del palacio de las oras (p. 3–118).

Libro de las taulas alfonsíes (p. 119–183). This is the original introduction to the Alphonsine tables.

Fragmentos numéricos de las taulas alfonsíes (some 80 p. of facsimile unnumbered). As explained above these are not fragments of the Alphonsine tables, but of some kind of universal ephemerides, possibly of a later date.

Vol. 5, part 1 (300 p., 1867). Los códices astronómicos verdaderos y espúrios del Rey D. Alfonso el Sabio. Las vindicias ó el centiloquio alfonsí. Estrellas que tenian nombre conocido en tiempo de D. Alfonso. Las mansiones ó casas de la luna, segun los libros alfonsíes.

Vol. 5, part 2. This second part was never published. It was planned to include comparative studies on the Alphonsine instruments, a collection of all the documents concerning Alfonso and his time, and a glossary.

Libro de las cruces. Elaborate analysis of it with translation of many extracts by José A. Sánchez Pérez (Isis, 14, 77–132, 4 figs., 1930).

Tabulae alphonsinae. For the original Spanish introduction, see Libros del saber (vol. 4, 1866).

First edition of the Latin version. Alfontii . . . celestium motuum tabule: nec non stellarum fixarum longitudines ac latitudines Alfontii tempore ad motus veritatem mira diligentia reducte. At primo Joannis Saxoniensis in tabulas Alfontii canones ordinati incipiunt faustissime (94 leaves; Venice, Ratdolt, 1483). Second edition, together with canones by Joannes Lucilius Santritter (114 leaves, Venice, Hamann, 1492). For an external description of these, see Gesamtkatalog der Wiegendrucke (vol. 2, 1–3, 1926; these two are the only Alfonsine incunabula). For a comparison of these editions and later ones, see A. Wegener (p. 165–171). Wegener quotes three editions of 1487, 1488, 1490, which are apparently ghosts.

Later editions: Venice 1518 (1521); by Lucas Gauricus of Naples, Venice, 1521, 1524; by Pascal Hamel (also spelled Hammel), Paris, 1545, 1553; by Francisco Garcia Ventanas, Madrid, 1641. According to Wegener, the numbers are the same in all printed tables.

Las siete partidas. First edition, Seville, 1491. Second, Seville, 1491. Later ones: Venice, 1501; Burgos, 1508, 1518, 1528; Venice, 1528; Medina del Campo, 1542; Alcala de Henares, 1542; Lyon, 1550. Critical edition by Lorenzo Galíndez de Carvajal and Gregorio López, Salamanca, 1555, 1565, 1576, etc. New critical edition by the Real Academia de la Historia (3 vols., Madrid, 1807). Opusculos legales, edited by the same academy (Madrid, 1836).

Primera crónica general. First edition, Zamora, 1541. Second, Valladolid, 1604. Third and better, Madrid, 1791-92. Ramón Menéndez Pidal: Estoria de España que mandó componer Alfonso el Sabio y se continuaba bajo Sancho IV en 1289 (vol. 1, Madrid, 1906).

P. de Gayangos: La gran conquista de Ultramar (Madrid, 1858). Earlier edition, Salamanca, 1503.

El tratado de ajedrez ordenado por mandádo del rey D. Alfonso en el año 1283. Facsimile reproduction of the Escorial MS. (Leipzig 1913).

Cantiguas de Santa Maria edited by the R. Spanish Academy (2 vols., Madrid, 1889).

General and historical criticism—Willy Herrmann: Alfons X als römischer King (Diss., 40 p., Berlin 1897). Joseph Jacobs: Jewish encyclopaedia (vol. 1, 377, 1901). R. Menéndez Pidal: La crónica general de España (50 p., Madrid 1916). Antonio Ballesteros y Beretta: Alfonso X, emperador electo de Alemania (96 p., Madrid 1918). Fritz Baer: Encyclopaedia judaica (vol. 2, 284, 1928).

Astronomy—Enrico Narducci: Intorno ad una traduzione italiana fatta nell' anno 1341 di una compilazione astronomica di Alfonso X (Giornale arcadico, vol. 42, 81-112, Roma 1864; not available). Eugen Gelcich: Die Instrumente und die wissenschaftlichen Hülfsmittel der Nautik (p. 84-90, Hamburgische Festschrift zur Erinnerung an die Entdeckung Amerika's, vol. 1, Hamburg, 1892). Alfred Wegener: Die Alfonsinischen Tafeln für den Gebrauch eines modernen Rechners (Diss., 63 p., 2 pl., Berlin 1905); Die astronomischen Werke Alfons X (Bibliotheca mathematica, vol. 6, 129-185, 1905); important; the study of the treatise marked no. 14 in my list above is particularly elaborate (p. 152-161). P. Duhem: Système du monde (vol. 2, 259-266, 1914). J. L. E. Dreyer: The original form of the Alfonsine tables (Monthly notices of the R. Astronom. Soc., vol. 80, 243-262, 1920; Isis, 3, 455; 4, 137). Joaquim Bensaude: Les légendes allemandes sur l'histoire des découvertes maritimes portugaises (Genève, 1917-1920, Annexe no. 2, Les tables alphonsines dans leur texte numérique original, p. 7-11). Claiming against A. Wegener that the tables published by Rico y Sinobas represent probably the original Alfonsine tables. Hugo Seemann and Th. Mittelberger: Das kugelförmige Astrolabe nach den Mitteilungen von Alfons X und den vorhandenen arabischen Quellen (Abhdl. zur Geschichte der Naturwissenschaften, Heft 8, 69 p., Erlangen 1925; Isis, 8, 743); description of the spherical astrolabe dealt with in the Libros del saber, my no. 9 above. Jose Soriano Viguera: Contribución al conocimiento de los trabajos astronómicos desarrollados en la Escuela de Alfonso X (Madrid 1926). Oiva Johannes Tallgren: Los nombres arabes de las estrellas y la transcripcion alfonsina (Homenaje a Menéndez Pidal, vol. 2, 634-718, Madrid 1925; Isis, 11, 175); Sur l'astronomie espagnole d'Alphonse X et son modèle arabe (Studia orientalia, 1, 342-345, Helsingfors 1925); Un point d'astronomie gréco-arabo-romane. A propos de l'astronomie espagnole d'Alphonse X (Neuphilologische Mitteilungen, vol. 29, 39-44, Helsinki 1928). Lynn Thorndike: Andalò di Negro, Profacius Judaeus, and the Alphonsine Tables (Isis, 10, 52-56, 1928). O. J. Tallgren: Survivance arabo-romane du Catalogue d'étoiles de Ptolémée (Studia orientalia, vol. 2, 202-283, Helsinki 1928; Isis, 12, 350). H. Rudy: Encyclopaedia judaica (vol. 2, 283, 1928; not up-to-date). José A. Sánchez Pérez: El libro de las cruces (Isis, 14, 77-132, 1930). O. J. Tallgren: Notas filológicas de astronomia alfonsina (Miscelânea em honra de D. Carolina Michaëlis de Vasconcellos, 7 p., Coimbra 1930).

Other scientific criticism—M. E. Chevreul: Examen d'un écrit alchimique intitulé Artefii clavis majoris sapientiae (Comptes rendus de l'Ac. des sciences, vol. 36, 33-82, 1867). L. Leclerc: Médecine arabe (vol. 2, 441-442, 1876). M. Steinschneider: Hebräische Übersetzungen (616-622, 1893). Hastings Rashdall: Universities of Europe in the Middle ages (vol. 2, 72-74, 1895). John Ferguson: Bibliotheca chemica (vol. 1, 24, 1926). E. O. v. Lippmann: Entstehung der Alchemie (498, 1919). Edward Luther Stevenson: Terrestrial and celestial globes (2 vols., New Haven, 1921; vol. 1, 40; Isis, 4, 549).

Literary criticism—Marqués de Valmar (Leopoldo Augusto de Cueto): Las cantiguas del rey D. Alfonso el Sabio (2d ed., 422 p., Madrid 1897). Aubrey F. G. Bell: Portuguese literature (42, Oxford 1922). John Brande Trend: Alfonso the Sage and other essays (224 p., London 1926).

Musical criticism—Julián Ribera y Tarragó: La musica de las Cantigas, estudio sobre su origen y naturaléza, con reproducciones fotograficas del texto y transcripción moderna (500 p., 10 pl., folio; Madrid 1922; fundamental); Abridged English version (296 p., Stanford 1929); Historia de la música árabe medieval y su influencia en la Española (355 p., Madrid 1927; Isis, 11, 496). John Brande Trend: Grove's Dictionary of music (vol. 1, 65, 1927).

JUDAH BEN MOSES

Judah ben Moses ha-Kohen. (Mosca el menor?). Jewish physician and astronomer who flourished in Toledo. One of the translators from Arabic into Spanish employed by Alfonso X. He was one of the two main authors of the Alfonsine tables in 1272 (the other being Isaac ibn Sid). Translations of the following works are ascribed to him: (1) Qusṭā ibn Lūqā. Treatise on the sphere. Libro de alcora (kurra means sphere). Translated with John of Aspa in 1259; revised and elaborated in 1277; (2) 'Abd al-Raḥmān al-Ṣūfī. Kitāb al-kawākib, Book of stars, Libro de las figuras, translated in 1256, revised and elaborated in 1276 with the collaboration of Samuel ha-Levi and others; (3) Ibn abī-l-Rijāl. Kitāb al-bāri', Libro complido, astrological treatise translated in 1256; (4) Lapidary by one Abolays (Abū-l-'Aysh?). De la propriedad de las piedras, dealing with 360 stones, one for each day of the year.

Soon after 1256 the Libro complido was translated into Latin by Aegidius de Thebaldis of Parma and Petrus de Regio (Pedro del Real), protonotary to Alfonso X; finally this Latin text was translated, thrice, into Hebrew! Judah may also be the translator of Ptolemy's Tetrabiblon together with 'Alī ibn Riḍwān's commentary, which Aegidius de Thebaldis was then ordered to translate from Spanish into Latin (another Latin translation had been made, c. 1136-1138 by Plato of Tivoli and Abraham bar Ḥiyya).

Text—Libro de alcora is included in Rico y Sinobas' edition of the Libros del saber (vol. 1, 153-208, 1863).

Libro de las figuras (ibidem, vol. 1, 1-145, 1863).

Extracts from Libro complido (ibidem, vol. 5, 1867). Latin text printed in Venice, 1485, 1525, and in Basel, 1551, 1571.

Lapidario del Rey D. Alfonso X. Facsimile reproduction of a splendid Escorial MS. which contains the description of 360 stones divided between the twelve signs of the zodiac. Introduction by Aureliano Fernandez-Guerra and Pedro de Madrazo and transcription of the text (Madrid 1881).

The Spanish translation of the Tetrabiblon is lost.

Criticism—L. Leclerc: Médecine arabe (vol. 2, 442-443, 1876). M. Steinschneider: Hebraeische Übersetzungen (525, 579, 979, 1893); Europäische Übersetzungen (3, 39, 1904). J. Horace Nunemaker: Noticias sobre la alquimia en el Lapidario de Alfonso X (Revista de filología española, vol. 16, 161-168, 1929); The lapidary of Alfonso X (Philological quarterly, vol. 8, 248-254, 1929); Some mediaeval Spanish terms of writing and illumination (Speculum, vol. 5, 420-424, 1930; Isis, 15, 409).

SAMUEL HA-LEVI

Samuel ha-Levi Abulafia. (The name Abulafia is derived from the Arabic Abū-l-'Āfiyat meaning Father of health; a number of Spanish Jews bore that name, a branch of the family being distinguished by the additional surname ha-Levi; from this Hebrew name derive the Italian name Bolaffi, the English name Bolaffey, etc.) This Samuel was one of the Jewish scholars employed by King Alfonso el Sabio to translate astronomical works from Arabic into Spanish. He flourished in Toledo. He translated the anonymous works: Fabrica y usos del relogio della candela (construction and use of the candle clock), and the Fabrica y usos del instrumento del levamento que en Arabigo se llama atazin (construction and use of the instrument of transportation called atazin?). The translation of the second work is also ascribed to Isaac ibn Sid. In 1276 he helped Judah ben Moses to revise and elaborate the Spanish text of the Book of stars of 'Abd al-Raḥmān al-Ṣūfī.

Text—The Fabrica is included in Rico y Sinobas' edition of the Libros del saber (vol. 4, 77-93, 1866). The book of stars (ibidem, vol. 1, 1-145, 1863).

The Libro del instrumento del levamento is not included in the Spanish Libros del saber, but it may be found in the Italian translation of 1341 kept in the Vatican library.

Criticism—Enrico Narducci: Intorno ad una traduzione italiana fatta nell' anno 1341 di una compilazione astronomica di Alfonso X (Giornale arcadico, vol. 42, 81-112, Roma 1864). M. Steinschneider: Hebraeische Übersetzungen (986, 1893); Europäische Übersetzungen (76, 1904). Moritz Kayserling: Jewish Encyclopaedia (vol. 1, 143, 1901; very brief note). M. Zobel: Encyclopaedia judaica (vol. 1, 650, 1928).

ISAAC IBN SID

Isaac ha-Ḥazzan, which means the precentor. He is also called in the Spanish documents Rabbi Zag (or Çag) and Aben Cayut (or Çayd). Hispano-Jewish astronomer, constructor of instruments, and translator from the Arabic into Spanish. He was the main collaborator of King Alfonso el Sabio, and flourished in Toledo c. 1263-1277. According to the Yesod 'olam of Isaac Israeli (first half of the fourteenth century), he made observations of eclipses in 1263-1266. He was one of the two authors of the famous Alphonsine Tables, 1272. He is said to have invented or improved various astronomical instruments.

He translated al-Battānī's Canons, and was the author of many (at least nine) of the translations and adaptations included in the Libros del saber. I shall mention these very briefly, quoting the numbers appended to each in my list of Alphonsine translations above.

8. Two books on armils.
9. Two books on the spherical astrolabe.
11. Book of atazir.
12. Two books of the universal plate, by 'Alī ibn Khalaf.
15. Book of quadrants, 1277.
16. Books on clocks. Out of the five books on clocks, four were composed by him.

To account for the movement of the equinoxes he is said to have introduced two periods of 49000 and 7000 years respectively for the precession and the "trepidation." One recognizes here a qabbalistic influence (notions of sabbath and jubilee extended to astronomy).

Text—See my note on Alfonso X. For the Libro del instrumento del levamento, see Samuel ha-Levi.

Criticism—M. Steinschneider: Hebraeische Übersetzungen (617, 975, 1893); Europäischen Übersetzungen (37, 1904). I. Broyde: Jewish Encyclopaedia (vol. 6, 632, 1904). Alfred Wegener: Die astronomischen Werke Alfons X (Bibliotheca mathematica, vol. 6, 176, 182, 1905). J. L. E. Dreyer: History of the planetary systems (278, 1906).

ABRAHAM OF TOLEDO

Don Abraham Alfaquin (the last word being derived from the Arabic al-ḥākim, the wise or the learned man, the physician). Spanish Jew. Physician to King Alfonso el Sabio and one of the scholars employed by him to translate scientific works from Arabic into Spanish. He translated:

1. A treatise of Ibn al-Haitham on the configuration of the universe; this free version or paraphrase was translated into Latin by an unknown author under the title De mundo et coelo. This same treatise was translated into Hebrew by Jacob ben Maḥir, and the Hebrew text was Latinized by Abraham de Balmes (second half of the fifteenth century). (2) A treatise of al-Zarqālī on the construction and the use, chiefly astrological, of his astrolabe. This had been translated into Spanish in 1255, for the same king, by Ferrando of Toledo. Abraham's translation, made in Burgos, 1277, was much better and was in its turn translated into Latin and Italian. (3) The seventieth chapter of the Qur'ān, Sūrat al-mu'ārij (chapter of the ascents). This same chapter was translated in 1264 from Spanish into French by Bonaventura de Sene.

Text—Libro de la açafeha in Libros del saber, edited by M. Rico y Sinobas (vol. 3, 135–237, 1863).

Criticism—M. Steinschneider: Notice sur un ouvrage astronomique inédit d'Ibn al-Haitham (Boncompagni's Bullettino, vol. 14, 721–741, 1881); Hebraeische Übersetzungen (559, 591, 972, 1893); Europäische Übersetzungen (3, 15, 1904). Louis Ginzberg: Jewish encyclopaedia (vol. 1, 121, 1901).

DINIS

Dinis (or Diniz) the Liberal, king of Portugal from 1279 to 1325. (Dinis is the Portuguese form of the old name Dionysios, Denis, etc.) Called the "Rei lavrador" (farmer king) and the "Father of his country." Born at Lisbon in 1261, died in 1325; buried in the monastery of São Dinis de Odivellas founded by himself near Lisbon. Grandson of Alfonso X. Educated by the Frenchman, Ayméric d'Ebrard of Cahors, afterwards bishop of Coimbra.

He developed the economic resources of Portugual, built canals and aqueducts, fostered agriculture, improved the methods of cultivation, planted pine forests upon the dunes of Leiria (which were later used to build the powerful Portuguese fleets), encouraged foreign trade, created schools and studios. In 1290 he founded a university in Lisbon, but transferred it in 1308 to Coimbra. He ordered the translation of many books from the Spanish, Latin, and Arabic into Portuguese; for example, the Cronica general of his grandfather (Historia geral de Hespanha).

Though there are a few earlier documents (e.g., a charter of 1192), the translations promoted by king Dinis may be considered the earliest monuments of Portuguese prose. Dinis was also a great poet, whose work was more abundant and more varied than that of every other trobador, excepting his grandfather. His Livro de trovas includes 138 poems; but it is possible that some of them were composed by other trobadores or jograes and ascribed to him.

Dinis was the first king to reign over Portugal with its modern boundaries, from the River Minho to Faro. His queen was Isabel, daughter of Pedro III of Aragon. She shared his throne for forty-three years, and is honored as the Queen Saint of Portugal.

Text—The Historia geral de Hespanha was incompletely edited in 1863.

Caetano Lopes de Moura: Cancioneiro d'elrei D. Diniz (232 p., Paris 1847). Enrico Molteni: Il canzoniere portoghese Colocci-Brancuti (Halle 1880). Henry R. Lang: Das Liederbuch des Königs Denis von Portugal (322 p., Halle 1894; partly published, 142 p., as a Strassburg thesis in Halle, 1892).

Criticism—Ruy de Pina: Chronica d'el-rei D. Diniz (2 vols., Lisbon 1907).

Aubrey F. G. Bell: Portuguese portraits (3–15, Oxford 1917); Portuguese literature (54, 59, Oxford 1922).

IV. FROM ARABIC INTO HEBREW

SOLOMON IBN AYYUB

Solomon ben Joseph ibn Ayyub·ha-Sefardi. Born or educated in Granada; flourished at Béziers. Hispano-Jewish physician and translator from Arabic into Hebrew. He translated:

1. Maimonides: Kitāb al-farā'iḍ, Sefer ha-mizwot, the book of divine commandments (Béziers 1240).

2, 3. Ibn Janāḥ: Kitāb al-tanbīh (Book of admonition, awakening), and Kitāb al-taswiya (Putting to rights), two grammatical treatises (Béziers 1254).

4. Ibn Rushd: Middle commentary on Aristotle's De coelo (1259).

5. Ibn Sīnā: Arjūzat, Sefer ha-arguzah, medical poem (1262).

He completed at Béziers in 1265 an original treatise on haemorrhoids, divided into seven parts, Ma'amar be-ṭeḥorim. It is interesting to compare it with the Maqāla fī-l-bawāṣīr of Maimonides which was translated into Hebrew under the title Ma'amar bi refu'at ha-ṭeḥorim.

Text—Edition of the Ma'amar 'al ha-ṭeḥorim by L. M. Herbert with a Hebrew preface by Alexander Marx (Ha-rofe' ha-ivri, vol. 1, 63–111, New York 1929–1930; Isis, 15, 409).

M. Peritz: Sever ha-mizwoth. Das Buch der Gesetze . . . im arabischen Urtexte nebst der hebräischen Übersetzung des Schelomoh ben Joseph ibn Ajub zum ersten Male vollständig hrsg. und mit einer deutschen Übersetzung und Anmerkungen versehen (Part 1, Breslau 1882).

Criticism—E. Renan: Rabbins français (591, 1877); Ecrivains juifs (458, 1893). M. Steinschneider: Hebraeische Übersetzungen (774, 928, 1893). Expressing doubts with regard to the earliest date, 1240, though it is given in the manuscript. Isaac Broydé: Jewish encyclopaedia (vol. 11, 453, 1905).

SHEM-ṬOB BEN ISAAC

Also called Babi ha-Ṭorṭosi. Born at Tortosa (on the Ebro, not far from its mouth) in 1196; he traveled in the Near East for business; after 1226 he began philosophical and scientific studies in Barcelona; later he flourished in Montpellier and Marseilles; he was still living in 1267. Hispano-Jewish physician and philosopher, translator from Arabic into Hebrew.

He translated Ibn Rushd's middle commentary on Aristotle's De anima, Bi'ur sefer ha-nefesh. But his main title to immortality rests on his translations of two of the greatest medical works of Islām: he began in 1254 and completed at Marseilles in 1258 (revised 1261) his translation of the Kitāb al-taṣrīf of Abū-l-Qāsim al-Zahrāwī, calling it Sefer ha-shimmush. In 1264 he translated the Kitāb al-Manṣūrī of al-Rāzī. Thus did Muslim medicine become available to the growing number of Jewish physicians who did not know Arabic. This implied a considerable extension of the Hebrew vocabulary relative to drugs and diseases. Besides those translations, Shem-ṭob transliterated various Arabic medical works in Hebrew characters.

His rather free translation of the Taṣrīf was preceded by an introduction dealing with the four elements, the four seasons and the diseases pertaining to each, and with medical astrology. Another Hebrew translation of the Taṣrīf was made at about the same time in southern France by Meshullam ben Jonah.

In his seventieth year, 1267, being in Marseilles, he began a translation of Hippocrates' Aphorisms which he finished in Tarascon within the same year. There are at least five Hebrew translations of that classic; Shem-ṭob's being of special interest because it includes Palladios'[3] commentary hitherto known only through a few quotations.

E. Renan: Rabbins français (592, 1877); Ecrivains juifs (731, 760, 1893). M. Steinschneider: Hebraeische Übersetzungen (148, 725, 741–748, 1893). Max Seligsohn: Jewish Encyclopaedia (vol. 11, 265, 1905). For Meshullam, see a short note by J. Z. Lauterbach: ibidem (vol. 8, 503, 1904). Alexander Marx: Mr. Bamberger's donation to the Seminary library (United Synagogue Recorder, vol. 8, 13–15, 1928); Brief note on a MS. of Shem-ṭob's translation of the Aphorisms (Isis, 11, 512); Register for the year 5689 of the Jewish Theological Seminary of America (140, New York 1928).

ZERAḤIAH GRACIAN

Zeraḥiah ben Isaac ben Shealtiel Gracian; Zeraḥiah Ḥen. Gracian (or in Hebrew, Ḥen) is the name of a prominent Hispano-Jewish family chiefly connected with Barcelona. Zeraḥiah was born in Barcelona or Toledo; he went to Rome c. 1277, and was still active there in 1288. Jewish philosopher, physician, and translator of philosophical and medical works from Arabic into Hebrew.

He wrote commentaries on Job, on Proverbs (1288) and on Maimonides' Moreh nebukim.

His philosophical translations include: Aristotle's Physics (Sefer ha-ṭeba'), Metaphysics (Mah she-aḥar ha-ṭeba'), De coelo et mundo (Ha-shamayim weha 'olam), De anima (Sefer ha-nefesh); Themistios' commentary on the De coelo; the neo-Platonic treatise De causis (Ha-bi'ur ha-ṭob ha-gamur); al-Fārābī's treatise on the nature of the soul (Ma'mar be-mahut ha-nefesh); Ibn Rushd's middle commentaries on Aristotle's Physics, Metaphysics, and De coelo.

His medical translations include: Galen's De causis et symptomatibus (Sefer he-ḥola'im weha-miqrim), and three chapters of his De compositione medicamento-

[3] Palladios the Iatrosophist, who flourished probably in the first half of the fifth century. See vol. 1, 392.

rum secundum genera, bearing the Greek title κατὰ γένη in Hebrew characters; the first of these Galenic texts (and probably also the second) was translated from the Arabic version made by Ḥunain ibn Isḥāq; the first two books of Ibn Sīnā's Qānūn; Maimonides' aphorisms (Rome 1277) and his treatise on coitus (jimā'). Most of these translations were made for Shabbethai ben Solomon, a Roman rabbi, who, in the great controversy caused by the Moreh nebukim, sided with Zeraḥiah against Hillel ben Samuel of Verona (q. v.).

Text—The commentaries on Job and on the Proverbs were published by Israel Schwarz, the first in his Tiqwat enosh (Berlin 1868), the second in Ha-shaḥar (vol. 2, passim)

The translation of al-Fārābī's Risālah fī māhiyyah al-nafs was published by Ẓebi Hirsch Edelmann in his Ḥemdah genuzah (Königsberg 1856).

Criticism—M. Steinschneider: Hebraeische Übersetzungen (1893). Max Seligsohn: Jewish Encyclopaedia (vol. 6, 63, 1904). U. Cassuto: Encyclopaedia judaica (vol. 7, 636–637, 1931).

For Shem-ṭob Ibn Falaquera and Isaac Albalag, see philosophical chapter; for Abraham ben Shem-ṭob, see medical one.

MOSES IBN TIBBON

Moses ben Samuel Ibn Tibbon. Provençal physician, mathematician, astronomer, and translator from Arabic into Hebrew. One of the greatest mediaeval translators. Born in Marseilles, flourished c. 1240–1283. His son, Judah ben Moses ibn Tibbon, was rabbi in Montpellier and took a prominent part in the dispute between the Maimonideans and anti-Maimonideans on the side of the former; he enlisted the cooperation of his relative, Jacob ben Maḥir, for the defense of the philosophical party.

Moses wrote a number of Biblical and Talmudic commentaries of no special importance. One of them deals with the weights and measures mentioned in the Old Testament and the Talmud.

His translations are so numerous that it is expedient to divide them into four groups: (a) philosophy and theology; (b) mathematics and astronomy; (c) mechanics and physics; (d) medicine. I have tried to give for each item the original Arabic title and the title of the Hebrew translation. In many cases I have also given the Latin title, and quoted that title first, in order to facilitate identification. For the sake of simplification, printed editions, if any, are mentioned at the end of each item.

Philosophy and theology

1 to 8. Ibn Rushd's commentaries on Aristotle. These are the most important of Moses' philosophical translations. All refer to the shortest commentaries (jāmi', synopsis), except no. 6 dealing with a middle commentary (talkhīṣ).

1. Physica auscultatio. Kitāb al-sama' al-ṭabī'ī. Ha-shma' ha-ṭib'i. Translated into Hebrew c. 1250.

Printed without Moses' name, Riva di Trento, 1559.

2. De coelo et mundo. Kitāb al-samā wal-'ālam. Kelale ha-shemayim weha-'olam.

3. De generatione et corruptione. Kitāb al-kūn wal-fasād. Sefer ha-hawayah weha-hefsed. Synopsis completed 1250. Levi ben Gerson wrote a commentary upon it in 1321.

4. Meteora. Kitāb al-āthār al-'ulwiyat. Sefer 'otot 'elyonot. The Hebrew summary was later Latinized by Elia Cretensis for Pico della Mirandola.

This Latin text was published at Venice, 1488, again 1489.

5. De anima. Kitāb al-nafs. Kelale sefer ha-nefesh. Hebrew synopsis completed, 1244. Levi ben Gerson wrote a commentary upon it in 1323.

6. Idem. Middle commentary completed by Ibn Rushd in 1181. Hebrew version, Bi'ur sefer ha-nefesh, 1261.

7. Parva naturalia. Ha-ḥush we ha-muḥash. Montpellier, 1254. Ibn Rushd's commentary was completed in Seville, 1170. The printed Latin text is translated from the Arabic.

8. Metaphysica. Mah she-aḥar ha-ṭeba'. Synopsis, 1258. This Hebrew synopsis was Latinized by Jacob Mantino.

This Latin text was printed in Rome, 1521; Bologna, 1523, etc.

9. Themistios (second half of the fourth century): Commentary on Book Λ of the Metaphysics. From the Arabic version by Isḥāq ibn Ḥunain, revised by Thābit ibn Qurra, translated into Hebrew in 1255. Part of it is included in Ibn Rushd's own commentary.

The Hebrew version was translated into Latin by Moses Finzi, and printed in Venice, 1576.

10. al-Baṭalyūsī (first half of the twelfth century): Kitāb al-ḥadā'iq (lost in Arabic). Ha-'agullot ha-ra'yoniyyot. Comparison of the world with an imaginary sphere.

Edited by D. Kaufmann: Die Spuren al-Bataljusi's in der jüdischen Religionsphilosophie (Budapest 1880). Moses replaced al-Baṭalyūsī's Qur'ānic quotations by Biblical ones.

11. al-Fārābī (first half of the tenth century): Kitāb al-mabādī (Book of origins), a philosophical and political treatise completed in Damascus, 942, revised in Cairo, 948–949. Translated in 1248 under the title Hatḥalot ha-nimẓa'ot ha-ṭib'iyyim.

Hebrew version edited by Hershell Filipowski (Leipzig 1849).

12 to 14. Three works of Maimonides.

12. Kitāb al-sirāj, commentary on the Mishnah. Fragment of treatise Pe'ah (field corners to be abandoned to the poor; Leviticus, 19, 9; 23, 22).

Edited by A. Geiger (Beiträge, 1847).

13. Kitāb al-farā'iḍ, Sefer ha-miẓwot. Translated very early, c. 1240. Moses explains that he is aware of the existence of an earlier Hebrew version by Abraham ben Ḥasdai, but that he has been able to avail himself of a revised Arabic text.

Printed in Constantinople (1516–1518), and in various editions of the Mishneh Torah.

14. Maqāla fī ṣinā'at al-manṭiq. The Arabic original is partly lost. Millot ha-higgayon, 1254. This translation has determined to some extent the Hebrew terminology on the subject.

Bad edition with Latin translation by Sebastian Münster: Logica sapientis Rabbi Simeonis (sic) (Basel, 1527). Edition with two anonymous commentaries, Venice 1550; again Cremona, 1566. Many later editions, generally with M. Mendelssohn's commentary, Francfort o. O., 1761, etc. S. Heilberg: Logicalische Terminologie . . . von Mendelssohn commentiert, übersetzt und mit einem Wortregister versehen (Breslau 1828).

Mathematics and astronomy

15. Euclid: Elements. Hebrew version called Shorashim or Yesodot, or Uqlides (Uqlidis), Montpellier, 1270. It is possible that Arabic commentaries by al-Fārābī and Ibn al-Haitham were also translated into Hebrew by Moses ibn Tibbon.

16. Geminos (first half of the first century B.C.): Εἰσαγωγὴ εἰς τὰ φαινόμενα. Introduction to Hipparchian astronomy. Translated, Naples, 1246. Ḥokmat ha-kokabim, or Ḥokmat ha-tekunah.

17. Theodosios of Bithynia (first half of the first century B. C.): Spherics. From the Arabic version by Qusṭā ibn Lūqā, and others; translated into Hebrew, in Montpellier, 1271. The Arabic text had been available to Latin readers for a long time thanks to the translations of Plato of Tivoli and Gerard of Cremona.

Latin text printed in a collection of spherics (Venice, 1518).

18. Jābir ibn Aflaḥ (first half of the twelfth century): Kitāb al-hai'a, or Iṣlāḥ al-majisṭī. Translated into Hebrew in 1274. Samuel ben Judah who corrected in 1335 a translation of the same work by Jacob ben Maḥir, knew Moses' translation only by hearsay. I wonder whether Moses' translation was actually made and whether there is not perhaps some confusion with his translation of al-Biṭrūjī (see below, no. 20). However the date quoted for this other astronomy is different (1259).

19. Muḥammad al-Ḥaṣṣār (second half of the twelfth century): Treatise on arithmetic and algebra, translated into Hebrew, Montpellier, 1271. Sefer ha-ḥeshbon. Divided into two parts (a) integers, 10 chapters; (b) fractions, 72 short chapters.

20. al-Biṭrūjī (second half of the twelfth century): Kitāb al-hai'a. Translated into Hebrew in 1259, Ma'amar be-tekunah. The Hebrew text was Latinized by Qalonymos ben David, 1528–1529.

Alpetragii planetarum theorica (Venice 1531). This is the Latin text derived from the Hebrew, not the direct Latin version made by Michael Scot in 1217.

Mechanics and Physics

21. Aristotle's Problems. From the Arabic version, Masā'il al-ṭabī'yat, by Ḥunain ibn Isḥāq; translated into Hebrew in 1264, She'elot ṭib'yot.

Medicine

22. Ibn Sīnā (first half of the eleventh century): Canticum. Arjūzat with Ibn Rushd's commentary. Bi'ur arguzah, 1260.

23. Ibn Sīnā: Al-qānūn al-ṣaghīr (The small canon). Translated Montpellier, 1272. Ha-seder ha-qaṭon.

24. Ibn al-Jazzār (second half of the tenth century): Zād al-musāfir (Viaticum peregrinantis). Translated in 1259. Ẓedat ha-derakim. Moses often quotes the Arabic technical terms, together with Hebrew equivalents. He criticizes the Latin translation by Constantine the African, and the Hebrew translation made from the Latin.

25. Ḥunain ibn Isḥāq (second half of the ninth century): Isagoge Johannitii ad tegni Galeni. Mabo el meleket ha-refu'ah, also She'elot (questions), the text being in the form of a catechism. Moses' version is undated.

26. al-Rāzī (second half of the ninth century): Kitāb al-aqrābādhīn. Antidotary. Translated into Hebrew, 1257.

27. al-Rāzī: Kitāb al-taqsīm wal-tashjīr (or Taqsīm al-'ilal). Division and distribution (of diseases). Translated into Hebrew in 1283, Ha-ḥilluq weha-ḥilluf.

28 to 30. Maimonides: Three medical treatises.

28. Maqāla fī tadbīr al-ṣiḥḥa. Regimen addressed, c. 1198, to al-Malik al-Afḍal. Translated in 1244 (this being one of Moses' earliest translations), under the title Ma'amar be hanhagat ha-beri'ut (Treatise on hygiene), also Miktab (letter).

Printed in Kerem ḥemed (vol. 3, 9 etc.). Edited by Jacob ben Moses Ẓebi: Dibre Mosheh (Warsaw 1886); by Jacob Saphir ha-Levi: Sefer hanhagat ha-beri'ut (Jerusalem 1885).

29. Al-sumūm wal-mutaḥarriz min al-adwiya al-qitālah. On poisons and antidotes. Undated. Translation under the title Ha-ma'amar ha-nikbad (The important treatise) or Ha-ma'amar be-teri'aq.

30. Commentary on Hippocrates' Aphorisms. Translated in 1257 or 1267.

Text—The texts already printed have been mentioned above, each under its own heading.

Criticism—Hermann Schapira: Mischnath ha-mmiddoth (Abhdl. zur Geschichte der Math. (p. 6, 1880). E. Renan: Rabbins français (593–595, 98–99, 750, 1877); Ecrivains juifs (1893). M. Steinschneider: Hebraeische Übersetzungen (1893, by index). Max Schloessinger: Jewish encyclopaedia (vol. 6, 545–548, 1906; careless).

JACOB BEN MAḤIR IBN TIBBON

Judaeo-Provençal mathematician, astronomer, zoologist. One of the greatest translators of scientific works from Arabic into Hebrew; he also helped to translate one of them into Latin. Born probably at Marseilles c. 1236; grandson of the great translator, Samuel ben Judah ibn Tibbon (first half of the thirteenth century); he studied in Lunel and flourished in Montpellier (he was called ha-Harri), where he died c. 1304. He was called in Provençal Don Profiat (Prophet) Tibbon, and in Latin Prophatius (Profacius) Judaeus. He was an energetic defender of the Maimonidean party and rallied to it the Montpellier community.

He was chiefly famous as an astronomer, and was quoted by some of the leading astronomers of the sixteenth century, Copernicus, Erasmus Reinhold, Cristof. Clavius, Kepler. He compiled new astronomical tables for the longitude of Montpellier, and the year beginning on March 1, 1300, and following. These tables were simply a modification of those of al-Zarqālī (second half of the eleventh century). They were written in Hebrew but soon translated into Latin (Almanach perpetuum Prophatii) and enjoyed much popularity.

Another original work of his was even more famous. That was the treatise containing the description and explanation of an instrument invented by him, the quadrans novus (or judaicus). This treatise was written by him in Hebrew in 1290 (or 1293, 1288). He called his instrument roba' Yisrael (quadrant of Israel; reference to Numbers 23, 10, and to his name Jacob), and the original Hebrew text was probably entitled Be'ur ha-keli ha-niqra roba' Yisrael. This text (a) had a singular fortune. It was translated into Latin (b) by Armengaud son of Blaise "secundum vocem eiusdem" (i.e., Jacob) (Montpellier, 1299). In 1301 Jacob prepared a revised edition, lost in Hebrew, but of which we have a Latin version (c). In the meanwhile another Latin version or rather elaboration (d) was made in Paris by Peter of St. Omer (Petrus de Sto. Audemaro). Both texts (c) and (d) were retranslated into Hebrew! Nor is this all. There were other Latin translations and commentaries, all of which prove the extraordinary popularity of this work.

The term quadrans novus was probably used in opposition to the quadrans vetus of Robert the Englishman (c. 1276), which Jacob's instrument superseded. The quadrans novus was entirely different from the quadrans vetus; it was far more complex, being meant to be of the same service as the astrolabe. A similar remark applies to the treatises describing these instruments; Jacob's treatise was entirely different from Robert's.

There is also ascribed to Jacob ben Maḥir a preface to the treatise Ḥeshbon mahlakot ha-kokabim of Abraham bar Ḥiyya (first half of the twelfth century), and a note on the calculation of chords extracted from the Almagest and appended to the same treatise.

The "Jacob's staff" may have been named after Jacob ben Maḥir, though the inventor seems to have been Levi ben Gershon (first half of the fourteenth century).

Far more important than his original treatises were Jacob's translations. He translated the following from Arabic into Hebrew (no. 8 was translated into Latin, but possibly also into Hebrew).

1. Autolycos of Pitane (second half of the fourth century B. C.): On the moving sphere. The Arabic text Kitāb al-kurra al-mutaḥarrakat had been prepared by Isḥāq ibn Ḥunain and Qusṭā ibn Lūqā. It was translated into Hebrew in 1273. (The same work had been translated from Arabic into Latin by Gerard of Cremona, De sphaera mota).

2. Euclid: Elements in 15 books. This was probably Jacob's first translation, c. 1255.

3. Euclid: Data. From the Arabic by Isḥāq ibn Ḥunain revised by Thābit ibn Qurra, Kitāb al-mafrūḍat (determined points or lines). Translated into Hebrew, 1272, Sefer ha-mattanot. The same Arabic text had been translated into Latin by Gerard of Cremona.

4. Menelaos of Alexandria (second half of the first century). Spherics. From the Arabic by Isḥāq ibn Ḥunain revised by Thābit ibn Qurra, etc. (the original Greek text is lost, its Arabic tradition is very complicated). Translated into Hebrew c. 1273? The same Arabic text had been translated into Latin by Gerard of Cremona.

5. Qusṭā ibn Lūqā (second half of the ninth century): Kitāb al-'amal bil-kurra al-fulkīya or al-kabīr (Use of the celestial sphere, or of the great sphere). Translated into Hebrew in 1256, Sefer ha-ma'aseh be-kaddur ha-galgal. The Hebrew version is divided into 65 chapters. The same work was translated into Spanish in 1259 by Judah ben Moses and John of Aspa.

6. Ibn al-Haitham (first half of the eleventh century): Fī hai'at al-'ālam (on the configuration of the world). Translated into Hebrew in 1271 (or 1275), Sefer ha-tekunah. Jacob's version was translated into Latin by Abraham de Balmes (second half of the fifteenth century). The Arabic text was translated into Spanish by Abraham of Toledo for Alfonso X.

7. Ibn al-Ṣaffār (first half of the eleventh century): Kitāb al-'amal bil-asṭurlāb (Use of the astrolabe). Translated into Hebrew, Perush (or Be'ur keli) ha-aẓṭurlab. This Arabic text had been translated into Latin by Plato of Tivoli (first half of the twelfth century).

8. al-Zarqālī (second half of the eleventh century): Kitāb al-'amal bil-ṣafīḥa al-zījīya (Use of the ṣafīḥa). Translated into Latin by Jacob ibn Maḥir and John of Brescia, Montpellier, 1263. Jacob translated the text into the vernacular, and John put it in Latin. The same Arabic text was translated into Spanish

in 1255–1256 by Ferrando of Toledo, then again in 1277 by Abraham of Toledo and one Bernaldo (see my note on Alfonso X, no. 13). There is a Hebrew version, Iggeret ha-ma'aseh be-luaḥ ha-niqra ẓofiḥah, which may have been made by Jacob, before or after his Latin version.

9. al-Ghazzālī (second half of the eleventh century): Philosophical treatise translated into Hebrew under the title Mozene ha-'iyyunim (Balance of speculations). I do not know the title of the Arabic original; it is not the Kitāb mīzān al-a'māl (Balance of deeds) which was translated into Hebrew by Abraham ibn Ḥasdai (first half of the thirteenth century). The ascription of this treatise to al-Ghazzālī has been doubted, but it is probably correct.

10. Jābir ibn Aflaḥ (first half of the twelfth century): Iṣlāḥ al-majisṭī. Jacob's translation, undated, was completed and revised later by Samuel ben Judah (1335). Another translation was made about the same time by Moses ibn Tibbon (1274). The Arabic text had been translated into Latin by Gerard of Cremona.

11. Ibn Rushd: Compendium of the organon. Translated into Hebrew in 1289 (not 1298); revised by Marsilli ben Judah at Tarascon, 1329, under the title Qiẓẓur ha-higgayon. The Hebrew version, that is Jacob's, was translated into Latin by Abraham de Balmes (second half of the fifteenth century) and was thus the basis of all printed editions.

Latin text printed in Aristotelis Opera, Venice 1550, etc. Hebrew text, entitled Kol meleket ha-higgayon (Riva di Trento, 1559).

12. Ibn Rushd: Commentary on Aristotelian zoology (de partibus XI–XIX, and de generatione animalium), completed by Ibn Rushd at Seville, 1169. Hebrew translation completed by Jacob ben Maḥir in 1302. The Hebrew version was translated into Latin by Jacob Mantino (d. 1549).

Mantino's Latin translation, Paraphrasis Averrois de partibus et generatione animalium, was printed in Rome, 1521, together with commentary by Levi ben Gershon. It is included in the Latin editions of Ibn Rushd (1550, etc.).

Summing up, out of these twelve translations, nine deal with mathematics and astronomy, two with philosophy, one with zoology. Two of the non-mathematical translations—Ibn Rushd's commentaries on Aristotelian logic and zoology—are of special importance. The earliest of these translations dates from c. 1255 (Euclid), or 1256 (Qusṭā); the latest from 1302 (Ibn Rushd's zoology); together they represent half a century of effort.

Text—The printed editions of translations have already been indicated.

M. Steinschneider: Prophatii prooemium in Almanach (Boncompagni's Bullettino, vol. 9, 595–614, 1876); Hebrew text with Latin translations. Giuseppe Boffito and C. Melzi d'Eril: Almanach Dantis Aligherii sive Profacii Judaei Montispessulani. Almanach perpetuum ad annum 1300 (i.e., 1301 N.S.) inchoatum. First edition (165 p., Florence 1908).

G. Boffito and C. Melzi d'Eril: Il quadrante d'Israel, facsimile edition (42 p., Florence 1922; Isis, 6, 149).

Criticism—S. Munk: Mélanges de philosophie juive et arabe (489, Paris 1859). Munk was the first to show the identity of Jacob ben Maḥir and Prophatius. Ernest Renan: Les rabbins français du commencement du quatorzième siècle (Histoire littéraire de la France, vol. 27, 599–623, 1877); Ecrivains juifs (1893, by index). M. Steinschneider: Über das Wort Almanach (Bibliotheca mathematica, 13–16, 1888); Hebraeische Übersetzungen (607–614, 976, and passim, 1893). I. Broydé: Jewish Encyclopaedia (vol. 6, 544, 1904). P. Duhem: Système du monde (vol. 3, 298–312, 1915). R. T. Gunther: Early science in Oxford (vol. 2,

163–169, 1923); apropos of the quadrant, drawings and specimens of which are illustrated. Lynn Thorndike: Andalò di Negro, Profacius, and the Alphonsine Tables (Isis, 10, 52–56, 1928); in defense of Jacob's Almanach against Duhem. Solomon Gandz: The astrolabe in Jewish literature (Hebrew Union College Annual, vol. 4, 469–486, Cincinnati 1927; Isis, 11, 227).

JACOB IBN ABBASSI

Jacob ben Moses ibn Abbassi ha-Bedarshi. Languedocian (ha-Bedarshi means of Béziers) or Spanish theologian and translator from Arabic into Hebrew. In 1297–1298, he was established at Huesca, in N. Aragon, and made a literal translation of Maimonides' commentary on the third order (Seder nashim) of the Mishnah. His introduction to this translation explains his scepticism with regard to natural studies and philosophical speculations, revealing incidentally his knowledge of Greek wisdom; the only way to perfection is the study of the Torah and the accomplishment of religious duties. The translation was dedicated to Solomon ben Adret.

According to Jacob's introduction, Maimonides' Kitāb al-sirāj was translated into Hebrew upon the initiative of the Roman community. Its emissary, R. Simḥah, traveled far and wide to obtain such a translation. He finally reached the Huesca community which undertook to translate the commentary relative to the first three orders of the Mishnah. Judah al-Ḥarizi's translation of the first order (zera'im) was completed by Joseph Ibn Alfawwal; the same Joseph translated also the second order (mo'ed). The third order was translated, as already said, by Jacob ibn Abbassi, who was supported by Ḥayyim ben Solomon ha-Rofe'.

Text—Jacob's translation was first printed in the complete edition of the Hebrew text of Maimonides' commentary (Naples 1492). Often reprinted in editions of the Mishnah and Talmud. Friedrich (or Mordecai) Weiss: Maimonides' Kommentar zum Mischnah Traktat Nazir, Abschn. i–iv (Inaug. diss., Heidelberg; 50 p., Berlin 1906). Edition of the Arabic text and of Jacob's Hebrew translation.

Criticism—Louis Ginzberg: Jewish encyclopaedia (vol. 1, 39, 1901). H. Brody: Encyclopaedia judaica (vol. 1, 179–180, 1928).

NATHAN HA-ME'ATI

Nathan ben Eliezer. Born probably in Cento, hence his name Me'ati, derived from the Hebrew equivalent of Cento (hundred), in the district of Ferrara. After long wanderings, he settled in Rome, where he was flourishing c. 1279–1283. One of the greatest translators of medical works from Arabic into Hebrew, he was nicknamed the Prince of Translators or the Italian Tibbonid. His activity in that direction was continued by his son, Solomon, and by his grandson, Samuel (first half of the fourteenth century). He translated into Hebrew:

1. The Aphorisms of Hippocrates with Galen's commentaries (from the Arabic).
2. Ibn Sīnā's Qānūn (see below).
3. The Muntakhab fī 'ilāj al-'ain (treatise on eye diseases) by 'Ammār ibn 'Alī; this translation was made for the famous papal physician Maestro Gajo (Isaac ben Mordecai).
4. Maimonides' Aphorisms.

The following translations are also ascribed to him.

1. A treatise on venesection by al-Rāzī, Ma'amar be-haqqazah.
2. Abū-l-Qāsim's Taṣrīf.

3. Ibn Zuhr's Kitāb al-aghdhiya, Sefer ha-mezonot.
4. An anonymous work on the causes of eclipses, Ma'amar 'al sibbot liqqut ha me'orot.

A translation from the Arabic of Galen's commentary upon Hippocrates' Airs waters and places, was begun by him, and completed by his son Solomon, in 1299

The most important of all these translations was of course his translation of the Qānūn, completed at Rome in 1279. Another Hebrew translation of the Qānūn was made almost at the same time, also in Rome, by Zeraḥiah Gracian (dealt with above). Gracian's translation does not seem to have been carried out beyond book II. Nathan's translation was revised by Joseph Ibn Vives al-Lorqi before 1402 (first half of the fifteenth century).

Text—For the translation of 'Ammār's Muntakhab, see vol. I (p. 729).

Maimonides' Aphorisms, Pirqe mosheh (Lemberg 1834; Vilna 1888). These are poor editions. The date printed on the Lemberg edition is 1804, but the real date is 1834.

The Hebrew translation of the Qānūn was first printed at Naples, 1491–1492, in three large volumes. (The first Arabic printed edition appeared only a century later, Rome, 1593.)

Criticism—M. Steinschneider: Hebraeische Übersetzungen (1893, passim). I. Broydé and Ismar Elbogen: Jewish Encyclopaedia (vol. 8, 398, 1904).

For Maestro Gajo, see M. Seligsohn: Jewish Encyclopaedia (vol. 5, 547, 1903).

SAMUEL BEN JACOB OF CAPUA

Flourished at Capua probably toward the end of the thirteenth century; that is, if he is identical with the father of the physician, Solomon ben Samuel of Capua. He translated from Arabic into Hebrew the treatise on purgatives and emetics written by Māsawaih al-Māridīnī (Mesuë junior, first half of the eleventh century). This translation is divided into two parts: 1. Canones generales; 2. Simplicia (the same subdivision occurs in the Latin version).

By way of correction to my note in vol. I (p. 728), I must say that there is considerable uncertainty with regard to this Mesuë junior and to his work. It would be better to call him pseudo-Mesuë, or rather pseudo-Mesuë I, to distinguish him from Mesuë the Third or pseudo-Mesuë II (first half of the thirteenth century). It is possible that the original work was not in Arabic, but in Latin, and was passed off as a translation from the Arabic to share the prestige of such translations. In the Latin text the author is named Joh. fil. Mesue fil. Hamech fil. Haly fil. Abdala regis (i.e., 'Abd al-Malik) Damascenus. For a similar case see my note on Serapion the Younger (first half of the twelfth century). According to Steinschneider, the original text of Mesuë's works (not only the one here considered but also the Antidotarium) was probably in Latin; it was translated from Latin into Arabic (sic) by a Sicilian Jew; this Arabic text is lost but there are Hebrew versions of it; these versions are anonymous except those ascribed to Samuel ben Jacob. Some of the Hebrew versions may have been made directly from the Latin. There is also a Greek translation of the first part (περὶ τοῦ συγγράμματος).

Criticism—M. Steinschneider: Hebraeische Übersetzungen (717–721, 1893); Europäische Übersetzungen (39–40, 1905). I. Broydé: Jewish Encyclopaedia (vol. 11, 19, 1905).

AḤIṬUB BEN ISAAC

Aḥiṭub ben Isaac. Rabbi, physician, and translator from Arabic into Hebrew, who flourished in Palermo towards the end of the thirteenth century His father Isaac was also a rabbi and physician, and his brother David a physician. He joined forces with Solomon ben Adret of Barcelona to resist Abraham Abulafia's qabbalistic propaganda in Sicily. He translated Maimonides' logic, Maqāla fī ṣinā'at al-manṭiq; this translation, Millot ha-higgayon, though superior in some ways to the earlier one by Moses ibn Tibbon (1254), did not supersede it. He wrote an ethical poem Maḥberet ha-ṭene, wherein he describes a journey to Paradise (cf. Dante and Immanuel ben Solomon, first half of the fourteenth century).

Text—Aḥiṭub's translation of Maimonides' maqāla was edited by M. Chamizer in the Festschrift dedicated to Hermann Cohen for his seventieth anniversary (423–456, Berlin 1912).

Criticism—U. Cassuto: Encyclopaedia judaica (vol. 1, 735, 1928).

V. FROM ARABIC INTO PERSIAN

See note on Nāṣir al-dīn al-Ṭūsī in the mathematical chapter.

VI. FROM ARABIC INTO SYRIAC

See note on Abū-l-Faraj in the philosophical chapter.

VII. FROM ARABIC (OR PERSIAN) INTO ARMENIAN

See note on Mekhitar of Ānī in the historical chapter.

VIII. FROM HEBREW INTO LATIN AND ROMANCE LANGUAGES

For Alfonso el Sabio see section III above. For Hermann the German, see section II above. For Abraham ben Shem-ṭob of Tortosa, see medical chapter.

MANFRED

King of Sicily. Born c. 1232; died at the battle of Benevento in 1266. He was a natural son of the emperor, Frederick II. Prince of Taranto; regent of Sicily after his father's death (1250). Aided by a Muslim army, he defeated the papal troops at Foggia in 1254 and became the virtual master of Sicily; in 1258 he was crowned king at Palermo. Aided by the Ghibellines of Italy, he defeated the Guelphs in 1260; the Pope (Urban IV, 1261–1264) then offered the Sicilian kingdom to Charles of Anjou, who defeated Manfred at Benevento in 1266.

The interest in Arabic and Hebrew learning shown by Frederick II was continued by Manfred (see my notes on Hermann the German and Bartholomew of Messina), and by his conqueror and successor, Charles of Anjou (1266–1282) (see my note on Moses of Palermo and Faraj ben Salīm).

In my note on Abraham ibn Ḥasdai (first half of the thirteenth century), I spoke of his translation from Arabic into Hebrew of the Book of the apple (Sefer ha-tappuaḥ), a pseudo-Aristotelian dialogue lost in Arabic. This text was translated from Hebrew into Latin under Manfred's direction. The translation is sometimes ascribed to himself, but supposing he had some knowledge of Hebrew, it is improbable that it was sufficient for such a task.

Text—Latin text of the Sefer ha-tappuaḥ together with the Hebrew text in Johann Justus Losius: Biga dissertationum quarum prima exhibet Sefer ha-tappuaḥ sive librum de pomo Aristotelis quod moribundus in manu gestaverit (Giessen 1706). German translation by J. Musen (Lemberg 1873). English translation by Isidor Kalisch (50 p., New York 1885).

Criticism—M. Steinschneider: Hebraeische Übersetzungen (267–270, 1893). August Karst: Geschichte Manfreds vom Tode Friedrichs II. bis zu seiner Krönung, 1250–58 (Berlin 1897). Karl Hampe: Urban IV. und Manfred, 1261–64 (109 p., Heidelberg 1905). Arnold Bergmann: Manfred, seine Geschichte vom Tode Urbans IV. bis zur Schlacht bei Benevent, 1264–66 (121 p., Heidelberg 1909). Adalbert, graf zu Erbach-Fürstenau: Die Manfredbibel (69 p., 14 pl.; Kunstgeschichtliche Forschungen hrsg. v. K. preuss. histor. Institut in Rom, vol. 1, Leipzig 1910). Helene Arndt: Studien zur inneren Regierungsgeschichte Manfreds (243 p., Heidelberg 1911).

JOHN OF CAPUA

Joannes de Capua, Campania, Campana. Italian Jew converted to Christianity. His original name is unknown. He flourished c. 1262–1278. Translator from Hebrew into Latin. He translated:

1. The Taisīr of Ibn Zuhr (first half of the twelfth century) from a Hebrew version. This translation in spite of its superiority was superseded by another made a few years later by Paravicius.
2. A treatise on diet by Maimonides, Maqāla fī tadbīr al-ṣiḥḥa, this translation being made at the request of the papal physician, Guglielmo Corvi.
3. The fables of Kalīla wa Dimna, from Rabbi Joel's (?) Hebrew version. This last translation, entitled Directorium vitae humanae, seems to have been the prototype of the many versions in various European vernaculars. If so it was the source of the Kalīla lore in western Europe, where it soon became as popular as in the East.

Text—Directorium humanae vitae, alias parabolae antiquorum sapientiae. First edition, without place or date (before 1483). Reprinted verbatim by Puntoni (Pisa 1884).

Many other incunabula in Latin and other languages. Exemplario contra los engaños del mundo (Burgos 1498). Buch der Weisheit oder der alten Weisen (Ulm 1485). Buch der Beispiele, etc.

Joseph Derenbourg: Deux versions hébraïques du livre de Kalilah et Dimnah (Bibliothèque de l'Ecole des hautes études, sci. philol., fasc. 49; Paris 1881), the Hebrew version of Rabbi Joel compared with the Directorium. New edition of Directorium prepared by same (Bibliothèque de l'Ecole des hautes études, sci. philol., fasc. 72; Paris 1887).

Joseph Jacobs: The earliest English version of the fables of Bidpai "The morall philosophie of Doni" by Sir T. North (337 p., London 1888). Reprint of first edition, 1570, with introduction and pedigree of Bidpai literature.

Criticism—M. Steinschneider: Hebraeische Übersetzungen des Mittelalters (748, 772, 875, 981, 1893). Gabriel Colin: Avenzoar (84, 1911).

PARAVICIUS

Or Paravicinus, Patavinus. Physician of Padua (?) who flourished in Venice c. 1281. In that year he translated the Hebrew version of Ibn Zuhr's Taisīr into Latin, with the assistance of a Jew called Jacob; it is probable that Jacob translated the Hebrew text into their common vernacular (Venetian), and that Paravicius retranslated this into Latin. This version is inferior to that prepared a few years before by John of Capua, yet it was printed while the other was not.

Text—Theicrisi dahalmodana vahaltadabir (Venice 1490). Again 1496, 1497, 1514, 1530; Lyon 1531 (twice) etc.
Criticism—M. Steinschneider: Hebraeische Übersetzungen (749, 1893). Gabriel Colin: Avenzoar (84, 1911).

HAGIN DEULACRES

Haginus filius Deulacres. Ḥayyim Gedaliah; Dieulacresse. Appointed chief rabbi of England in 1281, being the last before the expulsion of the Jews in 1290. He is mentioned here simply because he may be identical with the Hagin who translated Ibn Ezra's astrological work into French in 1273, in Henry Bate's house in Malines. He has also been identified with one of the translators into Hebrew of the Image du monde (q. v., Walter of Metz, first half of the thirteenth century). The best that can be said for these two identifications is that they are not unplausible, either on chronological or on scientific grounds. Hagin might have made these two translations, but there is nothing to prove that he made them. The name Ḥayyim (a Hebrew word meaning life) was common among mediaeval Jews.

The French translation of Ibn Ezra's astrological works, made by "Hagin le Juif" in 1273, was not written by himself but dictated to Obert de Montdidier. This explains the fact that it was written in Roman characters, a unique case, all other contemporary works of this kind being written in Hebrew characters.

E. Renan: Les rabbins français (507-509, 1877). M. Steinschneider: Hebraeische Übersetzungen (973, 1893). Joseph Jacobs: Jewish Encyclopaedia (vol. 6, 149, 1904). Raphael Levy: The astrological works of Abraham ibn Ezra (174 p., Baltimore 1927; Isis, 11, 171). Mainly devoted to Hagin's translation, with a glossary.

For Henry Bate, see mathematical chapter; for Armengaud son of Blaise, see section II above.

IX. FROM LATIN INTO ITALIAN, FRENCH, AND DUTCH

For Aldobrandin of Siena and Taddeo Alderotti, see medical chapter; for Jean de Meung and Jacob van Maerlant, see philosophical chapter.

X. FROM LATIN INTO HEBREW

DAVID CASLARI

David ben Abraham Caslari (the family name Caslari is derived from the place Caylar in Hérault, Languedoc; in Hebrew the name is spelled with *qof* and *sin*). David was also called Bongodas and entitled Maestro. Physician and translator from Latin into Hebrew, who was at Narbonne in 1284. He certainly flourished in the thirteenth century, for he was friend and correspondent of the great Languedocian poet, Abraham ben Isaac Bedersi, who was born c. 1230-1240 and died in all probability c. 1296-1300. He was probably the father of the physician, Abraham ben David Caslari, who flourished near Perpignan c. 1322-1329.

He translated into Hebrew Galen's treatise De inaequali intemperencie or De malitia complexionis diversae (Sefer ro'a mezeg mitḥalef). That translation was almost certainly made from the Latin. Galen's treatise had been translated from

Arabic into Latin by Gerard of Cremona. It is of course possible that Caslari's Hebrew version was only made in the fourteenth century.

Criticism—E. Renan: Les rabbins français (712, 715, 1877); Ecrivains juifs (646, 1893). M. Steinschneider: Hebraeische Übersetzungen (653, 1893). S. Kahn: Jewish Encyclopaedia (vol. 3, 599, 1902). J. Klatzkin: Encyclopaedia judaica (vol. 5, 74, 1930).

SOLOMON BEN MOSES OF MELGUEIL

Melgueil is probably the present Mauguio (Hérault) in Languedoc. Jewish French theologian and translator from Latin into Hebrew, who flourished probably in the second half of the thirteenth century. There is much uncertainty about him, and some works ascribed to him may be the works of namesakes. This Solomon is in all probability the author of a commentary on the Books of Kings and of the following translations:

1. Anonymous commentary on Aristotle's De somno et vigilia. Sefer ha-shenah we ha-yeqiẓah.
2. Ibn Sīnā: Summary of Aristotle's De coelo et mundo, Sefer ha-shammayim weha-'olam.
3. Platearius (first half of the twelfth century): Circa instans. The Hebrew title is simply a transliteration of the words Circa instans (Sirqa' iẓṭanẓ).
4. Ibn Rushd: Fragment of his metaphysics Haẓẓa'ah la-ḥokmah.

The significant point is that these translations were made from the Latin; this was natural enough for (3) but astonishing with regard to the other texts.

Criticism—E. Renan: Les rabbins français (575, 1877); Ecrivains juifs (686, 1893). M. Steinschneider: Hebraeische Übersetzungen (253, 283, 334, 822, 1893). Max Seligsohn: Jewish Encyclopaedia (vol. 11, 455, 1905).

For Hillel ben Samuel, see philosophical chapter.

XI. FROM LATIN INTO GREEK

HOLOBOLOS

Manuel Holobolos, Μανουὴλ ὁ Ὁλόβολος or Ὁλόβωλος; later he assumed the monastic name Maximos instead of Manuel. In 1261 he was a junior secretary in the cabinet of Michael VIII Palaeologos, but having fallen into disgrace, he retired soon afterwards to the monastery of Joannes Prodromos in Constantinople; in 1267 he was appointed professor of logic in the university led by Georgios Acropolites and rhetor of the church; in 1273 he fell again into disgrace because of his hostility to the union with the Latin church which was then advocated by the emperor for political reasons, and he retired into the monastery Τοῦ μεγάλου Ἀγροῦ near Sigriane[4] on the Sea of Marmora; he was still living in 1284.

He is chiefly remembered as a writer of devotional poetry, but is mentioned here as being one of the few Byzantines well acquainted with Latin. He wrote Greek translations and elaborations of logical and dialectical treatises of Boetius, De differentiis topicis and De syllogismo hypothetico; he commented upon the first book of Aristotle's Prior Analytics.

[4] This is the monastery founded by Theophanes Confessor (first half of the ninth century) to which I alluded in vol. 1, 577.

K. Krumbacher: Byzantinische Litteratur (546, 770–772, 780, 1897).

For Maximos Planudes, see the philosophical chapter; for Petros Theoctonicos, the chemical one.

XII. FROM CHINESE AND TIBETAN INTO MONGOLIAN

See the notes on the Introduction of Tibetan Buddhism into Mongolia, in the religious chapter; and on Kublai Khān in the philosophical chapter.

SUMMARY

ARISTOTELIAN TRADITION IN THE SECOND HALF OF THE THIRTEENTH CENTURY

The study of all of these translations enables us to obtain a general idea of the intellectual movement in various directions. We shall use that method in almost every one of the following chapters, but it is worth while to avail ourselves of it at once with regard to one topic of special importance, the growth of Aristotelian knowledge and tradition. The prestige of Aristotelian thought is evidenced by the number of new translations dating from this time; these translations did not necessarily supersede earlier ones, more often they were simply added to those. Thus Aristotelian literature increased all the time.

The following list does not profess to be complete, yet it is amply sufficient to illustrate the movement.

Logic—Simplicios' commentary on the Categories, translated by William of Moerbeke from Greek into Latin, 1266. Ibn Rushd's synopsis of the Organon, translated by Jacob ben Maḥir from Arabic into Hebrew, 1289. I may add to these Holobolos' commentary on the Prior analytics.

Physics—Ibn Rushd's summary of the Physica auscultatio translated by Moses ibn Tibbon c. 1250. Translation of the Physics and of Ibn Rushd's middle commentary by Zeraḥiah Gracian. Both translations from Arabic into Hebrew.

De coelo—From Arabic into Hebrew: Ibn Rushd's commentary translated by Solomon ibn Ayyub in 1259; Ibn Rushd's middle commentary, by Zeraḥiah Gracian.

From Greek into Latin: Simplicios' commentary translated by William of Moerbeke, 1271.

Finally, Ibn Sīnā's summary, translated from Latin into Hebrew (sic) by Solomon ben Moses of Melgueil.

De generatione et corruptione—Ibn Rushd's summary, translated by Moses ibn Tibbon from Arabic into Hebrew, 1250.

Meteorology—William of Moerbeke translated from Greek into Latin the fourth book and revised the others; he also translated the commentary by Alexander of Aphrodisias, 1260. Ibn Rushd's summary was translated from Arabic into Hebrew by Moses ibn Tibbon.

De anima—William of Moerbeke revised a translation from Greek into Latin.

From Arabic into Hebrew: The De anima and al-Fārābī's commentary were translated by Zeraḥiah Gracian; Ibn Rushd's synopsis, by Moses ibn Tibbon, 1244; Ibn Rushd's middle commentary by the same, 1261, and also by Shem-ṭob ben Isaac.

Parva naturalia—Ibn Rushd's synopsis translated from Arabic into Hebrew by Moses ibn Tibbon, 1254. A commentary of Alexander of Aphrodisias translated from Greek into Latin by William of Moerbeke. Finally a commentary on the De somno et vigilia translated from Latin into Hebrew by Solomon ben Moses of Melgueil.

Zoology—William of Moerbeke translated the History and generation of animals from Greek into Latin in 1260. Jacob ben Maḥir translated Ibn Rushd's commentary on the parts (xi–xix) and generation of animals from Arabic into Hebrew in 1302.

Problems—Translation from Greek into Latin by Bartholomew of Messina; and from Arabic into Hebrew, by Moses ibn Tibbon, 1264.

Metaphysics—William of Moerbeke translated book eleven from Greek into Latin, and revised the translation of other books. The following translations were made from the Arabic into Hebrew: Themistios' commentary, by Moses ibn Tibbon, 1255; Ibn Rushd's synopsis, by the same, 1258; Ibn Rushd's middle commentary by Zeraḥiah Gracian.

Ethics—Hermann the German translated from Arabic into Latin Ibn Rushd's middle commentary at Toledo 1240, and the Summa quorundam Alexandrinorum, three years later. The Magna moralia were translated from Greek into Latin c. 1262 by Bartholomew of Messina.

Economics—Translated from Greek into Latin by William of Moerbeke.

Politics—Translated from Greek into Latin by William of Moerbeke in 1260, at St. Thomas' request.

Rhetoric—Translated from Greek into Latin by William of Moerbeke, 1281. Al-Fārābī's commentary and Ibn Rushd's middle commentary translated from Arabic into Latin by Hermann the German.

Poetics—Ibn Rushd's middle commentary translated from Arabic into Latin by Hermann the German, 1256.

So much for the translations which prove the immense influence which Aristotle was then exerting upon the minds of Christian and Jewish philosophers. His writings and those of his Greek and Arabic commentators were to them like a gold mine which they were anxious to exploit. This extraordinary influence can still be shown in a different way. I have explained above that the fear of heresy was exceptionally high at the beginning of the thirteenth century. This was for the Church a period of extreme sensitiveness. The nervousness was such that every intellectual danger took at once extravagant proportions. Thus it is not very surprising that the Fourth Lateran Council (1215) forbade the teaching of Aristotle, except the logic and ethics. But gradually as the fear quieted down and as the real dangers were better appreciated, the interdiction was qualified and mollified.

The teaching of Aristotelian psychology was authorized by the Paris faculty of arts in 1252, and by 1255 the teaching of the whole Aristotelian knowledge, including the physics and metaphysics, was permitted. Urban IV (pope from 1261 to 1264) tried to reintroduce a partial interdiction, but he did it half-heartedly. It is possible that he was reassured by St. Thomas and William of Moerbeke, who met at his court.

We may thus say that by the middle of the thirteenth century ecclesiastical opposition to Aristotelianism had apparently come to an end. But soon afterwards the Church renewed its fight, not against Aristotelianism proper, but against the Averroistic form of it. To understand the true meaning of this the best way is to go back to my note on Ibn Rushd. In reality the fight was not against a new philosophy, but against some Aristotelian doctrines which could never be reconciled with Jewish, Christian, or Muslim theology. The old Aristotelianism had gradually been edulcorated; Averroism was but a revival of the original thought. Ideas which had been attenuated by centuries of habit became obnoxious again when Ibn Rushd had given them a new vigor and a new edge by his own creative effort. Hence this paradoxical result, that Aristotle was accepted by the Church, but Ibn Rushd, Aristotle's best exponent, rejected!

However it must be added that by the very fact that Averroism (I am speaking now of Latin Averroism) was persecuted, it naturally tended to be more subversive. It finally attracted to itself all the malcontents, and became so to say the intellectual citadel of the opposition to ecclesiastical and lay authorities.

The fight against Averroism was begun in earnest by Stephen Tempier, bishop of Paris from 1268 to 1279. He condemned it in his decree of 1270. This decree was followed by others; finally in 1277 he drew a list of 219 propositions formally censured. These propositions did not constitute a homogeneous whole. Apparently Stephen had made an effort to collect all the dangerous ideas, whatever their origin and scope, in order to sweep the University clean in one stroke. Most of these pernicious ideas were Aristotelian, some were more specifically Averroistic, some others were neo-Platonic, a few had been expounded by such men as Thomas Aquinas, Roger Bacon, Giles of Rome. However, thanks to the misconceptions to which I have already alluded, the decree of 1277 was generally understood as a condemnation of Averroism, or more precisely, of Siger of Brabant and Boetius of Dacia.

Other contemporary documents betray the same state of mind; for example, an Oxford publication of the end of the thirteenth century or beginning of the fourteenth century entitled Compilationes errorum omnium in Anglia et Parisiis condemnatorum; and the De erroribus philosophorum, a Spanish work, wrongly ascribed to Giles of Rome. The Errores is of special interest because the author took pains to exonerate Aristotle. In this he was right or wrong according to each one's prejudice. The "errors" were most of them Aristotelian, but new thought had given them a new lease of life and aggravated them. At bottom this was nothing but an episode in the long struggle between science and theology.

My contention is strengthened by the fact that the same struggle was going on at the same time among the Jews. But among them, instead of being focused upon Ibn Rushd, it was naturally centered upon their own great doctor, Maimonides. The more orthodox Jews began their fight against him early in the thirteenth century; I have already told that in 1234 rabbis of southern France went so far as to cause Maimonides' works to be burned by the Christian authorities. The Jewish communities of Spain and Southern France were divided into two hostile camps, the Maimonideans or philosophers, and the anti-Maimonideans who held that the Torah and Talmud were the only sources of sound knowledge. We shall come across many examples of both kinds, but especially of the first, further on.

Bibliography—See my notes on the Christian and Jewish philosophers in Chapter XLVI.

CHAPTER XLV

EDUCATION

(Second Half of Thirteenth Century)

I. CHRISTENDOM

CREATION OF NEW UNIVERSITIES

Very few new Universities were founded in the second half of the thirteenth century; none in Italy, none in France.

Spain

Valladolid—The University of Valladolid dates at least from the middle of the thirteenth century, and it was in fact a studium generale by the end of the century; yet it was not officially consecrated as such until 1346 by Clement VI (pope from 1342 to 1352). The point is that before 1346 it was a studium generale "respectu regni," but not in an ecumenical sense.

Seville—By the middle of the thirteenth century the Dominicans had recognized the necessity of organizing Arabic studies for missionary purposes. By 1265 such schools existed in Tunis and Murcia. Such a school may have been the nucleus of the university of Seville. Indeed a studium generale for the study of Latin and Arabic was established in Seville; a charter was granted to it by Alfonso el Sabio in 1254, and a bull by Alexander IV (pope from 1254 to 1261) in 1260. Nothing is known of the activities of that university.

Lerida—The university of Lerida (on the Segre) was founded by James II of Aragon in 1300, and it received in the same year a bull of privilege from Boniface VIII (pope from 1294 to 1303). It gradually died out in the fifteenth century.

Portugal

Lisbon and Coimbra—King Dinis founded a university at Lisbon which received in 1290 a bull of privilege from Nicholas IV (pope from 1288 to 1292). In 1308–1309, it was moved to Coimbra. In spite of many vicissitudes it has remained to this day the only national university of Portugal.

Hastings Rashdall: The universities of Europe (vol. 2, part 1, 1895).

ENGLISH COLLEGES

In England the two old Universities were soon broken into colleges, and these became, at least in appearance, more important than the Universities themselves. While on the continent the colleges or hospitals for scholars were subordinated to the Universities, the contrary was or appeared to be true in England. This was undoubtedly a result of the greater individualism of the English people.

Leaving out of account the Dominican monastery of Oxford (1221), and the Franciscan houses established at Oxford in 1224 and at Cambridge in 1224–1225, the earliest colleges date from the second half of the thirteenth century, as follows:

Oxford

Balliol (1260–1266)—In or about 1260 Sir John de Balliol (or Baliol, d. 1269) undertook to provide a perpetual maintenance for certain poor scholars of Oxford. Balliol College was established before 1266. The foundation was completed in 1282 by Devorguilla, Sir John's widow.

Merton (1263 or 1264)—This college was endowed in 1263 or 1264 by Walter de Merton, who was bishop of Rochester in 1274 and died in 1277. The original purpose was to provide for the education of theologians and jurists. The foundation was more clearly defined by the statutes of 1270. As we shall see in volume 3, Merton played a glorious part in the history of mathematics in the fourteenth century.

University (c. 1280)—In a sense the inception of University College was earlier than that of Balliol or Merton. It owes its origin to the bequest of William of Durham, archdeacon of Durham, who died in 1249. However nothing was done until c. 1280, when the earliest statutes were drawn; they were superseded by new ones in 1292.

To these early colleges might be added three monastic houses whose purpose was similar: to wit, Rewley, a Cistercian foundation dating from c. 1280; Gloucester Hall, a Benedictine house founded at Oxford in 1289, at first to accommodate the monks of St. Peter in Gloucester; Durham College, another Benedictine house originated at the same time for the monks of Durham.

Cambridge

The same system prevailed in the younger university of Cambridge, but only one college was established there as against the three Oxford ones.

Peterhouse (1284)—This earliest Cambridge college was modeled upon the Oxford colleges. It was founded in 1284 by Hugh of Balsham, who had been elected bishop of Ely in 1256 and died in 1286. The "Scholars of Ely" had first (1280) been placed in the Hospital of St. John, in charge of Regular Canons, but the experiment failed. In 1284 it was found necessary to separate the seculars from the regulars, and to accommodate them in another house, St. Peter's house, or Peterhouse.

Hastings Rashdall: The universities of Europe in the Middle Ages (vol. 2, part 2, Oxford, 1895).

ROBERT OF SORBON

Robertus de Sorbona. Born at Sorbon, near Rethel (Ardennes) in 1201; canon of Cambrai; later chaplain to St. Louis; in 1258 canon of the church of Paris and chancellor of the University of Paris; died in Paris, 1274. French theologian and moralist.

He wrote a few books on ethical and theological subjects, but is chiefly remembered because of his foundation in 1257, of the house of learning called after him, Sorbonne. His plan had already been authorized in 1252 by Queen Blanche (Louis IX being then in Palestine); in 1257 the king gave him a site in the Quartier Latin; the new establishment was sanctioned by the pope in 1259, 1263, 1268.

The original Sorbonne was neither a college, nor a faculty, nor a convent, but as I said, a house of learning and a modest hostelry for poor students and masters in theology (pauperes magistri de Sorbona). It soon obtained considerable influence. Robert also founded a preparatory college, named Collège de Calvi or "petite Sorbonne." The entrance examination required to be admitted into the Sorbonne was called Robertine, after the founder's baptismal name. The Sorbonne was responsible for the introduction of printing in France in 1469.

Text—Felix Chambon: De consciencia et De tribus dietis (87 p.; Collection de textes pour servir à l'étude de l'histoire, 35; Paris 1902).

Criticism—Henri Jadart: Robert de Sorbon et le village de Sorbon. Notice publiée à l'occasion du monument érigé à la mémoire du fondateur de la Sorbonne dans son pays natal (94 p., Reims 1888). Articles by M. Barroux in Grande Encyclopédie (vol. 30, 286–287, with abundant bibliography). Dorothy Louise Mackay: Le système d'examen au XIIIe siècle d'après le De conscientia de Robert de Sorbon (Mélanges Ferdinand Lot, 491–500, 1925).

History of the Sorbonne—Th. I. Duvernet: Histoire de la Sorbonne, dans laquelle on voit l'influence de la théologie sur l'ordre social (2 vols., Paris 1790). Alfred Franklin: La Sorbonne, ses origines, sa bibliothèque, les débuts de l'imprimerie à Paris, et la succession de Richelieu (2e éd., 293 p., Paris 1875). Octave Gréard: Nos adieux à la vieille Sorbonne (421 p., Paris 1893). Pierre Leguay: La Sorbonne (180 p., Paris 1910).

A facsimile of the charter granted by St. Louis to Robert of Sorbon in 1257 will be found, e.g., in Gustave Lanson: Histoire illustrée de la littérature française (vol. 1, 85, 1923). This early Sorbonne was located rue Coupe-Gueule in front of the Palais des Thermes (Cluny museum).

RICHARD DE FOURNIVAL

French poet and physician. Born at Amiens in 1201; chancellor of the church of Amiens; died c. 1260. His Biblionomia is a catalogue of his own library (of about 300 books) which he presented to the college founded in 1257 by Robert de Sorbonne; thus creating the first public library of Paris. He wrote chansons; La puissance d'amour, a kind of ars amandi; Conseils d'amour; Bestiaire d'amour. Though the purpose of the last work is erotic, it is a bestiary, wherein many animals are quoted.

Text—For the Biblionomia, see Léopold Delisle: Cabinet des Manuscrits (vol. 2, 518–536). Célestin Hippeau: Le bestaire d'amour (202 p., 48 woodcuts, Paris 1860; first edition). Paul Zarifopol: Kritischer Text der Lieder Richards de Fournival (Diss. Halle, 60 p., 1904).

Criticism—Paulin Paris: La vie et les ouvrages de Richard de Fournival (Bibliothèque de l'Ecole des Chartes, vol. 2, 32–56, 1840). Histoire littéraire de la France (vol. 23, 708–733, 1856; vol. 29, 456, 1885). Aleksander Birkenmayer: La bibliothèque de Richard et son sort ultérieur (in Polish, with French summary; Polish academy, 103 p., Cracow 1922; Isis, 5, 215).

GILBERT OF TOURNAY

Guibert or Gilbert; Gilbertus Tornacensis. Born in Tournay, Hainaut, flourished in Paris c. 1259. Franciscan educator and moralist who wrote (c. 1250 or 1262) a treatise on Christian education, Erudimentum doctrinae (or Rudimenta doctrinae christianae), of which the third part, De modo addiscendi, deals with the psychology and method of teaching. In 1259 he wrote for St. Louis—whom he seems to have accompanied in the Sixth Crusade—a treatise on the qualities and duties of princes (Eruditio regum et principum). This is an ethical treatise, largely based upon the Polycratus of John of Salisbury, essentially different from the Regimen principum of St. Thomas.

Text—A. De Poorter: Un traité de pédagogie mediévale, le De modo addiscendi (Revue néo-scolastique 195–229, 1922; extracts).

A. De Poorter: Le traité Eruditio regum et principum (Philosophes belges, 9, Louvain 1914; 107).

Another treatise, De pace et animi tranquillitate, has been edited by Longpré (Quaracchi, 1925).

Criticism—Kervyn de Lettenhove: Guibert de Tournai (22 p., Bruxelles 1860). E. H. J. Reusens: Biographie nationale de Belgique (vol. 8, 416–420, 1885). M. De Wulf: History of mediaeval philosophy (vol. 1, 390, 1926).

For the Enseignements of Saint Louis, see the introductory chapter; for Vincent of Beauvais, Albert the Great, Ramon Lull, see the philosophical chapter; for Martino da Fano, see the legal chapter; for Alfonso el Sabio and Dinis the Liberal, see the chapter on translators.

II. ISLĀM

MUḤAMMAD AL-RIQŪṬĪ

Abū Bakr Muḥammad ibn Aḥmad al-Riqūṭī al-Mursī. Hispano-Muslim philosopher, physician, mathematician. Born in the Valle de Ricote, in the province of Murcia. This province had been conquered from the Muslims in 1243 but continued for a time to be ruled by Muslim princes under Castilian tutelage. Such conditions were excellent for cultural exchanges. Murcia (and a little later Seville) became cultural centers rivaling Toledo. Al-Riqūṭī is here quoted to illustrate these conditions. Alfonso the Wise, then governor of Murcia, built for him a madrasa, wherein students of different nations were taught, each in his own language (Latin, Castilian, Arabic, Hebrew). Al-Riqūṭī was much honored by Alfonso and later by the second Naṣrid sulṭān of Granada, Muḥammad II al-Faqīh (1273–1302), who gave him a residence in the country near Granada. Al-Riqūṭī taught there medicine, mathematics, music, etc., and attended learned meetings at his patron's court.

His biography is included in the Iḥāṭa of Ibn al-Khaṭīb (second half of the fourteenth century), MS. of the Academy of history of Madrid (vol. 2, f. 153 verso). The substance of it was kindly communicated to me by D. Miguel Asín (20 Nov. 1927). H. Suter: Mathematiker und Astronomen der Araber (156, 1900). M. Asín: Islam and the Divine Comedy (245, London 1926).

III. CHINA AND MONGOLIA

See notes on Kublai Khān and Wang Ying-lin in the philosophical chapter.

IV. JAPAN

KANAZAWA-BUNKO

I have already indicated the importance of the Hōjō family. From 1200 to 1333 the head of that family was the actual ruler of Japan under the title of Shikken of Kamakura (that is, he was the prime minister of the Kamakura Shōgun).

A member of that illustrious family, Hōjō Sanetoki, grandson of Hōjō Yoshitoki, founded, c. 1270, a school and a large library (bunko) of Chinese and Japanese writings at Kanazawa (a village in Musashi, near Yokohama). The collection, called Kanazawa-bunko, was increased by Sanetoki's successors, his son and grandson, Akitoki and Sadaaki. When the Hōjō family lost its power in 1333, the school and library lost their importance. They were revived toward the middle of the fifteenth century by Uesugi Norizane (d. 1455). In the beginning of the seventeenth century under the Tokugawa Ieyasu (1542–1616), the library was annexed to the new one established by him at Edo.

E. Papinot: Historical dictionary of Japan (254, 1909). F. Brinkley: History of the Japanese people (449, 1914).

CHAPTER XLVI

PHILOSOPHIC AND CULTURAL BACKGROUND

(Second Half of Thirteenth Century)

I. EASTERN ISLĀM

AL-ABHARĪ

Al-Mufaḍḍal ibn 'Umar al-Abharī (not Abahrī), Athīr al-dīn. (There is a place called Abhar in Jibāl). Persian philosopher, logician, mathematician, astronomer, writing in Arabic. He studied under Kamāl al-dīn Ibn Yūnus. In 1228 he moved from Mūṣul to Irbil (Arbela). He died c. 1263. He wrote:

1. Hidāyat al-ḥikma. (Guide to wisdom) divided into three parts, dealing respectively with logic (manṭiq), physics (ṭabī'īyāt) and theology (ilāhīyāt). The popularity of this work is proved by many commentaries, notably the one composed by Mīr Ḥusain ibn Mu'īn al-dīn al-Maibudī (1475–1476).

2. Kitāb al-īsāghūjī. This is a summary of Porphyry's Isagoge. The Isagoge was well known to the Muslim world through translations directly from the Greek or from the Syriac, and through commentaries and elaborations. Al-Abharī's was the best known of these, and was in its turn the subject of many new elaborations or supercommentaries by Shams al-dīn Aḥmad ibn Ḥamza al-Fanārī (d. 1430–1431), by Zakarīya' ibn Muḥammad al-Anṣārī (1423–1520), by al-Ḥifnāwī (d. 1764–1765), etc. It was put in 94 rajaz verses by Al-Ṣadr ibn 'Abd al-Raḥmān al-Akhḍarī in 1534–1535, Al-sullam al-murawniq fī-l-manṭiq.

3. Astronomical tables, zīj (al-zīj al-shāmil?; comprehending tables).

4. Mukhtaṣar fī 'ilm al-hai'a. An astronomical summary in 22 chapters.

5. Risāla fī-l-asṭurlāb. On the astrolabe.

6. Kashf al-ḥaqā'iq fī taḥrīr al-daqā'iq.

7. Other astronomical treatises not well determined. There seem to be three of them but some may be identical with 3 or 4. One seems to deal with the sections of spheres.

A philosophical compilation of his, the Zubdat al-asrār (Cream of secrets), was translated into Syriac by Abū-l-Faraj.

Some of his works may belong to the first half of the thirteenth century.

Text—1. The commentary on the Hidāyat by Mīr Ḥusain al-Maibudī was printed at Calcutta, lithographed at Lucknow (no dates).

2. Shams al-dīn's commentary on the Īsāghūjī was printed in Constantinople, 1820. Editions with other commentaries, Cairo, 1305, 1306, 1310 H.

Al-sullam al-murawniq fī-l-manṭiq. Printed Cairo 1318 H. Many later editions with or without additional glosses, in Cairo and Fez.

Criticism—Ibn Khallikān (De Slane, vol. 3, 468, 1868). C. Brockelmann: Arabische Litteratur (vol. 1, 464–465, 1898); Encyclopaedia of Islām (vol. 1, 69, 1908). H. Suter: Mathematiker der Araber (145, 227, 1900). Moh. Ben Cheneb: Īsāghūjī (Encyclopaedia of Islām, vol. 2, 527, 1921). J. E. Sarkis: Dictionnaire de bibliographie arabe (290, 1928).

'ALĪ IBN 'UMAR AL-KĀTIBĪ

Najm al-dīn 'Alī ibn 'Umar al-Qazwīnī al-Kātibī (or Dabīrān, in Persian, the scribe). Persian philosopher and astronomer writing in Arabic. He flourished at the observatory of Marāgha under Nāṣir al-dīn al-Ṭūsī, and died in 1277. He prepared an edition of the Almagest. His main work is the Kitāb 'ain al-qawā'id fī-l-manṭiq wal-ḥikma (Source of the principles of logic and philosophy), of which a section is devoted to natural sciences and mathematics. The Kitāb ḥikmat al-'ain is a partial edition of the second part of the same work. He wrote another logical treatise entitled Al-risālat al-shamsīya fī-l-qawā'id al-manṭiqīya, and the Jāmi' al-daqā'iq fī kashf al-ḥaqā'iq, dealing with logic, physics and metaphysics. It includes a letter to Nāṣir al-dīn on the meaning of existence.

In the Ḥikmat al-'ain he discussed the hypothesis of the daily rotation of the earth. One might object, he said, that a bird flying in the direction of that motion would not be able to keep up with it. He considered that objection invalid, because the atmosphere might be rotating with the earth and carry the bird, yet he rejected the hypothesis because "all terrestrial motions take place in a straight line and therefore we cannot admit that the earth should move in a circle."

Text—The Risāla is appended to Aloys Sprenger's edition of 'Abd al-Razzāq's Dictionary of the technical terms of the Sufies (Calcutta 1845).

Criticism—A. Sprenger: The Copernican system of astronomy among the Arabs (Journal of the Asiatic Society of Bengal, vol. 25, 189, 1856). Contains the text referred to above in Arabic and English. C. Brockelmann: Arabische Litteratur (vol. 1, 466–467, 1898). H. Suter: Die Mathematiker und Astronomen der Araber (153, 1900).

For Ibn Wāṣil see the historical chapter; for Nāṣir al-dīn al-Ṭūsī, Shams al-dīn al-Samarqandī, Quṭb al-dīn al-Shīrāzī, see the mathematical chapter.

AL-QAZWĪNĪ

Abū Yaḥyā Zakarīyā ibn Muḥammad ibn Maḥmūd al-Qazwīnī. Born at Qazwīn, in 'Irāq 'Ajamī, Persia, 1203–1204; in 1232–1233 he was in Damascus; later qāḍī in Wāsiṭ and Ḥilla, two cities of 'Irāq; he died in 1283. He became acquainted with Ibn 'Arabī in Damascus, and was a pupil of al-Abharī. Persian encyclopaedist writing in Arabic; he has been called the mediaeval (or Muslim) Pliny,[1] a comparison justified by the abundance of his learning and his lack of critical spirit. He is the author of two large compilations, which have sometimes been considered as two parts of the same work, but are quite independent, a cosmography and a geography.

1. Cosmography. 'Ajā'ib al-makhlūqāt wa-gharā'ib al-mawjūdāt (marvels of created things and their singularities), divided into two parts dealing respectively with celestial things (planets, stars, angels, chronology!), and with terrestrial ones (four elements, minerals, plants, animals, man). This latter part also contains much geographical material which is repeated (often verbatim) in the Geography. There are four distinct recensions of this work, and its great popularity is proved by the existence of many extracts and of translations or paraphrases into Persian (at least two), Turkish (at least three), and Čaghatāi. It was used extensively by al-Damīrī (second half of the fourteenth century). It is possible that the longer

[1] Al-Mas'ūdī (first half of the tenth century) has also been compared to Pliny. (Vol. 1, 638).

recensions contain interpolations of a later time—e.g., chapters on the different races of mankind, on the various arts; information on the Turkish hordes extracted from the writings of Ibn Faḍlān and Abū Dulaf (both of the first half of the tenth century); notes on the Slavs, Khazars, etc. The establishment of the original text and its dating is thus exceedingly difficult, if not impossible. The two shorter versions are dated 1262–1263 and 1275–1276; these seem to be nearer to the original.

2. Geography. There are two distinct recensions. The first, dated 1262–1263, is entitled 'Ajā'ib al-buldān (marvels of the countries); the second, revised and much enlarged, dated 1275–1276, is entitled Āthār al-bilād wa-akhbār al-'ibād (Vestiges of the countries and stories of the servants; servants of God, i.e., the people). It is a description of the seven climes of the earth. For each clime the separate cities, countries, mountains, islands, lakes, rivers, etc., are classified in alphabetical order. In other words, instead of being one alphabetical dictionary, like Yāqūt's Mu'jam al-buldān (first half of the thirteenth century), it is a collection of seven dictionaries, one for each clime. Like Yāqūt's work, it contains not only geographical, but also historical, ethnographical, and biographical information. It would seem that the original MSS. were illustrated. Al-Qazwīnī's Geography was translated into Persian, and a summary of it was inserted into some Turkish versions of the Cosmography. It was abstracted in 1403–1404 by 'Abd al-Rashīd ibn Ṣāliḥ ibn Nūrī al Bākūwī (i.e., of Bākū) who added the latitude and longitude of the places mentioned.

The climes above mentioned are the Eratosthenian or Ptolemaic climes (κλίματες) adopted by most Arabic geographers and cartographers. The climes were latitudinal zones, the limits of which were somewhat arbitrarily determined by the length of the longest day. The first zone, c. 12° 40′ to 20° 27′, is nearest to the equator and corresponds to the shortest day, $12\frac{3}{4}$ hours; the seventh zone, c. 47° 12′ to 50° 20′ corresponds to the longest day, $15\frac{3}{4}$ hours.

See article iqlīm by H. T. Weir in Encyclopaedia of Islām (vol. 2, 460, 1919). Ernst Honigmann: Die sieben Klimata (Heidelberg 1929; Isis, 14, 270–276).

Text—The Arabic text of both works has been edited by Ferd. Wüstenfeld (2 vols., 892 p., Göttingen 1848–1849), the first part being the Cosmography, and the second the Geography. Wüstenfeld's text of the Cosmography is a very arbitrary one, probably far removed from the original. It is based mainly but not exclusively upon a late eighteenth century recension.

The Cosmography has often been printed in the East in the margins of al-Damīrī's Kitāb al-ḥayāt al-ḥayawān (Cairo 1305, 1309, 1330 H.).

L. Ideler: Untersuchungen über den Ursprung und die Bedeutung der Sternnamen (Berlin 1809). Astronomical part of the Cosmography in Arabic and German. Guil. Volck: Calendarium syriacum arabice latineque edidit et notis instruxit (46 p., Leipzig 1859). Explanation of the Syrian months.

Joh. Gildemeister: Excerpta ex Qazvinii opere geographico Indiam et Sindiam spectantia in his Scriptorum arabum de rebus indicis loci et opuscula inedita (Bonn 1838).

The first half of the Cosmography (Wüstenfeld, 1, 1–208) was translated into German by Hermann Ethé: Die Wunder der Schöpfung (644 p., Leipzig 1868; with notes by H. L. Fleischer). Julius Ruska: Das Steinbuch aus der Kosmographie (Heidelberg Progr., 1896; Wüstenfeld, 1, 208–245).

Georg Jacob: Ein arabischer Berichterstatter aus dem 10. oder 11. Jahrhundert über Fulda, Schleswig, Soest, Paderborn und andere deutsche Städte (20 p.,

Berlin 1890). Jonas Ansbacher: Die Abschnitte über die Geiste und wunderbaren Geschöpfe (Diss., 42 p., Erlangen 1905). Franz Taeschner: Die Psychologie Qazwinis (Tübinger Diss., 66 p., Kiel 1912).

E. Wiedemann: Aus der Botanik des muslimischen Volkes (Archiv für Geschichte der Naturwiss., vol. 3, 299–306); Beschreibung des Auges nach al-Qazwīnī (Eders Jahrbuch für Photographie, 67–73, Halle 1912); Über die Kriechtiere nach al-Qazwīnī nebst einigen Bemerkungen über die zoologischen Kenntnisse der Araber (Sitzungsber. d. phys. med. Ges., vol. 48, 228–285, Erlangen 1918; Isis, 4, 405, 431); Übersetzung und Besprechung des Abschnittes über die Pflanzen (ibidem, 286–321, 1918).

French translation of al-Bākūwī's summary by de Guigues: Exposition de ce qu'il y a de plus remarquable sur la terre, etc. (Notices et Extraits des MSS., vol. 2, 386–545, 1789).

Criticism—J. T. Reinaud: Géographie d'Aboulféda (vol 1, 143–150, 1848). L. Leclerc: Médecine arabe, (vol. 2, 135–136, 1876). C. Brockelmann: Arabische Litteratur (vol. 1, 481, 1898). H. Suter: Mathematiker und Astronomen der Araber (182, 1902). E. Wiedemann: Angaben bei Qazwīnī (Beiträge 5, Sitzungsber., Erlangen, vol. 37, 448–453, 1905); notes on Greek men of science. Edward G. Browne: Literary history of Persia (vol. 2, 1906, 482–483). Julius Ruska: Qazwīnīstudien (Der Islam, vol. 4, 14–66, 236–262, 1913. Discussion of the MSS., including fragments of the text); Über den falschen und den echten Qazwīnī (Mitt. zur Geschichte der Medizin, vol. 13, 183–188, 1914). E. Wiedemann: Über ein arabisches, eigentümliches Wasserrad und eine kohlenwasserhaltige Höhle auf Majorka nach al-Qazwīnī (Mit. zur Gesch. der Medizin, vol. 15, 368–370, 1916). Carra de Vaux: Penseurs de l'Islam (vol. 2, 34–40, 43–47, 250, 286, 309, 366, 1921). M. Streck: Encyclopaedia of Islām (vol. 2, 841–844, 1925). J. Stephenson: The zoological section of the Nuzhatu-l-qulūb (Isis, 11, 295–297, 1928). F. S. Bodenheimer: Materialien zur Geschichte der Entomologie (vol. 1, 156–165, 1928; vol. 2, 329, 1929; Isis, 13, 388–393; 14, 454–456). Extracts in German concerning insects, reproductions of figures in the illustrated MSS., list of insects quoted by Qazwīnī. J. E. Sarkis: Dictionnaire encyclopédique de bibliographie arabe (1507, Cairo 1929).

English translations of al-Qazwīnī's cosmography and geography and a systematic analysis of his scientific knowledge are badly needed.

AL-WAṬWĀṬ

Muḥammad ibn Ibrāhīm ibn Yaḥyā al-Waṭwāṭ Jamāl al-dīn al-Anṣārī al-Kutubī al-Warrāq (Kutubī is a bookseller, warrāq is a paperseller; in practice the two terms are almost equivalent. Waṭwāṭ is a bat or reremouse). Born in 1235, died in 1318. Muslim author of an ethical anthology, Ghurar al-khaṣā'iṣ al-wāḍiḥa wa 'urar al-naqā'iṣ al-fāḍiḥa, and of an encyclopaedia of natural science and geography, entitled Mabāhij al-fikar wa manāhij al-'ibar.

Text—The Mabāhij is still unpublished but there are Egyptian editions of the anthology (Būlāq 1284; Cairo 1299 H.).

Criticism—C. Brockelmann: Arabische Litteratur (vol. 2, 54, 78, 1902).

For al-Nawawī, see the legal chapter.

AL-BAIḌĀWĪ

'Abdallāh ibn 'Umar, Nāṣir al-dīn al Baiḍāwī. Persian Shāfi'ite theologian and historian, writing in Arabic and Persian. He flourished in Fārs (his father was chief justice there), then in Shīrāz, finally in Tabrīz, where he died in or after 1286.

He is chiefly known because of his commentary on the Qur'ān, Anwār al-tanzīl wa asrār al-ta'wīl (Lights of revelation and mysteries of interpretation). It is derived from the Kitāb al-kashshāf of al-Zamaksharī (first half of the twelfth century) but contains abundant materials taken from other sources. It is highly esteemed by the Sunnites who regard it almost as a holy book. Its fame can be measured by the number of MSS., printed and lithographed editions and super-commentaries.

His other works are the Minhāj al-wuṣūl ilā 'ilm al-uṣūl; Kitāb ṭawāli' al-anwār wa maṭāli' al-anẓār, on metaphysics, etc. All of these were composed in Arabic. He wrote in Persian, a brief and dull history of the world from Adam to 1275, Niẓām al-tawārīkh.

Text—Anwār al-tanzīl. Many eastern editions printed or lithographed in Būlāq, Stambūl, Cairo, Lucknow, Bombay, etc. Critical edition by H. O. Fleischer (2 vols., Leipzig 1844–1848).

D. S. Margoliouth: Chrestomathia baidawiana. The commentary on sura III translated and explained for the use of students (London 1894).

Winand Fell: Indices ad Beidhavii commentarium in Coranum (Leipzig 1878).

Many of the super-commentaries have also been published (see Brockelmann).

A commentary on the Minhāj al-wuṣūl, by 'Abd al-Raḥmān ibn Ḥasan al-Isnawī (d. 1370–1371) has been printed in the margins of the Kitāb al-taqrīr wal-takhbīr of Ibn Amīr al-Ḥajj (Būlāq, 1316 H.).

A commentary on the Ṭawāli' al-anwār by Maḥmūd ibn 'Abd al-Raḥmān al-Isfahānī (d. 1348) was printed in Cairo, 1323 H.

Abdallae Beidavaei Historia sinensis persice e gemino MS. ed. lat. quoque reddita ab Andrea Mullero Greifenhagio (Jena 1689). This is not Baiḍāwī's history, but an extract from the history of Rashīd al-dīn (first half of the fourteenth century).

Criticism—Theodor Nöldeke: Geschichte des Qorāns (Göttingen 1860; 2d ed. by Friedrich Schwally; Leipzig 1909, etc.). Carl Brockelmann: Arabische Litteratur (vol. 1, 416–418, 1898); Encyclopaedia of Islām (vol. 1, 590, 1911). E. G. Browne: Literary history of Persia (vol. 2, 487, 1906). J. E. Sarkis: Dictionnaire encyclopédique de bibliographie arabe (616–618, 1928).

MUḤAMMAD AL-TABRĪZĪ

Abū Bakr Muḥammad ibn Muḥammad al-Tabrīzī. Persian Muslim who flourished probably in the second half of the thirteenth century. He wrote in Arabic a commentary on Maimonides' introduction to the second part of the Dalālat al-ḥā'irīn. In that introduction Maimonides summarized Aristotelian philosophy in 25 propositions, upon which he then proceeded to establish his proof of the existence, unity, and incorporeality of God. Al-Tabrīzī's commentary is extant in two Hebrew translations, one of which was done in Majorca, c. 1347, by Isaac ben Nathan of Cordova (or Játiva), while the other is anonymous. The Hebrew translation was used by Moses ben Joshua of Narbonne (second half of the fourteenth century), and by Ḥasdai Qresqas in his Ōr Adonai (first half of the fifteenth century).

Text—Isaac's translation was published in Venice, 1574, by Saul ben Moses ha-Kohen. The other is unpublished.

Criticism—M. Steinschneider: Bodleian catalogue (1143, 1860); Hebraeische Übersetzungen (361, 1893). Arthur Zacharias Schwarz: Die hebraeischen Handschriften der Nationalbibliothek in Wien (nos. 141, 150, Leipzig 1925). Harry Austryn Wolfson: Crescas' critique of Aristotle (Harvard Press, Cambridge 1929; Isis, 14, 240–244).

MUḤAMMAD IBN DĀNIYĀL

Abū 'Abdallāh Muḥammad ibn Dāniyāl ibn Yūsuf al-Khuzā'ī al-Mūṣulī, Shams al-dīn. Muslim physician and author, possibly of Jewish or Christian origin; born c. 1265; died in 1310–1311. During the rule of Baybars, Baḥrī Mamlūk sulṭān of Egypt from 1260 to 1277, he composed a curious work entitled Ṭaif al-khayāl fī ma'rifat khayāl al-ẓill (Ghosts of the imagination, or knowledge of shadow plays). This work is the only extant specimen of the dramatic poetry of mediaeval Islām. Shadow plays (khayāl al-ẓill, or ẓill-i khayāl) were probably invented in India or Persia. We have indirect proof of their existence in other Muslim countries, even in Spain, as early as the eleventh century (see vol. 1, 713). Muḥammad's work contains interesting information on the civilization of his time; description of an Egyptian fair and of different characters appearing there, including a surgeon, pharmacist, herbalist, astrologer, woman cupper, snake charmer, quacks of various kinds, etc.

Text—Georg Jacob: Stücke aus Ibn Dāniyāl's Ṭaif al-khayāl 2. Heft (Erlangen 1910).

Criticism—Hājī Khalīfa (vol. 4, 174, 1845). C. Brockelmann: Arabische Litteratur (vol. 1, 495, 1898). Georg Jacob: Ein ägyptischer Jahrmarkt im 13. Jahrhundert (Sitzungsberichte der Bayerischen Ak., 10, 42 p., 1910). Th. Menzel: Khayāl-i ẓill (Encyclopaedia of Islām, vol. 2, 934, 1926). J. E. Sarkis: Dictionnaire encyclopédique de bibliographie arabe (100, 1928).

SA'DĪ

Musharrif al-dīn ibn Muṣliḥ al-dīn 'Abdallāh. His literary name, Sa'dī, was derived from the name of his father's patron, the Salgharid atābeg of Fārs, Sa'd ibn Zangī. The foremost didactic and lyrical poet of Persia and the one whose international influence has been greatest. He must be included in this survey on the same grounds as Firdawsī or Dante. Born at Shīrāz c. 1184; he died there almost a centenarian, c. 1283. The first third of his long life was spent in study, his education being completed at the Niẓāmīya of Baghdād, where he was deeply influenced by 'Umar al-Suhrawardī. The second third, in travel and song, his travels extending to Central Asia and India, Aethiopia, Yemen, Egypt, the Maghrib (?), Palestine, Asia Minor. The last third, after his return to Shīrāz, in meditation and the composition of his great works.

His main works are: 1. The Bustān (Garden, orchard), also called Sa'dī nāma, completed in 1257, a philosophic and didactic poem, divided into ten chapters.

2. The Gulistān (rose-garden), completed in 1258, a collection of moral stories told in prose, but with many poetical interludes. Both the Bustān and the Gulistān were dedicated to the Salgharid atābeg of Fārs, Abū Bakr, who ruled from 1226 to 1260.

3. The Dīwān, a collection of ghazal or short odes.

4. The Pand-nāma, a collection of counsels, comparable to 'Aṭṭār's work bearing the same title.

5. Many other poems, most of them in Persian, but a few in Arabic. One Arabic qaṣīda is an elegy on the destruction of the caliphate by the Mongols in 1258. A Persian poem deals with the same subject, being devoted to the last caliph, al-Musta'ṣim (1242–1258).

As opposed to the mystical poems of Farīd al-dīn 'Aṭṭār and of Jalāl al-dīn Rūmī, Sa'dī's poems are worldly and practical, sometimes cynical and Machiavellian. Their catholicity explains their worldwide influence and also their historical interest; they are a microcosmos of the eastern life of those days alike in its best and worst aspects.

It was long believed that Sa'dī was the first to write poetry in Hindustānī or Urdū, but that story is now discredited. Most of his work was written in Persian, but some poems were composed in Arabic, others in a mixture of Arabic and Persian, or in Persian dialects; one is said to have included sixteen languages and dialects.

Sa'dī has deeply influenced not only the literature of his own country but also that of India and of Turkey. His Gulistān was often translated into Hindustānī, and in 1391 it was translated into Egyptian Turkish by Saif al-Sarayī. The Bustān was translated into Turkish in 1354 by Taftāzānī. Moreover there are many Turkish imitations of and commentaries on Sa'dī's poems.

The Gulistān was printed in French in 1634; in Latin, 1651; in German, 1654; in English, 1774. The Bustān was first printed in Dutch, 1688. Thus by the end of the seventeenth century Sa'dī was already well known in western Europe. Outside of these translations, his influence was felt through many western writers, the earliest being La Fontaine, and the most important Voltaire and Goethe. To illustrate Sa'dī's influence at the end of the eighteenth century, I may recall that the founder of thermodynamics, Sadi Carnot (born in 1796) was named after him.

Text—Complete works (Kullīyāt). First edition in 2 vols., Calcutta 1791–1795 (in all, 496 leaves). Many other oriental editions.

Bustān—First independent edition, Calcutta 1824. Many later ones: Calcutta 1828; Tabrīz 1831; Cawnpore 1832, etc. First critical edition by K. H. Graf (480 p., Vienna 1858).

Unpublished Latin translation by Thomas Hyde (1636–1703). First printed translation, a Dutch one by D. H. (442 p., Amsterdam 1688). Poor German selection derived from the Dutch text (Hamburg 1696). German translation from the Persian by K. H. Graf (2 vols., Jena 1850). German selections in verse, by Ottokar Maria v. Schlechta Wssehrd (234 p., Vienna 1852). English translation by H. Wilberforce Clarke (London 1879). French translation by A. C. Barbier de Meynard (423 p., Paris 1880). German translation by Friedrich Rückert (296 p., Leipzig 1882).

Gulistān—First separate edition (Calcutta 1802). First complete edition, together with an English translation by Francis Gladwin (2 vols., Calcutta 1806). Critical edition by Edward B. Eastwick (378 p., Hertford 1850). Vocalized edition by A. Sprenger (250 p., Calcutta 1851), etc.

French translation by André du Ryer de Malezair (166 p., Paris 1634); by N. Semelet (Paris 1834); by Ch. Defrémery (358 p., Paris 1858). Latin translation by Georgius Gentius (Amsterdam 1651). German translation by Adam Olearius von Ascherleben (Hamburg 1654; used by Goethe); by K. H. Graf (Leipzig 1846). English selections by Stephen Sullivan (145 p., London 1774). English translation by Francis Gladwin (Calcutta 1806); by Edward B. Eastwick (312 p., Hertford 1852). The first four abwāb, translated in prose and verse by Sir Edwin Arnold (222 p., London 1899).

Dīwān. Sir Lucas White King: The odes (3 parts in the Bibliotheca indica, Calcutta 1919–1921).

General Criticism—E. G. Browne: Literary history of Persia (vol. 2, 525–539, 1906). A. V. Williams Jackson: Persia past and present (333-335, New York 1906). Account of Sa'dī's tomb in Shīrāz. Henri Massé: Essai sur le poète Saadi (Algiers thesis, 272 p., Paris 1919); Bibliographie de Saadi (60 p., Paris 1919). T. W. Haig and J. H. Kramers: Encyclopaedia of Islām (vol. 4, 36–39, 1924).

Special criticism—Karl Philipp: Beiträge zur Darstellung des persischen Lebens nach Sa'dī (Diss., 40 p., Halle a. S., 1901); Beiträge zur Kulturgeschichte Persiens nach Sa'dī (Der Islam, vol. 7, 92–101, 299–306, 1917). Dealing with military, legal, and medical (299–306) matters. Edmund O. v. Lippmann: Saadi über den Zucker (Die deutsche Zuckerindustrie, 521–522, Berlin 1927).

JALĀL AL-DĪN-I-RŪMĪ

Jalāl al-dīn Muḥammad al-Rūmī (meaning of Rūm, Asia Minor). Often called Mawlānā (our master). The greatest Ṣūfī poet of Persia. Born at Balkh, Khurāsān, in 1207–1208; political circumstances drove his father into exile and the family began to move westwards soon after his birth; it is said that in 1210 he received 'Aṭṭār's blessing in Nīshāpūr; after stopping for various lengths of time in Baghdād, Mecca, Damascus, Malaṭiya, Arzanjān, and Lāranda, they finally settled in Qūniya (ancient Iconium, then the capital of the Saljūq rulers of Rūm) c. 1226–1227. After his father's death in 1231, Jalāl al-dīn replaced him as professor in Qūniya: he spent the rest of his life in that city and was buried there in 1273. His spiritual education was guided from 1232 to 1241 by the Ṣūfī teacher Saiyid Burhān al-dīn Ḥusain Muḥaqqiq al-Tirmidhī; and he was deeply influenced in 1244–1246 by another Sūfī, the mysterious Shams-i-Tabrīzī.[2]

He founded the order of the Mawlawī or whirling dervishes. Qūniya is to this day the sacred center of that order, and all the grand masters (or Čelebi) are buried there near Jalāl al-dīn.

His main work is the Mathnawī, a philosophical poem, extremely discursive and heterogeneous, divided into six books and containing 26,660 couplets. (It exceeds in bulk the Iliad and Odyssey combined.) It was completed in 1273. It is an exposition of taṣawwuf woven around an immense variety of subjects. These Ṣūfī doctrines include as usual many foreign elements, neo-Platonic, Christian, Hindu. One of the main sources was the Egyptian Dhū-l-Nūn (second half of the ninth century). Jalāl al-dīn also wrote a Dīwān, that is, a collection of lyrical poems, and a treatise in prose called Fīhi mā fīhi (what is within is within).

In spite of obvious defects, the Mathnawī is one of the greatest poems of the world's literature. To Persians it is almost sacred; they call it "the Qur'ān in the Pahlawī language."

A son of Jalāl al-dīn, called Bahā' al-dīn Sulṭān Walad, wrote in 1301, a poem, Rabābnāma (Book of the rebec), which is the earliest important example of West-Turkish poetry.

Text—Mathnawī. Edited by Sulaimān Naḥīfī, with Turkish verse translation (Būlāq, 1268 H.). With Turkish commentary by Anqarāwī (6 vols., 1289 H.). Georg Rosen: Mesnewi (German translation of book 1, Leipzig 1849). English translation by Sir James William Redhouse (150 p., London 1881; book I in English verse); by E. H. Whinfield (London 1887 and 1898; whole poem abbreviated); by Charles Edward Wilson (2 vols., London 1901; English prose translation of book 2 and commentary).

Reynold A. Nicholson is preparing a critical and complete edition of the Mathnawī together with a complete English translation. It will fill six volumes of the E. J. W. Gibb Memorial Series. Vol. 1 has appeared (496 p., Leiden 1925); it contains

[2] That is, Shams al-dīn Muḥammad ibn 'Alī ibn Malikdād-i-Tabrīzī, a wandering darwīsh who was in Qūniya in 1244–1246 and disappeared soon afterwards. See R. A. Nicholson's study in Encyclopaedia of Islām (vol. 4, 744, 1929). For Saiyid Ḥusain Tirmidhī, see article by Köprülü Zāde Fu'ād (ibidem, vol. 4, 797, 1930).

the Persian text of books 1 and 2. Vol. 2 (1926) contains the English version of the same books. Vol. 3 (605 p., 1929) contains the text of books 3 and 4 (J. R. A. S., 127–131, 1930).

Dīwān. Rosenzweig: Auswahl aus den Divanen des grössten mystischen Dichters Persiens (Wien 1838). Rückert: Aus dem Dīwān (1819; extracts in German). F. A. G. Tholuck: Blütensammlung (53–191, Berlin 1825). R. A. Nicholson: Selected poems from the Dīwān-i-Shams-i-Tabrīz, edited and translated with an introduction, notes, and appendices (Cambridge 1898; warmly praised by E. G. Browne).

Selections in English from both the Mathnawī and the Dīwān by Frederick Hadland Davis (Wisdom of the East, 105 p., London 1912).

Criticism—Clément Huart: Konia. La ville des derviches tourneurs. Souvenirs d'un voyage en Asie mineure (270 p., map., pl., Paris 1897). E. G. Browne: Literary history of Persia (vol. 2, 515–525, 1906). Carra de Vaux: Djalāl al-dīn (Encyclopaedia of Islām, vol. 1, 1004–1006, 1912). D. S. Margoliouth: Mawlawīya (ibidem, vol. 3, 418–419, 1931).

II. EASTERN JEWS AND SAMARITANS

IBN KAMMŪNA

Sa'd ibn Manṣūr ibn Sa'd al-Isrā'īlī, 'Izz al-dawla, generally called Ibn Kammūna. Jewish philosopher, physician, alchemist, who flourished in Egypt, embraced Islām and died in 1277–1278. He wrote a number of treatises in Arabic: Al-ḥikmat al-jadīda (The new philosophy), dealing with logic (is the title a reference to the new illuministic philosophy ḥikmat al-ishrāq?); a risāla on the immortality of the soul; a commentary on Ibn Sīnā's logical treatise, Kitāb al-ishārāt wal-tanbīhāt (see vol. 1, 709), entitled Sharḥ al-ishārāt; a commentary completed in 1268–1269 on the philosophical treatise Kitāb al-talwīḥāt, of al-Suhrawardī (second half of the twelfth century); an opthalmological work called Al-kafī al-kabīr; remarks on the Talkhīs al-muḥaṣṣal, which Nāṣir al-dīn al-Ṭūsī had abstracted c. 1270 from Al-mabāḥith al-sharqīya of Fakhr al-dīn al-Rāzī (second half of the twelfth century); an alchemical treatise, Tadhkira fī-l-kīmiyā. After his conversion to Islām he wrote a treatise wherein he tried objectively to compare Judaism, Christianity, and Islām. This is called Tanqīḥ al-abḥāth fī-l-baḥth 'an al-milal al-thalāth (Extract of the questions concerning the dispute relative to the three religions). A digression comparing Rabbinic and Qaraite Judaism may be a later (Qaraite) interpolation.

Text—The part of Tanqīḥ dealing with Judaism was edited by Leo Hirschfeld: Sa'd ben Manṣūr und seine polemische Schrift (Berlin 1893; with German translation).

Criticism—Many MSS. of Ibn Kammūnā's work are quoted by Ḥājī Khalīfa, passim. C. Brockelmann: Arabische Litteratur (vol. 1, 437, 454, 507, 1898). M. Steinschneider: Arabische Literatur der Juden (239–240, 1902).

For the Samaritan, Muwaffak al-dīn, see the medical section.

AARON BEN JOSEPH

Aaron ben Joseph the Qaraite. (Often called "the Elder," to distinguish him from another Qaraite, Aaron ben Elijah of Nicomedia, "the Younger," born in Cairo c. 1300, died in Constantinople in 1369). Aaron ben Joseph was born in Sulchat (?), Crimea, c. 1260; flourished in Constantinople; died c. 1320. Physician, Qaraite theologian, liturgical poet. He studied the writings of Rashi, Ibn Ezra, Maimonides, Moses ben Naḥman, not to speak of earlier ones. He wrote his main work, the Mibḥar (Choice) in Constantinople, 1294. This is a commentary on the Pentateuch which became one of the main educational books of the Qaraites. A great many supercommentaries were devoted to it. He wrote a Hebrew grammar entitled Kalil yofi (Diadem of beauty). He tried to give some physiological explanations of the soul. In spite of his scientific training, and of his preference for the literal interpretation (peshaṭa) of the sacred writings, he had also some gematrical tendencies.

Text—Mibḥar. Hebrew extracts with Latin translation published by Johann Ludwig Frey: Excerpta nonnulla ex commentario inedito R. Aharonis b. Joseph Judaei Caraei (Amsterdam 1704). Complete Hebrew text with a commentary edited by Joseph Solomon ben Moses Yerushalmi (Kozlov 1835).

Kalil yofi, edited with additions by Isaac ben Judah Tishbi (Constantinople 1581).

Criticism—Kaufmann Kohler: Jewish Encyclopaedia (vol. 1, 14, 1901). For the younger Aaron, see article by same (ibidem, 9–10). J. N. Simchoni: Encyclopaedia judaica (vol. 1, 51–55, 1928).

III. WESTERN JEWS

For Solomon ibn Ayyub and Jacob ibn Abbassi, see the chapter on translators.

IBN FALAQUERA

Shem-ṭob ben Joseph Ibn Falaquera (Palquera). Hispano-Jewish philosopher born c. 1225; died after 1290. He wrote commentaries on the Bible (lost), and many philosophical treatises, the purpose of which was mainly to harmonize Jewish theology with Peripatetic philosophy as transmitted by Ibn Rushd and Maimonides.

He translated from Arabic into Hebrew:

1. Long extracts from the Yanbū' al-ḥayāt (Meqor ḥayyim, Fons vitae) of Ibn Gabirol. Thanks to his deep knowledge of Arabic literature, he was able to see Ibn Gabirol's activity in its true historical perspective. This translation of the Yanbū' al-ḥayāt may have influenced the Qabbalists, though they do not mention it.

2. Ibn Rushd's commentary on Aristotle's Physics and Metaphysics. This is not a translation stricto sensu, but the author declares that everything in this book, entitled De'ot ha-filusufim, is derived from Aristotle, according to Ibn Rushd's interpretation.

His other works are more original though more or less derived from Arabic writings. Nos. 3 to 7 were written by Shem-ṭob before he was 35.

3. Iggeret hanhagat ha-guf we ha-nefesh. Regimen of body and soul, in verse.

4. Ẓeri ha-yagon, Balm of sorrow. On resignation and fortitude in misfortune.

5. Iggeret ha-wikkuaḥ. Dialogue between a theologian and a philosopher on religion and philosophy. The purpose is to prove that Bible and Talmud are in harmony with the philosophic teaching. This was translated into Latin.

6. Reshit ḥokmah. Beginning of wisdom. Divided into three parts: (1) moral qualities needed to undertake philosophic and scientific studies; (2) survey of the sciences; (3) need of philosophy to obtain true happiness. It includes a translation of the "ethical epistles" of Aristotle (apocryphal writings transmitted

by Arabic writers, e.g., 'Alī ibn Riḍwān[3]). The end of part (3) discusses the views of Aristotle and Plato. The Reshit ḥokmah was also translated into Latin.

7. Sefer ha-ma'alot, Book of degrees. On the different degrees of human perfection.

8. Sefer ha-mebaqqesh. The seeker (after knowledge). Survey of knowledge, written in 1263, in prose and verse. It is an elaboration of no. 6.

9. Sefer ha-nefesh. On the soul. Explanation of the views of Muslim Peripatetics, chiefly Ibn Sīnā, in 20 chapters.

10. Shlemut ha-ma'asim, Perfection of works. Ethical tract in ten chapters.

11. Moreh ha-moreh. Guide to the Guide. Commentary on the philosophical part of the Moreh nebukim, composed in 1280. In the appendix Shem-ṭob corrects many errors of the Hebrew translation by Samuel ibn Tibbon.

12. Defense of the Moreh nebukim, against some French rabbis, written in 1290. Other works, Iggeret ha-musar, a collection of maxims, and Iggeret ha-ḥalom, on dreams, are lost.

Text—The numbers correspond to those mentioned above.

1. Meqor ḥayyim, extracts edited by Solomon Munk: Mélanges de philosophie juive (38 p., Paris 1859).

4. Ẓeri ha-yagon. The substance of this text was published with additions by one Saul ben Simeon (Cremona 1557). Later editions, Prague 1612; Hanau 1716.

5. Iggeret ha-wikkuaḥ (Constantinople 1570?). Later edition, Prague 1610.

7. Sefer ha-ma'alot. Edited by Ludwig Venetianer (Berlin 1891).

8. Sefer ha-mebaqqesh (The Hague, 1778–1779). French dedication by the editor, Mordecai ben Isaac Tama.

9. Sefer ha-nefesh, edited by Mordecai Loeb Bisliches (Lemberg 1835).

11. Moreh ha-moreh, edited by same (Pressburg 1837).

12. Defense of the Moreh nebukim, edited by same in Abba Mari Moses Yarḥi: Minḥat qena'ot, (Pressburg 1838).

Criticism—S. Munk: Mélanges de philosophie juive (274, 494, 1859). E. Renan: Averroës (183, 187, 1869). M. Steinschneider: Hebraeische Übersetzungen (5–9, 37–40, 270, 354, 1893). I. Broydé: Jewish encyclopaedia (vol. 5, 326, 1903; mainly derived from Munk).

ALBALAG

Isaac Albalag. Jewish philosopher and translator from Arabic into Hebrew, who flourished in northern Spain at the end of the thirteenth century and the beginning of the fourteenth. He tried to reconcile Jewish theology with the purer Aristotelian knowledge. In his refutations of al-Ghazzālī and Maimonides, he remarked that their errors were due to their knowing Aristotle only indirectly through the commentaries of al-Fārābī, Ibn Sīnā, and others. He was deeply influenced by Ibn Rushd, whom he considered a reliable interpreter of Aristotle (as opposed to Maimonides, not so reliable). Under this influence he tended to accept the theory of the eternity of the world. His attempts to reconcile positive knowledge with religion, as well as his study of al-Ghazzālī and Ibn Rushd, led him to a kind of double truth theory (see my discussion of this in my note on Ibn Rushd). He had some familiarity with Latin writings, and with those of the Qabbalists whose extravagances he denounced.

In 1292 or later (beginning of the fourteenth century ?) he translated the Maqāṣid

[3] Isis, 6, 505.

al-falāsifa (Tendencies of the philosophers) of al-Ghazzālī, under the title Tiqqun ha-filusufim, adding critical notes to defend Aristotle and the philosophers against the author. This translation or elaboration is not complete; it contains only the parts dealing with logic and metaphysics; the third part, physics, was translated in 1307 by Isaac ibn Polgar (or Pulqar). He wrote a Hebrew commentary on Ibn Rushd's talkhīṣ on the Aristotelian physics (partly lost).

Criticism—M. Steinschneider: Hebraeische Übersetzungen (116, 299–306, 1893). C. Brockelmann: Arabische Litteratur (vol. 1, 425, 1898). S. Horovitz: Jewish Encyclopaedia (vol. 1, 320, 1901). Heimann Auerbach: Albalag und seine Übersetzung des Maqāṣid al-Gazzālīs (Diss., Breslau 1907). M. Zobel: Encyclopaedia judaica (vol. 2, 104–107, 1928).

ABOAB

Isaac I Aboab or Abohab (Abū Hab). Judeo-Spanish theologian who lived about the end of the thirteenth century or the beginning of the fourteenth. (Not to be confused with his namesake, Isaac II Aboab, exegete, born at Toledo, 1430, died 1493). Isaac I was not a rabbi, but a business man who toward the end of his life set out to write popular works on Talmudic, religious, and ethical subjects. Only one of them is extant, but it is sufficient to establish his fame. The Menorat ha-maor (Candelabrum of light), is a collection of Talmudic stories, divided into seven sections (cf. seven branches of the candelabrum in the Tabernacle). It was soon translated into Spanish. Besides its educational influence this work is historically important, because it contributed more than any other contemporary book to the diffusion of Talmudic lore.

Text—First edition of the Menorah, Constantinople 1514. Later editions: Venice 1544; Mantua 1563; Venice 1595–1602; Venice 1623; Francfort o. M., 1687; etc.

Hebrew text with Spanish translation by J. Hages (Leghorn 1657; reprinted Amsterdam 1708). Hebrew text with commentary and Yiddish translation, by Moses Frankfurter (Amsterdam 1700). Hebrew text with German translation by Rafael J. Fürstenthal and Benzion Behrend (3 parts, Krotoschin, prov. Posen, 1848). New Yiddish version (Vilna 1880). German version by S. Bamberger (Hamburg 1923).

Criticism—M. Steinschneider: Cat. libr. heb. in Bibl. Bodl. (1071–1072, 1860). Samuel Baeck and Kaufmann Kohler: Jewish Encyclopaedia (vol. 1, 73, 1901). S. A. Horodezky: Encyclopaedia judaica (vol. 1, 343–345, 1928).

MOSES OF LEON

Moses ben Shem-Ṭob. Born at Leon, Spain, c. 1250; flourished at Guadajara, Valladolid and Avila; died at Arevalo in 1305. Jewish occultist. He was probably the author or editor of the most famous qabbalistic compilation, the so-called Sefer ha-zohar (Book of splendor). This title is derived from Daniel (XII, 3). The Zohar was written partly in Hebrew and partly in an obsolete Aramaic dialect and was self-ascribed to Simeon ben Yoḥai (first half of the second century); its title being Midrash of R. Shim'on ben Yoḥai (or Midrash ha-zohar). It is certainly, whoever may be the author, a much later compilation: it refers to the eclipse of Rome 1264, (1263?); mentions many ideas unknown before the thirteenth century and even states that it was not revealed before 1300–1306! But however young the compilation, most of its elements were very old.

The Zohar is a mystical commentary on the Torah. It deals with such subjects as astronomy, cosmogony, physiognomy, psychology, angelology, demonology, etc. An example of astronomical thought is a reference to the teaching of one rabbi Hamnuna the Elder[4] that "the earth turns like a sphere in a circle round itself and that some people are above and others below;"[5] a bit of Heraclidean knowledge which may have reached the editor of the Zohar in more than one way. Indeed the Zohar is an encyclopaedia of Jewish lore and theosophy derived, as all theosophical and mystical systems are, from an infinity of sources: neo-Pythagoreanism, neo-Platonism, Jewish occultism, Gnosticism, Hinduism, Ṣūfīsm, mysticism of many nations. The Platonic analogy between macrocosm and microcosm is extremely elaborated and other analogies are developed, e.g., between the shapes of the human body and those of Hebrew letters. Mystical interpretations of the Torah were obtained by considering the numerical values of the Hebrew letters,[6] using ciphers, detecting acrostics in various ways, or arranging the text in squares, and reading the lines vertically, backwards, or bustrophedon.

In the Zohar the theory of the ten sefirot is accepted as almost axiomatic. Much importance is paid to mystical psychology, to the idea of soul transmigrations, etc. The doctrine of four worlds is developed: (1) the 'aẓilutic world, of emanation ('azilut), where the sefirot dwell; (2) the beri'atic world, of creative ideas; (3) the yeẓiratic world, of creative formations; (2) the 'asiyyatic world, of creative matter.

There are four kinds of Biblical exegesis: peshaṭ (literal meaning), remez (allusion), derash (explanation), sod (mystery). The initials of these four words form the word pardes (paradise) which symbolizes the complete understanding. Those who see nothing in the Torah but its obvious meaning are as foolish as the men who mistake the clothes for the body, the body for the soul—or the jug for the wine which it contains. The real meaning of the Torah can be attained only by the complete Qabbalistic interpretation of it. There are four kinds of knowledge: external knowledge, internal knowledge, intuitive knowledge, knowledge through love. And above these are the seven ecstatic stages. It is not expedient to multiply these illustrations.

Perhaps the soundest part of the Zohar is the ethical, the insistency upon love as the only bridge between the individual souls and between these souls and God.

The recrudescence of Qabbalism at the end of the thirteenth century, and the apparition of the Zohar, are partly explained as reactions against the excessive intellectualism fostered by Ibn Rushd, Maimonides and their followers. The triumph of Jewish philosophy had repressed other fundamental tendencies beyond endurance—these emotional, sexual, and mystical needs which are normal constituents of human nature, Jewish or otherwise.

Though the Zohar did not supersede some of the earlier Qabbalistic treatises which it had assimilated (notably the Sefer yeẓirah and the Bahir), it obtained gradually more and more importance. Its success was so great that it finally came to represent the whole Qabbalah, or that it was considered as the fountain head of

[4] The name Hamnuna was worn by Babylonian amoraim of the third and fourth centuries, but this particular one is not identified.

[5] Zohar (vol. 3, fol. 10a, Amsterdam 1728) as quoted by J. L. E. Dreyer: History of the planetary systems (272, Cambridge 1906).

[6] The Hebrew script lent itself to this because the letters have numerical values and there are no numerals but these letters. Yet the same was the case for the Greek script, and gematria (defined in note 7), in spite of its Greek-Hebrew name, was essentially a Jewish disease, from which the ancient Greeks remained comparatively free.

it. Of course, this was wrong; but one thing is certain, it completed the establishment of the Qabbalah as a definite body of doctrine, and put it so to say on a level of equality with the two other great streams of Jewish thought, the orthodox or rabbinical and the Maimonidean or philosophical.

From the end of the thirteenth century on the number of Qabbalists or mequbbalim increased considerably, and some of them were found in every Jewish community. They were also called ba'ale ha-qabbalah, or maskilim (the wise; Daniel, 12, 10).

The influence of the Zohar was immense, and unfortunately not unmixed with evil. Indeed the Zohar contained admirable thoughts and some sound knowledge, but it was adulterated by so many superstitions and extravagances that the whole—and one has to judge it as a whole—became worthless and pernicious. It stimulated magical tendencies and encouraged immoderate dreams. It has always had an especially strong attraction for unbalanced minds, whose destruction it helps to complete, and the more surely because of the genuine jewels which are embedded in it.

However the historian of science must try to look at it without rationalistic bias from a purely historical point of view. The popularity of the Zohar and of the Qabbalah was partly due to the unparalleled miseries of Israel. Witness the Qabbalistic revivals which followed the expulsion of the Jews from Spain, and every other calamity which was never wanting very long. The Qabbalah was a reaction against rabbinical formalism, against the unbearable rationalism of the philosophers, above all against the increasing hardness of life in an atmosphere of contumely and persecution.

It should be noted that the Qabbalah did not influence only the mystically minded; of course it had a stronger hold on these, but in a sense every Jewish thinker was more or less affected by it, for good or for evil. A history of the Qabbalah is a cross section of the history of Jewish thought.

Moreover its influence was not by any means restricted to Judaism. Indeed the needs which the Zohar answered were specifically, but not exclusively, Jewish. The first Christian doctor to know of it was Ramon Lull. During the first half of the fourteenth century its fame spread rapidly in Jewish circles, and some of it percolated among the Gentiles. This external diffusion was considerably activated toward the middle of the fifteenth century because some baptized Jews sought to harmonize the teachings of the Qabbalah with those of the New Testament, and with such Christian ideas as the fall and redemption of man, the Trinity, etc. This Judeo-Christian movement started in Spain, one of the leaders being Pablo de Heredia (1405–1486). These converted Jews were then followed by Christians such as Pico della Mirandola, Paolo Rici, professor at Pavia, physician to Maximilian (emperor from 1493 to 1519), Johann Reuchlin, Heinrich Cornelius Agrippa von Nettesheim, Paracelsus, Robert Fludd, etc.

Text—Princeps edition. With a decision by Isaac ben Immanuel de Lattes (3 vols., Mantua 1558–1560). Another edition appeared at Cremona in the same year, 1558. Later editions among many: Lublin 1623–1624; Amsterdam 1715, 1728, 1772, 1805; Constantinople 1736; Leghorn 1791–1793, 1851, 1858; Jerusalem 1844–1846; Königsberg 1857, etc. There are innumerable commentaries, and almost every edition contains one or more of them and editorial notes.

Liber Sohar restitutus. Hebrew text with Latin translation by Christian Knorr von Rosenroth: Kabbala denudata (vol. 2, Sulzbach 1677–1684). Liber Sohar.

Collectanea de dictis et gestis R. Schimeon filii Jochai et discipulorum ejus. Opus quod Corpus cabbalae dici posset (782 p., folio, Sulzbach 1684).

S. L. MacGregor Mathers: Kabbala denudata. Englished from Knorr's Latin version (London 1887). French translation by Jean de Pauly: Le Zohar. Oeuvre posthume, revue et complétée par Emile Lafuma-Giraud (6 vols., Paris 1906–1911). Erich Bischoff: Die Elemente der Kabbalah. Übersetzungen, Erläuterungen und Abhandlungen (2 vols., Berlin 1913–1914).

Criticism—S. Munk: Mélanges de philosophie juive (275, 490, 1859). S. Karppe: Etude sur les origines et la nature du Zohar (614 p., Paris 1901). Maurice Fluegel: Philosophy, Qabbala and Vedānta (Baltimore 1902). Walter Begley: Biblia cabalistica (165 p., London 1903). Eliphas Lévi (i.e., Alphonse Louis Constant): Le Livre des Splendeurs (341 p., Paris 1894). Kaufmann Kohler and Louis Ginzberg: Jewish encyclopaedia (vol. 3, 456–479, 1902). Meyer Kayserling (ibidem, vol. 8, 7, 1904). Isaac Broydé (ibidem, vol. 12, 689–693, 1906). David Neumark: Geschichte der jüdischen Philosophie des Mittelalters (Berlin 1907). George Margoliouth: Doctrine of ether in the Kabbalah (Jewish quarterly review, vol. 20, 828, 1908). Christian David Ginsburg and Stanley Arthur Cook: Kabbalah (Encyclopaedia Britannica, 1911). Bernhard Pick: The cabala, its influence on Judaism and Christianity (109 p., Chicago 1913). Arthur Edward Waite: The secret doctrine in Israel (346 p., Boston 1914; Isis, 3, 87). Pierre Duhem: Le système du monde (vol. 5, 77–169, 1917). Paul Vulliaud: La Kabbale juive, histoire et doctrine (2 vols., Paris 1923). Second-hand compilation, to be used with great caution. However it includes valuable information, e.g., on the abundant misunderstandings of the Zohar or of "Rabbi Zohar." Samuel Aba Horodezky: Torat ha-qabbalah shel R. Moshe Qordoviro (386 p., Berlin 1924). Deeper study but over enthusiastic (Leo Jung in Jewish quarterly review, vol. 21, 199–201, 1930). Gerhard Scholem: Bibliographia Kabbalistica. Mit einem Anhang, Bibliographie des Zohar und seiner Kommentare (248 p., Leipzig 1927; Isis, 11, 514). Karl Preis: Die Medizin in der Kabbala (Schriften der Gesellschaft zur Förderung der Wissenschaft des Judentums, Nr. 35, 20 p., Frankfurt 1928; J. Q. R., 203–204, 1930).

ABRAHAM ABULAFIA

Abraham ben Samuel Abulafia. This Spanish Jew was one of the earliest Qabbalists. He was born at Saragossa, 1240, and died in or after 1291. He was educated in Tudela, Navarra, then traveled extensively, reaching Acre in Syria, then returned to Europe. He studied Maimonides' philosophy in Capua probably under the guidance of Hillel ben Samuel; c. 1271 he settled in Barcelona; in 1279 he was in Patras, Greece; in the following year he traveled to Rome to convert the Pope (Nicholas III) to his views (Qabbalistic Judaism); a little later while he was in Palermo, these views were condemned by Solomon ben Adret; in 1285–1286, he was working on the little island of Comino, near Malta. Starting from sound philosophical studies, from c. 1271 on, he drifted more and more in the mystical and qabbalistic direction, devoting a considerable energy to gematria[7] and other cryptographic delusions, and assuming prophetic pretensions. While in Sicily he announced that the Messiah would appear in 1290. He composed at least twenty-six works dealing with prophecies and Qabbalah. It is not the place to enumerate

[7] Gematria means a cryptograph obtained by giving numerical values to the letters of the Hebrew alphabet; it also means the application of this method to the interpretation of the Scriptures. The word gemaṭrya is the transcription of a mediaeval Hebrew word derived from the Greek γεωμετρία. S. A. Horodezky: Gematria (Encyclopaedia judaica, vol. 7, 170–179, 1931; received too late for use in this book).

them here, but Abraham's activity had to be mentioned because of its great, if evil, influence.

He laid particular stress upon the prophetical side of the Qabbalah, and developed Qabbalistic Trinitarianism, being probably stimulated in this by his discussions with Christians.

His main pupil was Joseph ben Abraham Giqaṭilia (see below).

Philipp Bloch and Kaufmann Kohler: Jewish Encyclopaedia (vol. 1, 140–142, 1901). G. Scholem: Encyclopaedia judaica (vol. 1, 637–641, 1928).

ṬODROS ABULAFIA

The name Abulafia derives from the Arabic Abū-l-'Āfiyat, meaning the father of health, the healthy one. From the Jewish-Spanish name Abulafia derive the Italian and English names, Bolaffi, Bolaffey, etc.

Ṭodros ben Joseph ben Ṭodros Abulafia (or in Catalan, Abenefeia). Judeo-Spanish Talmudist and Qabbalist. Born in 1234, died at Seville in or after 1298. He composed two qabbalistic works: (1) Sha'ar ha-razim (Gate of secrets), commentary on Psalm 19, written in 1298; (2) Oẓar ha-kabod (Treasure of glory), commentary on Talmud Zera'im and Mo'ed. The second of these works contains the earliest quotations from the Zohar and the earliest qabbalistic interpretations of the Talmudic haggadot.

Text—Partial edition of the Oẓar by Isaac ben Meir, at Torczyn (Novydvor 1808). Complete edition (Warsaw 1879). Dīwān transcribed by Saul Joseph, with preface by Moses Gaster (London 1926).

Criticism—Philipp Bloch: Jewish Encyclopaedia (vol. 1, 143, 1901). G. Scholem: Encyclopaedia judaica (vol. 1, 655–657, 1928).

GIQAṬILIA

Joseph ben Abraham Giqaṭilia (or Gikatilla), nicknamed Joseph Ba'al ha-nissim, the miracle-worker. Spanish Qabbalist. Born at Medinaceli, Castile, 1248; died at Peñafiel, after 1305. He studied the works of Ibn Gabirol, Ibn Ezra, Maimonides, but fell more and more under the influence of his master Abraham Abulafia, of whom he became the most distinguished disciple. He would not deserve to be mentioned in this survey but for the influence which he exerted, and not only upon the Jews but also upon Christians.

He wrote a criticism of the Moreh nebukim entitled Hassagot, based upon al-Ḥarizi's version. His other works were purely Qabbalistic. It will suffice to name a few titles: Ginnat egoz (garden of nuts), written in 1274; Sha'are orah or Sefer ha-orah, on the names of God; Sha'are ẓedeq or Sha'ar ha-shamayyim, on the ten spheres; Sefer ha-niqqud, on the mystical meaning of vowel points; Sodot ha-miẓwot, mysteries of the commandments; etc. The Sha'are orah was translated into Latin by Paul Rici and used by Reuchlin.

Text—Sefer ginnat egoz (folio, Hanau 1615).

Sefer ha-niqqud, included in Abraham ben Solomon 'Aqra: Sefer arze lebanon (Venice 1601). Separate edition (Cracow 1648).

Sha'are orah (Mantua 1561). Another edition, Riva di Trento 1561. Later editions, Cracow 1600; Offenbach 1715. Latin translation by Paul Rici: Portae lucis (Augsburg 1516). Reprinted in Joannes Pistorius: Artis cabalisticae . . . scriptores (vol. 1, Basel 1587), and in C. Knorr de Rosenroth: Kabbala denudata (2 vols., Sulzbach 1677–Francfort 1684).

Sefer sha'are ẓedeq (Riva di Trento 1561; Korzec 1785). Etc.

Criticism—M. Seligsohn: Jewish encyclopaedia (vol. 5, 665, 1903). S. A. Horodezky: Encyclopaedia judaica (vol. 7, 408–411, 1931).

MOSES BEN NAḤMAN

Moses ben Naḥman Gerondi. Spanish Talmudist and physician. Also called Naḥmanides, Ramban (meaning Rabbi M. b. N.), and Bonastruc da Porta (de Portas). Born in 1194 at Gerona, Catalonia (then a part of Aragon); rabbi of Gerona, and later chief rabbi of Catalonia until 1263 when he was exiled; after spending a few years in Castile and Southern France, he moved c. 1266–1267 to the Holy Land; he lived in Jerusalem and Acre; died c. 1270; buried in Haifa. He had been deeply influenced by the Talmudic school of northern France. He was ultra conservative, and naturally anti-Maimonidean, but with some moderation. He criticizes Abraham ibn Ezra more strongly than Maimonides.

In 1263, at the initiative of Ramon de Peñafort, he was obliged by James of Aragon (king from 1213 to 1276) to discuss publicly at Barcelona the respective merits of Christianity and Judaism with the apostate Pablo Christiani, a Dominican. The discussion lasted four days and seemed to turn to Moses' advantage but soon afterwards the Dominicans caused him to be exiled from Aragon, and the Talmud to be censored.

His main work is a commentary on the Pentateuch (Perush ha-Torah), composed in Palestine, hence, c. 1267–1270. This contains information on Palestinian topography and archaeology (e.g., on Hebrew and Samaritan coins). Moses loved to emphasize the miraculous aspects of the Bible. His interpretation was often apocalyptic and mystic, but not Qabbalistic stricto sensu, though he introduced quotations from the Bahir. According to him the three fundamental beliefs of Judaism were: creation ex nihilo (this suffices to show that he was not a Qabbalist), omniscience of God, and Providence.

He wrote various other works, commentaries on the Talmud and Halakah, devotional books, etc. I shall quote only the letters addressed from Palestine to his son Naḥman, and to a younger son, which contain information on Jerusalem and Acre and constitute a sort of ethical will.

Text—First edition of the Perush ha Torah (Lisbon 1480? or 1489?). Copies in the British Museum and in the Jewish Theological Seminary, New York.

The Wikkuaḥ, Moses' controversy with Pablo Christiani was published in the Milḥamot ḥobah (Constantinople 1710). Translated into Latin by Johann Christopher Wagenseil: Tela ignea Satanae (Altdorf 1681).

Criticism—Heinrich Denifle: Instrumentum disputationis de fide cum quodam. rabbi Moyse (Historisches Jahrbuch des Goerres-Gesellschaft, Munich 1887) Protocol of the discussion of 1263. Solomon Schechter: Studies in Judaism (vol. 1, 99–141, Philadelphia 1896). Isaac Broydé: Jewish encyclopaedia (vol. 9, 87–92, 1905). A. Lukyn Williams: The Jews. Christian apologists in Spain in the thirteenth century (Church quarterly review, vol. 102, 98–115, London, 1926). Jacob Mann: La lettre polémique de Jacob b. Elie à Pablo Christiani (Revue des études juives, vol. 82, 362–377, 1926). This Jacob was probably Jacob de Lattes ben Elijah ben Isaac of Carcassonne, a cousin of Pablo's; Pablo himself originated probably from Montpellier. S. Lieben: Pablo Christiani (Encyclopaedia judaica, vol. 5, 562, 1930).

SOLOMON BEN ADRET

Solomon ben Abraham ben Adret. Also called Rashba (i.e., Rabbi Sh. b. A.). Born at Barcelona, 1235; died in 1310. One of the most influential rabbis of his time, witness his nickname, El Rab d'España (The Rabbi of Spain). He was the main disciple of Moses ben Naḥman and through him had learned the Talmudic methods of northern France. He wrote a large number of responsa (some 3,000) which form a very valuable source for the study of contemporary Jewry, not only in Europe, but also in Asia Minor. He caused Maimonides' commentary on the Mishnah to be translated from Arabic into Hebrew. He refuted the attacks on Israel made by Ibn Ḥazm in his Kitāb al-milal wal-niḥal (first half of the eleventh century) and by Raymond Martin in his Pugio fidei (c. 1277). He resisted with equal vigor the forward movement of the rationalists (such as Levi ben Abraham ibn Ḥayyim), and the extravagances of the Qabbalists (e.g., of Abraham Abulafia, whom he openly condemned). In this fight for the preservation of the pure Jewish traditions he was associated with Abba Mari ben Moses ha-Yarḥi (q. v., first half of the fourteenth century).

In 1305, together with the other rabbis of Barcelona, he excommunicated those who studied philosophy (physics and metaphysics) before having completed their twenty-fifth year, unless they were physicians or were preparing themselves for the medical profession. After 1305 he devoted two other epistles to the criticism and condemnation of the philosophical movement which was undermining the Jewish faith. These three epistles are very important because of Solomon's commanding position in the rabbinical circles of Europe in the beginning of the fourteenth century.

Text—The earliest responsa of his to be printed appeared under Naḥmanides' name (1480?; Constantinople 1519).

Many partial editions of the Responsa. First part (Bologna 1539; Venice 1546; Hanau 1610, etc.). Second part (Leghorn 1657). Third part (Leghorn 1778). Fourth part (Salonica 1803). Fifth part (Leghorn 1825). Sixth and seventh (Warsaw 1865).

Talmudic novellae (Warsaw 1902).

Isidore Epstein: The Responsa of Rabbi Solomon ben Adreth, as a source of the history of Spain. Studies in the communal life of the Jews in Spain (132 p., London 1925).

Epistle prohibiting anyone under twenty-five years of age to study philosophy, in B. Halper: Post-Biblical Hebrew literature (Philadelphia 1921; one of his three epistles on the subject, in Hebrew and English).

Criticism—Moritz Kayserling: Jewish Encyclopaedia (vol. 1, 212, 1901). S. Bialoblocki: Encyclopaedia judaica (vol. 1, 907–911, 1928). B. Suler: Vidal Bonafos (Encyclopaedia judaica, vol. 4, 934, 1929).

AARON HA-LEVI

Aaron ha-Levi of Barcelona. Spanish Talmudist, moralist, and educator who flourished at the end of the thirteenth century. He studied the works of Maimonides and Moses ben Naḥman, and derived from them and other sources a work of a humbler kind, the Sefer ha-ḥinnuk (Book of consecration, or education), containing an enumeration of the 613 precepts of Mosaic Law, with simple explanations. The commandments are put in the same order as in the Sefer ha-miẓwot of Maimonides. The Ḥinnuk was immensely popular for centuries; it was translated into Spanish and Latin.

This Aaron is apparently different from another Aaron (ben Joseph) ha-Levi, also of Barcelona, a distinguished rabbi, author of responsa and Talmudic treatises, who was born about the middle of the century and died after 1300.

Text—Sefer ha-ḥinnuk. First edition (Bomberg, Venice 1523). Edition by Isaac ben Jacob of Herlisheim (Venice 1600). Later editions: Amsterdam 1721; with notes by Judah Rozanes, edited by M. J. Spiro (Brünn 1799); by Gabriel Hirsch Englaender (Vienna 1827); etc.

Minḥat ḥinnuk. Elaborate Hebrew commentary on the Ḥinnuk by Joseph ben Moses Babad, of Tarnopol (3 vols., Lemberg 1869).

The Spanish version is apparently lost.

Abbreviated version edited by Johann Heinrich Hottinger: Juris Hebraeorum leges CCLXI . . . . ductu R. Levi Barcelonitae (Zürich 1655).

Criticism—D. Rosin: Ein Compendium des jüdischen Gesetzes (Jahresbericht des jüdischen theologischen Seminars, Breslau 1871). Louis Ginzberg: Jewish Encyclopaedia (vol. 1, 15, 1901). S. Bialoblocki: Encyclopaedia judaica (vol. 1, 62–65, 1928). For Aaron ben Joseph, see ibidem (vol. 1, 57–60).

For Shem-ṭob ben Isaac and Zeraḥiah Gracian, see chapter on translators.

LEVI BEN ABRAHAM BEN ḤAYYIM

Languedocian Jewish philosopher, mathematician, and astronomer. Born between 1245 and 1250 at Villefranche-de-Confluent, Roussillon; he was in Montpellier in 1276; later we find him in Narbonne and Béziers; he was persecuted and excommunicated by the orthodox; in 1315 he retired in or near Arles, where he died soon afterwards. His father was Abraham ben Ḥayyim, rabbi of Narbonne (first half of the thirteenth century); one of his grandsons was Levi ben Gershon (first half of the fourteenth century). He was the leader of liberal Judaism in Languedoc and Provence; that is, the main advocate of the study of philosophy and positive knowledge. He compiled two Hebrew encyclopaedias:

1. Batte ha-nefesh weha-leḥashim (caskets for perfumes and amulets; title derived from Isaiah 3, 20), a popular work in Hebrew verse (1846 lines), written at Montpellier in 1276. It is divided into ten chapters and deals with ethics, logic, astronomy and astrology, physics, metaphysics, etc. Solomon de Lunas wrote a commentary upon the Batte, c. 1400 (This Solomon is probably identical with Solomon ben Menahem, alias Frat Maimon).

2. Liwyat ḥen (ornaments of grace) or Sefer ha-kolel (encyclopaedic book), containing six treatises dealing respectively with logic or arithmetic, geometry, astronomy and astrology, physics and psychology, metaphysics, theology and prophecy. The date of this work is unknown but Levi revised and expanded it at Arles in 1315.

In the year 1276 he wrote the Sefer ha-tekunah, a treatise on astronomy and astrology in forty chapters; the last chapter dealing with judicial astrology may be considered an independent work entitled Sha'ar ha-arba'im be-koḥot ha-kokabim.

Levi's views on astronomy and astrology were slavishly derived from Ibn Ezra; his philosophical guide was Maimonides.

Criticism—Ernest Renan: Les rabbins français (Histoire littéraire de la France, vol. 27, 628–647, 1877, analysis of Levi's works); Ecrivains juifs (1893). M. Steinschneider: Ersch und Grubers Allgemeine Encyklopädie (vol. 43, 294–295; reprinted in his Gesammelte Schriften, vol. 1, 228–233, 1925). Max Schloessinger: Jewish Encyclopaedia (vol. 8, 22–24, 1904).

GERSHON BEN SOLOMON

Judeo-Provençal or Judeo-Catalan encyclopaedist. The name Gershon is often spelled Gerson; in the Old Testament it is always written Gershon or Gershom. He is called Catalan in some MSS., and Arlesian in others. He lived at Arles and died at Perpignan(?) toward the end of the thirteenth century. Probably the father of Levi ben Gershon.

He compiled, c. 1280 (?), a Hebrew encyclopaedic treatise entitled Sha'ar ha-shamayim (Gate of heaven), derived from Greek and Arabic sources, or rather from their Hebrew translations, and containing long quotations from these; some Hebrew translations of Arabic writings are even included verbatim. This work is divided into three parts: (1) physics, i.e., natural phenomena, storms, volcanic eruptions, metals, plants, animals, man; (2) astronomy, largely derived from al-Farghānī, and from Ibn Sīnā's and Ibn Rushd's commentaries on the De coelo; (3) metaphysics, derived almost verbatim from Maimonides' Moreh nebukim.

Text—First edition, Venice 1547. Second by Wolf Heidenheim (Roedelheim 1801).

Criticism—E. Renan: Rabbins français (589–591, 576, 1877); Ecrivains juifs (475, 1893). M. Steinschneider: Hebraeische Übersetzungen (9–16, 1893); list of Gershon's sources. Moritz Kayserling: Jewish encyclopaedia (vol. 3, 618, 1902). I. Broydé: ibidem (vol. 5, 640, 1903). J. Ca.: Encyclopaedia Judaica (vol. 7, 320–321, 1931).

For Moses ibn Tibbon, Jacob ben Maḥir ibn Tibbon, Solomon ben Moses of Melgueil, Aḥiṭub ben Isaac, see the chapter on translators.

HILLEL BEN SAMUEL

Hillel ben Samuel of Verona. Italian philosopher, physician, Talmudist, translator from Latin into Hebrew. One of his grandfathers was the Talmudist, Eleazar ben Samuel of Verona. Hillel was born c. 1220; he died c. 1295. Educated in Barcelona, studied medicine in Montpellier, then practised in Rome. In 1260–1271 he practised medicine and taught philosophy in Capua; finally he retired to Forli.

He was a resolute Maimonidean, and when the anti-Maimonidean agitation spread to Italy he suggested to his friend Maestro Isaac Gajo, the pope's physician, to submit the controversy caused by the Moreh nebukim to a council of eastern rabbis for a final decision.

His main work, Tagmule ha-nefesh (Rewards of the soul) is a philosophical compilation reviewing the opinions of the Greeks, Muslims, Jews, and Christians. He was one of the first Jews having immediate access to the writings of the Latin scholastics. He wrote commentaries on the twenty-five fundamental propositions of Maimonides, Ha-qdamot; on the Haggadah, on the Song of songs, etc.

He translated from Latin into Hebrew:

1. De expositione bonitatis purae. That is, the pseudo-Aristotelian Liber de causis in the version made by Gerard of Cremona.

2. 'Alī ibn Riḍwān's commentary on Galen's Tegni, also from Gerard's version, Sefer ha-ṭegni.

3. The Chirurgia magna composed by Bruno da Longoburgo in 1252. Sefer karitot (or ẓirugiah).

Text—The Tagmule ha-nefesh was edited by Solomon Zalman Halberstam for the Meqiẓe nirdamim society (Lyck 1874). The commentary on Maimonides' 25 propositions is included in that edition.

Iggeret R. Hillel el R. Isaac ha-rofe' in Eliezer ben Solomon Ashkenasi: Ṭa'am zeqenim, edited by Raphael Kirchheim (Francfort o. M., 1854). Another edition in Ẓebi Hirsch Edelmann: Ḥemdah genuzah (Königsberg, 1856). Contains the two letters addressed to Isaac Gajo on the Maimonides' controversy.

Criticism—M. Steinschneider: Hebraeische Übersetzungen (262, 734, 788, 1893). A. Peiginsky: Jewish encyclopaedia (vol. 6, 401, 1904). Isaac Husik: Mediaeval philosophy (312–327, 1918).

ISAIAH BEN ELIJAH OF TRANI

Isaiah of Trani, the Younger. Italian Talmudist. Grandson, through his mother, of Isaiah ben Mali of Trani, who died c. 1250. His own birth and death dates are unknown. He wrote Biblical commentaries; a ritual code, Pirqe halakot, which was the first Italian one; a sort of critical introduction to the code, Qonṭres ha-re'ayot; etc. He was less liberal and less original than his grandfather, and I would not have mentioned him but for the fact that he was often confused with the latter.

Text—First edition of the Pirqe halakot by Meir ben Jacob Parenz, together with Alfasi's text (Venice 1552). Second edition by Joshua Boaz ben Simeon Baruch, together with Alfasi (3 vols., Sabionetta 1554–1555; including copious indices). Reprinted (3 vols., Riva di Trento 1558).

Criticism—Max Schloessinger: Jewish Encyclopaedia (vol. 6, 644, 1904).

JEHIEL 'ANAV

Jehiel ben Jekuthiel 'Anav. Moralist and copyist of manuscripts who flourished in Rome c. 1268–1289. He copied many Hebrew MSS. c. 1284–1289, some of which are still extant. His main work is an ethical treatise, Sefer beit ha-middot (or Ma'alot ha-middot, excellencies of virtue), describing many instances of right and wrong conduct. It is divided into twenty-four chapters each of which illustrates a good quality and its opposite. Jehiel derived its material not only from Jewish sources, but also from pagan and Christian ones. He composed an elegy on the destruction of the Roman synagogue by fire in 1268.

Text—Beit middot. First edition, Constantinople 1511. Later ones: Cremona 1556, 1565; Offenbach 1716; Constantinople 1763.

Criticism—Moses Güdemann: Das jüdische Unterrichtswesen (vol. 2, Vienna 1884). U. Cassuto: Encyclopaedia judaica (vol. 2, 800, 1928).

For Benjamin 'Anav, see the historical chapter.

MEIR BEN BARUCH

Meir of Rothenburg. German tosafist. The leader of Talmudic studies in Germany in his time; his influence spread abroad directly and also indirectly through his pupils, of whom the greatest was Asher ben Jehiel. He was sometimes called Me'or ha-golah (Light of the exile). Born at Worms sometime during the second eighth of the thirteenth century; studied in French yeshibot; was rabbi in various German cities, chiefly in Rothenburg an der Tauber (in Middle Franconia, not very far from Würzburg); he spent the last seven years of his life imprisoned in the fortress of Ensisheim (near Mühlhausen, Upper Alsace), and died there in 1293.

He was very conservative, defending orthodox Talmudism with equal strength against philosophical and against Qabbalistic tendencies. He wrote tosafot to several Talmudic treatises, responsa, various books on legal and ritual questions, etc. Nineteen piyyuṭim (liturgical poems) of his are preserved in the German maḥzor. One of them is an elegy dealing with the burning of the Talmud in Paris, 1244.

Text—Tosafot to the Mishnah Tractate Yoma (London 1648).

Various collections of Responsa. Cremona 1557; Prague 1608; Lemberg 1860; Berlin 1891.

Hilkot (or Seder) berakot (Riva di Trento 1558).

Hilkot abelut (or semaḥot) published by Judah ben Nathan ha Levi under the title Sefer maḥaneh lewiyyah (Leghorn 1819).

Commentary on the sixth order of the Mishnah, in Romm's edition of the Talmud (Vilna 1897).

Criticism—E. Renan: Rabbins français (452–471, 1877). Louis Ginsberg: Jewish encyclopaedia (vol. 8, 437–440, 1904).

ABRAHAM BEN ALEXANDER

Abraham ben Alexander of Cologne. German Qabbalist, disciple of Eleazar of Worms. He moved to Spain, and Solomon ben Adret, while still in his youth, heard him preach. Abraham wrote the treatise Sefer keter shem-ṭob (Crown of the good name), dealing with the sacred tetragram, which is of interest because it is a combination of German gematria with the Spanish sefirot ideas. That is, it illustrates the synthesis of German and Spanish Qabbalism. It has also been ascribed, but wrongly, to another pupil of Eleazar's, Menahem Ashkenazi.

Text—Keter shem-ṭob. First edition, Amsterdam 1810. Modern edition by Adolph Jellinek: Auswahl kabbalistischer Mystik (part 1, Leipzig 1853).

Criticism—Philipp Bloch: Jewish encyclopaedia (vol. 1, 100, 1901). G. Scholem: Encyclopaedia judaica (vol. 1, 414, 1928).

ASHER BEN JEHIEL

Often called Asheri. One of the greatest German tosafists and jurists. Born in Western Germany about the middle of the thirteenth century; studied under R. Meir of Rothenburg, of whom he was the most famous pupil; in 1281 he moved from Cologne to Coblenz, later to Worms; in 1303 persecutions obliged him to leave his country and go to Montpellier, Barcelona, and finally to Toledo. He spent some 23 years in Toledo, as rabbi and chief justice, and died there at the end of 1327. He joined Solomon ben Adret in the latter's struggle against the philosophical party. His great authority strengthened the reactionary movement initiated a generation earlier by Moses ben Naḥman. The successive and cumulative efforts of these two men, Moses and Asher, caused the scientific spirit of the Spanish Jews to be slowly quenched and replaced by a narrow and bigoted Talmudism.

He wrote considerably: responsa (more than a thousand), Talmudic commentaries, an ethical treatise Hanhagat ha-rosh (or Orḥot ḥayyim), etc. His main work was the Pisqe ha-rosh (or Hilkot ha-rosh, or Ha-Asheri), a code which was based upon Alfasi's Halakot and superseded it. The Piske ha-rosh was very popular; witness the number of MSS., editions, and commentaries.

His ethical will (ẓawwa'ah), addressed to his son, Judah ben Asher, is one of the best examples of this specifically Jewish kind of literature.

He caused his pupil, Isaac ben Joseph Israeli, to write in 1310 the astronomical treatise Yesod 'olam.

Text—First edition of Pisqe ha-rosh in Bomberg's edition of the Talmud (Venice 1520–1523). Many later editions; e.g., in almost every edition of the Talmud, under the heading Rosh (i.e., Rabbenu Asher).

Extracts from his will are included in Israel Abrahams: Hebrew ethical wills (vol. 1, 118–125, Philadelphia 1926; in Hebrew and English).

Hanhagah. First edition, Venice 1578.

Orḥot ḥayyim. Hebrew text with Yiddish translation by Yom-ṭob Heller and a sermon on the plague (Prague 1622), etc.

She'elot u-teshubot. First edition, Constantinople 1517 or 1522. Second and third, Venice 1552, 1607. Etc.

For other works, see Hebrew bibliographies.

Criticism—Gotthard Deutsch: Jewish encyclopaedia (vol. 2, 182, 1902). J. Freimann: Encyclopaedia judaica (vol. 3, 442–448, 1929).

IV. WESTERN CHRISTENDOM

PETER OF SPAIN

Petrus Hispanus. Also called Petrus Ulyssiponnensis or Compostellanus, names referring to Lisbon and Santiago de Compostela; Petrus Portugalensis; Petrus Juliani. Born at Lisbon between 1210 and 1220; son of the physician Julian; studied in Compostela, Paris, and from 1246 to 1250 in Siena; cardinal in 1273; elected pope in 1276 under the name of John XXI, he died accidentally eight months later in Viterbo, 1277.

Portuguese philosopher, physician, zoologist, one of the greatest logicians and psychologists of the thirteenth century. Dante referred to him in Paradiso (XII, 134).

He wrote many medical works and many commentaries on earlier works. The best known of his own medical works was the Treasure of the poor, Thesaurus pauperum, also entitled Summa experimentorum (also ascribed to his father Julian?). This little textbook was immensely popular, perhaps the most popular book of its kind until the sixteenth century; witness the number of MSS., editions, and translations into Italian, Spanish, Portuguese, and English; there were three Hebrew translations (Oẓar ha 'aniyim). Its popularity was due partly to its brevity and to its practical nature.

Next in importance was his treatise on eye diseases, Liber de morbis oculorum (or Liber de oculo, Breviarium de egritudinibus oculorum et curis). The MSS. of it vary considerably, but if one considers all the oculistic texts ascribed to Peter, one finds that they may be divided into three parts: (1) extract from the Kitāb al-malikī of 'Alī ibn 'Abbās (second half of the tenth century); (2) Tractatus mirabilis aquarum, dealing with twelve waters, the last two being the elixir of life and alcohol (aqua vite and aqua ardens). There are many Latin treatises of this kind (Liber de aquis qui dicitur 12 aquarum; Liber 12 aquarum alkimie; etc.)

the origin of which has not yet been determined;[8] (3) Zacharias' treatise (first half of the twelfth century).[8a]

Other medical treatises are ascribed to Peter, some of which may be apocryphal, or identical to others appearing under different titles: Summa de conservanda sanitate, Regimen sanitatis, Regimen salutis per omnes menses, Liber de morte et vita et de causis longitudinis ac brevitatis vite, Diete super cyrurgiam.

He wrote commentaries on the following medical works:

1–3. Hippocrates: De regimine acutorum, Prognostics, Aphorisms.

4–6. Galen: Microtegni, De crisibus, De diebus decretoriis.

7–8. Theophilos Protospatharios (first half of the seventh century): De pulsibus, De urinis.

9. Ḥunain ibn Isḥāq (second half of the ninth century): Isagoge ad Tegni. Peter added to this commentary an elaborate discussion De motu cordis.

10. Isḥāq al-Isrā'īlī (first half of the tenth century): Kitāb al-baul (De urinis).

11. Isḥāq al-Isrā'īlī: Kitāb al-adwiya al-mufrada wal-aghdhiya, Diaetae universales et particulares. A very full commentary in the scholastic style.

12. Ibn al-Jazzār (second half of the tenth century): Zād al-musāfir, Viaticum.

Summing up Peter's medical activity, it was not distinguished by originality, but was rather of the literary and didactic type. One at least of his works was immensely successful. Peter was practical and superstitious, yet relatively free from occultism.

The popularity of the Thesaurus pauperum, great as it was, was inferior to that of Peter's logical treatise, Summulae logicales. This was not an adaptation of Psellos' synopsis, but was partly derived from the Summa of Lambert of Auxerre (Dominican, fl. c. 1250). It deals not only with the old and new logic (logica vetus, logica nova), but also with the newest (logica modernorum), and is divided into seven books: (1) Liber peri hermenias; (2) praedicabilium; (3) praedicamentorum; (4) priorum; (5) topicorum; (6) elenchorum (fallaciae); (7) de terminorum proprietatibus (parva logicalia). This last book is the one representing the newest logic (properties of logical terms, their relation with grammatical terms). The aim throughout is practical, dialectical, rather than scientific.

The great success of Peter's Summulae is proved by the number of editions (some 45 had appeared before 1520) and commentaries. Buridan himself prepared a new edition (first half of the fourteenth century). It was not restricted to the Latin world, but extended to the Greek and Hebrew. There are many Hebrew translations, notably by Abraham ben Meshullam Abigdor (second half of the fourteenth century), and by Judah ben Samuel Shalom about the middle of the fifteenth century. A Greek version was made by Georgios Scholarios of Constantinople (religious name, Gennadios II, who died in or after 1464; the first patriarch after the Turkish conquest), Σύνοψις εἰς τὴν Ἀριστοτέλους λογικὴν ἐπιστήμην.

Speaking of Peter's logic, we may add that in his commentary on Isḥāq al-Isrā'īlī (no. 11 above) he devoted some attention to the study of the experimental

[8] A pseudo-Aristotelian treatise on the twelve waters appears in a thirteenth century Latin MS. pretending to be translated from the Arabic. "Liber Aristotelis de aquis secreti fluminis" (Digby 162). It would be worthwhile to search for the Arabic original. See Lynn Thorndike: History of magic (vol. 2, 251, 500, 797).

[8a] The following study on Zacharias reached me too late to be mentioned in the note devoted to him. Noè Scalinci: L'oculistica medioevale M° Zaccaria e le fonti della sua "Sisilacera" (Rivista di storia delle scienze, anno 22, 8–21, 1931).

method (via experimenti, as opposed to the via rationis), and though his effort ended in failure, it was an indication, among others, of the subconscious growth and pressure of the experimental point of view.

Peter composed an elaborate treatise on psychology, De anima. It was not simply a commentary on Aristotle's De anima and De sensu et sensato but was far more ambitious. It is divided into thirteen tractates, of which the last, subdivided into eight chapters, is a very remarkable history of the evolution of psychological ideas among the Greeks and Muslims. Special stress is laid on what might be called the physiological and medical aspects.

The Aristotelian tendencies of this work are noteworthy, considering that Peter gave proof later of opposite, Augustinian, tendencies. Indeed, it was during his brief pontificate that the bishop of Paris, Stephen Tempier, was ordered to investigate and censure the Aristotelian, Averroistic and Thomistic errors which were then being taught (1277).

Finally he wrote a long commentary on Aristotelian zoology as represented by the nineteen books of Michael Scot's version. This commentary was probably the first to be based on Scot's version, but it was soon superseded by the more elaborate and better one prepared by Albert the Great. It was more philosophical than zoological, being composed in the scholastic form of quaestiones disputatae and full of philosophical discussions.

Text—Thesaurus pauperum. First edition, Antwerp 1476. Many later ones: Antwerp 1497; Lyon 1525, etc. Italian translation, Tesoro dei poveri, Florence c. 1480; Venice 1494, 1500. Spanish translation, Alcala 1589, etc.

Liber de oculo. Albrecht Maria Berger: Die Ophthalmologie des Petrus Hispanus mit deutscher Übersetzung und Kommentar (München 1899). Italian translation of first part published by Franc. Zambrini in Scelta di curiosità letterarie (Bologna 1873).

Diete super cyrurgiam secundum magistrum Petrum Compostellanum edited by K. Sudhoff: Beiträge zur Geschichte der Chirurgie im Mittelalter (vol. 2, 395–398, 1918).

The commentaries on the works of Isḥāq al-Isrā'īlī are printed in the first Latin edition of Isḥāq's collected works. Omnia opera Ysaac (Lyon 1515; reprinted 1525).

Summulae logicales. Milan 1487; Cologne 1488; Venice 1496; Cologne 1499; etc. The editions of 1488, 1496 (?) and 1499 include a commentary by John Versor (second half of the fifteenth century).

General criticism—Francesco Cristofori: Di Pietro Ispano ricordato da Dante e dell' identità di lui con il papa Giovanni XXI provata (Nuovo giornale arcadico, serie 3, 44 p., Milano 1890). M. Steinschneider: Hebraeische Übersetzungen (470–474, 816–818, 1893). Richard Stapper: Papst Johannes XXI (Kirchengeschichtliche Studien, 4, 3, Münster 1898). G. Petella: Sull'identità di Pietro Ispano medico in Siena e poi papa col filosofo dantesco (Bullettino seneso di storia patria, anno 5, 277–329, 1899). Lynn Thorndike: History of magic (vol. 2, 488–516, 1923; with a list of MSS. of Thesaurus).

Philosophical criticism—C. Michalski: Les courants philosophiques à Oxford et à Paris pendant le XIVe siècle (Bull. de l'Académie polonaise, classe d'histoire, Année 1920; Cracovie 1921). Martin Grabmann: Ein ungedrucktes Lehrbuch der Psychologie des Petrus Hispanus (Spanische Forschungen der Görres-Gesellschaft, vol. 1, 166–173, Münster 1928; Isis, 13, 160); Mittelalterliche Aristotelesübersetzungen und Aristoteleskommentare (Sitzungsber. der bayer. Akad. der Wiss., Philos. Kl., 1925, 5; 98–113, 1928; Isis, 13, 205).

Medical criticism—G. B. Petella: Les connaissances occulistiques d'un médecin philosophe devenu pape (Janus, vol. 2, 405–420, 570–596, 1898). Pierre Pansier: Anonymi Tractatus de egritudinibus oculorum ex dictis sapientium veterum compilatis ejusdem Tractatus de quibusdam dubiis circa dicta oculorum concurrentibus. Précédés d'un aperçu sur la pratique de l'oculistique au moyen âge (Collectio ophtalmologica veterum auctorum, fasc. 2, 97–155, Paris 1908). M. Neuburger: Geschichte der Medizin (vol. 2, 368, 1911). Guglielmo Bilancioni: Pietro Ispano (Riv. di storia delle scienze mediche, anno XI, 1920; reprinted in Veteris vestigia flammae, 15–45, Roma 1922; Isis, 5, 475). Domenico Barduzzi: Pietro Spano (Riv. di storia delle scienze, anno 14, 118–121, 1923). David Riesman: A physician in the papal chair (Annals of medical history, 5, 291–300, 1923; Isis, 7, 192). Walter Wilke: Petrus Hispanus und seine Bedeutung für die Zahnheilkunde (Diss., 7 p., Leipzig 1924). Pietro Capparoni: Di una rara traduzione italiana del secolo XIV del Thesaurus pauperum (Rivista di storia delle scienze, 55–62, 1928).

For Alfonso X el Sabio, see the chapter on translators.

RAYMOND MARTIN

Raimaindo Martí, (Martin, Martini). Catalan Dominican and scholar. Born at Subirats, Catalonia; assumed the Dominican habit in 1236 and celebrated his jubilee in 1286. At a provincial chapter of his Order, held at Toledo in 1250, he was ordered to study oriental languages in the Dominican schools established for that purpose. He obtained a deep knowledge of Arabic and of rabbinical Hebrew. Later he was sent as a missionary to Tunis.

In 1264 Jaime el Conquistador commissioned him, together with the bishop of Barcelona, Raimundo de Peñafort, and two other Dominicans, Arnold of Segarra and Peter Janua (i.e., of Genoa), to examine and censure Hebrew writings, chiefly the Talmud; this being the first instance of Dominican censorship of the Talmud in Spain. They reported that some parts at least of the Talmud were acceptable from the Christian point of view, and thus that it was not necessary to burn the Talmud entirely.

Raymond Martin wrote various works of theology and apologetics: Capistrum Judaeorum (The Jew's muzzle); Explanatio symboli Apostolorum (c. 1256); Pugio fidei adversus Mauros et Judaeos (c. 1276–1278).

The "Dagger of faith" was published by him in Hebrew as well as in Latin. Many passages of it are identical with passages of St. Thomas' Summa contra Gentiles. According to Miguel Asín, St. Thomas used Martin's Arabic knowledge even as he used Moerbeke's Greek knowledge; according to Mandonnet, on the contrary, Martin was influenced by St. Thomas. A Latin-Arabic vocabulary is also ascribed to Raymond Martin.

Text—The Explanatio symboli Apostolorum ad institutionem fidelium edita was published by J. M. March y Battles (Anuari del Institut d'estudis catalans; Barcelona 1910).

Pugio fidei, rediscovered by Justus Scaliger (who ascribed it wrongly to Raimundo Sebon or Sabunde—it was also ascribed to Raimundo de Peñafort), edited by Joseph de Voisin (Paris 1651). Again by J. B. Carpzov with an anti-Semitic introduction (Leipzig 1667).

Vocabulista in Arabico, edited by Celestino Schiaparelli (Florence 1871) see vol. 1, 783.

Criticism—Antoine Touron: Histoire des hommes illustres de l'ordre de Saint Dominique (vol. 1, 489–504, Paris 1743). The same volume contains notes on

Raymond of Peñafort (p. 1–48) and on Arnold of Segarra (p. 505–508). R. Dozy: Supplément aux dictionnaires arabes (vol. 1, p. x, Leide 1881). Gotthold Weil: Jewish Encyclopaedia (vol. 8, 351, 1904). Miguel Asín: El Averroísmo teológico de Sto. Tomás (Homenage a D. Francisco Codera, p. 271–331, Zaragoza 1904); La Summa contra Gentiles y el Pugio fidei (Vergara 1905). Luis G. Alonso Getino: Por los mundos del tomismo (Ciencia tomista, vol. 3, 46–56, 1911). Marcelino Menéndez y Pelayo: Historia de los heterodoxos españoles (2d ed., vol. 3, 1917). Enciclopedia universal ilustrada (vol. 33, 451, Barcelona 1917). M. De Wulf: History of mediaeval philosophy (vol. 2, 43, 1927). M. Asín: Islam and the Divine Comedy (139, 140, 250, 1926).

ST. PETER PASCHAL

Pedro Pasqual; Petrus Paschalis. Born at Valencia in 1227, of captive or Mozarab parents; tutor to the son of the king of Aragon, he accompanied his charge to Toledo when the latter became archbishop; friar of the Order of Mercy; he visited Rome during the pontificate of Nicholas IV (1288–1292), then Paris; bishop of Jaén, 1296; made prisoner in 1297 by the Moors of Granada; martyred in 1300.

He had a deep knowledge of Arabic and of Islām, specially of the Qur'ān and the ḥadīth. During his captivity he wrote in Spanish a refutation of Islām, Impunaçion de la seta de Mahomah. He was very well acquainted with the eschatological views of the Muslim and with the legends of the isrā' and the mi'rāj which form the prototype of the Divine Comedy; he may have been one of the channels through which such traditions reached Dante.

Text—The Impunaçion was edited by Pedro Armengol y Cornet: El Obispo de Jaén sobre la seta mahometana, in Obras de San Pedro Pasqual (vol. 4, Rome 1908). La destructio de Hierusalem etc., edited by Ramón Miquel y Planas in Tractat de Scipio y Anibal, etc. (p. 49–106, Barcelona 1910).
Criticism—Miguel Asín: Islam and the Divine Comedy (250–252, 1926).

ARNOLD OF VILLANOVA

Arnaldus de Villa Nova, or Villanovanus, also Bacuone or Barchinone—i.e., from Barcelona. Born near Valencia c. 1234–1250; studied medicine at Naples, traveled extensively, flourishing in Paris, Montpellier, Barcelona, Rome, etc.; died at sea in 1311 on the way from Naples to Genoa; buried in Genoa.

Catalan physician, alchemist, astrologer, diplomat, social reformer, visionary. Translator of medical works from Arabic into Latin; he had some knowledge of Greek and Hebrew. One of the most extraordinary personalities of mediaeval times. He realized the value of natural science and suggested that it should be given more importance in education; he had some slight understanding of the experimental point of view and sometimes professed opposition to magic and sorcery; yet his own works are full of superstitious ideas. He was a famous medical practitioner, who was consulted by various kings of Aragon, and popes.

A great many writings have been ascribed to him, most of them dealing with medical subjects, others with chemistry, astrology, magic, theology, etc. Hauréau mentioned 123 items, of which 78 were then (1881) already published. Most of them are very short. Many are apocryphal; this seems to be especially true of the alchemical writings.

A complete enumeration would have no object, but I shall name the main writings, introducing explanations and additional information as expedient.

Medical works—1. Medicinalium introductionum speculum. A general treatise on medicine, one of the longest. Written at Montpellier, upon the model of Ḥunain ibn Isḥāq's Isagoge ad Tegni.

2. Liber de diversis intentionibus medicorum. Dealing also with medical generalities.

3. Regimen sanitatis ad regem Aragonum (Barcelona 1307). In 19 chapters. Many MSS., editions, and translations in Spanish and in Italian. It was translated into Hebrew by Israel ben Joseph ha-Levi—i.e., Israel Caslari—at Avignon, 1327, Ma'amar be-hanhagat ha-bri'ut; and again by an unknown author. See no. 10 below.

4. De conservanda juventute et retardanda senectute. Dedicated to Robert the Wise, king of Naples and Jerusalem; thus dating from 1309 or later, the last years of Arnold's life. This was a plagiarism of the Liber de conservatione juventutis of Roger Bacon, with a few additions, omissions, and modifications. For example, Arnold substituted his own prescriptions for Roger's. Arnold's treatise was translated into Italian; also into English by Jonas Drummond, in 1544.

5. De considerationibus operis medicinae. A large treatise dealing mainly with bloodletting.

6. Medicationis parabolae secundum instinctum veritatis aeternae. Three hundred and forty-five medical aphorisms compiled by Arnold, in Montpellier, 1300, with commentary by another. Hebrew translation by Abraham Abigdor, 1378.

7. Aphorismi speciales (Aphorismi de ingeniis nocivis, curativis et praeservativis morborum speciales corporis partes respicientes). Sequel to 6.

8. Liber de parte operativa. Large treatise containing many definitions and some prescriptions.

9. De regimine castra sequentium. Very short, on military hygiene.

10. Commentum super Regimen salernitanum. Arnold was probably the earliest editor of that twelfth century poem. See my note on the Regimen sanitatis salernitanum. See No. 3 above.

11. Breviarium practicae a capite usque ad plantam pedis cum capitulo generali de urinis et tractatu de omnibus febribus, peste, èmpiala et liparia. Encyclopaedia of practical medicine divided into four books: (1) head; (2) rest of the body; (3) women's diseases; (4) fevers. The Breviarium was often printed.

12. Practica summaria, seu regimen ad instantiam domini papae Clementis (i.e., Clement V, 1305–1314). After Arnold's death the pope took special pains to obtain possession of it. It was thus probably one of Arnold's last works.

13. Compendium regimenti acutorum. Explaining five different methods.

14. Regimen sive consilium quartanae.

15. Consilium sive regimen podagrae.

16. Tractatus de sterilitate tam ex parte viri quam ex parte mulieris. Also ascribed to Raymond of Moleriis, who was chancellor of Montpellier in 1338.

17. Compilatio de conceptione. Probably identical with Tractatus de impregnatione mulierum.

18. Tractatus de bonitate memoriae. Medical recipes to improve the memory!

19. Cautelae medicorum. Explaining bedside manners.

20. Tractatus de venenis.

21. Libellus de arte cognoscendi venena cum quis proponit ea alicui ministrare. This short treatise on poisons was more popular than no. 20; there are many MSS. and early editions of it.

22. Tractatus de dosibus theriacalibus.

23. Liber aphorismorum de graduationibus medicinarum per artem compositarum.

24. Simplicia. Aggregator practicus de simplicibus, seu herbolarium de virtutibus herbarum. Also called Areolae seu tabulae mag. Arnaldi. This treatise was translated into Hebrew; a copy of the Hebrew text was made in 1485 for the physician Jehiel Gershon.[9] It is apparently different from the Hebrew text mentioned below under no. 55.

25. Antidotarium clarificatum. A long treatise.

26. Liber de vinis. Written in Africa. Dealing not with ordinary wines, but with pharmaceutical ones. Arnold was one of the first Latin writers to insist upon the virtues of alcohol. Often printed in Latin and in German. Hebrew translation by Judah ben Solomon Nathan, 1358, Dbir be yiyinot.

27. Tractatus de aquis medicinalibus. Sequel to 26.

28–29. Liber de ornatu mulierum. Tractatus de decoratione. Including advice on sexual cleanliness for women.

30. De coitu.

31. Tractatus de conferentibus et nocentibus principalibus membris corporis nostri.

32. Recepta electuarii mirabilis praeservantis ab epidemia. Translated into Provençal.

33. Tractatus contra calculum.

34. Regimen curativum et praeservativum contra catarrhum.

35. De tremore cordis.

36. De epilepsia. In 26 chapters.

37. Tractatus de usu carnium pro sustentatione ordinis Carthusiensis contra Jacobitas. Defending vegetarianism.

38. Tractatus medicinae regales, sive descriptio receptarum.

39. De sanguine humano, to Jacob of Toledo (sive De maximo secreto medicinae). Explaining how an elixir of life may be obtained by distillation of human blood.

40. De phlebotomia. Different from no. 5.

41. De accidentibus senectutis et senii. Probably apocryphal.

42. Thesaurus pauperum. Different from the famous treatise of Peter of Spain bearing the same title. Published in Spanish, and often in French, but not in Latin.

43. Libellus regiminis de confortatione visus secundum sex res non naturales. How to improve one's eyesight (c. 1308). In two parts, of which the first deals with diet, and the second is a plagiarism from the Grabadin of Mesuë the Younger (Māsawaih al-Māridīnī, first half of the eleventh century).

44. Tractatus de urina.

45. A treatise on digestive and purgative drugs is lost in Latin but extant in two Hebrew versions made by Abraham Abigdor, in Montpellier, 1381, and by Ṭodros ben Moses Yom-ṭob, in 1394.

[9] That copy is now in the Library of the Jewish Theological Seminary, New York. See Register for 1929–1930, p. 181. The catch-words are in Romance or Hebrew.

Commentaries on ancient medical works—46. Hippocrates. Commentum super canonem, Vita brevis. Translated into Hebrew by one Gabriel.

47. Hippocrates. Abbreviatio libri Prognosticorum. Petrarca once owned a MS. of it.

48. Galen. Commentum super libello De mala complexione diversa cum textu Galieni. Long commentary.

49. Galen. Quaestiones super libro De mala complexione diversa. Questions in the usual scholastic style completing the preceding commentary.

Translations from Arabic into Latin—50. Galen: De tremore, palpitatione, rigore et convulsione. From the Arabic version by Ḥubaish ibn al-Ḥasan (second half of the ninth century). (Isis, 8, 696, no. 60.)

51. al-Kindī (first half of the ninth century): Risāla fī ma'rifat quwā'-l-adwiya al-murakkaba. De medicinarum compositarum gradibus.

52. Qusṭā ibn Lūqā (second half of the ninth century): De physicis ligaturis. This magical treatise has long been ascribed to Galen.

53. Ibn Sīnā (first half of the eleventh century): De viribus cordis. In 1282?

54. Abū-l-'Alā' Zuhr (Avenzoar's father, first half of the twelfth century): De conservatione corporis et regimine sanitatis. Arnold's authorship of this translation is doubtful.

55. Abū-l-Ṣalt Umaiya ibn 'Abd al-'Azīz (first half of the twelfth century): Kitāb al-adwiya al-mufrada. Albuzale de medicinis simplicibus. The same work was translated into Hebrew a century later by Judah ben Solomon Nathan.

Psychology—56. Expositiones visionum quae fiunt in somnis (Liber de pronosticationibus sompniorum). Ascribed by Lynn Thorndike (History of magic, 2, 300–302) to one William of Aragon, who wrote a commentary on Ptolemy's Centiloquium.

No. 18 might be called a psychological treatise.

Alchemy—A great many alchemical treatises are ascribed to Arnold. Most of them are probably apocryphal. I shall name the most important.

57. Thesaurus thesaurorum, Rosarius philosophorum ac omnium secretorum maximum secretum, etc. This is the largest treatise of this group. Judging by the number of MSS. it was very popular. It was translated into French, German, English, Italian.

58. Novum lumen. Translated into Italian and English.

59. Perfectum magisterium et gaudium . . . . ad regem Aragonum, quod quidem est Flos florum, thesaurus omnium. . . .

60. Epistola super alchymia ad regem Neapolitanum (Robert of Anjou?).

61. De lapide philosophorum (De secretis naturae; Thesaurus secretus operationum naturalium). Dialogue.

62. Cathena aurea (Opus magisterii, Ars magnae operationis). Ascribed to John of Gascony.

63. Novum testamentum. In three parts: (1) natural philosopher's stone; (2) artificial philosopher's stone; (3) transmutation.

64. Speculum alchymiae. Dialogue between a master and his disciple.

65. Practica.

66. Semita semitae, dedicated to Benedict XI? (pope from 1303 to 1304).

67. Quaestiones tam essentiales quam accidentales ad Bonifacium VIII (pope from 1294 to 1303). Thirty essential and twelve accidental questions on alchemy answered by Arnold.

68. Tractatus parabolarum. Chemical aphorisms.

69. Explicatio compendii alchemiae quod Joanni Garlandio tribuitur. Almost certainly apocryphal.

70. Rosa novella. Practical treatise for the making of the philosopher's stone. Four operations: to dissolve, distill, calcine, solidify.

Astrology and magic—52. See above.

71. Remedia contra maleficia. The maleficia meant in this title are mainly those creating sexual impotence.

72. Capitula astrologiae de judiciis infirmatum secundum motum planetarum (also called Compendium astrologiae; Astronomia; Brevis tractatus introductorius ad judicia astrologiae; Introductorium astrologiae pro medicis; etc.). Treatise on medical astrology, which remained popular for a long time. An abridged Hebrew version was made by Jacob ben Judah Cabret (Qabreṭ) in Barcelona, 1381; and a full Hebrew translation, in 17 chapters, Panim ba-mishpaṭ, by Solomon Abigdor, helped by his father Abraham, 1393. 73. Sigilla.

74. Libellus de improbatione maleficiorum. Letter addressed by Arnold to Jaspertus (Jasperto de Botonach, bishop of Valencia from 1276 to 1288) to show the folly of black magic and exorcisms.

75. Liber experimentorum. The experiments described are mainly astrological. According to the preface, they were published by Guillaume de Périsse, Arnold's secretary, after Arnold's death.

Theological and apocalyptic—Arnold wrote also a number of books the purpose of which was theological, apologetic, anticlerical, or apocalyptic. It will suffice to quote a few titles:

76. Collocutio Friderici regis Siciliae et mag. Arnaldi de Villanova. The title is absurd but the dialogue is of great interest.

77. Allocutio de his quae conveniunt homini secundum proprium dignitatem creaturae rationalis. Moral theology, divine rights and duties of kings.

78. Gladius veritatis adversus thomistas.

79. Speculatio adventus Antichristi.

80. De cymbalis Ecclesiae. Etc., etc.

Considering the vigor and extent of Arnold's literary activity in such dangerous fields as magic, anticlericalism, Joachimism, and prophecy, it is not surprising that he got into trouble with the Inquisition (Paris 1299, Valencia 1305); many of his writings were posthumously condemned in 1317 by the inquisitor of Tarragona.

Text—Collected writings—The first edition of Arnold's Opera appeared in Lyon, 1504. It contains 55 treatises, edited by Thomas Murchi of Genoa, physician to Louis XII (king, 1498 to 1515). It was reprinted the following year in Venice, and again in Lyon, 1509. The fourth edition, containing six additional treatises and a biography of Arnold by Symphorien Champier, appeared in Lyon, 1520. Reprinted, Lyon 1532; Basel 1585, with notes by Nicholas Taurellus (i.e., Nicholas Öchsle, died 1606).

Separate edition of medical writings, Praxis medicinalis universorum morborum humani corporis curandi viam ac methodum summa cum doctrina et certa experientia praescribens (Lyon 1586).

Chemical and astrological writings. Tractatus varii exoterici ac chymici (Lyon 1586); Opera chymica (Francfort 1602, 1603).

Editions of separate writings. The numbers refer to those of my own list above.

Medical—1. Medicinalium introductionum speculum. (144 leaves; Leipzig c. 1495.)

3. Regimen sanitatis ad regem Aragonum. Italian edition, 34 leaves, c. 1474 (?). Other editions: Paris 1573; Cologne 1586. Regimiento de sanidad (Seville 1526). See my separate note on the Regimen sanitatis.

4. De conservanda juventute. Published together with no. 31 (Leipzig 1511). Trattato del conservar la gioventù (Venice 1550). Charles Loomis Dana: The conservation of youth, translated by Jonas Drummond, with additions from the Breviarium (Woodstock, Vermont, 1912). Johann Schwartz: De conservanda juventute (Diss., 14 p., Leipzig 1923; Isis, 6, 149).

6. Parabolae. Many editions: Lyon 1534; Basel 1560, 1565. (See no. 31.) German translation by Paul Diepgen: Parabeln der Heilkunst (Klassiker der Medizin, 68 p., Leipzig 1922; Isis, 5, 217).

7. Aphorismi. They follow the Parabolae in the edition of 1534.

11. Breviarium. Many separate editions: Milano 1483; Pavia c. 1485; Venice 1494, 1497; Lyon 1532. Part 4 is included in the collection de febribus (Venice 1576). See no. 4.

15. Consilium podagrae. German version (Strassburg 1576).

16. Tractatus de sterilitate. Carl Arlt: Neuer Beitrag zur Geschichte der medizinischen Schule von Montpellier (Diss., Berlin 1902). Julius Pagel: De impedimentis conceptionis (Janus, 530–537, 1903). Edited by Arlt and Pagel as the work of Raymond of Moleriis. Arlt's thesis contains the first part dealing with sterility due to woman; Pagel's the latter part dealing with sterility due to man.

21. De arte cognoscendi venena. Mantua 1473; Padua 1473, c. 1474; Milano 1475; Rome 1475–1476. Printed with Peter of Abano's Libellus de venenis (Padua 1487).

24. Aggregator practicus de simplicibus. Venice 1499, 1520. See my note on printed herbals (second half of the fifteenth century).

25. Antidotarium clarificatum. (74 leaves, Valencia 1495.)

26. De vinis. (12 leaves, Paris c. 1500; Leipzig, later.) German translation by William of Hirnkofen (16 leaves, Esslingen 1478; Augsburg 1479; 1481, 1482; 1483, 1484; Strassburg c. 1483, c. 1484; Reutlingen c. 1485; Ulm 1499, 1500).

26 bis. De aqua vitae simplici et composita (22 leaves, Venice c. 1477–1478).

31. De conferentibus et nocentibus. Printed in Leipzig, 1511, together with no. 4; and in Basel, 1560, 1565, together with no. 6.

38. Tractatus medicinae regales. In Praxis medicinalis (81–87, 1586).

39. De sanguine humano. (De praestantia et virtutibus aquae humani sanguinis.) Edited in the De remediis secretis, ascribed to Conrad Gesner, first printed in Zurich, 1552; often reprinted in Latin, also in French, Italian, English. I do not know whether all editions contain no. 39; but it is in the edition of Lyon, 1572 (part 2, 289). Joannis de Rupescissa de consideratione quintae essentiae, accessere Arnaldi epistola de sanguino humano distillato, etc. (Basel 1597).

40. De phlebotomia. Lyon 1517.

41. De accidentibus senectutis et senii. Lyon 1517. Regimen senum et seniorum (20 leaves, Paris c. 1500).

42. Thesaurus pauperum. Tresor des povres, qui parle des maladies qui peuvent venir au corps humain et des remedes ordonnez contre icelles, etc. First edition, 1507. Second and third undated. Fourth, Paris 1618. Libro de medicina llamado Tesoro de los pobres (Seville 1543). Vincenzo di Giovanni: Ricette popolari del libro Thesaurus pauperum in antico volgare siciliano (Palermo 1878).

43. De confortatione visus. First edited by Pierre Pansier: Collectio opthalmologica veterum auctorum (35 p., Paris 1903).

Nos. 1 to 32 are included in Arnold's Opera (1504 etc.); nos. 33 to 37 in the edition of 1520, etc.

Commentaries on ancient medical works—No separate editions, but 46, 48, 49 are included in the Opera, 1504, etc.

Translations from Arabic into Latin—51. al-Kindī: De medicinarum compositarum gradibus (Strassburg 1531).

52. Qusṭā ibn Lūqā: De physicis ligaturis. Included in the Juntine edition of Galen (vol. 5), and in Arnold's Opera (1504, etc.).

53. Ibn Sīnā: De viribus cordis. Included in the Opera Avicennae (vol. 4, Venice 1520). Also in the Canon of 1595, etc. O. C. Gruner: The interpretation of Avicenna (Annals of medical history, vol. 3, 354–358, 1921).

54. Abū-l-'Alā' Zuhr: De conservatione corporis. Is this identical with the Latin text published at Basel in 1618?

Psychology—Nos. 18 and 56 are both included in the Opera omnia (1504, etc).

De somniorum interpretatione, and De mutatione aeris (Toulouse c. 1485).

Alchemy—Nos. 57 to 60 are included in Arnold's Opera (1504, etc.); no. 61 in the edition of 1520, etc.; no. 62 in the edition of 1586; nos. 57, 58, 64, in the Opera chymica (1602, 1603). German translation of nos. 57, 58, 64, published in Chymische Schrifften (Wien 1748).

57. Thesaurus thesaurorum. Included in Guglielmo Grataroio: Verae alchimiae artisque metallicae, etc. (Basel 1561). Also in Ars aurefira quam chemiam vocant (vol. 2, Basel 1610). Jean Jacques Manget: Bibliotheca chemica curiosa (vol. 1, Cologne 1702).

Abbreviated edition, Rosarius abbreviatus in Theatrum chimicum (vol. 4, 564).

Italian translation published by Giov. Bat. Nazari: Della tramutatione metallica (Brescia 1599).

Nos. 58, 59, 60, 64, 65, 66, 67, 68, are included in the same collections, each in at least two of them.

Nos. 61, 62, 70 are unpublished.

63. Novum testamentum was published by Manget alone (vol. 1, 704, 1702).

66. Semita semitae. De alchemia opuscula complura veterum philosophorum (Francfort 1550).

68. Tractatus parabolarum. Printed with commentary by Didacus Alvarez Chauca (Seville 1514).

69. Explicatio compendii alchimae quod Joanni Garlandio tribuitur. Published together with that Compendium (Basel 1560, 1571).

A few other editions are quoted by John Ferguson (1906).

For a chymeutic text in Greek ascribed to Arnold, see Catalogue des manuscripts alchimiques grecs (vol. 5, 95, 1928; Isis, 13, 547). Carlo Oreste Zuretti: Alcuni capitoli di un "manuale chemicum" greco (Studien zur Geschichte der Chemie, Festgabe E. O. v. Lippmann dargebracht, 55–74, 1927; Isis, 10, 135, 268).

Astrology and magic—Nos. 71, 72, 73, are included in the Opera (Lyon 1504, etc.).

73. Sigilla. Hauréau speaks of a new edition by A. Germain, which I was not able to identify.

74. De improbatione maleficiorum. First edition by Paul Diepgen: Archiv für Kulturgeschichte (vol. 9, 385–403, 1912).

75. Experimenta. Included in John Jacob de Maldiny: Mirabilia mundi (Augsburg 1754).

Theological and apocalyptic—76. Collocutio. Published by Matthias Flacius Illyricus (Francowitz): Catologus testium veritatis (357–376, Basel 1556); again by John Wolf: Lectiones (vol. 1, 565, 1600).

Rahonament fet per mestre Arnau de Vilanova en Avinyó denant lo papa e cardenals de les visions dels Reys Jaume Darago e Ffrederich Rey de Sicilia son frare (57 p., Recull de textes catalans antichs, vol. 11, Barcelona 1909).

General criticism—M. Menéndez y Pelayo: A. de Villanova, médico Catalán (Madrid 1879); Historia de los heterodoxos españoles (vol. 1, Madrid 1880; 2d ed., 1911). J. B. Hauréau: Histoire littéraire de la France (vol. 28, 26–126, 1881). E. Lalande: Arnauld de Villeneuve, sa vie et ses oeuvres (Paris 1896). Lynn Thorndike: History of magic (vol. 2, 841–861, 1923).

Paul Diepgen: Arnold als Politiker und Laientheologe (105 p., Abhdl. zur mittleren und neueren Geschichte, 9, Berlin 1909; throwing new light on Arnold's life from 1299 to the end); Studien zu Arnald (Archiv für Geschichte der Medizin, vol. 3, 115–130, 188–196, 369–396, 1909–1910; vol. 5, 88–120, 1911; vol. 6, 380–400, 1913; the last essay contains a bibliography).

Gesamtkatalog der Wiegendrucke (vol. 2, 684–699, 1926).

Medical criticism—L. Leclerc: Médecine arabe (vol. 2, 468, 1876). E. Gurlt: Geschichte der Chirurgie (vol. 2, 125–132, 1898). Joseph Frank Payne: Arnold on the therapeutic use of human blood (Janus, vol. 8, 432–435, 477–483, 1903). Apropos of treatise numbered 39 above. M. Neuburger: Geschichte der Medizin (vol. 2, 388–403, 1911). Therese Rennau: Die Gynäkologie des Arnold mit Erläuterungen (Diss., Freiburg i. B., 1912). Gustav Hoffmann: Zahnärztliches bei Arnaldus (Diss., 7 p., Leipzig 1923).

Other special criticism—M. Steinschneider: Hebraeische Übersetzungen (778–785, 1893); Europäische Übersetzungen (6, 1904). John Ferguson: Bibliotheca chemica (vol. 1, 43–47; vol. 2, 512, 1906). Ed. Bonnet: Sur une édition très rare de l'Herbarius, Paris, 1486 (Bull. de la Soc. bot. de France, 1911). Paul Diepgen: Traum und Traumdeutung (Berlin 1912). E. O. v. Lippmann (Entstehung der Alchemie (vol. 1, 494, 1919, vol. 2, 45, 1931).

RAMON LULL

Raymundus Lullius, "doctor illuminatus." Modern Catalan, Llull. Beat Ramon. Ramon is written without accent in Catalan; with accent, Ramón, in Castilian. Born of a wealthy Catalan family at Palma de Mallorca (Majorca) sometime between 1231 and 1235, probably in 1232; died, a martyr to his faith, at the end of 1315 or the beginning of 1316, either in Bugia, or on a Genoese ship on the way to Majorca. Since 1448 his remains have been lying in the Church of San Francisco in Palma.

Catalan philosopher, apostle, and writer. One of the greatest vernacular authors of mediaeval Europe, the patriarch of the Catalan language[10] and literature. Christian educator and missionary. Father of western orientalism. One of the champions of the struggle against Averroism. Inventor of a kind of generalized logic, ars magna. Extreme realist.

About 1246 he entered the personal service of James the Conqueror, king of Aragon; later he was tutor to the king's sons, Peter and James. After a few years of dissipation he was converted in 1263. From 1265 to 1274 he lived in Majorca, studying Arabic with a Moorish slave. After that he traveled considerably in western Europe, lecturing in universities, attending religious conferences, trying to interest kings and popes in his projects. For example, he was in Rome in 1277, 1285, 1288, 1290, 1295–1296; in Montpellier[11] in 1283–1284, 1287, 1289, 1296–1297, 1303–1304, 1305, 1308–1309; in Paris in 1286, 1298, 1306, 1309–1311; of course he returned very often to his native island; in 1301 he journeyed to the East, visiting Cyprus; in 1311 he attended the Council of Vienne (Dauphiné). He undertook three apostolic missions to Africa: Tunis, 1292; Bugia, 1307; Bugia and Tunis, 1314–1315. His death in 1315–1316 was the fruit of his last mission.

He professed as a Franciscan tertiary in 1295.

In spite of his continual moves from place to place, Ramon composed a very large

[10] I may recall that the earliest Catalan text dates from 1171. See my note on the Poema del Cid.

[11] From 1204 to 1349, Montpellier belonged to Aragon.

number of books, treatises, poems, many it is true very short, but some very long. By the time of his death, the catalogue of his writings included already more than 150 items, and that number was gradually increased in later catalogues, being swelled by many apocryphal publications. Between July 1312 and May 1314—being then about eighty years old—he wrote some 40 books and pamphlets. As these writings exist in Catalan and Latin MSS. (sometimes in both languages), it is not always possible to say which was the original language. Some of the most important were originally written in Catalan but promptly translated into Latin. One or two were written in Arabic by Ramon himself.

Because of the large number of his writings and the complexity of his activity, I shall divide my account in 28 sections, each dealing with a single work, class of works, or separate topic. For the reader's convenience the bibliography relative to each section is placed at the end of it, the general bibliography being given in sections 24 to 28. When a work has been fully described in the Histoire littéraire de la France (vol. 29, 1885), I have generally referred to that description as follows: (H. L., no. x, p. y).

Contents: (1) Libre de contemplació. (2) Discovery of the ars magna. Logical treatises. (3) Religious discussions. (4) Christian apologetics. (5) Chivalry and education. (6) Blanquerna. (7) Felix. (8) Catalan poems. (9) Tree of science. (10) Proverbs. (11) Anti-Averroism. (12) Phantasticus. (13) Philosophy. (14) Physics. (15) Mathematics and astronomy. (16) Medicine, (17) Alchemy. (18) Muslim influence. (19) Lull, a founder of western orientalism. (20) His missionary activity. (21) Dominicans vs. Franciscans. (22) Immaculate Conception. (23) History of Lullism.

(24) Collected editions. (25) Bibliographies. (26) Ancient biography and criticism. (27) Modern criticism. Biographical and general studies. (28) Special studies.

1. *Libre de contemplació en Deu*.—(Majorca, c. 1272.) Liber contemplationis in Deum. The Book of contemplation was first written, wholly or partly, in Arabic; later Ramon translated it into Catalan, this translation being completed c. 1272. It is an enormous encyclopaedia of practical theology, including satirical descriptions of various classes of people (e.g., physicians, lawyers). It already contains some of the typically Lullian notations, algebraical symbols and geometrical figures being occasionally used to represent thoughts or to abbreviate their expression. This was probably Ramon's first work; certainly the first large one; there are nearly a million words in the Catalan text. (H. L., no. 48, p. 220–235.)

Partial Latin edition by Jacques Lefebvre, of Etaples (Paris 1505).

Complete Catalan edition in the Obres (vols. 2 to 8, Palma 1906–1914). I shall no longer refer to the Obres except in section 24.

2. *Discovery of the ars magna. Logical treatises*—Ramon was convinced that the logical method could be improved, generalized, and used for the explanation of every kind of knowledge, and for the demonstration of every kind of truth. This idea seems to have occurred to him as a sort of illumination, during a period of retirement on Mount Randa (near Palma) in 1274, and he was possessed with it during the rest of his life. He wrote a large number of treatises to explain and exemplify his new method (ars magna, ars generalis). It was an extraordinary mix-

ture of sound logic and of graphical schemes (including the use of diagrams with movable parts), with arbitrary conventions and a kind of Qabbalism. Roger Bacon called it methodus imposturae. It was not, except that Ramon was carried away by his enthusiasm, and promised far more than he could accomplish. The worst side of it was nonsense; the best side, a premature and crude anticipation of what we now call mathematical logic (or algebra of logic, etc.).

According to its inventor, this method would enable one to evidence the essential unity of science, and to attain encyclopaedic and certain knowledge from above almost automatically; it would provide a kind of universal key to knowledge. Whenever he had mastered the rudiments of a new discipline (say law, or medicine) he proceeded to apply his method to it, and thus to give what he thought was a better exposition of it. In other words, he implicitly believed in the unity of nature and of knowledge, and tried to construct a philosophical synthesis representing that unity.

Failing to realize that no logical argument can be stronger than the premises upon which it is built, he imagined that the Truth (even religious truth) could be presented with such logical rigor that it would be impossible to deny one's acquiescence to it, that it would actually bind the mind (ligare intellectum). He had no conception of the experimental method, and did not see that in the last analysis no amount of logic can establish the reality and validity of a fact.

The first treatise wherein Ramon explained his method was probably written in 1274–1275 at the Cistercian monastery of Nostra Dona de la Real (near Palma) in 1274–1275. It was entitled Ars magna et major, or Ars compendiosa inveniendi veritatem (H. L., no 1, p. 74–79). It is an attempt to evidence all the possible combinations between a certain number of concepts by means of diagrams. All kinds of questions are solved to illustrate the method.

Ramon remained deeply interested in logic to the end of his life, and he wrote many other treatises on the subject (probably more than 40). Besides, almost every work of his proves the intensity of his logical prepossession; I quote only a few of his logical writings in chronological order.

Ars universalis seu lectura artis compendiosae inveniendi veritatem (H. L., nos. 2, 132). Supplement to the ars magna.

Ars demonstrativa, Montpellier 1283. (H. L., no. 13.) Various other treatises are supplements to, or explanations of, this one. It was a habit of Ramon's to re-explain the same subject and rewrite the same paper in various ways. Introductoria artis demonstrativae (H. L., no. 12). Lectura super figuras artis demonstrativae (H. L., no. 14). Compendium seu commentum artis demonstrativae (H. L., no. 16). Ars inveniendi particularia in universalibus (H. L., no. 17). Liber propositionum secundum artem demonstrativam (H. L., no. 18). Liber exponens figuram elementalem artis demonstrativae (H. L., no. 19). Regulae introductoriae in practicem artis demonstrativae (H. L., no. 20). Etc.

Quaestiones per artem demonstrativam seu inventivam solubiles. Montpellier 1287 (H. L., no. 21).

Ars inventiva veritatis, seu ars intellectiva veri, quae est instrumentum intellectivae potentiae. Montpellier 1289 (H. L., no. 34). Printed Valencia 1515. It would seem that Ramon translated this treatise into Arabic, in Genoa.

Ars amativa boni. Montpellier 1290. (H. L., no. 39.)

Compendium logicae Algazelis. Montpellier 1290. (H. L., no. 137.) It would seem that Ramon had first made a summary of al-Ghazzālī's logic in Arabic an that he translated it into Latin in 1290.

Tabula generalis. Begun on board ship in the harbor of Tunis, 1292, completed in Naples early in 1293. (H. L., no. 35.) Printed Valencia 1515. Many later works of Ramon's were developments of this Tabula.

Disputatio eremitae et Raymundi super aliquibus dubiis quaestionibus Sententiarum Petri Lombardi. Paris 1298 (H. L., no. 22.) It was natural enough that Ramon should apply his method to some of the difficulties of that famous textbook. Probably he heard it much discussed during his stay in Paris. Early editions: Lyon 1491, Palermo 1507, Venice 1507.

Liber de quadratura et triangulatura circuli. Paris 1299. (H. L., no. 160.) Not a mathematical treatise. Deals with the diagrams of Ramon's ars.

Aplicació de l'art general. Majorca 1300 (H. L., no. 100). Catalan poem, c. 1200 lines.

Brevis practica tabulae generalis. Genoa 1303 (H. L., no. 36). Lectura compendiosa tabulae generalis; Lectura super artem inventivam et tabulam generalem (H. L., nos. 37, 38). The second lectura was written during the pontificate of Boniface VIII (1294–1303).

Logica nova. Genoa 1303 (H. L., no. 56). Printed Valencia 1512, Palma 1744.

Ars generalis ad omnes scientias. About 1304 (H. L., no. 49). Very short. Printed Paris 1548, Lyon 1617, etc. Apocryphal?

Introductorium magnae artis generalis. Montpellier 1305 or 1306 (H. L., no. 131).

Ars brevis quae est de inventione mediorum juris (De inventione juris). Montpellier 1307 (H. L., no. 168).

Ars generalis ultima. Very long treatise, begun in Lyon, 1305, completed in Pisa, 1308 (H. L., no. 51). Often printed; Venice 1480, Barcelona 1501, etc. Spanish translation, Arte general para todas ciencias (Madrid 1598). French translation by the sieur de Vassy: Le grand et dernier art (Paris 1634). The Venetian edition of 1480 was the earliest Lullian printed edition.

Artificium, sive Ars brevis ad absolvendam omnium artium encyclopaediam. Ars brevis, quae est imago Artis generalis. Pisa 1308 (H. L., no. 50). This abbreviation of the Ars generalis ultima was even more popular than the latter. Often printed; Barcelona 1481, 1489; Lyon 1518; Paris 1578; etc. French translation, Paris 1632. The Ars brevis was translated into Hebrew in 1474, at Sinigaglia (nr. Ancona). The translation includes diagrams with movable wheels. This was the only logical treatise to be thus translated, but Ramon's thought must have been known before to the Jews, for Joseph ben Shem-ṭob Ibn Shem-ṭob was already denouncing it before 1451, together with Occam's philosophy.

Liber facilis scientiae. Paris 1311 (H. L., no. 31). Quaestiones supra librum facilis scientiae. Supplement to the preceding, written in Paris, presumably at the same time (H. L., no. 32).

De novo modo demonstrandi sive ars praedicativa magnitudinis. Majorca 1312 (H. L., no. 33).

Liber de quinque praedicabilibus et decem praedicamentis. Messina 1313 (H. L., no. 59). Printed Palma 1744.

This long list offers a good illustration of Ramon's continual moves from place to place and of his persistency.

Jordi Rubió y Balaguer: La logica del Gazzali posada en rims per En Ramon Lull (Anuari de l'Institut d'estudis Catalans, 311–354, 1913–1914). José Casadesús Vila: El Arte Magna (32 p., Barcelona 1917).

O. M. Dalton: A portable dial in the form of a book with figures derived from Raymond Lul (Archaeologia, vol. 25, 89–102, 2 pl., Oxford 1925). Made at Rome in 1593, it was used not only as a dial but as an instrumentum sciendi in the Lullian way (Isis, 13, 451).

3. *Religious discussions. Conversion of the infidels*—The main application of the ars magna was the conversion of unbelievers. The failure of the Crusades had proved the futility of the military method; the logical method would perhaps be more successful. If it were possible to establish absolutely the truth of Christianity and the error of other religions, conversions would naturally follow.

The earliest book of this kind, Libre del gentil, Liber de gentili et tribus sapientibus (H. L., no. 7), was written during the period of study in Majorca (1265–1274), probably in 1272–1273. A Jew, a Christian, and a Muslim explain in turn the superiority of their faiths to a gentile. Ramon was very well acquainted with the Jewish and Muslim religions and manners. The finest feature of this work is its spirit of toleration and fairness. In spite (or because) of his cocksureness, Ramon was amazingly gentle.

There are some points of contact between the Libre del gentil and the Kitāb al-ḥujjah wal-dalīl of Judah ha-Levi.

The Libre del gentil was perhaps first written in Arabic, afterward translated into Catalan and Latin by its author? There is a fifteenth century text in Arabic which is probably a revision of the original one. The Latin (or Catalan) text was early translated into Hebrew, into Spanish and into French.

Part of the French version was edited by Francisque Michel and Reinaud: Roman de Mahomet en vers du XIIIe siècle par Alexandre du Pont et Livre de la loi au Sarrasin en prose du XIVe siècle par R. Lulle (164 p., Paris 1831). Ch. V. Langlois: La vie spirituelle (La vie en france au Moyen âge, vol. 4, 327–381, 1928). The Castilian version was made in 1378 by Gonzalo Sánchez de Uceda.

Other treatises of this kind, in chronological order.

Liber Sancto Spiritu. Written in 1276–1278, or Montpellier 1275 (H. L., no. 8). Discussion between a Greek Christian and a Roman one in the presence of a Muslim.

Liber super psalmum Quicumque vult, sive liber Tartari et Christiani. Rome 1285 (H. L., no. 23). A Tartar interviews successively a Jew, a Muslim, and a Christian. Ramon was beginning to wonder whether the logical weapons were sufficient, perhaps some kind of crusading warfare was equally necessary. As years went on, his belief in the adequacy of peaceful methods decreased.

Liber de quinque sapientibus (H. L., no. 9). Discussion between a Latin, a Greek, a Nestorian, and a Jacobite, in the presence of a Muslim. This is followed by the Petitio Raymundi, an appeal to Celestine V (pope in 1294) for the defense and unification of the Christian faith. Printed Valencia 1510.

Petitio pro conversione infidelium. (H. L., no. 253). Addressed to Boniface VIII (pope from 1294 to 1303). Very similar to the Petitio addressed to Celestine V.

Liber de fine in quo traditur modus et doctrina, quo possunt omnes infideles ad fidei catholici veritatem breviter reduci, et Terra Sancta e manibus infidelium recuperari. Montpellier 1305 (H. L., no. 242).

De erroribus Judaeorum. Barcelona 1305 (H. L., no. 256).

Liber qui est disputatio Raymundi christiani et Hamar sarraceni. Pisa 1308 (H. L., no. 25). Printed Valencia 1510.

Liber de acquisitione Terrae Sanctae. Montpellier 1309 (H. L., 254).

Edition by Ephrem Longpré (Criterion, vol. 3, 266–278, Barcelona 1927).

Liber de quaestione valde alta et profunda. Paris 1311 (H. L., no. 217).
Disputatio fidelis et infidelis (H. L., no. 24). Undated, but addressed to the University of Paris.
Liber per quem poterit cognosci quae lex sit magis bona, magis magna et magis vera. Majorca 1312 (H. L., no. 219). Showing the superiority of the Christian law (i.e., religion) over the Jewish and Muslim.
De participatione Christianorum et Sarracenorum. Majorca 1312 (H. L., no 255).

4. *Christian apologetics*—These treatises are closely connected with those mentioned in §3. They are interesting as applications of Ramon's logical method to the subject least amenable to it, religious faith.
Liber de articulis fidei sacrosanctae et salutiferae legis christianae, sive liber Apostrophe. Rome 1296 (H. L., no. 27).
Liber ad probandum aliquos articulos fidei per syllogisticas rationes. Genoa 1303 (H. L, no. 218).
Liber de demonstratione per aequiparantiam. Montpellier 1304 (H. L., no. 30).
Supplicatio sacrae theologiae professoribus ac baccalaureis studii Parisiensis. Paris 1310 (H. L., no. 28).
Liber in quo declaratur quod fides sancta catholica est magis probabilis quam improbabilis. Paris 1310 (H. L., no. 79).
Liber mirandarum demonstrationum. Undated (H. L., no. 10). Divided into 200 chapters. According to the first Latin editor, Ivo Salzinger, this treatise was written in Limousin (i.e., Catalan).
Liber de quatuordecim articulis sacro-sanctae romanae catholicae fidei. Undated (H. L., no. 11).

5. *Chivalry and education*—While in Montpellier, Ramon wrote three books the purpose of which was mainly educational.
Liber de militia. Libre del orde de cavayleria. Written in Catalan in 1274–1275 (H. L., nos. 171, 258). This was very popular. It was translated into Latin, French, and English, and its influence can be traced in the works of the Infante Don Juan Manuel (1282–1347), grandson of San Fernando and nephew of Alfonso X el Sabio, and of the Catalan, Johanot Martorell, author of Tirant lo Blanch (c. 1460).

Catalan edition by Aguiló y Fuster (Barcelona 1879). Catalan and Castilian edition by J. R. de Luanco: Libro de la orden de caballeria (Barcelona 1901). French version printed in 1504 and 1505. English version from the French by William Caxton: Book of the ordre of chyualrey (c. 1484). Other English version also from the French by Sir Gilbert Hay (fl. 1456): Buke of the order of knychhede. Alfred T. P. Byles: The Book of the order of chivalry. Translated and printed by William Caxton . . . . together with Adam Loutfut's Scottish transcript (Early English text society, London 1926).

Liber doctrinae puerilis. Doctrina pueril. Montpellier 1274–1275 (H. L., no. 215). Written by Ramon for the education of his son Dominic. It deals with religion, giving an account not only of Christianity, but also of the two other laws (the Jewish and the Muslim), with the seven arts, medicine, mechanical arts, etc. Interesting views on the bringing up of children, on the training of the mind, etc.

Catalan edition by Obrador y Bennassar (Barcelona 1907). There is an early French version of it, Livre de l'enseignement puerill.

Liber de prima et secunda intentione. Libre de primera i segona entenció. Written in Montpellier c. 1283, also for his son Dominic; probably in Catalan (H. L., no. 46). This is a more advanced treatise than the Doctrina pueril; it deals almost exclusively with religion and theology.

6. *Blanquerna*—Montpellier c. 1283 (H. L., no. 76). This very long religious romance in Catalan is Ramon's greatest literary achievement and one of the masterpieces of the Christian Middle Ages. The concluding chapters describe distant countries: Barbary, Tartary, Abyssinia, Turkey, Georgia; e.g., one finds in it an account of the earliest European journey to the Sūdān (chapter 88).

Two opuscules supposed to have been written by the hero, Blanquerna, are appended to the main work, the Book of the lover and the beloved (Libre d amic e amat), and the Art of contemplation (Art de contemplació). The first of these is especially popular; indeed it is one of the golden books of the world literature. According to the author's own statement it was written after the manner of the Ṣūfīs. Many stories told in Blanquerna are derived from oriental sources. It is possible that the Book of the lover and the beloved was written some time before the romance itself.

First edition of Blanquerna, in Valencian dialect by Joan Bonlabi (Valencia 1521). Spanish translation (2 vols., Madrid 1881–1882, 1883). Other Spanish edition (Majorca 1749). English translation by E. Allison Peers (London 1926).

Innumerable editions of the Book of the lover and the beloved. Catalan editions by Obrador y Bennassar (Palma de Mallorca 1904; Barcelona 1905); by M. Olivar (Barcelona 1927). Spanish edition by Miguel Mir (Madrid 1903). French translation by Gabriel Chapuys (Paris 1586); other French edition (Paris 1632); French and Latin edition (Geneva 1890). Other French editions: Paris 1919, Paris 1921, etc. English translation by E. A. Peers (London 1923).

Francis Le Jau Frost: The Art of contemplació of Lull (Johns Hopkins thesis, 52 p., Baltimore 1903). Jean Henri Probst: La mystique de Lulle et l'Art de contemplació (Beitr. zur Gesch. der Philosophie des Mittelalters, vol. 13, 2, 134 p., Münster 1914; includes Catalan text). Art of contemplation, Englished by E. A. Peers (London 1925).

Charles de la Roncière: La découverte de l'Afrique au Moyen Age (vol. 1, 109–112, 1925). Apropos of the journey to the Sūdān described in Blanquerna.

7. *Libre appellat Felix de les maravelles del mon*—Paris 1286 (H. L., no. 257). This is another fantastic romance, very inferior to Blanquerna from the literary point of view. The intention is encyclopaedic, ethical, and as far as descriptions of contemporary life are concerned, satirical. It is divided into ten parts: God, angels, elements, heavens, plants, metals, beasts, man, paradise, hell.

The seventh part (of beasts) is a whole in itself, and was probably written before the rest. It is largely derived from oriental sources: Barlaam and Ioasaph, Kalīla wa Dimna, Alf laila wa laila; the story itself belongs to the cycle of Reynard the Fox. The eighth part (of man) fills more than half of the whole work.

Catalan edition of Felix by Gerónimo Rosselló (vol. 1, Palma 1873; vol. 2, Barcelona 1904). Liber Felix, o maravillas del mundo . . . . traducido de lemosin en español por un discipulo (2 vols., Palma 1750).

Konrad Hofmann: Ein katalanisches Thierepos von Ramón Lull (Bavarian Acad., München 1872). Llibre de les besties, edited by Obrador y Bennassar (Barcelona 1905). English version by E. A. Peers: The book of the beasts (100 p., London 1927).

8. *Catalan poems*—Of Ramon's many poetical compositions only three can be mentioned here.

Desconort (Disconsolateness). Rome 1295 (H. L., no. 97). His best poetical work, of biographical interest.

Lo cant de Ramon (Ramon's song). Probably Paris 1299 (H. L., no. 98).

Medicina de peccat (Medicine for sin). Majorca 1300 (H. L., no. 101). His longest poem, 6000 lines.

Gerónimo Rosselló: Obras rimadas de Ramón Lull. Escritas en idioma catalan-provenzal, publicadas por primera vez (Palma 1859).

9. *Tree of science*—Ramon's second longest work in Catalan, the Arbre de sciencia (Liber divinalis vocatus Arbor scientiae), was written in Rome, 1295–1296 (H. L., no. 72). The purpose is encyclopaedic. The image of a tree is used to show the relationships between ideas; Ramon describes 16 trees corresponding to as many groups of ideas. The last third of this work contains some 4000 questions and answers relative to its subject matter.

Many Latin editions: Barcelona 1505; Lyon 1615, 1635, 1637. Spanish translation by Alonso de Zepeda y Adrada (Brussels 1664, 1745). Catalan edition in the Obres edited by the Comissió editora Lulliana (vols. 11 to 13, 1917 ff.). See section 24.

The Arbre de filosofia d amor (Arbor philosophiae amoris) was composed near Paris in 1298 (H. L., no. 40). Ramon wrote it in Latin for Philippe le Bel, and translated it (or had it translated) into French for Philippe's queen, Jeanne of Navarre (the French version is lost). First edition, in Latin, Paris 1516.

Still another work built in the same artificial way is the Arbre de filosofia desijada (Arbor philosophiae desideratae), composed at an unknown time, long after 1283, for his son Dominic (H. L., no. 42). It might be classified with the educational books dealt with in §5. The image of the tree is here used as a mnemonic instrument.

10. *Proverbs*—Liber proverbiorum. Rome 1296 (H. L., no. 43). Collection of 6000 proverbs divided into three parts: the hundred names of God (see no. 18); scientific proverbs; moral proverbs.

First edition, Barcelona 1493. Later editions; Valencia 1507, 1510; Venice 1507; Paris 1516.

Liber de proverbis. Libre de mil proverbis, 1302 (H. L., no. 259). This collection of 1000 Catalan proverbs was composed by Ramon while he was sailing back from the East to Majorca.

A. Morel-Fatio: Proverbes rimés de Raimond Lull (Romania, vol. 11, 188–202, 1882).

11. *Anti-Averroism*—The Averroistic and revolutionary tendencies of some Parisian scholars provoked Ramon's anger. During his stay of 1297–1298, he

wrote his first anti-Averroistic treatise, Declaratio Raimondi per modum dialogi edita contra aliquorum philosophorum et eorum sequacium opiniones erroneas et damnatas a ven. patre domino episcopo Parisiensi[12] (H. L., no. 235). It is also entitled Liber contra errores Boetii et Sigerii (i.e., Boetius of Dacia and Siger of Brabant).

Edited by P. Otto Keicher: Lullus und seine Stellung zur arabischen Philosophie (89–221, Münster 1909).

During his stay of 1309–1311, much of his energy was devoted to his campaign against Averroism; witness the number of writings devoted to it.

Liber reprobationis aliquorum errorum Averrois. Paris, July, 1310 (H. L., no. 165).

Liber lamentationis philosophiae. Duodecim principia philosophiae. Paris, February, 1311 (H. L., no. 55).

First edition, Paris 1518. Many others: Strassburg 1598, 1617, 1651; Majorca 1606, 1745.

Liber contradictionis. Liber de centum syllogismis. Paris, February, 1311 (H. L., no. 70). Printed Palma 1746.

Sermones contra errores Averrois. Paris, April, 1311 (H. L., no. 164).

Liber de efficiente et effectu. Paris, May, 1311 (H. L., no. 67).

Liber de ente, quod simpliciter per se est existens et agens. Paris, September, 1311 (H. L., no. 200).

Disputatio Raymundi et Averroistae. Undated, probably Paris, 1311 (H. L., no. 166). Etc.

See additional list in Peers' biography, p. 345, 1929; mine is sufficient to show the intensity of Ramon's hostility to Averroism. See also P. Ephrem Longpré: Dictionnaire de théologie catholique (vol. 9, 1071–1141, Paris 1927).

12. *Phantasticus*—Vienne 1311–1312 (H. L., no. 54). Disputatio clerici et Raymundi phantastici. Written by Ramon during his attendance at the Council of Vienne.[13] Of autobiographical value. Ramon's description of himself as "fantastic" is typical. Printed Paris 1499.

13. *Philosophic writings not yet considered*—Liber chaos. Undated; anterior to Felix, 1286 (H. L., no. 124).

Liber de anima rationali. Rome 1296 (not 1294) (H. L., no. 44). Printed Alcala 1519.

Principia philosophiae complexa. Begun in Paris, finished in Majorca, 1300 (H. L., no. 130). Originally written in Catalan.

Disputatio fidei et intellectus. Montpellier 1303 (H. L., no. 26).

Liber de convenientia fidei et intellectus in objecto. Montpellier 1304 (H. L., no. 29). Printed Palma 1744.

Liber de ascensu et descensu intellectus. Montpellier 1304 (H. L., no. 62). Encyclopaedic treatise based upon the image of a ladder: stone, flame, plant, beast, man, heaven, angel, God. Printed Valencia 1512, again 1519; Palma 1744. Castilian version from the Latin, Majorca 1753.

[12] This is an allusion to the opinions condemned in 1277 by Stephen Tempier, bishop of Paris.

[13] That is, the Council which suppressed the Templars, and condemned various heresies.

Metaphysica nova et compendiosa. Paris 1309 (H. L., no. 61). Printed Paris 1516.

14. *Physics*—Liber de natura. Famagosta, Cyprus, 1301 (H. L., no. 68). Recommending the study of nature, a subject which Ramon was constitutionally unable to understand. The treatment is logical. Printed Palma 1740.

Liber de lumine. Montpellier 1303 (H. L., no. 87). More metaphysical than physical, and very obscure. Printed Majorca 1754.

Liber novus physicorum compendiosus. Paris 1309 (H. L., no. 60). Applying to physics the method of the ars nova. Printed Palma 1745.

15. *Mathematics and astronomy*—Ramon wrote a long treatise on astronomy in Paris, 1297: Tractatus novus de astronomia, (Ars astronomiae) (H. L., no. 169). As usual he attempts to apply his ars nova to the subject. He criticizes geomancy but not astrology. In fact, this treatise is largely astrological.

He wrote only one mathematical treatise, the Liber de nova et compendiosa geometria. Paris 1299 (H. L., no. 170). The Liber de quadratura et triangulatura circuli, written in Paris in the same year (H. L., no. 160), is not mathematical, but purely logical (see section 2).

It is clear that he had no real grasp of either mathematics or astronomy; he treated these subjects with the habitual conceit of a philosopher who believes he can dominate them without detailed and intimate knowledge.

16. *Medicine*—A number of medical treatises bear Ramon's name. Many are undated, some are apocryphal.

Liber de levitate et ponderositate elementorum. Naples c. 1293 (H. L., no. 86). Deals with posology. Printed Majorca 1752.

Liber de regionibus sanitatis et infirmitatis. Montpellier 1303 (H. L., no. 85). Printed Majorca 1752.

Liber de modo applicandi novam logicam ad scientiam juris et medicinae. After 1303 (H. L., no. 167).

Liber principiorum medicinae. Undated (H. L., no. 6). Carrying the logical method to the point of absurdity, and proving Ramon's utter ignorance of the experimental point of view.

Ars compendiosa medicinae. Undated (H. L., no. 84). Work of the same kind as the preceding. Printed Majorca 1752.

The Liber medicinae magnae, the Ars operativa medica, and the Libellus de conservatione vitae (H. L., nos. 88, 89, 91) are apocryphal.

Ramon's medical knowledge was but superficial, and his writings on the subject are negligible, except as illustrations of his logical obsession.

A treatise of Lull's on the composition of medicaments was translated into Hebrew.

17. *Alchemy*—The number of alchemical writings ascribed to Ramon Lull is so large (some 80), that no attempt will be made to list them. It is practically certain that all of them are apocryphal; none is mentioned in the contemporary bibliographies. Some of them were probably written by Raimundo de Tárrega (Tárrega in Catalonia, prov. of Lerida), converted Jew devoted to occultism, Dominican, who died in 1371.

Ramon Lull repeatedly expressed his opposition to alchemy, which he considered a fraud. According to him there is no possibility of metallic transmutation; the changes made by alchemists are superficial and transitory. Such views are expressed in the sixth part of Felix (Paris 1286) dealing with metals, the Quaestiones per artem demonstrativam solubiles (Montpellier 1287), the De novo modo demonstrandi (Majorca 1312), and probably in other writings.

However there is no doubt that the "Lullian" philosophy transmitted after Ramon's death included alchemy. The ascription of so many alchemical writings to the master is sufficient proof of that.

One of these apocryphal treatises, the Libre de la quinta esencia (Liber quintae essentiae), said to have been finished in Paris, 1319 (i.e., after Ramon's death), was translated into Hebrew.

For the very numerous editions of alchemical writings, see the Histoire littéraire (vol. 29, 1885). John Ferguson: Bibliotheca chemica (vol. 2, 49–57, 245, 594, Glasgow 1906).

José Ramon de Luanco: Lull considerado como alquimista (50 p., Barcelona 1870); La alquimia en España (2 vols., Barcelona 1889–1897). Tomás Aguiló: Algunos datos bibliográficos relativos a las obras químicas de Lulio (Museo Balear, vol. 1, 423–427, 1875). M. Berthelot: Sur quelques écrits alchimiques, en langue provençale, se rattachant à l'école de Raymond Lulle (Chimie au moyen âge, vol. 1, 351–356, 1893). E. O. v. Lippmann: Entstehung und Ausbreitung der Alchemie (1919). Dorothea Waley Singer: The alchemical testament attributed to Lull (Archeion, vol. 9, 43–52, 1928). The Testamentum and the Cantilena were both written in Catalan; Mrs. Singer confirms the improbability of the genuineness of these and other alchemical writings.

18. *Muslim influence*—We have already shown that Lull was deeply influenced by Arabic writings. See, e.g., sections 6 and 7, dealing with Blanquerna and Felix. He wrote a summary of al-Ghazzālī's logic (possibly first in Arabic, then in Latin, 1290). A Catalan poem of his on the hundred names of God, Els cent noms de Deu (Rome 1285; H. L., no. 96), was obviously inspired by the Muslim writings on the ninety-nine names of God (al-asmā' al-ḥusnā);[14] he intended to translate it into Arabic. It is probable that he was acquainted with some of the works of the great Spanish mystic Ibn 'Arabī (first half of the thirteenth century).

On the other hand, Ramon was one of the main channels through which Muslim lore was transmitted to Christendom. Considering his frequent stays in Italy, his writings must have been rapidly known in that country; they were probably one of the sources from which Dante derived his knowledge of Islām and Arabic literature.

Julián Ribera: Orígines de la filosofia de R. Lulio (Homenaje a Menéndez y Pelayo, vol. 2, 191–216, Madrid 1899); reprinted in Disertaciones y opúsculos (vol. 1, 151–179, 1928; Isis, 12, 161–163). Otto Keicher: Lullus und seine Stellung zur arabischen Philosophie (Beitr. zur Gesch. der Philos. des Mittelalters, vol. 7, 4, 223 p., Münster 1909). Includes a new text, the Declaratio Raymundi (see

[14] According to a Muslim legend quoted by Ramon, he who knows the hundredth Name will know all things. However there are far more than 99 names of God in Arabic. J. W. Redhouse collected 552 and did not believe that his list was complete; see his paper on The most comely names (Journal R. Asiatic Society, vol. 12, 1–69, 1880). Thomas Patrick Hughes: Dictionary of Islām (141, 1885). D. B. Macdonald: Encyclopaedia of Islām (vol. 1, 302–304, 1910); Aspects of Islām (116, New York 1911). "Seventy-two" names of God occur in the French romance Flamenca, composed c. 1234. Ch. V. Langlois: La vie en France au Moyen âge d'après des romans mondains du temps (2d ed., 149, Paris 1926).

section 11). Miguel Asín y Palacios: La escatologia musulmana en la Divina Comedia (Madrid 1919); English translation (London 1926; Isis, 10, 65–69).

19. *Ramon Lull, a founder of western orientalism*—Lull did not simply know Arabic, he could speak and write it. Various books of his were written in Arabic first (see sections 1, 2, 3), the most important being his Libre de contemplació (c. 1272). Inspired by his ideal of Christian propaganda he soon realized the need of schools where missionaries could obtain a practical knowledge of Arabic and Hebrew. In this he was probably influenced by his older countryman, Raymond of Peñafort (d. 1275), of whom it has been said that he founded such schools in Murcia, Tunis, and Barcelona (?). The Arabic college of Miramar (in Majorca) was founded by James II of Majorca and pope John XXI in 1276 at Lull's request; unfortunately it died out soon after 1292. (Another college of Arabic was established by Fra Joan de Puigventós in Valencia, 1281, and a school of Hebrew and Arabic was founded in Xátiva, 1291).

The necessity of creating oriental schools for missionaries was one of Lull's fixed ideas throughout his life. It is expressed in the Petitio Raymundi (Naples 1294; H. L., no. 9) addressed to Celestine V; in Phantasticus (Vienne 1311–1312; H. L., no. 54), again in the Petitio in concilio generali (Vienne 1311–1312; H. L., no. 252), and incidentally in other writings. In the petition to the council of Vienne, he recommended the establishment of such schools in Rome, Paris, and Toledo. The council decided to establish five of them; a normal one at the Roman curia, and four others in Bologna, Paris, Oxford, and Salamanca, wherein three languages would be taught, Hebrew, Chaldaean, and Arabic. These decisions were recorded by Ramon himself in his De participatiòne Christianorum et Sarracenorum (Majorca 1312; H. L., no. 255).

Hastings Rashdall: Universities of Europe in the Middle Ages (vol. 2, 96, 1895; only a brief reference).

20. *Ramon's missionary activity*—Ramon went three times to Africa as an ambassador of Christ to the Muslims, in 1292, 1307, 1314–1316; he died a martyr to his faith, in the course of his third mission. However his greatest contribution in this respect was his life-long insistence upon the necessity of a linguistic and logical (scientific) training for missionaries. His views on the subject were fully explained in the Libre de contemplació (c. 1272), in Blanquerna (c. 1283), etc. They were not realized until 1622 when the Congregation of propaganda (Congregatio de propaganda fide) was established by Gregory XV (pope from 1621 to 1623), and even until the foundation of the College of propaganda by Gregory's successor, Urban VIII (pope from 1623 to 1644).

21. *Dominicans vs. Franciscans*—The rivalry between the two great orders is well illustrated by Ramon's life. He oscillated between the two for a considerable time. He attended many chapters general of the Dominican Order: Montpellier 1283; Bologna 1285; Paris 1286; and later two chapters general of the Franciscans: Montpellier 1287; Rieti, in Umbria, 1289. He had hoped that the Dominicans would promote his ars magna and other ideas, but he found better support among the Franciscans, especially after Fra Ramon Gaufredi had been elected general (1289). During a spiritual crisis at Genoa, 1291–1292, he thought of assuming the Dominican habit. He finally became a Franciscan tertiary in 1295. In 1308 he spent some time in a Dominican monastery near Pisa. He made bequests to both

orders. The main persecutor of his memory and of his school was the Dominican, Nicholas Eymeric (1320–1399), inquisitor general of Aragon.

22. *Ramon upholder of the Immaculate Conception of Our Lady*—It is interesting to note that Ramon was one of the first doctors to claim that the Virgin Mary was conceived without original sin, notably in his Disputatio eremitae et Raymundi super aliquibus dubiis quaestionibus Sententiarum (Paris 1298; H. L., no. 22). This opinion was later defended by the Scotists, but vigorously opposed by the Dominicans. After centuries of discussion it became a dogma of the Roman Catholic Church in 1854 (Bull Ineffabilis Deus, of Pius IX). See my note on Duns Scotus below.

23. *History of Lullism*—During his last but one visit to his native island, in 1311–1312, Ramon founded the Lullian school (Escola lullista). After his death he soon acquired considerable fame.

Tres sabios hubo en el mundo
Adán, Salomón y Raymundo.

One enthusiast went so far as to say that the Old Testament was the work of God the Father, the New Testament of God the Son, and Ramon's writings of the Holy Spirit. As usual the weakest parts of Ramon's doctrine were especially admired and the mystical and occult aspects of Lullism (e.g., alchemy) absurdly magnified.

This was bound to cause a reaction, of which Nicholas Eymeric became the leader in 1366. Eymeric made immense efforts to prove Ramon's heterodoxy, but was finally defeated. In the fifteenth century Lullism became increasingly popular in Catalonia and Aragon. Chairs of Lullian science were established in 1408 at Cervera (not very far from Lerida), in 1478 at Barcelona, in 1481 at Mt. Randa (Majorca), in 1500 at Valencia. In the sixteenth century, thanks to the influence of Cardinal Jiménez de Cisneros (1436–1517), the teaching of Lullism was introduced into Castile, a chair being founded in 1518 at the University of Alcalá. Other early Lullists were Nicholas of Cues, Bessarion, and Pico della Mirandola. In 1483 a university was founded in Majorca (Estudi general de Palma). Further vicissitudes of Lullism do not concern us. One might say of Lullism, as was said of Averroism, that its history is a history of continual misunderstandings. Efforts were repeatedly made to get Ramon's books on the Index librorum prohibitorum;[15] on the other hand, processes in support of his sanctification or beatification failed one after another.

Miramar, where Ramon had established his oriental school in 1276, was occupied by the Archduke Louis Salvator of Austria from 1867 to his death in 1915, and considerably embellished. A community of Franciscan tertiaries was installed on Mt. Randa in 1913.

J. H. Probst: Le Lullisme de Raymond de Sebonde, Ramon de Sibiude (Toulouse 1912). Juan Alcover y Maspons: El Lulismo en Mallorca desde mediados de siglo XIX (Palma 1915). Joan Avinyó: Historia del Lulisme (Barcelona, 1925).

24. *Collected editions*—Ivo Salzinger (1669–1727): Lulli Opera (10 vols. folio, Mayence 1721–1742).

Jerónimo Rosselló: Obras de Ramón Lull. Textos originales, publicados e ilus-

[15] His name does not occur in the latest edition (1929; Isis, 14, 568).

trados con notas y variantes (3 vols., Palma de Mallorca, 1886–1892). Vol. 1 includes the Libre del gentil e los tres savis, Libre de primera e segona intenció, Libre de mil proverbis; vol. 2, Arbre de filosofía d amor, Libre de oració, Libre de Deu, de conexença de Deu, del es de Deu; vol. 3, Felix de les maravelles del mon.

New edition prepared by the Comissió editora lulliana, i.e., Mateu Obrador y Bennassar, Antoni Maria Alcover, Salvador Galmés, etc. (in progress; 14 vols. have appeared, 1906 sq., Palma de Mallorca). Vol. 1, Obre doctrinals: Doctrina pueril. Libre del orde de cavallería. Libre de clerecía. Art de confessió (1906); vols. 2 to 8, Libre de contemplació en Deu escrit a Mallorca e transladat d arabic en romanç vulgar devers lany 1272 (1906–1914); vol. 9, Blanquerna (1914); vol. 10, Libre de Sancta María. Hores de Sancta María. Libre de Benedicta tu in mulieribus (1915); vols. 11 to 13, Arbre de sciencia (1917–1926); vol. 14, Proberbis (1928).

25. *Bibliographies*—E. Littré and B. Hauréau: Histoire littéraire de la France (vol. 29, 67–386, 1885). Critical list of 313 works many of which are apocryphal. Reproduces on p. 72–74 the two early lists of Lull's writings, compiled in 1311 and a few years later. The list of the Histoire littéraire has been completed, with special respect to the Catalan MSS. and editions, by a number of Catalan scholars, Mateu Obrador y Benassar (Palma 1900), José María Batista y Roca (Barcelona 1916), Pedro Blanco Soto (Madrid 1916). Eliés Rogent and Estanislau Duràn: Bibliografía de les impressions lullianes. Amb un proemi, addicions i index de Ramon d'Alòs-Moner (Barcelona 1927).

Boletín de la Sociedad arquelógica Luliana (Palma 1885–1906). Revista Luliana (Barcelona 1901–1905).

26. *Ancient biography and criticism*—There are two contemporary biographies, both anonymous, the one in Latin, the other in Catalan. The Vita Beati Raymundi was published by J. B. Sollier in the Acta Sanctorum (Antwerp 1709; see below). The Catalan text of the Vida coetània was edited in the Boletín de la R. Acad. de buenas letras (vol. 15, 89–101, 1915). English translation by E. A. Peers: A life of Ramon Lull, written by an unknown hand about 1311 (85 p., London 1927; with text of the Latin Vita in appendix).

Agrippa von Nettesheim: In artem brevem Lulli commentaria (284 p., Solingen 1538). Valerius de Valeriis: Aureum sane opus in quo ea omnia breviter explicantur quae scientiarum omnium parens, Raymundus Lullus, tam in scientiarum arbore quam in arte generale tradit (188 p., Augsburg 1589). Ewald Vogel: De lapidis physici conditionibus liber. Quo duorum abditissimorum auctorum Gebri et R. Lullii methodica continetur explicatio (288 p., Cologne 1595). Johann Heinrich Alsted (1588–1638): Clavis artis lullianae et verae logices duos in libellos tributa (160 p., Strassburg 1652).

Acta Sanctorum junii tomus quintus (633–736, Antwerp, 1709) under the date of June 30, by J. B. Sollier and others.

Antonio Raymundo Pasqual: Vindiciae lullianae, sive demonstratio critica immunitatis doctrinae (4 vols., Avignon 1778). Elaborate biography in vol. 1. The same author wrote another biography in Catalan, which remained long unpublished (2 vols., Palma 1890).

27. *Modern criticism. Biographical and general studies*—Histoire littéraire de la France (vol. 29, 1–67, 1885). Homenatge al Doctor arcangelic (Barcelona 1901); Collection of essays. Samuel M. Zwemer: Lull, first missionary to the Muslems (194 p., New York 1902). The author is himself a missionary and an Arabic scholar; his account is interesting but needs checking. Havelock Ellis: Lull at Palma, in The soul of Spain (191–222, London 1908). Salvador Galmés: Vida compendiosa del Bt. Ramon Lull (Palma 1915). Lynn Thorndike: History of magic (vol. 2, 862–873, 1923). Lucien Graux: Le docteur illuminé (420 p., Paris 1927); a novel based upon Lull's life. E. Allison Peers: Ramon Lull (472 p.,

London 1929; Isis, 13, 368–370). Excellent biography, except that the author has not paid sufficient attention to Lull's logical and scientific works. Followed by a short but select bibliography.

28. *Special studies*—(In addition to those already mentioned in sections 1 to 23). Adolf Helfferich: Lull und die Anfänge der catalonischen Literatur (168 p., Berlin 1858). Juan O'Neille: R. Lull, iconografía (Museo balear, vol. 1, 435–442, 1875). Marcelino Menéndez y Pelayo: Historia de los heterodoxos españoles (vol. 1, 513–539, Madrid 1880; revised edition, 1917). Wilhelm Brambach: Des R. Lullus Leben und Werke in Bildern des 14. Jahrhunderts (Karlsruhe 1893). M. Steinschneider: Hebraeische Übersetzungen (475, 823–825, 1893). Salvador Bové: Lo Beat Ramón Lull y 'l descubriment de les Amériques (Revista luliana, vol. 1, 105–114, 1901). M. Menéndez y Pelayo: Orígines de la novela (vol. 1, Madrid 1905). Adam Gottron: Lulls Kreuzzugsideen (96 p., Berlin 1912). Jean Henri Probst: Caractère et origine des idées du bienheureux R. Lulle (Grenoble thesis, 354 p., Toulouse 1912).

For King Manfred and Bartholomew of Messina, see the chapter on translators.

ST. THOMAS AQUINAS

Contents: (1) Life and work. (2) Influence of Thomism in Christendom, and neo-Thomism. (3) Influence of Thomism upon Jewish philosophy.

(4) Text. (5) Hebrew translations. (6) Bibliographies. (7) Lexica. (8) Scholastic commentaries. (9) General criticism, biographies. (10) Philosophy and theology. (11) Politics, law and sociology. (12) Science. (13) St. Thomas and Judaism. (14) St. Thomas and Islām.

1. *Life and work*—Thomas ab Aquino. Born of a noble family in Roccasecca (in Campania), 1225; educated in Monte Cassino and Naples; assumed the Dominican habit at Naples, 1244; attended Albertus Magnus' lectures in Paris and Cologne; studied in Paris from 1252 to 1259; taught at the papal court (Anagni, Orvieto, Rome, Viterbo) from 1259 to 1268; it was during this last period that he met William of Moerbeke; in 1269 he returned to Paris, in 1272 again to Italy; he died in the Cistercian monastery of Fossanuova, between Naples and Rome, on March 7, 1274. Called by the schoolmen Doctor angelicus, communis, universalis. Canonized in 1323. The prince of Christian scholasticism. He was literarily active since c. 1252.

He was deeply influenced by Muslim philosophy, chiefly by al-Ghazzālī and Ibn Rushd, but his own point of view was fundamentally opposed to Averroism. He was deeply influenced also by Jewish philosophy, chiefly by Ibn Gabirol whom he took special pains to refute, Baḥya ben Joseph, and above all, Maimonides. In spite of his anti-Semitism his writings were studied with great care by later Jewish writers. Availing himself of the new translations prepared by William of Moerbeke, partly at his own request, he became the greatest Christian expositor of Aristotle's doctrines in the later Middle Ages. Indeed he was one of the first in Christendom who thoroughly understood these doctrines in their purity as opposed to neo-Platonic fancies. The aim of his life was to reconcile Aristotelian and Muslim knowledge with Christian theology. Though interested in science, he utterly failed to understand its true spirit and methods, and no scientific contribution can be credited to him. Indeed his mind was far too dogmatic to be capable of disinterested scientific curiosity. His master, Albert, was a more genuine man of science than he was, but Thomas had perhaps a better understanding of astronomical and physical subjects. His views on these subjects were partly suggested by Simplicios (first half of the sixth century), whose commentaries seem to have been introduced by him, with Moerbeke's assistance, to western Christendom. He believed in the reality of magic, which he carefully distinguished from legitimate science on one hand, and from legitimate miracles on the other, and considered evil. His views on divination, alchemy, and astrology were dominated by the same distinction. He had a vague conception of plant sexuality (see p. 62, note 45).

St. Thomas was a clear and forceful expositor, eclectic with regard to his sources, but as firm as a rock with regard to his own dogmatic purposes, very moderate both in his aims and methods and as simple and economical as possible in his teaching. Outside of his fundamental creed, he was capable of remarkable independence of thought; e.g., he said, "Locus ab auctoritate . . . . est infirmissimus." He was essentially an intellectualist, far more so than any other Christian philosopher; that is, he attached supreme importance to the act of understanding. His system, if not very original, is one of admirable congruity. Within the unbending frame of Christian dogmatics he offers us a complete and well-ordered explanation of the world.

The wisdom of Thomism is better appreciated if one realizes that it was a middle doctrine between two extremes, extreme Peripateticism or Averroism on the one hand, and extreme anti-Peripateticism or Scotism on the other. In this, St. Thomas' position was very similar to that of al-Ghazzālī in Islām.

He wrote commentaries on the four books of sentences of Peter the Lombard (1254–1256); Quaestiones disputatae (1256–1272); Quaestiones quodlibetales (1263–1272); commentaries on Plato's Timaeus, on Boetius, on Dionysios the Areopagite, on the Liber de causis. His most important works are his Aristotelian commentaries (Peri hermeneias, Posterior analytics, Physics, De coelo et mundo, De generatione et corruptione, Meteorologica, De somno et vigilia), composed in Italy and Paris, and the famous Summa theologica, at which he labored from c. 1267 to his death and left unfinished (a supplement to it was written by Reginald of Piperno, a close friend of his from 1261 on).

The following writings may still be mentioned: De principiis naturae (1255); Summa contra Gentiles (1258 to 1260 or 1264), written at the suggestion of Raymond of Peñafort;[16] De occultis operationibus naturae (1269–1272); Compendium theologiae (1271–1273). Considering the brevity of his life, the mass of his writings is as marvelous as their merit.

One of the most original parts of his work is the political and social philosophy. It is explained in the Summa theologica, in his commentary on Aristotle's Politics, and in a separate work composed for the education of Hugh II of Lusignan, king of Cyprus (who died in 1267 at the age of 14), the De regimine principum, in four books. This work was begun (Bk. I, Bk. II, chs. 1–4) by Thomas, and completed c.1274–1282 by his pupil Ptolemy of Lucques. We may safely assume that the whole represents Thomas' teaching. The core of this teaching is the view that the state exists for the good of the citizen rather than the citizen for the good of the state; individuals are the only social realities; every group must be subordinated to its members (Oportet eundem finem esse multitudinis humanae qui est hominis unius). This is a sort of declaration of the rights of man, which is original, if

[16] Apropos of the Summa contra Gentiles, see my note on Raymond Martin, above.

not with St. Thomas, at least with his time; these views may have been inspired in St. Thomas at least partly, by the great political and social changes which he was able to witness in France, England and Spain. They led him to the conception of a moderate democracy, of universal suffrage (if the citizens are sufficiently enlightened); sovereignty comes from God but is essentially vested in the people, who delegate it to a monarch or to another kind of government, this contract of delegation remaining always revocable (Regnum non propter regem, sed rex propter regnum).

On the other hand, it is noteworthy that St. Thomas, following Aristotle, considered slavery justified and useful (in this he was less liberal than Gregory the Great had proved himself to be, seven centuries earlier). He assimilated slavery to other forms of property, all of which were justified in his eyes, except that what we would call the right of eminent domain always belongs to God; man is a simple usufructuary. He did not realize that slavery was only a temporary institution, in spite of the fact that it had already evolved (and decreased) considerably since ancient times.

The taking of interest for the loan of money had been absolutely condemned by Aristotle (Politics, 1, chapter 3). St. Thomas took the same position. He considered commerce generally vile (turpe). It must be said in his defense that in those days money was almost always borrowed for consumption, seldom for constructive purposes. Thus St. Thomas considered the leasing of money wicked, but the leasing of a house justified, because money is useful only if it is consumed, while the house remains.

2. *Influence of Thomism in Christendom, and neo-Thomism*—Thomas' gigantic endeavor did not meet at once with unanimous approval among Christian doctors. An effort had already been made within his life time, in 1270, to have some of his views censured. In 1277 Stephen Tempier, bishop of Paris, acting in agreement with the University, condemned these views together with various Averroistic errors; this condemnation was confirmed by the University of Oxford in the same year at the initiative of the *Dominican*, Robert Kilwardby. However in 1278 Thomism became the official doctrine of the Dominican Order. This provoked a new form of opposition on the part of the Franciscan Order, and caused gradually a dogmatic schism between the two orders (1282 sq.). In Oxford this opposition was led by the Franciscan, John Peckham (1284, 1286). (See my notes on Peckham and William de la Mare.) In its turn this created a Dominican reaction in favor of Thomist philosophy.

Within a very short time the triumph of the latter was complete. It will suffice to record a few facts. At the council of Vienne in 1311–1312, St. Thomas was already named "doctor communis." During the council of Trent (1545–1563), his Summa theologica was placed upon the altar together with the Holy Scriptures and the Decretals. Pius V (pope from 1566 to 1572) declared him to be the fifth doctor of the church, the four others being Ambrose, Augustine, Jerome and Gregory the Great. Many other popes proclaimed the soundness and supreme value of St. Thomas' teachings. This triumph reached its culmination when Leo XIII (pope from 1878 to 1903) issued the encyclic Aeterni patris (August 4, 1879) wherein he set out at great length the superiority of St. Thomas' philosophy; a year later he wrote the brief "Cum hoc sit" (August 4, 1880), proclaiming St. Thomas the patron of all Catholic schools; he founded the Accademia Romana di S. Tommaso and ordered the publication of a new edition of St. Thomas' complete works. Leo XIII was genuinely interested in science (chiefly astronomy) and was convinced that the study of scholastic philosophy would favor the progress of scientific research.

The encyclic Aeterni patris of 1879, which established St. Thomas officially as the intellectual guide of the Roman Catholic Church, gave a considerable impetus to the neo-Thomist movement. Leo XIII's efforts in this direction were frequently and amply confirmed by his successors, Pius X (1903–1914), Benedict XV (1914–1922), Pius XI (1922–). To illustrate: In the new code of canonic law which appeared in 1917, during Benedict XV's pontificate, the study and teaching of philosophy, according to the method, doctrine and principles of St. Thomas, was formally enjoined (Canon 1366 §2); in the encyclic Fausto appetente die (June 29, 1921), issued by the same pope, the Church is made to proclaim that the doctrine of St. Thomas is its very own (Thomae doctrinam Ecclesia suam propriam edixit esse). This has been once more confirmed by Pius XI in the encyclic Studiorum ducem (i.e., St. Thomas) of 1924. It is thus sufficiently clear that Thomism is the official philosophy of the Roman Catholic Church; that it is as authoritative, for the members of that Church, as anything can be, short of the dogmas themselves; and that it is thus difficult, if not impossible, for these members to study it in a critical spirit.

For a general study of the neo-Thomist movement and of its antecedents, see F. Picavet: La restauration thomiste au XIXe siècle, in Esquisse d'une histoire des philosophies medièvales (Paris 1905; 2e éd., 233–313, 1907); Thomisme et modernisme dans le monde catholique, in Essais sur l'histoire des théologies et philosophies medièvales (346–368, 403, Paris 1913; both essays are very full). For later developments see L. Rougier: La scolastique et le thomisme (120, 810, Paris 1925). The texts of the encyclics and briefs are easy to obtain in many publications. For the encyclic Aeterni patris, I have used the text included in the Lettres apostoliques de S. S. Léon XIII (vol. 1, 43–75, Paris c. 1902; with French translation); this is a very remarkable document.

Many periodicals are devoted to neo-Thomist study and propaganda, mainly the Revue néo-scolastique publiée par la Société philosophique de Louvain, which began to appear in Louvain, 1894, the director being Désiré Mercier (later cardinal), and the secretary, Maurice De Wulf. The Rivista di filosofia neo-scolastica began to appear in Florence, 1909, the secretaries being Giulio Canella and Agostino Gemelli. The Revue thomiste. Questions du temps présent (Paris 1893, etc.) is of a more popular nature.

It is remarkable that the most important organ of this propaganda in the scientific world anteceded the encyclic Aeterni patris. I am thinking of the "Société scientifique de Bruxelles" founded in 1875 "to promote the study of mathematical, physical, natural, medical and economic sciences and to prove the harmony of these sciences with the teachings of Christian philosophy and revealed religion, in conformity with its motto: Nulla umquam inter fidem et rationem vera dissensio esse potest (Conc. Vaticanum, Const. de fide oath., C. IV)." This society of Roman Catholic scientists publishes very valuable annals, and a journal devoted to scientific subjects in general (Annales, since 1875; Revue des questions scientifiques, since 1877). These publications are among the best repertories of contemporary science available today; they also contain many contributions of special interest to historians of science (e.g., by P. Duhem, P. Mansion, H. Bosmans).

The neo-Thomist movement is the most conspicuous extension of mediaevalism in modern times. Its influence is very great within its own religious sphere, but because of its very sectarianism, limited. Its fate is subordinated to that of the Roman Catholic church; at least, it can hardly affect the non-Catholic world. It deserves, however, to be carefully studied, without prejudice, for it will help one better to understand medieval thought and also the trend of opinion of a large number of our contemporaries.

3. *Influence of Thomism upon Jewish philosophy*—Because of its Jewish origins and qualities, St. Thomas' philosophy drew the attention of some Jewish doctors. This is proved by the existence of a few Hebrew translations.

Leone Romano (1292–1350) translated at least one of St. Thomas' treatises, on ideas, Ma'amar ha-mashalim. After 1470, Elijah ben Joseph Ḥabillo translated the Quaestiones disputatae, Quaestio de anima, De animae facultatibus, Ma'amar be-koḥot ha-nefesh; the De universalibus, Ma'amar be-'inyan ha-kolel; and he wrote questions on the treatise on being and quality, She'elot ma'amar be-nimẓa ube-mahut. Abraham ben Joseph ibn Naḥmias translated the Commentaries on metaphysics, probably at Ocaña (prov. Toledo) in 1490. Extracts from the Summa contra Gentiles were translated by Jacob Ẓahalon (1630–1693). Isaac ben Judah Abravanel (1437–1508) mentions St. Thomas in his Mif'alot Elohim (printed in Venice, 1592).

To these Jewish translations may be added, if only for the sake of curiosity, the one made by the Italian Dominican and bishop Giuseppe Maria Ciantès (1602–1670). He translated the first three books of the Summa contra Gentiles into Hebrew to promote the conversion of the Jews.

4. *Text*—There are a large number of fifteenth century and other early editions. All previous editions have been superseded by the following: Sancti Thomae Aquinatis doctoris angelici Opera Omnia iussu impensaque Leonis XIII P. M. edita (14 vols., folio, Rome 1882–1926). Vol. 1 Commentaria in Aristotelis libros Peri hermeneias et Posteriorum Analyticorum cum synopsibus et annotationibus T. M. Zigliara (1882); 2. Commentaria in octo libros Physicorum Aristotelis (1884); 3. Commentaria in libros Aristotelis de coelo et mundo, de generatione et corruptione et meteorologicorum (1886); 4–12. Summa theologica cum commentariis cardinalis Caietani (1888–1906); 13–14. Summa contra Gentiles, with commentary by Franciscus de Silvestris of Ferrara (1918–1926).

The Summa Theologica was literally translated by the Fathers of the English Dominican province (10 vols., London 1911–1917). Joseph Rickaby: Aquinas Ethicus or the moral teaching of St. Thomas. A translation of the principal portions of the second part of the Summa theologica (2 vols., London 1896). Gonzague Truc: La pensée de St. Thomas; extraits choisis de la Somme théologique, avec texte latin, introduction, etc. (328 p., Paris 1925; Isis, 7, 538).

Summa contra Gentiles (De veritate catholicae fidei) literally translated by the English Dominican Fathers from the latest Leonine edition (4 vols., London 1923–1929). Joseph Rickaby: Of God and his creatures. Annotated translation with some abridgment (beautiful folio volume; London 1905).

Tratatto della pietra filosofale preceduto da una introduzione e seguito da un tratatto su l'Arte dell' alchimia, nelle quali opere sono rivelati i segreti per arrivare al bene su questa terra. Prima traduzione italiana dal testo latino (Todi 1913). According to Robert Steele (Singer's Studies, vol. 2, 149, 1921), this treatise is apocryphal; it was written by Fr. Thomas, chaplain to Robert, son of Charles of Anjou, in 1296. For other alchemical tracts, see Ferguson.

De regimine principum et rusticorum ad regem Cypri. First edition, undated incunabula. Later editions; Paris 1509, Cologne 1643.

Anthologies. H. C. O'Neill: New things and old in St. Thomas. Extracts translated (328 p., London 1909). Eugen Rolfes: Die Philosophie von Thomas von Aquin in Auszügen aus seinen Schriften herausgegeben und mit einer Einleitung und Anmerkungen versehen (Leipzig 1920); etc.

5. *Hebrew translations*—Ḥabillo's translation of the De anima, etc., was partly edited by Adolph Jellinek: Thomas von Aquino in der jüdischen Literatur (Leipzig 1853). Joseph Ciantès's partial translation of the Summa contra Gentiles was printed in Rome, 1657.

6. *Bibliographies*—Pierre Mandonnet: Des écrits authentiques de S. Thomas (2e. édition revue et corrigée, 158 p., Fribourg, Suisse, 1910). The first edition appeared in the Revue Thomiste, same year. Martin Grabmann: Die echten Schriften des hl. Thomas auf Grund der alten Kataloge und der handschriftlichen Überlieferung (Beiträge zur Gesch. der Philosophie des Mittelalters, 22, 1; 284 p., Münster 1920). P. Synave: Le catalogue officiel des oeuvres de St. Thomas (Archives d'histoire doctrinale du Moyen âge, vol. 3, 25–104, 1928; Isis, 13, 432). Apropos of the catalogue made by Bartholomew of Capua, 1319.

7. *Lexicon*—General index to the Summa theologica by A. C. Peltier (854 p., Paris 1861). This completed the Paris edition of the Summa (8 vols., 1856–1860). Ludwig Schultz: Thomas-Lexicon. Sammlung, Übersetzung und Erklärung der Kunstausdrücke und wissenschaftlichen Aussprüche (2. sehr vergrösserte Auflage, 1000 p., Paderborn 1895).

8. *Scholastic commentaries*—Many supercommentaries have been devoted to Aquinas' commentaries. Most of them are typically enough of inordinate length. It seems as if no such commentary could be taken seriously unless it were of gigantic size. One of less than six volumes would be decidedly infradig. I quote only a few for the sake of curiosity.

Joannes Baptista Gonet: Clypeus theologiae thomisticae contra novos ejus impugnatores (6 vols., Paris, 1875–1876). Joannes Capreolus: Defensiones theologiae divi Thomae de novo editae cura et studio RR. PP. Ceslai Paban et Thomae Pègues (7 vols., Tours, 1907–1908). Albert Farges: Etudes philosophiques pour vulgariser les théories d'Aristote et de S. Thomas et leur accord avec les sciences (9 vols., Paris 1890–1908). Thomas Pègues: Commentaire français littéral de la Somme théologique (10 vols., Toulouse 1907–1915).

9. *General criticism. Biographies*—P. J. Carle: Histoire de la vie et des écrits de S. Thomas (552 p., folio, Paris 1846; "tiré à 200 exemplaires pour être offert aux plus grands personnages du monde catholique, servir à l'expression du règne de Dieu et à l'exaltation de son Eglise"). Karl Werner: Der heilige Thomas (3 vols., Regensburg 1858–59). R. B. Vaughan: The life and labours of St. Thomas (2 vols., London 1871–1872). Abbé Philippe Reinhard de Liechty: Albert le Grand et Saint Thomas, ou la science au moyen âge (254 p., Paris 1880); includes a French translation of the encyclic of 1879. Rodolfo Maiocchi: S. Tommaso morì di veleno? (136 p., Modena 1889). Pius Cavanagh (O. P.): Life of S. Thomas. Illustrated (London 1890). Potthast (1062, 1896). Antonin D. Sertillanges: St. Thomas (2 vols., Paris 1910; 2d ed., 1912). Jos. Ant. Endres: Thomas von Aquin (107 p., 64 ill., Weltgeschichte in Karakterbildern; Mainz 1910); interesting from the iconographic standpoint. Placid Conway (O. P.): Saint Thomas (132 p., London 1911). Martin Grabmann: Thomas. Eine Einführung in seine Persönlichkeit und Gedankenswelt (176 p., Kempten 1912; 3rd improved ed., 1917; Italian translation, Milano 1920; English translation, 200 p., London 1929). Philip Henry Wicksteed: Dante and Aquinas (Jowett lectures, 293 p., London 1913); The reactions between dogma and philosophy illustrated from the works of St. Thomas (Hibbert lectures, 696 p., London 1920). Fr. P. Mandonnet (O. P.): L'entrée de St. Thomas chez les Frères prêcheurs fin avril 1244 (Congrès international d'histoire de Bruxelles, 1923). Etienne Gilson: St. Thomas d'Aquin

(Paris 1925). Henri Ghéon: Le triomphe de St. Thomas (Paris 1925). Aleksander Birkenmajer: Der Brief der pariser Artistenfakultät über den Tod des hl. Thomas (Beiträge zur Gesch. der Philosophie des Mittelalters, vol. 20, 5, p. 1–35, 211–213, Münster 1922); Neuer zu dem Briefe . . . . . (Xenia thomistica, Festschrift anlässlich des 600 jährigen Kanonisations-jübiläum, 18 p., Roma 1925). Paul Hartig: Albert der Grosse und Thomas von Aquino. Untersuchung zur Bedeutung volksheitlicher Verwurzelung im Mittelalter (Deutsche Vierteljahrsschrift für Literaturwissenschaft, vol. 5, 25–36, 1927; Isis, 13, 161).

10. *Philosophy and theology*—Giov. Maria Cornoldi: La filosofia scolastica di San Tammaso e di Dante (4th Italian ed., Rome 1889). Victor Lipperheide: Thomas und die platonische Ideenlehre (München 1890). E. V. Maumus: Thomas et la philosophie cartésienne (2 vols., Paris 1890). Hermann Koppehl: Die Verwandschaft Leibnizens mit Thomas in der Lehre vom Bösen (Diss., 128 p., Jena 1892). Thomas Esser: Die Lehre des hl. Thomas über die Möglichkeit einer anfangslosen Schöpfung (182 p., Münster 1895). Johannes Baron: Die Bedeutung der Phantasmen für die Entstehung der Begriffe bei Thomas. Ein Beitrag zur Geschichte des erkenntnistheoretischen Dualismus (Diss., 68 p., Münster 1902). Matthias Schiefferens: Die Lehre von der Willensfreiheit bei Thomas mit Berücksichtigung derselben Lehre bei Duns Skotus (Diss., Erlangen, 45 p., Münster 1904). Théodore de Regnon: La métaphysique des causes d'après S. Thomas et Albert le Grand (2e ed., Paris 1906). H. Dehove: Le réalisme thomiste comparé à l'idéalisme Kantien (245 p., Mém. de la faculté catholique, Lille 1907). Heinrich Weertz: Die Gotteslehre des Pseudo-Dionysius Areopagita und ihre Einwirkung auf Thomas (Diss., Bonn, 48 p., Köln 1908). Rudolf Eucken: Die Philosophie Thomas und die Kultur der Neuzeit (2. Aufl., Bad Sachsa 1910). Oskar Renz: Die Synteresis nach Thomas (246 p., Beitr. zur Gesch. der Phil. des Mitt., 10, 1, Münster 1911). Matthias Meier: Die Lehre Thomas de passionibus animae (175 p., ibidem, 11, 2, 1912). Theodor Steinbüchel: Der Zweckgedanke in der Philosophie Thomas (168 p., ibidem, 11, 1, 1912). Domenico Lanna: La teoria della conoscenza in San Tommaso (314 p., Bibl. d. Rivista di filosofia neoscolastica, 1913). Anselm Rohner: Das Schöpfungsproblem bei Maimonides, Albertus und Thomas (Beitr. zur Gesch. der Philos. des Mitt., 11, 5, 152 p., Münster 1913). Etienne Gilson: Index scolastico-cartésien (364 p., Paris 1913). Friedrich Beemelmans: Zeit und Ewigkeit nach Thomas (Beitr. zur Gesch. der Philos. des Mittelalters, 17, 1, 64 p., 1914). Günther Schulemann: Das Kausalprinzip in der philosophie Thomas (ibidem, 13, 5, 1915). Antonin D. Sertillanges: La philosophie morale de S. Thomas (594 p., Paris 1916). J. Durantel: Le retour à Dieu par l'intelligence et la volonté dans la philosophie de S. Thomas (Thèse, 432 p., Paris 1918); S. Thomas et le pseudo-Denis (Thèse, 278 p., Paris 1919). Etienne Gilson: Le thomisme (174 p., Strasbourg 1919; important, Isis, 5, 500); English translation from the third revised edition (302 p., Cambridge 1924); Etudes de philosophie médiévale (Strasbourg 1921). Maurice de Wulf: Philosophy and civilization in the Middle Ages (Princeton 1922); Mediaeval philosophy, illustrated from the system of Aquinas (152 p., Cambridge Mass., 1923). Aelred Whitacre: Veritas, the theology of St. Thomas (Aquinas sexcentenary lectures, Manchester University; 32 p., Oxford 1924). J. Fulton Sheen: God and intelligence in modern philosophy (London 1925). Martin Grabmann: Die Kulturphilosophie des hl. Thomas (217 p., Augsburg 1925). Louis Rougier: La scolastique et le thomisme (856 p., Paris 1925; Isis, 8, 219–221). M. De Wulf: Mediaeval philosophy (vol. 2, 3–37, 1926). Thomas Ohm: Die Stellung der Heiden zu Natur und Übernatur nach dem hl. Thomas (364 p., Münster i. W., 1927). Richard McKeon: Aquinas' doctrine of knowledge and its historical setting (Speculum, vol. 3, 425–444, 1928; Isis, 13, 162).

11. *Politics, law and sociology*—A great number of memoirs have been devoted to

this aspect of Aquinas' thought. To be sure, its study is essential if one would understand the political and social ideas of those days. Yet many of these memoirs have been written with a view to applying Thomas' ideas to the problems of our own time; that is, their purpose is not historical, but practical. Indeed neo-Thomism is not simply a religious but also a political movement.

Antonio Burri: Le teorie politiche di San Tommaso e il moderno diritto pubblico (157 p., Roma 1884). Georg von Hertling: Die Stellung des hl. Thomas zu den Problemen der philosophischen Rechts-, Staats- und Gesellschaftslehre (55 p., Münster 1887). Basilius Antoniades: Die Staatslehre des Thomas ab Aquino (133 p., Leipzig 1890). Cesare Augusto Bosone: Der Aufsatz de regimine principum. Ein Beitrag zur Kenntnis der Staatsphilosophie im Mittelalter (Diss., 68 p., Bonn 1894). Edouard Crahay: La politique de S. Thomas (180 p., Bibl. de l'Institut supérieur de philosophie, Louvain 1896). Max Maurenberger: Thomas Stellung zum Wirtschaftsleben seiner Zeit. (Diss., Leipzig, 128 p., Leipzig 1898). Franz Schraub: Die Eigentumslehre nach Thomas und dem modernen Sozialismus mit besonderer Berücksichtigung der beiderseitigen Weltanschauungen (470 p., Freiburg 1898). Fridolin Kuhn: Die Probleme des Naturrechts bei Thomas (Diss. München, 80 p., Erlangen 1909). Jacques Zeiller: L'idée de l'état dans S. Thomas (Paris 1910). Josef Vilmain: Die Staatslehre des Thomas (Diss. Heidelberg, 152 p., Leipzig 1910). Edmund Schreiber: Die volkswirtschaftlichen Anschauungen der Scholastik seit Thomas (Beitr. zur Gesch. der Nationalökonomie, 1, 254 p., Jena 1913). Joseph Anton Endres: De regimine principum (Beiträge zur Gesch. d. Philos d. Mittelalters, Festschrift, 261–267, 1913). Wilhelm Müller: Der Staat in seinen Beziehungen zur sittlichen Ordnung bei Thomas (Beitr. zur Gesch. der Philosophie des Mittelalters, 19, 1, 110 p., Münster 1916). Edward Francis Murphy: St. Thomas' political doctrine and democracy (Thesis, Catholic University of America, 311 p., Washington 1921). Victor Bouillon: La politique de Saint Thomas (Paris 1927).

12. *Science*—I do not know any complete study of Aquinas' scientific thought. The best investigations thus far we owe to P. Duhem, who is not by any means unbiassed: Etudes sur Léonard de Vinci (vol. 2, 1909; p. 70–72, on gravity; p. 74–75, on the reconciliation of the two propositions: the power of God is unlimited; there is only one universe and this universe is limited); Système du monde (vol. 3, 348–357, 1915, account of Aquinas' astronomy; vol. 5, 468–570, 1917; account of his philosophy). Duhem's conclusion is interesting: "Le thomisme n'est pas une doctrine philosophique; il est une aspiration et une tendance; il n'est pas une synthèse, mais un désir de synthèse . . . . Son désir de synthèse est si grand qu'il aveugle en lui le discernement du sens critique."

John Ferguson: Bibliotheca chemica (vol. 2, 446–448, 1906). Apropos of apocryphal alchemical writings, with long bibliography. E. O. v. Lippmann: Alchemie (493, 1919). Lynn Thorndike: History of magic (vol. 2, 593–615, 1923). Ämilian Schöpfer: Der hl. Thomas als Bahnbrecher der Wissenschaft (204 p., Innsbruck 1925).

13. *St. Thomas and Judaism*—Jacob Guttmann: Das Verhältniss des Thomas von Aquino zum Judenthum und zur jüdischen Litteratur (92 p., Göttingen 1891). Dealing mainly with Ibn Gabirol and Maimonides. M. Steinschneider: Hebraeische Ubersetzungen (483–487, 496, 1893). I. Broydé: Jewish encyclopaedia (vol. 2, 38–40, 1902). Henri Pirenne: La duchesse Aleyde de Brabant et le De regimine Judaeorum de St. Thomas (Bull. de la classe des lettres de l'Académie de Belgique, vol. 14, 43–55, 1928). St. Thomas wrote the De regimine Judaeorum at the request of the duchess who was the widow of Henry III of Brabant (d. 1261).

14. *St. Thomas and Islām*—Miguel Asín y Palacios: El Averroismo teologico de Santo Tomas (Zaragoza 1904); El justo medio en la creencia. Compendio de teologia dogmatica de Algazel (570 p., Madrid 1929; Isis, 13, 420).

ST. BONAVENTURE

John of Fidenza; born in 1221–1222 at Bagnorea, Tuscany; assumed the Franciscan habit c. 1240; studied theology in Paris, 1243–1245, attending the lectures of Alexander Hales and John of La Rochelle, whom he succeeded in 1248; in 1257 he became general of his Order; created cardinal by Gregory X (pope from 1271 to 1276); he died at Lyon in 1274 during the Council, which he was attending. "Doctor devotus, seraphicus." Canonized in 1482.

His philosophy continued the neo-Platonic tradition of St. Augustine, Dionysios the Areopagite, the schools of Chartres and Saint-Victor, Bernard of Clairvaux; he was more of a theophile and mystic than of a philosopher. His main scientific works, written before 1257, are a famous commentary on Peter Lombard's Sentences (1248 sq.); Quaestiones disputatae, especially De paupertate; De reductione artium ad theologiam, including a classification of knowledge. Of his later works, dealing mainly with religion and devotion, I mention only the Itinerarium mentis ad Deum (1259), and the life of St. Francis (1261).

His commentary on Peter Lombard gives us some idea of his scientific knowledge, which was rudimentary; in astronomy he defended the Aristotelian or Averroistic views versus the Ptolemaic. It is he who, as general of his Order, forbade Roger Bacon to continue his lectures in Oxford and obliged him to come to Paris that he might be watched more closely.

Text—An excellent edition of his collected works has been edited by the Franciscan St. Bonaventure College of Quaracchi (10 vols., 1882–1902; the last vol. contains biographical and critical studies and scholia).

His life of St. Francis (Legenda major) was abbreviated by himself (Legenda minor) and this shorter version is included in almost every Franciscan breviary.

General criticism—Joannes a Rubino and Antonius Maria a Vicetia: Lexicon bonaventurianum (Venice 1880). Leonhard Lemmens: Der hl. Bonaventura, Kardinal und Kirchenlehrer (Kempten 1909). Centennial number of the Franziskanische Studien (1921). Eusèbe Clop: St. Bonaventure (Paris 1922). Etienne Gilson: La philosophie de St. Bonaventure (Paris 1924). M. De Wulf: History of mediaeval philosophy (vol. 1, 362–375, 1926).

Special criticism—Kurt Ziesché: Die Naturlehre Bonaventuras (Fulda 1908). Eduard Lutz: Die Psychologie Bonaventuras (Beiträge zur Gesch. der Philosophie des Mittelalters, vol. 6, 226 p., Münster 1909). P. Duhem: Le système du monde (vol. 3, 407–410, 1915). Bonifaz Anton Luyckx: Die Erkenntnislehre Bonaventuras (Beiträge zur Geschichte der Philosophie des Mittelalters, vol. 23, 3, 330 p., Münster 1923). Bernhard Rosenmöller: Religiöse Erkenntnis nach Bonaventura (238 p., ibidem, vol. 25, 3, Münster 1925). Bernard Landry: La notion d'analogie chez St. Bonaventure et chez St. Thomas (Thèse, Louvain, 1922).

GILES OF ROME

Contents: (1) Life. (2) Thomism and anti-Averroism. (3) Aristotelian commentaries. (4) Classification of knowledge. (5) Other philosophical writings. (6) Theological writings. (7) De regimine principum. (8) Other political writings. (9) Physics and astronomy. (10) Medicine.

(11) Texts. (12) General criticism. (13) Special criticism. (14) Scientific criticism.

1. *Life*—Aegidius Romanus. Italian philosopher, theologian, and publicist. Frequently called Egidio Colonna (Aegidius de Columna), on the authority of the

Augustinian Jordan of Quedlinburg (in Saxony, d. 1380), but there is no reason to believe that he was a member of that illustrious Roman family. Born in or before 1247; became an Augustinian hermit; studied under St. Thomas; about 1282, he was tutor to the future Philip IV le Bel (born 1268; king of France from 1285 to 1314); he taught in Paris, but having taken the part of St. Thomas against the bishop of Paris, Stephen Tempier, he got into trouble with the university and did not receive the licentia docendi until 1285 after a retractation. He was in Bayeux, Normandy, in 1291. He became general of his order in 1292, archbishop of Bourges in 1295, and died in 1316.

2. *Thomism and anti-Averroism*—Giles was an ardent but eclectic Thomist. His writings against Stephen Tempier and also those against the Parisian Averroists were probably among his earlier publications. The most important was the Contra gradus et pluralitatem formarum, in which Tempier's pluralism was described as heretical. This was the treatise which caused his temporary disgrace; thus it was written in or before 1281.

Often printed: Padua 1493; Venice 1500, 1502; Naples 1525, etc.

Other treatises of this kind: De gradibus formarum accidentalium. Printed in Tres tractatus (see section 4); again Naples 1525.

De materia coeli contra Averroistas. Printed Padua 1493, Venice 1500, etc.

De intellectus possibilis pluralitate contra Averroistas. Printed together with the preceding. This was probably one of the treatises translated into Hebrew.

De erroribus philosophorum. Incomplete and apocryphal. Printed Vienna 1482, Venice 1581, etc.

3. *Aristotelian commentaries*—Giles seems to have commented upon the whole Aristotelian corpus, including the parts which had been previously forbidden (i.e., in 1215). Some of his commentaries being known only by title will not be mentioned.

Logic. In artem veterem expositio. That is, commentary on the Logica vetus or Vetus organum, including Porphyry's Isagoge, the Categories and Periermenias, the Liber sex principiorum of Gilbert de la Porrée. Printed Venice 1507, 1582; Bergamo 1594.

In libros Priorum analyticorum. Printed Venice 1499, 1504, 1516, 1522, 1598. Authorship uncertain; it is also ascribed to Robert Kilwardby.

In libros Posteriorum analyticorum. Printed Padua 1478; Venice 1488, 1491, 1495, 1500, 1513, 1530. Medium, or De medio demonstrationis. Appendix to preceding.

Commentary on the Elenchi, i.e., on the New logic. Printed Venice 1496, 1499, 1500, 1530.

Physics. In octo libros Physicorum. Printed Padua 1483, or 1493; Venice 1496, 1501, 1502 (twice).

De generatione et corruptione. Printed Naples, 1480; Venice 1493, 1498, 1505, 1518, 1520, 1567.

Psychology. In tres libros De anima. Printed Pavia 1491; Venice 1496, 1499, 1500, 1501? This was translated into Hebrew.

Rhetoric. In libros Rhetoricorum. This commentary was made on the basis of the Latin version completed by William of Moerbeke in 1281; it was made before 1285 and was thus a great novelty. The teaching of rhetoric was then a real innovation. Printed, together with al-Fārābī's commentary, in Venice 1481; again Venice 1555.

De differentia rhetoricae, politicae et ethicae. Short tract printed in Tres tractatus (see section 4).

Metaphysics. In Metaphysicorum duodecim libros quaestiones. Incomplete. Printed Venice 1499, 1501, 1552.

Ethics. De bona fortuna. Extracts from the Magna moralia and the Eudemian Ethics. Printed Venice 1496?, 1551.

De causis. Finally he composed, at Bayeux in 1291, a commentary on the pseudo-Aristotelian Liber de causis. (I do not say that the other commentaries were composed before; we do not know in which order they appeared.) Printed Venice 1550.

4. *Classification of knowledge*—The De partibus philosophiae essentialibus ac aliarum scientarum differentia et distinctione, c. 1280, was a real if modest contribution to this old subject, and it was the last mediaeval treatise showing some originality in the treatment of it. Printed with two other treatises in Tres tractatus, without place or date. Reprinted 1493?

5. *Other philosophical writings*—Two treatises De esse et essentia. The first, Quaestiones XIII, was printed in Venice 1493, 1503, 1504. The second, Aurea theoremata XXII, was printed in 1493. One of these treatises was translated into Hebrew.

6. *Theological writings*—Giles' theological teaching implied, as usual, commentaries on the Scriptures and on the Books of sentences of Peter the Lombard. His most important theological work was his commentaries on the Books of sentences. The commentary on book I was printed in Venice 1492, 1521, 1571?; the commentary on book II, completed in or after 1309, was printed in Venice 1482, 1581; the commentary on book III, left incomplete because of the author's death, was printed in Rome 1623 (careful edition with index rerum).

The most popular of his theological works was the Quodlibeta sex, though it was of very little value. It was often printed: Bologna 1481; Venice 1496, 1502, 1504, 1513; Naples 1525; Louvain 1646, 1648.

7. *De regimine principum*—Giles composed for his royal pupil not long before 1285 a treatise on the government of princes, De regimine principum libri III, largely based on Aristotle's ethics and politics, and on St. Thomas' treatise bearing the same title (though very different from the latter). Its three books deal respectively with the government of self, the government of the family, and civil government, or, with personal ethics, economics, and politics. The second book is divided into three parts dealing respectively with husband and wife, father and son (including a survey of physical, intellectual, and moral education, for both sexes and different ages), master and servant. His political views were far more advanced than those of Latini's Trésor. He showed a good deal of moderation and his sense of justice was tempered with Christian charity.

The popularity of this treatise is proved by the abundance of MSS., editions, and translations.

It was printed in 1473; Augsburg 1473; Rome 1482; Venice 1489, 1498, 1502; Rome 1556; Venice 1585, 1598; Rome 1607 (including the author's biography by Angelo Rocca, 1545–1620); Venice 1617. Still another edition, Leiden 1643, wrongly ascribed to St. Thomas.

It was translated into French by Henry of Gauchi (in Vermandois, Aisne; beginning of the fourteenth century)—not Henry of Ghent! Another French version was edited by Samuel Paul Molenaer: Li livres du gouvernement des rois. A thirteenth century version, now first published from the Kerr MS. (502 p., New York 1899; with long introduction). Extracts from a French version are included also in Louis de Baecker: Le droit de la femme (109–118, 1880).

A French version was translated into Hebrew, Sefer ha-nihugat ha-melekim, at an unknown time by an Italian Jew. There were at least two Italian versions. One of them was made from the French version of Henry of Gauchy by J. Nicholas de Guanto. An Italian version dated 1288 was edited by Francesco Corazzini: Del reggimento de' principi (Florence 1858). If the date is correct, this translation was made very soon after the publication of the original Latin text, thus presumably from this Latin text. It is one of the earliest texts in Italian prose. Another Italian version by Val. Averoni appeared in Florence, 1577. The Regimen principum was translated into Spanish by Bernard, bishop of Osma.[17] It was printed in Seville, 1494. A Catalan version was printed in Barcelona, 1480. There were also translations into English by Thomas Occlerc; into Portuguese; and into Dutch. For the last named, see Armin Tille: Eine mittelniederdeutsche Übersetzung (Z. f. d. gesamte Staatswiss., vol. 57, 484–496, Tübingen 1901).

Giles' treatise should not be confused with another on the same subject, Liber de informatione principum, written c. 1298—1314 by a Dominican. A French translation of it by the Carmelite friar, Jean Golein (c. 1320–1403): Le mirouer exemplaire et très fructueuse instruction selon la compilation de Gilles de Rome . . . du regime et gouvernment des roys, princes et grands seigneurs, was printed in Paris, 1517. Léopold Delisle: Histoire littéraire de la France (vol. 31, 35–47, 1893). Still another treatise of the same kind is the De eruditione principum, included among St. Thomas' works. It was probably composed by the Dominican, William Pérault. And of course there is St. Thomas' own treatise. All of which shows how much attention was paid to the subject by Christian doctors in the second half of the thirteenth century.

8. *Other political writings*—Giles wrote various other treatises dealing with lay or ecclesiastical politics. Some were devoted to the defense of ultramontanism. For example, a large treatise composed c. 1310, De ecclesiastica sive de summi pontificis potestate, was an application of Thomist philosophy to the justification of papal authority. Giuseppe Boffito and Giuseppe Ugo Oxilia: Un trattato inedito di Egidio Colonna, De ecclesiastica potestate (253 p., Florence 1908).

9. *Physics and astronomy*—Giles' views on physics and astronomy are explained in his Aristotelian commentaries mentioned above, and also in his discussion of Genesis: Hexaëmeron, seu de mondo sex diebus condito libri II (c. 1309). This was printed in Venice 1521, Padua 1549, Rome 1555.

Giles' sources were mainly patristic and Latin (Bede, Anselm, Hugh of Saint Victor). He preferred the astronomical views of Ptolemy and Simplicios to those of al-Biṭrūjī. However, like the majority of his contemporaries, he seemed to believe in the trepidation of the equinoxes rather than in a continuous precession.

[17] I do not find such a bishop in Gams's Series episcoporum (1873); yet he is named in the title of the edition of 1494.

As the Alphonsine Tables were hardly known in Paris before 1292, it is not surprising that he was not influenced by them.

In his De intentionibus in medio, he discussed the nature of light and concluded that it is something in the lighting object, not in the intermediary space, except "intentionally." If sun rays crossing a colored glass appear colored, their color is not real but "intentional." That opuscule was printed in Naples, 1525, together with others by the same author.

10. *Medicine*—The De corpore humano, or, De formatione corporis humani in utero. Largely derived from the Kitāb al-kullīyāt of Ibn Rushd. Printed in Paris 1515, Venice 1523, Rimini 1626. See Histoire littéraire (vol. 30, 463–465, 554, 563).

This treatise may have been known to Leonardo da Vinci. There is a reference to it in the Codex Atlanticus, though not in Leonardo's writing.

11. *Text*—The editions of separate texts have already been mentioned. There is no complete edition of his works. One was begun by the Augustinian, Christopher of Padua, but only the first volume appeared (folio, Rome 1554–1555), containing twenty works mainly theological. A smaller collection was published in Naples, 1525.

12. *General criticism*—Adolphe Franck: Réformateurs et publicistes de l'Europe (71–102, Paris 1864). Félix Lajard: Histoire littéraire de la France (vol. 30, 421–566, 1888). Contains a critical catalogue of Giles' writings, 73 in number plus 65 doubtful. Nicolo Mattioli: Studio critico sopra Egidio Romano Colonna (Antologia agostiniana, 1, 292 p., Rome 1896).

13. *Special criticism*—Victor Courdaveaux: Aegidii de regimine principum doctrina (86 p., Paris 1857). Carl Werner: Der Augustinismus des späteren Mittelalters (Wien 1883). M. Steinschneider: Hebraeische Übersetzungen (464, 491–494, 1893). Potthast (17, 1896) Ludwig Baur: Dominicus Gundissalinus (380–385, Münster 1903). P. Mandonnet: La carrière scolaire de Gilles de Rome (Revue des sciences philosophiques et théologiques, vol. 4, 481–499, 1910). Giuseppe Boffito: Saggio di bibliografia egidiana (Florence 1911). Adolph Dyroff: Aegidius von Colonna? Aegidius Conigiatus? (Philosophisches Jahrbuch, vol. 38, 18–25, Fulda 1925). Showing that the name Colonna is unwarranted.

14. *Scientific criticism*—P. Duhem: Système du monde (vol. 4, 106–119, 1916). J. Playfair McMurrich: Leonardo da Vinci (25, Baltimore 1930; Isis, 15, 342.)

LATINI

Ser Brunetto Latini (or Latino). Italian encyclopaedic writer and teacher, writing in Italian and French. Born in Florence at the beginning of the century; died there in 1295. He was a notary and a prominent member of the Guelf party; he was sent as ambassador of Florence to Alfonso the Wise in Toledo and Seville; upon his return in 1260, the Guelfs having been defeated, he was driven into exile and took refuge in France; in 1263 he was in Arras; in 1266 or 1267 he returned to Florence; during the following twelve years he held various offices in the government of that republic.

Already in the fourteenth century he was quoted as "maestro di Dante." His younger contemporary, Giovanni Villani said of him: "Fu cominciatore e maestro in digrossare i Fiorentini, e farli scorti in bene parlare e in sapere guidare e reggere la nostra republica secondo la politica" (Cronica, VIII, 10). He wrote considerably, chiefly during his exile in France. It was during that period (1260–1266–1267) that he translated Cicero's Rhetoric into Tuscan, and he wrote his masterpiece,

Li livres dou tresor (the treasure books). As this was written in French, we may place it toward the end of his exile, i.e., near but before 1266–1267. It is an intelligent if careless compilation which obtained considerable success. It is divided into three parts, of which the first is an encyclopaedia of the popular knowledge of his day, including an historical summary down to 1260 (with additions down to 1268); the second and third parts deal respectively with morals and politics (with special reference to the government of the Italian republics). The third part is the most original. The level of the first part is considerably lower than that of the Latin encyclopaedias. Latini had written before a smaller Treasure (Tesoretto) in Tuscan verse.

The popularity of the Trésor lasted very long; witness the abundant MSS. A curious testimony to it was Napoleon's intention of having a critical edition of the Trésor, with commentaries, published by the state. This intention however was not realized. The Trésor was translated into Tuscan by the Florentine, Bono Giamboni, in the fourteenth century or perhaps already during the author's lifetime.

The first part (divided into three in the Italian version) deals with the earth (geography), fishes (including crocodiles, whales, hippopotami, etc.), serpents, birds, and beasts. The geographical knowledge was derived from Pomponius Mela, Pliny, and above all, Solinus; the agricultural, from Palladius; the zoological, from the Provençal poem on falconry by Deudes de Prades, from Pliny, Solinus, St. Ambrose, Isidore of Seville, Hrabanus Maurus, Hugh of St. Victor, from the bestiaries composed by Philip of Thaon, William the Clerk (Guillaume le Clerc, a Norman trouvère, c. 1221) and Richard of Fournival; he was also acquainted with Marbode's lapidary and Hildegard's medicine. The two other parts reveal his familiarity with Aristotle's Ethics (probably through a Latin version of a Hispano-Arabic one), and with St. Martin of Braga (first bishop of Dumium, Portugal, d. 570–580), Isidore of Seville, Walter of Lille (Gualterius ab Insulis, fl. end of the twelfth century), William Pérault (Dominican of Peyraud, in Ardèche; d. 1260), Albertano of Brescia.

It is clear that a good deal of his information was rather old-fashioned. Yet he had had many contacts with Islām; for example, during his embassy in Toledo and Seville. His classification of knowledge was copied from Ibn Sīnā; he must have used bestiaries of Arabic origin; the Alexandrian romance told in the Tesoro suggests the Arabic tradition of it; he was acquainted with Ḥunain ibn Isḥāq; he had some knowledge of the Prophet Muḥammad and of the Muslim doctrines and customs. Finally the very titles of two of his works, Trésor, Tesoretto suggest some Arabic inspiration, for such a title was a commonplace in Arabic literature (kanz, khizānah, khazīnah, khazā'in). Considering that he was, if not Dante's teacher, at least a sort of older guide, some of the Arabic elements of the Divina commedia may have been transmitted by him.

Text—First edition of Li livres dou trésor by P. Chabaille (Collection de documents inédits sur l'histoire de France, 772 p., Paris 1863). Though this editor consulted some 40 MSS., his work was not done with sufficient care, and needs revision.

The Italian translation was printed long before the original text. The Italian version was divided into 9 parts instead of 3. It appeared in Treviso 1474, Venice 1528, 1533, and 1839, this last edition being due to Luigi Carrer. Edition by Luigi Gaiter (4 vols., Bologna 1878, 1877–1883).

Separate edition of the scientific books by Guido Battelli: I libri naturali del Tesoro (236 p., Florence 1917; with notes and illustrations).

Il tesoretto e il favoletto edited by Giov. Bat. Zannoni (322 p., Florence 1824); also by Berthold Wiese (Bibliotheca romanica, 106 p., Strassburg 1909).

Rettorica di Ser Brunetto Latini in volgar Fiorentino. First edition of this translation from Cicero, Roma 1546; reprinted Naples 1851. Critical edition by Francesco Maggini (Pubb. dell' Istituto di studii superiori, 190 p., Firenze 1915).

Cronica fiorentina attribuita a Latini. Appended to Pasquale Villari: I primi due secoli della storia di Firenze (2 vols., Florence 1893–1894).

General criticism—We owe the best general study to the Danish scholar Thor Sundby: Brunetto Latinos levnet og skrifter (350 p., Copenhagen 1869); Italian translation by Rodolfo Renier: Della vita e delle opere di Brunetto Latini. With appendices by Isidoro del Lungo and Adolfo Mussafia (536 p., Firenze 1884). This work contains a study of Latini's sources, especially those of the second part, and includes editions of the Moralium dogma of Walter of Lille (p. 391–474), and of the De arte loquendi et tacendi of Albertano of Brescia (p. 475–506). Unfortunately the author was not equipped to ravel out the Arabic sources.

Ch. V. Langlois: La connaissance de la nature et du monde au moyen âge (328–391, Paris 1911; reprinted, 1927, 355–390). Brief study followed by a summary of the scientific part of the Trésor.

Special criticism—Bart. Sorio: Il sistema di cronologia trattato del Tesoro (epithalamic publ., 24 p., Verona 1856). Umberto Marchesini: Latini notaio (idem; 11 p., Verona 1890); Due studi biografici su Latini (Atti dell' Istituto veneto, vol. 5, 65 p., 1887). Paget-Toynbee: Latini's obligations to Solinus (Romania, vol. 23, 62, 1894). Michele Scherillo: Alcuni capitoli della biografia di Dante (Torino 1896). Francesco Maggini: La rettorica italiana di Br. Latini (80 p., Pubb. dell' Istituto di studii superiori, Firenze 1912). Antonio Padula: Latini e il Pataffio (304 p., Milano 1921). Guido Battelli: Segreti di magia e medicina medievale cavati da un codice del Tesoro (Archivium Romanicum, vol. 5, 26 p., 1921). Apropos of the Italian translation traditionally ascribed to Bono Giamboni; the medical secrets, 41 in number, deal only with the animal kingdom. Miguel Asín: Islam and the Divine Comedy (252–254, London 1926; Isis, 10, 65–69). For the Arabic tradition of the Alexandrian romance see Emilio García Gómez: Un texto árabe occidental de la leyenda de Alejandro (346 p., Madrid 1929; Isis, 13, 494).

RISTORO D'AREZZO

Italian writer and scientist who flourished at Arezzo, Tuscany, c. 1282. He completed in Arezzo, 1282, an encyclopaedic treatise on the composition of the world, in Italian, Della composizione del mondo colle sue cagioni. It deals with astronomy, meteorology, geology, and to a large extent with astrology. His knowledge was not at all up to date, being largely derived from Latin translations of Arabic writings of the first half of the ninth century. He used al-Farghānī and Sahl ibn Bishr, probably also Abū Mā'shar, Isidore of Seville, and "Artephius." He may have had some slight contact with Aristotle's De coelo et mundo, Ibn Sīnā's Qānūn, and with Ibn Rushd's commentary on Aristotelian meteorology. His geological views were similar to those of Albert the Great and Thomas Aquinas, but this must be due to the use of common sources for there is no evidence that he knew their own compilations. He expressed the view that the scintillation of the stars originates in our eyes, not in the stars.

Text—First edition by Enrico Narducci (432 p., Rome 1859). Reprinted in the Bibliotheca rara directed by G. Daelli (vol. 54, 366 p., Milano 1864). This is not a critical edition; the best MS. has not been used.

Paul of Venice, who died in 1429, plagiarized Ristoro's Composizione in his De compositione mundi (Venice 1498; Paris 1513).

Criticism—P. Duhem: Etudes sur Léonard de Vinci (vol. 2, 319–327, 1909); Système du monde (vol. 4, 199–210, 1916). Alfred Michel: Die Sprache der Composizione del mondo nach Cod. Ricc. 2164 (Diss., 35 p., Halle 1905). Herbert Douglas Austin: Accredited citations in Ristoro's Composizione (Diss., Johns Hopkins, 52 p., Torino 1911).

For Bartholomew of Parma, see the mathematical chapter; for Taddeo Alderotti, the medical one.

VINCENT OF BEAUVAIS

Vincentius Bellovacensis; French Dominican and encyclopaedist. Born probably about the end of the twelfth century; in 1246 he was subprior of the Dominican monastery of Beauvais (34 m. SSW. Amiens); he died in 1264 or soon after. He was intimately connected with the royal family, being librarian and tutor to Louis IX, and tutor to the latter's sons.

He compiled an immense encyclopaedia, the Speculum maius, purposing to reflect "all things of all times." According to the original plan it was to be divided into four main parts dealing respectively with nature, doctrine (science), morality, and history (Speculum quadruplex naturale, doctrinale, morale, historiale). There is no doubt that the Speculum morale was not realized by himself; it was largely a summary of St. Thomas' Summa, and was completed between 1310 and 1325. Yet as it was a part of the original plan, and has been included in every printed edition of the Speculum maius it is better to mention it together with the rest.

The plan if not the substance of this encyclopaedia was entirely new. Its superiority over earlier ones was mainly due to the fact that Vincent had access to larger and better libraries and could command the services of amanuenses. Comparable in this to the Chinese encyclopaedias, it is essentially a collection of extracts, some of them very long. These extracts were apparently made with care and properly assigned to their respective authors. Thus Vincent quotes fully and explicitly from a large number of Latin, Greek, Arabic, and Hebrew writings (some 450 authors represented); the non-Latin works he knew only through Latin versions, but by his time these versions were already very abundant. This compilation must have taken considerable time, at least from 1244 to 1254, but probably much longer; the text was apparently revised at later dates for it contains many references to Albert the Great and even to St. Thomas.

On account of the vast number of his sources, it is not expedient to name them all. The main sources were Aristotle, Pliny, Dioscorides, the Physiologos, the Fathers of the Church, Palladius, Isidore, al-Rāzī (for chemistry as well as for medicine), Ibn Sīnā, Ibn Rushd, Adelard of Bath, William of Conches, Thomas of Cantimpré, Albert the Great, etc. However this compilation was more remarkable for its size than for its quality. The author did not take sufficient pains to assimilate its materials and transform them into an organic whole; like the Chinese compilers he was satisfied to quote the documents available to him without trying to remove or explain their contradictions. Not only does his work contain nothing new or original, but—unlike others of the same kind, as those of Pliny, al-Mas'ūdī, and the Chinese encyclopaedists—it has not even the value of a secondary repository of lost learning, for most of his sources are available to us otherwise, frequently in their original form. Moreover, aside from the works of his brother Dominicans,

Albert the Great and St. Thomas, Vincent made no effort to be up to date, and to integrate the newer knowledge with the older one. Thus the Speculum represents the knowledge which was generally accessible in the third quarter of the thirteenth century to the educated people of Western Christendom—not the people of genius, but the good, steady people. Its backwardness is especially apparent with regard to the more scientific subjects; e.g., he was not even acquainted with the innovations of his religious brother, Jordanus Nemorarius. We are not surprised to find in it not only the best popular lore of its time, but also many of its superstitions.

The Speculum naturale is an account of natural history in the form of a gigantic commentary on Genesis I. It contains a prologue followed by 32 books divided into 3718 chapters. It deals with meteorology, geography, geology, astronomy, botany, zoology, anatomy, physiology, psychology. The geological views were derived from Ibn Sīnā through Albert the Great. A similar remark applies to his astronomy. He reproduces al-Biṭrūjī's theory as distorted by Albert, and concludes in favor of the Ptolemaic conception. Much attention is paid to astrology, but he does not confuse it with astronomy. The chemistry is derived mainly from the De aluminibus et salibus of al-Rāzī as translated by Gerard of Cremona. He believed in the transmutation of metals and in other alchemic doctrines but with some qualifications probably inspired by Ibn Sīnā. The psychological part included naturally a long discussion of dreams. Considerable space was given to the consideration of plants and animals, not less than five books being devoted to the latter. According to Cuvier, his descriptions of fishes were better than those of Albert the Great.

The apocryphal letter on falconry addressed by Aquila Symmachos and Theodotion to Ptolemy, king of Egypt, was reproduced almost verbatim. The original text, whichever it was, is lost, but we have an early Catalan version which is possibly the earliest treatise on falconry in an European vernacular.

The Speculum doctrinale is divided into 17 books, 2374 chapters. It is a summary of theoretical and practical knowledge arranged in six major groups: literary, moral, mechanical, physical, mathematical, theological. This arrangement is suggestive of the poverty of Vincent's thought. The number six was probably inspired by the six days of creation and the six ages in the history of the world. The Speculum doctrinale deals with such subjects as grammar, logic, husbandry, law and government, various trades, medicine (456 chapters), physics, mathematics (including compotus), astronomy, astrology, music, weights and measures, surveying. It even includes a dictionary (c. 3200 words). It will be noticed that many subjects, such as astronomy, are dealt with in both the Speculum naturale and the Speculum doctrinale. My remarks relative to these subjects apply naturally to both Specula.

The Speculum historiale is a universal history, chiefly from the religious and ecclesiastical point of view, down to c. 1244, with later additions (to 1254). It is divided into 31 books and 3793 chapters. In 1244 Vincent wrote a briefer history, Memoriale omnium temporum (in 80 chapters), which was incorporated in the larger work. This Speculum was soon translated into Flemish by Jacob van Maerlant.

(The Speculum morale, composed by an unknown author between 1310 and 1325, is divided into 3 books and 381 sections. It deals with such subjects as passions and virtues, the incarnation and sufferings of Christ, death, purgatory, last judgment, resurrection, hell, paradise, sins, penitence.)

Vincent's fame is based upon his Speculum maius, which is in spite of its mediocrity one of the greatest monuments of learning of the Middle Ages. However he wrote a number of other treatises dealing with theological and religious questions and with education. Two of these may be quoted. The De eruditione filiorum regalium was written for Marguerite of Provence, wife of St. Louis, soon after the latter's return from the Crusade, between 1254 and 1260. It is a treatise on education in 51 chapters; one section deals with physical education. The Tractatus consolatorius de morte amici was addressed to St. Louis, c. 1260, when the latter had lost one of his children.

Text—The whole Speculum maius, including the Speculum morale, was printed for the first time by Joh. Mentelin in Strassburg, 1473–1476, this being the largest incunabula known; it consists of seven enormous folio volumes, often bound in ten. There has been some discussion apropos of the exact dates of the parts of this edition. See John Ferguson: Account of a copy of the first edition of the Speculum majus, 1473 (Transactions of the Archeological society of Glasgow, 1884; reprint, 25 p., 1885). Later editions: Nuremberg 1483–1486; Venice 1484, 1493–1494, 1591; by the Benedictines of Douai, 1624. There are also separate editions of the parts. French translation of Speculum historiale, printed 1495–1496.

The Tractatus consolatorius and the De eruditione filiorum regalium are included in the Opuscula (1 vol. folio, Basel 1484). The latter treatise was translated into German by Chr. Fr. Schlosser (Francfurt 1819).

The Catalan treatise on falconry "Libre dell nudriment he de la cura dels ocels los quals sepertãye ha cassa" was edited by Nicholas Rigault, librarian to Louis XIII: Ierakosophion. Rei accipitrariae scriptores (183–200, Paris 1612).

General criticism—Jacques Echard: Scriptores ordinis praedicatorum (1719–1721). P. C. F. Daunou: Histoire littéraire de la France (vol. 18, 449–519, 1835). Potthast (1095, 1896).

J. B. Bourgeat: Etudes sur Vincent (240 p., Paris 1856). Emile Mâle: L'art religieux du XIIIe siècle en France (4th ed., Paris 1919). As there are very striking analogies between the general economy of the Speculum majus and of the ornamentation of medieval cathedrals, chiefly that of Chartres, the author has modeled the plan of his book upon that of Vincent's encyclopaedia. He explains this is his second chapter. Lynn Thorndike: History of magic (vol. 2, 457–476, 1923). C. Oursel: Un exemplaire du Speculum majus provenant de la bibliothèque de Saint Louis (Bibliothèque de l'Ecole des chartes, vol. 85, 251–262, 1924).

Scientific criticism—E. H. F. Meyer: Geschichte der Botanik (vol. 3, 96–106, 1857). J. E. Harting: Bibliotheca accipitraria (110, 161, 175, London 1891). Alexis Rieunier: La médecine au moyen âge d'après le Speculum majus (Thèse, 60 p., Paris 1892). M. Berthelot: La chimie au moyen âge (vol. 1, 280–289, 1893). C. R. Beazley: Dawn of modern geography (3 vols., 1897–1906). Paul Diepgen: Traum und Traumdeutung (Berlin 1912). Ed. O. von Lippmann: Zur Geschichte der Verlötung von Bleirohren (Abhandlungen und Vorträge, vol. 2, 228–229, 1913; also Chemiker Z., 437, 1912). Apropos of a passage of the Speculum naturale, Bk. 8, of which Berthelot had spoken incorrectly as an example of autogenic soldering. P. Duhem: Etudes sur Léonard de Vinci (vol. 2, 318–319, 1909, mineralogy and geology); Système du monde (vol. 3, 346–348, 1915, astronomy). Fritz Jäger: Zahnärztliches aus den Werken Alberts des Grossen und seiner Schüler (Diss., 63 p., Leipzig 1921; superficial). F. S. Bodenheimer: Materialien zur Geschichte der Entomologie (vol. 1, 177–178, 1928; Isis, 13, 388). Robert Steele: Practical chemistry in the twelfth century. Rasis de aluminibus et salibus (Isis, 12, 10–46, 1929).

Philosophic and literary criticism—E. Boutaric: Vincent et la connaissance de l'antiquité classique au treizième siècle (Revue des questions historiques, vol. 17, 5–57, 1875). Richard Friedrich: Vincentius als Pädagog nach seiner Schrift De eruditione filiorum regalium (Diss., 44 p., Leipzig 1883). Ludwig Lieser: Vincenz als Kompilator und Philosoph. Eine Untersuchung seiner Seelenlehre im Speculum maius (Forschungen zur Geschichte der Philosophie und der Pädagogik, vol. 3, 214 p., Leipzig 1928).

JOHN OF MEUNG

Jean de Meun, or Meung. His original name was Jean Clopinel, or Chopinel. Born at Meung-sur-Loire, near Orléans, about the middle of the century; studied at the university of Paris and spent there the greatest part of his life; he died in 1305. French poet and encyclopaedist; translator from Latin into French.

He completed, c. 1268–1285 (before 1280?) the Roman de la Rose, which is one of the greatest poems of European literature.[18] The first part (4669 lines) had been written by William of Lorris[19] in the first third of the century; this is a literary work of considerable value but which does not concern us. John edited William's poem and composed an immense continuation (18,148 lines), which is of an entirely different nature: William was primarily a troubadour, writing for lords and ladies; John is primarily a satirist, a moralist, an encyclopaedist, writing for "bourgeois" like himself, despising women. Indeed these two poets represent two opposite poles of human thought, two opposite types of society; William, the past, John, the future. John's work, like that of his Flemish contemporary, Jacob van Maerlant, is a reaction against the artificiality of troubadour poetry, a sound revulsion from the conventionalities of chivalric courtesy; it is anticlerical, radical, naturalistic, somewhat cynical. To meet the demands of a new literary public, the rising class of burghers and artisans, and satisfy their growing need of information, it contains a summary of the knowledge generally available in those days; it is thus of considerable interest to the historian of thought. This knowledge was derived from the Latin translations of Plato, Aristotle, Ptolemy; from classical Latin literature in general (except Tacitus; it cannot be proved that he knew Lucretius); and from such authors as St. Augustine, Macrobius, Boetius, Alan of Lille, John of Salisbury, Roger Bacon, etc. Some 12000 lines of his poem (i.e., two-thirds of the whole) can be traced back to their sources; not less than 2000 lines to Ovid alone.

John of Meung translated into French Vegetius' De re militari (1284); the letters of Abaelard and Heloïse; the marvels of Ireland by Gerald the Welshman; Boetius' Consolation.

The translation of Boetius' Consolation is of particular importance. By the way this was the first great philosophical work of antiquity[20] to be fully translated into any vernacular, for we have an Anglo Saxon version of it by King Alfred the Great (second half of the ninth century). A Provençal translation was made at the end of the eleventh century (only the first 257 verses extant). Nor was John of Meung the first to Frenchify it.

There are three French versions anterior to his. The earliest of all was by

[18] This romance of the Rose should not be confused with an earlier one, Guillaume de Dôle ou la Rose, composed c. 1210, by Jean Renart. Ch. V. Langlois: La vie en France au Moyen âge d'après des romans mondains (2d ed., 72–106, Paris 1926).

[19] Lorris is in the same "pays" as Meung; Meung is SW of Orléans; Lorris is E of Orléans, nearer to Montargis.

[20] One may object to extending antiquity to Boetius' time, but his Consolation was in fact a mirror of ancient thought.

Simund de Freine,[21] canon of Hereford, friend of Gerald the Welshman, chaplain to the king of England in 1184. Simund's best known work, Speculum ecclesie, published in 1216, was very much discussed; but before that, possibly before the end of the twelfth century, he had written the Roman de philosophie, not a translation, but an abbreviated and simplified paraphrase of the Consolation. The first translation proper is anonymous and dates from the first half of the thirteenth century; another anonymous translation in Walloon dialect was probably made after the first anonymous and before John of Meung's.

To return to John, a paraphrase of a part of the Consolation was already included in his Roman de la rose. After the completion of that great work he seems to have devoted all of his time to prose translations into French. His translation of the Consolation, dedicated to Philippe le Bel, was apparently his last work; thus it may possibly belong to the first years of the fourteenth century. John's version was not the last mediaeval one: at least a dozen French versions and paraphrases appeared within a century and a half; and nothing could prove better the deep interest aroused in France by Boetius' noble book.

Alchemical writings ascribed to John of Meung are probably apocryphal.

Text—Le rommant de la rose, printed at Paris by Nicholas des Prez (1500? or before). The edition printed at Paris by Jehan du pré, c. 1495, was reprinted in 1878. Best edition by Ernest Langlois (5 vols., Société des anciens textes français, Paris 1914–1926). Translation in modern French by André Mary (Paris 1928).

Partial English translation, ascribed to Chaucer. The Romaunt of the Rose, from the unique Glasgow MS., parallel with its original, edited by Max Kaluza (Chaucer Society, publ. 83, London 1891). English translation by Frederick Startridge Ellis (3 vols., London 1900).

German translation by Heinrich Fährmann (facsimile edition folio, Wien 1921).

L'art de chevalerie, traduction du De re militari de Végèce, publié avec une étude sur cette traduction et sur Li abrejance de l'ordre de chevalerie de Jean Priorat (from Besançon, second half of the thirteenth century) par Ulysse Robert (Société des anciens textes français, 260 p., Paris 1897).

For the alchemical writings ascribed to Jean de Meung see John Ferguson: Bibliotheca chemica (vol. 2, 434, 1906).

Criticism. Generalities, and Roman de la Rose—Paulin Paris: Histoire littéraire de la France (vol. 23, 1–61, 1856; vol. 28, 391–439, 1881).

Felix Guillon: Jean Clopinel, le Roman de la Rose considéré comme document historique du règne de Philippe le Bel (235 p., Paris 1903). Francis William Bourdillon: The early editions of the Roman de la rose (Bibliographical Society, 232 p., London 1906). Luigi Foscolo Benedetto: Per la cronologia del Roman de la rose (Atti R. Accad. di Torino, vol. 44, 471–487, 1909); Il Roman de la rose e la letteratura italiana (259 p., Halle 1910). Charles Frederick Ward: The epistles on the Romance of the Rose and other documents (Thesis, 117 p., Chicago 1911; summary in Proc. R. Society of Canada, vol. 4, 191–204, 1911). Alfred Kuhn: Die Illustration des Rosenromans (Jahrbuch d. kunsthist. Samml. des Kaiserhauses, vol. 31, 1–66, 15 pl., Wien 1912). Dean Spruill Fansler: Chaucer and the Roman de la Rose (Columbia thesis, 270 p., New York 1914). Karl R. von Ettmayer: Der Rosenroman (Heidelberg 1919). L. Thuasne: Le roman de la rose (162 p., Paris 1929).

Translation of Boetius—Ernest Langlois: La traduction de Boèce (Romania, vol. 42, 331–369, Paris 1913). John Livingston Lowes: Chaucer's Boethius and Jean

[21] Alias Simon du Fresne, Fraxinetus or Ash. Miss M. Bateson: Dictionary of national biography (vol. 52, 263, 1897).

de Meun (Romanic Review, vol. 8, 383–400, New York 1917). Ch. V. Langlois: La vie spirituelle (La vie en France au moyen âge, vol. 4, 269–326, 1928). Contains analyses of, and extracts from, Simund de Freine's Roman de philosophie, John of Meung's paraphrase in the Roman de la Rose and translation, and a later translation.

Scientific criticism—Edmund O. von Lippmann: Alchemistische Poesie aus dem 13. Jahrhundert (Chemiker Z., 323–324, 1905; reprinted in his Abhandlungen und Vorträge, vol. 1, 103–109, 1926); Entstehung und Ausbreitung der Alchemie (500–503, 1919).

PETRUS DE TRABIBUS

French Franciscan who flourished toward the end of the century; disciple of Olivi (d. 1298). He wrote a commentary on the first two books of Peter Lombard's Sentences. He defended the theory of the plurality of forms against the Thomist doctrine of unity.

Ephrem Longpré: Pietro de Trabibus, un discepolo di Pier Giovanni Olivi (Studi francescani, già la Verna, anno 8 (19), 267–290, Arezzo 1922). Bernhard Jansen: Petrus de Trabibus. Seine spekulative Eigenart oder sein Verhältnis zu Olivi (Beiträge zur Geschichte der Philosophie des Mittelalters, Suppl. Bd. 2, 243–254, 1923). M. De Wulf: History of mediaeval philosophy (vol. 1, 387; vol. 2, 75, 1926).

For Robert of Sorbon, see chapter on education; for Peter Olivi, the physical chapter; for Armengaud son of Blaise, the chapter on translators; for Peter of Auvergne, the one on law.

ALBERT THE GREAT

Contents: (1) Life and thought. (2) Dates of Albert's scientific activity. (3) Aristotelian commentaries. (4) Mathematics and astronomy. (5) Chemistry, alchemy. (6) Meteorology and climatology. (7) Geology and mineralogy. (8) Botany. (9) Zoology. (10) Anatomy and medicine. (11) Apocryphal writings: the legendary Albert.

(12) Text. Collected editions. (13) Special editions. (14) Biography and general criticism. (15) Chronology. (16) Special criticism. (17) Science in general. (18) Philosophy. (19) Psychology.

1. *Life and thought*—Albertus Magnus, Doctor Universalis; Albrecht von Bollstädt. Born in 1193 (or 1195?, 1206–1207?) in Lauingen, Suabia; studied in Padova, assumed the Dominican habit in 1223; from 1228 on he taught in various Dominican schools of Germany; from 1245 to 1248 in Paris; from 1248 to 1254 in Cologne; in 1254 appointed provincial of the German province of his Order; in 1256 he was sent to the papal court to defend the teaching privileges of his Order against the University of Paris; bishop of Ratisbon from 1260 to 1262, when he returned to Cologne which became his habitual residence (his contemporaries called him Coloniensis); he died there on November 15, 1280.

Dominican philosopher, theologian and teacher. One of the most learned men of the Middle Ages. He knew neither Greek nor Arabic, but by his time the majority of Aristotelian, pseudo-Aristotelian and neo-Platonic works were already available in Latin; he had made a deep study of Aristotle, of the Timaeus, of the Liber de causis, of the Muslim philosophers. He wrote a series of encyclopaedic treatises dealing with almost every question of theology, philosophy, and natural science (but not mathematics), and of such comprehensiveness and mass that they constituted a real library.

Much of Albert's energy was spent in teaching or in organizing teaching. The overwhelming mass of his writings, together with the prestige accruing to him because of his teaching and of the high positions held by him, caused him to obtain considerable fame very early, even during his own lifetime. His activity seemed nothing short of miraculous. He was put on the same level as the very greatest. Bacon, who disliked him, said (Opus tertium, ed. J. S. Brewer, p. 30, 1859): "Nam sicut Aristoteles, Avicenna et Averroës allegantur in scholis, sic et ipse: et adhuc vivit et habuit in vita sua auctoritatem, quod nunquam homo habuit in doctrina." His influence was rapid and immense, but it could not last very long nor be very deep, because his work was too eclectic and too superficial. Thomas Aquinas and probably Thomas of Cantimpré attended his lectures, but he founded no school, the very impurity of his thought precluding this. His writings remained for centuries a treasury of information, wherein each philosopher, whether Thomist, or neo-Platonist, or otherwise, took what he needed; they never became authoritative in another way.

His philosophical and scientific works are based primarily upon Aristotle, but neither exclusively nor slavishly; they constitute a sort of paraphrase of Aristotle's writings containing abundant interpolations derived from Muslim and Jewish philosophy, various other sources, and even personal observation. Among the commentators he followed mainly al-Fārābī and Ibn Sīnā, and disagreed generally with Ibn Gabirol (whom he thought was a Christian anti-Aristotelian) and Ibn Rushd. He leaned heavily upon Maimonides, yet preserving his independence. In 1256, while he was at the papal residence in Anagni, he wrote at the request of Pope Alexander IV (1254–1261) a work against Averroism, De unitate intellectus contra Averroem; this is interesting because it shows that Averroism was then already sufficiently spread in the Latin schools to be considered dangerous. It is difficult to define his philosophy, because it is unsystematic, lacks precision, and involves many inconsistencies. Besides his efforts to reconcile his theories with Christian orthodoxy, he was always ready to include fresh information, whatever its source; he realized that scientific knowledge cannot be attained without investigation; he even recognized to a small extent the value of experimentalism; yet he was often uncritical and awed by his authorities. In spite of many original judgments, his immense work is thus not a real encyclopaedia, an organic synthesis, but a compilation; it does credit to his enormous energy and his intelligence, but it is not a true creation and does not constitute in itself a real intellectual progress.[22] Albert's main merit perhaps is to have contributed powerfully to the integration of Aristotelian knowledge into Latin culture. Unfortunately the knowledge thus transmitted was far from pure; it contained many neo-Platonic and other heterogeneous elements, and thus entailed misunderstandings similar to those of which Muslim philosophers had been the victims centuries before. To complete this account of Albert's general activity, we may add that in 1259 he was at Valenciennes, engaged in drawing up a new plan of studies for the Dominican Order; in this he was helped by Thomas Aquinas and Peter of Tarentaise.[23] The year before his

[22] Albert's works were very convenient and they stimulated scholarship and even scientific investigation; thus they contributed to the progress of science externally rather than internally (see Isis, I, 195).

[23] Peter of Tarentaise or Champagny (in Tarentaise, duchy of Savoy). Born c. 1225. Archbishop of Lyon, 1271. Pope for half a year in the year of his death, 1276, under the name of Innocent V. The first Dominican pope.

death he traveled to Paris to defend Thomas Aquinas, whose doctrines had been condemned by Stephen Tempier (1277).

He had the courage to reject some superstitious ideas (see examples in the zoological section), but he continued to believe in many others, and his writings are not deficient in "marvels" of the usual mediaeval type. This simply illustrates how difficult it is to eschew immemorial beliefs; only a few can be shaken off at a time.

As compared with St. Thomas, Albert was a weaker theologian and philosopher but a better scientist. Indeed he was the greatest naturalist of the Latin Middle Ages, the greatest between Pliny and the sixteenth century. Thanks to his scientific curiosity, he was to some extent comparable to his Franciscan contemporaries, Robert Grosseteste and Roger Bacon.

2. *Dates of Albert's scientific activity*—Albert's activity can be divided into three periods. During the period of youth he wrote a theological work entitled Summa de creaturis, and later, commentaries on the Sentences of Peter the Lombard (Bk. II, 1246; Bk. IV, 1249); the period of maturity was devoted to his paraphrases of Aristotle; during the third period his energy was largely absorbed by administrative duties; in 1270 he began the writing of his Summa theologica (unfinished). It is the middle period which interests us most: it began c. 1245–1248 and ended c. 1254–1260. By 1256 his scientific works were already composed, but he continued to improve them until c. 1274. In 1258 he lectured at Cologne on the De animalibus.

3. *Aristotelian commentaries*—Albert's scientific works were in the form of commentaries on or paraphrases of Aristotle. He did, or tried to do, for Christendom what Ibn Rushd had done for Islām, but he was very inferior intellectually to his Muslim predecessor, even as he was to his Jewish one, Maimonides; yet he was superior to both in his keener appreciation of the concrete facts of natural history.

I quote these commentaries, and a few other treatises closely related to them, as they were published by Father Jammy (1651) and later by Borgnet (1890–1899): De praedicabilibus liber I, De decem praedicamentis lib. 1, De sex principiis (i.e., Gilberti Porretani) lib. 1, De interpretatione lib. 2, De syllogismo simpliciter, id est, priorum analyticorum lib. 2, De demonstratione, id est, posteriorum analyticorum lib. 2, Topicorum lib. 8, De sophisticis elenchis lib. 2.

De physico auditu lib. 8 (i.e., physicorum lib. 8), De coelo et mundo lib. 4, De generatione et corruptione lib. 2, De meteoris lib. 4.

De anima lib. 3. A Hebrew translation of this commentary was begun but not completed by Leone Romano (first half of the fourteenth century).

Metaphysicorum lib. 13, Ethicorum lib. 10, Politicorum lib. 8.

Parva naturalia, sive De sensu et sensato lib. 1, De memoria et reminiscentia lib. 1, De somno et vigilia lib. 1, De motibus animalium lib. 2, De aetate sive de iuventute et senectute lib. 1, De spiritu et respiratione lib. 2, De morte et vita lib. 1, De nutrimento et nutribili lib. 1, De natura et origine animae lib. 1, De unitate intellectus contra Averroem lib. 1, De intellectu et intelligibili lib. 2, De natura locorum lib. 1 (i.e., geography, climatology). De causis proprietatum elementorum lib. 1, De passionibus aëris lib. 1, De principiis motus progressivi lib. 1.

De mineralibus lib. 5, De vegetabilibus et plantis lib. 7, De animalibus lib. 26.

To these commentaries might be added the two following, in spite of the fact that the former is far more neo-Platonic than Aristotelian, and that the latter is probably apocryphal.

De processu universitatis a causa prima lib. 1.

Philosophia pauperum, sive isagoge in libros Aristotelis de physico auditu, de coelo et mundo, de generatione et corruptione, de meteoris, et de anima. As the subtitle indicates, this is a general summary of Aristotelian physics.

4. *Mathematics and astronomy*—Albert had some interest in Pythagorean arithmetic but he was not a mathematician; much less so than Roger Bacon, who was at least able to appreciate the importance of the mathematical point of view. For this reason alone, he could not be a genuine encyclopaedist.

He observed a comet in 1240. His astronomical ideas were very poor; he was responsible for the diffusion of al-Biṭrūjī's theory in an absurdly simplified form; he finally accepted the Ptolemaic system.

Naturally he was much interested in astrology, and like all of his contemporaries believed in its validity. This is true whether the Speculum astronomiae is considered one of his works or is ascribed to Bacon. Besides the Speculum many arithmetical and astronomical treatises are ascribed to him, but these ascriptions are very doubtful (see Borgnet's edition, vol. 1, p. LVI, etc., 1890).

M. Steinschneider: Zum Speculum astronomiae des Albertus, über die darin angeführten Schriftsteller und Schriften (Z. für Mathematik, vol. 14, 357–396, 1871). P. Duhem: Etudes sur Léonard de Vinci (vol. 2, 64, 1909, on gravity); Système du monde (vol. 3, 327–345, 1915, astronomy; vol. 5, 412–467, 1917, philosophy). Lynn Thorndike: History of magic (vol. 2, 692–717, 1923). On the Speculum, with a list of MSS., defending the traditional ascription to Albert against Mandonnet who would attribute it to Bacon. According to Thorndike, the Speculum was written by Albert before 1277, when Averroism was condemned by the bishop of Paris, and perhaps even before 1256.

5. *Chemistry, alchemy*—The De mineralibus contains the description of various chemical substances (vitriol, alum, arsenic, etc.). It is difficult to appreciate his views on chemistry and alchemy, as we are not sure that the Libellus de alchimia, the least spurious of the alchemical writings ascribed to him, is authentic. But assuming it to be so, his chemical knowledge was not very advanced; it was on the level of Arabic knowledge before Ibn Sīnā. In the De minerabilibus (III, 9) he admits the theoretical possibility of the transmutation of metals, but remarks that gold obtained by alchemical means is not real gold (this is typical of Albert's eclectic and compromising manner).

The Libellus de alchimia is included in Jammy's Opera; also in Borgnet's (vol. 37, 545–573, 1898).

M. Berthelot: La chimie au moyen âge (vol. 1, 290–293, 1893). John Ferguson: Bibliotheca chemica (vol. 1, 15–17, 1906). L. de Launay: Un alchimiste du XIIIe siècle (Revue scientifique, 1913). H. Stadler: Über die erste Kohlenoxydvergiftung (Mit. zur Gesch. der Medizin, vol. 9, 102, 1910). Apropos of cases of death due to asphyxiation or to poisoning by carbon monoxide in De sensu et sensato (2, 13). E. O. v. Lippmann: Entstehung der Alchemie (vol. 1, 490–492, 1919; vol. 2, 8, 1931). E. J. Holmyard: Chemistry to the time of Dalton (34–36, 1925). Julius Ruska: Tabula smaragdina (Heidelberg, 1926; Isis, 9, 375–377). Fritz Paneth: Über eine alchemistische Handschrift des 14. Jahrhunderts und ihr Verhältnis zu Albertus Magnus' Buch De mineralibus (Archiv für Gesch. der Mathematik, vol. 12, 33–45, 1929; Isis, 13, 433); Über die Schrift Alberts des Grossen De alchimia (ibidem, vol. 12, 408–413, 1930; Isis, 15, 409). See my note on Petros Theoctonicos.

6. *Meteorology and climatology*—Albert's views on meteorology were simply a clear summary of those transmitted by the Muslims. Description of lunar rainbow. The De natura locorum is a treatise on climatology. It was edited by the Viennese humanist, Georg Tannstetter, alias Collimitius (d. 1535): Vienna 1514, Strassburg 1515.

Theodor Schmitt: Die Meteorologie und Klimatologie des Albertus Magnus (Diss., 116 p., Munich 1909).

7. *Geology and mineralogy*—The De mineralibus contains the description of some 95 precious stones or minerals. The notes devoted to them are based to some extent upon direct observations. Albert did not fear visiting loca metallica or alchemical laboratories. However the main substance was derived from Marbode, Thomas of Cantimpré, and Arnold the Saxon.

Albert's commentaries on the pseudo-Aristotelian De causis et proprietatibus elementorum, and on Aristotle's meteorology, contain his geological views, which are not at all new, on the movements of the sea, on erosion, on the generation of mountains, etc.; but he adds some new observations—e.g., about the withdrawal of the sea from Bruges. He claims that this withdrawal is purely accidental and temporary, not due to any astral influence. His main source besides the treatises commented upon were Theophrastos, the De mondo ascribed to Philon, Ovid's Metamorphoses, and above all Ibn Sīnā's De congelatione et conglutinatione lapidum (i.e., Liber de mineralibus Aristotelis). Albert's geology was essentially Plutonian; that is, he attached far more importance to eruptive motions than to the action of water. He minimized the displacements of the ocean with regard to the land areas, but did not deny them altogether, and explained by their means the presence of fossil shells in rocks.

P. Duhem: Etudes sur Léonard de Vinci (vol. 2, 309-317, 1909).

8. *Botany*—The De vegetabilibus based on Nicolaos Damascenos, Pliny, Palladius, etc., contains many novelties. We find in it rudiments of botanical geography, allusions to the relationship between galls and insects, studies of seeds and recognition of the embryo within.

A critical edition of the De vegetabilibus libri VII was begun by Ernest Meyer, and completed by Karl Jessen (804 p., Berlin 1867), with introduction and copious index.

Ernst Meyer: Geschichte der Botanik (vol. 4, 9-84, 1857); Albert der Grosse (Deutsches Museum, Nos. 38-39, 1858). Stephan Fellner: Albertus als Botaniker (Progr., Wien 1881). G. Wimmer: Deutsches Pflanzenleben nach Albertus (75 p., Halle a. S., 1908). Hermann Fischer: Mittelalterliche Pflanzenkunde (34-42, 157, etc., München 1929; Isis, 15, 367).

9. *Zoology*—The best parts of Albert's work were the botanical and zoological books. The zoology was based upon Michael Scot. It is divided into 26 books, of which the first nineteen are a paraphrase of Aristotle's three treatises. Books 20 to 26 contain new matter partly derived from personal observations or from direct information. Books 20 and 21 deal with generalities; book 20, with the nature of animals' bodies, their structure and forces; book 21, with perfect and imperfect animals, and the causes of their perfection or imperfection (this is a kind of comparative animal psychology). Books 22 to 26 are devoted to the description of

individual animals, these being introduced in each chapter in the alphabetical order of their Latin names. These books were a sort of appendix to the De natura rerum of Thomas of Cantimpré, who had sat at his feet in Cologne. Book 22: man, gressibilia (i.e., quadrupeds; our mammals, excepting bats, whales and seals); book 23: volatilia (i.e., birds and bats); book 24; aquatica or natatilia (i.e., fishes, whales, seals, cephalopods, shellfishes, water snails, and other aquatic animals); book 25: serpents (i.e., snakes, lizards, salamanders), including the varieties of snakes discussed in Ibn Sīnā's Qānūn; book 26: vermes (i.e., worms, insects, toads, frogs, landsnails). Many of these animals were here described for the first time.

Albert was undoubtedly a good observer but a poor theorist; he did not hesitate to introduce new facts, but his theories were slavishly derived from Aristotle or from Ibn Sīnā. He had had and improved many opportunities of observing things in the course of his long travels as provincial of his Order (the Dominican rule obliged him to travel afoot). He observed animals in the Danube region, in the vicinity of Cologne, Augsburg, Worms, Treves, in Friesland, Holland, Brabant, Italy; he studied the marine fauna of the North Sea (. . . . . experimenti causa navigans et exiens ad insulas et harenas manibus collegit, Book IV, 3). He also collected information from the many people of all classes he came across in the course of his missions.

While Bartholomew the Englishman quoted a great many authorities (105), Albert quoted only a few of them and often in disparagement. Besides Aristotle and Ibn Sīnā, the authors most often quoted in his De animalibus were Homer, Plato, Theophrastos, Pliny, Polemon, Galen, Solinus, al-Rāzī, Constantine the African, Ibn Rushd, the unknown Jew Jorach (Yorah?), etc.

He dealt with animals living in northern climates, and Cetacea. He gave a detailed description of whaling and walrus hunting; much space was devoted to the diseases of horses and of falcons, his knowledge of the latter being largely derived from Frederick II. He repeated many of Aristotle's errors and sometimes aggravated them; he confused bats with birds, and whales with fishes. On the other hand, he did not hesitate to reject many old superstitions; e.g., the notion of griffin, the pelican feeding its young with its own blood, the beaver's auto-castration, the incombustibility of the salamander, the birth of barnacle geese from trees, the self-combustion and resurrection of the phoenix, symbolizing the resurrection of Christ—in short, most of the fables which belong to the Physiologus tradition and had such immense vogue in mediaeval times. Like Ibn Sīnā, he considered fossils as petrified animals.

In brief, his zoology was essentially an Aristotelian renaissance, but it was more, for it contained many interesting observations; although many of these were incorrect, it marked a new beginning. In spite of the fact that Albert was not a true and pure naturalist, we may say that he was the foremost naturalist of the Middle Ages.

De animalibus libri XXVI nach der Cölner Urschrift herausgegeben von Hermann Stadler (Beitr. zur Gesch. der Philosophie des Mittelalters, vol. 15–16, 1712 p., Münster i. W., 1916–1920). This edition is based on a Cologne MS. which is probably the author's original! The first 19 books of this work are a paraphrase of Michael Scot's translation of Aristotle (historia animalium 10, de partibus animalium 4, de generatione animalium 5); books 20 and 21 deal with philosophic questions (de natura corporum animalium; de perfectis et imperfectis animalibus et causa perfectionis et imperfectionis); books 22–26 are devoted chiefly to the study of a large number of animals (113 quadrupeds, 114 birds, a long digression dealing with falconry, 139 "aquatic animals," 61 "serpents," 49 "worms"). Albertus' commentary is carefully distinguished throughout from his quotations by Stadler's marks. This remarkable edition is completed by elaborate indexes, notably one of the authors quoted by Albertus, and two others enumerating the words of Germanic and Arabic origin.

Partial German translation by Heinrich Mynsinger (fl. 1421–1465): Von den Falken, Pferden und Hunden. Edited by K. D. Hassler (100 p., Stuttgart 1863).

For criticism of the Latin editions see H. Stadler: Vorbemerkungen zur neuen Ausgabe der Tiergeschichte (Sitzungsber. der Bayer. Ak. der Wiss., Phil. Kl., 58 p., 3 pl., 1912); Zur Charakteristik der gangbarsten Ausgaben der Tiergeschichte (Archiv für Geschichte der Naturwiss, vol. 3, 465–474, 1912).

E. von Martens: Über die von Albertus Magnus erwähnten Landsäugethiere (Archiv für Naturgeschichte, vol. 24, 123–144, 1858). C. Jessen: Alberti historia animalium (Archiv für Naturgeschichte, vol. 33, 95–105, 1867). James Edmund Harting: Bibliotheca accipitraria (London 1891). H. Stadler: Geschichtlich-zoologische Studien über De animalibus (Mit. zur Geschichte der Medizin, vol. 6, 249–254, 1907); Albertus als Naturforscher und das Cölner Autogram seiner Tiergeschichte (Verhdl. der Gesellschaft deutscher Naturforscher, 80. Vers., 1, 29–37, 1909). Seb. Killermann: Die Vogelkunde des Albertus (106 p., Regensburg 1910; reviewed by Stadler in the Mit. zur Gesch. d. Med., vol. 10, 166–170, 1911). Fridtjof Nansen: In northern mists (vol. 2, 163, 1911). Franz Pelster: Alberts des Grossen neu aufgefundene Quaestionen zu De animalibus (Zeitschrift für katholische Theologie, vol. 4, 332–334, 1922). Questions collected by a student, Conrad of Austria, in 1258, when Albert was lecturing on the subject. Maurice Caullery: Histoire des sciences biologiques (23, 1924). Edward Heron-Allen: Barnacles in nature and myth (15, 1928; Isis, 12, 340). F. S. Bodenheimer: Materialien zur Geschichte der Entomologie (vol. 1, 170–177, 1928; Isis, 13, 388–392). Heinrich Balss: Albertus Magnus als Zoologe (Münchener Beiträge, Heft 11–12, 157 p., München 1928; Isis, 15, 213). G. Sarton: Jorach (Isis, 15, 171, 1931).

10. *Anatomy and medicine*—The anatomical part of the De animalibus is very similar to the Anatomia vivorum ascribed to Richard of Wendover (first half of the thirteenth century). This applies chiefly to the anatomical comparison between Aristotle and Galen almost equivalent in both texts, and concluding in both cases in Aristotle's favor. Albert must have used the Anatomia vivorum or the translation of Ibn Sīnā's Qānūn by Gerard of Cremona. He had no personal knowledge of anatomy, except the skeleton. After having surveyed human anatomy he quotes many facts of comparative anatomy, the organs of various animals being compared with those of man.

A number of medical works ascribed to Albert are of very doubtful authenticity; Liber de medicina; Experimenta medica; De secretis super Henricum de Saxonia de formato faetu (this Henry is said to have been Albert's disciple); De secretis naturae. Some of these titles cover probably different editions of the Secreta mulierum.

A treatise entitled in Hebrew She'elot u-teshubot (Questions and answers), dealing with the six natural things the body requires according to medical science, is also ascribed to "Albertus." It was translated into Hebrew by Moses ibn Shem-ṭob ibn Ḥabib of Lisbon (died at the beginning of the sixteenth century).[24]

Léon Moulé: La médecine vétérinaire en Europe au moyen âge (56–59, Paris 1900). Fritz Jäger: Zahnärztliches aus den Werken Alberts und seiner Schüler

[24] Samuel Poznanski: Jewish encyclopaedia (vol. 6, 125, 1904).

Thomas von Chantimpré und Vincenz von Beauvais (Diss., 64 p., Leipzig 1921; superficial).

11. *Apocryphal writings. The legendary Albert*—Various writings of uncertain authenticity have already been mentioned, but the apocrypha deserve to be considered separately, chiefly because Albert's popular fame was based upon two of these far more solidly than upon his own publications. In the introduction to Borgnet's edition (1890) no less than 112 apocryphal works are quoted.

The two best known of these works—indeed far better known than the authentic publications—are the Liber aggregationis, seu secretorum de virtutibus herbarum, lapidum et animalium quorundam, dealing with the magic properties of plants, stones, and animals; and the Secreta mulierum et virorum, dealing with astrological influences during pregnancy or menstruation, astrological superstitions, etc. Though Albert's own writings are not by any means free of them, much space is devoted in these apocrypha to other pseudo-sciences, such as oneirology and physiognomy, which were more and more deeply involved with astrology. It was chiefly on account of these two works that Albert obtained his extraordinary fame as a magician, that "ars albertina" came to mean magic, and that chap-books on "the white and black art of man and beast" are still being peddled under his name.

Many of these apocrypha are of a purely philosophic, theologic, or scientific nature, the most notable of these being the Philosophia pauperum (or Summa philosophiae naturalis, etc.), a summary of Aristotelian physics. This was a very popular text-book for a considerable time. Whether it was the work of our Albert, or of a contemporary, Albert of Orlamünde, or of another author is uncertain. It was translated into Hebrew under the title Qiẓẓur ha-filosofia ha-ṭib'yat (Summary of natural philosophy) by Abraham Shalom ben Isaac (d. 1492).

Lynn Thorndike: History of magic (vol. 2, 720–750, 1923). Including lists of MSS. of the Experiments or Secrets and of the De secretis mulierum. Ernest Wickersheimer: Henri de Saxe et le De secretis mulierum (Communication faite au 3e Congrès de l'art de guérir, 8 p., Anvers 1923). Whatever was the part of Albert in the composition of that work, that of Henry of Saxony (second half of the fifteenth century) was exceedingly small (Isis, 7, 192). Martin Grabmann: Die Philosophia pauperum und ihr Verfasser Albert von Orlamünde (Beiträge zur Geschichte der Philosophie des Mittelalters, vol. 20, 2, 64 p., Münster 1918). Alexander Birkenmaier: Krakowskie wydania tak zwanej Philosophia pauperum Alberta Wielkiego (16 p., Cracow 1924; Isis, 7, 190). Claiming that Grabmann's ascription of the Philosophia pauperum to Albert of Orlamünde is unproved; the textual difficulties involved are considerable.

12. *Text. Collected editions*—There are two very large editions of Albert's Opera. The earliest prepared by the Dominican, Peter Jammy, Opera quae hactenus haberi potuerunt, appeared in Lyon, 1651 (21 folio volumes). Vols. 1 to 6 contain the Aristotelian commentaries; vols. 7 and 8, commentaries on the Old Testament; vols. 9 to 11, commentaries on the New Testament; vol. 12, sermons; vol. 13, commentaries on Dionysios Areopagites and the Compendium theologicae veritatis; vols. 14 to 16, commentaries on the Books of sentences of Peter the Lombard; vols. 17–18, Summa theologiae; vol. 19, Summa de creaturis; vol. 20, treatises on the Holy Virgin; vol. 21, miscellanea, including the Philosophia pauperum, and the De alchimia libellus. There is an index rerum memorabilium to the Parva naturalia in vol. 5.

The second edition was prepared by Auguste Borgnet, helped later by Emile

Borgnet, both priests: Opera omnia ex editione lugdunensi religiose castigata et pro auctoritatibus ad fidem vulgatae versionis accuratiorumque patrologiae textuum revocata, auctaque B. Alberti vita ac bibliographia operum a PP. Quétif et Echard exaratis, etiam revisa et locupletata (38 quarto volumes, published under the auspices of Leo XIII, Paris 1890–1899). A superficial comparison of these two enormous collections shows that they are not essentially different. Their contents are the same though the order is somewhat different. For example, the Philosophia pauperum instead of being put almost at the end is brought nearer to the Aristotelian commentaries, which is more logical. The index to the Parva naturalia is reprinted. The main novelty is the biographical and bibliographical introduction covering 66 pages. There is nothing to indicate that the last volume to be published, vol. 38, 1899, was really meant to be the last. The editors possibly planned to publish a few more treatises not included in the Lyon edition; as far as I could see, judging from the scientific writings alone, they did not accomplish their task as faithfully as their title suggested.

Paul M. de Loë: Commentarium in librum Boethium de divisione. First edition (90 p., 6 pl., Bonn 1913). Including Boetius' text.

13. *Special editions*—I shall deal only with the texts of special interest to our readers. For the incunabula I have followed the admirable bibliography included in the Gesamtkatalog der Wiegendrucke (vol. 1, 264–451, 1925) containing 313 items and covering 187 columns.

Logica, lib. 1, 2. De praedicabilibus et praedicamentis, Pavia c. 1490. Liber 3, De sex principiis, Pavia c. 1490. Logica, Venice 1494 (322 leaves).

Physica. Venice 1488–1489, 1494–1495.

De coelo et mundo. Venice (1480, 1488?), 1490, 1495.

De generatione et corruptione. Venice 1495.

De meteoris. Venice 1488, 1494–1495.

De mineralibus. Padua 1476, Pavia 1491, Venice 1495, Cologne 1499, Augsburg 1519, Strassburg 1541, Cologne 1569. Delle cose minerali e metalliche libri cinque tradutte da Pietro Lauro (Venice 1557–1558).

De anima. Venice 1481, 1494.

Metaphysica. Venice 1494.

Ethica et politica. Venice 1520.

De intellectu et intelligibili. Venice 1472–1473, Leipzig 1489–1496. Also with the De anima, 1481, 1494.

De natura locorum. Vienna 1514, Strassburg 1515, Naples 1592–1594.

Speculum astronomicum. Lyon 1615.

Parva naturalia, Venice 1517.

De animalibus. Rome 1478; Mantua 1479; Venice 1495, 1519. Separate edition of the Tractatus de falconibus, asturibus et accipitribus, extracted from book 23 (Augsburg 1596–1598). For Stadler's edition (Münster i. W., 1916–1920) see section on zoology. Idem for a modern edition of the De vegetabilibus see section on botany.

Philosophia pauperum. Also entitled Philosophia naturalis, Physica pauperum, Summa naturalium, Summa philosophiae naturalis. Toulouse c. 1480; Barcelona 1482; Lerida c. 1485; Brescia 1490, 1493; Venice 1496. Summary printed in Leipzig, 1496, 1499.

De duabus sapientiis et de recapitulatione omnium librorum astronomie, Nuremberg c. 1493–1496.

De mirabilibus mundi. Venice c. 1472 (two), c. 1473; Vicenza 1475–1482; Colle c. 1478. Apocryphal treatise often printed together with the following.

Liber aggregationis, seu secretorum de virtutibus herbarum, lapidum et animalium quorundam. Paris, s.a.; Cologne c. 1499–1500.

Liber aggregationis together with De mirabilibus mundi: Strassburg c. 1478;

Reutlingen c. 1483; Speyer c. 1483; Cologne c. 1485; Strassburg 1490; Leipzig 1492; Strassburg 1493; Augsburg 1496; Vienna c. 1500. Ferrara c. 1477; Bologna 1478; Rome, not before 1480; Rome c. 1481; Bologna 1482; Rome c. 1485; Venice, not before 1487; Rome c. 1490; Naples c. 1490, 1493. Paris c. 1483, Geneva c. 1487; Southern France c. 1490; Lyon (?) c. 1490; Paris c. 1490; Lyon c. 1491–1492; Paris c. 1493; Paris c. 1500. London c. 1485.

Liber aggregationis, together with De mirabilibus mundi and other writings, to wit:

(1) With Parvum regimen sanitatis. Antwerp c. 1488; Cologne, after 1500.

(2) With Quaestiones naturales philosophorum: Antwerp c. 1487; c. 1491; not before 1494; 1498, 1499.

(3) With the preceding and also with the Quaestiones naturales of Adelard of Bath. Antwerp c. 1488–1491.

Translations of the Liber aggregationis. In French: soon after 1500. In Italian: Bologna 1493, 1494; Milano 1495; Venice 1495, c. 1496; Rome, after 1500. In Catalan: Barcelona 1499.

Secreta mulierum et virorum. (1) Cum commento. Cologne c. 1475; Germany c. 1480; Ulm c. 1480; Cologne 1481; Ulm c. 1482; Speyer c. 1483; Strassburg c. 1483; Reutlingen c. 1488; Leipzig c. 1490; c. 1492, 1494; Augsburg, not before 1494; Speyer, not before 1495; Augsburg c. 1500; Leipzig 1500. Antwerp c. 1484, c. 1488; not before 1496; after 1500. London c. 1483–1485. Geneva, not before 1487; Lyon c. 1488; Paris c. 1488; Southern France c. 1490; Paris, not before 1490, c. 1491–1493, c. 1492, c. 1493–1496, c. 1495–1497, c. 1496, after 1498; Rouen, after 1500.

(2) Cum commento novo, Cologne c. 1490, c. 1495.

(3) With commentary by Henry of Saxony. Perugia c. 1477; Venice 1478; Augsburg 1489; Vienna 1500?; Rome 1499 (or Venice, after 1500).

14. *Biography and general criticism*—Rodolph of Nijmegen (Rudolphus de Novimagio): Legenda litteralis beati Alberti Magni (Cologne, s.a., 1484, 1490). Peter of Prussia: Vita beati Alberti Magni (Cologne 1486; etc.) Ludovicus Valleoletanus (Lewis of Valladolid): Vita Alberti (Catalogus codicum hagiographicorum Bibliothecae regiae bruxellensis, 2; Brussels, 95–105, 1889). Vita beati Alberti (Analecta bollandiana, vol. 19, 272–284, 1900; i.e., the Legenda coloniensis). P. de Loë: De vita et scriptis Alberti (Analecta bollandiana, vols. 19 to 21, 1900 to 1902). This includes an unpublished life of 1483.

Quétif and Echard: Scriptores ordinis praedicatorum (vol. 1, Paris 1719). M. Weiss: Primordia novae bibliographiae b. Alberti (Paris 1898). Potthast (1147, 1896).

Daunou: Histoire littéraire de la France (vol. 19, 362–381, 1838). Joachim Sighart: Albertus, sein Leben und seine Wissenschaft (402 p., illustr., Ratisbon 1857; Englished, London 1876). Octave d'Assailly: Albert le Grand (456 p., Paris 1870). Albertus in Geschichte und Sage. Festschrift zur sechsten Säkularfeier seines Todestages (172 p., Cologne 1880). Georg Friedrich v. Hertling: Albertus (2d much improved edition, 192, p., Beiträge zur Geschichte der Philosophie des Mittelalters, vol. 14, Münster 1914; 1st ed., 1880). Franz Pelster: Kritische Studien zum Leben und zu den Schriften Alberts des Grossen (Ergänzungshefte zu den Stimmen der Zeit, zweite Reihe, 4, 196 p., Freiburg i.B., 1920). Lynn Thorndike: History of magic (vol. 2, 517–592, 1923). S. Foster Damon: A portrait of Albertus Magnus (Speculum, vol. 5, 102, 1 pl., 1930).

15. *Chronology*—Joseph Anton Endres: Das Geburtsjahr und die Chronologie in der ersten Lebenshälfte (Hist. Jahrbuch, vol. 31, 293–304, 1910); Chronologische Untersuchungen zu den philosophischen Kommentaren Alberts des Grossen (Festgabe Hertling, 95–108, Freiburg 1913). F. Überweg und M. Baumgartner: Geschichte der Philosophie (vol. 2, 10th ed., 466, 1915).

16. *Special criticism*—Paget Toynbee: Dante's obligations to Albertus (Dante studies and researches, London 1902). Lynn Thorndike: Vatican Latin MSS. in the history of science (Isis, 13, 55, 57, 1929).

M. Steinschneider: Hebraeische Übersetzungen (465, 494, 776, 1893). J. Guttmann: Jewish encyclopaedia (vol. 1, 323–324, 1901). H. Rudy: Encyclopaedia judaica (vol. 2, 120–123, 1928).

17. *Science in general*—L. Choulant: Albertus in seiner Bedeutung für die Naturwissenschaften (Janus, vol. 1, 152, 1846). F. A. Pouchet: Histoire des sciences naturelles au Moyen âge, ou Albert le Grand et son époque considérés comme point de départ de l'école expérimentale (660 p., Paris 1853). Franz Prangerl (S. J.): Studien über Albert den Grossen (Z. für katholische Theologie, vol. 36, 304–346, 512–549, 784–800, 1912). Hermann Stadler: Irrtümer des Albertus bei Benutzung des Aristoteles (Archiv für Geschichte der Naturwiss., vol. 6, 387–393, 1913); Zur Arbeitsweise des Albertus (Blätter für das Gymnasial-Schulwesen, vol. 52, 274–277, c. 1917). Franz Strunz: Albertus Magnus. Weisheit und Naturforschung im Mittelalter (190 p., 35 fig., Wien 1926; Isis, 10, 127). Arthur Schneider: Albertus, sein Leben und seine wissenschaftliche Bedeutung (Rektoratsrede, 38 p., Cologne 1927).

18. *Philosophy*—Ernst Degen: Welches sind die Beziehungen Alberts Liber de causis et processu universitatis zur Στοιχείωσις θεολογική des Proklus und was lehren uns dieselben? (Diss., 59 p., Munich 1903). H. Lauer: Die Moraltheologie Alberts mit besonderer Berücksichtigung ihrer Beziehung zur Lehre des heiligen Thomas (Freiburg 1911). Anselm Rohner: Das Schöpfungsproblem bei Maimonides, Albertus und Thomas von Aquin. (Beit. zur Gesch. der Phil. des Mittelalters, vol. 11, 5, 152 p., Münster 1913). Leopold Gaul: Alberts Verhältnis zu Plato (Beit. zur Gesch. des Phil. des Mittelalters, vol. 12, 1, 170 p., Münster i. W., 1913). Martin Grabmann: Drei ungedruckte Teile der Summa de creaturis Alberts aus den HS. nachgewiesen und gewürdigt (Quellen und Forschungen zur Geschichte der Dominikanerordens in Deutschland, 13, 88 p., Leipzig 1919). M. De Wulf: History of mediaeval philosophy (vol. 1, 393–406, 1926). Paul Hartig: Albert der Grosse und Thomas von Aquino. Untersuchung zur Bedeutung volkheitlicher Verwurzelung im Mittelalter (Deutsche Vierteljahrsschrift für Literaturwissenschaft, vol. 5, 25–36, 1927; Isis, 13, 161). Martin Grabmann: Der Einfluss Alberts auf das mittelalterliche Geistesleben (Z. für katholische Theologie, vol. 25, 153–182, 313–356, 1928).

19. *Psychology*—Arthur Schneider: Die Psychologie Alberts (Beitr. zur Gesch. der Philosophie des Mittelalters, vol. 4, part 5, 306 p., Münster 1903; incorporating the author's previous thesis on the subject, 1900). Paul Diepgen: Traum und Traumdeutung im Mittelalter (Berlin 1912; discussion of Albert's views on dreams). Claudius Franz Mayer: Die Personallehre in der Naturphilosophie von Albertus Magnus. Ein Beitrag zur Geschichte des Konstitutionsbegriff (Kyklos, vol. 2, 191–257, 1929).

For Hermann the German, see the chapter on translators; for Witelo, the chapter on physics.

ULRICH OF STRASSBURG

Ulrich son of Engelbert. Udalricus Engelberti; Udalricus de Argentina. German Dominican; disciple of Albert the Great in Cologne, lector in theology at Strassburg after 1248; provincial of his order from 1272 to 1277, when he was sent to Paris to lecture on Peter the Lombard's Sentences; but he died in Paris, 1277, before having begun his teaching. Neo-Platonist who was influenced mainly by the Liber de causis, Dionysios the Areopagite, Ibn Sīnā, and those of Albert's works which represented similar points of view. He wrote commentaries on Aristotle's Meteorologica and on Peter Lombard's Sentences, and an enormous philosophical treatise, De summo bono or Summa de theologia et philosophia (unfinished). His scientific knowledge was chiefly derived from Albert the Great.

Criticism—M. Grabmann: Studien über Ulrich von Strasburg (Z. für kathol. Theologie, 1905). P. Duhem: Système du monde (vol. 3, 358–363, 1915). Gustave Théry: Originalité du plan de la S. de bono d'Ulrich (Gand 1923). M. De Wulf: History of mediaeval philosophy (vol. 2, 119, 1926).

For William of Moerbeke, see the chapter on translators; for Henry Bate, the mathematical chapter.

SIGER OF BRABANT

Belgian philosopher, leader of the Parisian Averroists. He taught in Paris from c. 1266 to 1276, and was murdered in Orvieto (Umbria) c. 1281–1284. He wrote a few treatises on logic and philosophy, notably the De anima intellectiva, which seems to be an attempt to refute St. Thomas' treatise De unitate intellectus contra Averroistas; and commentaries or "quaestiones" on Aristotle: Metaphysics, Bks. I to V; Physics, Bks. I–IV, VIII; Meteorologica, Bks. I, II, IV; De somno et vigilia; De juventute et senectute; De vita et morte; De anima, Bks. I–II; De generatione et corruptione. In these commentaries he examines a number of moot questions (eternity of the world, unicity of the human intellect, identity of essence and existence, etc.) pointing out incompatibilities between reason and faith. In the De anima intellectiva he boldly accused Albert the Great and St. Thomas of misrepresenting Aristotle.

The condemnation pronounced in 1277 by Stephen Tempier, bishop of Paris—whom John XXI had charged to investigate philosophical teachings—was directed against the whole Peripatetic movement, but chiefly against the more radical faction, the advocates of extreme Averroism, led by Siger and by Boetius of Denmark. Siger was finally accussed of heresy, but died before being convicted.

His fame is largely based upon Dante's mention of him in Paradiso (10, 136).

"Essa è la luce eterna di Sigieri"

Did the poet place Siger in Paradise by mistake or does this show that his philosophy was even more eclectic than is generally supposed?

Text—Impossibilia, ein philosophische Streitschrift. First edited by Clemens Baeumker (Beiträge zur Geschichte der Philosophie des Mittelalters, vol. 2, 6, 208 p., 1898; biography and bibliography, 49–116). Other texts have been edited in the second part of Mandonnet's work quoted below.

Criticism—Gaston Paris: La poésie au moyen âge (2d. series, Paris 1895). Ch. V. Langlois: Siger (Revue de Paris, 1900, reprinted in Questions d'histoire et d'enseignement, Paris 1902). See also his article in the Grande Encyclopédie (c. 1901). Franz Bruckmüller: Untersuchungen über Sigers Anima intellectiva (Diss., München 1908). Pierre Félix Mandonnet: Siger et l'averroïsme latin au XIIIe siècle (Fribourg 1899; new ed. in 2 parts., Louvain 1911–1908; important). A. Counson: Biographie nationale de Belgique (vol. 22, 439–492, 1912). P. Duhem: Système du monde (vol. 5, 571–580, 1917). Martin Grabmann: Neuaufgefundene Quaestiones Sigers zu den Werken des Aristoteles (Miscellanea Ehrle, 1, 103–147, 1923); Neuaufgefundene Werke des Siger von Brabant und Boetius von Dacien

(Sitzungsber. der bayer. Ak., phil. Kl., 48 p., 1924). Salomon Reinach: L'énigme de Siger (Revue historique, 151, 34–46, 1926; Isis, 9, 153). M. De Wulf: History of mediaeval philosophy (vol. 2, 96–106, 1926).

HENRY OF GHENT

Flemish philosopher. Canon of Courtrai in 1267; archdeacon of Bruges in 1276; from that time on he flourished in Paris; doctor in theology in 1277; died in 1293. He has often been confused (e.g., in Histoire littéraire) with Henry Goethals of Ghent (a Gandavo), but it has been proved that Henry of Ghent was not Henry Goethals, Servite, member of the Sorbonne.

He was one of the most vigorous assailants, in the name of Catholic theology, of the two Aristotelian propositions: there cannot exist an infinite quantity; there cannot exist more than one universe. He was probably one of the advisers of Stephen Tempier, who formally condemned these propositions among many others in 1277. In 1282 he publicly denounced the ecclesiastical privileges of the mendicant orders. He wrote commentaries on Aristotle's Physics and Metaphysics, and on the Liber de causis, a treatise on logic, a Summa theologica, and XV Quodlibeta.

Text—Quodlibeta published in Paris, 1518; Venice 1608, 1613. Quodlibeta 1 to VIII edited by M. De Wulf, A. Pelzer, and J. Hoffmans in the collection Les philosophes belges (vols. 2 to 4, 1904–1914).

Summa theologica, printed in Paris, 1520, and Ferrara, 1646.

Criticism—Felix Lajard: Histoire littéraire de la France (vol. 20, 144–203, 1842). Alphonse Le Roy: Henry Goethals (Biographie nationale de Belgique, vol. 8, 51–66, 1884). M. De Wulf: Histoire de la philosophie scolastique dans les Pays Bas (Louvain 1895). P. Duhem: Etudes sur Léonard de Vinci (vol. 2, 446–455, 1909); apropos of Henry's opinions on the plurality of worlds, the vacuum, and infinity. M. De Wulf: History of mediaeval philosophy (vol. 2, 59–64, 1926). Martin Grabmann: Mittelalterliche Lateinische Aristotelesübersetzungen und Aristoteleskommentare (70–98, München 1928; Isis, 13, 205).

GILES OF LESSINES

Aegidius a Lessinia, Luscinus, Gilles de Lessines, etc. Born probably at Lessines in Hainaut c. 1230; spent most of his life in the abbey of St. James in Paris; died in or after 1304.

Belgian Dominican, philosopher and chronologist, astronomer; pupil of Albert the Great and St. Thomas. In 1270 he addressed a letter to Albert warning him of the impending condemnation of Thomism. He wrote a treatise on chronology, De concordia temporum, wherein he tried to fix historical dates by means of references to eclipses or other synchronisms; it stops at the year 1304. His most important work is a treatise on the unity of forms, De unitate formae, dated 1278, directed against Kilwardby; it contains an exposition and refutation of the pluralistic theory of forms which had been generally accepted before St. Thomas defended the opposite theory, the unity of substantial form. Giles' treatise is one of the most important among a good many devoted to the same controversy.

Giles of Lessines may possibly be identified with the Dominican Giles who wrote a treatise on the comet of 1264 (see §18 of my note on Roger Bacon).

Text—De unitate formae, edited by Maurice De Wulf, with an elaborate introduction and analysis (Les philosophes du moyen âge, vol. 1, 230 p., Louvain 1902, important).

Criticism—Emile Varenbergh: Biographie nationale de Belgique (vol. 7, 767–770, 1883). P. F. Mandonnet: Gilles et son traité de crepusculis (Revue Neoscolastique, 190, 1920). Aleksander Birkenmajer: Der Brief R. Kilwardbys an Peter von Conflans und die Streitschrift des Ägidius von Lessines (Beiträge zur Geschichte der Philosophie des Mittelalters, vol. 20, 5, p. 36–69, 213, Münster 1922). M. De Wulf: History of mediaeval philosophy (vol. 2, 11, 46, 1926).

GODFREY OF FONTAINES

Godefroid, Geoffroy; Galfridus, Gaufridus, etc. Born at Fontaines-les-Hozémont, near Liége; master of theology, Paris, 1286; canon of Liége, Paris and Cologne; member of the Sorbonne; died after 1303. Independent Thomist philosopher, who criticized the bishop of Paris, Stephen Tempier, and his successor, for their premature condemnation of Thomism. He wrote XIV Quodlibeta (c. 1286–1290). He conceived the possibity of a transmutation of sublunar things, different from the Aristotelian generation.

Text—The Quodlibeta I to VIII have been edited by M. De Wulf, A. Pelzer and J. Hoffmans (Les philosophes belges, vols. 2 to 4, Louvain 1904–1914).
Criticism—M. De Wulf: Etudes sur la vie, les oeuvres et l'influence de Godefroid de Fontaines (127 p., Mémoires Acad. Belgique, lettres, vol. 1, 1906). A. Pelzer: G. de Fontaines. Les manuscrits de ses Quolibets conservés à la Vaticane et dans quelques autres bibliothèques (Revue néo-scolastique, vol. 20, 365–388, 491–532, 1913). M. De Wulf: History of mediaeval philosophy (vol. 2, 55–59, 219, 1926).

MAERLANT

Jacob (de Coster) van Maerlant. Flemish poet, moralist, satirist. Born in the vicinity of Bruges, probably in Damme, c. 1235; was sexton (koster) in Maerlant (a place later incorporated with Briel in the Dutch island of East Voorne); c. 1267 he returned to Damme; he died there c. 1299.

He was the first great educator of his people and was justly called "vader der dietscher dichtren algader," meaning the father of all Nederlandish poets—the founder of Netherlandish literature.[25]

He translated rather freely a number of writings from French and Latin into his own language. At the beginning he translated various romances from the French; to wit, Alexanders geesten (i.e., gesta), the Alexandreis of Gautier de Chastillon (of Ronchin, Lille, fl. before 1179), the Boek van Merlijn (the Book of Merlin) by Robert of Boron (first half of the thirteenth century), the Historie van Troje (history of Troy) by Benoit de St. More (fl. 1180).

Later he wrote collections of poems, dealing with all sorts of questions—ethical, social, religious—in the form of dialogues between two friends Jacob and Martijn (representing possibly himself and Jan of Nassau, bishop of Utrecht, 1267–1288). These collections are three in number, called respectively Eerste Martijn, D'ander Martijn, Derde Martijn (First Martin, The other Martin, Third Martin). The third is also entitled Van der drievoudichede, because it deals with the Holy Trinity. These poems were parodied, imitated, and translated into Latin by Jan Bukelare (MS. dated 1453), and into French (printed 1480).

He translated before 1273 Bonaventura's life of St. Francis of Assisi, wrote a

[25] Netherlandish means at once Dutch and Flemish, two varieties of the same identical language, having the same grammar and dictionary. The difference between (literary) Flemish and Dutch is of the same nature as that between (literary) American and English.

number of devotional books, and a book denouncing clerical corruption (Der kerken claghe).

After some time he got tired of translating romances, and decided to devote his life to the diffusion of real knowledge. He thus produced an enormous amount of didactic poetry, mostly translated from the Latin. Though he loved France, he came to distrust more and more French writings. To him (as to many others of his contemporaries, the most serious minded), Latin was the language of true knowledge and his ambition was to make that knowledge available to his people. His didactic translations include:

1. Lapidarijs, a lapidary This is lost; it was in all probability a translation of Marbode's poem.

2. Sompniarijs, probably a book on dreams; also lost.

3. Heimelijcheit der heimelijcheden, c. 1266. Translation of the Secreta secretorum (vol. 1, 556).

4. Der naturen bloeme (Flowers of nature), c. 1264–1269. Free translation of the De natura rerum of Thomas of Cantimpré, which Maerlant ascribed to Albert the Great.

5. Scolastica or Rijmbijbel (27102 verses). Translation of the Historia scolastica of Peter the Eater (second half of the twelfth century). Maerlant added to this text a poem, Die wrake van Jherusalem, dealing with the destruction of Jerusalem by the Romans, completed by him in 1271.

6. Spieghel historiael (some 90,000 verses). Free translation of the Speculum historiale of Vincent of Beauvais. This is generally considered Maerlant's main work. It contains the history of the world down to c. 1250, but the translator has added interpolations concerning the Low Countries. Maerlant had divided the Speculum into four parts, of which he neglected the second. He began working at the first c. 1283; he did the third in 1284–1286; he was busy translating the fourth in 1288. This fourth part was completed by Lodewijk van Velthem, while the second was translated by Philip Utenbroeke of Damme.

His most interesting work to us is his translation of the De natura rerum. In his preface to it, Maerlant declared that he wrote it to publish the truth for the benefit of those "who are annoyed by romances and tired of lies." This attitude (contempt of chivalresque romance, love of prosaic truth) was largely influenced by the peculiar conditions of his milieu, the growth of municipal liberty and of democracy, nowhere more intense than in Flanders. Maerlant was not a political poet; he was essentially a moralist; but his love of truth, his anxiety to diffuse it, is a social phenomenon, a sure symptom of the progress of democracy. In its turn it was bound to influence that progress more than anything else. Privileges can flourish only in the darkness. Sooner or later, injustice as well as ignorance must wither in the light of truth.

Maerlant's influence was considerable in the Low Countries. He may be said to have formed a school to which belonged such men as his younger contemporaries, Gielijs van Molhem and Jan Praet, and later, Jan van Boendale (d. 1365) and Jan de Weert (d. 1362). Jan Praet wrote in 1299 the Vierden Martijn (the fourth Martin). That influence continued in the fifteenth century but then ceased, and his works were then almost forgotten until the end of the eighteenth century.

Text—Alexanders geesten. Edited by F. A. Snellaert (Brussels 1860–1861), and by Joh. Franck (Groningen 1882).

Boeck van Merlijn, edited by J. van Vloten (Leiden 1880–1882).

Historie van Troje. Partial edition by J. Verdam (Groningen 1873). Complete edition by Napoleon de Pauw and Edward Gaillard (4 parts, Ghent 1889–1892).

Strophische gedichten. Edited by Eelco Verwijs (Groningen 1880), by J. Franck and J. Verdam (390 p., Groningen 1898), by P. Leendertz, jr., and J. Verdam (Leiden 1918).

Sinte Franciscus leven. Edited by J. Tideman (Leiden 1848).

Heimelijcheit der heimelijcheden. Edited by J. Clarisse (Dordrecht 1838); by J. Kausler (Tübingen 1844), by A. A. Verdenius (Amsterdam 1917).

Der naturen bloeme. Edition of books I–IV by J. H. Bormans (Brussels 1857). Complete edition by Eelco Verwijs (2 vols., Groningen 1878).

Scolastica. Edited by J. David (3 vols., Brussels 1858–1859).

Spieghel historiael. First edition, Antwerp 1515 (with woodcuts). Parts 1 and 2 edited by J. A. Clignett and J. Steenwinkel (Leiden 1784–1785); part 3, by J. Steenwinkel and W. Bilderdijk (Amsterdam 1812); part 4, by J. H. Halbertsma (Deventer 1815) and by J. van Lennep (Amsterdam 1849). New edition by M. de Vries and E. Verwijs (3 vols., Leiden 1857–1863).

Criticism—See histories of Netherlandish literature; I have consulted W. J. A. Jonckbloet: Geschiedenis der Nederlandsche Letterkunde (4th. ed., vols. 1 and 2, by index). Martin: Allgemeine deutsche Biographie (vol. 20, 41–46, 1884). W. de Vreese: Biographie nationale de Belgique (vol. 13, 64–119, 1895; elaborate study with long bibliography). Potthast (757, 1896). H. Pirenne: Histoire de Belgique (vol. 1, 3d ed., 349–353, 1909). Pirenne has not completely understood the value of Maerlant's work, the social signification of the scientific urge. Miss A. J. Scholte: Nieuw nederlandsch biografisch woordenboek (vol. 7, 823–829, 1927). F. S. Bodenheimer: Materialien zur Geschichte der Zoologie (vol. 1, 179–181, 1928).

PETER THE IRISHMAN

Petrus Hibernicus, Petrus de Hibernia. Irish philosopher who flourished in Naples c. 1240–1260. Not to be mistaken for Petrus de Isernia (prov. of Campobasso, Abruzzi), who was professor of law in Naples, 1224.

Teacher of St. Thomas "in naturalibus" in Naples c. 1240–2. He discussed design in nature before King Manfred (c. 1258–1266). His interpretation of Aristotle was decidedly Averroistic.

Article by Miss Bateson in the Dictionary of National Biography (vol. 45, 52, 1896). Clemens Baeumker: Petrus de Hibernia, der Jugendlehrer des Thomas von Aquino und seine Disputation vor König Manfred (Sitzungsber. der Bayer. Ak. d. Wiss., Phil. Kl., 52 p., 1920). Containing (p. 41–49) the text of the disputation "utrum membra essent facta propter operaciones uel operationes essent facta propter membra" (Isis, 5, 214).

ROBERT KILWARDBY

Born in England; assumed the Dominican habit; taught in Paris and Oxford 1248–1261 (this was the time of his greatest literary activity); English provincial of his Order, 1261–1272; archbishop of Canterbury, 1272–1278; cardinal-bishop of Porto; died at Viterbo in 1279. English philosopher and grammarian.

In spite of his being a Dominican, he was distinctly anti-Thomist, and in 1277 he caused the University of Oxford to condemn a number of Thomist ideas. He wrote commentaries on Aristotle, Boetius, and Peter Lombard's Sentences. He composed two philosophical treatises: De unitate formarum and De ortu et divisione philosophiae. The latter was perhaps the most important work of its kind in mediaeval Christendom. It was an improvement upon Gundisalvo's treatise (first half of the twelfth century), itself derived from al-Fārābī, and embodied some of the views of Hugh of Saint Victor (first half of the twelfth century). After the analogy of the seven liberal arts, he divided the mechanical arts into a trivium (agriculture, dietetics, medicine), and a quadrivium (costuming, armor-making, architecture, commerce). His grammatical treatises, notably his commentary on Priscian, enjoyed much success.

Criticism—T. F. Tout: Dictionary of national biography (vol. 31, 120–122, 1892). Aleksander Birkenmajer: Der Brief Kilwardbys an Peter von Conflans und die Streitschrift des Ägidius von Lessines (Beiträge zur Gesch. der Philosophie des Mittelalters, vol. 20, 5, 36–69, 213, 1922). Lynn Thorndike: History of magic (vol. 2, 81–82, 1923). M. De Wulf: History of mediaeval philosophy (vol. 1, 392–393; vol. 2, 40, 1926).

THOMAS OF YORK

Thomas de Eboraco. English Franciscan. Obtained his master's degree in Oxford, 1253; taught in Cambridge; died in 1260. Moderate realist. Author, c. 1250–1260, of a large treatise, Super metaphysicam Aristotelis, conceived in a new way. It is divided into six books: (1) De creatore; rational theology; (2) origin of existence, beginning of the world (after Maimonides); principles of existence, matter, and form; (3) philosophia prima, further discussion of existence and causality; (4) de divisionibus entis; substantia prima, secunda; elaborate discussion of universals; (5) epistemology; an sit una veritas sola, an plures; (6) de ente in speciali (special metaphysics); psychology (not completed). This treatise was anterior to St. Thomas' Aristotelian commentaries. It was the first original attempt at metaphysical synthesis, in Christendom, posterior to the assimilation of the Aristotelian commentaries of Muslim and Jewish philosophers (Ibn Gabirol, Ibn Sīnā, al-Ghazzālī, Ibn Rushd, Maimonides).

Martin Grabmann: Die Metaphysik des Thomas von York (Baeumker Festschrift, 181–193, Münster 1913). F. Ueberweg and M. Baumgartner: Grundriss der Philosophie der patristischen und scholastischen Zeit (453, 1915). Auguste Pelzer: Les versions latines des ouvrages de morale, etc. (Revue néo-scolastique, vol. 23, 316–341, 378–412, see p. 403, 1921). M. De Wulf: History of mediaeval philosophy (vol. 1, 356–357, 1926).

For John Peckham, see the chapter on physics.

WILLIAM DE LA MARE

Oxford Franciscan who died in 1298. Disciple of St. Bonaventure. He wrote a commentary on the latter's Sentences (Bks. I–II), entitled Quaestiones disputatae, also Quodlibeta sophistica, but his main work was a series of annotations purporting to correct the Summa theologica of St. Thomas. That publication, called Correctorium fratris Thomae marked the beginning of Franciscan opposition to Thomism. It enumerated 117 Thomist errors or misconceptions. It was already well known in 1282 when the Franciscan chapter held at Strassburg decreed "quod non permittant multiplicari summam fratris Thomae nisi apud lectores notabiliter intelligentes et hoc nisi cum declarationibus fratris G. de Mara."[26]

[26] Analecta bollandiana, p. 292, 1899. Quoted by M. De Wulf (vol. 2, 37, 1926).

William's Correctorium was bitterly resented by the Dominicans; they affected to call it Corruptorium and produced a number of correctoria and defensoria of their own. One anonymous one was entitled Correctorium corruptorii (or Quare, after the first word of the refutation proper).

Text—Abbé P. Glorieux: Les premières polémiques thomistes. I. Le Correctorium corruptorii "quare." Edition critique (Bibliothèque thomiste, vol. 9; 508 p., Kain, Belgium, 1927). · Father Glorieux suggests that the author was probably the Dominican Richard Chapwell, whose views were condemned in 1280 by John Peckham, archbishop of Canterbury.

Criticism—Pierre Mandonnet: Premiers travaux de polémique thomiste (Revue des sciences philosophiques et théologiques, vol. 7, 46–70, 1913). Franz Ehrle: Der Kampf um die Lehre des hl. Thomas in den ersten fünfzig Jahren nach seinen Tod (Z. für katholische Theologie, 266–318, 1913). E. Longpré: G. de la Mare (France franciscaine, 1921–1922). M. De Wulf: History of mediaeval philosophy (vol. 1, 380; vol. 2, 37, 44, 71, 1926).

WILLIAM OF WARE

William Warre; Guaro, Varro, Varron. English philosopher. Born at Ware in Hertfordshire; entered the Franciscan order; lived, mainly in Paris, in the last quarter of the century. He is said to have been the pupil of Alexandre of Hales, and the teacher of Duns Scotus; the second statement is incorrect. He wrote commentaries on the Sentences of Peter Lombard, Quaestiones in IV libros sententiarum, of which there are many MSS., but which are still unpublished. I mention him chiefly because his astronomical discussions are literally borrowed from the Moreh nebukim. He does not give Maimonides' name but calls him The rabbi (Raby). This shows that the Franciscans of the end of the thirteenth century were studying Maimonides, perhaps as a sort of strange antidote to Ibn Rushd and Aristotle.

Text—Quaestiones disputatae de immaculata conceptione beatae Mariae Virginis (Quaracchi, 1904).

Criticism—Miss Bateson: Dictionary of national biography (vol. 61, 377, 1900). P. Duhem: Système du monde (vol. 3, 488–491, 1915). M. De Wulf: History of mediaeval philosophy (vol. 1, 389, 1926).

RICHARD OF MIDDLETON

Franciscan theologian and philosopher traditionally supposed to be English (or Scotch), hence his English name. But his usual (Latin) name, Ricardus de Media Villa, does not refer to a definite place in any country. He may have originated in Oxfordshire or Northamptonshire. He studied probably in Oxford and Paris; he obtained his master's degree in Paris in 1284–1285, and taught in Paris; for a few years after 1288 he was tutor to the son of Charles II of Anjou, St. Louis of Toulouse, then prisoner in Catalonia; he died at the end of the thirteenth century or the beginning of the fourteenth.

He was a theologian of the Franciscan school but with some eclectic tendencies. Though he was a disciple of St. Bonaventure, in some points he followed St. Thomas. In 1283 the general of his order appointed him with others to examine into the doctrines of Peter Olivi.

His main works are Quaestiones disputatae (end of 1284), Quodlibeta (1285–1287), and, best known of all, a commentary on the Books of sentences of Peter Lombard (c. 1285–1295).

He discussed many questions on the borderland of science and philosophy: infinity, plurality of worlds, motion, gravity, etc. He adopted the system of Ptolemy, disregarding the objections of al-Biṭrūjī and Ibn Rushd against it; the same attitude was taken about the same time by the French Franciscan Bernard of Verdun; it represents a turning point in astronomical thought.

Text—Super sententias Petri Lombardi. Complete editions, Venice 1489, 1509; Brescia 1591 (in 4 vols.). Separate editions of book I, Venice 1507; of books II, III, Venice 1509; of book IV, Venice 1489, 1499; Paris 1504, 1512.

Quodlibeta. Venice 1509, Brescia 1591.

Ferdinand M. Delorme: Quaestio disputata de privilegio Martini papae IV nunc primum edita (Quaracchi, 124 p., 1925). Martin IV was pope from 1281 to 1285.

De humanae cognitionis ratione anecdota quaedam S. Bonaventurae et nonnullorum ipsius discipulorum (Quaracchi, 1883).

Criticism—C. L. Kingsford: Dictionary of national biography (vol. 37, 356, 1894). P. Duhem: Etudes sur Léonard de Vinci (vol. 2, 1909; 368–373, on infinity; 411–414, plurality of worlds, 422–443, gravity); Système du monde (vol. 3, 1915; 484–488, astronomy). Edgar Hocedez: R. de Middleton, sa vie, ses oeuvres, sa doctrine (Spicilegium sacrum lovaniense, 7, 572 p., 1925; very elaborate study; Isis, 14, 479). Willibrord Lampen: De patria Richardi de Mediavilla (Archivum franciscanum historicum, vol. 18, 298–300, 1925). Claiming that Richard's native country is really unknown and that he should not be called Richard Middleton but R. de Mediavilla, leaving the question open. Margaret R. Toynbee: St. Louis of Toulouse and the process of canonization in the fourteenth century (275 p., Manchester 1930).

ROGER BACON

Contents: (1) Life. (2) General appreciation. (3) Dated writings. (4) The Opera of 1266–1267. (5) Questions on the Aristotelian treatises. (6) Logic. (7) Mathematics. (8) Astronomy and astrology. (9) Calendar. (10) Mechanics. (11) Optics. (12) Alchemy. (13) Natural history. (14) Geography. (15) Medicine. (16) Experimental science. (17) Philosophy. (18) Summa philosophiae. (19) Philology. (20 Biblical studies. (21) Attitude to Israel and to Islām. (22) Baconian legends.

(23 to 25) Text. (23) Earlier texts to be printed. (24) The three Opera and collections. (25) Separate editions not yet mentioned. (26 to 33) Criticism. (26) Bibliography of Bacon's writings. (27) General criticism. (28) Mathematics. (29) Astronomy and physics. (30) Chemistry. (31) Medicine. (32) Philosophy. (33) Baconian legends.

1. *Life*—Roger Bacon, English Franciscan, philosopher and scientist (c. 1214–1292). "Doctor mirabilis." Born at Ilchester, Somerset, c. 1214. Studied in Oxford under Grosseteste and possibly Adam Marsh; before 1236 he went to Paris, later seems to have traveled to Italy; dedicated a book to Innocent IV (1243–1254); returned to Paris, lectured there as a regent master of the university; returned to Oxford c. 1251. He assumed the Franciscan habit at some unknown time (between 1251 and 1257). Apparently he soon got into difficulties with his superiors. Soon after the publication in 1254 of the Liber introductorius ad Evangelium aeternum of Gerard of Borgo San Donnino, a censorship had been established by the Franciscan Order upon the writings of its own numbers. Happily for him, in 1266 he was ordered by Pope Clement IV (Guy de Foulques who had heard of him in France

and England) to send him copies of his writings, as secretly as possible. It was a great opportunity which Bacon improved, but this papal request made over the head of his superiors must have made him obnoxious to them. He sent four books to the pope in 1268, but unfortunately the latter died a few months later. After Stephen Tempier's condemnation of Averroism in 1277, the Franciscan censorship became probably more severe; at any rate in the following year Bacon was condemned for teaching "suspected novelties." It is said in a Franciscan chronicle (Chronica viginti quattuor generalium, to 1374) that he was imprisoned from 1278 to 1292, and no alternative residence has been suggested for him during that period. He died soon afterwards.

2. *General appreciation*—Bacon was essentially an encyclopaedist; that is, he was tormented with the idea of the unity of knowledge, and his life was a long effort better to grasp and to explain that unity. He denounced violently the evils of scholasticism, too violently in fact to obtain practical results. He realized the urgent need for philosophers and theologians to enlarge their basis of knowledge; they were not acquainted with the available scientific data and their mathematical and linguistic equipment was utterly insufficient. His greatest title to fame however, was his vindication of the experimental spirit. He was not himself an experimenter any more than he was a mathematician, but he clearly saw—better than anybody else in his time—that without experimentation and without mathematics, natural philosophy is very soon reduced to verbiage.

He also realized the utility of knowledge, and this was even more remarkable than to realize its unity, for the latter had been done instinctively by almost every philosopher. In the Opus majus and the Opus tertium he insists upon that utility repeatedly. This double point of view, unity (to be discovered experimentally and proved with the help of mathematics) and utility, led him to entirely new conceptions of knowledge, of learning, and of education.

Unfortunately he was of a quarrelsome disposition—a regular "kicker" or "mauvais coucheur"—and too temperamental to exert much influence upon his contemporaries; his immoderate criticism of the other leaders was bound to antagonize their followers instead of conciliating them. He detested Albert the Great and St. Thomas, not only because he was jealous of their tremendous success but also because he knew that their syntheses, though offered as complete and accepted as such, were incomplete in some essential respects. Moreover he was temperamentally opposed to them. Like the majority of his Franciscan brethren, he was an Augustinian (i.e., a Platonist), while they were Aristotelians. Bacon was a poorer philosopher perhaps than St. Thomas; that is, he was less able to construct a harmonious and authoritative synthesis; but he was a far better scientist; he was a poorer naturalist than Albert, but a better mathematician and physicist; he was a deeper encyclopaedist than both.

His accomplishments fell considerably short of his visions. Yet visions are very important, and we need seers as well as inventors. Bacon made few if any experiments, and no invention, not even gunpowder, can be definitely ascribed to him. He seems to have vaguely foreseen fundamental discoveries and inventions: the possibility of circumnavigating the world, of propelling boats by mechanical means, of flying, of taking advantage of the explosive property of powder, of improving sight by proper adjustments of lenses. One such anticipation would hardly deserve to be mentioned, but the combination of so many in a single head is very impressive.

As opposed to a dogmatic system like Thomism, Bacon's thoughts seem and are disconnected. His own philosophy was less a system than a method, a point of view. Hence its comparative failure was not surprising. St. Thomas founded a school, almost comparable in size and influence to the Academy and the Lyceum; Bacon founded none, but the majority of modern scientists feel more genuinely attracted to him than to any other mediaeval personality.

One should not confuse dogmatism with originality. Bacon's thought was less systematic, but on the whole more original than that of his great contemporaries. And the best proof of this is that he was a true harbinger of modern civilization, while St. Thomas (not to speak of the others) was destined to become the most perfect symbol of mediaevalism.

Of course, Bacon's originality—like any other—was limited. It consisted more in new arrangements and displacements of emphasis than in actual inventions. He borrowed materials from everywhere, and continued to a large extent the Oxford Franciscan tradition. He had no real followers and his fame increased but very slowly during the fourteenth and fifteenth centuries; much of it was a poor fame at that, a purely legendary one. The lack of incunabula editions confirms our impression that he was comparatively neglected by scholars before the sixteenth century. The first Baconian editions were printed only in 1541, 1542; and his most important work only in 1733.

3. *Dated writings*—The bibliography of Bacon's works is made especially difficult because of his habit of rewriting some of them many times and of using the same material over and over again in different ways. It will be best for our purpose to classify them by subject, and to consider separately those relative to each subject together with the ideas which they represent. But before doing this a chronological list of the dated writings will help in understanding the evolution of his thought.

c. 1243. Epistola de accidentibus senectutis. Probably begun before 1236; dedicated to Innocent IV (1243–1254).

c. 1236–1251 (probably 1245–1247). Questions relative to the Aristotelian Physics and Metaphysics, to the De plantis and the De causis.

c. 1256–1266. De speculis comburentibus. De mirabili potestate artis et naturae (chapters 1 to 6).

1263–1265. Compotus naturalium.

Before 1266. Began the compilation of the Compendium philosophiae (or Scriptum principale). A fragment of the metaphysical part, Metaphysica de viciis contractis in studio theologiae, was certainly written in or before 1266.

1266–1267. Opus majus. Tractatus de multiplicatione specierum (possibly a little anterior). Opus minus. Opus tertium.

1271. Compendium studii philosophiae.

c. 1277. Speculum astronomiae (ascribed to Bacon by Father Mandonnet, but to Albert the Great by others).

1292. Compendium studii theologiae. Bacon's last work.

Until about 1251, Bacon's activity was mainly of the scholastic or argumentative type. From that time on, the vision of a better and deeper knowledge grew upon him, and after years of study he was finally able to express it in the works composed at the Pope's request in 1266–1267. This was really the climax of his life, and one of the most important dates in the history of mediaeval thought. Let us consider these works first.

4. *The Opera of* 1266–1267—At the beginning of 1266 Bacon was engaged (and he had apparently been so engaged for years) in the compilation of a vast encyclopaedia, the Compendium philosophiae (or Scriptum principale), which was to consist of four volumes and treat of six sciences (hence, another name for it, Liber sex scientiarum); to wit, vol. 1, Grammar and Logic; vol. 2, Mathematics; vol. 3, Physics; vol. 4, Metaphysics and Morals. It is probable that by the time he received the command of Clement IV (papal mandate of June 22, 1266; this was a second request), he had already realized that his plan was too ambitious. It is possible that the Opus majus was already completed, or in a very advanced stage, when the mandate of June 22 reached him. At any rate the larger plan was abandoned, and instead of it Bacon wrote a series of four works which were sent to Clement IV in 1268; the Opus majus, the Opus minus, the Opus tertium, and the De multiplicatione specierum.

The Opus majus was divided into seven parts: (1) Causes of error; (2) Philosophy vs. theology; (3) Study of languages; (4) Mathematics (including astronomy, music, geography, etc.); (5) Optics or perspective; (6) Experimental science; (7) Morals.

The Tractatus de multiplicatione specierum was probably written before 1266; it was possibly a part of the Compendium philosophiae. A copy of it was sent to the Pope together with the Opus majus. I shall come back to it in sections 8 and 10.

The Opus minus was both an introduction and a supplement to the Opus majus. We have only fragments of it. It contained additional notes on astrology (De notitia caelestium), on the main points of the Opus majus, on alchemy (In enigmatibus; De rerum generatione ex elementis), on medicine (Remedia studii).

The Opus tertium was a work of the same kind as the preceding, i.e., a sort of supplement to the Opus majus. It deals with the relations of the different sciences to one another, with physics (vacuum, motion, and space), mathematics, astronomy alchemy, etc.

Bacon's ideas on almost every subject may be found in the Opus majus and its supplements. In the following sections, reference to them as well as to the more special treatises mentioned, will always be implied.

5. *Questions on the Aristotelian treatises*—During his stay in Paris (c. 1236–1251), Bacon discussed the Physics of Aristotle (Bks. I to VI), the Metaphysics (Bk. I, XII, and possibly Bks. II and IV), the De plantis and the De causis. The result of that teaching was the publication, not of commentaries, but of "questions" relative to special topics. These questions are of the purely scholastic type.

The text of the Physics used by Bacon was very close to the ancient translation direct from the Greek, also used by St. Thomas, which was then generally ascribed to Boetius. For the Metaphysics he used a similar translation and another of Arabic origin. The twelfth book of the Metaphysics was called by Bacon the eleventh; indeed the text known to Ibn Rushd did not include our eleventh book, and thus the twelfth (lambda) was the eleventh (kappa).

Other commentaries on Aristotelian or pseudo-Aristotelian treatises of which Bacon was (or may have been) the author: Tractatus ad declaranda quaedam obscure dicta in libro Secreti Secretorum. De somno et vigilia (2 books). In Meteora (probably a part of the Compendium philosophiae).

6. *Logic*—Bacon was well acquainted with the Aristotelian Organon and with the De sex principiis of Gilbert de la Porrée, but—and this is one of his originalities—he attached to logic only a subordinate importance. For him the main avenue to knowledge was not logic, but linguistic and mathematical ability. Logical ability he thought was almost instinctive, but languages and mathematics had to be learned.

However, he wrote a few treatises on logic: Prima petia (elementary), Summa de sophismatibus et distinctionibus, Summulae dialectices, De signis logicalibus, and the first volume of his Compendium was to be devoted to logic and grammar.

7. *Mathematics*—Bacon was not an original mathematician, and his knowledge of mathematics was very limited. But he was imbued with the Platonic idea of the transcendental importance of mathematics and he helped the diffusion of that idea. He was equally convinced of the practical utility of mathematics in almost every study, and explained it at great length.

Though the best source of knowledge (outside of revelation) is experimentation, the latter must be completed by mathematical treatment to bear all its fruits. This was a sort of anticipative conception of mathematical physics; very vague indeed, yet very fine.

He wrote Questiones naturales mathematice astronomice, etc. The fourth part of the Opus majus entitled De utilitate mathematicae is divided as follows: 1. Utilitas mathematicae in physicis; 2. Utilitas mathematicae in divinis; 3. Judicia astronomiae; 4. Correctio calendarii; 5. Geographia; 6. Astrologia. This is supplemented by sections of the Opus minus and the Opus tertium. Volume two of the projected Compendium was to be devoted to mathematics, and Bacon planned to subdivide it into nine sections as was done by al-Fārābī; i.e., one dealing with generalities, and four times two treating respectively the theory and applications of geometry, arithmetic, astronomy, and music.

8. *Astronomy and astrology*—The preceding section deals in part with astronomy, but this must be added. Bacon was well acquainted with Greek and Arabic astronomy and much interested in the subject, but like Grosseteste, he was never able to decide between Ptolemy and al-Biṭrūjī; he found that Ptolemy's system gave a better account of the observed facts, but that al-Biṭrūjī's was more consistent with the principles of natural philosophy. His influence can be traced in the work of the French Franciscan, Bernard of Verdun, and perhaps also in that of William of Saint Cloud. He had obtained some knowledge of the strange cosmological views (solid planetary spheres) of Ibn al-Haitham and of Muḥammad ibn Aḥmad al-Kharaqī.

He was deeply interested in astrology in which he believed implicitly. However he made a clear distinction between astrology and magic. Astrology itself he divided into two kinds; a legitimate kind, and a forbidden one, mere superstition. This was very sound, in spite of the fact that much if not all of Bacon's legitimate astrology was nothing but error and superstition from our point of view.

The theory of multiplication of species referred to in sections 10 and 11 had naturally an astrological aspect—for how were astrological influences transmitted through space?—which Bacon carefully amplified.

Outside of his encyclopaedic treatises, Bacon dealt with astronomy and astrology in the De cometis and the Thesaurus spirituum. For the Speculum astronomiae see my note on Albert the Great, section 4.

9. *Calendar*—Bacon continued Grosseteste's efforts to introduce a reform of the calendar which became more and more necessary as centuries went by. He devoted two special treatises to this question; the Compotus naturalium, written in 1263–1265, and the De termino Paschali. A Kalendarium ascribed to him was made by another Franciscan (?) at Toledo, 1292, or 1297. Bacon's Compotus is a complete and masterful treatise on the subject; it includes a full history of it wherein a large number of earlier authors—Greek, Arabic, Latin—are quoted and discussed, and an elaborate criticism of the ecclesiastical and lay calendars.

10. *Mechanics*—Bacon knew some of the mechanical writings of Jordanus Nemorarius (De ponderibus; Elementa super demonstrationem ponderis?) or of the latter's school, but in this field as in others he was chiefly influenced by Grosseteste. He investigated such subjects as force and its mathematical expression, and the impossibility of a vacuum. Following Adelard of Bath he explained the impossibility of vacuum by a theory of universal continuity. On the other hand he used it as an argument against the plurality of worlds.

He gave considerable thought also to the problems relative to what we would call action at a distance. How are mechanical forces, light, astrological influences, transmitted? He discussed these problems in the Opus majus, the Opus tertium and in a treatise ad hoc De multiplicatione specierum, which was sent by him to the Pope together with the Opus majus. Bacon called "species" what we would call "action" (I do not use a more definite term on purpose) and his Multiplicatio specierum was a study of the transmission of these actions, of the propagation of efficient causality.

11. *Optics or "perspective"*—Naturally that theory of multiplication of species was especially elaborated with a view to its optical applications. In this Bacon was walking in Grosseteste's footsteps; but he had a better knowledge of the Arabic writings, e.g., those of al-Kindī and of Ibn al-Haitham. In his turn he influenced John Peckham and William of Saint Cloud. His optics was essentially based upon that of the Ibn al-Haitham, with small additions and practical applications. He made experiments with mirrors and lenses, chiefly burning lenses, and foresaw vaguely both the compound microscope and the telescope. He influenced Leonard Digges, who died c. 1571. He had some understanding of spherical aberration and of its correction by the use of paraboloidal and hyperboloidal surfaces.

In opposition to Grosseteste he claimed that the passage of light through a medium cannot be instantaneous. Light is not an emanation of particles, but the transmission of a movement (Opus majus, Bridges, vol. 2, 72). However all this is too vaguely put to be considered an anticipation of the wave theory of light.

Bacon spent a considerable amount of money in these optical experiments. He sent a lens to the Pope to induce him to experiment himself (Opus tertium, Brewer, 111).

The following writings were especially devoted to optics: De speculis comburendis; Liber de visu (sive De mensurandis distantiis). Moreover the whole of part 5 of the Opus majus, De scientia perspectiva, dealt with it, and much space was given to it in the Opus tertium.

12. *Alchemy*—Gunpowder was discovered probably within Bacon's lifetime, but there is nothing to prove that he was the inventor (I discuss this question more fully in the section on gunpowder in the chemical chapter below). He mentioned

several times inflammable mixtures, such as were used for fireworks, and he described an explosive one which was probably gunpowder. He even suggested that its explosive power would be increased if the powder were enclosed in an instrument of solid material (Opus tertium, Little, 51, 1912).

His interest in alchemy is sufficiently proved by the fact that one of the four books of his Compendium philosophiae was to be entirely devoted to it, by the amount of space given to it in the Opus minus and the Opus tertium, and by the Tractatus expositorius enigmatum alchemiae which he communicated to Clement IV. He made a distinction between practical and speculative alchemy. He was opposed to the theory of the unity of matter (Opus tertium, Brewer, 120); his "primary matter" was not the primary constituent of all substances, but on the contrary a perfect and final blending of the elements.

A great many other alchemical writings are ascribed to him: Epistola de secretis operibus naturae et de nullitate magiae (or De mirabili potestate artis et naturae); Excerpta de libro Avicennae De anima; Breve breviarium (De naturis metallorum in ratione alkimica et artificiali transformatione; Caelestis alchymia; De naturis metallorum et ipsorum transmutatione; Breviloquium alkimiae);[27] Tractatus trium verborum (Epistolae tres ad Johannem Parisiensem); De leone viridi (on the manufacture of mercury, etc.); Speculum alchemiae (De transmutatione metallorum); Speculum secretorum (Liber secretorum de spiritu occulto); Speculum secretorum naturae de laude lapidis philosophorum; Editio super Geberem de tribus ordinibus medicine; Compendium alkymie; Epistola de spiritu occulto in sulphure et arsenico; Tractatus de quibusdam aquis alkimicis; De oleo stibii; De consideratione quintae essentiae, Semita recta alchemiae (Liber duodecim aquarum), etc. Some of these writings are probably apocryphal.

The most important of Bacon's chemical writings are the Tractatus expositorius and the Epistola de secretis operibus naturae. The ascription of the invention of gunpowder to him was based upon a cipher contained in this Epistola. However this cipher has no MS. authority whatever; it was probably nothing more than a copyist's blunder.

13. *Natural history*—In addition to his questions on the Aristotelian De plantis (or De vegetabilibus), Bacon had planned to deal with the "Scientia de plantarum natura et animalium . . . . praeterquam de homine" in the Compendium philosophiae.

14. *Geography*—The geographical section of the Opus majus (in the mathematical part) contained information on the less known countries of the world, derived not only from ancient geographers and from Aethicus Ister but also from recent travelers, notably William of Rubruquis. Bacon insisted upon the habitability of the southern hemisphere. He explained to the Pope the importance of undertaking a complete and accurate survey of the world, and appended to his treatise a parchment mappemonde whereupon the coordinates of the principal places were fixed (this map is lost). He indicated the possibility of reaching the Indies by sailing westward from Spain, and assumed that these countries were considerably nearer than they are. This was known indirectly to Columbus (through Peter of Ailly's Imago mundi) and may have been one of his incentives.

[27] It begins "Breve breviarium breviter abbreviatum sufficit intelligenti."

15. *Medicine*—Bacon wrote a number of medical treatises which were derived essentially from the Arabic writings and proved little originality (except one of them). Believing as he did in astrology, he naturally insisted upon the astrological side of medicine.

The longest and best known of these writings, the Liber de retardatione accidentium senectutis, was also the poorest. It was written relatively early (it was probably his first publication) when his mind was still undeveloped. In spite of its mediocrity it was plagiarized c. 1309–1311 by Arnold of Villanova under the title De conservanda juventute et retardanda senectute, and Villanova's edition was translated into Italian and into English. Bacon's own work was Englished by Richard Browne (London 1683).

Other medical writings ascribed to Bacon: Summaria expositio epistole predicte; De universali regimine senum et seniorum; De balneis senum et seniorum; De compositione quarundam medicinarum; Antidotarius; Liber (sermo) de conservatione juventutis; De graduatione medicinarum compositarum; Canones practici de medicinis compositis componendis; De erroribus medicorum.

The last named treatise, written when Bacon had finally discovered the experimental point of view, is by far the most valuable. His criticism of physicians and apothecaries leads him to summarize his philosophic and scientific ideals and to explain once more the supremacy of experimentation over authority or argument (Little's edition, 170, 1928; similar statements may be found in Opus majus, Bridges, vol. 2, 167; and in the Compendium studii, Brewer, 397). However the De erroribus is followed by miscellaneous notes on drugs and recipes (Dicitur quod pillule et trocisci . . .) which do not give us a very high idea of his own medical knowledge.

The Rogerina major and the Rogerina minor, two medical treatises, were not composed by Bacon; one was written by Roger Baron. They were printed in Venice, 1498.

16. *Experimental science*—Bacon's greatness as an experimental philosopher has been very much exaggerated. He made few experiments himself and in a sense he never understood the experimental method as we now understand it. Much of the praise bestowed upon him is based upon his own irresponsible statements. Like his countryman, Francis Bacon, more than three centuries later, he gave many precepts which he never followed himself. But what of it? Was it not—in his time—an immense achievement to speak of the superior value, of the indispensableness, of experimentation as he did repeatedly? (See references quoted in section 15.)

A whole part of the Opus majus, out of seven, was devoted to experimental science, and he came back to it in the two other Opera. He was careful to distinguish between external and internal experience (scientia experimentalis, per sensus exteriores; scientia interior, intuitiva), a distinction which was unfortunately lost by many of the later philosophers. Bacon was primarily interested in external or objective experience. To be sure some of the experiments proposed by him were fantastic, and in spite of his own efforts to separate experimentation from magic, he did not always succeed. However, the essential soundness of his experimental point of view is proved by his readiness to sacrifice theories to facts and to confess his own ignorance.

17. *Philosophy*—Bacon's philosophy is explained in his Aristotelian commentaries, in the Metaphysica de viciis contractis in studio theologiae (c. 1266)—we have only a fragment of it—in the Opus majus, and finally in his last work, the Compendium studii theologiae (1292). To appreciate it correctly, one must bear in mind that Bacon was not a philosopher stricto sensu; the apparent or real contradictions of his thought were due to the complexity of his nature, half seer, half scientist.

His main sources were Aristotle, St. Augustine, Isḥāq al-Isrā'īlī, Ibn Gabirol, Ibn Sīnā, Ibn Rushd, Pedro Alfonso, Grosseteste, and other English Franciscans. He was an Augustinian (i.e., a Platonist), a bold realist and pluralist, antagonistic to Thomism. Yet he deeply admired Aristotle and claimed to have a purer knowledge of him than was available in the Latin translations used by his contemporaries; he probably referred to the knowledge he had obtained through Ibn Rushd, but his understanding of Aristotle was far from perfect; witness his own inveterate Platonism.[28] For example, he took considerable pains to prove that Aristotle had not taught the theory of the eternity of the world (he had taught it of course).

He had a strong belief in the unity of knowledge, but that unity was accounted for by him as a subordination of all knowledge to theology. No knowledge would ever have been possible without divine revelation. It is interesting to compare these views with his experimental philosophy.

This mixture of mysticism and scientific positivism was Bacon's main characteristic; each ingredient would explain his growing impatience with metaphysical discussion; the combination of both was overpowering. Bacon was not a philosopher, but he was one of the greatest thinkers of all ages.

18. *Summa philosophiae*—This is perhaps the best place to speak of a large Baconian encyclopaedia entitled Tractatus difficilium ad scientiam veram universaliter spectantium. It was formerly ascribed to Robert Grosseteste, and was called in late MSS. Summa philosophiae domini Lincolniensis, or Summa Lincolniensis, but it is certainly a later work. Alexander of Hales and Albert the Great are quoted in it, and there is a reference (interpolated?) to the famous comet of 1264. Its spirit and language are clearly Baconian; it was probably composed not by Bacon but by a disciple of his.

It is divided into nineteen treatises, as follows: (1) rise of philosophy in Chaldaea and Egypt; history of Greek, Arabic, and Christian philosophy, etc.; (2) truth; (3) science; (4) matter; (5) form; (6) virtue;[29] (7) first cause; (8) universe, one but not eternal; (9) bodies, space, vacuum; (10) intelligence and intelligences; (11) rational soul; (12) sensitive soul; (13) vegetative soul; (14) light; (15) celestial spheres; (16) nature, universal and particular, and natural virtue; (17) four elements and qualities and their combinations; (18) meteorology, tides, saltness of the sea; (19) minerals, precious stones, seven metals, sulphur, mercury. It is interesting to compare this encyclopaedia with the De proprietatibus rerum of Bartholomew the Englishman, and the De natura rerum of Thomas of Cantimpré, both of which are also divided into nineteen parts. The three plans are very different.

The Summa philosophiae is especially remarkable because of the abundance of

[28] Si enim haberem potestatem super libros Aristotelis ego facerem omnes cremari, quia non est nisi temporis amissio studere in illis, et causa erroris et multiplicatio ignorantiae, ultra id quod valeat explicari (Compendium studii, Brewer, 469).

[29] Est autem virtus vigor alicuius actionis vel passionis causalis.

Muslim and Jewish elements which it contains. About thirty Muslim and Jewish doctors are quoted, ending with Maimonides whom the author thought had been converted to Christianity! This gives us a poor idea of his own orthodoxy.

Speaking of the comet of 1264, a treatise was devoted to it by the Dominican Giles, De essentia motu et significatione cometarum.[30]

The Summa philosophiae was edited by Ludwig Baur: Die philosophischen Werke des Robert Grosseteste (Beiträge zur Geschichte der Philosophie des Mittelalters, vol. 9, 275–643, Münster i. W., 1912). P. Duhem: Système du monde (vol. 3, 460–471, 1915). Duhem's discussion of the astronomical ideas of the Summa is followed (p. 472–484) by the analysis of a contemporary treatise on astronomy written by an unknown disciple of Bacon. Lynn Thorndike: History of magic (vol. 2, 448–453, 1923).

19. *Philology*—Bacon, realizing the supreme importance of the texts written in Greek, Hebrew and Arabic, insisted upon the necessity of studying these languages. This was really the first door to knowledge; the only means of approaching the sources of ancient wisdom. The third part of the Opus majus was entirely devoted to explaining the utility of linguistic studies, De utilitate grammaticae. The first volume of the Compendium philosophiae was planned to deal with grammar and logic. We have two important extracts from it, a complete Greek grammar, and incomplete Hebrew one.

While the need of languages for theological, philosophic and scientific purposes was foremost in his mind, he pointed out also other uses, diplomatic, missionary, and commercial. In his arguments for the study of Hebrew he anticipated Reuchlin. He realized that the best means of studying it was with the help of a Jew. He had a genuine interest in comparative philology. He suggested that Arabic, Hebrew, and Chaldaean were dialects of the same language. However it is doubtful whether he had any but the most superficial knowledge of Arabic.

He denounced the imperfection of the Latin versions of Aristotle and of the Bible. He insisted upon the urgency of recovering St. Jerome's text, and explained how it could be done. He thus laid down some of the principles of textual criticism.

To return to his Greek grammar, his work had been prepared for by Grosseteste and John Basingstoke, yet he was the first scholar in western Christendom to complete such a grammar for Latin use.

J. E. Sandys: History of classical scholarship (vol. 1, 3d. ed., 589–598, 1921).

20. *Biblical studies*—It is very misleading to represent Bacon as a sort of anticlerical prophet. He spoke ill of many clerics, but was not by any means anticlerical; he was or tried to be very orthodox, and considered the study of the Bible as of fundamental importance. Indeed the moral necessity of knowing the Holy Scriptures as exactly as possible was his primary argument for the study of Hebrew and Greek. All knowledge is explicitly or implicitly set forth in the Bible, and no effort should be spared to make that knowledge as clear and available as possible. In short, Bacon was in many respects what we would call a "fundamentalist," preaching repeatedly a return to the Bible, away from modern works such as the Books of sentences of Peter the Lombard to which theologians were giving undue importance.

[30] There are many Dominicans named Giles who flourished c. 1264–1300. He might be identical, e.g., with Giles of Lessines who was interested in eclipses (see above).

Like the majority of his contemporaries, Bacon believed in the approaching epiphany of Antichrist, and he made a special study of that problem.

21. *Attitude to Israel and to Islām*—His Hebrew studies and his need of Jewish collaboration may have induced him to consider the Jews with more kindness than was usual. At any rate his toleration of them was very remarkable and may have helped to make him obnoxious to other people. He shared the belief of most Jews and of many of his own contemporaries that the Hebrew culture was the original one from which the Greek had been derived at a later time. (According to various Jewish traditions, Aristotle had obtained his knowledge from Jewish sources, or was himself of Jewish race, or had become a Jewish proselyte).[31] In the Opus tertium (Brewer, p. 28) he says a good word for the Jews who lived in Palestine at the time of the Crucifixion.

One of his arguments for the study of Hebrew and Arabic was the need of these languages to convert unbelievers to Christianity. He realized the utter futility of the Crusades with respect to their avowed purpose. Persuasion will succeed where violence must fail, but people cannot be persuaded unless they be evangelized in their own language (Opus majus, Bridges, 120–125). In this respect he makes one think of Ramon Lull; he was a very poor orientalist as compared with Ramon, but he was far more consistent in his distrust of material strength.

22. *Baconian legends*—The experiments made or suggested by Bacon, his visionary inventions, failed to be appreciated for a considerable time, or rather, what is worse, they were misunderstood, and there emerged gradually the legend of Friar Bacon, the wonderworker. All sorts of magical powers were ascribed to him. This legend can be traced back to the fourteenth century; by 1385 it was already known in such a distant country as Dalmatia. It grew rapidly in the fifteenth and sixteenth century and was finally established by a play of Robert Greene (1560?–1592): "The honorable historie of Frier Bacon and Frier Bongay" (played with various "magical" properties; printed 1594, 1630, etc.), and by a London chapbook dating from about the same time: "The famous historie of Frier Bacon containing the wonderful things that he did in his life, also the manner of his death with the lives and deaths of the two conjurers Bungey and Vandermast" (reprinted 1627, 1638, etc.).

This aspect of the Baconian legend has been recently reinforced by the discovery "in an ancient castle in Southern Europe" of an ancient MS. written in cipher and ascribed to Bacon. If authentic, Bacon should be credited with the invention and actual use of telescope and compound microscope, and with the discovery of seminiferous tubes, cells with nuclei, spermatozoa, etc. Such inventions and discoveries in that time would have been truly magical. Needless to say, they are entirely unsubstantiated. (Isis, 11, 141–145).

An entirely different legend dating from modern times represents him as a martyr of science and of the freedom of thought. This is doubly misleading, for Bacon was a scientist but not a free thinker, as this phrase is generally understood. He was a very original thinker, a forerunner of modern science; he was outspoken and uncautious, yet very orthodox, and in many ways, a fundamentalist. On the other hand, if he was imprisoned by order of his Franciscan superiors this was

[31] Louis Ginzberg: Aristotle in Jewish legend (Jewish encyclopaedia, vol. 2, 98, 1902). Joseph Heller: Encyclopaedia judaica (vol. 3, 338–340, 1929).

apparently a matter of internal discipline. Granted that he suffered for the originality of his mind and the eccentricities of his character, his martyrdom is not established, and he was not in any sense a forerunner of the modern rationalists, nor even of the Reformers. For him, theology was still the crown of all knowledge, and the Bible its repository.

23. *Text. Earlier texts to be printed*—The best proof of Bacon's eclipse is the absence of incunabula editions, and the rarity of sixteenth century ones and of translations. For example, it is remarkable that none of his works was translated into Hebrew.

The first books to be printed were alchemical, the Speculum alchemiae, the Epistola de secretis operibus naturae, and the De consideratione quintae essentiae. The first and third are doubtful; the second is probably genuine, except perhaps the last five chapters.

The Speculum alchemiae was printed in Nuremberg, 1541. It was reprinted in the Theatrum chemicum of Lazarus Zetzner (Strassburg 1659), in the Thesaurus of Jean Jacques Manget (Geneva 1702). French translation, 1557; reprinted 1612, 1627, under the title Miroir de maistre Jean Mehun (i.e., John of Meung). English translation, 1597, and in the Medicina practica of William Salmon (London 1692, 1707).

The Epistola de secretis was first printed in Paris, 1542. Later editions: Oxford, 1594; Hamburg 1618; in Zetzner's and Manget's collections above mentioned, 1659, 1702; in Brewer's Opera inedita (1859). French translation by Jacques Girard de Tournus (Lyon 1557; Paris 1558). English translation, together with the Speculum (London 1597, 1659). New English translation by Tenney L. Davis: Letter concerning the marvelous power of art and of nature and concerning the nullity of magic (76 p., Easton, Pa., 1923; Isis, 7, 537).

The De consideratione quintae essentiae was printed in Basel, 1561, 1597.

The next work to appear in print was medical, De retardandis senectutis accidentibus et de sensibus conservandis. First edition by John Williams (Oxford 1590). New edition 1928, see below. Englished by Richard Browne: The cure of old age and preservation of youth (London 1683).

A number of alchemical tracts were printed in Francfort, 1603: De arte chymiae scripta (reprinted in 1620 under the title Thesaurus chemicus). That collection included the Excerpta libro Avicennae de anima, Breve breviarium, Tractatus trium verborum, De leone viridi, Speculum secretorum.

The Specula mathematica in quibus de specierum multiplicatione . . . . agitur edited by Ludwig Combach (Francfort 1614) included fragments of the Opus majus and the De speculis comburentibus.

The De oleo stibii was printed in the Currus triumphalis antimonii fratris Basilii Valentini (Toulouse 1646).

This ends the list of the early publications; considering the number of Bacon's writings, it is astonishingly small, and the main works were left out.

24. *Text. The three Opera and collections*—First edition of the Opus majus by Samuel Jebb (folio vol., London 1733). Improved edition, Accedit prologus galeatus in reliqua ejusdem auctoris (Venice 1750). These two editions included only parts I to VI. New edition, including part VII, by John Henry Bridges (2 vols., Oxford 1897), with notes and index. Unfortunately the text of the first three parts was unsatisfactory and Bridges was obliged to publish a revised edition of them in a third volume (204 p., London 1900); with corrections and additional notes. For the history of Bridges' edition, see his biography by his niece, Suzan Liveing (278 p., London 1926; Isis, 10, 208). English translation of the Opus majus by Robert Belle Burke (2 vols., 894 p., 8 pl., Philadelphia 1928). Translation based upon Bridges' corrected text with index, but without notes (Isis, 11, 138–141).

Tractatus de multiplicatione specierum. Published by Jebb between parts V and VI of the Opus majus, and by Bridges at the end of it. It is indeed an independent work, though sent to Clement IV together with the Opus. See also Bridges (vol. 3, 183–186).

John Sherren Brewer: Opera quaedam hactenus inedita. Vol. I containing I. Opus tertium, II. Opus minus; III. Compendium philosophiae (no more published; 673 p., London 1859). This includes also the letters exchanged between Clement IV and Bacon in 1266.

Further editions of the Opus minus. F. A. Gasquet: An unpublished fragment (English historical review, vol. 12, 494–517, 1897). Part II of the Opus minus, De notitia caelestium, may be identical with the treatise on astrology included in Bridges' edition (vol. 1, 376–404).

For the Opus tertium, see Pierre Duhem: Un fragment inédit de l'Opus tertium (198 p., Quaracchi 1909). This text was entitled in the Parisian MS. used by Duhem, Liber tertius Alpetragii, i.e., it was ascribed to al-Biṭrūjī. It deals with optics and astronomy—including a careful analysis of the systems of Ptolemy and al-Biṭrūjī without conclusion in favor of the one or the other—experimental science, morals, alchemy, generation and corruption. The alchemical part (p. 181–190) is Bacon's Tractatus expositorius enigmatum alchemiae. A. G. Little: Part of the Opus tertium including a fragment now printed for the first time (British Society of Franciscan studies, vol. 4, 140 p., Aberdeen 1912). This fragment (p. 1–19) fills the gap remaining between the texts edited by Brewer and by Duhem; the rest of Little's text is essentially the same as Duhem's.

The lack of a complete edition of Bacon's work is a real shame. In 1921 more than half of his writings was still unpublished. Apropos of the celebration of Bacon's seventh centenary in Oxford, 1914 (Isis, 2, 164; Nature, 100, 138, 1917), it was decided to publish his unknown works as fast as possible. In the meanwhile, a series of Bacon editions had been undertaken by Robert Steele under the general title Opera hactenus inedita Rogeri Baconi (Oxford University Press). The following parts have appeared (edited by Steele unless otherwise stated).

(1) Metaphysica. De viciis contractis in studio theologiae (64 p., 1905).

(2–3) Liber primus communium naturalium (318 p., 1911).

(4) Liber secundus communium naturalium. De celestibus (p. 309–456).

(5) Secretum secretorum, cum glossis et notulis. Tractatus brevis et utilis ad declarandum quedam obscure dicta. Accedunt versio anglicana ex arabico edita per A. S. Fulton, versio vetusta anglo-normanica nunc primum edita (382 p., 1920). For the original Secretum secretorum, the Sirr al-asrār, see vol. 1, 556. Bacon completed this edition of it c. 1257, and added an introduction to it c. 1270. He considered the Secretum as a genuine Aristotelian work and was much influenced by it.

(6) Compotus. Accedunt compotus Roberti Grossecapitis, Massa compoti Alexandri de Villa Dei (330 p., 1926).

(7) Questiones supra undecimum prime philosophie Aristotelis (Metaphysica XII). (172 p., 1926.)

(8) Questiones supra libros physicorum Aristotelis (306 p., 1928). Nos. 7 and 8 were edited by Steele and Ferdinand M. Delorme.

(9) De retardatione accidentium senectutis. Cum aliis opusculis de rebus medicinalibus. Edited by A. G. Little and E. Withington (268 p., 1928; Isis, 13, 110–111). The same book has appeared simultaneously as part 14 of the publications of the British Society of Franciscan studies. The alii opusculi are: Summaria expositio epistole predicte, De universali regimine senum et seniorum, De balneis senum et seniorum, De compositione quarundam medicinarum, Antidotarius, Liber (sermo) de conservatione juventutis, De graduatione medicinarum, De erroribus medicorum. In appendix: Extract from the Liber sex scientiarum; De diebus criticis (two treatises).

Of these two treatises De diebus criticis, the first had been edited before by Friedrich Palitzsch: Bacons zweite (astrologische) Schrift über die kritischen Tage (Diss., 38 p., Leipzig 1918), the second, by Hans Elfferding: Bacons Schriften über die kritischen Tage (Diss., 48 p., Erfurt 1913). The new editors suggest that the first may have been composed by Bacon and Grosseteste in collaboration; the genuineness of the second is doubtful.

(10) Questiones super libros primie philosophie Aristotelis (Metaphysica, I, II, V–X). Edited by Steele and Ferdinand M. Delorme (392 p., 1930).

25. *Text. Separate editions not yet mentioned*—Edmond Nolan and S. A. Hirsch: The Greek grammar of Bacon and a fragment of his Hebrew grammar (287 p., Cambridge, 1902).

Compendium studii theologiae edited by Hastings Rashdall (British Society of Franciscan studies, vol. 3, Aberdeen 1911; text, p. 25–69).

26. *Bibliography of Bacon's writings*—A bibliography compiled by A. G. Little was printed in appendix to Rashdall's edition of the Compendium studii theologiae (71–118, 1911). A revised edition of it appeared in 1914 in the Bacon Essays, collected by Little (p. 375–426).

27. *General criticism*—Emile Charles: Bacon. Sa vie, ses ouvrages, ses doctrines d'après des textes inédits (thesis, 432 p., Paris 1861). M. W. Ivanovsky in the Chrestomathy on mediaeval history edited by P. G. Vinogradoff (Moscow 1898; in Russian).

The seventh centenary in 1914 was the occasion of many publications. John Henry Bridges: The life and work of Bacon. Edited with additional notes and tables by H. Gordon Jones (173 p., London 1914). This is an improved edition of Bridges' preface to the Opus majus, 1897. Bacon essays collected and edited by A. G. Little (434 p., Oxford 1914). The contributors were A. G. Little, Ludwig Baur on Grosseteste's influence; François Picavet; Cardinal Gasquet on Bacon's criticism of the Latin Vulgate; S. A. Hirsch on philology; D. E. Smith on mathematics; Eilhard Wiedemann and Sebastian Vogl on optics; J. Würschmidt on scientific method apropos of Bacon's De speculis, P. Duhem on the vacuum; M. M. Pattison Muir on alchemy, H. W. L. Hime on gunpowder; E. Withington on medicine; Sir John Edwin Sandys on Bacon in English literature. The excellent bibliography completing this volume has already been mentioned.

Collections of commemorative essays were published in the Rivista di filosofia neo-scolastica (anno 6, fasc. 6, Firenze 1914) and in the Open Court (vol. 28, p. 449 sq., Chicago 1914; Isis, 3, 324). See also J. Thirion in the Revue des questions scientifiques (vol. 26, 227–240, Bruxelles 1914); Sir John Edwin Sandys in the Proceedings of the British Academy (vol. 6, 18 p., London 1914). A pageant of the thirteenth century for the 700th anniversary of Bacon given by Columbia University, the plan and the notes by John J. Cross, the text by John Erskine, the illustrations by Claggett Wilson (75 p., New York 1914).

Robert Steele: Bacon and the state of science in the thirteenth century (Studies in the history of science, vol. 2, 121–150, Oxford 1921; Isis, 4, 404). Lynn Thorndike: History of magic (vol. 2, 616–717, 1923). The last 26 p. deal with the Speculum astronomiae traditionally ascribed to Albert the Great, but which Father Mandonnet considers Baconian; Thorndike favors the ascription to Albert. A. G. Little: R. Bacon (Annual lecture on a master mind, British Academy, vol. 14, 34 p., London 1928; Isis, 13, 430).

28. *Mathematics*—David Eugene Smith: The place of R. Bacon in the history of mathematics (Commemoration Essays, 153–183, 1914).

29. *Astronomy and physics*—Sebastian Vogl: Die Physik Bacons (Diss., Erlangen 1906). P. Duhem: Origines de la statique (vol. 1, 354–355, 1905; showing that Bacon knew some of the writings of the Nemorarius school); Etudes sur Léonard de Vinci (vol. 2, 366, 1909, statics; 410–411, against the plurality of worlds

and the possibility of vacuum); Système du monde (vol. 3, 260–277, 1915; Bacon's lectures on Aristotelian physics; 411–442, compotus, opus majus; 499–520, on astronomical canons which may possibly be ascribed to Bacon and on the camera obscura with the text of a Bordeaux MS. relative to the latter; vol. 5, 375–411, 1917, Bacon's lectures on Aristotelian physics and metaphysics). Essays in the Bacon Essays by E. Wiedemann, S. Vogl, J. Würschmidt, P. Duhem (Oxford 1914). Theodore Otto Wedel: The mediaeval attitude toward astrology particularly in England (New Haven 1920; Isis, 4, 186). Charles Singer: Steps leading to the invention of the first optical apparatus (Studies in the history and method of science, vol. 2, 394–398, Oxford 1921; very clear account; see also vol. I. of same series, pl. 38). Raoul Carton: L'expérience physique chez Roger Bacon (thèse, 188 p., Paris 1924; Isis, 8, 540). Adam Bednarski: Die anatomischen Augenbilder in den Handschriften des Roger Bacon, Johann Peckham und Witelo (Archiv für Geschichte der Medizin, vol. 24, 60–78, 16 figs., 1931).

30. *Chemistry*—John Ferguson: Bibliotheca chemica (vol. 1, 63–66, 1906). Bacon Essays, contributions by M. M. Pattison Muir and H. W. L. Hime (Oxford 1914). Henry W. L. Hime: The origin of artillery (112–116, London 1915). E. O. von Lippmann: Entstehung der Alchemie (493, 1919). Lynn Thorndike: History of magic (vol. 2, 668–691, 1923). Tenney L. Davis: Bacon's gunpowder (Army ordnance, 3, 280, 1923); Bacon's formula was 6 parts of saltpeter, 5 of charcoal and 5 of sulphur. Ad. Clement: Sur l'indication de la composition de la poudre à feu chez Bacon (Archivio di storia della scienza, 7, 4–5, 1926; Isis, 10, 127). Tenney L. Davis: Bacon's De mirabili potestate. Query 6 (Isis, 9, 425, 1927; 11, 127, 1928). Robert Steele: Luru vopo vir can utriet (Nature, 121, 208–209, 1928); these words have no MS. authority whatever (Isis, 11, 428). T. L. Davis: Bacon's gunpowder and his secret wisdom (Industrial and engineering chemistry, 20, 772, etc., 1928; reprint, 6 p.).

Karl Sudhoff: Eine alchemistische Schrift des 13. Jahrhunderts, betitelt Speculum alkimiae minus, eines bisher unbekannten Mönches Simeon von Köln (Archiv für Gesch. der Naturwiss., vol. 9, 53–67, 1922; Isis, 8, 743). This text is the one generally ascribed to Bacon; see Aleksander Birkenmajer: Simeon von Köln oder Roger Bacon? (Franziskanische Studien, vol. 11, 307, 1924). Brother Simon of Cologne is otherwise unknown.

31. *Medicine*—Article by E. Withington in Bacon Essays (Oxford 1914). R. Steele: A mediaeval panacea (Proc. R. Soc. of med., hist. sect., vol. 10, 93, London 1917). Tenney L. Davis: Bacon's sound views on the practice of medicine (Medical Life, vol. 31, 473–478, 1924). Else Förster: Bacon's De retardandis senectutis accidentibus et de sensibus conservandis and Villanova's De conservanda iuventute et retardanda senectute (Diss., 19 p., Leipzig 1924). The author compares both treatises, claiming that Villanova's treatise was not influenced by Bacon's anterior treatise on the same subject. Clement Charles Julian Webb: Bacon on Alphonse of Poitiers (Essays presented to R. L. Poole, 290–300, Oxford 1927; Isis, 11, 175). For the anatomy of the eye, see §29 (Bednarski, 1931).

32. *Philosophy*—G. A. Manser: Bacon und seine Gewährsmänner, speziel Aristoteles (Jahrbuch für Philosophie und spekulative Theologie, vol. 27, 1912). Clemens Baeumker: Bacons Naturphilosophie, insbesondere seine Lehren von Materie und Form, Individuation und Universalität (revised reprint from Franziskanische Studien, 3, 80 p., Münster i. W., 1916). Bacon Essays, contributions by A. G. Little, Ludwig Baur, F. Picavet (Oxford 1924). Raoul Carton: L'expérience mystique chez Bacon (376 p., Paris 1924); La synthèse doctrinale de Bacon (150 p., Paris 1924; Isis, 8, 540). M. De Wulf: Mediaeval philosophy (vol. 2, 134–146, 1926). Andrew George Little: Thomas Docking and his relation to Bacon (Essays presented to Reginald Lane Poole, 301–331, Oxford 1927; Isis, 11, 175).

33. *Baconian legends*—Greene's play was reprinted in Adolphus William Ward:

Old English drama (Oxford 1878). The chapbook in William John Thoms: Early English prose romances (vol. 1, 1858). In his story, The merchant and the friar (2d ed., 258 p., London 1844), Sir Francis Palgrave represented Bacon as the expounder of mediaeval science but his main purpose was to explain some important passages of the ancient English constitution. See J. E. Sandys' essay in Little's collection (359–372, 1914).

Abbé P. Feret: Histoire des emprisonnements de Bacon (Revue des questions historiques, vol. 50, 119–142, 1891).

Facsimiles of the MS. dealt with in section 22 have appeared in the Illustrated London News (May 20, 1920). John M. Manly: The most mysterious manuscript in the world (Harper's Magazine, July, 1921; Isis, 4, 404). William Romaine Newbold: The cipher of R. Bacon. Edited with foreword and notes by Roland Grubb Kent (256 p., 33 pl., Philadelphia 1928). Elaborate study of the cipher and of the contents of the MS. as far as it was deciphered at the time of Newbold's death; fantastic (Isis, 11, 141–145). Raoul Carton: Le chiffre de R. Bacon (Revue d'histoire de la philosophie, 3, 31–66, 165–179, 1929; Isis, 13, 429).

DUNS. SCOT

Scotch Franciscan, philosopher, theologian; the most influential philosopher of his order. Joannes Duns Scotus. Doctor subtilis. Born in Ulster, or more probably in Northumberland; probably in 1265; studied in Oxford where he learned to love science and to hate Thomism; he assumed the Franciscan habit, when and where is unknown; he taught in Oxford and Paris; in 1308 he went to Cologne, and he died there within that year.

A survey of his thought is especially difficult because of the number of doubtful writings, which some critics ascribe to him and others not, and of the uncertain chronological order of those accepted as authentic. A detailed analysis would at once involve discussions as to the authenticity or date of this or that work, and therefore it will answer our purpose best to speak of his activity and thought only in a more general way.

Duns Scot's most important work was his questions on the Sentences of Peter Lombard, often called Opus oxoniense which would suggest that it was written in Oxford. However it seems to have been composed c. 1301–1305; i.e., partly in Paris. He also wrote Quaestiones in metaphysicam, De primo principio, Reportata parisiensa (a second commentary on the Sentences, collected by his Paris students), Quodlibeta.

The ascriptions of the commentaries on the Organon and on the De anima are doubtful. The following works are now considered apocryphal: commentaries on the Physics and Meteorology (the latter is now ascribed to another English Franciscan, Simon Tunsted, d. 1369), Expositio in XII libros metaphysicorum (Metaphysica textualis), Theoremata (posterior to William of Occam), Quaestiones disputatae de rerum principio, Grammatica speculativa. The alchemical treatises, Tractatus ad album et rubrum, De veritate et virtute lapidis philosophici, are certainly apocryphal.

The Grammatica speculativa (or, De modis significandi) was one of the earliest attempts to treat the subject philosophically. See my notes on John of Garland (first half of the thirteenth century), and on Siger of Courtrai (first half of the fourteenth century). It has been ascribed to Thomas of Erfurt (first half of the fourteenth century), to Albert of Saxony (second half of the fourteenth century), and to others.

To return to Duns Scot. He was a sharp but constructive critic of contemporary thought, especially of Thomism. Indeed the movement named after him, Scotism, was largely a movement of opposition against Thomism. It represented an extreme form of realism and anti-intellectualism. In contrast with St. Thomas' attempts to harmonize faith and reason, the sphere of rational thought was gradually restricted by the Scotists. Critics of the neo-scholastic school have taken pains to minimize the differences between Duns Scot and St. Thomas; making allowances for possible exaggerations in that direction, it is clear that the differences are not as great as was thought when various writings ascribed to Duns Scot were wrongly believed to be genuine.

It is probable that whatever differences there were between Scotism and Thomism they were accentuated by the growing rivalry and hostility between the Franciscans and Dominicans. To illustrate that hostility, it is well to say a few words concerning one of the main bones of contention. Duns Scot defended the doctrine of the Immaculate Conception (i.e., that the Virgin Mother of Christ herself had been conceived without original sin); the Dominicans opposed it; Duns Scot was supported by the Franciscans and later by the Jesuits and the Sorbonne. After more than five and a half centuries of bickering, the matter was finally settled in favor of the Franciscan party. The bull Ineffabilis Deus, issued by Pius IX on Dec. 8, 1854, established the doctrine of the Immaculate Conception as a dogma of the Roman Catholic Church. (It includes a brief history of the movement which led to the pontifical definition of the new dogma.) Before 1855, Thomists opposed that doctrine on St. Thomas' authority; since 1855 they teach it on the same authority.

Duns Scot tried to be well informed on scientific subjects. His astronomy, inspired by Bernard of Verdun and other Franciscans, was distinctly pro-Ptolemaic. Of course this was of a piece with his general attitude, which was anti-Aristotelian.

He had been influenced by Ibn Sīnā and Maimonides, but above all by Ibn Gabirol. His anti-intellectualism had the unexpected good result of preparing for the divorce between philosophy and theology, a process of dissolution greatly accelerated by Occam and the Occamists during the fourteenth century. In proportion as the domain of rational thought was narrowed, the alliance between theology and philosophy became more and more unsatisfactory to the philosophers. Duns had hoped to increase their subjugation; instead of which he caused their revolt and their final emancipation. So great was the influence of Ibn Gabirol upon Duns Scot that the history of Scotism is necessarily a history of Avicebronism. This special stream of thought can be easily followed until the very end of the sixteenth century among the Italian neo-Platonists; e.g., traces of Avicebronism can be detected in the writings of Giordano Bruno.

To understand the favor with which Scotism was received it suffices to bear in mind that it was a sort of mystical reaction against Aristotelianism, and Aristotelianism, in whatever form, could never be a popular doctrine; it demanded too much effort. Scotism represented the extreme right of philosophical thought, while Averroism represented the extreme left. St. Thomas, like al-Ghazzālī two centuries before (Isis, 13, 420), was trying to keep the middle path between these two extremes. The popular success of the extreme right, of what we might call the "fundamentalists," was not surprising. With regard to Duns Scot, this success is sufficiently proved by the great number of early editions.

However, it had its unpleasant side, which is immortalized to this day by the

English word "dunce." Indeed that word is derived from Duns' own name. The Scotists were the defenders of scholastic traditions against Thomism and other novelties; before the end of the sixteenth century they had become the symbols of scholasticism at its worst, and obscurantism; they were already so much ridiculed by humanists and reformers, that a "Duns man," or a dunce, came to mean a hair-splitting reasoner, a cavilling sophist, a dullard, and a fool.

Duns Scot's attitude to the Jews was far less charitable than that of St. Thomas. For example, he favored the forcible baptism of children (and even of parents!) which St. Thomas justly denounced.

Text—1. Opus oxoniense. Questiones super IV libros Sententiarum. First printed, in an abbreviated form, edited by John of Cologne, together with the Quodlibeta, the questions on the Metaphysics, and the De anima (388 leaves, Venice 1472). Complete editions: Venice 1477; Nuremberg 1481; Venice 1490?, 1497; Paris 1513, 1518; Venice 1597; Paris 1600; Valencia 1603; Saragossa 1614; Venice 1617; Antwerp 1620 (edition followed by Wadding in 1639); Paris 1661; Zug 1702. Modern edition by M. Fernandez Garcia (2 vols., Quaracchi 1913–1914).

There were also many editions of separate books. Book I, Venice 1472, 1506; Coimbra 1609.

Book II. Venice 1474.

Book III. Valencia 1624.

Book IV. Nuremberg 1474; Paris 1497; 1519.

2. Reportata parisiensia. First edition of book 1, as abridged by William of Alnwick (d. 1449), Bologna 1478. Second edition of book 1 by Thomas Penketh (d. 1487), Venice 1481. Later editions, presumably complete: Venice 1505; Paris 1517–1518; Venice 1522, 1607; Cologne 1635.

3. Quaestiones quodlibetales. First edition by Thomas Penketh, Venice 1474. Later editions: Venice 1477, 1490? 1497; Paris 1513, 1519; Lyon 1520, 1530.

4. Quaestiones super libros Metaphysicorum. Venice 1497, 1499.

5. Conclusiones utilissimae metaphysicae. Venice 1503.

6. Expositio in XII libros Metaphysicorum. Venice 1501; Paris 1520.

7. Quaestiones de anima. Venice 1485?, 1517.

8. Logicalia. Barcelona 1475?; Venice 1483, 1485, 1490, 1492, 1493, 1497; Paris 1504; Venice 1512, 1583, 1600, 1610; Ursel 1622.

9. Quaestiones in VIII libros Physicorum. Paris 1513 (under the name of John Marsilius of Inghen), Venice 1516, 1617; Cologne 1618.

10. Grammatica speculativa. St. Albans 1480 (under the name of Albert of Saxony); London 1497?; Venice 1499, 1512; London 1515; Paris 1520, 1605. Modern edition by M. Fernandez Garcia (Quaracchi 1902).

11. Quaestiones disputatae de rerum principio, edited by M. Fernandez Garcia (Quaracchi 1910).

Opera omnia edited by Luc Wadding and others, together with a biography by Wadding, and notes (12 vols., folio, Lyon 1639). Reprinted without the biography and with various other additions and subtractions by L. Vives (26 vols., quarto, Paris 1891–1895).

General criticism—Parthenius Minges: Catholic encyclopaedia (vol. 5, 194–199, 1909). M. Fernandez Garcia: De vita scriptis et doctrina B. Joannis Duns Scoti (Quaracchi 1910). Charles Reginald Schiller Harris: Duns Scotus (2 vols., 790 p., Oxford 1927; Isis, 13, 430). Includes a long but uncritical bibliography (vol. 1, 316–360).

Special criticism—M. Steinschneider: Hebraeische Übersetzungen (477, 1893). Certain philosophical questions were translated into Hebrew by Elijah Ḥabillo (second half of the fifteenth century). J. Guttmann: Jewish encyclopaedia (vol. 5, 14–15, 1903).

F. M. Paolini: Monumenta cultus immemorabilis publici et ecclesiastici antiquissimi et extensissimi quibus fulcitur causa servi Dei Ioannis Duns Scoti (Rome 1907). Documents for the process of beatification.

Martin Grabmann: Die Entwicklung der mittelalterlichen Sprachlogik (Phil. Jahrbuch, vol. 35, Fulda 1922); De Thoma Erfordiensi, auctore grammaticae quae Ioanni Duns Scoto adscribitur speculativae (Archivum franciscanum historicum, vol. 15, 273–277, 1922).

Ch. Balič: Quelques précisions fournies par la tradition manuscrite sur la vie, les oeuvres et l'attitude doctrinale de Jean Duns Scot (Revue d'histoire ecclésiastique (vol. 22, 551–566, 1926).

A. G. Little: The Franciscan school at Oxford in the thirteenth century (Archivum franciscanum historicum, vol. 19, 869–872, 1926).

Philosophic criticism—Karl Werner: Die Psychologie und Erkenntnislehre des Duns Scotus (Denkschr. der Ak. der Wiss., Wien 1877); Die Scholastik des späteren Mittelalters (vol. 1, Wien 1881). E. Pluzanski: Essai sur la philosophie de Duns Scot (Paris 1887; Italian translation, Florence 1892). Parthenius Minges: Ist Duns Scotus indeterminist (Beiträge zur Gesch. der Philosophie des Mittelalters, vol. 5, 4, 148 p., 1905); Der angeblich exzessive Realismus des Duns Scotus (Beiträge, 1908). The same author has published a long series of papers on Duns Scotus, chiefly theological, between 1902 and 1919. Bernard Landry: Duns Scot (Les grands philosophes, 372 p., Paris, 1922; Isis, 5, 500). Ephrem Longpré: La philosophie du bienheureux Duns Scot (Paris 1924). Articles first published in Etudes franciscaines, severe criticism of Landry's work. Ch. Balič: Les commentaires de Duns Scot sur les quatre livres des Sentences (Bibliothèque de la Revue d'histoire ecclésiastique, fasc. 1, Louvain 1927; 386 p. plus schematic tables of the MSS. and editions). E. Belmond: Duns Scot métaphysicien (Revue de philosophie, 29, 405–423, 1929).

Scientific criticism—P. Duhem: Origines de la statique (vol. 2, 326–335, 1906; the treatise on meteors falsely ascribed to Duns Scot was probably written by Simon Tunsted); Système du monde (vol. 3, 491–499, 1915; astronomy).

BOETIUS OF DACIA

Boethius de Dacia. Danish philosopher, who flourished in Paris c. 1277. His name is generally bracketed with that of Siger of Brabant; they were the main defenders of Averroism in the University of Paris and were condemned together in 1277.

Boetius wrote commentaries on Aristotelian logic and on the fourth book of the Meteorology, a treatise on speculative grammar (De modis significandi), De somno et vigilia, De summo bono. Apparently Boetius was far less important than Siger.

P. Doncoeur: Boèce le Dace (Revue des sciences philosophiques et théologiques, vol. 4, 500–511, 1910). Martin Grabmann: Neu aufgefundene Werke des Siger von Brabant und Boetius von Dacien (Sitzungsber. Bayer. Ak., phil. Kl., 48 p., 1924). See my note on Siger of Brabant, above.

V. EASTERN CHRISTENDOM

THEODOROS II LASCARIS

Θεόδωρος Λάσκαρις, Son of Joannes III Ducas Batatzes, whom he succeeded; grandson of Theodoros I Lascaris. Born at Nicaea, 1222. Byzantine emperor at Nicaea from 1254 to his premature death at Magnesia on the Hermos (NW. Lydia) in 1258. In 1255–1256 he recovered Thrace from the Bulgarians.

Pupil of Nicephoros Blemmydes and Georgios Acropolites. In spite of continued ill-health he was able to devote much time to philosophic and theological studies. However he was more of a rhetorician, in the Byzantine tradition, than of a philosopher. He wrote prayers, poems, 218 letters many of which deal with philosophical and literary subjects, homilies, a polemical work against the Latins, an obituary of the emperor Frederick II, eulogies of Nicaea, of his father, of Georgios Acropolites, etc. His main works are a treatise on the unity of nature, Περὶ τῆς κοινωνίας τῶν ἐν τῃ φύσει, containing not only philosophic but also mathematic and scientific considerations, and a theological treatise, Χριστιανικῆς θεολογίας λόγοι ὀκτώ. According to him the unity of nature is due to the fact that all things, animate or inanimate, are made out of four elements; the diversities are due to the diverse combinations (κράσεις) of these elements. A prayer of his to the Virgin has become a part of the orthodox liturgies.

Text—De communione naturali, Latin edition by Claud. Auberius (Basel 1561). Greek text in Migne's Greek Patrology (140, 1267–1296).

Edition of the letters except one by Niccola Festa (R. Istituto di studi superiori, Florence 1898).

The funeral oration of Frederick II is printed at the end of Pappadopoulos' work (p. 183–189).

Criticism—Joh. Dräseke: Theodoros Laskaris (Byzantinische Zeitschrift, vol. 3, 498–515, 1894). K. Krumbacher: Byzantinische Litteratur (95, 478, 1047, etc., 1897). Jean B. Pappadopoulos: Théodore II Lascaris (207 p., Paris 1908).

NICEPHOROS BLEMMYDES

Νικηφόρος ὁ Βλεμμύδης (better than Βλεμμίδης). Born at Constantinople in 1197 or 1198; flourished at the court of Nicaea; before 1235 he retired into a monastery near Ephesus and died in 1272. Byzantine man of letters (one of the best known among them), philosopher, geographer. He wrote elementary treatises on logic and physics, Εἰσαγωγικῆς ἐπιτομῆς βιβλίον α', ἐπιτομὴ λογικῆς βιβλίον β', περὶ φυσικῆς ἀκροάσεως; a geographical summary, Γεωγραφία συνοπτική, largely based upon Dionysios Periegetes (second half of the first century); a short treatise on the (spherical) shape and the size of the earth and the seven climata, Ἑτέρα ἱστορία περὶ τῆς γῆς ἐν συνόψει; a treatise on alchemy, Περὶ χρυσοποιΐας, etc. The conceited and egotistic autobiographies, which he wrote in 1264 and 1265, contain valuable historical information.

Text—Treatises on logic and physics in Migne's Greek patrology (vol. 142, 527–1634).

Geographical treatises. F. A. G. Spohn: Nicephori Blemmidae duo opuscula geographica (62 p., Leipzig 1818; with commentary and map). New edition in Greek and Latin (Upsala 1818). C. Müller: Geographi graeci minores (vol. 2, 458–476, 1865).

Autobiographies. Edited by Aug. Heisenberg (Leipzig 1896; with biographical introduction).

The alchemical treatise is included in Berthelot's Collection des anciens alchimistes grecs (vol. 3, 452–457, 1888).

Criticism—Latin introduction to Heisenberg's edition (1896). K. Krumbacher: Byzantinische Litteratur (1897, 445–449, 633). Ernst Honigmann: Die sieben Klimata (p. 99, Heidelberg 1927; Isis, 14, 270–276).

For Manuel Holobolos, see chapter on translators.

SOPHONIAS

Σοφονίας. Byzantine monk who was probably a contemporary of Georgios Pachymeres. He wrote paraphrases of a number of Aristotelian works: Περὶ ψυχῆς, περὶ μνήμης, περὶ ὕπνου, κατηγορίαι, σοφιστικοὶ ἔλεγχοι, πρότερα ἀναλυτικά.

Text—Paraphrase of the Περὶ ψυχῆς edited by Michael Hayduck (Comm. in Aristotelem graeca, vol. 23, Berlin 1883–1884). The anonymous paraphrases of the Κατηγορίαι and of the Σοφιστικοὶ ἔλεγχοι, edited by Hayduck, and the paraphrase of the first book of Analytica priora ascribed to Themistios and edited by Max Wallies, all in the same volume, are probably also Sophonias' work.

Criticism—K. Krumbacher: Byzantinische Litteratur (430–431, 1897).

GEORGIOS PACHYMERES

Γεώργιος ὁ Παχυμέρης. The greatest Byzantine polyhistor of his century. Born in Nicaea, 1242; flourished in Constantinople under the Palaeologoi from 1261 on when the Latin empire came to an end; died after 1308, c. 1310. He occupied important lay and ecclesiastical offices: ἱερομνήμων, πρωτέκδικος, βασιλικὸς δικαιοφύλαξ, etc.

His main work is a great chronicle of contemporary events, in 13 books, forming a continuation to that of Georgios Acropolites, from 1261 (or 1255) to 1308. It is largely devoted, as we would expect, to the discussion of the theological controversies which engrossed the thoughts of his contemporaries. This chronicle was much praised by Edward Gibbon.

Next in importance are a summary of Aristotelian philosophy undertaken at the instance of Nicephoros Blemmydes, and a treatise on the quadrivium, Σύνταγμα τῶν τεσσάρων μαθημάτων, ἀριθμητικῆς, μουσικῆς, γεωμετρίας καὶ ἀστρονομίας (also called Τετράβιβλον). The first part contains a paraphrase of the first book of Diophantos, and extracts from Euclid and Nicomachos. Pachymeres was acquainted with the Hindu numerals.

He also wrote a number of letters, rhetorical essays, declamations, and a long autobiographical poem.

The chronicle contains a description of the giraffe which Michael Palaeologos had received in 1257 from the king of Aethiopia. This was not the first one to be seen in Europe, for the emperor Frederick II had obtained one from the sulṭān of Egypt in exchange for a white bear.

Text—The Historia Byzantina was edited by Peter Poussines (Rome 1666–1669). Also by Imm. Bekker in the Corpus hist. byzant. (2 vols., Bonn 1835; with indexes).

The Quadrivium has not yet been completely published. The paraphrase of Diophantos in the first part has been edited by P. Tannery in his Diophanti Opera (vol. 2, 78–122, 1895). The second part (music) has been edited by H. Vincent with a notice on ancient and medieval music (Notices et extraits, vol. 16 (2), 362–553, 1847). Part of the fourth part has been included in Th. H. Martin: Theonis Smyrnaei liber de astronomia (Paris 1849). P. Tannery had prepared a complete edition (Isis, 4, 344). Mme. Tannery wrote to me in Oct. 1922 that it was ready for the press and would appear eventually with some other Greek texts.

Neither is the Aristotelian commentary fully printed. The logic appeared in Venice, 1532, together with Psellos' compendium; also in Paris, 1548, 1581; Oxford 1669. But there is a complete Latin translation by Philippus Becchius (Bale 1560).

Fragments of the Aristotelian commentary: Περὶ ἀτόμων γραμμῶν (de lineis insecabilibus) in Is. Casaubon's edition of Aristotle (vol. 1, 745–752, Lyon 1590). Ch. Emile Ruelle: Deux morceaux inédits de Pachymère sur l'arc-en-ciel (Annuaire de l'Association des études grecques, 32 p., 1873).

Criticism—E. Narducci: Di un codice archetipo e sconosciuto dello Περὶ τῶν τεσσάρων μαθημάτων (Rend. d. Lincei, vol. 7, 191–196, 1891; vol. 1, 153–156, 1892). Potthast (889, 1896). K. Krumbacher: Geschichte der byzantinischen Litteratur (2 Aufl., 288–291, 1897).

Gustave Loisel: Histoire des ménageries (vol. 1, 144, 1912). Berthold Laufer: The giraffe in history and art (66, Chicago 1928; Isis, 11, 536).

P. Tannery: Les chiffres arabes dans les manuscrits grecs (Revue archéologique, vol. 7, 355–360, 1886; reprinted in his Mémoires, vol. 4, 199–205, 1920).

MAXIMOS PLANUDES

Μάξιμος ὁ Πλανούδης. Byzantine monk, mathematician, grammarian, archaeologist, man of letters, translator from Latin into Greek. Born c. 1260 in Nicomedia; his baptismal name was Manuel, but he assumed the name Maximos when he began a new life as a monk; in 1296 he was sent by Andronicos II Palaeologos (emp. 1282–1328) as ambassador to Venice, and this gave him the opportunity of mastering the Latin language; he died in 1310.

He translated a number of Latin works into Greek. This was a pioneer undertaking of the greatest importance for it bridged the increasing gap separating Rome from Byzantium and thus prepared for the Greek renaissance of western Europe. He translated the Praecepta of Cato the Censor, the Metamorphoses and Heroïdes[32] of Ovid, Cicero's Somnium Scipionis together with Macrobius' commentary, the De bello gallico of Caesar, the Ars minor of Donatus, Augustine's De trinitate, Boetius' De consolatione, possibly St. Thomas' Summa theologica. He was one of the first Greek scholars to study Latin theology with some care. His translations were much used by the early Latin humanists for the study of Greek; that of Boetius' Consolation is still occasionally used for that purpose.

His main mathematical work was a commentary on the first two books of Diophantos. He also wrote (c. 1300) an arithmetic after the Hindu method, Ψηφοφορία κατ' Ἰνδοὺς ἡ λεγομένη μεγάλη. This seems to be based upon an earlier Greek work of the same kind, the Ἀρχὴ τῆς μεγάλης καὶ Ἰνδικῆς ψηφοφορίας written in 1252. The numerals used in the Ἀρχή were of the Italian type; those of Planudes' treatise, of the Arabic one. Planudes' treatise deals with integers and with sexagesimal fractions. It explains methods of computation which are called Hindu, and occasionally others. For example, for the extraction of the square root, the Hindu method is first explained (i.e., essentially the one used to this day), then another approximate which the author claims as his own, but which is considerably older.[33] If $A^2 = a^2 + b$ (b being small in comparison with a), then A is approximately equal to $a + \frac{b}{2a}$. He also explains the casting out of nines, ascribing its discovery to the Hindus.

A canon on uroscopy is ascribed to him, entitled Περὶ τῶν ὑελίων πασῶν τῶν ἀσθενειῶν ἐν τοῖς ἀνθρώποις ἐπερχομένων στίχοι.

[32] His translation of the Heroides was based upon a MS. superior to our existing MSS. (J. E. Sandys: History of classical scholarship, vol. 1, 3d. ed., 428, 1921).

[33] It can be traced back to Heron of Alexandria and possibly to Archimedes. Johannes Tropfke: Geschichte der Elementar-Mathematik (2d. ed., vol. 2, 136, 1921).

He was also the author of two grammatical treatises, Περὶ γραμματικῆς in the form of a dialogue and Περὶ συντάξεως.

He compiled three anthologies; (1) A disordered collection of historical and geographical extracts, Συναγωγὴ ἐκλεγεῖσα ἀπὸ διαφόρων βιβλίων, including fragments of Plato, Aristotle, Strabon, Dion Chrysostomos (second half of the first century), Pausanias, Dion Cassios, Synesios, Joannes Laurentios Lydos (first half of the sixth century), Constantinos Manasses. (2) A collection of popular proverbs, Παροιμίαι δημώδεις. (3) A collection of epigrams, Ἀνθολογία διαφόρων ἐπιγραμμάτων, the so-called Anthologia Planudea, dated 1301 (autograph MS. in San Marco, Venice). This was an abridgment and rearrangement of the anthology compiled by Constantinos Cephalas (Κωνσταντῖνος ὁ Κεφαλᾶς, fl. c. 917) about the beginning of the tenth century. Until 1607, when the Anthologia Palatina was found (Cephalas' anthology was so called after the Palatine Library in Heidelberg where its MS. was discovered), we knew the "Greek Anthology" only through Planude's collection.

Finally, Planudes wrote scholia to Theocritos and to the rhetor Hermogenes (second half of the second century), a biography of Aesopos, an eulogy of Claudios Ptolemaeos, theological discussions, 121 letters (chiefly of the period 1292–1300), declamations, poems, etc.

Text—Theological works in Migne's Greek patrology (vol. 147, 967–1178).

M. Treu: Maximi Planudis epistolae (Breslau 1890). Translation of Boetius' Consolation edited by E. A. Bétant (Geneva 1871), of Cato's Sentences (Basel 1533, Leiden 1598, Cygneae 1672), of Ovid's Metamorphoses, by Jean François Boissonade (Paris 1822), of a few Heroides, in Carl Dilthey: De Callimachi Cydippa (Leipzig 1863), of Cicero and Macrobius in Chr. Fr. Matthaei: Varia graeca (Moscow 1811), of Caesar, by Ant. Baumstark (Freiburg 1834).

Das Rechenbuch des Planudes. Greek edition of the Ψηφοφορία by C. J. Gerhardt (60 p., Halle 1865). German translation by H. Waeschke (Halle 1878). The scholia to Diophantos are included in P. Tannery's edition of the latter (vol. 2, 125–255, 1895). A Latin translation had appeared long before in G. Xylander's edition of Diophantos (Basel 1575).

The canon on uroscopy will be found in Julius Ludwig Ideler: Physici et medici graeci minores (vol. 2, 318–322, 1842). Textual criticism by Robert Fuchs in Rheinisches Museum (vol. 49, 535–538, 1894).

Grammatical texts edited by Ludwig Bachmann: Anecdota graeca (vol. 2, 1–166, 1828) and by Jean François Boissonade: Anecdota graeca (vol. 1, 408, 1829).

The earliest edition of the Greek anthology, by Janus Lascaris (Florence 1494) contained only the Planudean anthology. Anthologia graeca epigrammatum Palatina cum Planudea edited by Hugo Stadtmüller (Leipzig 1894–1906). Greek and English texts by W. R. Paton (Loeb library, 5 vols., London 1916–1918).

General criticism—K. Krumbacher: Byzantinische Litteratur (2d ed., 99, 543–546, 727–728, 1897).

Mathematical criticism—C. J. Gerhardt: Über das Rechenbuch des Planudes (Monatsber. der Berliner Akad., 38–40, 1867). A. Steen, H. G. Zeuthen: Planudes' Problemer (Tidsskr. for math., vol. 2, 139–147, 1884). Paul Tannery: Las chiffres arabes dans les manuscrits grecs (Revue archéologique, vol. 7, 355–360, 1886; reprinted in Mémoires, vol. 4, 199–205, 1920). Sir Thomas Heath: Greek mathematics (vol. 2, 546–549, 1921).

ABŪ-L-FARAJ OR BARHEBRAEUS

Syriac historian, grammarian, philosopher, theologian, physician, astronomer, man of letters, translator from Arabic into Syriac. Born 1226, died 1286.

Abū-l-Faraj Yūḥannā ibn al-'Ibrī al-Malaṭī. Bar 'Ebhrāyā. Bar Hebraeus. His father was a Jewish physician, named Aaron, who had been baptized. Yūḥannā was born in Melitene (Malaṭīya, Upper Euphrates) in 1225–1226; he lived in Antioch, then in Syrian Tripolis, where he received logical and medical instruction from a Nestorian named Jacob. In 1246 he was appointed (Jacobite) bishop of Gūbōs (near Melitene) and assumed the name of Gregorius; without going into the details of his ecclesiastical career it will suffice to say that he ended it as mafriān of Takrīt (on the Tigris), i.e., as primate of the eastern Jacobites, from 1264 to his death.[34] The needs of his diocese, sorely afflicted by the Mongol raids, obliged him to travel considerably. He resided in many places; e.g., in Baghdād from 1264 to 1277, but mostly in Mūṣul and in Marāgha and Tabrīz, two cities east of Lake Urmīya in Adharbāyjān. In 1285 he completed the reconstruction and decoration of the monastery of Barṭallā (near Mūṣul) which had been intrusted by him to Greek artists. In 1286 he died in Marāgha. His moral authority is illustrated by the fact that the Greeks, Armenians, and Nestorians shared the grief of his own people. He was buried in the monastery of Mar Mattai near Mūṣul.

Abū-l-Faraj was an encyclopaedist who wrote in Syriac, and subsidiarily in Arabic. He tried to make available to his people as much of the Arabic learning as possible, and his voluminous writings give us a complete view of Syriac science and civilization in his time. He was to the Syriac world what Vincent of Beauvais or Albert the Great was to the Latin, but unfortunately the Syriac language did not survive him very long. He was the last Syriac writer of importance.[35]

Contents: (1) Astronomy. (2) Medicine. (3) History and geography. (4) Philology. (5) Philosophy. (6) Theology. (7) Alia. (8) General criticism.

1. *Astronomy*—Abū-l-Faraj wrote at Marāgha in 1279 an astronomical treatise called Sullāqā haunānāyā (ascent of the mind); it is a summary of the Almagest, probably the edition of astronomical lectures delivered by him in Marāgha at some time between 1272 and 1279. Indeed we know that he lectured at Marāgha on Euclid in 1268, and on Ptolemy in 1272–1273. This is the only astronomical textbook of any importance in the Syriac language. An anonymous elementary treatise on the calendar may have been composed by him. He compiled elementary astronomical tables (zīj); these may be identical with the calendar just mentioned. He took pains to prove that the earth cannot be in motion, either rectilinear or circular.

Partial edition by Richard J. H. Gottheil: Adscensus mentis (Berlin 1890). François Nau: Le livre de l'ascension de l'esprit sur la forme du ciel et de la terre (Bibliothèque de l'Ecole des hautes études, Sci. philol., 121; 2 vols., Paris 1899–1900; Syriac text with French translation).

[34] The mafriān was second in importance only to the Jacobite patriarch who was then Mar Ignatius III.

[35] Ever since the Muslim conquest, Syriac had been losing ground to Arabic. By the fourteenth century it had almost completely ceased to be used except for liturgical purposes. At the present time it is no longer spoken except perhaps in a few mountainous districts, and if so by very few people in a very corrupted form.

H. Suter: Mathematiker und Astronomen der Araber (154, 1900). J. L. E. Dreyer: History of the planetary systems (255, 257, 259, 277, 1906). G. Furlani: Bruchstücke einer syrischen Paraphrase der Elemente des Eukleides (Z. für Semitistik, vol. 3, 27–52, 212–235, 1924; Isis, 8, 536, 742). Apropos of a Syriac translation of an Arabic paraphrase of Euclid; the Arabic model was probably al-Ḥajjāj (first half of the ninth century), the Syriac translator possibly Barhebraeus.

2. *Medicine and botany*—Though he composed many medical works, none has come down to us. He compiled an anthology of medical opinions, a summary of Dioscorides' materia medica with illustrations, Kĕthābhā dhĕ Dhiosqorīdhīs; he translated the medical questions of Ḥunain ibn Isḥāq, adding a commentary upon them (not completed), and the Kitāb al-adwiya al-mufrada of al-Ghāfiqī; he began a translation of the Qānūn of Ibn Sīnā. He is said to have written in Arabic commentaries on Hippocrates' Aphorisms[36] and on the Galenic treatises *περὶ τῶν καθ' Ἱπποκράτην στοιχείων* (De elementis) and *περὶ κρασέων* (De temperamentis).

F. Wüstenfeld: Geschichte der arabischen Aerzte (145–146, 1840). J. G. Wenrich: De auctorum graecorum versionibus (242, 1842). L. Leclerc: Médecine arabe (vol. 2, 147–151, 1876). M. Steinschneider: Die arabischen Übersetzungen aus dem Griechischen (Z. der deutschen morg. Ges., vol. 50, 368, 1896). Ch. Singer: The herbal in antiquity (49, 1927; Isis, 10, 519).

3. *History and geography*—His main work is a Syriac chronicle, Makhtĕbhānūth zabhnē, divided into two main parts, a lay one (Chronicon Syriacum) and an ecclesiastical one (Chronicon ecclesiasticum). The first part is a universal history from the creation down to 1286, for which he made use of Arabic and Persian sources as well as of Syriac ones. For example, for the Mongol events he used al-Juwainī's chronicle. His main Syriac source up to 1196 was the chronicle of Michael the Elder.

The ecclesiastical history was divided in its turn into two parts: (1) history of the Old Testament, of ancient Christendom, of the patriarchs of the church of Antioch, and of the monophysite patriarchs down to 1285; (2) history of the eastern church of Syria, of the Jacobite patriarchs, and of the Nestorian catholicoi, to 1286. To this second part were added autobiographical notes, and later a life of the author by his brother Bar-ṣaumā Ṣafī, and a continuation to 1288. Other continuations of both ecclesiastical parts extend to 1495–1496.

Toward the end of his life he composed an Arabic abridgment of the lay history under the title Mukhtaṣar ta'rīkh ad-duwal. To this he added a summary of Biblical history and an account of the scientific literature available in Arabic. This account was largely derived from Ibn al-Qifṭī. Abū-l-Faraj is perhaps best remembered because of his Mukhtaṣar; it was that book that gave credence to the story of the burning of the library of Alexandria by order of the caliph 'Umar (also borrowed from Ibn al-Qifṭī).[37]

His history contained a map of the climates, which, imperfect as it was, was the best specimen of Syriac cartography.

The Mukhtaṣar was first published by Edward Pococke (1604–1691), with a Latin translation: Historia compendiosa dynastiarum historiam complectens universalem

[36] This is very probably a confusion with the commentary composed by his contemporary Abū-l-Faraj Ibn al-Quff, dealt with in the medical section, below.

[37] On that story, see vol. 1, 466.

a mundo condito usque ad tempora authoris res Orientalium accuratissime describens (447 p., Oxford 1663; with a Latin translation). Supplementum in quo historiae orientalis series a Gregorii Abul-Faragii exitu ad nostra usque tempora compendiose deducitur (72 p., Oxford 1663). New edition by Anṭūn Ṣāliḥānī (623 p., Beirut 1890; with indexes). German translation by G. L. Bauer: Des Gregorius Abulfaradsch Kurze Geschichte der Dynastien (2 vols., Leipzig 1783–1785).

Chronicon Syriacum, edited by P. I. Bruns and G. W. Kirsch, with Latin translation (2 vols., Leipzig 1789). Chronicon Syriacum e cod. MSS. emendatum ac punctis vocalibus adnotationisque locupletatum by Father Bedjan (Paris 1890).

Chronicon ecclesiasticum edited by J. B. Abbeloos and Th. J. Lamy (2 vols. in 3, Louvain 1872–1877). Syriac text with Latin translation.

F. Wüstenfeld: Geschichtschreiber der Araber (146–147, 1881). Heinrich Gelzer: Sextus Julius Africanus (vol. 2, 401–409, 1885). Konrad Miller: Mappae arabicae (vol. 1, 9, 1926; Isis, 9, 458–462).

4. *Philology*—He continued the efforts of the earlier Syriac grammarians, especially of Jacob of Edessa (second half of the seventh century), and wrote various grammatical treatises. His larger work, the Kĕthābhā dhĕ-ṣemhē (Book of rays) was modeled upon the Arabic grammar of al-Zamakhsharī (first half of the twelfth century), being divided into four parts (noun, verb, particles, generalities). A smaller grammar, Kĕthābhā dhĕ-ghrammatikī was written in verse. A third grammar, still shorter and in prose, the Kĕthābhā dha-bhĕlēṣūṣīthā (Book of the spark), remained incomplete.

Abbé Paulin Martin: Oeuvres grammaticales d'Aboul-Faradj (2 vols., Paris 1872; autographic edition of the first two grammars). The second grammar had been published before, incompletely, by Ernest Bertheau: Grammatica linguae syriacae in metro ephraemeo (Göttingen 1843). Axel Moberg: Buch der Strahlen, die grössere Grammatik, übersetzt nach einem kritisch berichtigten Texte (Leipzig, 1907–1913); Le livre des splendeurs, Texte syriaque avec introduction et notes, (278 p., Lund 1922).

5. *Philosophy*—He made an immense effort to transmit the Aristotelian philosophy to his people. To that effect he compiled the following works:

(1) Kĕthābhā dhĕ-bhābhāthā (Book of the pupils of the eye), dealing with logic and dialectics. It is divided into eight parts, of which the first is an introduction on the utility of logic, and the seven others summarize respectively Porphyry's Isagoge, the Categories, De interpretatione, Analytica priora, Topica, Analytica posteriora, Sophistici elenchi.

Curt Steyer: Buch der Pupillen, hrg. und teilweise übersetzt (Leipzig 1908).

(2) Kĕthābhā dha-sĕwādh sophia (Book of the speech of wisdom), dealing with dialectics, physics, metaphysics, theology.

(3) Ḥēwath ḥekhmĕthā (Cream of wisdom), or Ḥekmath ḥekhmāthā (Sapientia sapientiarum), is a large encyclopaedia of Aristotelian knowledge, divided into four main parts: (a) logic; (b) physics; (c) metaphysics; (d) ethics, economics, politics, physiognomy. We might call this work the Syriac summa.

(4) Tēgĕrath tēgĕrāthā (Mercatura mercaturarum). This is derived from the 'Uyūn al-ḥikma of Ibn Sīnā.

(5) Poem on the soul, summarizing the Aristotelian views.

(6) Treatise on the soul. Available in Arabic, Mukhtaṣar fī 'ilm al-nafs. Edited by Paul Sbath (70 p., Cairo 1928; analysis in Isis, 13, 428).

To these must be added the translations of two philosophical compendia from Arabic into Syriac.

(7) Ibn Sīnā: Kitāb al-ishārāt wal-tanbīhāt (Book of signs and admonitions), Kĕthābhā dhĕ-remzē wa mĕ'īrānwāthā.

(8) al-Mufaḍḍal al-Abharī (second half of the thirteenth century): Zubdat al-asrār (Cream of secrets).

The edition of some minor philosophical works is being prepared at the Oriental Institute of Chicago by Herman Janssens.

6. *Theology*—His main work in this field was the Auṣar razē (storehouse of mysteries), a critical and doctrinal commentary on the Old and New Testaments, based on the Pĕshīṭtā but also on Hebrew, Greek, and other texts. His other theological works are:

Mĕnārath qudhshē (Lamp of the sanctuary), dealing with the twelve "bases" on which the church is established: (1) knowledge in general; (2) nature of the universe; (3) theology; (4) incarnation; (5) angelology; (6) priesthood; (7) evil spirits; (8) soul; (9) free will, freedom, and fate; (10) resurrection; (11) end of the world, last judgment; (12) paradise.

Kĕthābhā dhĕ-zalgē (Book of rays), similar to the preceding, divided into ten sections. Translated into Arabic.

Kĕthābhā dh'īthiqōn (i.e., τῶν ἠθικῶν) on ethics and devotion, composed at Marāgha in 1279. Twice translated into Arabic. Divided into four parts: (1) exercises of body and soul—prayer, study, manual work, vigils, etc.; (2) regimen of the body; (3) purification of the soul; (4) embellishment of the soul.

Kĕthābhā dhĕ-yaunā (Book of the dove), dealing also with devotion but more briefly; (1) training of the body for the ascetic life; (2) training of the soul; (3) spiritual peace; (4) autobiographical notes. Also translated into Arabic.

Kĕthābhā dhĕ-huddāyē (Book of directions). Ecclesiastical manual for the Jacobite church. Translated into Arabic. Etc.

Extracts from the Storehouse of mysteries have been published at various times, but no complete edition has as yet appeared. A complete critical edition with English translation and notes is being prepared by members of the Oriental Institute of Chicago; the first volume due to the collaboration of Martin Sprengling and Graham will appear in 1931; the other volumes, probably three more, are well along in preparation and should follow within the next two or three years.

W. E. W. Carr: Commentary on the Gospels from the Horreum mysteriorum (490 p., London 1925; Syriac and English).

Richard J. H. Gottheil: A list of plants and their properties (lithographed for private circulation, 34 p., Berlin 1886; extract from the Mĕnārath qudhshē); Contributions to the history of geography, II. Candelabrum sanctorum and Liber radiorum (Hebraica, vol. 7, 39–55, 1890).

Paul Bedjan: Ethicon seu moralia Gregorii Bar Hebraei (Paris 1898; includes the Liber columbae).

Kĕthābā dhĕ-yaunā. Syriac text edited by Gabriel Cardahi (Rome 1898). Translation by A. J. Wensinck: Book of the dove together with some chapters from the Ethicon (Leiden 1919; with valuable introduction).

A Latin translation of the Kĕthābhā dhĕ-huddāyē was published by G. A.

Assemani: Ecclesiae Antiochenae Syrorum Nomocanon in Angelo Mai: Scriptorum veterum nova collectio (vol. 10, part 2, 1–268, Rome 1838). Edition of the Syriac text by P. Bedjan: Nomocanon (Paris 1898).

F. Nau: Deux textes de Bar Hebraeus sur Mahomet et le Qoran (Journal asiatique, vol. 211, 311–329, 1927).

F. S. Marsh: The book which is called the Book of the holy Hierotheos with extracts from the prolegomena and commentary of Theodosios of Antioch[38] and from the Book of excerpts and other works of Bar-Hebraeus (London 1927; Syriac and English).

Carlo A. Nallino: Il diritto musulmano nel nomecanone siriaco cristiano di Barhebreo (Rivista degli studi orientali, vol. 9, 542–580, 1923); Ancora il libro siro-romano di diritto e Barhebreo (ibidem, vol. 10, 78–86, 1923).

7. *Alia*—Of his other writings it will suffice to mention philosophical poems, a treatise on the interpretation of dreams, Pushshāq ḥelmē, and a collection of humorous stories, the Kĕthābhā dhĕ-thunnāyē mĕghaḥḥĕkhānē. There was an Arabic translation of the last named work (itself more Arabic in spirit than Syriac) entitled Kitāb daf' al-hamm (Driving away of care) which is lost.

The poem Bona lex sed melior philosophia was published by E. Renan: De philosophia peripatetica apud Syros (Paris 1852). Various poems edited by Caesar von Lengerke (1836–1838) and by the Maronite Augustinus al-Shabābī (Rome 1877). Carmen de divina sapientia, edited by Gabriel Sionita (1638) and by Yūḥannā Nuṭayn al-Dar'ūnī (Rome 1880).

E. A. W. Budge: Laughable stories. Syriac text with English translation (London 1897); Oriental wit and humour, translated from the Syriac (London 1899). Budge's edition of the Syriac text was reviewed by René Basset: Contes syriaques (Revue des traditions populaires, June 1907; reprinted in his Mélanges africains et orientaux, 317–324, Paris 1915).

8. *General criticism*—Theodor Nöldeke: Sketches from Eastern history (236–256, Edinburgh 1892). William Wright: Short history of Syriac literature (London, 265–281, 1894). Rubens Duval: Littérature syriaque (3d. ed. Paris 1907). C. Brockelmann: Encyclopaedia of Islām (vol. 1, 657–658, 1911). Anton Baumstark: Geschichte der syrischen Literatur (312–320, Bonn 1922).

J. E. Sarkis: Dictionnaire encyclopédique de bibliographie arabe (339–340, Cairo 1928).

'ABHD-ĪSHŌ' BAR BĔRĪKHĀ

Mar 'Abd Yeshua. Ebediesus Sobiensis. Nestorian theologian and man of letters writing in Syriac, and subsidiarily in Arabic. Bishop of Sinjār (W. of Mūṣul, in Jazīrah), in 1284–1285, and before 1290–1291, metropolitan of Nisībis[39] and Armenia; died in 1318.

'Abhd-īshō' was to the Nestorian Syrians what Abū-l-Faraj was to the Jacobites, though on a much smaller scale, and each was the last great writer of his people.

[38] That is, Romanus the physician, a monk in the monastery of Qartamīn, who was elected Jacobite patriarch at Amid in 887 and assumed the name of Theodosios; he died in 896. He wrote in Syriac a medical summa (kunnāshā) which was much esteemed but is lost.

W. Wright: Syriac literature (206, London 1894). R. Duval: Littérature syriaque (391, Paris 1907). A. Baumstark: Syrische Literatur (280, Bonn 1922).

[39] Syriac, Ṣōbhā (hence his name Sobiensis); Arabic, Naṣībīn; on the Hirmās river, in Jazīrah.

He wrote commentaries on the Old and New Testaments, a treatise on the secrets of Greek philosophy, the Kĕthābhā skolastiqos (i.e., σχολαστικός), against all the heresies, a poem on the calendar, letters, poems, etc. His main theological work was the Margānīthā (Pearl), written in 1297–1298. It is divided into five parts: God, creation, Christian dispensation, sacraments, things that prefigure the world to come. He translated this book himself into Arabic in 1312, and large extracts from the Arabic version were quoted by 'Amr ibn Mattā in the Majdal. His main poetical effort was the Paradise of Eden, a collection of fifty poems, probably inspired by the fifty Maqāmāt of al-Ḥarīrī; it was published by him in 1291; then again with a commentary in 1316. In 1298 he compiled a catalogue of Biblical and ecclesiastical writings (ending with a list of his own publications). He wrote a commentary on the epistle of Aristotle to Alexandre on alchemy. His Kunnāshā dhĕ-qānōnē (Collections of canons) is the Nestorian equivalent of the Kĕthābhā dhĕ-huddāyē of Abū-l-Faraj. In 1315–1316 he compiled a table of the ecclesiastical ordinances and laws.

Text—Ebediesu metropolitae Sobae et Armeniae Collectio canonum ad usum ecclesiae Nestorianorum. Praecedit Epitome canonum apostolicorum auctore eodem Ebediesu. Ebediesu liber margaritae, seu de veritate christianae religionis. Both works are edited in Syriac, and translated into Latin by G. A. Assemani, in Angelo Mai: Scriptorum veterum nova collectio (vol. 10, part 1, 3–331; part 2, 317–366, Rome 1838).

The catalogue of his writings, made in 1298, was published by Abraham Ecchellensis (Rome 1653), again by Giuseppe Simone Assemani: Bibliotheca orientalis (vol. 3, Rome 1728).

Mimeographed edition of Margānīthā by J. E. Kelaita (Urmīyah 1908). Abraham Yohannan: The book of the pearl (94 p., New York 1916).

The Margānīthā and the catalogue of Biblical and ecclesiastical writings were Englished by George Percy Badger: The Nestorians and their rituals (vol. 2, 361–422, London 1852).

Enrico Gismondi: Carmina selecta ex libro Paradisus Eden (Beirut 1888; extracts in Syriac and Latin). Gabriel Cardahi: Pardaisa dha 'Edhen seu Paradisus Eden (Beirut 1889; edition of first half).

The alchemical tract is apparently lost.

Criticism—G. P. Badger: The Nestorians (2 vols., London 1852). William Wright: Syriac literature (285–289, 1894). A. Baumstark: Geschichte der syrischen Literatur (323–325, 1922).

For John of Erzinjān, see mathematical chapter.

VI. CHINA

KUBLAI KHĀN

Chinese emperor of Mongol origin. Born probably in 1214. Ruled from 1260 to his death in 1294. Established the Yüan[2] (13744) dynasty in 1271.

His name is written in many ways. For example, the first sound is represented in Arabic script by a kāf, a qāf, also by a khā. This would lead to a whole series of English transcriptions: Qūbīlai, Qublāi, Khubilāy, Kublai, etc. Khān is a Turkish sovereign title, adopted by the Mongols. Kublai Khān was the "Great Khān" who received Marco Polo in 1274, and Coleridge's Kubla Khan. In Chinese he was called Shih[4] Tsu[3] (9969, 11826), and in Japanese, Koppitsuretsu.

He was the grandson of Chingiz Khān, the nephew of Ogotāy. While his brother Mangū was ruling the Mongol empire (1248–1259), he was entrusted (1251 sq.) with the management of the Chinese provinces. When Mangū died, he secured the throne, and soon afterwards began the conquest of the provinces ruled by the southern Sung dynasty, south of the Yang[2] Tze[3] Kiang[1] (12876, 12317, 1208). By 1279 he was the sole master of China, and his rule extended as far west as Arabia, Russia, and Poland. On the other hand, his expeditions against other eastern countries—Japan (1274, 1280–1281), Burma, Champa (1278), Cambodia, even Java (1294)—ended in failure.

In 1267 he ordered the building of a new capital at Khānbaliq (the Khān's town, also written Cambaluc, etc.) on the site of the present Tartar city of Peiping. His summer capital was Qaraqorum, on the Orkhon, in Mongolia.

He also built the northern portion of the Grand Canal, connecting Khānbaliq with the Huang[2] ho[2] (5124, 3936), i.e. the Yellow River; the other part, connecting the Yellow River with the old Sung capital Hangchow, was much older. The portion built by him was some 500 miles in length; the total length of the Grand Canal is about 1200 miles.

See Dominique Gandar: Le canal impérial (Variétés sinologiques, no. 4, 80 p., maps and plans, Shanghai 1894).

The Huang ho was explored up to its sources (in the Kokonor region) in 1280. He sent missions to distant countries; e.g., to S. India, E. Africa, even to Madagascar. In 1287 he received envoys from the East Indies and from Ceylon.

Kublai Khān continued the efforts of Chingiz Khān to educate his peoples. In 1287 he reorganized the imperial academy, Han[4]-lin[2] yüan[4] (3828, 7157, 13752), founded by Ming Huang (first half of the eighth century, vol. 1, 512).

Chingiz' efforts to give a written form to the Mongolian language were also continued by order of Kublai. In 1269 a Lama called Phagspa (or Phagpa, Bashpa; in Chinese, Pa[1]-ssŭ[1]-pa[1], 8510, 10271, 8510) introduced a new Mongol alphabet derived from the Tibetan and written vertically. It was this same Phagspa who converted Kublai to Buddhism. He died in 1279.

A government printing press had existed in Khānbaliq since 1236, and Kublai greatly increased its importance by adding to its stock quantities of blocks obtained in Kiangsi or in Hangchow, when the southern capital was conquered. In 1293 he ordered the unification of the government press with the academy, and the printing of books in Mongolian as well as in Chinese.

Though Kublai had become under Phagspa's influence an ardent Lamaist, he was also a Confucianist, and was tolerant of other religions, except Taoism. For example, he was favorably disposed to the Muslim, except during a few years (Aḥmad's revolt, 1282–1289). In 1281 he caused all Taoist works save the Tao tê ching, to be burned. He sent an envoy to Turfan to obtain copies of Buddhist scriptures. The Tibetan canon was collated with Chinese and Sanskrit texts by a company of 29 Tibetan, Uighūr, Chinese, and Hindu scholars working under the direction of Saskyā Paṇḍita; this led later, after Kublai's death, to the translation of the Kanjur (vol. 1, 467) into Mongolian about 1310 by Saskyā Lāma Ch'os-Kyi Od-zer.

I have explained above that Chu Hsi had revised the annals composed by Ssŭ-ma Kuang. In 1282 that revision, entitled T'ung chien kang mu, was translated by Kublai's order into Mongolian. This same work was later translated into Manchu by order of the emperor K'ang Hsi (1708) and the substance of it put into French by Father Joseph de Mailla (1669–1748) and published after the latter's death (Histoire générale de la Chine, 13 large vols., Paris 1777–1785).

Kublai ordered the calendar to be reformed in 1267 by Cha-ma-li-ting, and again in 1276 by Kuo Shou-ching. For the astronomical instruments which he provided see my note on the latter.

In 1273 a work on agriculture and sericulture was compiled at his request, the Nung² sang¹ chi⁴* yao⁴ (8408, 9566, 943, 12889). It included seven books divided into ten sections: precepts, ploughing, sowing, planting mulberry trees, rearing silkworms, vegetables, fruits, bamboo and forest trees, medicinal plants, breeding cattle. New editions of this work appeared several times during the Yüan dynasty.

Kublai was a great administrator. A new code of criminal law was prepared during his reign. Laws and statutes were collected and clearly set forth; they dealt with such subjects as poll taxes, duties, regulations of the issue of paper money, sea transportation, river conservancy, postal service, official uniforms, sacrificial prayers, posthumous titles, etc.

For a better appreciation of the exchanges between East and West at the Mongolian capital, I may still add that Kublai and his successors had a special guard of Christian soldiers. These were the Alains, in Chinese A⁴ su²* (1, 10330), who had been imported from the Caucasus in Mangū's time (1248–1259), nomadic northern Iranians probably related to the ancient Sarmatae and also to the present day Ossetes of the Caucasus. About 1275 a large number of Alains were treacherously killed at the siege of Chen-ch'ao, and the revenues of that city were given by Kublai to their families. The descendants of those Alains sent an embassy to Benedict XII (pope in Avignon, 1334–1342) in 1336–1338; the embassy included Andrew and William de Nassio, and fourteen Alains.

Sources—The best Chinese source is the official history of the Yüan dynasty, Yüan shih, compiled by Sung⁴ Lien² (10462, 7132) who died in 1381. A considerable amount of new information will be found in the Hsin¹ Yüan² shih³ (4574, 13744, 9893), i.e., the new history of the Yüan dynasty, compiled by Ko¹ Shao⁴-min² (6039, 9773, 7926) and recently published at the expense of the late president Hsü² Shih⁴-ch'ang¹ (4748, 9969, 427). It includes 257 books bound in 60 vols. in 12 cases.

The best non-Chinese oriental source is the Jāmi' al-tawārīkh, written in Persian by Faḍl Allāh Rashīd al-dīn in 1310–1311.

See histories of the Mongols, mainly that by Sir Henry Hoyle Howorth (4 vols., 1876–1927; Isis, 11, 501), and the histories of China. For Marco Polo, see the note devoted to him.

Biographies—H. A. Giles: Chinese biographical dictionary (386–388, 1898). Encyclopaedia sinica (271, 1917). W. Barthold: Encyclopaedia of Islām (vol. 2, 1091, 1927). See notes by same on Khānbaliq and Qaraqorum (ibidem, 898, 740). Sir Henry Yule: Encyclopaedia Britannica (vol. 13, 509–510, 1929). René Grousset: Histoire de l'Extrême-Orient (448–493, 1929; Isis, 14, 437–441).

Special criticism—Lawrence Austine Waddell: The Buddhism of Tibet (15,8 London 1895). A Wylie: Chinese literature (94, 1902). Th. F. Carter: Invention of printing in China (61, 1925; Isis, 8, 361–373).

For 'Īsā the Mongol, see my note in mathematical chapter.

MA TUAN-LIN

Ma^3 Tuan^1-lin^2 (7576, 12138, 7165). Chinese encyclopaedist. Born in Lo^{4*}-p'ing^2 (7331, 9310), Shansi, in the thirteenth century; he was still living in 1280, for he survived the Sung dynasty; after its fall he retired to his native place.

His main work is the great encyclopaedia in 348 books called Wên^2 hsien^4 t'ung^1 k'ao^3 (12633, 4530, 12294, 5966), completed c. 1280, published in 1319. It is an extension of Tu^4 Yu^4's (12043, 13437) encyclopaedia (first half of ninth century). Tu Yu's nine divisions were expanded into nineteen, and five new divisions were added (including bibliography, uranography, phenomena). The period embraced in Ma's encyclopaedia extends from the beginnings of Chinese tradition to the early part of the thirteenth century. A supplement to it, in 254 books, was compiled by Wang^2 Ch'i^2 (12493, 1011) in 1586; a revision of this supplement was ordered by Ch'ien Lung (emperor from 1736 to 1796) in 1747 and completed in 1772. A further extension of the work, in 266 books, was compiled during the same reign.

The Wên^2 hsien^4 t'ung^1 k'ao^3, Tu^4 Yu^4's T'ung^1 tien^3 (first half of ninth century) and the historical encyclopaedia, T'ung^1 chih^4 (12294, 1918), compiled by Chêng^4 Ch'iao^2 (724, 1407) (second half of the twelfth century), are often spoken of as the Three T'ung, San' T'ung^1 (9552, 12294). Each of these three works was revised twice in Ch'ien Lung's reign; hence the phrase the Nine T'ung, Chiu^3 t'ung^1 (2263, 12294).

Text—The Library of Congress has four different editions of the Wên hsien t'ung k'ao including a Ming palace one published in 1524 in 100 large volumes beautifully printed after a Yüan edition of the Chih-chêng period (1341–1368). It has the San T'ung, both in the original and in the Ch'ien Lung revised edition.

Marquis d'Hervey de Saint-Denys: Ethnographie des peuples étrangers à la Chine. Traduit du chinois avec commentaire (2 vols., Paris 1876–1883). The last 25 books of the 348 constituting the Wên hsien t'ung k'ao deal with the historical and ethnographical description of foreign countries. Rémusat had planned to translate these 25 books but was not able to accomplish his design. The Marquis d'Hervey undertook the translation which was to fill four large quarto volumes: I. Eastern peoples (from the Chinese point of view—i.e., Korea, Japan, Kamchatka); II. Southern; III. Western; IV. Northern. I have seen only vols. I and II; they contain abundant notes.

Criticism—Abel Rémusat: Biographie universelle (vol. 27, 461–464, 1820) J. H. Klaproth. Notice sur l'encyclopédie de Ma Touan lin (Nouveau Journal. Asiatique, reprint, 78 p., Paris 1832). W. Vissering: On Chinese currency, coin and paper money (Leiden 1877; largely based upon vols. 8 and 9 of Ma Tuan-lin's encyclopaedia). Alexander Wylie: Notes on Chinese literature (69, 1902). Giles: Chinese biographical dictionary (570, 1898).

WANG YING-LIN

Wang^2 Ying^1-lin^2 (12493, 13294, 7186). Chinese encyclopaedist and educator. Born in the Ning^2 po^1 (8325, 9336) prefecture in Chehkiang in 1223, died in 1296.

His main work is the Sea of Jade, Yü^{4*} hai^3 (13630, 3767), an encyclopaedia in 200 books divided into 21 sections and containing more than 240 articles plus 13 appendices.

The authorship of the Three character classic, San^1 tzŭ^4 ching^1 (9552, 12324, 2122), has also been ascribed to him. This is the most popular schoolbook of China even to this day; it is the first book put in the hands of children. It contains 560 different characters and deals with a great variety of subjects in rhymed doggerel, three characters to a line. It has also been ascribed to Liang[2] Ying[1]-shêng[1] (7021, 13294, 9879) of the Ming dynasty. In fact a copy of it bears Liang's name as the author, together with a preface by Fu[4] Kuang[1]-tsê (3632, 6389, 11669). The editions of it vary somewhat, and various adaptations have been published from time to time to use the venerable textbook as a vehicle for this or that propaganda. For example, such adaptations have been prepared by Catholic and Protestant missionaries, and also by the T'ai P'ing rebels (1851–1865).

The San tzŭ ching should not be confused with the Ch'ien[1] tzŭ[4] wên[2] (1725, 12324, 12633) or Thousand Character Essay, another popular school book ascribed to Chou[1] Hsing[1]-ssŭ[4] (2450, 4611, 10258) (first half of sixth century).

His free utterances about the comet of 1264 got Wang into trouble.

Text—The Yü Hai was published for the first time in 1351.

The editions of the San tzŭ ching are of course innumerable. I will mention only the following Western editions: S. C. Malan: The threefold San-tsze-king, as issued (1) by Wang-Po-keou; (2) by Protestant missionaries; (3) by the rebel chief Tae-ping-wang. Put into English with notes (78 p., London 1856). Abel des Michels: Chinese text with Annamite transcription and French translation (Paris 1882). Walter Brooks Brouner and Fung Yuet Mow: Chinese made easy (New York 1904). H. A. Giles: Chinese and English texts (2d. ed., Shanghai 1910).

The Library of Congress has the Yü hai in 240 volumes and 204 chüan, with a preface dated 1738. It also has the San tzŭ ching, the Ch'ien tzŭ wên, and the T'ai P'ing san tzŭ ching.

Criticism—Alexander Wylie: Notes on Chinese literature (162, 184, 1902). Giles: Chinese biographical dictionary (853, 1898). Encyclopaedia Sinica (498, 1917).

CHAPTER XLVII

MATHEMATICS AND ASTRONOMY

(Second Half of Thirteenth Century)

I. WESTERN CHRISTENDOM

DIFFUSION OF HINDU NUMERALS IN WESTERN EUROPE

The Hindu numerals continued their diffusion in the second half of the thirteenth century, steadily but slowly. As we might expect, it was in Italy that they were first put to practical purposes. We know indirectly that they were already used by business people before the end of the century, because the bankers of Florence were forbidden in 1299 to do so. Besides the statutes of the university of Padua ordered that the stationer should keep a list of books for sale with the prices marked "non per cifras sed per literas claras."

These two examples are mentioned by Isaac Taylor: The alphabet (vol. 2, 263, 1883), who does not state the date of the Paduan statutes referred to.

There was a set of astronomical tables in Boncompagni's library bearing the date 1264 written with Hindu numerals. Narducci's Catalogo (p. 130), quoted in D. E. Smith and L. C. Karpinski: The Hindu Arabic numerals (139, 1911).

For the study of mathematical translations see my notes on John of Brescia, Armengaud son of Blaise, Alfonso X el Sabio, Judah ben Moses, Samuel ha-Levi, Isaac ibn Sid, and Hagin Deulacres in the chapter on translators.

For Ramon Lull, see philosophical chapter.

CAMPANUS

Giovanni Campano da Novara (near Milan). Italian mathematician and astronomer. He was chaplain to Urban IV (pope from 1261 to 1264), and was canon in Paris or flourished for a time in Paris; he was still living in 1292.

He was much influenced by Robert Grosseteste and praised by Bacon. His own influence seems to have been felt mainly in Paris; e.g., by William of St. Cloud.

He wrote a number of treatises on mathematics, astronomy, and possibly a commentary on Ptolemy's treatise on music (Ἁρμονικά).

He is chiefly known because of his edition of the Latin text of Euclid's Elements (Books I to XV, all of which he ascribed to Euclid), completed in 1254 (?). This text was obviously based upon the translation by Adelard of Bath (first half of the twelfth century). In fact it is less a new translation than a commentary on Adelard's in the compilation of which Campanus availed himself of other Arabic sources. This was the first edition of Euclid to be printed (Venice 1482). It contains some interesting mathematical items. The consideration of the angle of contingence (Nemorarius) between a curve and its tangent, smaller than any angle between two straight lines, led Campanus to the study of continuous quantities (quantitates continuae). He proved the irrationality of the golden section[1] by a mathematical induction ending in a reductio ad absurdum. He calculated the sum of the angles of a stellated pentagon. Another mathematical treatise, De quadratura circuli, is so poor that one would like to doubt his authorship of it; yet Albert of Saxony, a century later, mentioned him as the author.

He wrote various astronomical treatises: Compotus major, Theoretica planetarum (ad Urban's request, thus before 1265), Tractatus de sphaera (after the Theoretica), Tractatus de sphaera solida, Tractatus de quadrante composito. The two last named describe astronomical instruments; the sphaera solida is a sort of armillary sphere, the quadrant was often called instrumentum Campani and was much used by Parisian astronomers; the Tractatus de quadrante composito, judging by the number of MSS. was perhaps the most popular of his writings.

In the Compotus major he explains the precession and trepidation of equinoxes which he knew through Robert Grosseteste, and probably from other sources as well. The Theoretica planetarum (or Theoretica Campani) was a general astronomical treatise. He explained among other things the old theory according to which the greatest distance of a planet must be equal to the nearest distance of the next one (this theory may be traced back at least to Proclos, and is often found in mediaeval writings).

The Demonstrationes Campani super theoreticas is apparently apocryphal. It quotes the Alphonsine Tables which were probably not yet known to Campanus; it elaborates considerably the theory just mentioned in the same manner as in Bacon's Opus tertium. It is probably posterior to Bacon.

Text—Campanus' edition of Euclid was printed in Venice, 1482, by Erhard Ratdolt, with geometrical drawings in the wide margins. This was the first printed mathematical book of any importance. Other editions appeared in Ulm, 1486, and Vicenza, 1491. The first complete translation from the Greek, by Bartolomeo Zamberti, appeared in Venice, 1505, yet Luca Pacioli reedited Campanus' text, with many emendations, in Venice, 1509. The new Latin translation from the Greek by Federigo Commandino of Urbino (Pesaro, 1572), with ancient scholia, was the mother of all subsequent editions down to the beginning of the nineteenth century.

Tetragonismus, id est circuli quadratura per Campanum, Archimedem syracusatum atque Boetium. Edited by Luca Gaurico (1475–1558) (Venice 1503).

Compotus major included in the astronomical collections edited by Octaviano Scot: Sphera cum commentis (Venice 1518) and by Luca Antonio de Giunta: Sphera mundi noviter recognita cum commentariis et authoribus (Venice 1518, again 1531). Description of these two collections in Duhem (vol 3, 246.)

De sphaera, and De sphaera solida are included in the same collections.

Criticism—Daunou: Histoire littéraire de la France (vol. 21, 248–254, 1847). H. Weissenborn: Die Übersetzungen des Euklid durch Campano und Zamberti (Halle a.S., 1882). P. Riccardi: Biblioteca matematica italiana (219–220, 1887). J. L. Heiberg; Euklid's Elemente im Mittelalter (Z. für Math., vol. 35, hist. Abt., 48–58, 81–100, 1890). D. E. Smith: Rara arithmetica (433, Boston 1908). Apropos of a MS. of the Elements in G. A. Plimpton's library, which is believed to be the copy given by Campanus to Urban IV before the latter's pontificate, i.e., before August 29, 1261. P. Duhem: Système du monde (vol. 3, 317–326, 1915; vol. 4, 119–124, 1916). Ernst Zinner: Verzeichnis der astronomischen Hand-

[1] This term is relatively modern. The division of a straight line in extreme and mean ratio was called by Proclos "the section"; by Luca Pacioli (1509) the "divine proportion."

schriften des deutschen Kulturgebietes (71–73, München 1925; Isis, 15, 193–195.) Maria Teresa Zapelloni: Il postulato di Campano e i fondamenti dell'aritmetica (Periodico di matematiche, vol. 8, 175–184, 1928).

GERARD OF SABBIONETA

Gherardo da Sabbioneta. Famous Italian astrologer who flourished c. 1255–1259. He has been confused with the translator, Gerard of Cremona; of course he may have been called Gerard of Cremona himself, Sabbioneta (better than Sabbionetta) being a place not far from Cremona.

He composed a treatise on geomancy (Geomantiae astronomiae libellus) and an astronomical summary (Theorica planetarum). The latter is a summary of Ptolemaic astronomy as explained by al-Farghānī and al-Battānī. It has often been ascribed to Gerard of Cremona; in some MSS. it is also ascribed to John of Seville, Robert Grosseteste, Simon Bredon, and Walter Brit (Brithus, Bryte, or Brytte). The Oxford texts are longer, and represent probably an elaboration of the original. The Theorica enjoyed some popularity and was twice translated into Hebrew; by Judah ben Samuel Shalom Astruc (middle of the fifteenth century) under the title 'Iyun shib'a kokabe lakot (Calculation of the seven planets), and by an anonymous translator (this second translation is accompanied by a copy of the Latin text in Hebrew vocalized script).

Text—Geomantia first printed with the works of H. C. Agrippa (Lyon, s.a.). It was translated into French by the sieur de Salerne (Paris 1615, etc.) Géomancie astronomique de Gérard de Crémone, pour savoir les choses passées, les présentes et les futures. Traduite par le sieur de Salerne. Dernière édition (Paris 1687).

Theoretica planetarum. First edition, Ferrara 1472. Often reprinted: Venice 1478. Also with Sacrobosco's Sphera mundi, Bologna 1477, 1480; Venice 1478, etc.

Criticism—B. Boncompagni: Della vita e delle opere di Gherardo Cremonese e di Gherardo da Sabbionetta (Atti d. Accad. d. Nuovi Lincei, Roma 1851). P. Riccardi: Biblioteca matematica italiana (1887–1893). M. Steinschneider: Hebraeische Übersetzungen (631, 1893). A. A. Björnbo: Walter Brytes Theorica planetarum (Bibliotheca mathematica, vol. 6, 112–113, 1905). Apropos of Bryte's elaboration of Gerard's work, Cod.Digby 15. P. Duhem: Le système du monde (vol. 3, 219–223, 234, 1915).

Duhem claims that the Theorica was really composed by the translator, Gerard of Cremona in Toledo, that it was already quoted in the London tables composed c. 1232, and considers it the oldest treatise on theoretical astronomy of Latin scholasticism.

Ernst Zinner: Verzeichnis der astronomischen Handschriften (283–286, München 1925; Isis 15, 193–195).

JOHN OF SICILY

Joannes de Sicilia. Italian astronomer who flourished in Paris c. 1290. He wrote in Paris in that year a criticism of the Toledan tables, i.e., of the astronomical ideas upon which these were based. The Toledan tables were considered then and there the most up to date (this was not surprising considering that the Alphonsine tables were published only c. 1272; they were only known in Paris by 1292). He resolutely rejected the idea of the trepidation of the equinoxes, and went back to Ptolemy. His work was influenced to some extent by Bacon's Opus tertium.

The identification of John of Sicily with John of Messina, one of the translators employed by Alfonso X in 1276, must be rejected if only because in that case John of Sicily would certainly have known of the Alphonsine tables. See my note on Bartholomew of Messina.

Text—Expositio Joannis de Sicilia super canones Arzachelis. Latin MS. 7281, Bibliothèque nationale, Paris.

Criticism—M. Steinschneider: Die europäischen Übersetzungen aus dem Arabischen (51, Wien 1904). P. Duhem: Système du monde (vol. 4, 6–10, 1916).

BARTHOLOMEW OF PARMA

Italian astrologer and geomancer. Born in Parma; flourished in Bologna c. 1286–1297. He wrote many treatises, most of them astrological. I mention only the dated ones. Liber de occultis, 1280; Breviloquium astrologiae, Bologna 1286; Breviloquium or Ars geomantiae, Bologna 1288; Tractatus sphaerae, Bologna 1297.

A Philosophia Boëtii must also be ascribed to him; it is nothing but an amplification of the περὶ διδάξεων of William of Conches (first half of the twelfth century).

His best known work is the Ars geomantiae. This was the most elaborate treatise on geomancy of that age, even as Bonatti's Liber astronomicus was the most elaborate treatise on astrology. For the nature and history of geomancy see my note on Hugh of Santalla (first half of the twelfth century); needless to say I do not profess to write a complete history of that subject. This work attracted attention, for a few years later, in 1294, he wrote an abridgment of it for two German friends (MSS. in Latin and Italian), and in 1295 he composed another abridgment. One of these texts was translated into French before the end of the fourteenth century.

The Tractatus sphaerae is more scientific than Bartholomew's other writings, and he flattered himself that it was superior to Sacrobosco's famous work. It is more ambitious, yet worthless. It includes much material stupidly plagiarized from William of Conches.

Text—The Tractatus sphaerae was edited by Enrico Narducci in Boncompagni's Bullettino (vol. 17, 43–120, 165–218, with facsim. 1884). That edition was made from a MS. of the Bibliot. Vittorio Emanuele, Codice Santa Croce nº 228, which is possibly autograph.

Criticism—Enrico Narducci: Intorno al Tractatus sphaerae di Bartolomeo da Parma e ad altri scritti del medesimo autore. Memoir prefaced to Narducci's edition of the Tractatus (p. 1–42, 1884). See also a note by the same author in the trans. of the Accademia dei Lincei (vol. 8, 284–287, 1884). Giuseppe Boffito: Dante e Bartolomeo da Parma a proposito di Par. 1, 37, sgg., Conv., III, 5, ecc. (Rendiconti del R. Ist. lombardo, vol. 35, 10 p., 1902). P. Duhem: Système du monde (vol. 4, 210–222, 1916). Lynn Thorndike: History of magic (vol. 2, 835–838, 1923). Ernst Zinner: Verzeichnis der astronomischen Handschriften (239, München 1925; Isis, 15, 193–195).

GUIDO BONATTI

Guido Bonatus de Forlivio (Foroliviensis). Guido of Forlì. Famous Italian astrologer. Born in Cascia, on the upper Arno, Tuscany; he soon left his native country; in 1223 he was in Ravenna and in Bologna, where he had a violent quarrel with John of Vicenza; in 1233, being in Forlì, he offered advice to Frederick II; in 1259 he entered the service of Ezzelino III da Romano, who died in that same year; and in 1260 he became astrologer to Guido di Montefeltro, count of Urbino (d. 1298); after a journey to Paris he died c. 1297.

He represents the type of the professional astrologer who could then be found in the household of almost every king or prince. But he was not simply a practical astrologer, he was also the foremost defender and theorist of astrology—extreme astrology, without compromise. Dante placed him in the eighth circle of Hell (Inferno, 20, 118), and Pico della Mirandola, while acknowledging his authority, spoke of him with the utmost contempt. He composed, after 1261 or after 1277, an elaborate work, Liber astronomicus, which was exclusively astrological. It is naturally based upon the Arabic literature on the subject, but contains many facts taken from his own experience.

The Liber astronomicus (or Astronomiae tractatus decem) begins with a general introduction defining and defending astrology. The following treatises (which vary somewhat in number according to the division of that text in various MSS.) deal with the signs of the zodiac, planets, conjunctions, astrological judgments, and finally meteorology—i.e., astrological forecasts of the weather. The astronomical part, reduced to very little, was derived from al-Farghānī.

It was translated into Italian toward the end of the fifteenth century, by Francesco Strigatti. A German translation was published in 1572, and an English one as late as 1676! I do not know of a Hebrew version, but one Eliezer compiled in the sixteenth century an astrological collection including extracts from Bonatti among many others.

Text—The Liber astronomicus was first printed by Erhard Ratdolt (Augsburg 1491), this first edition (422 leaves quarto) being prepared by the Bavarian astrologer Johann Engel (Angelus). Second edition by Melchior Sessa (Venice 1506). This seems to be simply a reprint of the first. Third edition, Guidonis Bonati de Astronomia tractatus X, universum quod ad iudiciariam rationem nativitatum aëris tempestatum attinet comprehendentes (Basel 1550).

Auslegung des menschlichen Gebuhrtstunden (Basel 1572). William Lilly: Anima astrologiae, or a guide for astrologers, being the considerations of the famous G. Bonatus rendered into English, as also the choicest aphorisms of Cardan's VII segments (London 1676).

Criticism—Baldassare Boncompagni: Della vita e delle opere di Guido Bonatti (167 p., Roma 1851; reprinted from the Giornale arcadico, vols. 123–124). M. Steinschneider: Hebraeische Übersetzungen (531, 1893). P. Duhem: Système du monde (vol. 4, 188–199, 1916). Gustav Hellmann: Die Wettervorhersage im ausgehenden Mittelalter (179–181, 1917; Isis, 4, 185). Lynn Thorndike: History of magic (vol. 2, 825–840, 1923; with a list of MSS. of the Liber astronomicus). Ernst Zinner: Verzeichnis der astronomischen Handschriften (61, München 1925; Isis, 15, 193–195).

For St. Thomas Aquinas, St. Bonaventure, Giles of Rome, and Ristoro of Arezzo, see philosophical chapter.

BERNARD OF TRILIA

Bernard of La Treille. Languedocian Dominican and astronomer. Born at Nîmes c. 1240; entered the Dominican order; taught in Montpellier, Avignon, and at the school of St. James in Paris; provincial of Provence, 1291; died in 1292.

Pupil of Albert the Great. He wrote a commentary on Sacrobosco (Quaestiones de sphera) dealing largely with astrology, but also with physics and astronomy.

In the controversy relative to the Ptolemaic eccentrics and epicycles vs. the Aristotelian homocentric spheres, he was distinctly Ptolemaic. He continued Albert's endeavor to reconcile the Hipparchian theory of continuous precession with Thābit's trepidation.

He composed a number of theological treatises: Quodlibeta (1279–1287), De cognitione animae conjunctae corpori, De cognitione animae separatae, De distinctione esse et essentiae, Quaestiones de spiritualibus creaturis, etc. They show that his philosophy was essentially Thomistic; he was one of the earliest Thomists.

Text—The Questiones de sphera are still unpublished. MS. 171 of the municipal library of Laon, Aisne, France.

Criticism—M. Baumgartner: Überwegs Grundriss (10th ed., 504, 518, 180*, 1915). P. Duhem: Système du monde (vol. 3, 363–383, 1915). M. De Wulf: History of mediaeval philosophy (vol. 2, 46, 1926).

BERNARD OF VERDUN[2]

French Franciscan astronomer, who flourished probably toward the end of the thirteenth century. His main work is an astronomical treatise, Tractatus optimus super totam astrologiam, which is of considerable importance. It deals with astronomy as well as with astrology. (Note that the words astrologia and astronomia were then almost interchangeable; an astrological treatise might be called Liber astronomicus, while another like this one bearing the word Astrologia in its title would be of special astronomical importance.) It contains a careful comparison of the homocentric theories of Aristotle, al-Biṭrūjī and Ibn Rushd, with the Ptolemaic theory of excentrics and epicycles as elaborated by Ibn al-Haitham. Bernard was well acquainted with Bacon's astronomical writings, but replaced Bacon's indecision by a vigorous decision in favor of Ptolemaic astronomy. He also rejected Thābit's trepidation, and accounted for the increase of longitude of the stars by a continuous precession. The writings of Bernard of Verdun and of his contemporary, the English Franciscan, Richard of Middleton, mark the beginning of the complete Ptolemaic supremacy.

Text—Bernard's Astrologia is still unpublished. For MSS. see Duhem (p. 443) and Lynn Thorndike: Vatican Latin manuscripts (Isis, 13, 65, 1929).

Criticism—E. Littré: Histoire littéraire de la France (vol. 21, 317–320, 1847). P. Duhem: De l'influence exercée par Bacon sur Bernard de Verdun, in Un fragment inédit de l'Opus tertium (64–69, 1909); Système du monde (vol. 3, 442–460, 1915). Ernst Zinner: Verzeichnis der astronomischen Handschriften (350, München 1925; Isis, 15, 193–195). Quoting but one MS.

WILLIAM OF SAINT CLOUD

Guilelmus de Sancto Clodoaldo. French astronomer. Flourished in Paris (?) c. 1292–1296.

He seems to have been one of the founders of the astronomical school of Paris. He was a remarkable observer. In 1285 he observed the sun indirectly by means of a camera obscura. He invented an instrument, directorium, the description of which is lost (he mentions it in his calendar of 1296). In 1290 he determined experimentally the obliquity of the ecliptic, his result being 23°34′ (the value for

[2] Everybody knows one Verdun, the old city on the Meuse (Virodunum), but there are and were other places of that name in France. We do not know from which Bernard hailed.

that year computed by means of Le Verrier's formula is c. 23°32′30″); this was the only direct determination of that quantity by a Christian astronomer of mediaeval times; Nicholas of Cues made use of it in his report on the reform of the calendar presented to the council of Basel in 1436.

He compiled an almanac giving the positions of the planets for the period 1292–1311, and a perpetual calendar dedicated in 1296 to Queen Marie of France (the second wife and widow of Philippe III le Hardi; queen from 1274 to 1321).

In the table of planets, compiled in 1292, he criticized the anterior tables, viz., those of Ptolemy, Alexandria, Tolosa, and Toledo (not the Alphonsine tables, which he probably did not know). However the corrections he applied to these tables were purely empirical.

Queen Marie's Calendar gives the hour at which the sun will enter each zodiacal sign in 1296, and contains a table making it possible to determine rapidly the same data for a period of four centuries (two centuries before and after 1296). That calendar is preceded by an introduction setting forth the great practical value of scientific research. Does this betray Bacon's influence or is it simply a sign of the changing times?

According to Zinner, this William (fl. 1292–1294), magister and canon in Saint Cloud, Paris, was of English origin. He calls him William the Englishman, and said he wrote a calendar for Queen Elizabeth (?).

E. Littré: Histoire littéraire de la France (vol. 25, 63–74, 1869). P. Duhem: Système du monde (vol. 4, 10–19, 580, 1916). Lynn Thorndike: History of magic (vol. 2, 262, 668, 1923). According to Thorndike the tables referred to the period 1285–1321. Ernst Zinner: Verzeichnis der astronomischen Handschriften (92, Munich 1925; Isis, 15, 193–195).

THE ASTROLOGER TO BALDWIN II OF COURTENAY

A great astrological treatise, entitled Introductoire d'astronomie, was written in the Île-de-France dialect c. 1270 by an unknown astrologer for Baldwin II of Courtenay, the last effective ruler of the Latin empire of Constantinople. (Emperor from 1228 to 1273, he was actually in power from 1240 to 1261). It is preceded by an astrological poem of 394 lines, also in French. The treatise and the poem belong together and were in all probability composed by the same author.

They are of special interest for two reasons. First, because of their being written in French. Second, because of their remarkable backwardness. They do not represent the astronomy of their age, but are a late echo of an obsolete tradition. The author states very clearly and distinctly that Mercury and Venus circulate around the sun. This might seem an imperfect anticipation of Copernicus, but is in fact a relic of pre-Ptolemaic astronomy. The Introductoire continued the tradition of Heraclides of Pontos (second half of the fourth century B. C.) which had been preserved by Chalcidius, Macrobius, Martianus Capella, and less purely by philosophers of the school of Chartres, such as William of Conches.

Text—Bibliothèque Nationale, fonds français, no. 1353 (olim 7485).

Criticism—Paulin Paris: Histoire littéraire de la France (vol. 21, 423–433, 1847). Wilhelm Foerster: Zur Geschichte der Astronomie im 13. und 14. Jahrh. (Mitt. der Vereinigung von Freunden der Astronomie, 7 p., Berlin 1913; not seen). P. Duhem: Système du monde (vol. 3, 130–152, 1915).

ANIANUS

Magister Anianus. Author of the earliest compotus[3] to appear in print (Paris 1483). Nothing is known of his life, but it is probable that he was a French monk; he may have flourished at the Benedictine monastery of Aniane, not far from Montpellier; he lived probably in the second half of the thirteenth century. His Compotus manualis (so called, because all explanations were based upon the use of the hand) was written in Latin verse (c. 250 Leonine lines). It was largely based upon earlier works of the same kind, but it enjoyed far more popularity than any other, being very frequently copied and printed until the abundance of cheap calendars drove it out of business.

Anianus' poem may be divided as follows: (1) the solar cycle (leap year, planets, zodiac, order of holy days); (2) the lunar cycle (saltus lunae, epacts, regulares, embolismic years); (3) moveable and immoveable festivals (claves festorum); (4) seasons (terms and quarters of the year, vigils, perilous or "Egyptian" days, litterae tabulares). The popularity of this Compotus was partly due to the many mnemonic lines which it contained. It should be noted that many of these—e.g., the most famous, helping to remember the signs of the zodiac and the number of days of each month—were already commonplace in Anianus' time.

Text—First edition by Guy Marchand, undated (Paris 1483). First dated edition, Strassburg 1488. About thirty-five incunabula editions; nineteen more before 1516; then very few more.

Christopher Wordsworth: The ancient calendar of the University of Oxford from documents of the fourteenth to the seventeenth century, together with the Computus manualis ad usum Oxoniensium from C. Kyrfoth's edition, Oxon., 1519–1520 (Oxford historical society, vol. 45, 325 p., 7 facsim., Oxford 1904; elaborate study).

David Eugene Smith: Le comput manuel de Magister Anianus (Documents scientifiques du XVe siècle, 4, 107 p., many illustrations, Paris 1928; Isis, 11, 385–387). This contains the text of the edition of 1488, and the abridged French translation printed in 1483, together with very complete introduction and notes.

Criticism—D. E. Smith: Rara arithmetica (31–35, 1908; superseded by the notes to his edition of 1928). Florian Cajori: Comparison of methods of determining calendar dates by finger reckoning (Archeion, vol. 9, 31–42, 1928).

For Vincent of Beauvais, see philosophical chapter; for Peter the Stranger, and Villard of Honnecourt, see physical chapter; for William Durand, see legal chapter.

FRENCH ANONYMOUS ALGORISMS

Two algorisms of this time were composed by unknown authors in French (Picard dialect). One dating from c. 1275 is represented by two MSS., Bibliothèque Sainte-Geneviève, Paris (no. 2200), and Bibliothèque Nationale, Paris (MS. français 2021). This text containing about 800 words is essentially a translation of the Carmen de algorismo of Alexander of Villedieu (first half of the thirteenth century). It was first published by Charles Henry, together with the oldest

[3] Or computus., I think it is better to write compotus and to refer this word in this acceptation to componere rather than to computare. It should be noted that the word computus is also used in the sense of computation (ars jactandi computum). Very often too the two meanings, simple arithmetic and calculation of the calendar, are mixed.

French treatise on geometry (Boncompagni's Bullettino, vol. 15, 53–70, Rome 1882). New edition by Victor Mortet: Le plus ancien traité français d'algorisme (Bibliotheca mathematica, vol. 9, 55–64, 1908). This includes a comparison with the Carmen de algorismo. See also Suzan Rose Benedict: A comparative study of the early treatises introducing the Hindu art of reckoning (Thesis, University of Michigan, 1914).

The second text represented by a Bodleian MS. (Selden supra 26) was only edited in 1928 by E. G. R. Waters: A thirteenth century algorism in French verse, with introduction by Louis C. Karpinski (Isis, 11, 45–84, 1928; 13, 160). Includes 2 pl. facsimile, English translation, and glossary. It is more important than the first text, for it is longer (it is a poem of 519 lines), more complete, and more independent. It is closer to the Carmen de algorismo than to any other algorism, but is not slavishly derived from it. In some respects it is similar to Sacrobosco's treatise, or to the Salem MS. It contains two rules for learning the multiplication table between 5 times 5 and 10 times 10; in modern notation

$$d^2 = 10\,[d - (10 - d)] + (10 - d)^2$$
$$a\,b = 10\,[a - (10 - b)] + (10 - a)\,(10 - b)$$

The second rule (of which the first is a special case) appears also in the Salem MS., and in twelfth century algorisms. The first rule is found in Ocreatus (first half of the twelfth century) as an application of the regula Nicomachi.

In both French algorisms six fundamental operations are dealt with, duplication and mediation being considered separate operations.

ROBERT THE ENGLISHMAN[4]

Robertus Anglicus.[4] English astronomer who flourished in Paris (?) and Montpellier c. 1271; Christian neo-Platonist. He wrote a treatise on the astrolabe (De astrolabio canones), a commentary on Sacrobosco's sphere, in Paris or Montpellier, 1271; a treatise on the quadrant, in Montpellier, before 1276.

The commentary on Sacrobosco deals with astronomy and astrology. The astronomical part is partly derived from the De substantia orbis of Ibn Rushd, some of whose ideas were adopted by Robert; e.g., the heavens could not stop, or if they did, every motion in the sublunar world would also cease (this was one of the propositions condemned by the bishop of Paris in 1277). He conceived the celestial orbs in the same way as Thābit ibn Qurra, rather than in the way of Ibn al-Haitham. He did not enter into the great contemporary controversy between the Ptolemaic and Alpetragian theories.

The treatise on the quadrant describes very well an astronomical instrument by means of which angular altitudes could be measured; e.g., the altitude of the sun (hence, with the help of solar tables, its place in the ecliptic), and also the hours of the day (again with the help of tables). It was very popular; witness the number of MSS., and the translations into Greek, Hebrew, and German (1477); it was plagiarized in the Margarita philosophica of Gregory Reisch (at least in the edition of 1508). The Greek version, entitled περὶ τοῦ τετραγώνου, is anonymous and undated (fourteenth or fifteenth century).

This treatise is also ascribed to one John the Englishman, Joannes Anglicus de Monte Pessulano. Robert and John represent probably the same person. Of

[4] The same name was also applied to Robert of Chester (first half of the twelfth century), and conceivably to other English Roberts living abroad.

eleven MSS. (quoted by Tannery), all beginning in the same way (Geometriae duae sunt partes theorica et practica), some bear the name of John, others that of Robert.[5]

The quadrant described was probably invented in the second half of the twelfth century and the invention was hardly more than the adaptation of an Arabic instrument to Christian and western needs; it was called quadrans vetus when it was superseded by the quadrans novus invented and described by Jacob ben Maḥir c. 1290.

Text—Roberti Anglici de astrolabio canones (Colle c. 1478).

Paul Tannery: Le traité du quadrant de maitre Robert Anglès. Texte latin et ancienne traduction grecque (Notices et extraits, vol. 35 (2), 561–640, 1897; with important introduction, 561–592). Reprinted in his Mémoires (vol. 5, 118–197). Maximilian Curtze: Der Tractatus quadratis in deutscher Übersetzung aus dem Jahre 1477 (Abhdl. zur Geschichte der Mathematik, 9, 43–63, 1899); Tractatus de quantitatibus terre et stellarum et primo de terra (Z. für Mathematik, hist. Abt. vol. 45, 41–46, 1900). This text is an appendix to the Tractatus quadrantis.

Criticism—M. Steinschneider: Hebraeische Übersetzungen (612, 1893); Johannes Anglicus und sein Quadrant (Bibliotheca mathematica, 102–104, 1896); Europäische Übersetzungen aus dem Arabischen (66, 1904). This last work ascribes to Robert two translations from the Arabic: (1) al-Kindī, De judiciis, 1272; (2) anonymous treatise De proportione et proportionalitate. There is no sufficient reason to identify this translator with the astronomer.

Paul Tannery: Magister Robertus Anglicus in Montepessulano (Bibliotheca mathematica, 3–6, 1897; Mémoires, vol. 5, 112–117, also 355); Traité du quadrant (Bulletin des sciences mathématiques, vol. 23, 145–150, 1899; Mémoires, vol. 5, 198–203). P. Mansion: Note on Tannery's edition (Annales de la Société scientifique de Bruxelles, vol. 22, 83–84, 1898). P. Duhem: Système du monde (vol. 3, 291–298, 1915). R. T. Gunther: Early science in Oxford (vol. 2, 157–163, 1923; apropos of the quadrant). Ernst Zinner: Verzeichnis der astronomischen Handschriften (91–92, Munich 1925; Isis 15, 193–195).

For Bacon, William of Ware, and Richard Middleton, see philosophical chapter; for John Peckham, see the physical one.

HENRY BATE

Henry of Malines. Flemish astronomer, astrologer, neo-Platonic philosopher. Born in Malines (Mechelen) near Antwerp, in 1246 (not 1244); flourished in Liége and Malines; canon and cantor of the cathedral of Liége; in 1292 he was in Orvieto; died in or after 1310.

Having met William of Moerbeke at the council of Lyon, 1274, after his return to Malines the same year he wrote a treatise on the astrolabe, Magistralis compositio astrolabii. This was primarily astrological. Bate did not invent a new type of astrolabe, but he may have elaborated the astrological applications of that instrument.

He made many astronomical observations which enabled him to compile new tables for his native city, Tabulae machlinienses. He prepared three editions of them, the earliest before 1281.

[5] The two abbreviations Ro. and Jo. could easily be confused.

In that same year 1281 he wrote an astrological autobiography, Liber servi Dei de Machlinia super inquisitione et verificatione navitatis propriae.

He translated astrological treatises of Ibn Ezra into Latin. These had been translated from Hebrew into French in Bate's house in Malines, 1273–1274, by a Jew called Hagin. Bate retranslated them from French into Latin (Liber de planetarum conjunctionibus et de revolutionibus annorum mundi) in 1281 and later; the last one in Orvieto, 1292 (De luminaribus sive de diebus criticis). An original treatise bearing the same title, De diebus criticis, is also ascribed to him. At an unknown date, but probably during this same period, he wrote a commentary on the De magnis conjunctionibus et annorum revolutionibus, an astrological treatise composed by Abū Ma'shar, or rather by al-Kindī (vol. 1, 568).

He criticized the Alphonsine Tables in the Tractatus super defectibus tabularum Alfonsii (lost). The date of that tractatus is not known, but it cannot have been before 1292–1296, for the Tables were not known in Paris until that time. Until then the best tables were those of al-Zarqālī (second half of the eleventh century) and their derivatives.

At some time between 1280 to 1300 (1310), he composed a vast theological encyclopaedia in 23 books, the Speculum divinorum et quorundam naturalium. Its contents and arrangement were probably inspired by the decision of the university of Paris, 1255, permitting the teaching of the whole Aristotelian knowledge. The Speculum deals successively with men, spiritual creatures, and God. It contains many digressions on physical problems; e.g., nature of matter, optics, physiology and psychology, winds, comets, bees, thunder, time and motion, celestial orbs and revolutions, etc. It includes (book 22) an attempt to explain celestial phenomena without excentrics or epicycles, but in a manner different from al-Biṭrūjī's. It is largely a compilation derived from the Greek, Arabic, and Latin authors. Among the latter, Albert the Great and St. Thomas are often quoted. The general point of view is the neo-Platonic compromise between Aristotle and Plato. It exerted but little influence upon later philosophers, Nicholas of Cues being almost alone in quoting it.

On January 31, 1310, he observed an annular eclipse of the sun. (Indeed such an eclipse was visible in Flanders on that day.)

Henry Bate was one of the best astronomers of his time, or to put it in another way, one of the most scientifically minded astrologers, for he was first and last an astrologer. He exerted a deep influence upon later astrologers down to the sixteenth century.

Text—The Magistralis compositio was printed together with Abraham Judei de nativitatibus (Ratdolt, Venice 1485).

Other astrological writings were printed in Venice, 1507.

Criticism—E. Littré: Histoire littéraire (vol. 26, 558–562, 1873). M. De Wulf: Henri Bate (Bull. de l'Académie de Belgique, lettres, 465–481, 1909). P. Duhem: Système du monde (vol. 4, 19–28, 1916). Alexander Birkenmajer: Henri Bate (La Pologne an Congrès international d'histoire de Bruxelles, 13 p., Cracow 1923; Isis, 7, 188). J. Fr. Schroeter: Sonnenfinsternisse (48, 128, map 86b, Kristiania 1923; Isis, 6, 208). Lynn Thorndike: History of magic (vol. 2, 926–930, 1923); Vatican Latin MSS. (Isis, 13, 75, 1929). Ernst Zinner: Verzeichnis der astronomischen Handschriften (47, München 1925; Isis, 15, 193–195).

For William of Moerbeke, see chapter on translators; for Albert the Great, see the philosophical chapter; for Witelo, see the physical one.

LEOPOLD OF AUSTRIA

Leopoldus de Austria. Leopoldus ducatus Austriae filius. Literally translated, son of the duchy of Austria. Does this mean a native of that duchy, as when we speak of a son of Nebraska? Or should ducatus be read ducis, son of the duke of Austria? The second hypothesis is confirmed by the title of an early French version. I call him simply Leopold of Austria, which leaves the question open.

Austrian astronomer and meteorologist, who flourished probably in the middle or the second half of the thirteenth century. He composed an astronomical treatise which was professedly a compilation,[6] entitled Compilatio de astrorum scientia, divided into ten treatises. The purpose was primarily astrological, but this implied an astronomical basis. Leopold was a poor theorist; he was thrown into confusion by the conflicting theories and was not able to reach a clear conclusion with regard to the main controversies of the time, continuous precession vs. trepidation, and Ptolemaism vs. Alpetragianism. He was acquainted with the tables of al-Zarqālī, and was probably posterior to William the Englishman (fl. c. 1231). A very large part of his work was derived from the Kitāb al-madkhal of Abū Ma'shar (first half of the ninth century). To account for the distances of the planets, he explained the old theory according to which each of the concentric spheres must be thick enough to contain the eccentricity, plus half of the diameter of the epicycle, plus half the diameter of the planet. He postulated ten celestial spheres, of which the last three were respectively the spheres of the fixed stars, and of the signs, and finally the firmament (the immobile empyrean).

The most interesting part of the Compilatio was the sixth devoted to meteorology, De mutatione aeris. This was also the most influential, witness a similar work by Firmin of Belleval (first half of the fourteenth century) wherein Leopold was often quoted. This meteorology was entirely astrological; as stated at the very beginning, "omnis mutatio aeris fit aut ex natura signorum aut stellarum quae in eis sunt." It includes at the end a number of weather signs, such as were known to the peasants (agricolae dicunt), a few a little more theoretical, rules with regard to the meaning of thunder for each month (already mentioned by Bede), etc.

A French translation of Leopold's Compilatio (Li compilacions Leupol le fil le duc d'Austeriche de le science des estoiles) was owned by Mary of Luxemburg, queen of France (d. 1324). This shows that Leopold can hardly be placed after the second half of the thirteenth century.

Text—The Compilatio was first printed by Erhard Ratdolt (110 fol., many figures, Augsburg 1489). Second edition printed by Melchior Sessa (94 fol., Venice 1520). Does not seem to differ materially from the first.

Criticism—S. Günther: Allgemeine deutsche Biographie (vol. 18, 404, 1883). P. Duhem: Système du monde (vol. 3, 312–317, 1915). Gustav Hellmann: Die Wettervorhersage im ausgehenden Mittelalter (176–179, Berlin 1917; Isis, 4, 185). Ernst Zinner: Verzeichnis der astronomischen Handschriften (202, Munich 1925; Isis, 15, 193–195).

PETER OF DACIA

Petrus Philomeni (or Philomena) de Dacia. Peter Ingvarssön. Danish Dominican, mathematician and physician. Studied in Paris, flourished in the monastery

[6] This is not inferred from the title but from a very definite statement in the preface.

of Roskilde, near Copenhagen, towards the end of the thirteenth century. He composed: 1. An excellent commentary on Sacrobosco's algorismus, of about 18000 words, completed in Paris c. 1291. 2. A calendar for the year 1292 and following. 3. A compotus (?) c. 1300. 4. Multiplication tables from 1 × 1 to 49 × 49, in sexagesimal numbers. 5. Various medical treatises dealing with bloodletting, medical astrology, hygiene, etc.

Peter explained arithmetic progressions. In the extraction of the cubic root of a number having more than three figures, Peter was apparently the first to suggest a means of finding the second figure of the root (division by $3a^2$ if a is the first figure). He conceived the generation of a surface by the continuous movement or 'flowing' (fluere) of a line, and the generation of a solid by the "flowing" of a surface.

Text—Max Curtze: Petri Philumeni de Dacia in Algorismum vulgarem Johannis de Sacrobosco commentarius (112 p., Copenhagen 1897; together with the algorism itself).

There is a MS. of a calendar ascribed to Peter of Dacia, and supposed to have been owned by him, in the new royal collection (N.K.S., no. 275 quarto) in the Royal Library of Copenhagen. This so-called Petri de Dacia Kalendarium simply reproduces a calendar made by Grosseteste (first half of the thirteenth century). But Peter wrote another calendar, based upon Grosseteste, yet independent. There are two versions of it: (1) in French, Codex Havniensis Thott, 240 in 2°, Copenhagen; (2) in Latin, Calendarium Magistri Petri de Dacia, Codex no. 20, College of Arms, London.

The medical texts written by him are short; one somewhat larger (Royal Library, Copenhagen, G. k. S. = Old royal Collection, 4to, 1810) wherein he calls himself Frater Petrus Inguari studiosus roskildensis, was investigated by the late J. W. S Johnsson who was planning an edition of it (private communication, Dec. 1927).

Criticism—G. Eneström: Anteckningar om matematikern Petrus de Dacia och hans skrifter (Vetensk. Akad., Öfversigt, vol. 42 and 43, Stockholm 1885–1886). B. Boncompagni: Sur un MS. d'un traité de géométrie attribué à Petrus (Bibliotheca Mathematica, 196, 1885). M. Cantor: Geschichte der Mathematik (vol. 2, second edition, 90, 1899). G. Eneström: Über die Geschichte der Kubikwurzelausziehung im Mittelalter (Bibliotheca mathematica, vol. 14, 83, 1914). Suzan R. Benedict: Comparative study of early arithmetics (Ann Arbor 1914). P. Duhem: Système du monde (vol. 4, 29–30, 1916). K. Kålund: Alfraeði íslenzk (vol. 2, xxxix, 1914–1916, commentary written by N. Beckman). Ernst Zinner: Verzeichnis der astronomischen Handschriften (77, Munich 1925; Isis, 15, 193–195). In some MSS. this Peter is apparently called Petrus Danus de S. Audomaro (i.e., Saint Omer, Pas-de-Calais).

II. EASTERN CHRISTENDOM

For Greek mathematics, see the notes on Nicholas Blemmydes, Georgios Pachymeres, and Maximos Planudes in the philosophical chapter.

For Syriac mathematics, see the notes on Abū-l-Faraj and 'Abhd īshō' bar Bĕrīkhā in the philosophical chapter.

JOHN OF ERZINJĀN

Also called John Bluss, or the Blue. Armenian moralist, grammarian, astronomer, translator from Latin into Armenian. Born at Erzinjān, between Erzerum and Sīwās, c. 1271 (or before?); studied at the monastery of Mt. Sepuh (Kohanam

Dagh); traveled across Armenia and Syria to Jerusalem; taught at the monastery of Dsordsor (?); died at Mt. Sepuh in 1326. His main works are: 1. An astronomical treatise composed in 1284 at the request of a Georgian prince and of the bishop of Tiflīs. 2. Later at the request of an Armenian prince he rewrote this treatise in verse. 3. An Armenian grammar modeled upon the Greek grammar of Dionysios Thrax (second half of the second century B. C.). He was commanded by Jacob I the Learned (catholicos from 1267 to 1286) to put together all the explanations given by earlier Armenian grammarians; he completed this compilation in 1293 and divided it into 30 chapters. 4. A collection of religious and moral precepts; a similar work was also published by him in vulgar Armenian, all his other works being in the classical language. 5. Two hagiological discourses made at Sepuh in 1288. 6. In 1316 he completed the commentary on the Gospel according to St. Matthew, begun by Nerses the Graceful, upon Chrysostomos' example. 7. A translation from the Latin of St. Thomas Aquinas' treatise on sacraments. This work had been sent to Cilicia by the pope, John XXII (1316–1334). It was translated twice into Armenian; by John, and by the bishop Zacharias of Dsordsor.

Text—1. Astronomical treatise printed in 1792 in New Nakhichevan, Russian Armenia.

3. The grammar was printed at Venice in 1815.

5. The two hagiological discourses were published twice in Constantinople (1737, 1824).

6. Commentary on St. Matthew (Constantinople 1825).

Criticism—C. F. Neumann: Geschichte der armenischen Literatur (193–196, 202, 1836).

For Mekhitar of Ānī, see the note on Mekhitar of Aïri-vankh in the historical chapter.

III. ISRAEL

For Moses ibn Tibbon and Jacob ben Maḥir ibn Tibbon, see chapter on translators; for Gershon ben Solomon and Levi ben Abraham ben Ḥayyim, see philosophical chapter; for Benjamin 'Anav, see historical chapter.

IV. WESTERN ISLĀM

IBN AL-BANNĀ'

Moroccan mathematician and astronomer. Abū-l-'Abbās Aḥmad ibn Muḥammad ibn 'Uthmān al-Azdī Ibn al-Bannā' (son of the architect). Born at Marrākush c. 1256; studied there and in Fās, became a ṣūfī; died at Marrākush in 1321 or a few years later.

A great many writings are ascribed to him (51, even 74), most of them mathematical and astronomical. I shall first deal with the most popular, the Talkhīṣ; then more briefly with a few others.

1. The Talkhīṣ fī a'māl al-ḥisāb (summary of the operations of calculation) is an arithmetical summary derived from the work of Muḥammad ibn 'Abdallāh al-Ḥaṣṣār. It contains many interesting features: improved treatment of fractions; constant use of Hindu numerals, in their western form of course (ghubār)[7]; sums

[7] On the ḥurūf al-ghubār, see vol. 1, 648, 649, 663, 670. Solomon Gandz: The origin of the ghubār numerals (to appear in Isis, vol. 16 or 17).

of squares and cubes; casting out of nines, eights, and sevens; rule of double false position.

$$\sqrt{(a^2 + r)} \approx a + \frac{r}{2a}, \text{ if } r \leqslant a$$

$$\approx a + \frac{r}{2a+1}, \text{ if } r > a$$

The popularity of Ibn al-Bannā's Talkhīṣ is proved by many commentaries, of which the following may be mentioned:

(a) By one of his pupils, 'Abd al-'Azīz ibn 'Alī ibn Dā'ūd al-Huwārī.

(b) By Abū Zakarīyā Muḥammad al-Ishbīlī (end of fourteenth century or beginning of fifteenth).

(c) By the Egyptian Ibn al-Majidī (1359–1447).

(d) By the Spaniard, al-Qalaṣādī (d. 1486).

There are also anonymous commentaries, and one, Raf' al-ḥijāb (Lifting up of the veil) by the author himself.

The other treatises of Ibn al-Bannā' may be divided roughly into seven groups: geometry, arithmetic, algebra, astronomy, astrolabe, astrology, calendar.

2. *Geometry*—He wrote an introduction to Euclid and a treatise on the measurement of surfaces, Risāla fī 'ilm al-masāḥa.

3. *Arithmetic*—Outside of the Talkhīṣ and of the Raf' al-ḥijāb, he composed four discourses on calculation (Al-maqālāt fī-l-ḥisāb) dealing respectively with integers, fractions, roots, and proportions. Also the Tanbīh al-albāb (Awakening of minds); the Mukhtaṣar kāfil li-l-muṭallib (A compendium which is a surety to the investigator); a treatise on binomials (dhawāt al-asmā) and apotomes (munfaṣalāt)—i.e., quantities of the form $a \pm \sqrt{b}$ or $\sqrt{a} \pm \sqrt{b}$; on proportions; on inheritance problems.

4. *Algebra*—Kitāb al-uṣūl wal-muqaddamāt fī-l-jabr wal-muqābala (Principles of and introduction to algebra). Kitāb fī-l-jabr wal-muqābala (may be identical with preceding).

5. *Astronomy*—Kitāb minhāj al-ṭālib li ta'dīl al-kawākib (The way of those who wish to account for the movements of the stars). According to Ibn Khaldūn, this was an extract from the tables of Ibn Isḥāq.[8]

Qānūn li-tarḥīl al-shams wal-qamar fī-l-manāzil wa ma'rifat auqāt al-lail wal-nahār (Rule to determine the stations of sun and moon and know the times of night and day). Determination of the qibla. Heliacal settings of stars. Kitāb al-yasāra fī-taqwīm al-kawākib al-sayyāra (Book of ease, tables of the wandering stars).

6. *Astrolabe*—Treatise on the astrolabe. On the use of the ṣafīḥa of al-Zarqālī.

7. *Astrology*—Madkhal al-nujūm wa ṭabā'i' al-ḥurūf (Introduction of stars and properties of letters). Kitāb fi aḥkām al-nujūm, on judicial astrology. It is probable that the treatises mentioned in sections 5 and 6 are also partly astrological.

8. *Calendar*—Kitāb al-manākh (hence our word almanac). This seems to be the earliest literary use of the word manākh in this sense.

Ibn al-Bannā's popularity as a mathematical teacher is proved by the success of his Talkhīṣ which lasted at least two centuries, and by the admiration which Ibn Khaldūn expressed. He was the teacher of Abū 'Abdallāh Muḥammad ibn Ibrāhīm al Abbalī (d. c. 1368), who in his turn was Ibn Khaldūn's teacher.

[8] That is Aḥmad (ibn 'Alī) ibn Isḥāq al-Tamīmī, who lived in Tunis at the beginning of the thirteenth century. His tables, wherein he made use of the observations of a Sicilian Jew, were very popular in western Islām. (H. Suter: Mathematiker, 142, 1900.)

Text—French translation of the Talkhīṣ by Aristide Marre (Atti de' Nuovi Lincei, vol. 17, 289–319, 1864; reprint, Rome 1865). Extracts from Ibn al Majidī's commentary (c) were translated by Franz Woepcke: Passages relatifs à des sommations de séries de cubes (Rome 1864). Extract from al-Qalaṣādī's commentary translated by the same (Journal asiatique, vol. 1, 58–62, 1863).

Criticism—Ibn Khaldūn: Prolégomènes (de Slane's translation, vol. 1, 245, vol. 3, 132–134, 149). Aristide Marre: Biographie d'Ibn al-Bannā' (Atti de' Nuovi Lincei, vol. 19, 1865). Includes text and translation of the biography by Aḥmad Bābā of Timbuktu (1556–1626). M. Steinschneider: Rectification de quelques erreurs (Boncompagni's Bulletino, vol. 10, 313–314, 1877). L. Rodet: Sur les méthodes d'approximation chez les anciens (Bull. de la Société mathématique de France, vol. 7, 159–167, 1879). A. Favaro: Sulla costruzione delle equazioni (Modena, 1878). H. Suter: Die Mathematiker und Astronomen der Araber (162–164, 220, 227, 1900); Das Rechenbuch des Abū Zakarīyā al-Haṣṣār (Bibliotheca Mathematica, vol. 2, 12–40, 1901). C. Brockelmann: Arabische Litteratur (vol. 2, 255, 710, 1902). M. Cantor: Geschichte der Mathematik (vol. 1^3, 805–810, 1907). H. Suter and Mohammed ben Cheneb: Encyclopaedia of Islām (vol. 2, 367, 1916). George Sarton: Tacuinum, taqwīm. With a digression on the word almanac (Isis, 10, 490–493, 1928).

For Muḥyī al-dīn al-Maghribī, see the section on Eastern Islām.

V. EASTERN ISLĀM

MUḤAMMAD IBN ABĪ BAKR AL-FĀRISĪ

Persian mathematician and astronomer who seems to have flourished in Yaman in the second half of the thirteenth century. He wrote two astronomical works: 1. Nihāyat al-idrāk fī asrār 'ulūm al-aflāk (The highest understanding on the secrets of the science of the spheres). 2. The Ma'ārij al-fikr al-wahīj (Stairs of the burning thought), explaining the difficulties of astronomical tables.

The second work was composed for al-Muẓaffar Yūsuf ibn 'Umar (prince of Yaman from c. 1249 to 1295). It was probably identical with the Zīj Muḥammad quoted by Ḥājī Khalīfa (vol. 3, 567), of which the latter says that it was based upon the observations of Farīd al-dīn Abū-l-Ḥasan 'Alī ibn 'Abd al-Karīm al-Shirwānī, called al-Fahhād (fl. c. 1145–1174). There are two MSS. of the Ma'ārij written in Hebrew script. This work is probably posterior to 1266.

A magical treatise, Āyāt al-āfāq min khawāṣṣ al-aufāq (Signs of the universe from the most appropriate properties), dealing with magic squares (?), is ascribed to an author of exactly the same name, but who is mentioned as having died in 1350–1351. This date is not incompatible with the other facts, if Muḥammad composed his Ma'ārij toward the end of al-Muẓaffar's rule.

Criticism—Ḥājī Khalīfa: Lexicon (vol. 3, 567; vol. 6, 176). H. Suter: Mathematiker (139, 218, 1900; 175, 1902). C. Brockelmann: Arabische Litteratur (vol. 1, 474; vol. 2, 214; 1898–1902).

According to Ḥājī (vol. 6), followed by Brockelmann, Muḥammad died in 1231–1232; but this does not tally with his other statement (vol. 3). The facts which we know favor my assumption that Muḥammad flourished in the second half of the thirteenth century.

NĀṢIR AL-DĪN AL-ṬŪSĪ

Persian philosopher, mathematician, astronomer, physician, and scientist who wrote in Arabic and Persian. One of the greatest mathematicians and scientists of Islām. Born in 1201, died in 1274.

Contents: (1) Life. (2) Writings with special reference to the Mutawassiṭāt. (3) Arithmetic. (4) Geometry. (5) Trigonometry. (6) Observatory and library of Marāgha. (7) Instruments used in Marāgha. (8) Astronomical tables. (9) Astronomical theories. The Tadhkira. (10) Other astronomical treatises. (11) Calendar. (12) Other astrological treatises. (13) Other superstitions. (14) Optics. (15) Mineralogy. (16) Music. (17) Geography. (18) Medicine. (19) Logic and classification of knowledge. (20) Philosophy. (21) Theology. (22) Ethics. (23) Poetry. (24) Nāṣir al-dīn's sons.
(25) Text. (26) Oriental sources. (27) Criticism.

1. *Life*—Abū Jaʻfar Muḥammad ibn Muḥammad ibn al-Ḥasan, Nāṣir al-dīn al-Ṭūsī, al-Muḥaqqiq, the investigator (Nāṣir is often written naṣīr; both words, which look far more different in the Arabic script than in our own, are derived from the same root and have the same meaning—auxiliary, defender; nāṣir al-dīn is a title of honor meaning defender of the faith; I shall always write nāṣir for the sake of consistency). Born in February, 1201, in Sāvah,[9] or in Ṭūs, Khurāsān. His main teacher was Kamāl al-dīn Ibn Yūnus. He was kidnapped by Nāṣir al-dīn ʻAbd al-Raḥmān (Raḥīm?) ibn abī Manṣūr, the Ismāʻīlī governor of Quhistān, and sent to Alamūt—the great Ismāʻīlī stronghold[10]—where he remained, if not a prisoner at least an unwilling guest, until its capture by the Mongols in 1256. Upon our Nāṣir's advice, the Grand Master of the Assassins, Rukn al-dīn Khūrshāh, gave himself up to the Mongol chief, Hūlāgū Khān (Īl-khān of Persia, 1256–1265), and Nāṣir himself entered the latter's service. Nāṣir was probably in Hūlāgū's train when the latter sacked Baghdād in February 1258 and put an end to the ʻAbbāsid caliphate. He remained in the Mongol service, becoming a wazīr and obtaining increasing influence over Hūlāgū by his astrological knowledge; it is said that Hūlāgū did not dare to undertake anything without his astrologer's advice. Nāṣir al-dīn was finally appointed administrator of the waqf[11] revenues; part of these revenues may have been used to build and endow the observatory and library of Marāgha. Nāṣir al-dīn resided in that city from 1259 almost until the end of his life. In 1274 he went to Baghdād, where he died in June of that year. He was a Shīʻa, of the sect of the Shīʻī-Imāmī (or Twelvers).

2. *Writings with special reference to the Mutawassiṭāt*—A large number of writings on many subjects are ascribed to him. Not less than 56 are listed by Brockelmann, and that list is not complete. I shall deal with all of the scientific writings about which we know something, and with the most important of the others. My list including 64 items is largely independent of Brockelmann's.

His knowledge was largely derived from Greek sources of which he had made a deep study. It is said that he knew Greek, but there is no definite proof of it and such knowledge was not considered necessary in his time. He knew the Greek mathematicians through the Arabic translations and commentaries; he prepared

[9] This is probably Sāvah in Jibāl, between Hamadān and Ray.
[10] Near Qazwīn in Jibāl. For the Ismāʻīlī and the "Assassins" see vol. 1, 752, 593.
[11] Waqf (pl. awqāf), religious property in mortmain.

translations of some Greek texts from Arabic into Persian; he edited a large collection of the Arabic versions and elaborations. This is the work called (1) Kitāb al-mutawassiṭāt bain al-handasa wal-hai'a (The middle books between geometry and astronomy). By "middle books" was probably meant the books to be studied in addition to the Elements and the Almagest. This collection included Arabic versions or rather elaborations of treatises by Autolycos, Aristarchos, Euclid, Apollonios, Archimedes, Hypsicles, Theodosios, Menelaos, Ptolemy; also Arabic treatises by Thābit ibn Qurra; later other Arabic treatises by the Banū Mūsā and Nāṣir al-dīn himself were added to it.

It is clear that the Mutawassiṭāt were the equivalent of the "little astronomy" (ὁ μικρὸς ἀστρονομούμενος τόπος) plus a few Arabic accretions. The "little astronomy" indeed was a collection of Greek writings by the authors above mentioned; it was so called in opposition to the Μεγάλη σύνταξις.[12] Together with the Elements and the Almagest, the Mutawassiṭāt constituted the bulk of ancient classics available to the Muslims.

As it is not easy to distinguish between plain versions, elaborations, commentaries, and original works, I shall quote the different treatises which seem to belong to the Mutawassiṭāt together with the other treatises dealing with the same subjects, in the following sections. It should be remembered that these sections are provided simply to make a survey of Nāṣir al-dīn's work more easy; they are not by any means exclusive: astronomy cannot be entirely dissociated from geometry on one side and from astrology on the other; treatises on arithmetic or on the calendar are, or may be, partly astrological, etc.

The treatises which belong, or might belong, to the Mutawassiṭāt, are generally published separately and are often quoted (e.g., by Ibn Shākir) independently of the Mutawassiṭāt as if they were separate works. There is a MS. of the whole collection in Constantinople (Aya Sophia, 2760) entitled Majmū'a fī-l-hai'a walhandasa (Astronomical and geometrical collection).

M. Steinschneider: Die mittleren Bücher der Araber und ihre Bearbeiter (Zeitschrift für Mathematik und Physik, vol. 10, 456–498, 1865).

3. *Arithmetic and algebra*—The (2) Mukhtaṣar bi-jāmi' al-ḥisāb bil-takht walturāb (summary of the whole of computation with table (?) and earth) is extant in Persian and Arabic.

(3) On the proof that the sum of two odd squares cannot be a square.

(4) Inheritance problems. (May be of arithmetical interest).

(5) Kitāb al-jabr wal-muqābala. Treatise on algebra.

4. *Geometry*—In his astronomical treatise Tadhkira, to be dealt with in section 9, Nāṣir al-dīn proved that if a circle internally touches another circle of double diameter and if the two circles turn or roll uniformly in opposite directions, remaining tangent and the speed of the smaller being twice greater than that of the other, then the original point of contact of the smaller circle will move along a diameter of the greater circle.

He wrote a number of geometrical treatises or commentaries as follows:

(6) Treatise on Euclid's postulates (al-uṣūl al-mauḍū'a).

(7) Discussion of the fifth postulate, addressed to Qaiṣar ibn Abī-l-Qāsim

[12] P. Tannery: Recherches sur l'histoire de l'astronomie ancienne (35, Paris 1893).

(both Qaiṣar and Nāṣir al-dīn were disciples of Kamāl al-dīn Ibn Yūnus). This treatise may be a part of the preceding one. Nāṣir al-dīn's discussion was remarkably elaborate. The work of Girolamo Saccheri (Euclides ab omni naevo vindicatus, Milan 1733) was largely derived from the start made by Nāṣir al-dīn.

Latin translation published by John Wallis: De postulato quinto, et definitione quinta lib. 6 Euclidis (Wallis operum mathematicorum volumen alterum, 665–678, Oxford, 1693; the translation itself is on p. 669–673). An earlier publication of that translation, 1651(?) was not available to me.

Roberto Bonola: Non-Euclidean geometry (Chicago 1912).

(8) Qawā'id al-handasa (Principles of geometry).

(9 to 16) Probably parts of the Mutawassiṭāt.

(8–9) Two redactions of the Elements of Euclid, Taḥrīr al-uṣūl, a longer and a shorter one. Though this was not by any means his chief achievement, Nāṣir al-dīn was best known among mathematicians for centuries for his share in the Euclidian tradition. As opposed to Euclid, he multiplied the special cases; e.g., not less than 16 for the Pythagorean theorem! This was obviously a backward step.

H. Suter: Einiges aus Nassir ed-Dins Euklidausgabe (Bibliotheca mathematica, 3–6, 1892). Eilhard Wiedemann: Zu der Redaktion von Euklids Elementen durch Naṣīr al-dīn al-Ṭūsī (Beiträge, 73; Sitzungsberichte der Phys. med. Sozietät, vol. 58, 228–236, Erlangen 1928). Contains translation of the preface and of the beginning of the first book, with notes.

(8) Longer redaction of the Elements. Together with notes and additions by al-Ḥajjāj ibn Yūsuf ibn Maṭar (first half of the ninth century), and by Thābit ibn Qurra (second half of the ninth century). Euclidis Elementorum geometricorum libri tredecim. Ex traditione Nasiridini Tusini nunc primum arabice impressi (Rome 1594).

(9) Shorter redaction of the Elements, including the fifteen books. Printed Constantinople, 1801. Books I to VI, printed Calcutta, 1824. There is a Commentary on this shorter version by one Abū Isḥāq. Suter suggests the latter's identification with Abū Isḥāq al-'Aṭṭār al-Jazūlī, teacher of Ibn al-Bannā', but without good reason (Mathematiker der Araber, 162, note 82 on p. 220, 1900).

(10) 105 Problems on the Elements.

(11) Version of Euclid's Data.

(12) Edition of the Data of Thābit ibn Qurra, Taḥrīr al-mafrūḍāt li Thābit ibn Qurra.

(13) Version of Apollonios' Conics, Books I to VII.

(14) Archimedes on the sphere and the cylinder, after Thābit ibn Qurra and Isḥāq ibn Ḥunain.

(15) Archimedes on the division of the circle, idem.

(16) Archimedes Lemnata after Thābit ibn Qurra with commentary by 'Alī ibn Aḥmad al-Nasawī (first half of the eleventh century).

5. *Trigonometry*—Nāṣir al-dīn's permanent fame is based primarily upon his trigonometry, which marked the culmination of the ancient and mediaeval efforts in that special direction.

(17) He prepared a new edition of Menelaos' spherics, after Abū Naṣr Manṣūr ibn 'Alī (second half of the tenth century).

He wrote a separate treatise on this subject, (18) Kitāb shakl al-qaṭṭā' (Kitāb da'āwī al-shakl al-ma'rūf bil-qaṭṭā', or Kashf al-qanā' 'an asrār shakl al-qaṭṭā'). Shakl al-qaṭṭā' means the figure of the sector, referring to Menelaos' theorem about the triangle cut by a transversal; in the mediaeval Latin translations this became the figura cata or the regula catta (vol. 1, 598).

The Shakl al-qaṭṭā' is divided into five books of which books 3 and 4 deal respectively with plane and spherical trigonometry. It was the first textbook wherein trigonometry was considered independently from astronomy, for its own sake, and it was the greatest of its kind in mediaeval times. It was very elaborate. It included the first explicit formulation of the sine law relative to plane triangles, together with two proofs of it; and the six fundamental formulae for the solution of spherical right angled triangles. Moreover it showed how to solve other triangles as well, replacing if necessary the consideration of angles by that of sides and vice versa by means of polar triangles. Of course he did not define the polar triangles, but his method implied their consideration. Polar triangles were not clearly explained until the time of Francis Vieta (1593) and Willebrord Snell (1627).

Greco-Arabic trigonometry was continued (probably independently of Nāsir al-dīn) in Hebrew by Levi ben Gershon (c. 1321), and in Latin by Richard Wallingford (d. 1335) and finally by Regiomontanus (c. 1464). To appreciate Nāṣir al-dīn's achievement it will suffice to realize that his Shakl al-qaṭṭā' was almost the Arabic equivalent of Regiomontanus' De triangulis omnimodis libri quinque, posthumously printed in 1533.

The Shakl al-qaṭṭā' was edited and translated into French by Alexandre Carathéodory pasha: Traité du quadrilatère (Constantinople 1891). Reviewed by H. Suter in Bibliotheca mathematica (1-8, 1893).

A. v. Braunmühl: Nassir Eddin und Regiomontan (Abhdl. d. Leopold. Akademie der Naturforscher, vol. 71, 31-67, 2 pl., Halle 1897); Geschichte der Trigonometrie (vol. 1, 65-71, 1900). John David Bond: The development of trigonometric methods down to the close of the fifteenth century (Isis, 4, 295-323, 1922). Joh. Tropfke: Geschichte der Elementar-Mathematik (vol. 5, 126, 1923). H. Bürger and K. Kohl: Geschichte des Transversalensatzes (Abhdl. zur Geschichte der Naturwissenschaften, 7, 85-89, and passim, Erlangen 1924; Isis, 8, 799).

6. *Observatory and library of Marāgha*—I have already alluded (in §1) to Nāṣir al-dīn's long residence in Marāgha (1259-1274). Marāgha is a town in Adharbāijān, east of Lake Urmīya and south of Tabrīz; it became a favorite residence of the Īlkhān Hūlāgū. After having defeated al-Musta'ṣim, the last caliph, he ordered the establishment of an observatory and of a library[13] near that city, the execution of his plans being entrusted to Nāṣir al-dīn. The construction was begun and probably completed in 1259.

The observatory was built on a fortified hill to the west of the city. The foundations of it are still extant; the leveled area on the hill measures 137 x 347 metres.

V. Minorsky: Marāgha (Encyclopaedia of Islām, vol. 3, 261-266, 1930).

The observatory was equipped with the very best instruments, some of which were probably obtained from Baghdād and Alamūt. The library is said (by Ibn

[13] Such a plan had already been conceived by the Great Khān, Mangū (1248-1257), and it is told (by Khwāndamīr) that when he sent Hūlāgū to Persia he ordered him to get hold of Nāṣir al-dīn for that very purpose.

Shākir) to have contained more than 400,000 volumes (?), which the Mongol armies had collected in Syria, Mesopotamia, and Persia. The whole establishment was richly endowed. It reminds one of earlier scientific institutions, such as the Bayt al-ḥikma organized in Baghdād by al-Ma'mūn (first half of the ninth century), and the Dār al-ḥikma founded in Cairo by al-Ḥākim (first half of the eleventh century). The climate of Marāgha was very favorable for astronomical observations. There is no evidence that the observatory lasted more than two generations. After work had stopped in Marāgha, no other observatory of equal importance was established in eastern Islām until the time of Ulūgh Beg (Samarkand 1420).

Nāṣir al-dīn was the first director of the observatory, and was later succeeded by two of his sons (see section 24). According to the preface of his tables, he had the following collaborators: 'Alī ibn 'Umar al-Qazwīnī (d. 1277), Mu'ayyad al-dīn al-'Urḍī al-Dimishqī, Fakhr al-dīn al-Khalāṭī of Tiflīs, Fakhr al-din al-Marāghī of Mūṣul. Two other astronomers who worked in Marāgha at about the same time were Muḥyī al-dīn al-Maghribī and the illustrious Abū-l-Faraj (c. 1268–1279). (All of these men are dealt with separately in this volume, except the two Fakhr al-dīn). Finally we may still mention 'Abd al-Razzāq ibn Aḥmad ibn Muḥammad al-Shaibānī, called Ibn al-Fūṭī (1244–1323), made prisoner in the sack of Baghdād, assistant to Nāṣir al-dīn and later keeper of the Marāgha library.[14]

It is said that Hūlāgū had brought from China a number of Chinese astronomers and scientists, among them one Fao-mun-ji (?),[15] through whom Nāṣir al-dīn obtained his knowledge of Chinese astronomy and of their calendar. I have not been able to check this statement made by Constantin Mouradja d'Ohsson: Histoire des Mongols (vol. 3, 265, 1834–1835). However see my note on Muḥyī al-dīn al-Maghribī below (section 3).

7. *Instruments used in Marāgha*—A list of these instruments will be found below in my note on al-'Urḍī who described them. Here is another list made from a different point of view by Khwāndamīr (first half of the sixteenth century): tamāthīl-i-ashkāl-i-aflāk (representations of the shapes of the spheres); tadwīrāt, epicycles; ḥawāmīl, deferents: dawā'ir-i-mauhumā wa ṣuwar wa burūj-i-duwāzdagāna (imaginary circles, constellations, and signs of the zodiac).

Nāṣir al-dīn has been named the inventor of the turquet (torquetum), an instrument containing two graduated circles in two perpendicular planes. The same invention has been ascribed also to Franco of Liége (second half of the eleventh century), and to Jābir ibn Aflaḥ (first half of the twelfth century). The second of these ascriptions, made by Regiomontanus, is quite plausible; Jābir could have invented that instrument as well as Nāṣir al-dīn. The first is less likely. It is based upon the existence (in the Halliwell collection) of a MS. entitled Tractatus torquati secundum magistrum Franconem. Whatever its origin, the introduction of the turquet into the Latin West was largely due to Regiomontanus; it became very popular in the fifteenth and sixteenth centuries.

The linear astrolabe, sometimes called Ṭūsī's staff, was not named after Nāṣir al-dīn, but after al-Muẓaffar al-Ṭūsī (d. c. 1213).

Nāṣir al-dīn wrote a treatise on the sine quadrant (19) Nuzhat al-nāẓir (The observer's delight). Another treatise of his, on the astrolabe, is extant in Persian

[14] For other possible collaborators see E. Wiedemann (Beitr. 78, 299, 1928).

[15] "Le docteur Fao-moun-dji, plus connu sous le nom de Sing-Sing, ou de savant." The Chinese characters are not given, hence the correct form of these names can not be ascertained.

(20) Risālat-i-bīst bāb dar ma'rifat-i-uṣṭurlāb (Twenty chapters on the science of the astrolabe). There is a commentary upon it by 'Abd al-'Alī ibn Muḥammad ibn al-Ḥusain al-Barjandī (d. c. 1523).

Amable Jourdain: Mémoire sur l'observatoire de Méragah et sur quelques instruments employés pour y observer, suivi d'une notice sur la vie et les ouvrages de Nassyr-Eddin (Magasin encyclopédique, vol. 6, 1809; reprint, 64 p., Paris 1810). Hugo J. Seemann: Die Instrumente der Sternwarte zu Marāgha (Sitzungsber. der physik. med. Sozietät, vol. 60, 15–126, Erlangen 1928; Isis, 13, 111–113).

A Latin text written before 1350 (MS. Ashmole 1522, Bodleian), describing the turquet was edited by R. T. Gunther: Early science in Oxford (vol. 2, 370–375, 1923; Isis, 6, 449–453). See also same vol. (35–37) for another description and working drawings.

8. *Astronomical tables*—The main fruit of the short-lived Marāgha observatory was the compilation of new tables, called (21) Al-zīj al-īlkhānī (The tables of the Īlkhān). They were compiled by order of Hūlāgū (Īlkhān from 1256 to 1265). We may assume that the work was begun in 1259 or soon after. Nāṣir al-dīn claimed that thirty years would be needed to compile the tables, because this was the shortest period during which the planetary cycles were completed, but Hūlāgū gave him only twelve years to accomplish his task. Nāṣir promised to try and succeeded in completing the tables within twelve years; thus they were completed c. 1272.

It is probable that the Zīj īlkhānī were originally written in Persian. The work is divided into four books devoted respectively to (a) Chinese, Greek, Arabic, and Persian chronology, (b) motions of the planets, (c) ephemerides, and (d) astrological operations. It was translated into Arabic by Shihāb al-dīn al-Ḥalabī,[16] and again by (Yaḥyā ibn?) 'Alī ibn al-Rifā'ī al-Ḥusainī in 1527–1528 under the title Ḥall al-zīj (Solution of the tables). There is a copy of the tables by a son of Nāṣir al-dīn, Aṣīl al-dīn al-Ḥasan, and a commentary by al-Ḥasan ibn Muḥammad al-Nīsābūrī (first half of the fourteenth century) entitled Kashf al-ḥaqā'iq (Unveiling of the truths). 'Alī Shāh ibn Muḥammad al-Khwārizmī (fl. c. 1301) composed another commentary called Al-'umdat al-īlkhānīya (The Īlkhānic support). The Tauḍīḥ-i zīj īlkhānī is an elaboration of the tables by al-Ḥasan ibn al-Ḥusain Shāhinshāh al-Simnānī (or Samnānī), written in 1392–1393, and the Tauḍīḥ was commented upon by Maḥmūd Shāh Khuljī. Finally Jamshīd ibn Mas'ūd al-Kāshī (d. c. 1436), the first director of Ulūgh Beg's observatory in Samarqand, compiled a sort of supplement to the Īlkhānic tables, entitled Zīj-i Khāqānī (Tables of the Great Khān).

The tables of Nāṣir al-dīn were based upon new observations, but also (according to his own statement) upon earlier ones, namely those of Hipparchos, Ptolemy, al-Ma'mūn's astronomers, al-Battānī, Ibn al-A'lam, Ibn Yūnus.

These tables were immensely popular in the East, including China. They continued to be used even after the publication of new tables by Ulūgh Beg (c. 1437).

A part of al-Khuljī's commentary was edited by John Greaves (1602–1652): Astronomia quaedam ex traditione Shah Cholgii Persae una cum hypothesibus planetarum (London 1650).

[16] Possibly identical with Abū-l-'Abbās Aḥmad ibn Ibrāhīm ibn Khalīl al-Ḥalabī, of Damascus (d. 1455).

R. Ramsay Wright: Über die Schrift Astronomia quaedam von Greaves (Beiträge, 77; Sitzungsber. der phys. med. Soz., vol. 58, 381–386, Erlangen 1928).

9. *Astronomical theories. The Tadhkira*—Outside of the Zīj, Nāṣir al-dīn wrote many astronomical treatises.

The most important is the (22) Tadhkira fī 'ilm al-hai'a (Memorial of astronomy often called Al-tadhkira al-Nāṣirīya, not after the author, but after his first patron Nāṣir al-dīn, governor of Quhistān. It was thus composed some time before 1256. There seem to have been two editions of it.

The popularity of the Tadhkira is proved by the number of commentaries and super-commentaries devoted to it, namely: (a) the Bayān maqāṣid al-tadhkira (Explanation of the aims of the Tadhkira) by Muḥammad ibn 'Alī ibn al-Ḥusain al-Ḥimādhī, with notes by Maḥmūd ibn Mas'ūd Quṭb al-dīn al-Shīrāzī (d. 1310–1311); (b) the Tauḍīḥ al-tadhkira (Illustration of the T.) written in 1311–1312 by al-Ḥasan ibn Muḥammad al-Nīsābūrī; (c) a commentary by 'Alī ibn Muḥammad al-Jurjānī (d. 1413–1414); (d) another by Qāḍīzāda al-Rūmī (d. c. 1441); (e) still another by Aḥmad ibn Muḥammad (or Muḥammad ibn Aḥmad?) al-Khafarī, written in 1525; etc. The Tadhkira was translated into Persian under the title Risāla-i-hai'a, or Risāla-i-mu'īnīya (after a Shāh called Mu'īn). A Turkish commentary was composed in 1414 by Fatḥ Allāh Shirwānī.

The Tadhkira is a very condensed summary of astronomy, and hence somewhat difficult to understand. This may help to explain the number of commentaries. It is the main source for the study of Nāṣir al-dīn's astronomical ideas. It is divided into four chapters: (a) Geometrical and cinematical introduction. Discussion of rest, simple and complex motions, etc. (b) General astronomical notions. Secular change of the obliquity of the ecliptic, trepidation of the equinoxes. Discussion of the cosmological views of Ibn al-Haitham, who conceived planetary orbits in the shape of solid spherical surfaces (or discs), having different sizes and centers, and tangent to one another. Another part of the same chapter (translated by Carra de Vaux) contains interesting criticisms of the Almagest, chiefly with regard to the anomalies of the Moon and the motion in latitude of the planets (notably Mercury and Venus); also the proposition of a new system to replace the complicated Ptolemaic machinery of deferents and epicycles. (c) The earth and influences exerted upon it by celestial bodies. Geodesy after the astronomers of al-Ma'mūn, Qusṭā ibn Lūqā, and al-Bīrūnī. Account of seas, of sea winds, etc. (d) Sizes and distances of the planets.

In his criticism of the Almagest Nāṣir al-dīn showed considerable ingenuity, but his system was just as complicated as Ptolemy's and hardly better. The positive part of the Tadhkira was soon forgotten, but the negative part—his new and forceful criticism of Ptolemaic astronomy—was an additional step toward the Copernican reform.

A complete edition and translation of the Tadhkira is much to be desired. Extracts from it have been published in French by Carra de Vaux: Les sphères célestes selon Nasīr-Eddīn Attūsī, in appendix to P. Tannery: Recherches sur l'histoire de l'astronomie ancienne (337–361, Paris 1893).

Carra de Vaux: L'Almageste d'Abū'l Wéfa (Journal asiatique, vol. 19, 459, 1892). J. L. E. Dreyer: History of the planetary systems (268–271, 1906).

10. *Other astronomical treatises*—(23) Zubdat al-hai'a (The cream of astronomy), or Zubdat al-idrāk fī hai'a al-aflāk. Extant in Arabic and Persian.

(24) Kitāb al-tashīl[17] fī-l-nujūm (The stars made easy).

(25) On the trajectory, size, and distance of Mercury.

(26 to 33) Probably parts of the Mutawassiṭāt. Some of these writings are partly astrological.

(26) Autolycos: Risings and settings, after Thābit ibn Qurra, Fī-l-ṭulū' walghurūb.

(27) Autolycos: On the moving sphere, also after Thābit.

(28) Aristarchos. On the sizes and distances of Sun and Moon.

(29) Euclid: Phaenomena.

(30) Hypsicles: On the ascension of stars (Τὸ ἀναφορικόν). After al-Kindī and Qusṭā ibn Lūqā.

(31) Theodosios: Spherics.

(32) Theodosios: Days and nights.

(33) Theodosios: Habitations. After Qusṭā ibn Lūqā.

(34) Ptolemy: Almagest. Taḥrīr al-majisṭī (1247). This recension (taḥrīr) reproduced the original rather closely, but with additions, e.g., on proportions (after pseudo-Euclid), on armillary spheres, on new observations. There is but little criticism of Ptolemy's views; his criticism is set forth in the Tadhkira (see section 9). The Taḥrīr was commented upon by Muḥammad ibn Ashraf Shams al-dīn al-Samarqandī (fl. 1276); by al-Ḥasan ibn Muḥammad Niẓām al-dīn al-Nīsābūrī in 1304–1305; by 'Abd al-'Alī ibn Muḥammad Niẓām al-dīn al-Barjandī (d. c. 1523).

11. *Calendar*—(35) Mukhtaṣar fi' 'ilm al-tanjīm wa-ma'rifat al-taqwīm (Summary of astrology and of the calendar). This is also extant in Persian under the title Risāla-i-sī faṣl (Treatise in thirty chapters). There is a Persian commentary by one Badr al-Ṭabarī, and two Arabic ones by 'Abd al-Wāḥid ibn Muḥammad dated 1394–1395, and by an anonym.

(36) Kitāb al-bāri' fī 'ulūm al-taqwīm wa-ḥarakāt al-aflāk wa-aḥkām al-nujūm (The excellent book on the calendar, the movements of the spheres, and judicial astrology).

Treatises 35 and 36 are both devoted to astrology as well as to the calendar—which is not unusual; witness many modern calendars. They may be partly or wholly identical.

12. *Other astrological treatises*—See nos. 2, 35, and 36. The two following nos. 37 and 38 were probably parts of the Mutawassiṭāt.

(37) Ptolemy: Τετράβιβλον (Quadripartitum). In Persian.

(38) Pseudo-Ptolemy: Καρπός (Liber fructus, Centiloquium). In Arabic and Persian.

(38 bis?) Fāl nāma. Book of presages.

Note that the Zīj īlkhānī was also to a large extent astrological, the fourth or last part entirely so.

13. *Other superstitions*—(39) Kitāb al-wāfī fī 'ilm al-raml (The perfect treatise on the science of sand, i.e., geomancy). Also entitled Al-risāla al-sulṭānīya fī khaṭṭ al-raml (Sultanian epistle on the sand figure).

(40) Ikhtiyārāt (Choices, i.e., of propitious days). In Turkish.

[17] Read tas-hīl!

14. *Optics*—(41) Taḥrīr kitāb al-manāẓir. Recension of Euclid's Optics, probably a part of the Mutawassiṭāt. It is set forth in the preface that we perceive objects because of the light rays emanating from them, but that everything happens as if the rays emanated from our eyes.

(42) Mabāḥīth fī in'ikās al-shu'ā'āt wa in'iṭāfihā (Research on the reflection and deflection of rays). Contains a proof of the equality of the angles of incidence and reflection.

German translation by Eilhard Wiedemann: Über die Reflexion und Umbiegung des Lichtes (Eder's Jahrbuch für Photographie, 21, 38–44, 1907).

(43) Answer to 'Alī ibn 'Umar al-Qazwīnī (d. 1277) concerning Ibn Sīnā's theory on the influence of heat and cold upon the colors of dry and moist bodies.

Abbreviated translation by E. Wiedemann: Über die Entstehung der Farben nach Naṣīr al-Dīn al Tūsī (Jahrbuch für Photographie, 22, 86–91, 1908).

E. Wiedemann: Über optische Täuschungen nach Fakhr al-dīn al-Rāzī und Naṣīr al-dīn al-Ṭūsī (Beiträge 33, Sitzungsber. der phys. med. Societät, vol. 45, 154–167, 1913–1914).

15. *Mineralogy*—(44) Tansūq-nāma-i-Īlkhānī. Persian lapidary.

E. G. Browne: Literary history of Persia (vol. 2, 485, 1906).

16. *Music*—(45) Kitāb fī 'ilm al-mūsīqī. In Arabic.

(46) Kanz al-tuḥaf. Persian treatise also ascribed to Nāṣir al-dīn. If genuine it may be a translation of 45.

According to a Turkish tradition, Nāṣir al-dīn invented a kind of flute, mahtar dūdūk (chapel flute). His musical theories were elaborated by his greatest disciple, Quṭb al-dīn al-Shīrāzī (see below).

Evliyā Chelebī (or Efendi): Narrative of travels in Europe, Asia, and Africa in the seventeenth century. Translated from the Turkish by Joseph von Hammer (vol. 1, part 2, 237, London; part 1 dated 1846). H. G. Farmer: History of Arabian music (226, London 1929; Isis, 13, 375).

17. *Geography*—(47) Kitāb ṣūrat al-aqālīm. This is not simply a Persian translation of the Ṣuwar al-aqālīm of al-Balkhī (first half of the tenth century). The MSS. contain maps.

Moreover we must expect Nāsir al-dīn's tables and other astronomical works to contain geographical coordinates. The third chapter of the Tadhkira deals with geodesy, and ends with a description of the seas, sea-winds, etc.

Demetrios Alexandrides: *Δύο πίνακες γεωγραφικοί, ὁ μὲν Νασσὶρ Ἐδδινοῦ Πέρσου, ὁ δὲ Οὐλοὺγ Μπέϊ Ταтάρου* (80, p., Vienna 1807). Persian tables giving the longitude and latitude of many cities, with Greek translation.

J. T. Reinaud: Geographie d'Aboulféda (vol. 1, 138–141, 1848; nothing purely geographical). Hans von Mžik: Ptolemaeus und die Karten der arabischen Geographen (Mitt. der geograph. Ges., vol. 58, Wien 1915). Konrad Miller: Mappae arabicae (vol. 1, part 1, p. 22, Stuttgart 1926; Isis, 9, 458).

18. *Medicine*—Nāṣir al-dīn brought Hūlāgū an illustrated book dealing with the preparation of the daryāq al-farūkī (i.e., the best kind of treacle).[18] It is not said that he was the author of it.

In 1270–1271 (or 1273) he was called upon to treat Hūlāgū's son and successor, Abāqā (Īlkhān from 1265 to 1281), who had been gored by a wild cow. His treatment was successful.

E. G. Browne: Literary history of Persia (vol. 3, 18, 1920).

Two medical writings are ascribed to him.

(48) Notes on the Kullīyāt (introductory generalities) of Ibn Sīnā's Qānūn.

(49) Kitāb al-bāb al-bāhīya fī-l-tarākīb al-sulṭānīya. A regimen for the ailing son of the sulṭān of Qāzān (i.e., the Khanate of Kazan around the town of Kazan on the Volga, the foundation of which is traditionally ascribed to Bātū, Khān of the Golden Horde, 1224–1256). This regimen is divided into three parts of which the first two deal with dietetics and health rules, and the third with sexual intercourse and means of favoring it. It was translated into Turkish.

L. Leclerc: Médecine arabe (vol. 2, 137–139, 1876; poor account).

19. *Logic and classification of knowledge*—Two treatises are mainly devoted to logic.

(50) Kitāb al-tajrīd fī 'ilm al-manṭiq (Compendium of logic). One of Nāṣir al-dīn's disciples, al-Ḥasan ibn Yūsuf Ibn al-Muṭahhar al-Ḥillī (d. 1325–1326), wrote a commentary upon it, entitled Sharḥ tajrīd al-manṭiq.

(51) Commentary on the Kitāb al-ishārāt wal-tanbīhāt of Ibn Sīnā, in answer to the objections made by Fakhr al-dīn al-Rāzī (second half of the twelfth century).

In at least two other treatises Nāṣir al-dīn discussed the classification of knowledge. The first of these was his ethical treatise Akhlāq-i-Nāṣirī to be dealt with in section 22. The classification of knowledge explained in that work is as follows:

I. Speculative: (a) Metaphysics; theology; (b) Mathematics (including music, optics, mechanics); (c) Natural sciences (elements, science of transformations, meteorology, mineralogy, botany, zoology, psychology, medicine, astrology, agriculture, etc.).

II. Practical: (a) Ethics; (b) Domestic economy; (c) Politics. Logic is left out of the classification, being considered as a general tool.

J. Stephenson: The classification of the sciences according to Nasiruddin Tusi (Isis, 5, 329–338, 1923; 11, 428). Translation of a part of the introduction of the Akhlāq.

The other is the (52) Kitāb aqsām al-ḥikma (Divisions of philosophy).

20. *Philosophy*—Nāsir al-dīn's popular fame is based upon a large number of philosophical and theological treatises. I shall mention briefly the most important.

(53) Kitāb al-fuṣūl. On metaphysics. Written in Persian and translated into Arabic by al-Jurjānī (Muḥammad ibn 'Alī? or 'Alī ibn Muḥammad?). There is an anonymous commentary upon it entitled Al-anwār al-Jalālīya.

(54) Risāla fī ithbāt al-jauhar al-mufāriq (al-'aql al-kullī). On intelligence and

[18] The Arabic and Persian words daryāq, tiryāq, etc. as well as the English one treacle, are derived from the Greek θηριακή, ἡ θηριακὴ ἀντίδοτος, an antidote against the bites of poisonous animals, hence universal and sovereign remedy.

its limits. Commentaries by one Shams al-dīn al-Kashshī, and by Muḥammad ibn As'ad al-Dauwānī al-Ṣiddīqī[19] (d. 1501–1502).

The following items (55 to 59) are in the nature of commentaries on earlier works.

(55) Glosses on the writings of al-Fārābī dealing with intellectual education as a path to happiness and wisdom.

(56) Talkhīṣ al-muḥaṣṣal. Composed in 1270–1271. One of many commentaries on the Kitāb muḥaṣṣal afkār al-mutaqaddimīn wal-muta'akhkhirīn (al-muḥaṣṣal min nihāyat al-'uqūl fī 'ilm al-uṣūl) by Fakhr al-dīn al-Rāzī. It includes consideration of various scientific questions; e.g., optical illusions, apropos of which he shows that they are due less to sensual lapses than to errors of judgment.

(57) Reply to Ja'far ibn Muḥammad al-Ḥillī al-Muḥaqqiq (d. c. 1277) on the nature of taste.

(58) Commentary on the Sharḥ al-muḥaqqiq, dealing with the absolute existence of God, by 'Alī ibn 'Umar al-Qazwīnī al-Kātibī (d. 1277).

(59) Discussion of the views on generality and particularity expressed by the same 'Alī. See also no. 43.

21. *Theology*—(60) Jawāhir al-farā'id al-Nāṣirīya. Probably so called after Nāṣir al-dīn, governor of Quhistān. Deals with law (fiqh). · Commentary by 'Ali ibn Muḥammad al-Jurjānī (d. Shīrāz, 1413–1414).

(61) Tajrīd al-'aqā'id (al-kalām). Dealing with scholastic philosophy; this is perhaps his best known work; a large number of commentaries, supercommentaries, and super-supercommentaries, have been devoted to it by Arabic and Turkish authors. I can quote only a few commentaries: by al-Ḥasan ibn Yūsuf Ibn al-Muṭahhar al-Ḥillī (d. 1326); Al-sharḥ al-qadīm by Maḥmūd al-Isfahānī (d. 1348–1349); Al-sharḥ al-jadīd by 'Alī ibn Muḥammad al-Qūshjī (d. 1474–1475); Al-sharḥ al-tajwīd, by Muḥammad ibn Aḥmad ibn Sulaimān Ibn Kamāl pāshā (d. 1533–1534). The most popular of these commentaries was the Sharḥ qadīm which was commented upon by 'Alī ibn Muḥammad al-Jurjānī, by Muḥammad ibn Ibrāhīm Khaṭībzāde (d. 1495–1496), by Aḥmad ibn Muṣṭafā Ṭāshköprīzāde (d. 1560–1561), etc. There are also many supercommentaries on the Sharḥ jadīd.

(62) Kitāb qawā'id al-'aqā'id. Five chapters on the essence and qualities of God, the meaning of prophecy, the resurrection, etc.

22. *Ethics*—Nāsir al-dīn wrote two ethical treatises, the first of which was immensely popular.

(63) Akhlāq-i-Nāṣirī, Nasirian ethics. (The Arabic and Persian word akhlāq is equivalent to characteres in Greek and Latin). Thus called after the Ismā'īlī governor Nāṣir al-dīn; hence written before 1256. Translated into Arabic under the title Risāla fī-taḥqīq al-'ilm. This work was the continuation of an old Islāmic tradition which was itself derived from Aristotelian and Platonic ethics through the neo-Pythagorean Bryson. It was very successful and its popularity has continued to this day. It has inspired other Persian works of the same kind, notably the Akhlāq-i-Jalālī by Jalāl al-dīn Muḥammad ibn As'ad al-Dauwānī (d. 1501), and the Akhlāq-i-Muḥsinī composed by Ḥusain-i-Kāshifī in 1494–1495.

[19] Al-Ṣiddīqī is short for al-Bakrī al-Ṣiddīqī, ansāb reserved for those claiming descent from the caliph Abū Bakr.

There are many lithographic and printed editions of these Akhlāq, principally in India. For example, the Akhlāq-i-Nāṣirī was printed in Bombay 1267H., Calcutta 1269, Lucknow 1286, etc. This text is much used by Anglo-Indians for the study of Persian. A part of the introduction was Englished by J. Stephenson (Isis, 5, 329–338, 1923; see above section 19).

For a general study on the akhlāq literature, Martin Plessner: Der οἰκονομικός des Neupythagoreers Bryson und sein Einfluss auf die islamische Wissenschaft (Heidelberg 1928; Isis, 13, 529). Contains (p. 52–104) long extracts from the Akhlāq-i-Nāṣirī in German.

(64) Auṣāf al-ashrāf fī-l-siyar wal-sulūk. This second ethical treatise, also in Persian, was composed after the first one. It is of Ṣūfī inspiration. It was translated into Arabic by Muḥammad ibn 'Alī al-Jurjānī c. 1329–1330.

23. *Poetry*—Nāṣir al-dīn wrote poems in Persian, few of which have come down to us. Some of the Rubā'īyāt published under the name of 'Umar al-Khayyāmī have been ascribed to him, but almost every Persian poet seems to be represented in that collection!

24. *Nāṣir al-dīn's sons*—Three sons of his are named: Ṣadr al-dīn 'Alī, Aṣīl al-dīn al-Ḥasan, and Fakhr al-dīn Aḥmad. Ṣadr al-dīn succeeded his father, and was in his turn succeeded by Aṣīl al-dīn. The latter made a copy of the Zīj īlkhānī. He went to Syria with Ghāzān Maḥmūd (Īlkhān of Persia, 1295–1304); and after his return was appointed governor of Baghdād; he died disgraced in 1314–1315. According to one al-Ḥasan ibn Aḥmad al Ḥakīm who visited the observatory when Ṣadr al-dīn was directing it, there were then working there Shams al dīn al-Mu'ayyad al-'Urḍī, Shams al-dīn al-Shīrāzī, Kamāl al-dīn al-Īkī (or Aikī), and Ḥusām al-dīn of Syria (would this last one be identical with Abū-l-Faraj?). The scientific institute of Marāgha does not seem to have survived Nāṣir al-dīn's children.

25. *Text*—For the editions of Nāṣir al-dīn's works, see the sections above wherein each of them is dealt with. The number of critical editions and translations is surprisingly small.

26. *Oriental sources—Arabic*: Mu'ayyad al-dīn al-'Urḍī al-Dimishqī, one of Nāṣir al-dīn's collaborators (see below).

Abū-l-Fidā' (d. 1331): Mukhtaṣar ta'rīkh al-bashar.

Muḥammad Ibn Shākir al-Kutubī (d. 1363): Fawāt al-wafayāt.

Hājī Khalīfa (d. 1658): Kashf al-ẓunūn.

Syriac: Abū-l-Faraj (d. 1286): Makhtĕbhānūth zabhnē.

Persian: Rashīd al-dīn Faḍl Allāh (d. 1318): Jāmi' al-tawārīkh.

Mīrkhwānd (d. 1498): Rawḍat al-ṣafā.

Khwāndamīr: Ḥabīb al-siyar (1523).

27. *Criticism*—C. Brockelmann: Arabische Litteratur (vol. 1, 508–512, 1898). H. Suter: Die Mathematiker und Astronomen der Araber (146–153, 1900; this is the longest note in the whole volume; 175, 1902). Max Horten: Die philosophischen Ansichten von Rāzī und Ṭūsī, mit einem Anhang, Die griechischen Philosophen in der Vorstellungswelt von Rāzī und Ṭūsī (Bonn 1910); Die speculative und positive Theologie des Islām nach Rāzī und ihre Kritik durch Ṭūsī (Leipzig 1912). E. G. Browne: Literary history of Persia (vols. 2 and 3, 1906, 1920). R. Strothmann: Shī'a (Encyclopaedia of Islām, vol. 4, 350–358, 1926); Die Zwölfer-Schī'a. Zwei religionsgeschichtliche Characterbilder aus der Mongolenzeit (195 p., Leipzig 1926). The personalities dealt with are the theologian Raḍī al-dīn 'Alī ibn Mūsā

al-Ṭā'ūsī and Nāṣir al-dīn al-Ṭūsī, who is described as the type of Shī'ite politician, a master in the art of dissimulation. Eilhard Wiedemann: Zum Leben von Nāṣir al-dīn al-Ṭūsī (Beiträge, 75, Sitzungsber. der physik. med. Soz., 58, 363–379, 1928). Nāṣir al-dīn al-Ṭūsī (Beiträge, 78, Sitzungsber., 60, 289–316, 1928; Isis, 14, 480).

AL-'URḌĪ

Mu'ayyad al-dīn al-'Urḍī al-Dimishqī. Syrian astronomer, architect, and engineer. Dates of birth and death unknown, but he was a contemporary of Nāṣir al-dīn.

He began his technical career in Syria; he did some engineering (hydraulic) work in Damascus and constructed there an astronomical instrument for al-Manṣūr Ibrāhīm (king of Ḥimṣ, 1239–1245) who took it with him to Ḥimṣ (Emesa). It was probably during his stay in Damascus that al-'Urḍī taught geometry to the Christian physician Abū-l-Faraj Ibn Ya'qūb ibn Isḥāq ibn al-Quff, Amīn al-dawla (1233–1286).

In or soon after 1259 he was in Marāgha, being one of the four astronomers who worked with Nāṣir al-dīn al-Ṭūsī to organize Hūlāgū's observatory and to collect observations for the Īlkhānic tables. He was a friend of al-Ṭūsī, who speaks of him in the preface of these tables. A foundry and a toolshop were connected with the observatory, and the instruments, remarkable for their precision, were apparently constructed under al-'Urḍī's supervision (c. 1261). He also built a mosque and a palace.

Al-'Urḍī was in all probability the author of a treatise describing the astronomical instruments used in Marāgha. That anonymous treatise is entitled Risāla fī kaifīya al-arṣād wa mā yuḥtāja ilā 'ilmihi wa 'amalihi min ṭuruq al-muwaddīya ilā ma'rifa 'audāt al-kawākib (The art of astronomical observations and the theoretical and practical knowledge needed to make them, and the methods leading to the understanding of the regularities of the stars). The following instruments are described: (1) mural quadrant; (2) armillary sphere; (3) solstitial armil; (4) equinoctial armil; (5) Hipparch's diopter (alidade); (6) instrument with two quadrants; (7) instrument with two limbs; (7) instrument to determine sines and azimuths; (9) instrument to determine sines and versed sines; (10) the perfect instrument (this is the universal instrument of which he had already built a model while in Syria); (11) parallactic ruler (after Ptolemy). These instruments are not only described but their construction and use are explained at least to some extent. Many technical details, such as may be found in the Libros del saber, are unfortunately missing, nor do we have any information on the observatory itself, the general disposition of the apparatus within the observatory, the technique of the observations, the daily routine, etc. Note that the instruments nos. 8 and 9 were used to determine sines and versed sines; that is, they were trigonometrical rather than astronomical instruments. Al-'Urḍī's descriptions prove that the need of precise instruments and methods was keenly realized. Much importance was already attached to such things as the stability and correctness of the instruments and of each of their parts, the trueness of their divisions, the leveling of the horizontal surfaces, etc. This treatise seems to be incomplete, for it deals only with the instruments, and not, as announced in the preface, with the observations and the proofs (i.e., the theories underlying them). For more information on the observatory and instruments, see my note on Nāṣir al-dīn, sections 6 and 7.

Al-'Urḍī wrote two other treatises: 2. Risāla fi 'amal al-kura al-kāmila (Construction of the perfect sphere). 3. On the determination of the distance between the center of the sun and the apogee. Astronomical tables and a treatise on Ptolemaic astronomy are also ascribed to him.

He had two sons, Shams al-dīn and Muḥammad, who joined him later in Marāgha (he had gone there alone). Shams al-dīn wrote an account of al-Ṭūsī's teachers; he was in Marāgha when Ṣadr al-dīn was director (see my note on Nāṣir al-dīn, section 24). The other son, Muḥammad, constructed in 1279 (or 1289) a celestial globe, for which see the note on early Arabic celestial globes below. By that time the heyday of the observatory of Marāgha was already over, for Hūlāgū had died in 1265 and his successors had no interest in science.

Text—Amable Jourdain: Mémoire sur l'observatoire de Méragha et les instruments employés pour y observer (Magasin encyclopédique, vol. 6, 43, etc., 1809; tiré à part, 64 p., Paris 1810; abbreviated French version of the main work ascribed to al-'Urḍī). Hugo J. Seemann: Die Instrumente der Sternwarte zu Marāgha nach den Mitteilungen von al-'Urḍī (Sitzungsber. der physik. med. Soz., vol. 60, 15–126, Erlangen 1928; German translation with abundant notes; Isis, 13, 111–113).

EARLY ARABIC CELESTIAL GLOBES

The globe constructed by Muḥammad ibn Mu'ayyad al-'Urḍī is one of the earliest extant, in fact the fourth or fifth one out of five anterior to the fourteenth century. It is worthwhile to enumerate these five globes.

Globe I. Made at Valencia in 1080–1081 by Ibrāhīm ibn Sa'īd al-Sahlī, with the assistance of his son, Muḥammad. Diameter 209 mm. Made of two empty brass hemispheres soldered together. Forty-seven constellations are engraved upon its surface, including 1015 stars, the respective magnitudes of which are indicated. Kept in the University of Florence.

Ferdinando Meucci: Il globo celeste del secolo XI esistente nel Gabinetto degli strumenti antichi del R. Istituto di studi superiori (20 p., 2 pl., Florence 1878).

Globe II. Made somewhere in the Near East in 1225–1226 by Qaiṣar ibn abī-l-Qāsim. Two brass hemispheres upon four supporting feet, with horizon and meridian circles. Preserved in the National Museum, Naples.

Giuseppe Simone Assemani: Globus coelestis cufico-arabicus Veliterni Musei Borgiani, etc. (Patavii 1790).

Globe III. Made by Muḥammad ibn Hilāl, astronomer of Mūṣul, in 1275–1276. It is made of brass, and is apparently of Persian workmanship. Diameter, 240 mm. (It is the largest of the five.) Forty-seven constellations are represented, together with zodiacal signs, and the words sharq, gharb, shimāl, janūb (meaning E, W, N, S) on the circumference of the horizon. Preserved in the rooms of the Royal Asiatic Society, London.

Bernhard Dorn: Description of a celestial globe belonging to Sir John Malcolm, deposited in the Museum of the Royal Society (Transactions of the Royal Asiatic Society, vol. 2, 371–392, 1830).

Globe IV. This is the one made by Muḥammad ibn Mu'ayyad al-'Urḍī in 1279 (or 1289). It is composed of two brass hemispheres separated by the ecliptic.

Diameter 140 mm. Horizon circle, and two movable half circles attached to the zenith point by a pivot. These circles being graduated enable one to determine the declination and right ascension of any star. Forty-eight constellations, the equator, and the ecliptic are inlaid with silver or gold. Preserved in the mathematical "salon" of Dresden.

G. W. S. Beigel: Nachricht von einer arabischen Himmelskugel (Astronomisches Jahrbuch, 97, Berlin 1808). Adolph Dreschler: Der arabische Himmelsglobus angefertigt 1279 zu Maragha (14 p., 8 pl., Dresden 1873).

Globe V. (I call it V, but the date is uncertain, and it might be anterior to one or more of the others). Undated globe in the Bibliothèque Nationale, Paris. Diameter 190 mm. Forty-nine constellations. The engravings on the surface are very similar to those of globe IV.

Louis Amélie Sédillot: Mémoire sur les instruments astronomiques des Arabes 116–141, Paris 1841); Matériaux pour servir à l'histoire comparée des sciences mathématiques chez les Grecs et chez les orientaux (vol. 1, 334, Paris 1845).

To these five early globes may be added two later ones: Bibliothèque Nationale, Paris, c. 150 mm., 1573–1574; Library of Leningrad, c. 190 mm., 1701–1702. It is probable that there are many more globes anterior to the Leningrad one, but far less so that the number of the earlier ones (before 1300) will be much increased.

Ludewig Ideler: Untersuchungen über den Ursprung und die Bedeutung der Sternnamen (526 p., Berlin 1809). Edward Luther Stevenson: Terrestrial and celestial globes (vol. 1, 26–34, New Haven 1921; Isis, 4, 549–553).

With the study of globes might be connected that of illustrated MSS. representing constellations. I saw such a MS. in the Metropolitan Museum, New York, a Persian MS. of c. 1300, and there are probably others. The subject would deserve investigation.

MUḤYĪ AL-DĪN AL-MAGHRIBĪ

Muḥyī al-milla wal-dīn Yaḥyā ibn Muḥammad ibn Abī-l-Shukr al-Maghribī al-Andalusī. Hispano-Muslim mathematician and astronomer. He flourished for a time in Syria, then in Marāgha. He was not one of the original astronomers[20] of that observatory, but must have joined them pretty soon after its foundation (1259), for it is said that he was a guest of Hūlāgū, who died in 1265, and he seems to have made observations in 1264–1265. The time and place of his death cannot be determined. He probably survived Nāṣir al-dīn, who died in 1274. He met Abū-l-Faraj in Marāgha, but the latter was there at various times between 1268 and 1286.

His writings will be considered in the following order: (1) Geometry and trigonometry. (2) Editions of Greek classics. (3) Chronology. (4) Astrology. (5) Astrolabe.

1. *Geometry and trigonometry*—(1) Kitāb shakl al-qaṭṭā'. Probably his most important original work. It was composed after the treatise of Nāṣir al-dīn bearing the same title (no. 18 in my list of Nāṣir's writings), and is partly based upon it. Yet it contains original developments; for example, two proofs are given of

[20] Quoted in section 6 of my note on Nāṣir al-dīn.

the sine theorem for right angled spherical triangles, and one of them is different from the proofs given by Nāṣir al-dīn; this theorem is then generalized for other triangles.

2. *Editions of the Greek classics*—All of these editions, except that of Euclid, are entitled Tahdhīb (purification), while those of Nāṣir al-dīn are called Taḥrīr (redaction).

(2) Euclid: Elements.

(3) Apollonios: Conics. With brief preface.

(4) Theodosios: Spherics.

Carra de Vaux: Remaniement des Sphériques de Théodose par Iahia ibn Muhammed ibn Abī Schukr Almaghrabī Alandalusī (Journal asiatique, vol. 17, 287–295, 1891).

(5) Menelaos: Spherics. This might be considered at the same time as the Shakl al-qaṭṭā' above mentioned.

(6) Khulāṣat al-mijisṭī (Essence of the Almagest). Extract from the Almagest made at Marāgha at the request of Abū-l-Faraj. He added an appendix based upon the latest observations, then gave the whole work to the library of Abū-l-Ḥasan 'Alī ibn Muḥammad ibn al-Ḥasan al-Ṭūsī; this was the son and successor of Nāṣir al-dīn. The Khulāṣat was thus probably completed at Marāgha after 1274.

The Khulāṣat contains a new determination of the obliquity of the ecliptic made at Marāgha in 1264, 23°30′ (the real value in 1250 was 23°32′19″).

3. *Chronology*—(7) Risālat al-Khiṭā' wal-Īghūr (Memoir on the Chinese and the Uighūr). Deals with the chronology and calendar of these peoples. The production of such a work is typical of the internationalism of the Marāgha observatory. It would tend to substantiate the presence there of Chinese astronomers (see section 6 of my note on Nāṣir al-dīn).

4. *Astrology*—Many of his writings were devoted to astrology; the briefest mention of these astrological writings should suffice. (One or two of them may be identical with one or two others).

(8) Kitāb al-madkhal al-mufīd fī ḥukm al-mawālid (useful introduction to the judgment of births).

(9) Kitāb al-nujūm (Book of stars).

(10) Kitab al-ḥukm[21] 'alā qirānāt al-kawākib fī-l-burūj al-ithnā 'ashar (Judgments relative to the conjunctions of planets in the twelve signs of the zodiac).

(11) Kaifīyat al-ḥukm 'alā taḥwīl sinī-l-'ālam (Mode of judgment relative to the return of the years of the world). Also called Kitāb al-nujūm.

(12) Kitāb al-jāmi' al-ṣaghīr (Small compendium).

(13) 'Umdat al-ḥāsib wa ghunyat al-ṭālib (Prop of the calculator and wealth of the searcher). Collection of astronomical tables and rules for astrological purposes.

5. *Astrolabe*—(14) Tasṭīḥ al-asṭurlāb (The flattening of the astrolabe). May be partly astrological.

There is still a treatise entitled Tāj al-azjāj wa ghunyat al-muḥtāj (Crown of the

[21] Or, in the plural, al-aḥkām.

tables and wealth of the one in need), ascribed to Abū 'Abdallāh Muḥammad ibn Abī-l-Shukr al-Maghribī. This author is probably identical either with the scientist to whom the present note is devoted (the words "Yaḥyā ibn" having fallen out), or with the latter's father. The Tāj is a collection of astronomical, geographical, and chronological tables.

Criticism—C. Brockelmann: Arabische Litteratur (vol. 1, 474, 1898). H. Suter: Die Mathematiker der Araber (155, 219, 1900; 176, 1902). H. Bürger and K. Kohl: Zur Geschichte des Transversalensatzes (Abhdl. zur Gesch. der Naturwiss., Heft 7, 55–57, 67, 70, 71, 73–75, 89, Erlangen 1924; Isis, 8, 799). Oskar Schirmer: Studien zur Astronomie der Araber (Sitzungsber. der physik. med. Soz., vol. 58, p. 59, 1926; Isis, 9, 560–561).

QUṬB AL-DĪN AL-SHĪRĀZĪ

Persian mathematician, astronomer, optician, physician, philosopher, ṣūfī, who wrote in Arabic and subsidiarily in Persian. One of the greatest Persian scientists of all times (1236–1311).

Contents: (1) Life. (2) Geometry. (3) Astronomy and geography. (4) Optics. (5) Mechanics. (6) Medicine. (7) Encyclopaedic treatise. (8) Philosophy. (9) Qur'ān and ḥadīth. (10) Text. (11) Criticism.

1. *Life*—Maḥmūd ibn Mas'ūd ibn Muṣliḥ, Quṭb al-dīn al-Shīrāzī. Born in Shīrāz, 1236. He belonged to a family of learned men, and received part of his medical training from his father and his uncles in Shīrāz. Later he sat at the feet of Nāṣir al-dīn al-Ṭūsī and became his most famous pupil. He traveled extensively in Khurāsān, the two 'Irāq, Persia, and Rūm (Asia Minor), and finally entered the service of the Īl-Khān of Persia, Aḥmad (1281–1284) and Arghūn (1284–1291). In 1282–1283 he was qāḍī in Sīvās and Malaṭiyah. Aḥmad sent him on an embassy to al-Manṣūr Sayf al-dīn Qalā'ūn (Mamlūk sulṭān, 1279–1290) to notify the latter of his conversion to Islām and to conclude a treaty of peace. Quṭb al-dīn must have remained some time in Egypt, judging by the amount of materials which he collected in that country. He finally returned eastward and settled down in Tabrīz, where he died in 1311.

He wrote many scientific treatises which will be examined in order of subjects.

2. *Geometry*—There is in a library of Constantinople (Yani jāmi', 796) a Persian translation of Nāṣir al-dīn's redaction of Euclid's Elements, which is ascribed to Quṭb al-dīn. If this translation was made by him, it was one of his few writings in Persian. It would seem that he wrote primarily in Arabic, but there are Persian MSS. of some of his writings.

There is appended to his great astronomical treatise Nihāyat (see below) a little treatise which had been communicated to him by an author whom he does not name. As he fully discusses it, and as the real author is unknown, I shall count it as one of his own writings (in any case the commentary, which might bear the same title, is his own). It is entitled (2) Fī ḥarakāt al-daḥraja wa nisba bain al-mustawī wal-munhanī (On the motion of rolling and the relation between the straight and the crooked). It examines the paradox whether a straight line is really shorter than an arc.

3. *Astronomy and geography*—His main publications were astronomical and medical. Among the astronomical ones, by far the most important was the

(3) Nihāyat al-idrāk fī dirāyat al-aflāk (Highest understanding of the knowledge of the spheres). This is a very comprehensive account not only of astronomy, but of many related subjects, such as geodesy, meteorology, mechanics, and optics. It is based upon the work of Nāṣir al-dīn, chiefly upon the Tadhkira, but is more elaborate, and contains novelties; e.g., a fuller discussion of the cosmological views of Ibn al-Haitham and of Muḥammad ibn Aḥmad al-Kharaqī (first half of the twelfth century). Ibn al-Haitham (and Nāṣir al-dīn) conceived the spherical surfaces relative to the planetary orbits as tangent; Quṭb al-dīn suggests that there might be some space between them. The Nihāyat includes a long discussion as to whether the earth is at rest or not, concluding in favor of the first alternative. The earth is an immobile sphere placed at the center of the universe. The author's views are on the whole Ptolemaic, though he was naturally well aware of the criticisms to which the Almagest has been subjected.

Like other astronomical handbooks, the Nihāyat is also partly geographical. For example, it contains an account of the seas, and a description of the climates; the latter is very similar to that of al-Bīrūnī. When Arghūn's Genoese envoy, Buscarello de' Ghizolfi, was on his way to Europe in 1289, Quṭb al-dīn explained the envoy's travels to the Īl-Khān by means of a map.

(4) Ikhtiyārāt-i Muẓaffarī. Selections from the Nihāyat in Persian, made for one Muẓaffar.

(5) Kitāb al-tuḥfa al-shāhīya fī-l-hai'a (The royal present on astronomy). A work of about the same scope as the Nihāyat. There is a commentary on it by 'Alī ibn Muḥammad al-Qūshjī (d. 1474-1475).

(6) Kitāb fa'altu falā talūm fī-l-hai'a (Book I have composed but don't blame it, on astronomy).

(7) Kitāb al-tabṣira fī-l-hai'a. Treatise on astronomy.

(8) Sharḥ al-tadhkira al-Nāṣirīya. Commentary on Nāṣir al-dīn's Tadhkira and on the Bayān maqāṣid al-tadhkira of Muḥammad ibn 'Alī al-Ḥimādhī.

(9) Kharīdat al-'ajā'ib (The wonderful pearl).

(10) Extract from the Iṣlāḥ al-majisṭī of Jābir ibn Aflaḥ.

4. *Optics*—The very remarkable optical views of Quṭb al-dīn are found in his astronomical works. In the Nihāyat he discusses questions of geometrical optics, the nature of vision, and finally the rainbow. He was the first to give a satisfactory account of the rainbow (excepting of course, the colors). He explained it by the study of the passage of a ray of light through a transparent sphere (drop of water): the ray is refracted twice and reflected once (or twice in the case of the secondary rainbow). This explanation is essentially similar to that of Descartes.

It was through him that Kamāl al-dīn al Fārisī (d. c. 1320), who was his most famous disciple, learned to know the Kitāb al-manāẓir of Ibn al-Haitham upon which he (Kamāl) wrote a commentary (Tanqīḥ). Thus Quṭb al-dīn was an important link in the transmission of Ibn al-Haitham's optics.

5. *Mechanics*—The same Nihāyat contains also his views on mechanics. For example, his rejection of the hypothesis of a rotating earth was essentially based upon the following argument. There are two sorts of natural motions: rectilinear and circular; bodies endowed with either of these two motions cannot move naturally in another way. Sublunar motions are rectilinear. Similar views were also ex-

pressed by an older contemporary, 'Ali ibn 'Umar al-Qazwīnī (d. 1277), whom Quṭb al-dīn may have known directly or through his teacher Nāṣir al-dīn.

6. *Medicine*—His most important medical work is a commentary on the Kullīyāt (the generalities) of Ibn Sīnā's Qānūn. He conceived early in life the idea of writing it, and kept thinking of it and accumulating materials for it during his travels and his stay in Egypt. This is told by himself in the preface which is a valuable autobiographical document. It was called (11) Kitāb nuzhat al-ḥukamā' wa-rawḍat al-aṭibbā' (Delight of the wise and garden of the physicians), and also Kitāb al-tuḥfa al-sa'dīya fi-l-ṭibb (Present to Sa'd, on medicine) because it was dedicated to Muḥammad Sa'd al-dīn, wazīr to Aḥmad Khān. As the latter ruled only until 1284, we may assume that the Tuḥfa al-sa'dīya was completed soon after Quṭb al-dīn's return from Egypt.

According to his preface, Quṭb al-dīn made use of the writings of Fakhr al-dīn al-Rāzī and of the earlier commentaries or discussions by Ibn al-Tilmīdh, Ibn Jamī', 'Abd al-Laṭīf, al-As'ad al-Maḥallī, Ibn al-Quff, Ibn al-Nafīs, etc. Most of these writings were obtained by him in Egypt.

(11 bis) Sharḥ kullīyāt al-qānūn. This is probably another title, or another recension, of the preceding.

(12) Risāla fi bayān al-ḥāja ilā-l-ṭibb wa ādāb al-aṭibbā' wa-waṣāyāhum (Explanation of the necessity of medicine and of the manners and duties of physicians). Apparently a treatise on medical deontology.

(13) Risāla fī-l-baraṣ. On leprosy.

(14) Commentary on Ibn Sīnā's Arjūzat (Cantica).

(15) The ascription to him of a treatise on eye-diseases is apparently erroneous (Hirschberg 1905).

7. *Encyclopaedic treatise*—(16) Durrat al-tāj lighurrat al-dībāj fī-l-ḥikma (Pearls of the crown, best introduction to wisdom). Encyclopaedic treatise available in Arabic and Persian.

8. *Philosophy*—(17) Sharḥ ḥikmat al-ishrāq. Commentary on the Kitāb ḥikmat al-ishrāq of Yaḥyā al-Suhrawardī (second half of the twelfth century).

His philosophical interest is proved also by the fact that the Muḥākamāt which Quṭb al-dīn Muḥammad ibn Muḥammad al-Rāzī al-Taḥtānī (d. 1364–1365) composed in 1354–1355 was inspired by him. The purpose of the Muḥākamāt was to explain the differences of opinion between Fakhr al-dīn al-Rāzī and Nāṣir al-dīn with regard to the Kitāb al-ishārāt wal-tanbīhāt of Ibn Sīnā. After Hājī Khalīfa (Lexicon, vol. 1, p. 301–303, 1835) who speaks of the two Quṭb al-dīn as contemporaries!

9. *Qur'ān and ḥadīth.* Toward the end of his life, Quṭb al-dīn was more and more interested in taṣawwuf (i.e. sufism) and religious matters. He composed commentaries on the ḥadīth and on the Qur'ān.

(18) Fatḥ al-mannān fī tafsīr al-Qur'ān.

(19) Fī mushkilāt al-Qur'ān.

(20) Commentary on the Kitāb al-kashshāf 'an ḥaqā'iq al-tanzīl of al-Zamakhsharī (first half of the twelfth century).

10. *Text*—None of his works has been edited, and none translated except the short fragments included in Wiedemann's numerous papers quoted below, and in Seippel's Fontes.

11. *Criticism*—E. Wiedemann: Zu den optischen Kenntnissen von Quṭb al-dīn (Archiv für Geschichte der Naturwissenschaften, vol. 3, 187–193, 1911); Über die Dimensionen der Erde nach muslimischen Gelehrten (ibidem, 250–255); Über die Gestalt, Lage und Bewegung der Erde sowie philosophisch-astronomische Betrachtungen von Quṭb al-dīn (ibidem, 395–422, 1912); Über das Meer, über die Klimate (Beiträge, 27, Sitzungsber. der phys. med. Soz., vol. 44, 27–35, Erlangen 1912); Über die angebliche Verwendung des Pendels bei den Arabern (Z. für Physik, vol. 10, 267–268, 1922; Quṭb al-dīn referred to a plumb-line, not to a pendulum); Über Erscheinungen bei der Dämmerung und bei Sonnenfinsternissen (Archiv für Geschichte der Medizin, vol. 15, 43–52, 1923); Inhalt eines Gefässes in verschiedenen Abständen vom Erdmittelpunkt (Z. für Physik, vol. 13, 59–60, 1923); article in Encyclopaedia of Islām (vol. 2, 1166–1167, 1928); Über eine Schrift über die Bewegung des Rollens und die Beziehung zwischen dem Geraden und dem Gekrümmten (Beiträge, 71; Sitzungsber. der phys. med. Soz., vol. 58, 219–224, 1928; Isis, 14, 481).

F. Wüstenfeld: Arabische Aerzte (148–149, 1840). L. Leclerc: Médecine arabe (vol. 2, 129–130, 1876). Alexander Seippel: Rerum normannicarum fontes arabici (part 1, Christiania 1896; in Arabic). H. Suter: Mathematiker und Astronomen der Araber (158, 1900; 176, 1902). C. Brockelmann: Arabische Litteratur (vol. 2, 211, 1902). J. Hirschberg: Die arabischen Lehrbücher der Augenheilkunde (Abhdl. d. preuss. Ak., 93, 1905). Fridtjof Nansen: In northern mists (vol. 2, 211, 1911). Henry George Farmer: History of Arabian music (203, 1929; Isis, 13, 375). Ernest Honigmann: Die sieben Klimata (162, 167, 170, 178, Heidelberg 1929; Isis, 14, 270–276).

MUḤAMMAD IBN ASHRAF AL-SAMARQANDĪ

Shams al-dīn Muḥammad ibn Ashraf al-Ḥusainī al-Samarqandī. Muslim mathematician, astronomer, logician who flourished about 1276. He wrote in Arabic and subsidiarily in Persian.

His popularity is based upon a treatise on dialectics, Risāla fī ādāb al-baḥth, which was immensely successful, if one may judge by the number of commentaries and supercommentaries devoted to it. He wrote two other logical treatises, the Kitāb al-qusṭās (balance, justice), and the Kitāb 'ain al-naẓar fī-l-manṭiq (The source of speculation, dealing with logic). The two terms naẓar and baḥth are often used together; the first means speculation, the second discussion; ahl al-baḥth wal-naẓar are people trained in the discussion of philosophical subjects.

His mathematical writings include the Kitāb ashkāl al-ta'sīs (Figures or difficulties of the foundation), also called Risāla al-riyāḍiyā, explaining thirty-five propositions of the first book of Euclid's Elements; and a star calendar for the year 1276–1277, A'māl-i taqwīm-i kawākib-i thābita (Arrangement of the tables of the stars). The A'māl-i taqwīm is in Persian, all the other works here mentioned in Arabic.

A commentary on the Ashkāl al-ta'sīs was composed by Mūsā ibn Maḥmūd Qāḍī Zāda al-Rūmī who died in 1412–1413.

Finally he wrote a treatise on dogmatics entitled Kitāb al-ṣaḥā'if (Book of leaves).

There is a possibility that he was the original author of an astronomical work which was freely translated in 1323 from Persian into Greek, but it is more probable that the author called Σὰμψ Μπουχαρῆς in the Greek version was another Shams al-dīn (a title fairly common)—e.g., Shams al-dīn Muḥammad ibn Mubārakshāh al-Bukhārī (d. c. 1339); indeed μπουχαρής is the equivalent of Bukhārī. This question will be fully discussed in vol. 3.

Criticism—C. Brockelmann: Arabische Litteratur (vol. 1, 468, 1898). H. Suter: Die Mathematiker und Astronomen der Araber (157, 1900; 176, 1902). Carra de Vaux: Baḥth (Encyclopaedia of Islām, vol. 1, 587, 1911).

For al-Abharī, 'Alī ibn 'Umar al-Kātibī, al-Qazwīnī, see philosophical chapter.

VI. CHINA

For Kublai Khān, see the note in the philosophical section.

'ĪSĀ THE MONGOL

'Isā tarjamān (interpreter). Named in Chinese Ai⁴-hsieh¹* (15, 4371). Nestorian physician and astronomer in the Mongolian service (1227–1308). He was employed by the Great Khān Kuyuk (1246–1248), and later by Kublai who appointed him director of the astronomical bureau in 1263. He seems to have inspired the edict of 1279 directed by Kublai against Muslim propaganda in China. In 1284 he accompanied Būlād[22] as envoy to the new Īl-khān of Persia, Arghūn (1284–1291). After his return he was appointed Christian commissary in 1291, then member of the imperial academy Han⁴-lin² yüan⁴ (3828, 7157, 13752), finally minister. His four sons continued their allegiance to the Nestorian faith and held important posts at the Mongolian court.

Henri Cordier: Histoire générale de la Chine (vol. 2, 387, 1920). René Grousset: Histoire de l'Extrême-Orient (465, 1929; Isis, 14, 437).

CHA-MA-LI-TING

Or Cha²*-ma³-lu³-ting¹ (127, 7576, 7388, 11253). This is obviously a Chinese transcription of the Arabic name Jamāl al-dīn, but I prefer the Chinese form because it is more specific and also because what little we know of this Jamāl we owe to Chinese, not to Arabic, sources. Persian astronomer who devised for Kublai Khān in 1267 a new calendar—Yeh-lü's calendar had never been adopted—called the Ten thousand years calendar, Wan⁴-nien² li⁴* (12486, 8301, 6923). It was probably so named because it was a development of an ancient Persian system based on a period of ten thousand years; or the words ten thousand may simply mean perpetual. This calendar is lost. He introduced seven Persian astronomical instruments, among them an armillary sphere constructed for the latitude of 36°, probably to be used in the college of P'ing²-yang² (9310, 12883), Shansi, in latitude 36°6'. See my note on Yeh-lü Ch'u-ts'ai (first half of thirteenth century).

Alexander Wylie: Chinese researches (part 3, 16, 1897). Yule's Marco Polo (3d. ed., vol. 1, 455, 1903). Y. Mikami: Development of Chinese mathematics (100, 1913).

HSÜ HÊNG

Hsü³ Hêng² (4761, 3913). Chinese astronomer. Born at Hsin¹-chêng⁴ (4574, 724), Honan, in 1209; died in 1281. Canonized under the name Wên² Chêng⁴ (12633, 687); his tablet was placed in 1313 in the Confucian temple. Grand secre-

[22] In Chinese Pu⁴ la¹* (9479, 6662).

tary and president of the astronomical board under Kublai Khān. He wrote a work on the calendar, Shou^{4} jih^{4*} li^{4*} (10017, 5642, 6923).

Text—The Library of Congress has Hsü Hêng's collected works under his style name, Hsü^{3} Lu^{3} Cha^{1} Chi^{2*} (4761, 7388, 134, 906) in vol. 35 of the Chêng^{4} i^{2} t'ang^{2} ch'üan^{2} shu^{1} (687, 5354, 10760, 3176, 10024), but the Shou jih li is not included in it.
Criticism—Giles: Chinese biographical dictionary (303, 1898).

KUO SHOU-CHING

Kuo^{1*} Shou^{3}-ching^{4} (6617, 10012, 2144). Born at Hsing^{2}-t'ai^{2} (4618, 10577) in 1231; from 1262 he flourished at the Mongol court; died in 1316. Chinese astronomer and mathematician. In 1276 he was ordered by Kublai Khān to compute a new calendar. This calendar, called the Shou-shih calendar, Shou^{4}-shih^{2} li^{4*} (10017, 9921, 6923), was completed in 1280; it remained in use from 1281 to 1367. It was probably Kuo who introduced spherical trignometry, as developed by the Muslims, into China. The Muslim origin of this trigonometry cannot be proved, as Kuo's works are apparently lost, but is highly probable. (See my note on Cha-ma-li-ting.) He made many astronomical observations and constructed remarkable instruments. The epoch of his observations was the winter solstice of 1280 accurately determined by him. He sent assistants into various parts of China to determine latitudes and longitudes (with reference to Pei-ping). He wrote many works on astronomical subjects.

Two of Kuo's instruments, dated 1279, are still extant in Pei-ping: an armillary sphere and a "compendium instrument." They had been removed by German troops in 1900 or 1901 and taken to Potsdam. The Treaty of Versailles stipulated that they were to be restored. They arrived in China in Oct. 1920. These instruments should not be mistaken for those built by the Jesuits in the seventeenth and eighteenth centuries. The best proof of their Mongol origin is the division of the circle into 365 1/4 degrees, each degree into 100 minutes, each minute into 100 seconds. For instance, Kuo found for the obliquity of the ecliptic the value 23°90′ 30″, which is equivalent, according to our division of the circle, to a little more than 23°33′40″.

Text—The Yüan Annals, Yüan^{2} Shih^{3} (13744, 9893)—for which see my note on Sung^{4} Lien^{2} (10462, 7132), second half of fourteenth century—contain the text of the Shou-shih li (ch. 52–55) and an important biography of Kuo (ch. 164).
Criticism—Antoine Gaubil (1689–1759): Traité d'astronomie chinoise; Observations mathématiques, etc. (Paris 1729–1732, not seen). Alexandre Wylie: The Mongol astronomical instruments in China (27 p., 2 pl., Chinese researches, part 3, 1897). This includes the relevant Chinese texts. Yule's Marco Polo (3d. ed., vol. 1, 448–454, 3 pl., 1903). Y. Mikami: Development of mathematics in China (98–108, 1913). Contains an analysis of Kuo's spherical trigonometry derived from the "Principles of the ta^{4}-t'ung^{3} (10470, 12316) calendar," a Ming work. L. Gauchet (S. J.): Note sur la trigonométrie sphérique de Kouo Cheou-King (T'oung Pao, vol. 18, 151–174, 1917). Examples in Chinese and in French translation. Father Gauchet claims that Kuo could find in Chinese mathematics everything that he needed for his trigonometrical purposes and that foreign inspiration was unnecessary; interesting but highly conjectural.

YANG HUI

Yang[2] Hui[1] (12878, 5154). Nom-de-plume, Ch'ien[1] Kuang[1] (1722, 6389). Born at Ch'ien[2]-t'ang[2] (1736, 10768); flourished c. 1261–1275. Chinese mathematician. He wrote, in 1261, the Analysis of the arithmetical rules, in nine sections, Hsiang[2]-chieh[2] chiu[3]-chang[1] suan[4]-shu[4]* (4279, 1515, 2263, 390, 10378, 10053), which is a commentary on that old Chinese classic (see my note on Chang[1] Ts'ang[1] (416, 11596), first half of second century B. C.). Later he wrote a supplement to that commentary and an arithmetical work in six books entitled Yang[2] Hui[1] suan[4]-fa[2]* (12878, 5154, 10378, 3366); one of these books, Hsü[4]* ku[3] chai[1]* ch'i[2] suan[4] fa[2]* (4773, 6188, 228, 798, 10378, 3366), is dated 1275–1276. Graphic illustration of the sum of an arithmetical progression.

$$1 + (1 + 2) + (1 + 2 + 3) + \ldots\ldots + (1 + 2 + \ldots\ldots + n) = \frac{n}{6}(n + 1)(n + 2)$$

$$\Sigma_1^n i^2 = \frac{n}{3}\left(n + \frac{1}{2}\right)(n + 1)$$

Problems dealing with proportions, "alternate exchange," hu[4] huan[4] (4972, 5080), and compound proportions, "doubled alternate exchange," chung[4] (2880) hu-huan. Linear equations with 4 or 5 unknown quantities. Computations by means of decimal fractions. Graphic explanation of quadratic equation. Solution of numerical equations by a method similar to Ch'in's, called "accumulating involution," tsang ching fang[1] (?, ?, 3435)[23].

Strangely enough Yang Hui seems to be independent from Ch'in and Li, for he does not name them nor speak of the celestial element, t'ien[1]-yüan[2] (11208, 13744). He quotes another mathematician, his teacher Liu[2] I[2]* (7270, 5485), native of Chung[1]-shan[1] (2875, 9663), of whom we know nothing.

Text—A critical edition of the Hsiang-chieh was published in 1842 by Sung[4] Ching[3]-ch'ang[1] (10462, 2143, 427).

The Library of Congress has the Hsiang-chieh chiu-chang suan-fa[2]* (3366); the Yang Hui suan fa, the Hsü ku chai ch'i suan fa and other writings by this same author in the I[2] chia[4] t'ang[2] ts'ung[1] shu[1] (5353, 1143, 10760, 12039, 10024), vols. 51–55.

A Korean edition of the Yang Hui suan-fa is mentioned in Maurice Courant: Bibliographie coréenne (vol. 3, p. 1–2, 1896), the Korean title (as quoted by Courant) being Song yang houi san pep.

Criticism—A. Wylie: Notes on Chinese literature (117, 1902). Yoshio Mikami: Development of mathematics in China (84–88, 1913). Smith and Mikami: Japanese mathematics (21, 22, 51, 116, 1914; Isis, 2, 410; according to them Seki Kōwa made a special study of Yang Hui in 1661). Louis Van Hée: The Ch'ou-jen chuan of Yüan Yüan (Isis, 8, 112, 1926).

[23] This method is mentioned by Smith and Mikami (51, 1914), but they do not give the Chinese text and I have failed to identify the characters which might be represented by the words tsang ching. The relevant passage in Yang Hui's works was kindly communicated to me by Y. Mikami, but it does not contain any such characters. Yang Hui states that Liu I wrote the treatise I[4]-ku[3] kên[1]-yüan[2] (5460, 6188, 5974, 13704), wherein two hundred problems were solved by the method called yen[3]-tuan[4] so[3]-fang[1] (13130, 12140, 10204, 3435), which was superior to all anterior methods.

CHAPTER XLVIII

PHYSICS, TECHNOLOGY AND MUSIC

(Second Half of Thirteenth Century)

I. OPTICS

THE INVENTION OF SPECTACLES

Spectacles appear to have been invented some time in the second half of the thirteenth century. At least they cannot be traced back to an earlier date. We find two records of them in Italy referring respectively to the years c. 1285 and 1289, and two inventors of that time are named: Salvino degl' Armati (d. 1317), and Alessandro della Spina (d. 1313).

To be sure magnifying (or burning) glasses or lenses had been used long before that time; they were already referred to by Aristophanes, in the Clouds (c. 424 B.C.), by Pliny the Elder (?),[1] and by Seneca. The magnifying and burning properties of lenses may have been discovered accidentally more than once. There is of course a great difference between a magnifying glass—which may be used, e.g., to read fine script even as we still do to-day—and real spectacles, though there are so many ways of bridging the gap that it is difficult to know where to draw the line. In both Italian records the word occhiali is used, a plural, which favors the hypothesis that real spectacles are meant.

Before dealing with these Italian records, it is necessary to discuss a Chinese one which may be anterior, though I doubt it.

The earliest Chinese mention of spectacles occurs in the Tung[1] tien[3] ch'ing[1] lu[4]* (12294, 11177, 2188, 7386) written by Chao[4] Hsi[1]-ku[3]* (498, 4048, 6248), a member of the imperial Sung family. Chao had borrowed his own information from the "account of people of the Yüan dynasty", Yüan[2] jên[2] hsiao[3] shuo[1]* (13744, 5624, 4294, 10164). He speaks of glasses called ai[4]-tai[4] (21, 10561),[2] by means of which old people can read fine script which they could not read otherwise, and says that they come from Central Asia. Other works of about the same time, the Pai[4] shih[3] lei[4] pien[1] (8563, 9893, 6853, 9178), and the Fang[1] chou[1] tsa[2]* yen[2] (3435, 2446, 11454, 13025),[2a] also refer to the Central Asiatic origin. On the other hand, according to the K'ang[1]-hsi[1] tzŭ[4]-tien[3] (5908, 4115, 12324, 11177), the dictionary produced under the patronage of the Ch'ing emperor K'ang-hsi (c. 1717), spectacles were

[1] Reference to a smaragdus, Natural History, book 37, chapter 5. It is not clear whether or not that smaragdus was actually used as a lens (Isis, 14, 465).

[2] These words mean cloudy, obscure, the glasses being used to relieve the cloudiness of sight.

[2a] I am not sure that these two titles are correctly represented as they are quoted by Berthold Laufer (op. cit., 380–381) without the Chinese characters. No further information could be elicited from the author. The sequences of Chinese characters quoted by me are plausible, but the works themselves are unknown to me. This may serve to illustrate the need of giving either the Chinese characters or equivalent numbers; the lack of them in this instance obliged me to waste a considerable amount of time and even then my doubts were not alleviated.

introduced into China from Malacca; this would postpone the introduction at least until the fifteenth century. Assuming the reality of the earlier introduction, it is probable that Central Asia was not the real origin but only an intermediary; the origin might be in India or in the West?

It is difficult to date this earliest Chinese record. Laufer suggests c. 1260, but I do not see how such an early date can be arrived at. The Yüan jên siao shuo can hardly have been written before the Yüan dynasty was well under way. The end of the thirteenth century seems to me to be the earliest possibility.

At a later time the name of Chinese glasses was changed from ai-tai to yen[3]-ching[4] (13129, 2170), which means eye-mirror (cf. German, Augenspiegel). The new name is definite enough but it dates only from the XVIIIth century.

Berthold Laufer: Zur Geschichte der Brillen (Mitt. zur Geschichte der Medizin, vol. 6, 379–385, 1907). T. Naba: The Chin-mu in Huai Nan Tzŭ (in Japanese; Shina-gaku, vol. 3, no. 8, July 1924). Discussion of a reference to a golden-eye, chin[1]-mu[4]* (2032, 8080), by the Han Taoist Huai[2] Nan[2] Tzŭ[3] (5034, 8128, 12317). The author reviews the Chinese literature on spectacles and concludes that the chin-mu was something else.

Nothing has been shown to prove or suggest a Muslim origin. Let us now pass to the West.

1. A Dominican friar of Pisa, named Giordano da Rivalto, preaching in Piacenza on February 23, 1305, said: "Non è ancora venti anni che si trovò l'arte di fare gli occhiali, che fanno veder bene, che è una delle migliori arti e delle più necessarie, che'l mondo abbia." (Vocabolario degli accademici della Crusca, under occhiale). He added that he himself had seen and spoken to the man who invented the spectacles and first made them. On the basis of this testimony, the invention is often dated c. 1285. If we must take it literally the discovery occurred some time after 1285.

2. Francesco Redi published at Florence in 1678 a letter dealing with the discovery of spectacles (an improved edition dated Florence, 1690, is entitled Lettera intorno all' invenzione degli occhiali, 15 p.). He quoted from a MS. in his possession, dated 1289, the following passage: "Mi truovo cosi gravoso di anni, che non avrei valenza de leggere e scrivere senza vętri appelati okiali, truovati novellamente per la commodità delli poveri veki quando affiebolano del vedere."

It should be noted that the dates of (1) and (2) tally very well. As to the discoverer, two names have been put forward; Salvino degl' Armati, and Alessandro della Spina.

Leopoldo del Migliore in his Fiorenze, città nobilissima, illustrata (p. 431, Florence 1684), speaks of a tombstone in Santa Maria Maggiore at Florence bearing the inscription: "Qvi diace Salvino d'Armato degl' Armati di Fir., Inventor degli occhiali. Dio gli perdoni la peccata. Anno D. MCCCXVII." This monument was originally in the cloister of Santa Maria Maggiore; it disappeared for a time, but is now in the chapel of the Virgin Mary in that church.[2b]

Alessandro della Spina, Dominican residing at the Santa Catarina monastery of Pisa, died in 1313. A contemporary chronicle of the convent said that he was one of the first to make spectacles.

[2b] Dr. Andrea Corsini of Florence kindly sent me the following information which reached me during proofreading. The chapel of the Virgin in Santa Maria Maggiore contains a marble head said to represent Salvino, and a marble tablet bearing the epitaph quoted above, but no tomb; or rather the tomb below is not Salvino's.

According to Isidoro Del Lungo, Salvino's invention is a fable; Alessandro della Spina would be the real inventor. According to G. Albertotti (1922), the invention was made some time before, more probably at Venice where documents relative to the manufacture of eye-glasses date back to the second half of the thirteenth century. The by-laws of Venetian guilds refer in the chapter De cristalleriis (1284) to roidi da ogli as well as to lapides ad legendum.

A passage in the great Heidelberg MS. of songs ascribed to the Minnesänger Missener the Elder, c. 1270, is not convincing, for the word spiegel may refer to a magnifying glass as well as to spectacles.

Grosse Heidelberger Liederhandschrift (folio 342), edited by Fridrich Pfaff (1118, Heidelberg 1899). Quoted by F. M. Feldhaus: Geschichtsblätter für Technik und Industrie (vol. 6, 245, 1919).

Indirect testimonies help to establish the fact that spectacles were actually made and used about the end of the thirteenth century or the beginning of the fourteenth. Bernard de Gordon, physician in Montpellier (c. 1285–1308), speaks of spectacles in his Lilium medicinae, composed in 1303 (printed, Lyon 1474). In the earlier MS. text of the Lilium the spectacles are called oculus berillinus which would suggest that at first a single eyeglass was used, and how shall we differentiate such a single glass from a magnifying glass? In later texts of the Lilium, oculus is replaced by ocularia. In his Chirurgia magna (1363) Guy de Chauliac speaks of a maker of glasses, ocularius vitri aut beryllorum; and in the following year Petrarca mentions ocularia.

The earliest mention of spectacles in an account occurs in 1316 "Item in oculis de vitro cum capsula (VI solidi bononienses)". The earliest illustration of them is found in the frescoes of Treviso, made in 1352 by Tommaso Barisino of Mòdena. It is a portrait of the Dominican cardinal Ugone di Provenza, wearing eye-glasses. This Ugone di Provenza is the earliest person represented with eye glasses; of course this portrait does not prove that he actually used them.

It is remarkable that at least three Dominicans are mentioned apropos of that invention: Giordane da Rivalto, Alessandro della Spina, and Ugone di Provenza.[3] This would suggest that these learned friars had an important share if not in the invention itself, at least in its diffusion.

It would seem that spectacles were first made in two centers from which they spread gradually to other countries. The very first of these centers was probably Venice, or let us say North Italy, where spectacles were soon called occhiali (from oculare; the same word reappeared in the seventeenth century in cannocchiale, for telescope). The other center was in the southern part of the Netherlands, and there spectacles were called bril or brillen (derived from beryllus). Compare the French word béricle used to designate the pieces of magnifying glass or crystal which were placed in the walls of reliquaries to enable people better to see the objects contained in them. This may have been the origin of the more general use of magnifying glasses—movable ones—and later of spectacles.

Bibliography—Apart from the earlier Florentine authorities already mentioned—F. Redi (1678) and L. del Migliore (1684)—the following accounts may be quoted. Emil Bock: Die Brille und ihre Geschichte (Wien 1903). Carl Barck: History of

[3] I have failed to identify this Hugh of Provence, who according to Albertotti (1922) was Dominican, cardinal, and blessed. Would it be Hugh of Saint Cher?

spectacles (Chicago 1907; largely based on Bock). G. H. Oliver: History of the invention and discovery of spectacles (London 1913). R. Greeff: Die historische Entwicklung der Brille (Wiesbaden 1913). Prof. Greeff owned what is probably the most complete collection of spectacles in existence. It contains about 600 pairs of spectacles and 200 prints. It is now, I believe, included in the Jena collection. F. M. Feldhaus: Die Technik (137–143, 1914). Isidoro del Lungo: Le vicende di un' impostura erudita (Archivio storico italiano, vol. 78, p. 5–53, 1920). G. Albertotti: Lettera intorno all' invenzione degli occhiali (24 p., 3 pl., Roma 1922; Isis, 5, 499). Edm. O. von Lippmann: Zur Geschichte der Brille (Mitt. zur Geschichte der Medizin, 278, 1927; brief note).

Much historical information will be found in Moritz von Rohr: Die Brille als optisches Instrument (3. Aufl., Hdb. der gesamten Augenheilkunde, 268 p., 112 fig., Berlin 1921). The last part of it is historical and the text is full of historical references. See also M. von Rohr: Die Entwicklung der Brille, 9, (Die Naturwissenschaften, 284–286, 1922; Isis, 5, 301); Thomas Young oration (Transactions of the Optical Society, 1923–1924); Aus der Geschichte der Brille mit besonderer Berücksichtigung der auf der Greeffschen beruhenden Jenaischen Sammlung (Beiträge zur Geschichte der Technik und Industrie, vol. 17, 30–50, 1927; vol. 18, 95–117, 1928).

Casey A. Wood: The first scientific work on spectacles (Annals of medical history, vol. 3, 150–155, 1921; Isis, 5, 512). Apropos of the Uso de los antoios para todo genero de vistas by Benito Daca de Valdez (Seville 1623).

WITELO

Vitellius, Vitellio, Vitelo. Polish physicist and philosopher. Born in the duchy of Silesia, then a fief of Poland, c. 1230; it is probable that one of his parents was Thuringian, for he called himself Thuringo-polonus, also filius Polonorum et Thuringorum. He was educated in Paris c. 1253; after a short stay in his own country he continued his studies in Padua (canon law!) c. 1262–1268, and Viterbo, 1269; he died probably in the Premonstratensian monastery of Witow, near Piotrków, Poland, at an unknown date.

His main work is a treatise on Optics or Perspective, composed between 1270 and 1278. It shows little improvement, from the theoretical point of view, upon the optics of Ibn al-Haitham from which it is largely derived. The results of new experiments on refraction which it includes are hardly superior to Ptolemy's. His theory of the rainbow, though superior to Aristotle's, was inferior to that of his Muslim contemporaries. He noticed the necessity of refraction as well as of reflection of solar light, but did not attempt any further description. He recommended giving a paraboloidal shape to burning mirrors.

Though this work did not contain considerable novelty, it was an important link in the transmission of Greco-Arabic optics. The importance ascribed to him by the pioneers of modern optics is proved by Kepler's treatise Ad Vitellionem paralipomena quibus astronomiae pars optica traditur (Francfort 1604).

It is more original from the psychological point of view; e.g., it contains observations on ordinary perception (aspectus simplex), and attentive perception, spontaneous and unconscious reasoning which affects our vision, perception of the third dimension of space, etc.

It was dedicated to William of Moerbeke whom he had met in Viterbo, 1269, and whose philosophical views he seems to have shared. These views—neo-Platonism as explained by Proclos and by Muslim philosophers, chiefly Ibn Sīnā—were set forth in the preface to his Perspectiva. Witelo also wrote two theological treatises, De natura daemonum, and De primaria causa paenitentiae.

The De intelligentiis formerly ascribed to him is an earlier work (c. 1225).

Text—Vitellionis περὶ ὀπτικῆς, id est de natura, ratione et protectione radiorum visus, luminum, colorum, atque formarum, quam volgo perspectivam vocant libri X. First edition by Georg Tannstetter (i.e., Collimitius, 1483–1535) and Peter Apian (1495–1552) (297 leaves, Nuremberg 1535). Reprinted under the same title in 1551. Third edition by Friedrich Risner (d. 1580): Opticae libri decem, instaurati atque aucti infinitisque erroribus quibus antea scatebant expurgati (Basel 1572; appended to Risner's Latin edition of Ibn al-Haitham).

The De natura daemonum, De primaria causa paenitentiae, and related texts by other authors, were edited by Aleksander Birkenmayer: Studja nad Witelonem, 1 (149 p., Cracow 1921; Isis, 5, 214).

The apocryphal Liber de intelligentiis was edited by C. Baeumker in the memoir quoted below (1–71, 1908). Philosophical extracts from the Perspectiva are included in the same memoir (p. 127–179).

Criticism—Maximilien Curtze: Sur l'orthographe du nom et sur la patrie de Witelo (Boncompagni's Bullettino, vol. 4, 49–77, 1871). Including Bernardino Baldi's account of him. B. Boncompagni: Intorno ad un manoscritto dell' Ottica di Vitellione citato da Fra Luca Pacioli (ibidem, 78–81). Robert Knott: Allgemeine deutsche Biographie (vol. 43, 556–558, 1898). M. Steinschneider: Europäische Übersetzungen (82, 1904). Clemens Baeumker: Witelo ein Philosoph und Naturforscher des 13. Jahrhunderts. (Beitr. zur Geschichte der Philosophie des Mittelalters, vol. 3, 2, 700 p., Münster 1908); Zur Biographie des Witelo (Historisches Jahrbuch, vol. 33, 359–361, 1912). E. Gerland: Geschichte der Physik (198–200, 1913). P. Duhem: Système du monde (vol. 5, 358–374, 1917). Apropos of the De intelligentiis, which he refuses to ascribe to Witelo. This writing was already well known at the time of Aquinas' activity. Duhem would place it about 1250 or a little before. Aleksander Birkenmajer: Studies on Witelo (in Polish with French summaries in the Bull. of the Polish Academy, Cracow, 1919–1922, 1925; in four parts). Part 1 contains two new texts, see above (Isis, 5, 214). Part 2 deals with the De intelligentiis, concluding that it is apocryphal. Part 3, with the sources of Witelo's philosophy. Part 4, with Witelo's stay in Padova (Isis, 8, 741). A. Birkenmajer: Witelo e lo studio di Padova (Omaggio dell' Accademia polacca alla Università di Padova, 147–168, 1922). Italian translation of the fourth of the Polish memoirs. Clemens Baeumker: Zur Frage nach Abfassungszeit und Verfasser des irrtümlich Witelo zugeschriebenen Liber de intelligentiis (Miscellanea F. Ehrle, 1, 87–102, 1923). Lynn Thorndike: History of magic (vol. 2, 454–456, 638, 643). M. De Wulf: History of mediaeval philosophy (vol. 2, 118, 1926). Adam Bednarski: Die anatomischen Augenbilder in den Handschriften des Roger Bacon, Johann Peckham, und Witelo (Archiv für Geschichte der Medizin, vol. 24, 50–78, 16 fig., 1931).

JOHN PECKHAM

English theologian, mathematician, and physicist. Joannes Pisanus, Londinensis (these names are incorrect). Born in Sussex; studied at Oxford and assumed the Franciscan habit; went to Paris c. 1250; returned to Oxford c. 1270; provincial of the English Franciscans, 1276; c. 1278 he lectured in Rome; archbishop of Canterbury from 1279 to his death, at Mortlake, in 1292. Buried in the cathedral of Canterbury.

He wrote four treatises on scientific subjects: (1) the Perspectiva communis, a treatise on optics or perspective, divided into three parts, of which the second and third deal respectively with reflection and refraction; this treatise enjoyed a very long popularity (it was reprinted as late as 1627!); (2) Theorica planetarum; (3) Tractatus sphaerae; (4) De numeris (?).

His optics was largely derived from Ibn al-Haitham. Hence it is not surprising to find in it references to the camera obscura, even as we find them in the contemporary works of Bacon and Witelo. There is a description of the eye, and the printed editions contain a diagram of it which was probably the earliest to appear in print.[4]

The Tractatus de oculo morali ascribed to Peckham in the princeps (Augsburg, s. a., 1475?) is apocryphal. It has also been ascribed to Robert Grosseteste; but the real author was Peter of Limoges[5] (d. 1306). The purpose of the De oculo morali is purely ethical but it contains a description of the eye, together with a brief account of eye diseases and their treatment. It has been called the first ophthalmological treatise to be printed, but this is doubly incorrect, first because it is not a bona fide ophthalmological treatise, second because the De oculis of Benvenutus Grassus was printed in all probability[6] before (Ferrara 1474).

To return to Peckham, he wrote a great many treatises on other subjects: the Bible, theology, religion. I shall quote only a few. Two collections of theological questions: Quaestiones quodlibeticae and Quaestiones ordinariae. Commentaries on Aristotle's Ethics, and on the Sentences of Peter the Lombard (this last work was quoted by Peter Olivi in 1285). The Tractatus pauperis contra insipientem novellarum haeresum confictorem circa Evangelicam perfectionem, in defense of the mendicant orders, and especially of the Franciscans against the writings of William of Saint Amour, notably his De periculis novissimorum temporum (c. 1255). Tractatus contra Rogerium (O. P.) obloquentem contra suum ordinem. A life of St. Anthony of Padua (1195–1231), written at the request of Jerome of Ascoli (general of the Franciscans, 1274; pope Nicholas IV, 1288–1292). Finally, he composed many religious poems of which the best known is the Nightingale or Philomela (wrongly ascribed to St. Bonaventure and others).

While in Paris he met St. Thomas and defended him. Yet he was a disciple of St. Bonaventure (also in Paris), and was more and more deeply imbued with Franciscan ideals. Eventually he became a strong defender of the older scholasticism against Thomism as well as against Averroism. He continued Kilwardby's campaign against Thomism, condemning it in 1284, and again in 1286 in spite (or perhaps because) of the fact that it was since 1278 the official doctrine of the Dominicans.

Text—The Perspectiva communis was first edited by Facio Cardano (Milano 1482). This Facio (1444–1524), physician and lawyer in Milano, was the father of the famous mathematician Gerolamo Cardano (1501–1576). Other editions: Leipzig 1504; Venice 1504, 1505?; Cologne 1508; Nuremberg 1542, by Georg

[4] At any rate, the edition of 1504 contains the diagram. Presumably the earlier edition contained it too, but even if it did not, I know of but one other printed diagram of the eye, that is, the one contained in the Margarita philosophiae of G. Reisch (Strassburg 1504), which may be earlier. Reisch's diagram is reproduced in C. Singer: Fasciculo di medicina (vol. 2, fig. 71, Florence 1925).

[5] This Peter of Limoges flourished at the Sorbonne in Paris c. 1272; he was canon of Evreux. See B. Hauréau: Histoire littéraire de la France (vol. 26, 460–467, 1873).

[6] I cannot be categorical because both works, De oculo morali, and De oculis, are undated.

Hartmann (1489–1564); Cologne 1542, 1627. Italian translation, I tre libri della Perspettiva commune (Venice 1593).

A part of the Tractatus pauperis is included in the Firmamentum trium ordinum ordinum beatissimi Francisci (Venice 1513).

The Philomela has often been printed in the works of St. Bonaventure (vol. 6, 424–427, Mayence 1609; etc). German translation, Nachtigall des hlg. Bonaventura (Munich 1612); Spanish translation (Madrid 1788). English imitation written c. 1460.

Canticum pauperis Fr. Joannis Peckham (Bibliotheca franciscana ascetica medii aevi, vol. 4, p. 133–205; Quaracchi 1905). Tractatus tres de paupertate. Cum bibliographia ediderunt C. L. Kingsford, A. G. Little, F. Tocco (British Society of Franciscan studies, 2, Aberdeen 1910). Johannis Pechami quaestiones tractantes de anima. First edition by Hieronymus Spettmann (Beitr. zur Gesch. der Phil. des Mittelalters, vol. 19, 5, 262 p., Münster 1918).

Charles Trice Martin: Registrum Fr. Joannis Peckham (3 vols., Rolls series, London 1882–1885). Contains Peckham's letters, 720 in number (1279–1292).

Liber (s. Tractatus) de oculo morali. First edition, Augsburg, s.a., 1475? Later editions: Venice 1496, 1503. Italian translation printed in Venice 1496.

Criticism—C. L. Kingsford: Dictionary of national biography (vol. 44, 190–197, 1895). P. Duhem: Système du monde (vol. 3, 515–517, 525, 527, 1915). Hieronymus Spettmann: Die Psychologie des J. Pecham (Beitr. zur Gesch. der Philos. des Mittelalters, vol. 20, 6, 112 p., Münster 1919); Der Ethikkomentar des J. Peckham (Beitr. zur Gesch. der Philos. des Mittelalters, Suppl. Bd. 2, 221–242, 1923). M. De Wulf: History of mediaeval philosophy (vol. 1, 378–381; vol. 2, 41–43, 1926). A Bednarski: Anatomical drawing of the eye by Peckham (Archiv. hist. i filoz. med., vol. 9, 73–80, 1929; in Polish); Das anatomische Augenbild von J. Peckham (Archiv für Geschichte der Medizin, vol. 22, 352–356, 1929; presumably a translation of the Polish paper).

For other optical investigations see my notes on Bacon, Peter the Stranger, William of Moerbeke, Giles of Rome, Nāṣir al-dīn al-Ṭūsī, Quṭb al-dīn al-Shīrāzī.

II. WEIGHTS AND MEASURES

See my notes on Moses ibn Tibbon and al-Kūhīn al-'Aṭṭār.

III. MAGNETISM

PETER THE STRANGER

French physicist who flourished c. 1269. One of the greatest physicists of mediaeval times.

Petrus Peregrinus de Maharn curia (Maricurtia). The name Peregrinus (stranger) was often given to Crusaders; our Peter was in the army of Crusaders which besieged Lucera in 1269. He hailed from Maricourt in Picardy.

He was the teacher of Roger Bacon, who speaks of him in the Opus tertium and in the Opus maius as the greatest experimental scientist of the time, one of the greatest mathematicians, a complete alchemist, a man acquainted with the theory and practice of all the technical arts.

He wrote a treatise on the astrolabe, Nova compositio astrolabii particularis, after 1261; and a letter on the magnet in 1269. He planned to compose a treatise on mirrors, De operibus speculorum.

The letter on the magnet Epistola ad Sygerum de Foucaucourt militem de magnete, was written in 1269 at the siege of Lucera dei Pagani (or Lucera di Puglia, where the emperor Frederick II had established a Muslim colony).[7] As this letter is one of the greatest monuments of experimental research in the Middle Ages, it deserves to be examined in detail.

It is divided into two parts dealing respectively with theory and applications. The first, by far the longer, is divided into ten chapters: (1) purpose of the work; (2) explanation of experimental method; (3) how to recognize loadstones; (4) two methods for determining the poles; (5) how to distinguish the septentrional pole from the meridional; (6) how a magnet affects another; (7) how to magnetize a piece of iron by rubbing it with a magnet; (8) how a magnet attracts iron; (9) why one kind of pole attracts the other kind; (10) origin of the natural virtue of a magnet (the magnet is directed virtu Dei or nutu Dei). Construction of a magnetic terrella (a magnet of spherical shape) moving together with the firmament, to illustrate cosmic motions. In such a terrella all the magnetic forces seem to derive from two opposite poles. First vague suggestion of terrestrial magnetism, inducing the virtue of particular magnets.

In the second part he describes three instruments: (1) one to determine directly the azimuths of stars. This is a kind of portable compass and sundial; (2) another and better instrument of the same kind; (3) an attempt to create a perpetuum mobile by means of magnets.

The instrument described in chapter 1 of part 2 is in fact a compass of an improved type—a floating compass provided with a fiducial line and a circle divided into 360 degrees. The compass described in chapter 2 is made of a needle turning on a metallic pivot within a box covered by a glass or crystal lid, together with a graduated circle and an alidade provided with two sights.

To sum up, the Epistola was not only a summary of magnetic knowledge; it added considerably to it and was a splendid and rare exemplar of the experimental method. We find in it descriptions of floated and pivoted compasses, of the two kinds of poles, their attractions and repulsions; magnetization by contact; inversion of the poles; breaking of a magnetic needle into smaller ones; exertion of magnetic force through water, glass; etc.

Text—First edition by Achilles Pirmin Gasser, a physician of Lindau, who died in Augsburg (1505–1577): Petri Peregrini Maricortensis De magnete seu rota perpetui motus, libellus . . . . nunc primum promulgatus (Augsburg 1558). Second edition by John Taisnier:[8] Opusculum perpetua memoria dignissimum de natura magnetis et eius effectibus. Item de moto continuo. Demonstratio proportionum motuum localium contra Aristotelem et alios philosophos (Cologne 1562). Poor edition without the author's name, place or date. Third edition by Tiberius Cavallo: A treatise on magnetism in theory and practice with original experiments. The third edition with a supplement (London 1800). The supplement contains "an account with extracts of a curious letter of Peter Adsiger on the properties of the magnet," with English translation of the extracts quoted. Poor edition; the author's name, Peter Adsiger, is a misreading of "ad Sigerum," which had been made previously by Melchissédech Thévenot: Recueil de voyages (29, Paris 1681). Fourth edition by G. Libri: Histoire des sciences mathématiques en Italie (vol. 2, 487–502, 1838). All of these editions are uncritical, but the first has the value of a MS.

A much better edition was given by Timoteo Bertelli in the memoir quoted below

[7] See the last section of my note on Frederick II.

[8] John Taisnier (1508–after 1562). See article by Henri Bosmans: Biographie nationale de Belgique (vol. 24, 499–511, 1929, Isis, 12, 99).

(p. 70–89, 1868). Bertelli's edition was revised by Gustav Hellmann: Rara magnetica (Neudrucke von Schriften und Karten über Meteorologie und Erdmagnetismus, no. 10, Berlin 1898).

For more information on these editions and on the MSS. see the third and last part of Schlund's memoir (1912).

Latin text and English version with an introductory history of experimental science in the Middle Ages by Charles Sanders Pierce (c. 1894). I have only seen the prospectus (16 p.) of this edition of 300 copies; I do not believe it was actually published. Facsimile edition of one of the MSS., written by an English hand c. 1390 (8 leaves; Quaritch, London 1900; 50 copies). English translation by Silvanus P. Thompson from the printed Latin versions of Gasser 1558, Bertelli 1868, and Hellmann 1898, and amended by reference to the MS. in his possession dated 1391 (printed in the Caxton type by the Chiswick Press, London 1902; 240 copies). English translation by Brother Arnold (i.e., Joseph Charles Mertens) with introduction by Brother Potamian (i.e., M. F. O'Reilly), (60 p., New York 1904).

Criticism—Timoteo Bertelli: Sopra Peregrino e la sua epistola (32 p., Bull. di bibliografia delle scienze mat., vol. 1, Roma 1868). Fontès: Deux mathématiciens peu connus du XIIIe siècle (Mém. de l'Acad. des sciences de Toulouse, vol. 9, 382–384, 1897; unimportant, derived from Bertelli). P. Duhem: Origines de la statique (vol. 1, 57, 1905). On perpetual motion. S. P. Thompson: Peregrinus and his epistola (32 p., London 1907). Erhard Schlund: Peregrinus, sein Leben und seine Schriften (Archivum franciscanum historicum, vol. 4, 436–455, 633–643, 1911; vol. 5, 22–40, 1912; important). F. Picavet: Le maitre des expériences, Pierre de Maricourt. In Essais sur l'histoire générale et comparée des théologies et des philosophies médiévales (233–254, 1913). Paul Fleury Mottelay: Bibliographical history of electricity and magnetism (45–54, with two facsimiles, 1922; Isis, 6, 104–107).

IV. MECHANICS, TECHNOLOGY, ENGINEERING

PETER OLIVI

French physicist and theologian. Petrus Joannis Olivi (the form Petrus Joannes is incorrect), Pierre fils de Jean Olivi. Born in Sérignan, Languedoc, 1248–1249; assumed the Franciscan habit in Béziers, 1260–1261; studied probably in Paris; died in Narbonne, 1298.

Since the time of Joannes Philoponos (first half of the sixth century), he was the first author to explain more or less clearly the theory of the impetus (Codex Vatic. lat., 1116), which was a vague anticipation of the concept of inertia. Indeed in his solution of the 22nd objection to Quaestio 31, he asks how the "vis formativa" can bring about the existence of a living being, and answers, "Vis formativa non agit nisi sicut virtus instrumentalis alicuius principalis agentis"—a view which he explains by means of the following comparison: "sicut suo modo impulsus seu inclinationes datae proiectis a proiectoribus movent ipsa proiecta etiam in absentia proicientium" (also other texts to the same effect).

In his Quaestiones he discusses very elaborately a number of philosophical and theological problems. He wrote considerably: Postilla super Genesim, and other commentaries on the Old and New Testaments; a commentary on the Sentences of Peter the Lombard, a Tractatus de quantitate; and various tracts on the Franciscan observance, discussing such questions as evangelical perfection and poverty. A treatise of his on monachal poverty was directed against St. Thomas.

He opposed Thomism and to some extent neo-Platonism but was not an Augustinian. He tried to reestablish primitive poverty into his order, and was supported by the more radical elements of it (the Spirituals). Richard of Middleton and others were appointed by the general of the Franciscans in 1278, 1283, 1288, to examine into his doctrines. These were repeatedly censured by the chapter of Strassburg, 1282, by the University in 1283, etc. Some of his philosophical ideas were censured at the same time.

Text—There are two early editions of the Quaestiones, the one without place or date, the other printed in Venice, 1509. The text of some questions was discovered only in 1878–1880. New edition of the Quaestiones by Bernhard Jansen (Quaracchi 1922 ff.).

Criticism—Franz Ehrle: Petrus Johannis Olivi, sein Leben und seine Schriften (Archiv für Litteratur- und Kirchengeschichte des Mittelalters, vol. 3, 409–552, 1887; very elaborate study). Brother René of Nantes: Pierre de Jean Olivi (Etudes franciscaines, vol. 16, 472–488, 1906; vol. 17, 146–163, 283–304, 1907). Deals with Olivi's theological views and troubles. Bernhard Jansen: Olivi, der älteste scholastische Vertreter des heutigen Bewegungsbegriffs (Philosophisches Jahrbuch der Görresgesellschaft, vol. 33, 137–152, Fulda, 1920; Isis, 4, 584); Petrus de Trabibus, seine spekulative Eigenart oder sein Verhältnis zu Olivi (Beiträge zur Gesch. der Philos. des Mittelalters, Supp. Bd. 2, 243–254, 1923). Edgar Hocedez: Richard de Middleton (443–453, Louvain 1925).

VILLARD DE HONNECOURT

French architect and engineer, who originated probably in Honnecourt on the Scheldt, near Cambrai, Picardy, about the beginning of the thirteenth century. His first and last architectural works, as far as we know, were done c. 1235 at Vaucelles, near Honnecourt, and before 1257 at St. Quentin; the choir of St. Quentin's cathedral was consecrated in 1257. He left an album of drawings, from which we gather that he worked not only in these places but also in Cambrai, Laon, Reims, Meaux, Chartres, Lausanne, and even in Hungary. This album (33 leaves of parchment, c. 24 x 16 cm.) is not only a unique document for the history of mediaeval architecture; it also contains a number of drawings which reveal Villard as a humble forerunner of Leonardo da Vinci. They deal with architectural plans, construction, masonry, woodwork, practical geometry, artistic anatomy, studies in proportion and symmetry, machines of various kinds including war engines, perpetual motion, sketches of animals from life (molluscs, crustacea, insects, birds, porcupine, lion, etc.). Upon the last leaf there is a recipe to preserve the natural colorations of the flowers kept in a herbarium.

Text—The Album was published in facsimile for the first time by J. B. A. Lassus (1807–1857) (Paris 1858; with notes and glossary; posthumously edited by Alfred Darcel). Facsimile of the sketchbook of Wilars de Honecort, with commentaries and descriptions by J. B. A. Lassus and J. Quicherat, edited by Robert Willis (255 p., 53 pl., 43 ill., London 1859). Bibliothèque nationale, département des manuscrits. Album de Villard. Reproduction des 66 p. et dessins du MS. français 19093 de la Bibliothèque nationale (Paris 1906).

Criticism—Jules Quicherat: Revue archéologique (vol. 6, 65–80, 164–188, 211–226, 3 pl., 1849). Ernest Renan: L'art au moyen âge et les causes de sa décadence (Revue des deux mondes, vol. 40, 203–228, 1862); reprinted in Mélanges d'histoire et de voyage (209–252, 1890); Histoire littéraire de la France (vol. 25, 1–9, 1869). Viollet-le-Duc: Revue archéologique (vol. 7, 1863). C. Enlart: Villard et les Cisterciens (Bibliothèque de l'Ecole des Chartes, vol. 56, 1895). H. Schimank: Der Weg zur Erkenntnis des Energieprinzips (Dresden 1929).

For other information on mechanics, technology, and engineering, see my notes on Bacon, 'Alī ibn 'Umar al-Kātibī, Quṭb al-dīn al-Shīrāzī, Peter the Stranger, William of Moerbeke, al-'Urḍī, Samuel ha-Levi, Kublai Khān, al-Ḥasan al-Rammāḥ.

A-LAO-WA-TING

A^4-lao^3-wa^3-ting^1 (1, 6783, 12420, 11253) or La-pu-tan (?). Both these names are Chinese transcriptions of unknown Arabic names ('Alā al-dīn?). Muslim military engineer who was in the Mongol service c. 1271, and died in 1312. He was employed by Kublai Khān in 1271, together with his countryman I-ssŭ-ma-yin, at Hangchow and other places. He constructed ballistic engines (not cannons!) for the Mongols. About 1300 (?) he was succeeded by his son, Ma^3-ha^{1*}-sha^1 (7576, 3754, 9624).

Giles: Chinese biographical dictionary (p. 1, 1898). Gustave Schlegel: On the invention and use of fire-arms and gunpowder in China, prior to the arrival of Europeans (T'oung Pao, vol. 3, 1–11, 1902). Schlegel claims that the Mongols used gunpowder already in 1232; I believe this is wrong; see my note on gunpowder (second half of thirteenth century). Yoshio Mikami: Development of mathematics in China (100, 1913).

I-SSŬ-MA-YIN

I^{4*}-ssŭ^1-ma^3-yin^1 (5395, 10271, 7576, 13215). Chinese transcription of an unknown Arabic name (Ismā'īl?). Born in Turkestan; was in the Mongol service c. 1271; died in 1330 (Mikami says 1274 ?). Muslim military engineer who worked with A-lao-wa-ting. He was present at the siege of Hsiang^1-yang^2 (4266, 12883) in 1273, and constructed for it a mangonel of tremendous power. He was succeeded by his son Ya^4-ku^3 (12810, 6188), i.e., Ya'qūb.

Giles: Chinese biographical dictionary (351, 1898). Y. Mikami: Development of mathematics in China (100, 1913).

V. MUSIC

See my notes on Alfonso X el Sabio, Salimbene of Parma, Georgios Pachymeres, Nāṣir al-dīn al-Ṭūsī, Quṭb al-dīn al-Shīrāzī.

ṢAFĪ AL-DĪN

Ṣafī al-dīn 'Abd al-Mu'mīn ibn Faqīr (or Fākhir) al-Urmawī al-Baghdādī. One of the greatest theorists of music in Islām. His family originated from Urmīyah in Adharbāyjān, but he was born in Baghdād in the first quarter of thirteenth century. He was librarian, scribe, and chief minstrel to the last 'Abbāsid caliph, al-Musta'ṣim (1242–1258). When Baghdād was sacked by the Mongols (1258). Hūlāgū spared him together with his family and property. Ṣafī al-din entered the Mongol service and became tutor to the two sons of Hūlāgū's wazīr, Bahā' al-dīn Muḥammad (1240–1279) and Sharaf al-dīn Hārūn (d. 1286). When Bahā' al-dīn was appointed governor of al-'Irāq and 'Irāq 'Ajamī in 1265, Ṣafī al-dīn went with him to Iṣfahān. After the death or ruin of his patrons he fell on evil days, and died in a debtor's prison in 1294.

Ṣafī al-dīn wrote at least three treatises:

1. Kitāb al-adwār (Book of musical modes), composed probably in 1252.
2. Risālat al-sharafīya, c. 1267. So named after his pupil Sharaf al-dīn. It is also a treatise on music, and was very authoritative, judging by the number of commentaries devoted to it. It is derived from al-Fārābī's treatise, which it simplified and improved.
3. Fī 'ulūm al-'arūḍ wal-qawāfī wal-badī', on prosody, rhyme and rhetoric.

He invented two stringed instruments, the mughnī, an archlute (in Iṣfahān), and the nuzha, a kind of psaltery.

It is from him that we hear that the Muslims used the Nicomachean notation for recording their melodies. He was one of the founders of the so called "systematist" school; Sir Hubert Parry considers the "systematist" scale the most perfect ever devised.[9]

Text—Baron Carra de Vaux: Le Traité des rapports musicaux ou l'Epitre à Scharaf ed-dīn (Journal Asiatique, vol. 18, 279–355, 1891). This is a very elaborate analysis amounting almost to a translation.

Criticism—C. Brockelmann: Arabische Litteratur (vol. 1, 496, 1898). Father Collangettes: Etude sur la musique arabe (Journal asiatique, vol. 4, 365–422, 1904; vol. 8, 149–190, 1906; not continued). Jules Rouanet: La musique arabe (Lavignac's Encyclopédie de la musique, vol. 5, 1922). Carra de Vaux: Les penseurs de l'Islam (vol. 4, 342, 363, 1923). J. B. Trend: Grove's Dictionary of music (vol. 4, 498, 1928).

Henry George Farmer: The Arabian influence on musical theory (Journal R. Asiatic Soc., 79, 1925; Isis, 8, 508); History of Arabian music (by index; see on pl. opposite p. 202 an extract from the Kitāb al-adwār showing Ṣafī al-dīn's notation; London 1929; Isis, 13, 375–376); Greek theorists of music in Arabic translation (Isis, 13, 332, 1930).

[9] Art of music (1893) as quoted by Farmer, 1925.

CHAPTER XLIX

CHEMISTRY

(Second Half of Thirteenth Century)

I. GUNPOWDER AND PYROTECHNICS

THE INVENTION OF GUNPOWDER

Ordinary gunpowder or "black powder" is an explosive mixture of saltpeter, sulphur, and charcoal. Of course, sulphur and charcoal have been known from time immemorial. The "invention" of gunpowder implied thus essentially a knowledge of saltpeter and of the proper mixture.

To clear the ground it will be well to speak of saltpeter first and to define it. This is the more necessary in that this word, sal petrae, or its equivalent, niter, has been taken to mean many different things. The word niter (*νίτρον*, nitrum, natron) was frequently used by the ancients but they meant by it potash or soda or any other alkaline salt. For example, some such salt, sodium carbonate, was extracted from the famous natron lakes of Egypt by the early Egyptians for many purposes: embalming, cleansing, perhaps also to cure meat, to help in smelting ores, and as medicine.

The Hebrew word neter occurs in Proverbs (25, 20) but it may refer to any alkaline salt which an acid would cause to effervesce; it also occurs in Jeremiah (2, 22), where it refers to a lye or soap. In the Kitāb al-uṣūl of Ibn Janāḥ (first half of the eleventh century) it is translated: (1) alum, (2) nitre; (3) chalk (or perhaps, fuller's earth).

There was some sort of saltpeter industry in al-Baṣra in the ninth century, for we hear in 869 of a rebellion of the negro slaves (zinj) who were employed in it.[1] But here again it is highly probable that another alkali, or rather any kind of alkali soil, is meant.

It has been claimed that the earliest clear reference to real saltpeter (potassium nitrate) is found in the work of Ibn al-Baiṭār under bārūd. He identified the substance bārūd known in Morocco, with the flower of asīyūs, i.e., the stone of Assos (*λίθος ἄσσιος*) mentioned by Dioscorides and Galen, and said that the Egyptian physicians called it Chinese snow (talj al-ṣīnī). Thus this reference would send us back to Greek or Chinese sources. But there is nothing to prove that bārūd meant saltpeter. The thing thus called by Ibn al-Baiṭār may have been almost any kind of nitrous efflorescence. The stone of Assos may have been alunite. The fact that the word bārūd (or bārūt) is used in modern Arabic, Persian, and Turkish to designate gunpowder is of course irrelevant.

Our modern word saltpeter is still full of ambiguity. When used alone it is

[1] R. A. Nicholson: Literary history of the Arabs (273, 1907). Theodor Nöldeke: Sketches from eastern history (145, London 1852). Mr. Nicholson kindly wrote me that al-Ṭabarī called these slaves shūrajī, makers of shūraj, by which is probably meant the alkaline substance. Al-Ṭabarī did not use the word bārūd in that connection.

supposed to mean potassium nitrate, that is, the very substance needed to make gunpowder. Yet when we speak of the saltpeter industry we mean Chile saltpeter, i.e., sodium nitrate (too deliquescent to be used for gunpowder), and when we speak of wall saltpeter we mean calcium nitrate.

It is probable that potassium nitrate was known in the West (and possibly also in China) about the middle of the thirteenth century. This implies that its identity had been distinguished and that means had been invented for leaching it out of other substances and purifying it. Such invention would lead to that of gunpowder, or rather would be almost simultaneous with it, for the making of gunpowder would create a need of pure saltpeter.

Let us now consider the three possible sources of that invention: the Chinese, the Muslim, and the Latin.

1. *The Chinese contribution*—We have seen that the Egyptians gave to some kind of alkali the name of Chinese snow. On the other hand it has been claimed that the Chinese were acquainted with gunpowder as early as the T'ang dynasty. This is entirely unproved; it cannot even be proved that they were then already acquainted with other pyrotechnic devices comparable to the Greek fire which was known in the west in the second half of the seventh century (vol. 1, 494). But they used such devices in the battles of 1161 and 1162, and again at the battle of 1232 against the Mongols. The claim that they used guns in 1232 is due to a misunderstanding of the texts. If they used gunpowder at all it was in the form of hand grenades or rockets.

The Chinese may have discovered saltpeter, or else that discovery may have been transmitted to them by the Muslims whom they had plenty of opportunities of meeting either at home or abroad. It should be noted that saltpeter would be more abundant and more obvious in a tropical climate than in a cold one. For centuries after the invention of gunpowder the growing European demand for saltpeter was met by importations from India, this important business being largely monopolized by Venice.

Gustave Schlegel: On the invention and use of fire-arms and gunpowder in China (T'oung Pao, vol. 3, 1–11, 1902; in defense of the Chinese invention). P. Pelliot (ibidem, vol. 21, 432–434, 1922).

2. *The Muslim contribution*—The assumption that Muslims had some knowledge of saltpeter is corroborated by the study of the work of al-Ḥasan al-Rammāḥ (second half of the thirteenth century), who described methods of purifying that substance. On the other hand there is no mention of gunpowder in any Arabic or Persian text of the thirteenth century. They may speak of bārūd, but there is nothing to show that gunpowder was meant. One of the Arabic recipes quoted by Berthelot suggests a western origin (Chimie au moyen âge, vol. 2, 198, 1893).

3. *The Latin contribution*—The discussion of Latin claims rests upon the works of two men: Marc the Greek, and Roger Bacon.

The Liber ignium of the former marks the climax of a long Greek-Arabic tradition; it contains materials of many ages, and the gunpowder recipe represents the latest stage of its evolution. Indeed that recipe is included only in the latest edition of the text represented by a MS. of c. 1300. Thus it was probably discovered in the second half of the thirteenth century.

As to Bacon there is no reason for ascribing the invention of gunpowder to him.

The part of the Epistola de secretis operibus naturae upon which such ascription is founded is apocryphal, if not the whole epistola. The cipher supposed to contain a recipe of gunpowder has no MS. authority whatever, and the interpretations which have been made of it are fantastic. However Bacon may have known something of gunpowder, and he was certainly acquainted with various inflammable and pyrotechnic substances.

In the Opus tertium (Little, 51, 1912) Bacon speaks of a powder the explosive power of which would be increased if it were enclosed in an instrument of solid material. Was this gunpowder?

Bacon's suggestion makes us realize that the great invention which revolutionized the world was not after all that of saltpeter, nor even of gunpowder, but the application of explosive power to the propulsion of missiles. This last step—the invention of firearms—does not seem to have been made before the second quarter of the fourteenth century. I shall discuss it in vol. 3.

In conclusion, it is very probable that gunpowder was invented before the end of the thirteenth century; but even so, it is certain that nobody understood as yet the implications of that invention. If the reader insists that an invention can only be considered as made when it is fully understood, then gunpowder was not discovered before the fourteenth century; on the same principle, Columbus did not discover America. There is no proof that gunpowder was invented by the Chinese; it may have been invented by Muslims, but there seems to be a stronger probability that the invention was made in the Latin world, that is, in western Europe.

S. J. von Romocki: Geschichte der Explosivstoffe (2 vols., Berlin 1895, Hannover 1896). E. O. von Lippmann: Zur Geschichte des Schiesspulvers und der älteren Feuerwaffen (Z. für Naturwiss. 295, 1898; reprinted in Abhdl. und Vortr., vol. 1, 125–189, 1906). Lieut. Col. Henry W. L. Hime: Gunpowder and ammunition (256 p., London 1904). Includes an interpretation of Bacon's ciphered recipe of gunpowder. A revised edition of this work was printed in a later work by the same author: Origin of artillery (London 1915). Oscar Guttmann: Monumenta pulveris pyrii. Reproductions of ancient pictures concerning the history of gunpowder, with explanatory notes (102 fig., London 1906). Sumptuous publication of which only 270 copies have been printed. F. M. Feldhaus: Die Technik (894, 911–914, 1914); Ein Feuerangriff um 1290 (Zeitschrift für historische Waffenkunde, vol. 7, 236–237, 1 fig., 1916; Geschichtsblätter für Technik, vol. 3, 338, 1916; vol. 5, 178, 1918). Arthur Marshall: Explosives (640 p., London 1915; revised edition 1917). Tenney L. Davis: Bacon's letter concerning the marvelous power of art (76 p., Easton, Pa., 1923; translation of the Epistola with introduction; Isis, 7, 537); Roger Bacon's gunpowder (Army Ordnance, vol. 3, 280, 1923; Isis, 7, 537). Lynn Thorndike: History of magic (vol. 2, 688–691, 1923). Showing the fantasticality of Hime's interpretation. Bernhard Rathgen: Das Geschütz im Mittelalter (Berlin 1928; chapter 12, p. 95–108, powder and saltpeter; Isis, 13, 125–127). Robert Steele: Luru vopo vir can utriet (Nature, 121, 208–209, 1928; Isis, 11, 428).

MARC THE GREEK

Unknown author of a collection of recipes who flourished probably in the second half of the thirteenth century. Indeed that collection, entitled Liber ignium ad comburendos hostes, was probably composed in that period, certainly not before. These recipes are obviously of many ages—Egyptian, Hellenistic, Byzantine, Arabic, Latin, contemporary. They deal with incendiary and pyrotechnic substances, Greek fire, phosphorescent substances, explosive substances containing saltpeter, etc. The explosive substances are among the latest additions. Indeed there are two important versions of the text, an older one represented by the Munich MS. 197 (written in 1438), and a younger represented by the earlier Paris MS. 7156 (c. 1300). (There are many other MSS.) The recipe for gunpowder is not included in the Munich MS. yet it is probably the earliest recipe of its kind.

It is possible that the Liber ignium was originally written in Greek; one Latin MS. at least bore a Greek title, Περὶ τῶν πυρῶν; it is also possible that the Greek text was translated into Arabic and later from Arabic into Latin. The Latin text contains words obviously derived from Arabic words such as qiṭrān (liquid pitch or tar) and anbīq (alembic), but this does not prove that it was translated from the Arabic. Collections of recipes invite interpolations. It is clear that it is practically impossible to distinguish between a series of versions, each with its own accretions, and a series of treatises containing the same accretions. However, it does not matter very much whether the borrowings were in the form of straight translations, or free translations, or more independent compositions. It is the borrowings themselves that matter, irrespective of their form.

The very title, Liber ignium ad comburendos hostes, and the recipe for Greek fire suggest a Byzantine transmission. See my note on Callinicos (second half of the seventh century). There is no reason to believe (as Berthelot did) that the sal coctum mentioned in the recipe for Greek fire was saltpeter.

Among the latest accretions of the Liber ignium are recipes for the distillation of terebentinum, oleum laterinum (brick oil) and aqua ardens (alcohol), and finally the recipe for gunpowder. In this last one, saltpeter is carefully defined, which would suggest that it was a comparative novelty "Sal petrosum est minera terrae . . . . reperitur in scrophulis contra lapides." The recipe for gunpowder is as follows: "Take 1 lb. of live sulphur, 2 lb. of charcoal from the lime or willow, 6 lb. of saltpeter. Let the three substances be very finely powdered upon a marble slab (and then mixed together).[2]

Text—First edition of the Liber ignium by Gabriel de La Porte du Theil (Paris an XII, 1804). New independent edition by Ferdinand Hoefer: Histoire de la chimie (vol. 1, 491, 1842). Latin edition with French translation in M. Berthelot: La chimie au moyen âge (vol. 1, 100–135, 1893).

Criticism—Johann Beckmann: Beiträge zur Geschichte der Erfindungen (vol. 5, 570, Leipzig 1805). Hermann Kopp: Beiträge zur Geschichte der Chemie (vol. 3, 95, 1875). M. Berthelot (Annales de chimie et de physique, vol. 24, 433–521, 1891). E. O. von Lippmann: Entstehung der Alchemie (477–482, Berlin 1919). E. J. Holmyard: Chemistry to the time of Dalton (38, London 1925; Isis, 8, 616). Lynn Thorndike: History of magic (vol. 2, 252, 738, 784–788, 797, 1923); Vatican Latin MSS. (Isis, 13, 83, 1929.) D. W. Singer: Catalogue of Latin and vernacular MSS. in Great Britain (633–634, Brussels 1930; Isis, 12, 168–169; 15, 299). For other MSS. of the same kind see ibidem (632–638).

AL-ḤASAN AL-RAMMĀḤ

al-Ḥasan al-Rammāḥ (the lancer) Najm al-dīn al-Aḥdab (the hunchback). Muslim writer on military subjects. He flourished probably in Syria; he died in 1294–1295 in his thirties; thus his literary activity can hardly be anterior to 1280.

[2] After Holmyard.

He wrote two treatises on horsemanship and the art of war: (1) Kitāb al-furūsīya wal-munāṣab al-ḥarbīya (Horsemanship and war stratagems); (2) Nihāyat al-su'ūl wal-umnīya fī ta'allum a'māl al-furūsīya. The second was dedicated to an amīr of Damascus.

The first treatise deals with all that a military officer is supposed to know: military operations, means of using lances, bows, siege engines; how to fight at sea; how to communicate fire, etc. It contains various pyrotechnic recipes which remind one of those included in the Liber ignium of Marc the Greek. Both works must have been partly derived from the same sources. Al-Ḥasan considered saltpeter the fundamental substance of pyrotechnics. He explained methods of preparing and purifying it by means of potash and of repeated crystallizations. This is far more important than it may seem, for the impurities of saltpeter are hygroscopic and thus tend to destroy its value. To discover saltpeter and its uses was one thing, to purify it was another.

Text—Extracts of the Kitāb al-furūsīya in Arabic and French are given by Joseph Toussaint Reinaud and Ildephonse Favé: Histoire de l'artillerie. 1ère partie. Du feu grégeois, des feux de guerre et des origines de la poudre à canon (Paris 1845).

Criticism—J. T. Reinaud: De l'art militaire chez les Arabes (Journal asiatique, vol. 12, 193–237, 1848). Deals with al-Ḥasan's treatise and various others of the same kind. M. Berthelot: La chimie au moyen âge (vol. 1, 133; vol. 2, 198, 1893). Apropos of an Arabic treatise containing pyrotechnic recipes similar to al-Ḥasan's, one of which is entitled "Formule de la graine franque des Patrices," suggesting a western origin. C. Brockelmann: Arabische Litteratur (vol. 1, 496, 1898; only four lines). E. O. v. Lippmann: Entstehung der Alchemie (394, 1919).

II. GLASS MANUFACTURE

The making of glass dates back to very early times in Egypt and Mesopotamia. The blowing of it was invented during the Augustan age in Sidon, and Alexandria soon became the main commercial center for its distribution. It was probably from Alexandria that the art finally reached China in the fifth century (vol. 1, 389). In the meanwhile it developed in many places in Europe and the Near East. Abundant examples of ancient and mediaeval glass of many countries, East and West, may be examined in every large museum.

At the time of which we are now speaking, Venice had become the greatest center of fabrication. Glass manufacture was already existing there in the eleventh century; the Venetian prosperity and power which was one of the results of the Crusades (especially of the fourth one, 1202–1204) gave it a tremendous stimulus. The activity of Venetian glass works in the thirteenth century is proved by many archival documents. They are mentioned in a treaty concluded in 1277 between the doge Jacopo Contarini and Bohemund VII, prince of Antioch. One of the articles deals with the exportation of cullet (verre brisé, groisil), i.e., old broken glass which was indispensable to facilitate the fusion of the new glass. On the other hand Venice took drastic measures to prohibit the exportation of cullet and the emigration of craftsmen to other countries. In 1291 the whole industry was ordered to be moved to the island of Murano, a separate borough of the city, where there were already a few glass works.

The industry was very prosperous, partly because of the commercial supremacy of Venice, partly because the necessary materials were easily obtainable; wood from Eastern Venetia and the lower Alps, salt from Dalmatia, soda ash (rocchetta, salicor), from Egypt or from Alicante in Spain, clay from Vicenza, sand from the Lido and a finer kind from Verona, etc. Moreover by the end of the century the common use of glass, both for vessels and windows, had increased considerably.

It is difficult to say how much the technique was improved. The technique of ancient glass makers (meaning Roman ones) was already very advanced; every essential point had been mastered by them. The best mediaeval account of glass manufacture was that given by Theophile the Priest about the end of the eleventh century. I may recall that the golden age of Venetian glass did not occur until much later, in the sixteenth century.

Anton Kisa: Das Glass im Altertume (3 pts., Leipzig 1908). Robert Schmidt: Das Glass (2te vermehrte und verbesserte Auflage; Handbücher der staatlichen Museen zu Berlin, 1922). Emile Turrière: Le développement de l'industrie verrière d'art depuis l'époque vénitienne jusqu'à la fondation des verreries d'optique (Isis, 7, 77-104, 1925). E. O. v. Lippmann: Entstehung und Ausbreitung der Alchemie (vol. 2, 93-97, Berlin 1931; Isis 16).

III. COLORS AND PIGMENTS. LIMNING

PETER OF SAINT OMER

1. Petrus de Sancto Audemaro. Canon in Saint Omer, Artois (Pas-de-Calais). He composed probably in the second half of the thirteenth century a Liber de coloribus faciendis, which contains a list of substances available for painting, with recipes for the preparation of various pigments and their use. Oil painting is mentioned; it was made with linseed oil mixed with some sort of resin, called vernix or glassa. See my note on Theophile the Priest (first half of the twelfth century).

2. One Peter of Saint Omer was a doctor in theology in Paris, 1288; in 1296 he was chancellor of Notre Dame, and librarian of the Church and University; he was still living in 1308.

3. One Peter of Saint Omer composed (c. 1309?) a Latin elaboration of the Hebrew treatise on the quadrant by Jacob ben Maḥir ibn Tibbon (second half of the thirteenth century). In the fourteenth century this elaboration was retranslated into Hebrew.

It is impossible to say whether these three Peters are identical or not; their identity is not unplausible, but it is unproved. For a fourth Peter of Saint Omer, see my note on Peter of Dacia.

E. Renan: Histoire littéraire de la France (vol. 27, 615, 1877). Paul Meyer (ibidem, vol. 32, 574, 1898).

Charles Dalbon: Les origines de la peinture à l'huile (19, 77, Paris 1904).

D. W. Singer: Catalogue of Latin and vernacular MSS. in Great Britain (Brussels 1930; Isis, 12, 168-169; 15, 299). Section XVII, Pigments (p. 589-621), will refer the reader to many treatises de coloribus, de distemperandis coloribus ad scribendum vel illuminandum, ad faciendum incaustum, ad delendum litteram insensibiliter de pergameno, de tincturis pannorum, ad litteras aureas vel argenteas scribendas, etc. However the MSS. anterior to the fourteenth century are but few in number.

ABRAHAM IBN ḤAYYIM

Abraham ben Judah Ibn Ḥayyim. Spanish or Portuguese Jew who copied and limned manuscripts c. 1262. He wrote (1) a little treatise on the calendar ('ibbur, meaning intercalation); (2) another, in the Portuguese language (?) on the composition and use of colors for the illustration of MSS.; (3) still another on the means of adorning Hebrew characters.

The second of these treatises was finished at Loulé, Portugal, in 1262, but the MS. in which this statement occurs (Bib. Palatina, Parma) seems to be a later elaboration. This MS. is in Portuguese, written in Hebrew cursive. Was the original possibly in Hebrew? The Parma text is divided into 45 chapters; it deals with such subjects as how to make gold paint, blue color, rose color (e.g., with brazil wood!), red lead, verdigris, carmine, vermilion; how to color bones, boxwood; how to make chess men; how to make glue, varnish, etc.

If the author is identical with Abraham ben Ḥayyim, rabbi of Narbonne, he flourished in that city until c. 1240 when he moved to Villafranca (Villefranche-de-Confluent, Roussillon). This identification, suggested by Steinschneider, is uncertain. There were probably many Jews called Abraham ibn Ḥayyim, both names being common. (The word ḥayyim, meaning life, is found in a great many Jewish names; there are many variants either of the original word or of translations of it: Hyam, Hayem, Heine, Hain, Hagin, Agim, Vita, Vida, Anvidal, Vives, Zoë).

Text—David S. Blondheim: An old Portuguese work on a manuscript illustration (Jewish quarterly review, vol. 19, 97–135, 1928; vol. 20, 89, 1929; Isis, 12, 358). Text in Hebrew script with English translation.

Criticism—Max Seligsohn: Jewish encyclopaedia (vol. 6, 272, 1904). Carlo Bernheimer: Paleografia ebraica (333–336, Florence 1924). Rachel Wischnitzer-Bernstein and H. Brody: Encyclopaedia judaica (vol. 1, 426, 492, 1928). David S. Blondheim: Additional note (Jewish quarterly review, vol. 20, 283–284, 1930). The century in the date 1262 rests purely upon conjecture; the opuscule was almost certainly composed in Loulé; it is probable that Abraham ibn Ḥayyim wrote it not later than 1462.

IV. STRONG AND MEDICINAL WATERS

See my notes on Peter of Spain, Theodoric Borgognoni, Albert the Great, Arnold of Villanova, Ramon Lull, Marc the Greek.

V. ALCHEMICAL THEORY AND PRACTICE

PETROS THEOCTONICOS

Πέτρος ὁ Θεοκτόνικος Unknown translator from Latin into Greek who flourished at some unknown time in the thirteenth or fourteenth century? He translated into Greek an alchemical treatise, Semita recta, ascribed to Albert the Great (I place him here, in order that students of Albert's writings may easily refer to this Greek translation). It is included in a great chemical Greek MS. (Bibliothèque nationale, Paris, 2419, fol. 279 to 288) copied by Georgios Midiates (Γεώργιος ὁ Μειδιάτης) c. 1462. It begins: Ἀρχὴ τῆς εὐθείας ὁδοῦ τοῦ μεγάλου διδασκάλου κύρου πέτρου τοῦ Θεοκτονίκου πρὸς τὴν τέχνην τῆς ἀρχημίας. (The right road to alchemy by the great master Petros Theoctonicos); and ends: ἕως ὧδε ἐτελειώθη ἡ ὁδὸς ἡ καθαρὰ τοῦ ἀδελφοῦ Ἀμπέρτου τοῦ Θεοκτόνικου τοῦ μεγάλου φιλοσόφου τῆς ἀρκιμίας (Here ends the clean road of the brother Ampertos Theoctonicos, the great philosopher of alchemy). The last name Ampertos Theoctonicos might be a corruption of Albertus Teutonicus?

The Greek text is essentially the same as the Latin one. Among the few variations may be quoted a list of authorities (given in Greek, not in Latin): Hermes, Ibn Sīnā, al-Rāzī, Plato, Jābir, Aristotle, etc. The Latin text states that alchemy was invented by one Alchimus, from whom it derived its Greek name.

The contents of both texts may be summarized as follows: There are no essential differences between metals, only accidental ones. They must be reduced to their primary substance. Description of furnaces and of the four volatile spirits: mercury, sulphur, arsenic, ammoniac salt. Various salts: tartar, verdigris, cinnabar, ceruse, minium. Description of various operations: sublimation, calcination, coagulation, fixation of a volatile substance, solution, etc.

Text—The Latin text is printed in vol. 21 of the works of Albert the Great, and in vol. 2 of the Theatrum chemicum.

Criticism—M. Berthelot: Collection des anciens alchimistes grecs (vol. 1, 207–209, 1887). Henri Lebègue: Catalogue des manuscrits alchimiques grecs (vol. 1, Parisini; 65, Bruxelles 1924; Isis, 7, 507).

See my notes on Vincent of Beauvais, Albert the Great, Bacon, Villanova, Lull.

THE LATIN TREATISES ASCRIBED TO GEBER

A number of Latin treatises are ascribed to one unknown Geber: (1) Summa perfectionis; (2) Liber de investigatione perfectionis; (3) Liber de inventione veritatis sive perfectionis; (4) Liber fornacum, (5) Testamentum Geberis. The first is by far the longest and most important. We may consider it the main chemical textbook of mediaeval Christendom. The earliest MS. (Staatsbibliothek Munich, Cod. lab. 353) dates from the end of the thirteenth century, and as the Summa perfectionis is mentioned neither by Albert the Great nor by Bacon, we may assume that the text was not much anterior to the MS. There is another MS. of about the same time in Florence (Cod. Riccardianus, 933). The treatises nos. 2 to 4 are referred to in the Summa.

Before discussing its authorship, let us give a brief analysis of the Summa. It is divided into two books, subdivided respectively into four and three parts, which we shall number consecutively from *a* to *g*. (a) bodily and mental impediments to chemical practice, qualities required; (b) arguments against alchemy (i.e., belief in the possibility of transmutation of metals, etc.) and their refutation; (c) natural principles of metallic bodies. Metals are made of sulphur and mercury. There are six metals: gold, silver, lead, tin, copper, iron. Definition and qualities of each; (d) methods, such as sublimation, descension, distillation, calcination, solution, coagulation, fixation, ceration (softening to the consistency of wax); (e) nature of the different substances; (f) preparation of each toward its transmutation by means of medicines or elixirs. Medicines are of three orders of efficacy, the third order being the most efficacious; (g) methods of analysis to ascertain whether transmutation has succeeded or not: cupellation (cineritium), cement, ignition, fusion, exposition over vapors, extinction, admixtion of burning sulphur, calcination and reduction.

The Sum of perfection or the Perfect magistery was an elaborate treatise on the art, at once theoretical and practical. In fact it was the most elaborate in Latin, but it was not more elaborate than various Arabic treatises. Its Arabic origin is incontrovertible. One finds many identical statements, for example, in treatises by al-Rāzī (second half of the ninth century); same purposes, same principles, same methods, same instruments. The Latin text is perhaps a little more concrete, and the descriptions more complete and more accurate, but this may easily be disputed. Were the Summa and the other Latin treatises translations from the Arabic or elaborations of such translations? It is difficult to say and it does not matter much. Was Geber, as the name would imply, the Persian alchemist Jābir ibn Ḥaiyān? That is, are these Latin treatises translations of the Arabic ones written in the second half of the eighth century by that Jābir? Probably not.

The sulphur theory of metals above mentioned (Summa perfectionis, part c) is also explicitly found in the Kitab al-īḍāḥ (Book of elucidation) ascribed to Jābir; see Holmyard's edition (p. 54, Paris 1928). However, according to E. O v. Lippmann that theory can be traced back to Hellenistic times (Isis, 11, 166).

To solve the many problems involved we must wait until all the Arabic and Persian treatises ascribed to Jābir, al-Rāzī, al-Kāthī, and others have been carefully edited. Julius Ruska of Berlin, Eric John Holmyard of Bristol, and Henry Ernest Stapleton of Calcutta, together with their assistants, are deeply engaged in these investigations. A recent discovery by Ruska's assistant, Paul Kraus, has still further increased the complexity of the question. According to that discovery all of the Arabic Jābir literature is apocryphal, and was forged in the first half of the tenth century under the stimulation of Qarmaṭian propaganda.[3]

To return to the Latin treatises ascribed to Geber, whether they be translations or elaborations, they represent the amount of Arabic chemical knowledge made available to Latin reading people toward the end of the thirteenth century; or, to put it otherwise, they represent the best Latin knowledge on chemistry in that period. However the influence of that Geberian knowledge was hardly felt before the following century.

Thus far I have spoken only of the Summa perfectionis, by far the largest of these works. Let us say a few words of the others.

2. Liber de investigatione perfectionis. Earliest MS. in Florence (Cod. Riccardianus, 933; thirteenth century). Other MS., Bodleian West. MS. 19039, containing other writings dated 1466. This treatise includes the earliest description of the preparation of nitric acid and aqua regia.

3. Liber de inventione veritatis sive perfectionis.

4. Liber fornacum. Nos. 3 and 4 are unknown in MS.; they are known only through the printed editions.

5. Testamentum. Sixteenth century MS. in Cambridge, Trinity College, no. 1380, 25.

Text—The earliest printed book bearing Geber's name is the Liber qui flos naturarum vocatur (s. l, 1473). This has nothing to do with the chemical Geberian literature; it is a popular treatise on organotherapy. Ernst Darmstaedter: Die Geber-Inkunabel Hain 7504 (Archiv für Geschichte der Medizin, vol. 16, 214–217, 1925).

The earliest printed edition of one of the alchemical treatises appeared c. 1481, probably in Rome (printer of Vitruvius). It contains the Summa together with the Liber trium verborum ascribed to Khālid ibn Yazīd, the Epistola Alexandri imperatoris, the Liber investigationis magisterii, etc. Other editions: Rome c. 1510–1520; Strassburg 1529, 1531; Nuremberg 1541; Venice 1542; Bern 1545; Leiden 1668; Danzig 1682; etc. Many of these editions contain woodcuts representing chemical operations. Six plates of the Nuremberg edition of 1541 have been reproduced by Darmstaedter (1922).

[3] About which see vol. 1, 593, 660.

German translation: Strassburg 1529 or 1530, again 1625; Francfort 1710, Vienna 1751, 1753.

French translations: 1672, 1678, 1741.

English translation by Richard Russell (London 1678; again 1686). Another translation of the Summa by William Salmon: Medicina practica (London 1692). Russell's translation was reedited by E. J. Holmyard: The works of Geber (304 p., London 1928; Isis, 13, 150).

Ernst Darmstaedter: Die Alchemie des Geber; übersetzt und erklärt (212 p., Berlin 1922). Critical German translation with abundant notes and alchemical glossary (Isis, 5, 451–455). The same author has edited the Liber misericordiae Geber after the Riccardianus 933, Florence, end of the thirteenth century (Archiv für Geschichte der Medizin, vol. 17, 181–197, 1925; Isis, 8, 737). This is an actual translation of the Kitāb al-raḥma ascribed to Jābir. He also edited the Liber claritatis totius alkimicae artis, also ascribed to Geber, after a Bologna MS. (cod. lat. 164 = 153 of the fourteenth century) in the Archivio di storia della scienza (vol. 6, 319–330, 1925; vol. 7, 257–266, 1926; vol. 8, 95–103, 214–226, 1927; Isis, 9, 153; 10, 130).

Criticism—The Geber and Jābir questions being closely related, see my note on Jābir ibn Ḥaiyān (vol. 1, 532–533), and various additions to it published in the critical bibliographies of Isis (nineteenth and following, vol. 8, etc.). I shall mention only Eric John Holmyard: The Arabic works of Jābir ibn Ḥayyān (vol. 1, part 1 of Arabic text, 186 p., Paris 1928; Isis, 13, 150). Günther Bugge: Das Buch der grossen Chemiker (Berlin 1929; Isis, 15, 298). This volume contains articles on Jābir and pseudo-Geber by Julius Ruska (18–31, 60–69). J. Ruska: Die bisherigen Versuche das Dschābirproblem zu lösen (Dritter Jahresbericht des Forschungs-Institut für Geschichte der Naturwissenschaften in Berlin, 9–22, 1930; Isis, 15, 399). Paul Kraus: Dschābir ibn Ḥajjān und die Isma'īlijjia (ibidem, 23–42, 1930; Isis, 15, 399); Studien zu Jābir ibn Ḥayyān.1.Das Wissenschaftsgebäude der Jābirschriften, 2.Die Jābir-Legende (Isis, 15, 7–30, 1931). E. O. v. Lippmann: Entstehung und Ausbreitung der Alchemie (vol. 2, 71–76, 89–92, 1931; Isis, 16).

ABŪ-L-QĀSIM AL-'IRĀQĪ

Abū-l-Qāsim Muḥammad ibn Aḥmad al-Sīmawī al-'Irāqī. Muslim alchemist who flourished in the second half of the thirteenth century. He made experiments and wrote a number of treatises on alchemy. The earliest and most important is the

1. Kitāb al-'ilm al-muktasab fī zirā'at al-dhahab (Knowledge acquired concerning the cultivation of gold). It contains a clear account of what we might call the more radical alchemical doctrine, as opposed, e.g., to the more moderate views of Ibn Sīnā. The central theory of kīmīyā is that concerning the six metals (tin, lead, iron, copper, silver, gold) and their transmutation. The differences between these metals are purely accidental. They form an ascending scale leading to the pure metallic substance, gold. Tin and lead are preparatory steps to silver; as compared with gold, copper and iron contain too much heat, tin and lead too much cold; etc. This suggests a method of procedure: the metals are treated with elixirs (al-iksīr, essence, philosopher's stone), which remove the accidental differences. The theoretical part is very logical; the practical directions, as usual, are sadly deficient. The Zirā'at al-dhahab ends with a mass of quotations from earlier authors, most of them Greek, corroborating the author's views. Many (8) of Abū-l-Qāsim's quotations can be identified word for word with passages of the

Compositio alchemiae (1144) of Robert of Chester, purporting to be a translation of a treatise by Khālid ibn Yazīd. An extensive commentary on the Zirā'at al-dhahab was composed by 'Alī ibn Aidamur al-Jildakī (d. 1342–1343), who did not name the author, under the title Nihāyat al-ṭalab (End of the search).

The other works may be dealt with more briefly.

2. Zubdat al-ṭalab fī zar' al-dhahab (Cream of the search upon the sowing of gold).

3. Commentary on the dīwān of alchemical poems Shudhūr al-dhahab (Particles of gold) composed by Ibn Arfa' ra'sahu (d. 1196–1197). It is not certain that this commentary was completed.

4. 'Arf al-abīr fī 'ilm al-iksīr (Perfume of saffron upon the knowledge of the elixir). Discussing al-Rāzī's allusions to the elixir.

5. Kitāb al-durar al-makhtūm bi-l-ṣūr (Pearls sealed with figures). On the elixir.

The books 2 to 5 seem lost.

6. Kitāb al-aqālīm al-sab'a fī-l-'ilm al-mausūm bil-ṣan'a (The seven climes on the science called art [of alchemy]). Deals with the social aspect of alchemy, the obligation of secrecy, with references to Jābir ibn Ḥaiyān's "practical" attitude on the subject (i.e., the giving of instructions, which are apparently simple and clear, yet cannot be understood except by those who are fully initiated!)

7. 'Uyūn al-ḥaqā'iq wa īḍāḥ al-ṭarā'iq (Sources of the truths and explanation of the ways). Composed between 1260 and 1277 upon the basis of work carried out between 1250 and 1257. Deals with magic. Divided into 30 chapters, of which the 24th is devoted to simples and the 27th to the magical properties of metals.

8. Kitāb al-kanz al-afkhar wal-sirr al-a'ẓam fī taṣrīf al-ḥajar al-mukarram (The most glorious treasure and greatest secret concerning the transmutation of the noble stones). Alchemical parable derived from the sayings of the ṣūfī Ibn 'Arabī (d. 1240). It includes a series of "Decknamen" (secret names) and signs for the seven metals (i.e., those mentioned above plus mercury), the iksīr, sulphur, arsenic, copper oxide, vitriols, etc., also names of apparatus, with drawings representing them.

9. Kitāb al-najāt wal-ittiṣāl bi 'ain al-ḥayāt (Salvation and conjunction with the source of life); etc.

Text—The 'Ilm al-muktasab was edited and Englished by E. J. Holmyard (115 p., Paris 1923; Isis, 7, 124–128).

Lithographic edition of the 'Uyūn al-haqā'iq. Without place or date (Bombay? end of nineteenth century?).

Criticism—Ḥājī Khalīfa (vol. 5, 9879; vol. 6, 13599). C. Brockelmann: Arabische Litteratur (vol. 1, 496, 1898). J. Ruska and E. Wiedemann: Alchemistische Decknamen (Beiträge, 67, Sitzungsber., 56, 17–36, Erlangen 1926). E. J. Holmyard: Abū l-Qāsim al-'Irāqī (Isis, 8, 403–426, 1926; important). J. Ruska: Zu E. J. Holmyard's Ausgabe des Kitāb al-'ilm al-muktasab (Islam, vol. 15, 103–105, 1926).

See notes on Nicholas Blemmydes, 'Abhd-īshō' bar Bĕrīkha, Ibn Kammūna.

CHAPTER L

GEOGRAPHY

(Second Half of Thirteenth Century)

I. LATIN CHRISTIANS

PORTOLANI

One calls portolani (sing., portolano) the books containing sailing directions for navigators, descriptions of harbors, safe itineraries, etc., and generally illustrated with charts. As these charts were or became the essential features of these sailing books, the name portolani is generally restricted to them. This note refers mainly to the charts.

The earliest portolano (chart) extant, the undated Carte pisane, dates from the end of the thirteenth century, and is apparently a copy of older ones. At any rate the relative perfection of the early portolani implies the existence of many previous ones. One would think that the earliest portolani date back at least to the eleventh century. There is a fragment of the text of one in Adam of Bremen (d. c. 1076). The origin of portolani is not yet known and one wonders whether it is knowable. It may be multiple. As maritime commerce developed, the need of reliable sailing directions increased and became acute. The making of portolani was such an obvious means of satisfying these needs that it would not be surprising if it had begun in more than one country. Our reference to Adam of Bremen suggests the possibility of a Scandinavian origin. On the other hand a Byzantine origin is very plausible. According to Nordenskiöld (Periplus, 1897) the prototype was probably Catalan, because the unit of length used on all portolani seems to be the Catalan legua. But the adoption of this legua or portolan mile might be posterior to the invention of the chart itself, and its frequent occurrence would point to the supremacy of Catalan mapmasters rather than to their initiative. The language of these early maps is Latin, Catalan, Italian, or a sort of Mediterranean lingua franca composed of various Romance elements.

It is certain that a great many early maps were made by Italians, Pisans and Genoese (chiefly the latter). An interesting theory has been defended by Charles de la Roncière, according to which the "normal portolano" was probably established by sailors in the service of Benedetto Zaccaria, a famous Genoese admiral in the Byzantine service, brother-in-law of Michael VIII Palaeologos (emperor from 1261 to 1282). This is a sort of combination of the Italian and Byzantine origins.

The notion of "normal portolano" instead of "first portolano" is very good, for it allows for the existence of many local charts anterior to the first cartographical synthesis of this type. It is well also to bear in mind that many portolani were in all probability private and secret documents which their owners had no wish to divulge.

Whatever their origin, these portolani which had reached by the end of the thirteenth century a high degree of perfection, might be called the first true maps. To quote Beazley (op. cit. 3, 512), "Nothing in the history of geography is more significant; at no point perhaps is there a more impressive advance in human knowledge than when we pass from the highest designs of the pre-portolan type—designs on the whole quite abreast of Ptolemy's—to that Carte pisane with which opens the great series of the mediaeval peripli."

And yet that Carte pisane (Bibliothèque nationale, Paris) was decidedly inferior to the portolani which appeared soon afterwards; e.g., that of Giovanni da Carignano (c. 1320) and others to be dealt with in vol. 3. It was so called (by Jomard) because it was believed that it belonged to a Pisan family. It shows the Mediterranean coasts; the ocean coast of Europe up to Holland; England (very badly); the Crimean peninsula (much exaggerated), and a small part of the coasts of the Black sea. The earliest dated portolano, that of Pietro Vesconte, appeared in 1311.

Here is an indirect proof of the existence of portolani anterior to the earliest extant. In 1270 St. Louis sailed from Aiguesmortes to Tunis on a Genoese ship. After six days navigation, as the coasts of Sardinia were not yet visible the king became anxious, but the officers showed him his position on a map, and declared that they were nearing Cagliari. This is the earliest reference to the use of a map aboard ship (after the Gesta Ludovici IX by William of Nangis, a contemporary account). Another reference is found in the Arbor scientiae of Ramon Lull (1295–1296). How do mariners find their way across the sea? Says Lull, "ad hoc instrumentum habent chartam, compassum, acum, et stellam maris." This establishes the use of the compass and of a chart. The chronicle of England of Roger of Howden also suggests the availability of some kind of portolani or sailing directions.

The great merit of the early portolani was due to their experimental origin and to the fact that they were made, not to illustrate fanciful conceits, but to satisfy practical and urgent needs. They were essentially based upon the experience of sailors using log and compass, that is, on the direct determination of distances and azimuths.[1] Hence they are often called "compass-charts" to distinguish them on the one hand from the more learned and theoretical works based on Ptolemaic tradition and on a few astronomical determinations, on the other hand from the monastic maps largely inspired by Biblical and patristic conceptions. They are on the whole remarkably accurate but as they were made for sailors they were naturally restricted to the coast lines and to the towns and natural features in the immediate neighborhood of the coasts. They contain no indications of longitudes and latitudes but instead networks of loxodromes or rhumb-lines proceeding from a number of crossing points regularly distributed over the map. While most features of the portolani are copied from chart to chart often in the most slavish way (e.g., conventional shapes of some islands, symbols, use of colors), it is remarkable that these networks are different in almost every specimen.

The wind rose which became (and has remained) a striking feature of every compass, is of course considerably earlier than the magnetic needle. The concept of eight symmetrical winds can be traced back to the Horologion or Tower of winds, built at Athens by Andronicos Cyrrhestes[1a] in the first century B. C. These eight

[1] The earliest portolani may have been made without a compass, the azimuths being determined by observations of the sun, moon and stars.

[1a] Andronicos of Cyrrhus (or Cyrus) in Syria. For the Horologion, see Walther Judeich: Topographie von Athen (333, München 1905).

winds appear in many early portolani, each being designated by the initial of its name; Tramontano, Greco, Levante, Scirocco, Ostro, Africo (Libeccio), Ponente, Maestro. But the Eastern wind (Levante) was often represented by a cross, and the northern (Tramontano) by a spear head out of which developed later the traditional fleur-de-lis. In the course of time the points or rhumbs of the wind rose increased in number from 8 to 16, 24, and finally 32. The Carte pisane had 16 winds, but the portolano of Giovanni da Carignano has already 32. The 32 rhumbs are clearly mentioned by Chaucer: "Now thy horizon is divided into 24 parts by the azimuths, in signification of the 24 parts of the world (albeit shipmen reckon with 32 parts)" (Treatise on the astrolabe, ed. by R. T. Gunther, 90, 1929).

I have spoken only of western portolani because these are far better known, but there were also Eastern (Muslim) portolani, and it is as yet impossible to say which were the first. As I have already remarked, I believe that the need of charts was so widespread and so urgent, and the idea of making them so obvious, that I do not understand why it should be necessary to postulate a single instead of a multiple origin. For example, Muslim sailors had been navigating across the eastern seas, all the way to the China coast and the East Indies, from the ninth century on; they had charts; Marco Polo refers to them (see Yule's editions by index); is it not conceivable that some of these charts were made, after centuries of experience, before the portolani devoted to the Mediterranean and Atlantic coasts?

However, there are but very few Arabic or Muslim portolani as compared with the western ones. The earliest extant is the so-called Maugrabin chart of the Ambrogiana in Milano. It has only sixteen rhumbs. It is probably of the fourteenth century, probably of the beginning, posterior to the Carte pisane. Its scale is decimal, but the same feature characterizes the chart of Giovanni da Carignano. A part of it is reproduced by Charles de la Roncière (pl. 4, 1925). Most of the Arabic maps that have come down to us—e.g., the Idrīsī maps—are of an entirely different type, sui generis, the work of theoretical cartographers rather than of mapmakers trying to meet the practical demands of sailors (Isis, 9, 458–462).

The following fact is an indirect evidence of the existence of Muslim charts. The Īl-khān of Persia, Arghūn, had sent a political agent to Europe in 1289 to obtain allies against the Muslims. This agent was the Genoese Buscarello de' Ghizolfi, and the original letter of Arghūn to Philip le Bel (a roll 6½ feet long written in Mongolian, Uighūr script) is still preserved in the Archives nationales, Paris. While Buscarello was proceeding on his journey, Quṭb al-dīn al-Shīrāzī was able to show his movements on a map to the Īl-Khān. See also my note on Sahl ibn Abān and other "Lions" of the sea in chapter VIII.

Bibliography—(vol. 1, 767). Carlo Errera: Atlanti e carte nautiche dal secolo XIV al XVII conservate nelle bibliotheche di Milano (Rivista geografica italiana (vol. 3, 90, etc., 1896). A. E. Nordenskiöld: Periplus: An essay on the early history of charts and sailing instructions (folio, 218 p., 60 large maps on pl. and 100 smaller ones in the text; Stockholm 1897). Edgar Blochet: Contribution à l'étude de la cartographie chez les Musulmans (Bulletin de l'Académie d'Hippone; reprint, Paris 1899). C. R. Beazley: Dawn of modern geography (vol. 3, chiefly p. 512–528, 1906). Brief examination of the early portolani, c. 1300 to 1420, considered under about eleven groups or isolated examples; though excellent when made it is now a little out of date. Konrad Kretschmer: Die italienischen Portolane des Mittelalters (Veröff. des Instituts für Meereskunde, Berlin, 13, 796 p., Berlin 1909).

A very elaborate study, a review of which by Carlo Errera will be found in the Rivista geografica italiana (anno 18, 25 p., 1911). Charles de la Roncière: La découverte de l'Afrique au Moyen âge (vol. 1, 37-44, 53-55, Cairo 1925).

MONASTIC MAPS

While the portolani symbolized geographical progress, they can hardly be considered as representing the geographical thought of the age. The portolani were made by practical men for seafaring people; they remained largely unknown to the landsmen. These are naturally in overwhelming majority, and it is upon them that the task of promoting and keeping knowledge is primarily devolved. The main sources of geographical knowledge in western Christendom—e.g, in the monasteries where learning was best appreciated—were still Pliny, the Antonine itinerary, Solinus, Orosius, Martianus Capella, Aethicus, etc., not to speak of the Alexander romance, the bestiaries and the herbals. The news of geographical discoveries filtered very slowly.

As we are primarily interested in scientific progress, that is, in the efforts of an exceedingly small élite, not in the stagnation of the learned nor in the regression of the mass, I shall make no attempt to give a complete account of the average geographical knowledge of the time, but a good idea of it will be obtained by the consideration of three typical maps.

Though very different in their details, these maps are based upon the same general conception. The universe has the form of a circle or wheel, of which Jerusalem is the hub, and the ocean the rim.

1. *The Psalter map*—This map dating from the middle of the thirteenth century is so called because it is included in a MS. of the Book of Psalms (British Museum, Add. 6806). It is of circular shape, diameter 8.5 cm., but in spite of its small size it contains no less than 145 inscriptions. It represents a semi-mythical debased kind of geography. The winds have classical names: Aquilo and Septentrio for N, Zephyrus for W, Auster or Nothus for S, Eurus or Euro-Nothus for the E and SE; but Vulturnus is placed in NNE instead of SE (compare with the Italian wind-names of the portolani).

Anton Springer: Die Psalter Imitationen (Leipzig 1880). C. R. Beazley: Dawn of modern geography (vol. 2, 568, with facsimile, 617-621, 1901).

2. *The Hereford map*—This map, painted on parchment, is much larger. It is kept in the cathedral of Hereford (in Herefordshire on the Welsh border). Its size is 162 by 132 cm., the diameter of the circle is 132 mm. It is ascribed to one "Richard de Haldingham e de Lafford" (Richard de Bello?) who appears as treasurer of Lincoln cathedral c. 1270-1276, and as prebendary of Hereford in 1305, and was still living in 1312. The Hereford map was probably painted c. 1276-1283. It bears the inscription "Descriptio Orosii de ormesta mundi." It contains a great many data, some geographical, some others fantastic.

A full size facsimile copy was edited by Francis Tebbs Havergal (London 1869). Vicomte de Santarem: Essai sur l'histoire de la cosmographie et de la cartographie pendant le Moyen âge (vol. 2, 288-434, 1850). D'Avezac: Note sur la mappemonde historiée de la cathédrale de Hereford, détermination de sa date et de ses sources (Paris 1862; would place it as late as 1314). W. L. Bevan and H. W. Phillott: Mediaeval geography, an essay in illustration of the Hereford mappa mundi (230 p., London 1873–1874). R. D. Benedict: The Hereford map and the legend of St. Brandan (Bull. American geographical soc., vol. 24, 321–365, 1892). Konrad Miller: Die Herefordkarte (Die ältesten Weltkarte, 4, 54 p., facsmile 3/7 of original size; Stuttgart 1896). C. R. Beazley: Dawn of modern geography (vol. 3, 528, 1906).

3. *The Ebstorf map*—This map is larger still, almost six times larger than the Hereford map, its dimensions being 358 cm. by 356 cm. It was made also on parchment and was kept in the Benedictine monastery of Ebstorf between Hanover and Lüneburg until 1833 when it was discovered and moved to Hanover (first described in the Vaterländisches Archiv, 1834). It is now preserved in the museum of the historical society of Lower Saxony in Hanover. It was made in that region, probably in Lüneburg, c. 1270–1284.

Full size facsimile by Ernst Sommerbrodt, Die Ebstorfer Weltkarte (100 p., quarto, 25 pl. folio, Hannover 1891). Konrad Miller: Die Ebstorfkarte (Die ältesten Weltkarten, 5, 79 p., Stuttgart, 1896; reduced facsimile). C. R. Beazley: Dawn of modern geography (vol. 3, 528, 1906).

For mappae mundi in general, see Michael C. Andrews: The study and classification of medieval mappae mundi (Archaeologia, vol. 75, 61–76, 2 pl., 1926; Isis, 14, 515).

See notes on Matthew Paris, Bacon, and Albert the Great.

CHRISTIAN PILGRIMS

The most important pilgrim of this age was Burchard of Mount Sion, who will be dealt with presently; but a few anonymous itineraries and descriptions will help the reader to complete his vision of the Holy Land as it appeared to Christian eyes in the second half of the thirteenth century.

About 1261. "Rothelin"—One of the continuations of the Historia hierosolymitana of William of Tyre (d. c. 1186), the so-called continuation Rothelin, covering the period 1229 to 1261, contains a valuable description of the Holy Land.

Often published. Recueil des historiens des croisades (Lois, vol. 2, 107–115, 1843). Etc. Melchior de Vogüé: Les églises de la Terre sainte (436–451, Paris 1860). Paulin Paris: Guillaume de Tyr et ses continuateurs (vol. 2, 475–496, Paris 1880). H. Michelant and G. Raynaud: Itinéraires français (Publications de la Société de l'Orient latin, 179–199, Geneva 1882).

R. Röhricht: Bibliotheca geographica Palaestinae (53, 1890). A. Molinier: Sources de l'histoire de France (vol. 3, 122, 1903).

English translation in James T. Barclay: The city of the great king (368–377, Philadelphia 1857).

About 1265–1268. Chemins et pèlerinages de la Terre sainte—A guide book composed c. 1265–1268. There are two versions of it, one written by a Provençal, the other by an Englishman.

Both edited by H. Michelant and G. Raynaud: Itinéraires (179–199, 1882). R. Röhricht (54, 1890).

1270–1273. Mauritius—Norwegian (?) Franciscan, who traveled to the Holy Land in 1270–1273, and wrote a brief account of his journey.

Itinerarium in terram sanctam auctore Fratre Mauritio, edited by Gustav Storm: Monumenta historica Norvegiae (165–168, Kristiania 1880).

Storm (p. xxxvii-ix). P. Riant: Expéditions et pèlerinages des Scandinaves en Terre sainte (72, 357, 412, 1865). R. Röhricht (55, 1890).

About 1280. Pèlerinages et pardouns de Acre.
About 1289–1291. La devise des chemins de Babiloine.
About 1290. Les casaus de Sur.

These three were also edited by Michelant and Raynaud. See Röhricht (55, 61 1890).

Finally there are a number of anonymous itineraries and descriptions dating from the thirteenth century but to which no particular year can be assigned. Some twenty-five are in Latin, four in French, one in German.

BURCHARD OF MOUNT SION

Burchardus de Monte Sion. German Dominican who traveled to the Holy Land c. 1273 and remained there about ten years, then returned to Europe. He settled probably at or near Magdeburg and wrote there an account of his experiences, Descriptio Terrae Sanctae, which is one of the best mediaeval descriptions of the Holy Land. It is elaborate and relatively critical. His description of the Near East is centered upon Acre, the country around that city being divided into four principal quarters, corresponding to the four cardinal points, and then subdivided into twelve smaller parts, corresponding to the twelve winds. The measurements of distances are particularly good. The accounts of Acre and Jerusalem contain much information which is new and accurate. In his judgment of Eastern Christians (Jacobites, Armenians, Georgians, Nestorians), the author showed remarkable toleration and charity; but the inhabitants of the Holy Land, and above all the Latin Christians who were settled there, he considered beyond contempt.

There are two versions of the Descriptio; the earlier was accompanied by a map; the second version was a revised elaboration of the former. Burchard derived some information from James of Vitry and from John of Würzburg (or from a common source), but the bulk of his description was the fruit of his own observations.

This Burchard should not be confused with two other travelers to the Near East bearing the same name: Burchard of Strassburg (fl. 1175), and Burchard (or Brocard)—another German Dominican—who went to Persia c. 1308 and wrote the Directorium ad passiagium faciendum in Terram Sanctam in 1330. The last named and Burchard of Mount Sion might be identical, but their identity is not proved and is not plausible. For further discussion see vol. 3.

Text—First edition in the Rudimentum nouiciorum . . . . per mag. Lucam Brandis de Schasz (fol. 164–188, with map, Lubeck 1475). Many later editions of various kinds: Basel 1494; first separate edition, Venice 1519; Paris 1532; Antwerp 1536; Basel 1537; Paris 1544; Wittenberg 1554; Basel 1555; Wittenberg 1579, 1587; Magdeburg 1587, 1593; Ingolstadt 1604; Amsterdam 1703, 1704, 1707; Leuwarden 1717; Paris 1719; Venice 1722, 1746.

J. C. M. Laurent: Peregrinatores medii aevi quattuor (Leipzig 1864, again 1873). Critical edition with valuable notes. New edition by W. A. Neumann (Geneva 1880).

Burchard's Descriptio was translated into French in 1458 by Jean Mielot of Gaissart, canon in Lille. Another French version is included in La mer des hystoires (Paris 1488, 1516, 1536).

German translation by Michel Herr: Fleyssige Beschreybung der Örter im heyligen Land gelegen durch Bruder Burcarden eyn Munch beschrieben. Included in Die neue Welt der Landschaften und Inseln (Strassburg 1534; Nuremberg 1583; etc). Other German editions in Reysbuch (1584, 1609), and in J. H. Jäck: Taschenbibliothek der wichtigsten See- und Landreisen (Nuremberg 1827).

Dutch version in Kanaan en d'omliggende landen vertoont in een woordenboek (Leeuwarden 1717).

English translation by Aubrey Stewart, with geographical notes by C. R. Conder (Palestine Pilgrims' Text Society, 30, London 1896).

Criticism—V. Leclerc: Histoire littéraire de la France (vol. 21, 180–215, 838, 1847). R. Röhricht: Bibliotheca geographica Palaestinae (56–60, 1890). Potthast (177, 1896). C. R. Beazley: Dawn of modern geography (vol. 3, 382–390, 1906).

RUBRUQUIS

Guilielmus de Rubruquis. William of Rubruquis, Willem van Ruysbroeck (Rubruck, Rusbouck, etc.). Flemish Franciscan and traveler to the East c. 1253–1255. One of the greatest European travelers before Marco Polo. Born probably near St. Omer in Flanders (now Département du Nord, France).

William was sent by St. Louis to Mongolia (or Tartary) as an unofficial representative in 1253. Unofficial, because the king had sent before (1248–1251) an official mission led by friar Andrew of Longjumeau and had been offended by the impertinent reply of the Mongolian queen (Joinville). William left Constantinople in May 1253, sailed to the Crimea, crossed South Russia and a large part of Asia, finally reaching the Mongolian capital Qaraqorum in April 1254 (the difference in longitude between Constantinople and Qaraqorum is more than 73°). He left Qaraqorum in August and reached Tripoli, Syria, a year later. The narrative of his immense journey is a document of very great importance for the students of geography, ethnography, religion and language; it is one of the best narratives of its kind in existence.

He was the first to describe the Caspian as an inland sea, to indicate the sources and course of the Don and the Volga, the identity of Cathay and Seres, the true position of the Balkhash Lake and of the Central Asian depression of which this lake is the eastern limit. He gave good descriptions of Qaraqorum and of the Mongol court, of the Nestorians of China, of Lamaism and of Uighūr customs, and was the first European to mention Korea and some of the North Asiatic tribes. He was the first European also to mention the wild ass (kūlan) of Central Asia, the great sheep of the Pamirs (argali, ovis argali, ovis poli), the use of the halsband for sparrow-hawks, etc. He gave a good account of the Crimean Goths, and distinguished between Tartars and Mongols. He was very interested in languages, knew Arabic, learned Mongolian, and was able to recognize the affinities of languages and dialects (e.g., of the Slavonic languages); he described Chinese, Tangut, Uighūr and Tibetan writings.

Rubruquis' relation is far more elaborate than Carpini's, but it is less orderly and less lucid—and Carpini was the pioneer.

It was praised and used by Roger Bacon; on the other hand it was not quoted by Vincent of Beauvais, nor by the fourteenth century authors.

Text—Opere dilettevole da intendere nella qual si contiene duo itinerarj in Tartari per alcuni frati dell' ordine minore (Vinegia 1537). Parts of the text are included in Hakluyt's Principal navigations (London 1598). Pierre Bergeron: Relation des voyages en Tartarie du Fr. Guillaume de Rubruquis (Paris 1634).

The first edition of the Latin text was given in vol. 4 of the Recueil de Voyages publié par la Société de Géographie (199–396, Paris 1839). Itinerarium fratris Willelmi de Rubruk ad partes orientales. Prefatory notes by D'Avezac, Francisque Michel, Thomas Wright.

French translation by Louis de Backer (Bibl. orientale elzévirienne, 13, Paris 1877).

English translation with abundant notes by William Woodville Rockhill (Hakluyt Society, London 1900). C. Raymond Beazley: The texts and versions of Carpini and Rubruquis as printed by Hakluyt in 1598 together with some shorter pieces (Hakluyt Society, London 1903).

German translation by Hermann Herbst (227 p., map, Leipzig 1925).

Criticism—Franz Max Schmidt: Über Rubruk's Reise (Z. der Ges. für Erdkunde zu Berlin, vol. 20, 161–253, 1885). Emil Bretschneider: Medieval researches from Eastern Asiatic sources (London 1888). C. R. Beazley: Dawn of modern geography (vols. 2–3, 1901–1906). Achatius Batton (O. F. M.): Wilhelm von Rubruk (Franziskanische Studien, Beiheft 6, 90 p., Münster i. W., 1921). Joseph de Ghellinck: Les Franciscains en Chine aux XIIIe et XIVe siècles (Xaveriana, no. 42, 40 p., Louvain 1927).

BUSCARELLO DE' GHIZOLFI

Buscarello or Buscarel, Ghizolfi or Ghisolfi. Genoese diplomat in the service of Arghūn (Īl-Khān of Persia, 1284–1291). He was sent by Arghūn to the Roman curia and to the French and English courts; in 1291 Galfridus (Geoffrey) de Langele, envoy of Edward I of England, met him in Genoa; they went together to Persia by way of Trebizond where there was at that time a flourishing Genoese colony.

Cornelio Desimoni: I conti dell' ambasciata al chan di Persia nel 1292 (Atti della Società ligure di storia patria, vol. 13, 537–700, Genova 1879); Notes et observations sur les actes du notaire génois Lamberto di Sambuceto (Revue de l'orient latin, vol. 2, 1–34, 216–234, 1894). J. B. Chabot: Notes sur les relations du roi Argoun avec l'occident (Revue de l'orient latin, vol. 2, 566–640, 1894). Including the text of many diplomatic documents and a facsimile of Arghūn's letter to Philippe le Bel, dated 1289. That curious document is kept in the Archives nationales, Paris. It is a roll six and a half feet long and eleven inches high in cotton paper. It is written in Mongolian, Uighūr script, with a Chinese seal. C. R. Beazley: The dawn of modern geography (vol. 3, 475, 492, 1906). G. I. Bratianu: Recherches sur le commerce génois dans la mer Noire au treizième siècle (360 p., 5 pl., 1 map; Paris 1929).

JOHN OF MONTECORVINO

Giovanni di Montecorvino; Joannes de Monte Corvino. Italian missionary to India and to China (c. 1247–c. 1328).

Born probably at Montecorvino, district of Salerno, in 1246 or 1247; assumed the Franciscan habit; in 1272 he took part in the negotiations for the reunion of the Latin and Greek churches carried on by Michael Palaeologos and Gregory X. Sometime later he was sent as a missionary to the East and reached the court of the Īl-khān of Persia. He returned to Rome with letters from Arghūn in 1289, and was sent back as a legate, bearing letters from Nicholas IV (the first Franciscan pope, 1288–1292), dated 1289, addressed to Arghūn, Kublai Khān, Kaydū,[2] and also to the Emperor of Ethiopia and other Christian kings of the East. In Tabrīz he was joined by a trader, Peter of Lucolongo, and together they proceeded to India. They traveled by sea, sailing probably from Ormuz, then down the Malabar Coast and up the Coromandel Coast ("St. Thomas' country"). John remained about a year in the Madras region founding there the earliest Catholic mission in India (c. 1291); the Dominican Nicholas of Pistoia was there too and died during John's stay. From India, John proceeded to Cathay, also by sea; he worked there alone from 1292 to 1303–1304, when he was joined by the Franciscan Arnold of Cologne (Arnoldus Alemannus de provincia Coloniae). In 1305 he was established in Khānbaliq (Peiping), and in high favor with the Great Khān. He failed to convert the latter, but had better luck at first with the Nestorians. He converted many of them, including their prince George "of the family of Prester John of India." But after George's death (1299) the Nestorians reverted to their own faith and did their best to impede the Catholic propaganda. However John was building churches and translating the New Testament and Psalms into Mongolian; he caused six Biblical scenes to be painted, with inscriptions in Latin, Persian and Uighūr. The arrival of an impious Lombard surgeon (c. 1301) disturbed him very much. He wrote home for help, recommending that missionaries be sent by the inland route across Russia and the steppes rather than by the sea route which he had followed; along the former it would be possible to reach Khānbaliq in five or six months, while the sea journey would take two years. In 1305 he built a new church in Peiping, quite near the Khān's palace, and in spite of the Nestorian enmity made many new converts. Not very long before February 1306 he received in Khānbaliq a deputation of Ethiopians asking him to visit their country.

In 1307 Clement V (pope from 1305 to 1314) created the archbishopric of Khānbaliq, appointed John the first archbishop, and nominated seven suffragan bishops. Of these seven, only three reached Cathay (in 1308): Andrew of Perugia, Gerard, and Peregrine; three more suffragans were nominated in 1311, of whom at least one, Peter of Florence, reached Cathay. Another bishopric was created in Zayton[3] c. 1313. These two bishoprics did not last very long. The Christians were expulsed from Khānbaliq in 1369; later bishops were non-resident; the bishopric of Zayton ceased in 1362.

John of Montecorvino died c. 1328, presumably in Peiping.

What we know of John's activity is essentially derived from his own reports. His first letter written from the Coromandel Coast, in 1291–1292, is known only through an Italian version made by the Dominican Menentillus of Spoleto for another Dominican, Bartholomew of San Concordio (1262–1347). It contains an account of the Coromandel Coast, which is very valuable not only because it is the earliest Latin Christian account of India, but also for intrinsic reasons. It describes the climate, the monsoons, the peoples of India, and its products (ginger, dye-wood, spices, cinnamon, etc.), Hinduism, Hindu manners and customs; it bears testimony

[2] Kaydū (d. c. 1301); grandson of Ogotāy, Kublai's rival.

[3] Zayton (Zeyton, Zaytūn, etc.), the great mediaeval port of China, was probably Ch'üan Chow, in Fukien, or else it was Chang Chou, near Amoy (opposite Formosa). Encyclopaedia sinica (114, 1917). Sir Henry Yule: The book of M. Polo (3d ed. by H. Cordier, vol. 2, 1903). Henri Cordier: Ser Marco Polo (100, 1920).

to the influence which Muslims enjoyed, while Christians and Jews were despised. Finally John realized the vast extent and the diversity of that continent.

Two other letters written from Khānbaliq in 1305 and 1306 contain information on his apostolic work in China and the incidents connected therewith summarized above. The letter of 1305 was transmitted to Rome by the intermediary of the Franciscans in Sarai, on the lower Volga; it was also communicated to the Franciscans and Dominicans in Tabrīz. The letter of 1306 probably followed the same road; it was brought to the Roman curia by the Franciscan Thomas of Tolentino, who had traveled in Armenia and who died a martyr at Tana (on Salsette I., near Bombay) in 1322.

Text—Luke Wadding (1588–1657): Annales Minorum (2nd ed., vol. 6, 69–72, 91–92, 1733). F. Kunstmann in Münchner Gelehrte Anzeigen (no. 22, 171–175, 1855). Englished in Yule's Cathay (2d. ed., vol. 3, 1914, with abundant notes). See also centennial publication quoted below.

Criticism—C. R. Beazley: Dawn of modern geography (vol. 3, 162–178, 1906). A. C. Moule: Documents relating to the mission of the minor friars to China in the thirteenth and fourteenth centuries (Journal R. Asiatic Society, 533–599, 1914). Joseph de Ghellinck: Les Franciscains en Chine (Xaveriana, no. 44, 40 p., Louvain 1927). Acta ordinis fratrum minorum . . . . Primo Sinarum apostolo et archiepiscopo Ioanni a Monte Corvino sexcentesimo exeunte ab eius obitu reverenter dicata (vol. 47, 179–232, illustr., Quaracchi 1928). Centennial publication containing a new edition of the Vita et gesta fr. Ioannis de Monte Corvino by Jerome Gobulovich, together with John's letters and other documents. Joseph de Ghellinck: Jean de Monte-Corvino (Revue d'histoire des missions, vol. 5, 506–544, Paris 1928); John of Monte Corvino, first archbishop of Peking (International review of missions, 18, 83–96, 1929). A. C. Moule: Christians in China before the year 1550 (London 1930; Isis, 15, 458).

THE POLO FAMILY

The Venetian Andrea Polo of San Felice had three sons: Marco, who made his will in 1280; Niccolò, who died before 1300; and Maffeo, who made his will in 1309. These three brothers were partners in the same business. Marco the elder, Marco of San Severo, had resided in Constantinople, and he had a house in Sudaq (Crimea), one of the most prosperous harbors of the time. In his will of 1280 that house was bequeathed to the local Franciscan mission. Niccolò and Maffeo were established for a time in Constantinople, whence they moved to Sudaq, which was then a part of the Khānate of western Kipchak.[4] In or about 1260–1261 they traveled in other parts of the Khānate, visiting Baraka (Khān from 1256 to 1266). They went to one of his two residences, or probably to both: Sarai on the Lower Volga, and Bulghar near the junction of the Volga and the Kama (not very far from Kazan). Hostilities between the Hordes obliged them to move eastwards from Bulghar across the steppes; they finally reached Bukhārā where they remained three years during part of which Burāq Khān was ruling (Chagatāy Khān from 1266 to 1270). From Bukhārā they traveled in the train of a Tartar embassy to the court of Kublai Khān. By this time the two brothers had a good knowledge of Mongolian. Kublai sent them back as his envoys to the pope with letters in "Turkish" (Uighūr). After three years traveling they reached the port of Ayas in Little Armenia (Aegae, Cilicia). By that time Clement IV (pope from 1265

[4] The Blue Horde of western Kipchak, one of the Khānates of the Golden Horde.

to 1268) was dead, and no successor was elected until 1271. They sailed from Ayas in April, 1269, to Acre, to Negropont, and finally to Venice. In Venice, Niccolò found his son, Marco the Younger, who was then fifteen years of age. Their achievements up to that time are explained in the Book of Marco Polo (Prologue, chapters 1 to 9); for their later achievements see my note on Marco Polo below.

Niccolò and Maffeo were primarily merchants but they must be counted among the greatest mediaeval travelers.

MARCO POLO

Venetian merchant and explorer. Born c. 1254, the son of Niccolò, died in Venice, 1324. Also called Marchus Paulus Milioni, Marco Milione (probably because of his exaggerations—or what were believed to be his exaggerations—and his fondness for large numbers).

The greatest traveler of mediaeval times in Christendom. He was the first to cross the whole continent of Asia, from the Mediterranean Sea to the Pacific Ocean (during their first journey, his father and uncle met Kublai Khān at a camp of his inside of Mongolia; as to John of Montecorvino, his crossing occurred a little later, c. 1292, and a great part of it was by sea). He was the first to give an adequate description of China, and his accounts of many other eastern countries (Ciampa, Siam, Burma, Laos country, Java, Sumatra, Nicobar and Adaman Is.; Abyssinia, Socotra, Zanzibar coast, Madagascar; W. and S. India, Baluchistan, Russia) were fuller than those available before. He was the first to give the West a glimpse of Japan.

Niccolò, Maffeo, and the young Marco left Venice in 1271; they went to Acre, then to Jerusalem, Ayas, returned to Acre to receive the apostolic letters addressed to the Great Khān by the newly appointed pope Gregory X, then to Ormuz. This would suggest that their first intention was to sail around India, but instead of this they proceeded overland via Balkh, Badakhshān, the Pamir, Kashgar, Yarkand, Khotan, Lop Nor, the Gobi Desert, etc., reaching Shangtu (Coleridge's Xanadu) where they were welcomed by Kublai Khān probably in 1275. For seventeen years they lived under his rule. Much of that time was probably spent in the imperial capital, Khānbaliq. Marco was especially high in the Khān's favor, and was sent by him on long errands to the West, as far as Yünnan and Tibet, and to N. Burma and Ciampa (S. Cochin-China). It would seem that he was even for a while governor of the great city of Yangchow (near Nanking). He knew the four scripts used by the Mongols (the following scripts are probably meant: Uighūr, Tibetan, Arabic, Chinese).

The Poli received leave to return to their own country at the beginning of 1292 when they sailed from Zaiton, escorting a new bride sent to Arghūn, the Īl-Khān of Persia, and carrying imperial messages for the pope and the main kings of Christendom. The sailing from Zaiton to Java and Sumatra took three months; in Sumatra they stayed five months; the sailing from Sumatra to Ormuz occupied eighteen months; in all the journey from Zaiton to Ormuz consumed two years and two months, their numbers being reduced from 600 to 18. From Ormuz they continued via Trebizond, Constantinople, Negropont, reaching Venice at the end of 1295.

Marco Polo took part in the naval battle between the fleets of Genoa and Venice off Curzola, Dalmatia, on Sept. 7, 1298, and was made a prisoner. During his Genoese captivity (1298–1299), he dictated a narrative of his travels to a fellow prisoner, Rustichello (or Rusticiano) of Pisa, who wrote it in French; or else Rustichello wrote his French narrative on the basis of Marco's notes.[5]

After a prologue explaining the personal circumstances of his own travels and those of his father and uncle, Marco deals successively with the different countries of Asia which he came across, reciting the "diversities," peculiarities, sights, products, and manners of each. He gives a particularly full account of Mongolian administration.

Marco was a merchant, a business man, very intelligent and full of curiosity, an intrepid traveler, but he was not in any sense a geographer. It is impossible to reconstruct his itineraries except in a very broad manner, for his indications of distances and directions are very poor and often misleading. He was not interested in geography proper, but he was deeply interested in men, their customs and wares. He was very orthodox yet could admire some features of the Buddhist religion. Making allowance for a certain fondness for superlatives and big numbers, he was a careful observer and a good reporter.

It is impossible to examine in detail a work encyclopaedic in its scope, but a few of the facts mentioned or described by him may be quoted by way of illustration.

Natural features and minerals: Naphtha springs in the Caucasian country (Baku), often observed before; the Caspian, an inland sea; description of the Gobi desert; coal and its use for heating; asbestos ("salamander"), tutty (crude zinc oxide) in Kūhbanān, Kirmān province, etc.

Plants: Dried melons of Shaburqān; mountain rhubarb; indigo, ginger; pepper; dyewood, rice (and rice wine), etc.

Animals: Georgian goshawks, the finest in the world; saker and lanier falcons in Badakhshān, ovis poli (already described by Rubruquis); fat-tailed sheep; humped oxen, and black partridges in the Rūdhbār district, Kirmān province; etc.

Institutions, religions and customs: Nestorians and Jacobites and their numerous and widespread establishments; Buddhists; Lamas; Mongolian manners and customs, their use of kumiss; description of the immense city of Khānbaliq; imperial roads, post and courier service; patriarchal organization of the empire; paper currency; Tartar cycles of twelve years; astrology; Grand Canal completed by Kublai; fire regulations; registration of the people; harbor of Zaiton; Chinese ocean-going ships, some of them with watertight compartments; manufacture of porcelain and cotton goods (muslin), etc.

These lists might be lengthened considerably, but it is perhaps more interesting to mention a number of items which are *not* dealt with in Polo's reminiscences: there is no mention of the Great Wall, of tea, of the compressed feet of Chinese women ("golden lilies"), of the use of cormorants for fishing, of Chinese printing, of the peculiarities of the Chinese script. The account of Mongol history is inaccurate, inferior to Carpini's; that of Chinese customs, often inferior to Rubruquis'.

Marco's stories were so extraordinary that they were received with much incredulity. This helps to explain that his influence was slow in making itself felt. His contemporaries hardly mentioned him. The only one to refer to him in a

[5] This Rustichello wrote in French some romances of the Round Table cycle. Bear in mind that Marco's contemporaries, Aldobrandino of Siena and Brunetto Latini of Florence also wrote in French.

scientific way was Peter of Abano in his Conciliator (c. 1303). Half a century later, John of Ypres paid much attention to him. The Catalan map of 1375 takes full account of the Polian explorations. Later Prince Henry the Navigator and Columbus were influenced by them. Finally, Marco's description of Russia and of the far-northern lands is said to have inspired prince Rupert (1619-1682) and to have led indirectly to the creation of the Hudson's Bay company.

Text—The original French text of Marco's work was not published until 1824 (see below), but up to that time a great many translations and translations of translations had appeared. Let us first mention a few of these.

Marco's narrative was first published in German: Nuremberg 1477. This was reprinted in Augsburg 1481.

These German texts were followed by two Latin ones: Zwolle 1483?, and Antwerp 1485. The version printed in 1485 is very important for it was made by the Bolognese Dominican, Francesco Pipino, before Polo's death. Columbus' own copy of it, with many autograph notes is kept in the Colombina, Seville. Simón de la Rosa y Lopéz: Biblioteca Colombina (vol. 2, Seville 1891).

Finally, two incunabula are in Italian: Venice 1496; reprinted Brescia 1500.

The first editions of translations in other languages are: Portuguese (Lisbon 1502) from Pipino's text; Spanish (Seville 1503), from the Italian; French (Paris 1556), from Grynaeus' Latin text, see below; English by John Frampton (London 1579), from the Spanish; etc.

Simon Grynaeus' Latin edition in his Novus orbis regionum (Paris 1532; reprinted Basel 1537, 1555) is very different from Pipino's (Antwerp 1485), additions being derived from another, Portuguese (?), translation. The first French edition of this French work was a translation of Grynaeus' bastard text!

The Italian text was established very early, within Polo's lifetime. Special attention must be paid to the text included by Giovanni Battista Ramusio (1485-1557) in his Navigationi e viaggi (vol. 2, 1559) for it contains interpolations of direct Polian origin not found anywhere else. Giov. Bat. Baldelli-Boni: Il Milione di Marco Polo. Testo di lingua del secolo decimoterzo ora per la prima volta pubblicato ed illustrato. Il Milione di Messer Marco Polo Viniziano secondo la lezione ramusiana illustrato e comentato (2 vols., Florence 1827). It was count Baldelli-Boni who first proved that the original text was French. Vincenzo Lazari: I viaggi di Marco Polo tradotti per la prima volta dall'originale francese di Rusticiano di Pisa, pubblicati per cura di Lodovico Pasini (Venice 1847). Adolfo Bartoli: I viaggi secondo la lezione del Codice Magliabechiano più antico reintegrati col testo francese (Florence 1863).

The original French text (Bibliothèque nationale, Paris) was edited by J. B. G. Roux de Rochelle, and formed vol. 1 of the Recueil de voyages et de mémoires published by the Société de géographie (Paris 1824) together with a Latin text, tables to both, glossary, and geographical index. Guillaume Pauthier: Le livre de Marco Polo, publié pour la première fois d'après trois MSS. inédits de Paris présentant la rédaction primitive du livre revue par Marc Pol lui-même et donnée par lui, en 1307, à Thiébault de Cépoy (2 parts, Paris 1865). This is an elaboration of the first text, less accurate but better written and possibly approved by Polo. Pauthier has added many notes, some of them derived from Chinese documents. Revision of Pauthier's edition, translation into modern French with additional notes extracted from Chinese sources by A. J. H. Charignon (2 vols., Peking 1924-1926; Isis, 11, 427).

A Spanish version dating from between 1231 and 1375 (Escorial MS.) was edited by Hermann Knust and R. Stuebe (140 p., Leipzig 1902).

Facsimile of a French MS. of the fourteenth century of the Royal Library,

Stockholm, published by A. E. Nordenskiöld (Stockholm 1882). Charles V of France owned five copies of Marco Polo; the Stockholm MS. was one of them.

John Frampton (fl. 1577–1596) translated Marco's Travels into English in 1579. That Elizabethan translation has recently been edited with introduction, notes, and appendices by Norman Mosley Penzer (400 p., London 1929).

The most popular English translation is that by William Marsden (London 1818), now included in Everyman's Library, and often revised.

The best English edition is the one prepared by Colonel Sir Henry Yule (1820–1889). First published in London 1871 (2 vols.); second edition 1874–1875; third edition revised throughout by Henri Cordier, with a memoir of Henry Yule by his daughter Amy Frances Yule (2 vols., 1392 p., many pl., maps, London 1903). This is a real encyclopaedia of the subject, indispensable to every student not only of Polo but of this period. It has been completed by a volume of addenda compiled by Henri Cordier: Ser Marco Polo (171 p., London 1920; Isis, 4, 136).

A new critical edition has been prepared by Luigi Foscolo Benedetto, the French edition published by the Société de géographie of Paris in 1824 being used as the basic text. Benedetto has been able to obtain new information from an Ambrosiana MS. which contains some of Ramusio's material and other hitherto unknown. Benedetto's text, Il Milione (500 p., with splendid illustrations, Florence 1928; Isis, 11, 135–138), is superior to the one represented by Yule's translation.

The modern popularity of Marco Polo is proved by the continual appearance of new editions of all kinds, with or without illustrations. There is no point in naming them, as they are not meant for scholars (many of them are registered in Isis as they appear).

For the sake of curiosity, I shall mention only two more editions. Whitley Stokes: The Gaelic abridgment of the Book of Ser Marco Polo (Z. für celtische Philologie, vol. 1, 245–273, 362–438, Halle 1896–1897). Japanese piratical publication of the second edition of Yule's Marco Polo (1900), see Bull. Ecole française d'Extrême Orient (vol. 4, 769).

There is a magnificent Marco Polo MS. in the Pierpont Morgan Library, New York (no. 723b). It apparently contains the French text revised by Thiébault de Cépoy (see above); written and limned in France, late in the fourteenth century (Isis, 16).

Biography and general criticism—The best general source of information is the Yule-Cordier edition above mentioned. Placido Zurla: Di Marco Polo e degli altri viaggiatori veneziani più illustri, con appendice sopra le antiche mappe lavorate in Venezia (2 vols., Venice 1818–1819). C. R. Beazley: Dawn of modern geography (vol. 3, 15–160, 1906). Ch. V. Langlois: Histoire littéraire de la France (Vol. 35, 232–259, 1921). Gabriel Bonvalot: Les chercheurs de routes: Marco Polo (254 p., Paris 1924; Isis, 10, 127, popular account).

Special criticism—W. S. Ament: Marco in Cambaluc, a comparison of foreign and native accounts (Journal of the Peking Oriental Society, vol. 3, 97–122, 1892). Cesare Augusto Levi: Il vero segreto di Dante e Marco (37 p., Treviso, 1905). Dante Olivieri: Una famiglia di codici italiani (Atti Istituto veneto, vol. 64, 1639–1665, Venezia 1905). Emilio Teza: I viaggi di Marco nella vecchia versione boema (14 p., ibidem, vol. 67, 747–758, 1908). J. Witte: Das Buch des M. Polo als Quelle für die Religionsgeschichte (126 p., Berlin 1916). Giuseppe Caraci: Un capitolo del Milione (Rivista geografica italiana, an. 31, 12–42, 1924). Comparison of Ramusian with French text. Ad. Aug. Michieli: Il Milione del M. Polo e un cronista del 1300 (La geografia, an. 12, 153–166, 1924). Latin summary of Polo's travels in the Chronica imaginis mundi of Fra Iacopo d'Acqui, 1328–1334 (Isis, 7, 538); I carattere morale de M. Polo (L'Universo, 341–346, 1925; Isis, 8, 742). A. C. Moule: Carriages in M. Polo's Quinsai or Hang-chou (T'oung-Pao, 24, 66–69, 1925); A lost manuscript of Marco Polo (Journal Royal Asiatic Society,

406–408, 1928). G. Orlandini: M. Polo e la sua famiglia (68 p., Archivio veneto-tridentino, vol. 9, 1926). Giovanni Vacca: Le divisament dou monde di Marco Polo (Rivista geografica italiana, 35, 51–60, 1928; Isis, 15, 214). G. I. Bratianu: Recherches sur le commerce génois dans la mer Noire au treizième siècle (360 p., 5 pl., 1 map, Paris 1929).

Scientific criticism—E. H. F. Meyer: Geschichte der Botanik (vol. 4, 114–131, 1857). G. Giuseppe Bianconi: Degli scritti di Marco e dell' uccello ruc da lui menzionato (Mem. dell' Accad. di Bologna, (2) vols. 2 and 7, 1862–1868). Edmund O. von Lippmann: Chemisches bei Marco Polo (Z. für angewandte Chemie, vol. 21, 1778–1788, 1908; Abhdl. und Vorträge, vol. 2, 258–287, 1913). This memoir has been translated into Italian with additional notes by Icilio Guareschi in the Suppl. annuale all' Enciclopedia di chimica (vol. 24, 1908). Louis J. Bragman: Some medical observations of Marco Polo (Medical Life, vol. 34, 313–315, 1927).

RICOLDO DI MONTE CROCE

Ricoldus de Monte Crucis. Also called mistakenly Ricardus Florentinus. Born at Monte Croce near Florence in 1242, died in Florence 1320. He assumed the Dominican habit at Florence 1267; was in Pisa in 1272; he sailed to Acre in 1286 or 1287. He traveled in Palestine and Syria, then to Tabrīz via Lesser Armenia, Sivas and Erzerum; he spent many months in Tabrīz, and preached there in Arabic, then proceeded to Baghdād via Nineveh and Mūṣul; he remained many years in Baghdād. His accounts in the Itinerary and in his letters contain valuable information on the Mongols and other peoples met by him, on the Nestorian communities, on Muslim life and religion, on Baghdād under Muslim rule, etc. In the vicinity of Mt. Ararat he noticed that all rivers flowed eastward toward the Sea of India; he concluded that the Hindus lied when they claimed that the Flood did not reach them. While in Mūṣul he heard of the fall of Acre (1291), and the end of Christian power in Syria cut him off from communication with his Order. He reappeared in Florence in 1301.

He wrote a refutation of the Qur'ān and of Islām which obtained considerable success. It was translated into Greek by Demetrios Cydones (second half of the fourteenth century), then retranslated from Greek into Latin by Bartholomew Pincernus de Montearduo. Finally it was translated into German by Martin Luther. It was often printed in Latin, Greek, and German.

Ricoldo may have been one of the channels through which Muslim knowledge reached Dante.

Text—Itinerarius, or, Liber peregrinacionis, edited by J. C. M. Laurent: Peregrinatores medii aevi quattuor (101–141, Leipzig 1864).

Italian translation by Vincenzio Fineschi: Itinerario ai paesi orientali di Fra R. de Monte di Croce (78 p., Florence 1793). F. L. Polidori, F. Grottanelli, L. Banchi: Viaggio in Terra Santa, volgarizzamento del secolo XIV (42 p., Siena 1864, per nozze Loreta-Zambrini).

R. Röhricht: Epistolae quinque commentatoriae de perditione Acconis 1291 (Archives de l'orient latin, vol. 2, 258–296, 1884). Extract with French translation in Comte Henry de Castries: L'Islam 290–295, 1922).

Improbatio (or Confutatio) Alcorani. First printed Seville 1500. Often reprinted in various ways. Contenta Ricoldi contra sectam mahumeticam (86 p., Paris 1511). Theodorus Bibliander: Machumetis eiusque successorum vitae ac doctrina . . . . Adiunctae sunt confutationes multorum authorum, etc. (vol.

2, 83-178, Basel, 1543). Latin translation from the Greek, (1520?). Greek-Latin edition (1543). Propugnaculum fidei toti christianiae religioni adversum mendacia et deliramenta Saracenorum, etc. (219 p., Venice 1607). Etc.

Verlegung des Alcoran, verdeutscht durch Martin Luther (84 p., Wittenberg 1542). Kurzer Inhalt des gotteslästerlichen Alcorans . . . . samt derselben Widerlegung (155 p., Nuremberg 1684). Etc.

Criticism—Louis de Backer: L'extrême orient au moyen âge (256-333, Paris 1877). R. Röhricht: Bibliotheca geographica Palaestinae (61, 1890). C. R. Beazley: Dawn of modern geography (vol. 3, 192-202, 390-391, 1906).

LANZAROTE MALOCELLO

Lanciloto, Lansalot, Lancelot; Malocello, Maroxello, Marucelu, Maloisel, etc. Genoese navigator and conqueror, who is said to have rediscovered the northern Canaries (the Fortunate Islands of the ancients, αἱ τῶν μακάρων νῆσοι) c. 1270-1275 and to have made an attempt (finally unsuccessful) to colonize them. According to Petrarch (b. 1304) this happened within the memory of his parents. The most northeasterly of the Canaries, Lanzarote, was thus called after Lanzarote Malocello, and the name already appeared on early portolani (Angelino Dulcert 1339, Laurentian 1351) together with the red cross of Genoa.

Malocello's discovery may have been anticipated by Muslim sailors—e.g., by one Khashkhāsh of Cordova to whom al-Mas'ūdī referred in his Murūj al-dhahab—or by the Maghrurīn (the Deceived ones), referred to by al-Idrīsī (Climate 4, section 1). The Maghrurīn were eight cousins who set out from Lisbon and sailed about eleven days eastward, then in a southerly direction for twelve days, when they reached the Isle of sheep (Jazīrat al-ghanam) which was inhabited; after twelve days more navigation they landed in another island where they were made prisoners, etc. The first island may have been Madeira; the second, one of the Canaries.

These accounts are not dated, but Kashkhāf's venture must be anterior to 957, when al-Mas'ūdī died; and the Maghrurīn must have set out from Lisbon before 1147 when that city ceased to be in Muslim hands.

For Khashkhāf, see the Société asiatique edition of the Murūj al-dhahab (vol. 1, 258, Paris 1861).

For the Maghrurīn, see Amédée Jaubert's translation of al-Idrīsī (vol. 2, 26-29, Paris 1840).

For Malocello, see C. R. Beazley: Dawn of modern geography (vol. 3, 411-414, 1906).

THE BROTHERS VIVALDI

Ugolino and Vadino Vivaldo. Genoese navigators. In May, 1291, Ugolino Vivaldo and Tedisio Doria[6] equipped two galleys in Genoa. Ugolino set out in them together with his brother Vadino (Guido) and two Franciscans. Their definite purpose was to find the sea-way round Africa toward India; their main motive was commercial, though the presence of the Franciscans suggests a religious afterthought. They sailed out of the Gibraltar Straits and followed the African coast down beyond Cape Nun (28°46'N.), after which all trace of them was lost.

Some time before 1315, Sorleone Vivaldo, son of Ugolino, undertook a series of

[6] Or D'Oria. Son of Lamba Doria, the Genoese admiral who defeated the Venetian fleet at Curzola, 1298, and made Marco Polo prisoner. See note on Marco Polo.

expeditions in the hope of finding traces of his father and uncle. In the course of one of these expeditions he reached Magadoxo (Mogdishu) on the Eastern African coast (Italian Somaliland).

C. R. Beazley: Dawn of modern geography (vol. 3, 414–419, 1906). Charles de La Roncière: La découverte de l'Afrique au Moyen âge (vol. 1, 50, 1925).

See note on Ramon Lull for an account of the earliest European journey to the Sūdān.

BEGINNINGS OF THE HANSEATIC LEAGUE

The needs of international commerce created gradually an association of German and other towns called the Hanseatic League. Its history is primarily economic, secondarily political, and does not concern us except in a very indirect way. The beginnings were naturally obscure, yet can be traced back without doubt to the thirteenth century, even to some extent to the first half of it. By 1241 Lübeck and Hamburg had already reached some sort of agreement to safeguard their commercial enterprises in the Baltic and the North Seas. By 1256, Lüneburg, Wismar, Rostock, and Stralsund had already joined them. The movement of German colonization east of the Elbe increased the impetus toward the consolidation of commercial efforts.

An association of German merchants existed also at Wisby, in Gothland, as early as the beginning of the thirteenth century, but this association and others of the same kind in England, France, and Flanders were gradually subordinated to the greater association of the Hanseatic towns, centered in Lübeck.

The Hanseatic League did not reach its full power until the second half of the fourteenth century; its very name was not adopted before 1360, and its golden age did not extend beyond the fifteenth century when geographical discoveries diverted the world's trade into new channels.

However as long as it lasted it helped to organize and improve international commerce, maritime regulations, etc., and to that extent it exerted not simply a purely economic but a cultural influence.

James Westfall Thompson: An economic and social history of the Middle Ages (New York 1928). Edwin Francis Gay: Hanseatic league (Encyclopaedia Britannica, vol. 11, 162–165, 1929).

II. EASTERN CHRISTIANS

See notes on Nicephoros Blemmydes, Maximos Planudes, Abū-l-Faraj, Bar Sauma, and Vardan the Great.

KING HAYTON

Hayton the Elder. Haython, Hethum, Hetūm, Hayton I. King of the Latin Kingdom of New (or Little) Armenia—i.e., the ancient Cilicia and the Taurus—from 1225 to 1269; then a monk; he died in 1271–1272. To defend his kingdom against the Saracens and the Byzantines, he sought the protection of the Franks and that far more valuable of the Mongols. On the accession of Kuyuk, the third Great Khān, in 1246, Hayton sent to him as an ambassador his brother Sempad, constable of his kingdom. Sempad was away four years and during that time he wrote a letter to his king from Samarqand, wherein he gave an exaggerated account of the Christian tendencies of the Mongols. Some time after the accession of Mangū, the fourth Great Khān, in 1248, Hayton himself was invited to visit the Western Ḫorde upon the Volga and the imperial court in Mongolia. Hayton reached the first Tartar camp at Kars, Georgia, in the early spring of 1254; he then proceeded with an escort across the pass of Derbent and towards the camp of the Blue Horde, north of the Caspian sea, thence to the camp of the Great Khān, which he reached on Sept. 14. He remained there until Nov. 1, when he started his home journey, via Barkul, Urumtsi, Lake Sairam, the Ili valley, Talas, Otrar, Jizak, Samarqand, Bukhārā, Marw, Tabrīz, etc. He reached his country in July 1255.

A brief narrative of his journey was written in Armenian by his secretary, Cyriacus of Gandzak (d. 1272). It is unfortunately but too brief. It contains curious references to Chinese Buddhism.

Text—The Armenian text was translated into Russian by Prince Argutinski in Sibirski Vyestnik (69 sq., 1822); this Russian text was put into French by Julius Klaproth in Journal Asiatique (vol. 12, 273 sq., 1833). M. Brosset published a French translation from the Armenian in the Mémoires de l'académie de St. Pétersbourg (1870). A new Russian translation by K. P. Patkanov appeared in 1874. Partial English translation by E. Bretschneider: Medieval researches from Eastern Asiatic sources (vol. 1, 164–172, London 1888).

Criticism—C. R. Beazley: Dawn of modern geography (vol. 2, 381–391, 1901).

III. WESTERN JEWS

JACOB OF PARIS

Rabbi Jacob. Jewish pilgrim to the Holy Land c. 1258. About the middle of the thirteenth century the Talmudical school of Paris had already superseded the schools of Troyes and Ramerupt and had become the main center of rabbinical learning in France, if not in the whole of northern Europe. This was partly due to the prestige of a great rabbi, Jehiel ben Joseph.[7] However, various ordinances of Louis IX had decreased Jewish wealth, and rabbi Jehiel was obliged to send an emissary to the eastern synagogues to ask for financial help. This emissary was rabbi Jacob, otherwise unknown. He wrote a brief account of his journey, containing a list of eighty sepulchers visited by him in the Holy Land. An anonymous itinerary from Paris to Saint Jean d'Acre, also written in Hebrew at about the same time, was possibly composed by him.

Text—French translation with notes by Eliacin Carmoly: Itinéraires de la Terre sainte (171–216, Bruxelles 1847). Hebrew text in J. D. Eisenstein: Ozar massaoth (New York 1926; Isis, 11, 147).

Criticism—R. Röhricht: Bibliotheca geographica Palaestinae (53, 1890). For Hebrew geographical literature in general, see Josef Heller: Geographische Literatur (Encyclopaedia judaica, vol. 7, 260–271, 1931).

[7] Also called Jehiel the Holy, the Wise, the Elder, or in French, Sir Vives. Born at Meaux at the end of the twelfth century; died in Palestine in 1286. Isaac Broydé: Jewish Encyclopedia (vol. 7, 82, 1904).

IV. WESTERN MUSLIMS

IBN SA'ĪD AL-MAGHRIBĪ

Abū-l-Ḥasan 'Alī ibn Mūsā ibn Muḥammad al-Maghribī. Born in 1208–1209 or 1214 near Granada, studied in Seville; traveled extensively and lived in many Muslim cities East and West; he was the guest of Hūlāgū (Īl-Khān of Persia from 1256 to 1265) in Armenia; he died at Damascus 1274–1275, or at Tunis 1286–1287. Hispano-Muslim historian and geographer.

His main work is a geographical treatise, Kitāb basṭ al-arḍ fī ṭūlhā wal-'arḍ (Extent of the earth in length and breadth), also called Kitāb al-jaghrāfīya. It is based upon Ptolemy and al-Idrīsī, but contains many facts discovered since the latter's time, and the geographical coordinates of every important place (these were lacking in al-Idrīsī). Abū-l-Fidā' (first half of the fourteenth century) used this work considerably, but seems to have lost much of his confidence in it toward the end of his life, and the final edition of his Taqwīm al-buldān is free from errors due to Ibn Sa'īd which may be found in an earlier version.

While in Baghdād (c. 1251, i.e., before the Mongol invasion), Ibn Sa'īd saw there thirty-six libraries. He knew of the mouth of the Senegal. He gives some brief account of the northern countries of Europe where white bears are found; Iceland is called the island of white falcons; true falcons are obtained in Denmark.

His historical works are less important. He completed two chronicles begun by his father; the one dealing with the West, Kitāb al-mughrib fī-akhbār ahl al-maghrib (Book of singularities concerning the people of the West); the other dealing with the East, Kitāb al-mushriq fi akhbār ahl al-mashriq (Book throwing light upon the people of the East). We may also quote his history of pre-Islāmic Arabia, Kitāb nashwat al-ṭarab fi ta'rīkh jāhilīyat al-'Arab (The smell of joy, or chronicles of the pagan Arabs.

Text—K. Vollers: Fragmente aus dem Mughrib des Ibn Sa'īd. 1. Bericht über die Handschrift und das Leben des Aḥmed ibn Ṭūlūn von Ibn Sa'īd nach Ibn ed-Dājä (Semitische Studien, 1, Berlin 1894). Reviewed by M. J. de Goeje (Z. d. Deutschen Morgenl. Ges., vol. 49, 706–710, 1895). K. L. Tallquist: Edition of Book 4 of the Mughrib (Leiden 1899).

The Baṣt was much used by Abū-l-Fidā'; the very MS. used by him is now in the Bibliothèque Nationale, Paris. It is still unpublished.

A fragment of another geographical work, Geographica et historica orbis descriptio appeared in the Boll. ital. degli studi orientali (388–392, 1881).

Criticism—J. T. Reinaud: Géographie d'Aboulféda (vol. 1, 141–143, 1848). F. Wüstenfeld: Geschichtschreiber der Araber (no. 353, 135–137, 1881). C. Brockelmann: Arabische Litteratur (vol. 1, 336–337, 1898). Francisco Pons Boigues: Ensayo bio-bibliográfico (Madrid, 306–310, 1898). Quoting fourteen works ascribed to Ibn Sa'īd; according to some authors he was said to have written 400! Fridtjof Nansen: In northern mists (vol. 2, 177, 208, 1911). Encyclopaedia of Islām (vol. 2, 414, 1918). Konrad Miller: Mappae arabicae (vol. 1, 1, p. 21, 1926). Fritz Trummeter: Ibn Sa'īd's Geschichte der vorislamischen Araber (67 p., Stuttgart, 1928; OLZ, 33, 129, 1930).

AL-'ABDARĪ

Abū Muḥammad Muḥammad ibn Muḥammad ibn 'Alī, al-Abdarī (i.e., descendant of 'Abd al-Dār ibn Quṣaij ibn Kilāb ibn Murra of the tribe of Quraish). Hispano-Muslim traveler. Born in Valencia, flourished c. 1289 and after.

He left Mogador (on W. coast of Morocco) in 1289 to accomplish the Pilgrimage; he made the whole journey both ways by land, thus crossing the whole of N. Africa twice. He began in Tlemcen (Algeria), a description of the N. African countries, entitled Al-riḥla al-maghribīya, which contains accurate topographical data and valuable information on the Muslim life and scholarship of his day.

Text—A critical edition and complete translation of the Riḥlat al-'Abdarī are badly needed.

Criticism—Auguste Cherbonneau: Notice et extraits du voyage d'el-Abdery à travers l'Afrique septentrionale (Journal asiatique, vol. 4, 144–176, 1854). Analysis and extracts. C. Brockelmann: Arabische Litteratur (vol. 1, 482, 1898). F. Pons Boigues: Ensayo bio-bibliográfico (310–313, 1898). Motylinski: Itinéraires entre Tripoli et l'Egypte. Extraits des relations de voyage d'el Abdery, el Aiachi, Moulay Aḥmed et el-Ourtilani (Bulletin de la Société de géographie d'Alger, vol. 5, 69–140, 1900). For al-'Abdarī, see p. 70–77. Mohammed ben Cheneb: Encyclopaedia of Islām (vol. 1, 67, 1908).

MUḤAMMAD IBN RUSHAID

Abū 'Abdallāh Muḥammad ibn 'Umar Muḥib al-dīn al-Sabtī al-Fihrī al-Andalusī. Moroccan historian, traditionalist, and geographer. Born at Ceuta in 1259; studied there and in Fās; in 1284–1285 he made the Pilgrimage together with the historian and preacher, Muḥammad ibn 'Abd al-Raḥmān Ibn al-Ḥakīm al-Zubaidī al-Lakhmī al-Ishbilī of Ronda (assassinated in 1309); after their return together they settled in Granada in 1292–1293; after his companion's death, Muḥammad ibn Rushaid returned to his own country, Morocco, and died in Fās, 1321.

He wrote books on tradition, biographies, and two itineraries.

1. Riḥlatāni. Two itineraries, the one relative to Spain, the other to Africa, both containing information on the natural history as well as on the literary history of these countries.

2. Kitāb silsilat al-samā' wa ifādat al-naṣīḥ. Completed at Ceuta in 1290–1291. Notices on the Spanish traditionalists and legists.

3. Kitāb al-sanan al-abyan wal-mawrid al-am'an. Lives of al-Bukhārī and Muslim.

4. Mal' al-'aiba fī mā jama'a biṭūl al-ghaiba fī-l-raḥla ilā Makka wa Ṭaiba. Notices on the learned men who lived in Cairo and Alexandria c. 1300.

Michael Casiri: Bibliotheca arabico-hispana escurialensis (vol. 2, 86, 1770). The Escorial contains other itineraries of the same kind; see, e.g., ibidem, p. 151, 165. J. T. Reinaud: Géographie d'Aboulféda (vol. 1, 127, 1848). F. Wüstenfeld: Geschichtschreiber der Araber (no. 375, 152, 1881). F. Pons Boigues: Ensay bio-bibliográfico (317, Madrid 1898). C. Brockelmann: Arabische Litteratur (vol. 2, 245, 1902).

V. EASTERN MUSLIMS

See my notes on Nāṣir al-dīn al-Ṭūsī, Quṭb al-dīn al-Shīrāzī, al-Qazwīnī, al-Waṭwāṭ, al-Juwainī.

VI. CHINESE

CH'ANG TÊ

Ch'ang² Tê²* (440, 10845). Flourished c. 1259. Chinese traveler. He traveled in 1259 fom Qaraqorum to Western Asia, being sent by the Mongol emperor Mangū Khān to the latter's brother Hūlāgū, who had then just overthrown the Caliphate and destroyed Baghdād (1258). The narrative of his journey, Hsi¹ shih³ chi⁴ (4031, 9896, 923) was taken down by Liu² Yü⁴* (7270, 13689). It is not a diary of Hūlāgū's army, but a narrative of Ch'ang's own travels with some account of Hūlāgu's conquests. Ch'ang Tê's work has much less geographical value than that of Ch'iu Ch'ang-ch'un (first half of thirteenth century), but its historical value is greater. It should be compared with the account given in Persian at the beginning of the following century by Rashīd al-dīn.

Text—The Library of Congress has the Hsi shih chi in the Ch'i² fu³ ts'ung¹ shu¹ (1066, 3627, 12039 ,10024), vol. 101; in the Hsüeh²* ching¹ t'ao³ yüan² (4839, 2163, 10838, 13700), vol. 68; in the Ku³ chin¹ shuo¹* hai³ (6188, 2027, 10164, 3767), vol. 5, and in four other collections of reprints.

French translation of the Hsi shih chi by Abel Rémusat: Mélanges asiatiques (vol. 1, 171 sq., 1825); also by G. Pauthier in the Introduction to his Marco Polo (1865). These translations are incomplete and imperfect. A translation into English based upon four Chinese editions has been included by E. V. Bretschneider in his Mediaeval researches (vol. 1, 109–156, 1888; with abundant notes).

YEH-LÜ HSI-LIANG

Yeh¹-lü⁴* Hsi¹-liang⁴ (12974, 7548, 4048, 7035). Great grandson of Yeh-lü Ch'u-ts'ai, the great Mongol educator dealt with above. He was born near Qaraqorum. He traveled to Central Asia in 1260–1263; an account of his peregrinations is included in his biography in the Yüan² shih³ (13744, 9893), chapter 180.

Text—Chapter 180 of Yüan-shih was Englished by Emile Vasilievich Bretschneider: Mediaeval researches from Eastern Asiatic sources (vol. 1, 157–163, 1888), with notes.

Another itinerary of almost the same time, but anonymous, was edited and translated by A. C. Moule: Hang Chou to Shang-tu, A. D. 1276 (T'oung Pao, vol. 16, 393–419, 1915).

CHOU TA-KUAN

Chou¹ Ta²*-Kuan¹ (2450, 10473, 6263). Styled Ts'ao³-t'ing² (11634, 11286). Born at Yung³-chia¹ (13504, 1158), Chehkiang; flourished in 1296–1297. Chinese traveler who accompanied, in 1296, an envoy sent by the Yüan court to Cambodia. They were back home in 1297. Chou wrote a "Memoir on Cambodian customs." Chên¹ la⁴* fêng¹ t'u³ chi⁴ (589, 6667, 3554, 12099, 923), which is a faithful account of the heyday of that civilization. He gives valuable information on Angkor-Vat and on Khmer customs.

Angkor-Vat is a magnificent group of temples dating from the twelfth and thirteenth centuries. It represents the latest period of Khmer art.[8] By 1450 the old Khmer civilization had vanished and Angkor-Vat was buried in the jungle. Chou Ta-kuan's description of Angkor-Vat was remarkably accurate; it was not only the

[8] The Pre-Khmer or Indo-Khmer art dates from the sixth and seventh centuries. Khmer art itself began in the ninth century (Angkor Thom).

first description, but also the last until modern times. The ruins of Angkor were noticed by a few missionaries: Ribadeneira and Gabriel of Santo Antonio at the end of the sixteenth century, Chevreuil at the end of the seventeenth century, Langenois in 1783; they were mentioned by Father Bouillevaux in 1856; but their real discoverer was Henri Mouhot (1826–1861), a French naturalist in the English service, on January 22, 1861.

Text—The T'u chi was included in vol. 63 of the ts'ung[1] shu[1] (12039, 10024) entitled Shuo[1*] fu[1] (10164, 3650) compiled by T'ao[2] Tsung[1]-i[2] (10831, 11976, 5455) (born c. 1320, still living in 1399) probably before the end of the Yüan dynasty. For other Chinese editions see Pelliot's introduction to his translation quoted below (1902). The Library of Congress has the Shuo fu and four other ts'ung shu containing the T'u chi.

Abel Rémusat: Description du royaume de Cambodge par un voyageur chinois qui a visité cette contrée à la fin du XIIIe siècle (98 p., 1 map, Paris 1819; French translation of a poor text). Paul Pelliot: Mémoires sur les coutumes du Cambodge (Bull. de l'Ecole française d'Extrême-Orient, vol. 2, 123–177, 1902; French translation with abundant notes). New popular edition by Pelliot: Angkor vu au XIIIe siècle par un ambassadeur chinois (Collection des classiques de l'Orient, Paris c. 1924).

Criticism—See histories of Cambodia; e.g., Georges Maspero: L'empire Khmer (Phnom-Penh, 1903). Adhémard Leclère: Histoire du Cambodge depuis le ler siècle de notre ère (Paris 1914). G. Groslier: Recherches sur les Cambodgiens (Paris 1921; Isis, 4, 607). George Coedès: Notes sur Tcheou Ta-kouan (Bulletin de l'Ecole française d'Extrême Orient, vol. 18, 4–9, 1918). Paul Pelliot: Quelques remarques sur le Chouo fou (T'oung Pao, 23, 163–220, 1924). Elaborate discussion of the vicissitudes of the Shuo fu above mentioned, a late Yüan or early Ming ts'ung shu containing the T'u chi.

For Angkor-Vat, see Henri Mouhot, Travels in the central parts of Indo-China (2 vols., London 1864). H. Marchal: Guide archéologique aux temples d'Angkor (218 p., Paris 1928). Louis Finot: Le temple d'Angkor Vat. Première partie: L'architecture du monument (Mémoires archéologiques publiés par l'Ecole française d'Extrême Orient: 2 vols., 41 p., 150 pl., Paris 1929; Isis, 15, 208). René Grousset: Histoire de l'Extrême-orient (Paris 1929; Isis, 14, 437–441). See histories of Asiatic art.

BAR ṢAUMA

Rabban Bar Ṣauma (meaning in Syriac, son of fasting). Christian (Nestorian) priest born in Peiping; died in Baghdād in 1293. The first identified Chinese to reach Western Europe, in 1287–1288.

Another Chinese Nestorian, Marcos Bainiel, born in 1244, son of an archdeacon living in Tung-sheng (Tokhto) in Shansi, came to Rabban Ṣauma to receive religious instruction, and eventually became a monk. They decided to go together on a pilgrimage to Jerusalem. They went via Tangut, the Desert of Lob, Khotan, Kashgar, Ṭūs, Marāgha, Baghdād, Armenia, Georgia. Here their progress was stopped and they were obliged to return to Baghdād. Marcos was appointed metropolitan and Bar Ṣauma, visitator general; soon afterward, in 1281, the patriarch of the Nestorians having died, Marcos was appointed in his stead[9] being named

[9] This Patriarchate was the traditional see of Seleucia-Ctesiphon, then located in Baghdād. Yaballaha did not know Syriac, but it was found expedient to appoint him, as the temporal rulers were Mongols and he was the only eligible candidate who was at all acquainted with their language and customs.

Yaballaha III (meaning, God has given); he remained in power until his death in 1317.

Before continuing this story, I must introduce another personage, Arghūn, Īl-Khān of the Western Mongols (1284–1291). Like his predecessors, he was pro-Christian; and he thought of uniting his forces with Christian forces to defeat the common enemy, Islām. He had a Christian wife, some of his coins bore Christian legends;[10] his son was baptized in 1289, but he himself would not be baptized except in Jerusalem, which was not to be. In 1285 he sent an embassy to Honorius IV (pope from 1285 to 1287), to bespeak an alliance against the Saracens; in 1287 in conjunction with the patriarch Yaballaha III, he sent another mission to Rome, headed by Bar Ṣauma and including two other Christians, Sabadinus and Thomas de Anfusis, and the interpreter Uguetus (Thomas and Uguetus had taken part in the first mission); in 1289–1290 he sent a third mission conducted by Buscarello de' Ghizolfi; and soon afterward, a fourth and last one, headed by a Christian convert, Chagan. On the other hand the legate John de Monte Corvino came to Arghūn's court in 1290–1291. Arghūn, wishing a new Chinese wife, applied to Kublai Khān, who selected one for him and put her in Marco Polo's charge. On their arrival, Arghūn had died (1291). To complete this story I may say that these diplomatic efforts failed ultimately. After much flirtation with Christendom, the Īl-Khāns finally decided to cast their lot with the Muslims (at the end of the century).

To return to Bar Ṣauma's mission, he went to Constantinople, then by sea to Italy. He witnessed the Aetna eruption of June 18, 1287, and reached Naples on June 24. Thence to Rome where he could not accomplish his mission, pope Honorius IV having just died (April 3, 1287). He traveled to Genoa, noticing its democratic institutions; to Paris where he visited the university, counting—so he says—30,000 students; was received by the king of France, Philip IV, and in Gascony by the king of England, Edward I; wintered at Genoa, marveling at its soft climate, then returned to Rome, Nicholas IV having been elected pope in the meanwhile (Feb. 22, 1288); the first Franciscan pope. He left Rome soon after Easter, 1288, returning to Baghdād, where he died in 1293.

Bar Ṣauma wrote a diary of his journey in Persian, which has come down to us in an abbreviated Syriac translation. It is interesting to note that in his first journey across China and Central Asia, he followed essentially the same road as Marco Polo, though in the opposite direction; in fact they may have met.

Text—A translation of the text into modern Syriac was published in the Journal of the American Protestant Mission at Urmia (1885–1886). First edition of the Syriac text by Father Paul Bedjan of the Chaldaean Church (1888). Improved edition by same: Histoire de Mar-Iabalaha (Paris 1895). French translation made by Jean Baptiste Chabot from the unrevised text in Revue de l'Orient latin (vol. 1, 567–610, 1893; vol. 2, 73–143, 235–304, 1894; with abundant notes and various complementary documents). Partial English translation by James Alan Montgomery: The history of Yaballaha III (82 p., New York 1927). This contains the part of greatest interest to us, with a valuable commentary (Isis, 10, 129). Complete English translation by Sir E. A. Wallis Budge: The monks of Kublai Khān, or the History of the life and travels of Rabban Sāwmā, etc. (352 p., 16 pl., 6 ill., London 1928; Isis, 13, 160).

[10] Montgomery: loc. cit. (p. 17, footnote).

Criticism—H. H. Hall in Proceedings of the American Oriental Soc. (p. iv–vii, Oct. 1886; p. clxxxi, 1889). Chabot and Montgomery's editions quoted above. P. Pelliot: Les Mongols et la papauté (Revue de l'art chrétien, vol. 23, sq., 1923 sq). A. C. Moule: Important review of Montgomery's translation (Journal R. Asiatic Society, 448–453, 1928). A. C. Moule: Christians in China (94–127, London 1930; Isis, 15, 458).

See my notes on Kublai Khān and Kuo Shou-ching.

CHAPTER LI

NATURAL HISTORY

(Second Half of Thirteenth Century)

I. WESTERN CHRISTENDOM

See notes on Villard de Honnecourt, Rubruquis, Marco Polo, Richard of Fournival, Peter of Spain, Vincent of Beauvais, Albert the Great, and Bacon.

Also the notes on Simon of Genoa, King Dinis, Walter de Henley, and on falconry in the first half of the thirteenth century.

"KING DANCUS"

One of the earliest Latin writers on falconry, repeatedly quoted in later times, is supposed to be one Dancus (Danchus, Daulcus, Dalcus), king of Armenia. There never was such a king in Armenia, and the other circumstances relative to his authorship of a book on falconry are equally mythical. According to Jean de Franchières, who flourished under Louis XI (king, 1461–1483), king Dancus was a famous falconer; he was visited by Galatian, king of Egypt, and later by Galatian's son, Atanacio; Dancus had an assistant called Martino, who had previously been falconer to King Roger of Hungary. All these kings are equally fictitious.

However we have a French text entitled Le livre du Roi Dancus, one of the earliest French texts on falconry, dated 1284. (The French translations made by Daniel of Cremona for Enzio are a little earlier.) It is probable that this is the actual date of the treatise, or that it is very near to it. It is possible that the treatise was originally written in French, not in Latin. There are Italian and Latin versions of it, but apparently later than the French.

Text—H. Martin Dairvault: Le livre du roi Dancus. Texte français inédit. Suivi d'un Traité de fauconnerie, également inédit d'après Albert le Grand (Paris 1883).

Guillaume Tardif: Le livre de l'art de faulconnerie et des chiens de chasse (Paris 1492). New edition of Tardif's work by Ernest Jullien (2 vols., Paris 1882). William Tardif of Puy-en-Velay (i.e., Le Puy, Haute-Loire) was professor at the College of Navarre and reader to Charles VIII (king, 1483–1498). According to his own statement his treatise was a translation of the Latin works of king "Danchus, qui premier trouva et escrivit l'art de faulconnerie," "Moamus," "Guillinus," and "Guicennas."

Francesco Zambrini: Libro delle nature degli uccelli fatto per lo re Danchi, testo antico Tuscano (Scelta di curiosità lett., 140, Bologna 1874). Containing splendid facsimiles of miniatures.

The Latin version is in a British Museum MS. of the fifteenth century (Add. 20774, f. 79). "Aliae rubricae de infirmitatibus et medicinis secundum Danchum regem," beginning, "Danchus rex stabat in suo pallatio."

Critical comparisons of all these texts are needed to clear up the many problems involved.

Criticism.—James Edmund Harting: Bibliotheca accipitraria (66, 71, 159, 181, London 1891). Léon Moulé: La médecine vétérinaire en Europe au Moyen âge (65, Paris 1900).

II. GREEKS

See note on Demetrios Pepagomenos.

III. WESTERN ISRAEL

See notes on Judah ben Moses, Jacob ben Maḥir, Gershon ben Solomon.

IV. ISLĀM

BAILAK AL-QABAJAQĪ

Muslim mineralogist who flourished in Cairo c. 1242–1282. He wrote in 1282–1283 the Kitāb kanz al-tijār fī ma'rifat al-aḥjār (Treasure of merchants concerning the knowledge of [precious] stones), which he dedicated to the sulṭān al-Manṣūr II Sayf al-dīn Qalā'ūn (Baḥrī Mamlūk, ruling from 1279 to 1290). This was largely derived from al-Tīfāshī (first half of the thirteenth century). He quotes twenty-three authors, Hermes, Apollonios, Aristotle, Ptolemy among the Greeks; al-Mas'ūdī, al-Bīrūnī, al-Ghazzālī among the Muslims. The Kanz al-tijār contains a description of the floating compass and its use by sailors, which he had witnessed in the eastern Mediterranean Sea in 1242–1243.

Julius Klaproth: Lettre à A. de Humboldt sur l'invention de la boussole (57, Paris 1834; containing Arabic text with translation). M. Steinschneider: Arabische Lapidarien (Z. der deutschen morgenländischen Ges., vol. 49, 256, 1895). C. Brockelmann: Arabische Litteratur (vol. 1, 495, 1898). Carra de Vaux: Penseurs de l'Islam (vol. 2, 371, 1921). E. Wiedemann: Maghnaṭīs (Encyclopaedia of Islām, vol. 3, 106, 1928).

'ABD AL-MU'MIN AL-DIMYĀṬĪ

Abū Muḥammad 'Abd al-Mu'min ibn Khalaf, Sharaf al-dīn al-Tūnī al-Dimyāṭī al-Shāfi'ī. Egyptian traditionalist and writer. Born in the island of Tūna near Dimyāṭ (Damietta) in 1217, educated in Damietta, he was the first professor at the college al-Manṣūrīya founded in Cairo by the Mamlūk sulṭān al-Manṣūr Qalā'ūn (ruled from 1279 to 1290); he taught also at the college al-Ẓāhirīya; he died in 1306.

His main work is the Kitāb faḍl al-khail (Excellence of horses), a collection of traditions concerning horses. It is divided into 8 chapters: (1) the merit of horses used in the jihād (holy war); (2) the castration of horses, a forbidden thing; (3) the choosing of horses, the colors to be preferred; (4) markings of evil omen; (5) competitions for prizes are forbidden, except with regard to horses and camels; (6) spoils belonging to the rider; (7) Muslim horses free from taxation; (8) names of the Prophet's horses. It is clear that the purpose of this work is mainly traditional and legal; but the student of natural history may find in it some little bits of information concerning Arabian horses.

A summary of it, entitled Qaṭr al-sail fī amr al-khail (Dropping of the flood in the matter of horses) was made by 'Umar ibn Raslān al-Bulqainī (d. 1402–1403).

Ḥājī Khalīfa (ed. Flügel, vol. 4, 562, no. 9535). F. Wüstenfeld: Geschichtschreiber der Araber (no. 379, 153, 1881). Léon Moulé: La médecine vétérinaire arabe (37, 1896). C. Brockelmann: Arabische Litteratur (vol. 2, 73, 1902).

See notes on al-Waṭwāṭ, al-Qazwīnī, Nāṣir al-dīn al-Ṭūsī, Muḥammad ibn Rushaid.

ILLUSTRATIONS OF ARABIC MANUSCRIPTS

There are beautifully illuminated Arabic (and Persian) MSS. of the thirteenth century representing plants and animals. I have often thought of investigating the subject but have had no time, and do not wish to delay the publication of this volume because of it. This is thus simply a note of warning to the reader. Of course a similar remark might be made with regard to western MSS. These are far better known, yet a general study of them from the point of view of the naturalist and of scientific iconography is still badly needed.

To return to the Arabic MSS., such illustrations as I have in mind may be found in copies of Dioscorides (representations of herbs), and of other medical writings, in cosmographies like that of al-Qazwīnī, in copies of the Manāfi' al-ḥayawān (The uses or virtues of animals). There is a magnificent example of an illustrated work bearing the last named title in the Pierpont Morgan Library in New York (dated 1291 or 1295). I have seen fine specimens of isolated pictures of plants and animals in the Metropolitan Museum, New York, in the Museum of Fine Arts, Boston, and in the Freer Gallery, Washington (five minatures from a thirteenth century Manāfi' al-ḥayawān). Some would probably be found in any large collection of Islamic MSS., and in many smaller ones.

The subject of oriental illustrated MSS. of Dioscorides is indicated, but not dealt with, by Charles Singer: The herbal in antiquity (Journal of Hellenic studies, vol. 47, p. 48, 1927; Isis, 10, 519–521).

Sir Thomas W. Arnold and Adolf Grohmann: The Islamic book. A contribution to its art and history from the seventh to the eighteenth century (130 p., 104 pl., Leipzig 1929). This beautiful volume is very disappointing from our point of view. However the following plates may arrest the reader's attention: 31 to 35, and 38. Four of these are taken from a Vienna MS. (National Library A. F. 10 of the first half of the thirteenth century), the Arabic translation of the first book of Galen's treatise on electuaries by John the Grammarian (see my vol. 1, 480); pl. 35 is taken from a Munich MS. (Cod. Arab. 464) of al-Qazwīnī's 'Ajā'ib al-makhlūqāt, dated 1279; pl. 38, from an Edinburgh MS. (Univ. Lib. no. 161) of al-Bīrūnī's Al-āthār al-bāqiya, dated 1307. The last named plate shows physicians about to perform the Caesarean operation (?).

Arménag Bey Sakisian: La miniature persane du XIIe au XVIIe siècle (190 p., 106 pl., Paris 1929).

V. CHINA

CH'ÊN CHIṆG-I

Ch'ên[2] Ching[3]-i[2] (658, 2143, 5438). Style name, Fei[2]-t'un[4] (3484, 12241). Born at T'ien[1]-t'ai[2] (11208, 10583), Chehkiang. He completed in 1256 a botanical encyclopaedia in 58 books, entitled Ch'üan[2]-fang[1] pei[4]-tsu[3] (3176, 3448, 8804, 11826). It deals with a large number of plants from the botanical, historical and literary points of view. It is divided into two main parts: the Ch'ien^{2} chi^{2*} (1737, 906) devoted to flowers (27 books); and the Hou^{4} chi^{2*} (4025, 906) or supplement, devoted to fruits, plants in general, herbs, trees, agriculture and sericulture, vegetables and medicinal plants (31 books). In imitation of ancient works, the material concerning each plant is classified in two sections: shih^{4} shih^{2*} tsu^{3} (9990, 9947, 11826) or prose descriptions, and fu^{4} yung^{4} tsu^{3} (3748, 13508, 11826) or poetical descriptions. This work contains abundant quotations from earlier writings; for example, the chapter on the lychee is largely a reproduction of the Li^{4}-chih^{1}-p'u^{3} by Ts'ai^{4} Hsiang^{1} (second half of eleventh century, vol. 1, 766).

Text—No printed copies of the Ch'üan-fang pei-tsu are known. There are many MSS. in Chinese libraries, and one bound in 20 vols. in the Library of Congress. This last copy was revised and edited by a Sung scholar, Chu^{1} Mu^{4*} (2544, 8073). It is thus possible that there were two editions of this work, the original, and the one revised by Chu Mu. A preface written by one Han^{2} Ching^{4} (3827, 2167) states that the book was presented to the Sung emperor Li^{3}-tsung^{1} (6879, 11976), who ruled from 1224 to 1264; this confirms the date (1256) given above.

Criticism—Hsü^{4*} Wên^{2}-hsien^{4} t'ung^{1}-k'ao^{3} (4773, 12633, 4530, 12294, 5966), chüan^{4} (3146) 186. Walter T. Swingle: Report of the Librarian of Congress (328–330, 1926; Isis, 10, 239). The Library of Congress has two Chinese editions, and one Korean, of the Wên hsien t'ung k'ao.

See note on Kublai Khān.

LI K'AN

Li^{3} K'an^{4} (6884, 5863). Flourished at the beginning of the Yüan dynasty. Chinese artist and botanist. He published in 1299 a treatise on the bamboo, in seven books, Ch'u^{4*} p'u^{3} hsiang^{2} lu^{4*} (2626, 9515, 4279, 7386), which became a standard work. It is divided into four sections: outline drawings of the bamboo, ink paintings of the bamboo, drawings of the bamboo under various conditions, drawings of various species of bamboo.

Though the purpose of this treatise is primarily artistic, it has also some scientific interest, especially the fourth section. For a proper appreciation of this characteristic mixture of artistic and scientific elements, one must read a Chinese treatise on painting, such as the Chieh^{4} tzŭ^{3} yüan^{2} hua^{4} ch'uan^{2} (1525, 12317, 13740, 5013, 2740), which was printed for the first time only in 1679 (second part in 1701), but represents very old Chinese traditions.

Text—The text of the treatise is included in the Yung^{3}-lo^{4*} Ta^{4}-tien^{3} (13504, 7331, 10470, 11177), q.v., first half of fifteenth century. Later editions were extracted from that encyclopaedia.

The Library of Congress has the Ch'u p'u hsiang lu with illustrations in the Chih^{1} pu^{1*} tsu^{2*} chai^{1} ts'ung^{1} shu^{1} (1783, 9456, 11840, 234, 12039, 10024), vols. 189–191; and the text without illustrations in the reprint entitled Wang^{2} shih^{4} shu^{1} hua^{4} yüan^{3} (12493, 9978, 10024, 5013, 13718), vol. 10.

It also has the Chieh tzŭ yüan hua ch'uan in the original edition of 1679 and 1701, and also in later editions. The Chieh tzŭ was translated into French by Raphaël Petrucci: Les enseignements de la peinture du jardin grand comme un grain de moutarde (532 p., folio, c. 500 illustr., Paris 1918; Isis, 4, 345–347).

Criticism—A. Wylie: Chinese painting (136, 1902). L. Wieger: La Chine (341, 530, 1920).

CHINESE ORNITHOLOGY

The earliest Chinese ornithological treatise is one called Ch'in[2] ching[1] (2099, 2122), treatise on birds, of which the earliest version may be very ancient, even anterior to the Han dynasty. This version is lost, however, and the text bearing that title now seems to have been written about the end of the Sung dynasty (1279), in spite of the fact that it is ascribed to much earlier writers, one Shih[1] K'uang[4] (9909, 6415), with a commentary by Chang[1] Hua[2] (416, 5005) of the Chin[4] (2069) dynasty, 265–420.

Text—The Library of Congress has the Ch'in ching in vol. 31 of the T'ang[2] sung[4] ts'ung[1] shu[1] (10767, 10462, 12039, 10024).
Criticism—A. Wylie: Chinese literature (153, 1902).

VI. JAPAN

KOREMUNE TOMOTOSHI

Japanese scholar who completed in 1282 the Honzō iroha shō. This is an index of the names of plants mentioned in the Chêng[4] lei[4] pên[3] ts'ao[3] (726, 6853, 8846, 11634) and other medical works. The Chêng lei pên ts'ao, published in China in 1108 and introduced soon afterwards into Japan, remained the standard work on materia medica in the latter country until the importation of the Pên ts'ao kang[1] mu[4]* (5900, 8080; kammu in Japanese) in 1607.

Mitsutaro Shirai: Scientific Japan (215–216, Tokyo 1925; Isis, 10, 83).

See my note on Seia in the medical chapter.

CHAPTER LII

MEDICINE

(Second Half of Thirteenth Century)

I. WESTERN CHRISTIANS

JORDAN RUFFO

Giordano Ruffo (or Rufo), Jordanus Ruffus (Rufus), Jourdain Ruf, etc. Calabrian veterinarian who flourished at the court of Frederick II Hohenstaufen, and died after 1250.

He completed c. 1252 and dedicated to Frederick's memory a treatise on the veterinary art, or more exactly on the medical treatment of horses, Liber mareschalchiae, in 76 chapters. It is derived from the Mulomedicina Chironis (vol. 1, 375) but also largely from personal experience. It was the first western treatise of its kind and was very popular; most of the later treatises were more or less dependent on it. It is the main representative of mediaeval veterinary medicine as opposed to the ancient mulomedicinae on the one hand, and to Carlo Ruini's treatise on the other (Dell' anotomia e del infermità del cavallo, 2 vols., Bologna 1598).

So many MSS. of it exist, in many languages (Latin, Italian, Sicilian dialect, German, French), that it is difficult to determine the original language (Sicilian? Latin?). There is also a Hebrew translation.

Text—First Latin edition by Hieronymus Molin (Padua 1818).

First Italian edition. Arte de cognoscere la natura d'caval laqual vulgarmente se chiama arte de mareschalci translata de latino di Miser Zordan Russo in vulgare per frate Gabriele Bruno (Venice 1492). This Gabriel Bruno was a Venetian Franciscan who flourished c. 1480. Later editions: Venice 1554, 1561; Bologna 1561; Venice 1563.

A fragment of a Neapolitan text is included in A. Bruce Whyte: Histoire des langues romanes (vol. 2, 153–156, Paris 1841).

Criticism—M. Steinschneider: Hebraeische Übersetzungen (807, 1893). L. Moulé: Histoire de la médecine vétérinaire (Fasc. 3, 25–30, 1900). Including list of MSS. Luigi Savastano: Pietro dei Crescenzi (p. 8, Acireale 1922; Isis, 6, 151). Robert Roth: Die Pferdeheilkunde des Jordanus Ruffus (Diss., Berlin 1928; includes a partial German translation).

See my notes on Faraj ben Salim, John of Capua, Bartholomew of Messina, Bartholomew Spadafora, Moses of Palermo.

JOHN OF PROCIDA

Giovanni da Procida. Procida is an islet in the gulf of Naples which belonged to his family, a noble Ghibelline family. Born c. 1210–1225 and educated in Salerno, he became physician and counsellor to Frederick II and later to Manfred.

After the latter's defeat and death (1266), the victor, Charles of Anjou, included John in his proscription of the Ghibellines and confiscated his estates. John took refuge at the court of Peter III of Aragon, then traveled to various other courts in southern Europe and even to Constantinople, as Peter's agent, to intrigue against the French rule in Sicily; he went to Sicily himself, and fanned the popular discontent, culminating in the so-called Sicilian Vespers, the massacre of the French, which broke out on Easter Monday at vesper time in 1282. He died c. 1298–1302.

He practised medicine until the last years of his life. He is said to have written a medical treatise, Utilissima practica brevis, which is lost. He was long remembered in the Neapolitan pharmacopoeia by a plaster called "empiastro di Giovanni da Procida." He compiled a collection of maxims ascribed to ancient philosophers.

Text—Liber philosophorum moralium . . . . quem transtulit de Greco in Latinum magister Johannes de Procida, edited in Salvatore de Renzi's Collectio salernitana (vol. 3, 69–150, Naples 1854). I have read a part of this; it does not sound at all like a translation from the Greek.

Criticism—S. de Renzi: Collectio salernitana (vol. 1, 311, 1852; vol. 3, 151–204, with portrait). Nouvelle biographie générale (vol. 41, 66–68, 1862). A. Hirsch: Biographisches Lexikon (vol. 2, 560, 1885).

La cronica del ribellamentu di Sicilia contra re Carlu, edited by Vincenzo di Giovanni (Soc. siciliana per la storia patria, Ricordi e documenti del Vespro siciliano, I, ix–xxiv, 1–85, 1882); edition with Italian translation by Filippo Evola (Palermo 1882).

See my notes on Bonacosa, Paravicius, and on the Borgognoni.

BRUNO DA LONGOBURGO

Italian surgeon who flourished c. 1252 at Padua. He was probably born at Longobucco (Cosenza) in Calabria, and educated at Salerno; he practised medicine in Padua and Verona.

His main surgical work, the Chirurgia magna, was completed at Padua in January 1252, and dedicated to one Andrew of Vicenza. It was largely derived from Arabic authors: al-Rāzī, Ḥunain ibn Isḥāq, Yaḥyā ibn Sarāfyūn, Abū-l-Qāsim, 'Alī ibn 'Abbās, Ibn Sīnā, and Ibn Rushd, plus some others transmitted by Constantine the African. His Arabic knowledge was derived from Latin translations. Bruno's Chirurgia magna represents a new stage in the Arabicization of Latin surgery. He was especially indebted to Abū-l-Qāsim, but he was himself an experienced surgeon, and refers many times to his own observations. Some time after 1252 he composed, at the request of one Lazarus of Padua, an abridgment of his treatise, entitled Chirurgia minor (or Chirurgia parva) and divided into 23 chapters.

The Chirurgia magna is divided into two books each containing 20 chapters. Book I deals with solutiones continuitatis, some of which are simplices, i.e., do not involve a loss of substance (wounds, fractures, luxations); others, compositae, i.e., involve such a loss (certain wounds, ulcers); healing requires for the former a iunctio partium solutarum, for the latter a regeneratio substantie deperdite. Book II deals with a great variety of other subjects: eye diseases, polypi in the nose, affections of the lips, mouth, and gullet, dentistry, earache, erysipelas, oedemata, cancer, bubo, dropsy, herniae, castration, warts, haemorrhoids, stones and lithotomy, etc.

Bruno recommended the dry process of wound healing (against the festering process), and spoke of healing by the first and by the second intention (prima, secunda intentio, in chapter 2 of book 1).

The Chirurgia magna was promptly translated into Hebrew by Hillel ben Samuel (died c. 1295), Sefer keritut (Book of cutting off).

Text—Both the Chirurgia magna and parva are included in the Collectio chirurgica veneta, not in the first edition (1497), but in the second (1498) and following (1499, 1513, 1519, 1546).
Criticism—M. Steinschneider: Hebraeische Übersetzungen (788, 1893). E. Gurlt: Geschichte der Chirurgie (vol. 1, 725–740, 1898).

WILLIAM OF SALICETO

Guglielmo da Saliceto, Guilelmus Placentinus. Italian physician and surgeon, the greatest surgeon of his time. Born c. 1210 at Saliceto, near Piacenza—hence his name Magister Placentinus—studied medicine and taught it in Bologna; in 1275 he was town physician in Verona; he died c. 1280 or later.

He began in Bologna c. 1271 the writing of a Cyrurgia and completed it in Verona 1275. Later he wrote a general treatise on medicine, Summa conservationis et curationis. It would seem that after the completion of the Summa he prepared an improved edition of the Cyrurgia. Lanfranchi was his pupil.

The Cyrurgia was dedicated to Buono del Garbo, a Bolognese surgeon, son-in-law of Taddeo Alderotti, and father of the Florentine physician Dino del Garbo (d. 1327). It is divided into five books: Book 1 deals with a great variety of subjects (roughly the same kind of subjects as in book II of Bruno's Chirurgia magna); book 2 with injuries and contusions in various parts of the body; book 3 with fractures and luxations; book 4 with surgical anatomy. This was the first attempt to write a topographical anatomy. It is not based upon human dissection; it is largely derived from earlier Latin anatomies; however a practising surgeon must necessarily make many anatomical observations, and such are found in the Cyrurgia (e.g., reference to intrathoracic organs of a wounded man). Special attention is paid to veins for the sake of venesection, in various kinds of luxations and herniae; book 5 deals with cauterization and drugs.

William did not mention as many authorities as Bruno; he quoted Galen and a few Arabians, also some contemporaries, but he was on the whole far more independent. His independence of Arabic tradition shows itself best in his reaction against excessive cauterization (as practised by the Muslim surgeons); he recommended the use of the scalpel instead of the cauter.

The Summa conservationis et curationis is also divided into five books: (1) special pathology and therapeutics a capite ad calcem; (2) fevers, in 38 chapters; (3) cosmetics (decoratio) and dermatology; (4) toxicology; (5) materia medica, antidotary in 32 chapters. The authors most often quoted are Hippocrates, Galen, al-Rāzī, and Ibn Sīnā. The Summa contains excellent advice with regard to bedside manners, diagnostic enquiries, gynaecology, hygiene and diet for every age of life. It is clear that William was not only an experienced surgeon, but also a very learned and very wise physician.

His works contain many good clinical cases. He realized the venereal contagion of certain ailments and indicated prophylactic measures. He gave a good account of melancholia and described a remarkable case of durities renum (Summa, book 1) which was the first indication of the group of symptoms associated with Bright's disease.

The Cyrurgia was very popular. There are early translations of it into Italian,

English and Bohemian, a translation into French by Nicole Prévost (medical student in Paris, 1472), and two partial translations into Hebrew. There is also a partial Hebrew translation of the Summa.

Text—The Cyrurgia was first printed in Piacenza 1476, then in Venice 1490, 1502, etc. Italian version, La cirosia vulgarmente fatta (1486). Nicole Prévost's French version, La Cyrurgie (Lyon 1492). Reprinted Paris 1505, 1596. New French edition by Paul Pifteau: La chirurgie de Guillaume Salicet (Toulouse 1898). Bohemian version (Prague 1867).

The Summa conservationis was first printed in Piacenza 1475 or 1476, then again in Venice 1489, 1490; Leipzig 1495, etc.

Many editions contain both works.

Criticism—M. Steinschneider: Hebraeische Übersetzungen (801–802, 1893). Hermann Grunow: Diätetik des W. Saliceto (Diss., Berlin 1895). Eugen Loewy: Beiträge zur Kenntnis und Würdigung des W. Saliceto als Arzt (Diss., Berlin 1897). Wilhelm Herkner: Kosmetik und Toxicologie nach W. Saliceto (Diss., Berlin 1897). Oscar Basch: Materialien zur Beurteilung des W. Saliceto als Arzt (Diss., Berlin 1898). E. Gurlt: Geschichte der Chirurgie (vol. 1, 754–765, 1898). Julius Pagel: Handbuch der Geschichte der Medizin (vol. 1, 719, 1902). M. Neuburger: Geschichte der Medizin (vol. 2, 380–384, 1911). K. Sudhoff: Beiträge zur Geschichte der Chirurgie im Mittelalter (vol. 2, 399–416, 1918). Includes various texts ascribed to Saliceto: De urinis; de hiis que ingrossant virile membrum et augmentant; flebotomia; consilium super impregnatione; etc.; also biographical data. Franz Otto Schaarschmidt: Die Anatomie des W. von Saliceto (Diss., 75 p., Leipzig 1919; Isis, 4, 585). Hans Georg Neugebauer: Die chirurgisch-klinische Kasuistik in den beiden Bearbeitungen der Chirurgia (Diss., 40 p., Leipzig 1924). Charles Singer: The evolution of anatomy (71, 170, New York 1926).

NOTE ON JOHN OF CARBONDALA

Having wrongly interpreted the explicit of a MS. of the Cyrurgia, entitled De operatione manuali, Vincenzo Malacarne concluded that the author was one Giovanni da Carbondala, surgeon of Santhià (Vercelli, Piedmont), c. 1275. Tiraboschi showed Malacarne his error, which the latter acknowledged. However it was reproduced in various works. I mention it here with the hope of eliminating it.

V. Malacarne: Delle opere de' medici e de' cerusici che nacquero o florirono primo del secolo XVI negli stati della real casa di Savoja (vol. 1, 24, Torino 1786). Girolamo Tiraboschi: Storia della letteratura italiana (vol. 4, 245, 1788). Hoefer: Nouvelle biographie générale (vol. 8, 676, 1855). Gerol. Boccardo: Nuova enciclopedia italiana (vol. 4, 1128, 1877). Unger: Hirsch's Biographisches Lexikon (vol. 1, 662, 1884; also in new edition, vol. 1, 827, 1929).

LANFRANCHI

Lanfranco, Lanfranc, Alanfranc, etc. Lanfrancus Mediolanensis. Italian surgeon who flourished in France and may be called the founder of French surgery. Died probably before 1306.

He originated in Milano; was a disciple of William of Saliceto, practised in Milano until his banishment by the Visconti c. 1290. He then proceeded to Lyon where he wrote the Chirurgia parva for the education of his sons; later he practised in other provincial cities of France, finally reaching Paris in or about 1295, where he obtained considerable success as a practitioner and teacher. Soon after his arrival in Paris he joined the surgeon's guild, Confrérie de Saint Côme, founded c. 1271 by Jean Pitart (?).

His teaching seems to have been a real clinical teaching, which was then a great novelty. He insisted upon the importance of the study of good clinical cases, and upon the necessity for surgeons to have a complete knowledge of medicine. By so doing he did much to raise the standards and the status of French surgeons. In 1296 he dedicated to Philip le Bel (king from 1285 to 1314) his great work, the Chirurgia magna.

His main sources were (roughly in chronological order), Hippocrates, Aristotle, Galen, Alexander Iatrosophista[1], Ḥunain ibn Isḥāq, al-Rāzī, Isḥāq al-Isrā'īlī, 'Alī ibn 'Abbās, Abū-l-Qāsim, Ibn Sīnā, Constantine the African, Copho, Ibn Sarābī, Matthew Platearius, Ibn Rushd, Maurus, Giles of Corbeil, Roger of Salerno, Mesuë the Third, Roland of Parma, Theodoric Borgognoni, and naturally his master William of Saliceto.

The Chirurgia parva is a surgical summary divided into 16 chapters.

The Chirurgia magna (Practica que dicitur ars completa totius cyrurgiae) is divided into five treatises: (1) Definition of surgery; qualities of the surgeon (he should be a complete physician), deontology, purposes of surgery. Anatomical and physiological summary. Wounds and ulcers. (2) Wounds of special parts, a capite ad calcem, together with the anatomy of these parts. (3) Other medical treatments, also a capite ad calcem, which are not properly or necessarily surgical. Hair and skin diseases; apostemata; eye, ear, nose, and throat ailments; herniae, stones and lithotomy, sexual malformations, hermaphroditism, dropsy, haemorrhoids, bloodletting, etc. (4) Fractures and luxations. (5) Antidotary.

It would be difficult to indicate all the novelties of the Chirurgia magna. The following may be quoted: e.g., excellent description of concussion of the brain, and of the symptoms of fracture of the skull; reaction against excessive trepanation—it should be restricted to cases when fragments of the skull are depressed or the dura mater is irritated; same moderation with regard to herniae—in most cases he recommends the use of trusses instead of the radical operation. He seemed to have been less prejudiced against cauterization than William of Saliceto. On the whole he gives one the impression of being a very experienced and wise surgeon and physician.

Various early translations extended Lanfranchi's influence outside of the Latin world (many surgeons did not read Latin, or did not read it with sufficient ease). The Chirurgia magna was twice translated into English before the middle of the fifteenth century; and one of these translations, dating from c. 1380, was the earliest surgical and anatomical work to appear in that language; the other was made some

[1] According to an investigation kindly made for me during proofreading by Miss M. C. Welborn, Alexander is quoted but once the in Chirurgia magna (doctrina 3, tract. 3, cap. 12) and the reference (nobilis Alexander) is not clear. Of course Lanfranchi was acquainted with Alexander of Tralles through Roger and Roland. I cannot remember now why I wrote Alexander "Iatrosophista." The term ἰατροσοφιστής, meaning a teacher of medicine or a learned physician, goes back at least to the beginning of the fifth century, e.g., Palladios (vol. 1, 392); hence it would be a correct designation of Alexander of Tralles as opposed to earlier physicians, such as Alexander Philalethes of Laodicea, first half of first century (Pauly-Wissowa, vol. 1, 1459, 1894), and Alexander of Aphrodisias, first half of third century. Other Byzantine designations which we shall come across in this volume were ἀκτουάριος, meaning court physician, and μυρεψός, unguentarius.

forty years later. A French translation was made by a surgeon of Lyon, William Ivoire (or Yvoire), c. 1490. The Chirurgia parva was translated into Spanish; and into German by the botanist, Otto Brunfels (d. 1531).

Both works were translated into Hebrew by unknown translators; the Chirurgia parva under the title Alanfranqina; the Chirurgia magna under the title Ḥokmah nishlamat be melakat ha-yad. A Hebrew text of the Parva is followed by a summary of the antidotary, which forms the fifth part of the Magna. There is also a Spanish translation of the antidotary in Hebrew script. The Hebrew transmission caused the author's name to be erroneously transformed into Leon Franco (Leon, Leo, Leone, being frequently chosen as a new name by Romanic Jews whose original name was Judah).

Text—Both texts are included in the Collectio chirurgica veneta, though not in the first edition of 1497 (Venice 1498, 1499, 1513, 1519, 1546).

The Chirurgia magna was first printed in Latin in Venice 1490, but the French translation by Guillaume Ivoire had appeared before (260 leaves, Lyon c. 1479). English translation, Lanfrank's Science of cirurgie, edited from the Bodleian Ashmole MS. 1396 (c. 1380) and the British Museum additional MS. 12056 (c. 1420), by Robert von Fleischhacker (Early English Text Society, 102, Part 1, Text, 355 p., London 1894).

Chirurgia parva. La cirurgia menor (Seville 1495). Otto Brunfels: Ein nutzlichs Wundertzney Büchlein des hochberümbten Lanfranci aus Fürbit des wolerfarnen Meister Gregorij Fleugaus Chyrurgen und Wundarzt zu Strasburg (47 p., Zwickaw 1529). John Halle: A most excellent and learned worke of chyrurgerie, called Chirurgia parva Lanfranci, Lanfranke of Mylayne his briefe: reduced from dyvers translations to our vulgar or usual frase and now first published in the Englyshe prynte by John Halle chirurgien etc. (London 1565).

Dutch edition, Chyrurgie Langrancks (Antwerp 1529).

Criticism—M. Steinschneider: Leon (Ersch und Grubers Encycklopädie, vol. 43, 118–122; reprinted in Gesammelte Schriften, vol. 1, 216, 1925); Hebraeische Übersetzungen (807, 1893).

Emile Littré: Histoire littéraire de la France (vol. 25, 284–294, 1869). E. Gurlt: Geschichte der Chirurgie (vol. 1, 765–791, 1898). Julius Pagel: Puschmann's Handbuch (vol. 1, 722–727, 1902). Albert Werk: Die angebliche practica avium et equorum des Lanfrancus de Mediolano. Ein Beitrag zur Geschichte der Veterinärmedizin im 14. Jahrh. (Diss., Giessen, 75 p., Danzig 1909.) This treatise on veterinary art attached to the Chirurgie is apocryphal, and dates from the second half of the fourteenth century. M. Neuburger: Geschichte der Medizin (vol. 2, 385–388, 1911). Romanus Johannes Schaefer: Starlehre und Staroperation bei den mittelalterlichen Chirurgen im Abendlande (Georg Sticker Festgabe, 49–53, 1930; Isis, 15, 214).

HUMAN DISSECTIONS

It would seem that human dissections began to be made in Christendom in the second half of the thirteenth century. I say in Christendom, because dissections were almost certainly practised in Greek and Hellenistic times. Such dissections are implied in the Hippocratic treatises on fractures and dislocations (περὶ ἀγμῶν, περὶ ἄρθρων ἐμβολῆς) dating from the beginning of the fourth century B. C., if not earlier (vol. 1, 119), and they were certainly made by the great Alexandrian anatomists, Herophilos and Erasistratos (first half of the third century B. C.). To return to mediaeval times and to Christendom, the first traces of dissections appear in this time. It is probable that the earliest dissections were made not for anatomical but for legal reasons, post-mortem examinations to determine the cause of death. It is not surprising that they seem to have been made in Bologna, which was then at once the greatest school of law and the greatest school of surgery and medicine of Europe.

Some evidence of human dissection may be found in the Cyrurgia of William of Saliceto, completed in 1275, and post-mortems are referred to by Taddeo Alderotti who taught in Bologna from 1260 on and died in 1303. The Franciscan Salimbene of Parma (died in or after 1288) refers in his Latin chronicle to the opening of a corpse and examination of the heart by a physician of Cremona in 1286. This is the earliest definite reference to a post-mortem. The first formal account of one was made a few years later, in 1302, by Bartolommeo da Varignana. There is a curious drawing illustrating a dissection scene, in a Bodleian MS. (MS. Ashmole 399, fo. 34r) dating from about the same time (1300 ± 25).

In the absence of other evidence, we may assume temporarily that human dissections began to be practised in Bologna before 1275; but such dissections or post-mortem examinations must have remained very rare occurrences in the thirteenth century; in the first half of the fourteenth century their number increased considerably.

This fact alone would suffice to disprove the theory according to which such dissections were forbidden by the church in 1300: for before 1300 they were very rare, after 1300 they became more common, as I shall show in vol. 3.

The church did not formally prohibit dissections, but in 1300 Boniface VIII (pope from 1294 to 1303) issued the bull De sepulturis, forbidding the cutting up of corpses and their boiling in order to separate the bones from the flesh. This strange practice had grown largely as a result of the Crusades; its purpose was to make possible the repatriation of the bones of people who died in distant countries and the proper burial of their bones in their own parish.

However if Boniface's bull was not directed against dissection, the church must have shown its hostility to it, or distrust of it, in other ways. It is highly probable that the early dissections were controlled by ecclesiastical authorities, and such control, though irksome at times, must have been also a protection for the anatomists and surgeons properly engaged in their duties. That some sort of control and even prohibition existed is proved by a statement in the preface of the anatomy by Guido of Vigevano (1345): "Quia prohibitum est ab Ecclesia, facere anathomiam in corpore humano . . . ."

It is certain that the Christians had strong prejudices against dissection, for such prejudices are still deeply rooted to-day. Nor were these prejudices peculiar to the Christians; they were shared by Muslims and Jews, if anything with greater force, because of the Semitic abhorrence of blood. The relatively low status of surgeons, as compared with physicians, was largely due to that repulsion. There can be no doubt that the progress of anatomical studies was considerably delayed by such psychological conditions, and the delays must have been greater in mediaeval times when social and personal inhibitions due to prejudice were incomparably stronger, and when there was no organized means of resisting them.

James J. Walsh: The popes and science (Knights of Columbus edition, 28–60, New York 1913). The Latin text of the bull De sepulturis is given on p. 413–414. "Corpora defunctorum exenternantes, et ea immaniter decoquentes ut ossa a carnibus separata ferant sepelienda in terram suam, ipso facto sunt excommunicati" etc.

Further notes on the thirteenth century anatomy.

Christoph Ferckel: Literarische Quellen der Anatomie im 13. Jahrhundert (Archiv für Gesch. d. Naturw., vol. 6, 78–82, 1913). Charles Singer: Thirteenth century miniatures illustrating medical practice (Proc. R. S. of Med., hist. section, vol. 9, 29–42, 1916); Note on a thirteenth century diagram of the male genitalia (ibidem, vol. 9, 212–214, 1916); A thirteenth century drawing of the anatomy of the uterus and adnexa (ibidem, vol. 9, 43–47, 1916). Karl Sudhoff: Graphische Darstellungen innerer Körperorgane (Archiv für Geschichte der Medizin, vol. 7, 367–378, 3 pl., 1914; Isis, 3, 326); Die Oxforder anatomische Fünfbilderserie der Cod. Ashmole 399 (ibidem, vol. 7, 363–366; 5 pl., 1914; Isis, 3, 326); Die Anatomie und die Kirche im Mittelalter (Mit. zur Gesch. d. Med., vol. 14, 92, 1915; Isis, 3, 326). Christoph Ferckel: Diagramme der Sexualorgane in mittelalterlichen Handschriften (Archiv für Geschichte der Medizin, vol. 10, 255, 1917). One ninth century and five thirteenth century drawings. Ludwig Choulant: History and bibliography of anatomic illustration, translated by Mortimer Frank (Chicago 1920; Isis, 4, 357). Karl Sudhoff: Neue Uterus-Zeichnungen in einer bisher unbekannt gebliebenen Mustio-Handschrift zu Vicenza (Archiv für Geschichte der Medizin, vol. 17, 1–11, 1 pl., 1925). Charles Singer: Evolution of anatomy (71–74, 1926). See my note on Giles of Rome.

JOHN OF PARMA

Giovanni da Parma. Author of a short treatise on medicine, Practicella. He was probably a Franciscan, flourishing about and after 1250.

There are many other Johns of Parma, and one of them, Giovanni Buralli, born at Parma c. 1209, was the seventh general of the Franciscans, from 1247 to 1257, and died in 1289.

Moritz Arndt Mehner: Johannes von Parma und seine Practicella (Diss., 42 p., Leipzig 1918; Isis, 4, 585). Includes the text of the Practicella and a list of the drugs mentioned.

ALDOBRANDIN OF SIENA

Aldobrandinus de Senis, Aldobrandino da Siena, Aldebrandin de Sienne; and many variants: Halebrandis, Helebrandis, Albrandas; sometimes also Florence instead of Siena.

Tuscan physician, who became physician to Beatrice of Savoy, countess of Provence (wife of Raymond Berenger IV), and later possibly to her son-in-law, St. Louis; he died in Troyes, Champagne, 1287. He wrote c. 1256–1257 a medical treatise, Le régime du corps, at Beatrice's request, on the occasion of a journey which she undertook to visit her four daughters, the Queen of France, the Queen of England, the Queen of Germany (i.e., the wife of Richard, earl of Cornwall, elected king of the Romans in 1257), and the countess of Anjou (later Queen of Sicily).

The Régime du corps is divided into four main parts dealing respectively with (1) general hygiene, De garder le cors tot ausi le bien sain com le mal sain generaument; (2) special hygiene of various organs, De garder cascun menbre par lui (hair, eyes, ears, teeth and gums, face, stomach, liver, heart); (3) dietetics, Des simples coses qu'il convient a oume user (cereals, beverages, meat, birds, beans, fruits, herbs, fish, varia); (4) physiognomy.

Parts 1 and 2 are derived mainly from Ibn Sīnā, and secondarily from al-Rāzī and

'Ali ibn 'Abbās; part 3 is an adaptation of the Kitāb al-adwiya al-mufrada wal-aghdhiya of Isḥāq al-Isrā'īlī; part 4 is translated almost verbatim from the Kitāb al-Manṣūrī of al-Rāzī (book 2, chs. 26 to 58). Needless to say, all these Arabic texts were known to Aldobrandin only through Latin translations. Besides the authors already quoted, he was also acquainted with Ḥunain ibn Isḥāq and Constantine the African.

The most important part from the purely medical point of view is the first. It deals with such subjects as air (climate), eating, drinking, sexual life, bathing, bloodletting, purgation, use of cupping glasses and leeches (but hardly any mention of clysters), hygiene of pregnant women and of babies, hygiene of travelers, how to protect oneself against plagues, etc.

Le Régime du corps is the first monument of French medical literature, and one of the first of French scientific literature. It was a little earlier than Li livres dou tresor of Brunetto Latini (c. 1266). It is written in a strange dialect, Picard-Walloon, with but very few Italianisms. The chapter on pediatrics in book 1 contains by far the earliest examples of the words papa and maman.

The popularity of the Régime du corps is proved by the abundance of MSS., at least 35, plus many others in Italian representing two different versions. One of these Italian versions, completed in 1310 by Zucchero Bencivenni, notary of Florence, is an important text from the linguistic point of view.

Text—First edition, Le livre pour garder la santé du corps (78 leaves, Lyon c. 1481). This is the only French incunabulum, but there are two other partial editions in Italian. Philosomia degli uomini, in verse, by Battista Caracino (4 leaves, Florence c. 1489; again c. 1492–1500). These three incunabula are the only ones quoted in the Gesamtkatalog der Wiegendrucke (vol. 1, 423–424, 1925).

There are various other partial editions in Italian, most of which, if not all, represent the Bencivenni version. Giuseppe Manuzzi: Il libro delle segrete cose delle donne (22 p., Florence 1863); Libro della cura delle malattie (58 p., Florence 1863). E. Teza: Trattatello di fisiognomonia (Bologna 1864). G. Manuzzi: Trattato di fisionomia (Florence 1865–1867). Otto Targioni Tozzetti: Le quattro stagioni e come l'uomo si dee guardare il corpo in ciascheduno tempo del'anno (Leghorn 1871); Trattatello (Leghorn 1872; chapter on pediatrics). G. Manuzzi: Trattato dei cinque sensi dell' uomo (32 p., Florence 1872). Picielleesse (i.e.. Luigi Savorini): Dottrina a guardare il visaggio e donarli bello colore (Forum Cornelii, 1872). Francesco Zambrini: Del conservare i capelli e i denti (Imola 1876); Ammaestramenti a conservare la sanita del corpo e come la femmina si dee guardare quanto e incincta e come governare il fanciullo si tosto ch'è nato (Bologna 1889).

Critical edition of the original French text by Louis Landouzy and Roger Pépin: Le régime du corps (340 p., Paris 1911). With preface by Antoine Thomas, curious illustrations from the MSS., a valuable introduction by the main editor, Pépin, and a very elaborate glossary.

Criticism—Emile Littré: Histoire littéraire de la France (vol. 21, 415–418, 1847). Antoine Thomas: L'identité d'Aldebrandin de Sienne (Romania, vol. 35, 454–456, 1906; Janus, 545, 646, 1906). J. B. Soalhat: Les idées de maistre Alebrand de Florence sur la puériculture (Thèse, Paris 1908). E. O. von Lippmann: Aldebrandino's Régime du Corps (Chemiker Zeitung, 1912; also Abhdl. und Vorträge, vol. 2, 237–249, 1913). Examination from the chemical standpoint.

SIMON OF GENOA

Simon Januensis or Geniates a Cordo, Simon de Cordo. Italian lexicographer, botanist, physician, who flourished about the end of the thirteenth century. He was canon of Rouen, physician to Nicholas IV (pope from 1288 to 1292), and chaplain to Boniface VIII (pope from 1294 to 1303).

He devoted some thirty years of his life to the compilation of a dictionary of materica medica entitled Synonyma medicinae or Clavis sanationis. This work, completed during Nicholas' papacy if not earlier, with a dedication to and a preface by the mathematician Giovanni Campano, was based at once upon linguistic and botanical investigations. The philologic point of view was predominant. Because of the juxtaposition of technical terms derived from a great variety of sources and from at least three languages (Greek, Arabic, and Latin), the medicinal nomenclature (including of course the botanical one) had then become extremely confusing. Simon addressed himself—and was the first to do so in full earnest—to the gigantic task of putting order into that chaos. He succeeded in doing this only to some extent, but the success of his effort must be judged in the light of the great difficulties to be overcome and of his pioneering spirit. The Synonyma contained some 6000 articles; it was one of the most erudite works of his time; it was deemed indispensable at least until the middle of the sixteenth century and it is still very useful to-day for the study of mediaeval terminology. Simon is said to have traveled extensively in order to collect his materials.

According to his own statements, his main sources were (I quote them roughly in chronological sequence) Celsus, Dioscorides (of which he used two Latin versions), the ophthalmological treatise of Demosthenes Philalethes (now lost), Pliny, Galen, Oribasios, Theodorus Priscianus, Cassius Felix, Moschion, Alexander Iatrosophista, Isidore of Seville, Paulos Aegineta, Ibn Māsawaih, al-Rāzī, Isḥāq al-Isrā'īlī, Abū-l-Qāsim, 'Ali ibn 'Abbās, Ibn Sīnā, Gariopontus, Constantine the African, Nicholas of Salerno, Ibn Sarābī. The most striking fact about these sources is that none is very old, say pre-Christian, or none very recent. The latest in my list is Ibn Sarābī who flourished before Ibn al-Baiṭār (d. 1248). Most of these texts were available in Latin, and it is probable that Simon read them in Latin. He showed some freedom in using them, and did not hesitate to criticize even Ibn Sīnā.

With the help of Abraham ben Shem-ṭob, acting as dragoman, he translated from the Arabic, or more probably from the Hebrew, the materia medica (bk. 28) of the Kitāb al-taṣrīf of Abū-l-Qāsim (Liber servitoris), and the Kitāb al-adwiya al-mufrada (Liber de simplici medicina) of Ibn Sarābī. See my note on Abraham ben Shem-ṭob below.

Some MSS. of the Clavis sanationis contain additions by one Mundinus de Foro Julio or Friulensis. This author (not to be confused with his contemporary the great anatomist Mondino de' Luzzi, d. 1326) was born in Cividale del Friùli (near Udine, Venetia), practised medicine in Padua, and died in 1340.[1a]

Text—Synonyma medicinae seu Clauis sanationis. First edition, Ferrara 1471–1472? This edition seems to be lost except for a fragment of 21 leaves in the Bodleian. Later editions: Milano 1473 (157 leaves, folio, two columns); Padua 1474 (162 leaves folio); Venice 1486, 1507, 1510, 1513, 1514; Lyon 1534.

Liber servitoris liber XXVIII Bulchasin Benaberazerin translatus a Simone

[1a] According to A. Hirsch: Biographisches Lexikon der Aerzte (vol. 4, 264, 1886).

Januensi interprete Abraam judeo tortuosiensi (64 leaves quarto, Venice 1471). Later editions: Naples 1478, Venice 1479; etc.

Liber Serapionis aggregatus in medicinis simplicibus (185 leaves folio, Milano 1473). Later editions: Venice 1479, Strassburg 1531, Venice 1552; etc.

Criticism—Ernst H. F. Meyer: Geschichte der Botanik (vol. 4, 159–167, 1857). L. Leclerc: Médecine arabe (vol. 2, 470, 1876). Julius Pagel: Puschmann's Handbuch (vol. 1, 679–681, 1902). Pierre Guigues: Les noms arabes dans Sérapion, Liber de simplici medicina. Essai de restitution et d'identification de noms arabes de médicaments usités au Moyen âge (137 p., reprinted from Journal asiatique, 1905; Paris, 1905; the reprint has 4 additional p. of errata; Arabic index). Hermann Fischer: Mittelalterliche Pflanzenkunde (70–74, München 1929; Isis, 15, 367–370).

M. Steinschneider: Abhandlung über Synonyma (appended to Julius Pagel's edition of Henri de Mondeville, Berlin 1892); Hebraeische Übersetzungen (737, 740, 800, 1022, 1893); Europaeische Übersetzungen (76, 1904).

TADDEO ALDEROTTI

Thaddaeus Florentinus. Italian physician, one of the founders of the medical school of Bologna.

Born in Florence c. 1223; brought up in dire poverty, his education could not be started until relatively late; c. 1245 and following years he studied medicine and philosophy in Bologna; in 1260 he began to teach in Bologna, and nine years later to write; he died in 1303.

Under the influence of the law school of Bologna, then at the full tide of its prosperity, he taught medicine in the scholastic manner, great importance being given by him to the logical elaboration of the subject. He was far surpassed in that direction a little later by Peter of Abano (d. c. 1317). In spite of these dialectic proclivities, he was a practical and very successful physician.

He attended dissections of animals, and probably human autopsies. Indeed there are a few hints of post-mortem examinations in his writings, and we may safely assume that, though such examinations were very exceptional before the fourteenth century, they were occasionally practised within his time. However his anatomical knowledge was largely derived from the writings of the Greek and Arabic physicians.

He made clinical observations, the most valuable of which were collected in his Consilia medicinalia, which inaugurated (or more exactly reestablished) a new type of medical literature of exceptional importance for the progress of medicine.

He wrote abundant commentaries on Hippocrates, Galen, and on the Isagoge of Ḥunain ibn Isḥāq, and a treatise on hygiene (De conservanda sanitate) which he translated into Italian. He was also very well acquainted with the Qānūn and other writings of Ibn Sīnā, and his library contained not only the works already mentioned, but also the Liber Almansoris of al-Rāzī, the Practica of Yaḥyā ibn Sarāfyūn, etc.

He translated from Latin into Italian the Ethics of Aristotle. This was the translation criticized by Dante in the Convivio (1, 10), though the phrase "ciò fu Taddeo ippocratista" is a gloss; there may be another reference to this Taddeo in Paradiso (XII, 83).

He criticized the translations of Constantine the African, and praised those of Burgundio of Pisa. He realized the necessity of direct translations of the medical classics from Greek into Latin and encouraged their preparation.

His influence was truly considerable, and was multiplied by his famous pupils Bartolomeo da Varignana, Henry de Mondeville, and Mondino de' Luzzi. Remembering perhaps the insecurity of his own youth, he exacted enormous fees from his patients, notably from Honorius IV (pope from 1285 to 1287).

His writings contain autobiographical references; e.g., to his somnambulism (Comm. on Isagoge, ch. 10).

A little treatise on the treatment of fever was translated into Hebrew, Kelal qaẓer 'al minhag ha-qadaḥot, by Moses ben Immanuel in 1468. Another Hebrew text ascribed to him by an unknown translator is entitled Lequṭim (Gleanings).

Text—Commentaria in artem parvam Galeni (Naples 1522).

Expositiones in arduum aphorismorum Hippocratis volumen, in divinum prognosticorum Hippocratis librum, in praeclarum regiminis acutorum Hippocratis opus, in subtilissimum Joannitii isagogarum libellum (Venice 1527). Considering the brevity of the Isagoge, Taddeo's commentary is very long. A part of it was translated into German by Robert von Töply: Mann und Weib (Wiener klinische Rundschau, 1899).

Thaddaeus de Florentia: De regimine sanitatis, together with Benedictus de Nursia: De conservatione sanitatis (140 leaves, Bologna 1477). Described in William Osler: Incunabula medica (no. 129, Oxford 1923). The De regimine sanitatis is not Taddeo's in spite of the title; is it the one by John of Seville?

Giuseppe Manuzzi: Libello per conservare la sanità con una ricetta inedita di Maestro Taddeo da Firenze, volgarizzato nel buon secolo della lingua (12 p., Firenze 1863).

The Consilia medicinalia are still unpublished, except for a few fragments quoted below.

Criticism—A. Hirsch: Biographisches Lexikon (vol. 5, 606, 1887). M. Steinschneider: Hebraeische Übersetzungen (832, 1893). Julius Pagel: Handbuch der Geschichte der Medizin (vol. 1, 668–669, 1902). M. Neuburger: Geschichte der Medizin (vol. 2, 373–377, 1911). Edmund O. von Lippmann: Thaddäus über den Weingeist (Archiv für Geschichte der Medizin, vol. 7, 379–389, 1914). On the medical value of alcohol; contains the text of the end of the Consilia (Isis, 3, 325). Aldo Mieli: Pagine di storia della chimica (p. 146–155, Roma 1922). Herbert Löschburg: Zahnärztliches aus den Consilien des Thaddäus (Diss., 54 p., Leipzig 1922). Text of the Consilia relating to dentistry, with commentary, biography and bibliography. C. Singer: Evolution of anatomy (72, 1926). L. Thorndike: Vatican Latin MSS. (Isis, 13, 71, 1929).

WILLIAM CORVI

William of Brescia, Guglielmo Corvi, Guilelmus Brixiensis. Italian physician (1250–c. 1326).

Born at Canneto near Brescia in 1250; professor of logic in Padua 1274–1279; later studied medicine at Bologna under Taddeo Alderotti; physician to Boniface VIII (pope, 1294 to 1303), then to Clement V (pope, 1305–1314) whom he followed to Avignon, perhaps also to John XXII (pope, 1316–1334); he obtained from these popes various ecclesiastical honors—e.g., the archdiaconate of Bologna in 1313; however he continued to reside in Avignon until his departure for Paris sometime after Clement's death; he spent the end of his life in Paris, dying in or after 1326.

His main work is a textbook on practical medicine entitled Aggregatoris dictorum illustrium medicorum ad unamquamque egritudinem a capite ad pedes practica, but generally called, for short, Aggregator, or Aggregator brixiensis (Aggregator also became the author's nickname). William continued the scholastic tendencies of his master Taddeo, and his Aggregator is an uncritical compilation of as many medical opinions as he could collect on every disease, arranged from head to foot. The Aggregator was often taken as a model by subsequent writers; it represents a type of medical literature of which there are many other examples and which is not yet entirely extirpated.

He wrote various shorter treatises, less ambitious but possibly more valuable, on fevers, on stones in the kidneys and the bladder, on surgery, etc. The plague treatise ascribed to him is apocryphal; it is derived from a treatise by Pietro da Tossignano (d. 1407).

Finally he wrote a number of consilia. Judging from those available to me he was a good observer, but not wise enough for his learning, of which he was unable to free himself. He was a very erudite but not a creative physician.

Text—The Aggregator brixiensis was printed in Venice 1500 and 1508. I can vouch only for the second of these editions.

Erich Walter Georg Schmidt: Die Bedeutung Wilhelms von Brescia als Verfasser von Konsilien (Diss., 60 p., Leipzig 1922). Includes the text of a few consilia, with lists of drugs and of sources (Isis, 5, 501).

Walter Georg Zieger: Ein Traktat Wilhelm's von Brescia über Nieren- und Blasensteine (Diss., 26 p., Leipzig 1925; Isis, 8, 744).

Criticism—Julius Pagel: Puschmann's Handbuch (vol. 1, 673, 1902). Fabio Glissenti: Nuovi documenti su Guglielmo Corvi (11 p., Brescia 1914; reviewed in Mitt. zur Geschichte der Medizin, vol. 15, 151). K. Sudhoff: Beiträge zur Geschichte der Chirurgie (vol. 2, 419–421, 1918). Giving the beginning and contents of the Cyrurgia magistri Wilhelmi de Brixia. K. Sudhoff: Ein tractatus de pestilentia domini Guilelmi Brixiensis? (Archiv für Geschichte der Medizin, vol. 16, 112–114, vol. 17, 243, 1925.)

JOHN OF AQUILA

Unknown physician who flourished probably in the thirteenth century, and who was probably a Frenchman. He composed a Latin poem (582 lines) on bloodletting, De flebotomia (verse 491 is French). He may be the author of another medical treatise, in Latin prose, De duricie et apostemate matricis vera et experta nota. Gilbert the Englishman being quoted in this second treatise, it can hardly have been written before the second half of the thirteenth century; but even if John is the author of both works, the De flebotomia may be somewhat earlier than the other.

Arthur Morgenstern: Das Aderlassgedicht des Johannes von Aquila und seine Stellung in der Aderlasslehre des Mittelalters, samt den Abdruck der lateinischen Übersetzung der Schrift Peri flebotomia Ypocratis nach den Handschriften in Brüssel und Dresden (Diss., Leipzig, 80 p., Leipzig 1917). Contains list of writings on bloodletting down to the present one.

See my note on Giovanni dell' Aquila (second half of the fifteenth century).

THE FOUR MASTERS

A famous commentary on the Practica chirurgiae of Roger of Salerno (fl. c.1170) and on the Chirurgia of Roland of Parma (beginning of the thirteenth century) was composed by four masters, Quattuor magistri, at an unknown time. I have already referred to it in my note on Roland. It is entitled Glossulae quatuor magistrorum, scilicet Archimathaei, Petroncelli, Platearii et Ferrarii super cyrurgiam Rogerii et Rolandi. This title is obviously absurd, since the four masters named were all anterior to Roland, and some of them even to Roger. These Glossulae were probably composed in France c. 1260–1270; certainly not much later for they were already known to the Flemish surgeon Jan Yperman (d. 1330–1331). On the other hand they may possibly be earlier at least in their original form, and date from Roger's own time; Roland's name would then have been added to the title of a later edition to increase its up-to-dateness. It is possible also that the "four masters" never existed except in the imagination of an enterprising commentator who tried to give more weight to his own work.

Whatever the exact date and origin of the Glossulae, they are divided in the same way as Roger's Practica and Roland's Chirurgia; i.e., into four books. In fact, for a proper study of mediaeval surgery it is well to consider these three texts together as a single body of practice and doctrine, representing the accumulation of a century of experience.

Text—The Glossulae were first edited by Charles Daremberg, in S. de Renzi: Collectio salernitana (vol. 2, 497–724, 1853). Daremberg's introduction was translated into Italian and annotated by de Renzi (ibidem, vol. 3, 205–254, 1854).

An earlier text was edited by Francesco Puccinotti: Storia della medicina (vol. 2, 662–795, 1859).

Criticism—A. Hirsch: Biographisches Lexikon (vol. 6, 108, 1888). E. Gurlt: Geschichte der Chirurgie (vol. 1, 703–720, 1898). Contains an analysis of the three treatises, indicating many peculiarities of each. Karl Sudhoff: Beiträge zur Geschichte der Chirurgie im Mittelalter (vol. 2, by index, 1918).

JOHN OF SAINT AMAND

Joannes de Sancto Amando. Belgian physician who flourished in Paris and died at the beginning of the fourteenth century.

John was born at Tournai in Hainaut, or at Saint Amand en Pévèle near Valenciennes; he studied medicine probably in Paris, and taught there for a long time; he was canon of Tournai, where he died full of years, probably before 1312. He was primarily a compiler, and wrote summaries of Greek and Arabic medicine and materia medica. His manner was largely dialectical and uncritical, yet he could make eventually good observations and tried to react against excessive scholasticism and against the more superstitious practices of his day (he was by no means free either of superstition or of scholasticism); he had even some inkling of the experimental method and he discussed it; he helped to revive the study of Hippocrates and Galen, and his compilations were one of the main channels through which the Arabicized Greek medicine flowed into western Christendom and especially into France.

His fame is based upon two works: (1) a commentary on the antidotary of Nicholas of Salerno, Expositio sive additio super antidotarium Nicolai, which shared the popularity of the antidotary itself and increased it; (2) a medical compendium called Revocativum memoriae.

The commentary on Nicholas is a treatise on general therapeutics centered upon the actions of drugs. It is divided into three main parts, dealing respectively with digestion (i.e., πέψις), evacuation (spontaneous, or artificial by means of purgation, bloodletting, leeches, etc.), restauration or upbuilding. Much importance is attached to bloodletting, uroscopy, and calendric diet. The Arabic polypharmacy is not too much in evidence. The main sources are Hippocrates, Aristotle, Galen, al-Rāzī, Ḥunain ibn Isḥāq, Isḥāq al-Isrā'īlī, 'Alī ibn 'Abbās, Ibn Sīnā, Constantine the African, Ibn Sarābī, Platearius, Roger of Salerno. The commentary was twice translated into Hebrew; one of these translations was made in 1403 by Isaac ben Abraham Cabret.[2]

The Revocativum memoriae is composed of three parts which might be considered independent works: (a) Areolae; (b) Concordantiae; (3) Abbreviationes librorum Galeni.

The Areolae or Tractatus de virtutibus et operationibus medicinarum simplicium et compositarum is a materia medica arranged, first, in the alphabetical order of pharmacodynamic headings (abstersiva, adustiva, aperitiva, attractiva, corrosiva, consolidantia, confortativa, constrictiva, constringentia sanguinem, exsiccativa, frangentia acuitatem, dissolventia ventositatem, conglutinativa, incisiva, inflativa, lenitiva, lavativa, mundificativa, maturativa, putrefacienta, diuretica, resolutiva, rubificantia, subtiliativa, styptica, stupefactiva, vesicantia); then in order of organs, ending with a list of purgatives; this is followed by directions on the making up of prescriptions, and a defense of compound drugs. The main sources are Galen, Ibn Sīnā, Māsawaih al-Māridīnī, Ibn Sarābī, and Nicholas of Salerno.

The Concordantiae, which forms the main part of the Revocativum, is a collection of sentences extracted mainly from Galen and Ibn Sīnā, and arranged in alphabetical order of pathological subjects. The differences of opinion are indicated by the author who then proceeds to explain them away, hence the title concordantiae. It is a real dictionary of internal pathology. It was continued or amplified in the fourteenth century by a Parisian physician called Peter de Saint Flour[3] (Petrus de Sancto Floro).

The Abbreviationes librorum Galeni (operum omnium rememorationes, divisiones, sententiae summariae) gives the contents of the main writings of Galen. It is a sort of Galenic epitome.

The number of MSS. shows the popularity of John's works. They were often quoted; e.g., by Guy de Chauliac and Jacques Despars; and they were also imitated.

Text—The Expositio sive additio super antidotarium Nicolai was printed in Venice 1485, together with Māsawaih al-Māridīnī (Mesuë junior), and was often reprinted in the Venetian editions of Mesuë (Venice 1527, 1549, 1562, 1589).

Parts of it have been printed separately: the De balneis in the Venetian collection bearing the same title (Venice 1553, 1581); De usu idoneo auxiliorum in Christopher Heyll: Artificialis medicatio (Mayence 1534); Flebotomia in K. Günther's paper quoted below.

Julius Pagel: Die Areolae (165 p., Berlin 1894).

Julius Pagel: Die Concordantiae nebst einem Nachtrage über die Concordantiae des Petrus de Sancto Floro (488 p., Berlin 1895); Neue literarische Beiträge zur mittelalterlichen Medizin (Berlin 1896).

Other parts of the Revocativum have been published by Pagel's pupils as follows: Otto Paderstein: Über Joh. de Sancto Amando nebst einem Teil des Revocativum (Diss., Berlin 1892). K. Eicksen: Historisches über Krisen und kritische Tage (Diss., Berlin 1893). A. Müller-Kypke: Über die Ars parva Galeni, aus dem

[2] The name is spelled Qabreṭ or Qabriṭ in Hebrew script. I write Cabret, because it is really of Spanish origin. This Cabret will be dealt with in vol. 3.

[3] There is a town of that name in Auvergne (Cantal).

Revocativum (Diss., Berlin 1893). F. Petzold: Über die Schrift des Hippocrates "Von der Lebensordnung in akuten Krankheiten "nebst dem Schluss des Revocativum (Diss., Berlin 1894). R. Reichel: Zur Literaturgeschichte der antiken Arzneimittellehre (Diss., Berlin 1894). H. Ehlers: Zur Pharmakologie des Mittelalters unter besonderer Berücksichtigung der Areolae (Diss., Berlin 1895).

Criticism—E. Littré: Histoire littéraire de la France (vol. 21, 254–266, 1847). Biographisches Lexikon der Aerzte (vol. 1, 117, 1884; in new edition, p. 108). Victor Jacques: Biographie nationale de Belgique (vol. 10, 415–418, 1889; unsatisfactory). M. Steinschneider: Hebraeische Übersetzungen (806, 1893). Max Neuburger: Geschichte der Medizin (vol. 2, 370–372, 1911). Alexander Tschirch: Handbuch der Pharmacognosie (vol. 1, 873, 1909). Kurt Günther: Johannes de Sancto Amando und ein Aderlasstraktat unter seinem Namen (Diss., 36 p., Leipzig 1922). Containing text of the Flebotomia which is a part of John's commentary on Nicholas' Antidotary (Isis, 5, 500). Lynn Thorndike: History of magic (vol. 2, 510–513, 1923).

PETER OF CAPESTANG

French physician who flourished c. 1299–1313 in Montpellier. Capestang is in Languedoc, near Béziers. He wrote a short regimen on how to avoid paralysis, and questions on Hippocrates' Regimen acutorum. In 1299 he took steps toward the translation of Ibn Zuhr's Taisīr.

Ernest Wickersheimer: Pour éviter la paralysie. Conseils de Maitre Pierre de Capestang (Bull. soc. hist. méd., 18, 103–106, 1924; Isis, 7, 192).

See notes on Vincent of Beauvais and Armengaud son of Blaise, and the reference to Peter of Limoges in my note on John Peckham.

VETERINARY MEDICINE IN SPAIN IN THE THIRTEENTH CENTURY

There are a number of Spanish treatises on farriery and the veterinary art dating apparently from the thirteenth century but which cannot be dated exactly and the authors of which are unknown to me.

1. Jacme de Castro: Libro de fechos de caballos (Libro de menescalia del fecho de los cavallos e de las cavalzadas), in 130 chapters.
2. Juan Alvarez Salamiellas (or Salamillas): Libro de menescalcia, de albeiteria et fisica de las bestias. A MS. in the Bibliothèque nationale, Paris, contains very curious illustrations.
3. Fray Bernardo Portuguès: Los siete libros de albeiteria. It is explained in the introduction that the horse doctor must know astronomy (for astrological purposes), the virtues of herbs, the anatomy of the horse, its ailments and methods of curing them.

Léon Moulé: Histoire de la médecine vétérinaire en Europe au moyen âge (33–34, Paris 1900).

See notes on Peter of Spain, Arnold of Villanova, Ramon Lull; on Bacon; on William of Moerbeke and Jacob van Maerlant; on Albert the Great; on Peter of Dacia.

A GERMAN TREATISE ON MATERIA MEDICA OF THE SECOND HALF OF THE THIRTEENTH CENTURY

A German translation of the Introductiones et experimenta Bartholomaei magistri in practicam Hippocratis, Galieni, Constantini, graecorum medicorum, was made in Bavaria in the second half of the thirteenth century. (The Bartholomew referred to in the title is Bartholomew of England). It is one of the oldest German treatises on the subject.

Franz Pfeiffer: Zwei deutsche Arzneibücher aus dem 12. und 13. Jahrhundert (Sitzungsber., Phil. Kl., Wiener Akad., vol. 42, 110–200, 1863). The first of these texts, "Liber de naturali facultate incipit. Hie beginnet daz arzinbuoch Ypocratis . . . ." was probably composed in Schaffhausen about the middle of the twelfth century; the second, "Ditze buoch dihte ein meister der hiez Bartholomêus . . . ." much longer (some 30 printed pages), is the one to which this note is devoted. The texts are followed by a glossary.

Joseph Haupt: Über das md. Arzneibuch des Meisters Bartholomaeus (Sitzungsber., Phil. Kl., Wiener Akad. vol. 71, 451–566, 1872). Karl Sudhoff: Der Abschnitt über die Kräfte der Verbena (Eisenkraut) aus dem Münchener Cod. lat. 614 (13.–14. Jahrh.) (Archiv für Geschichte der Medizin, vol. 12, 83–84, 1920).

NICHOLAS OF POLAND

Nicholas de Bodlys (?), Nicholas of Bohemia(?) Polish physician and Dominican. He studied medicine in Montpellier where he is said to have resided some twenty years. He was probably there in 1270; a little later we find him at the court of Leszek III Czarny (Leszek the Black, king of Poland, 1279–1288). He composed in or after 1270 the Antipocras, or Liber empericorum, a medical poem with a prose prologue; another work of the same kind, but in prose, the Experimenta, though ascribed to him, is probably by another writer and may be later. The German Cyrurgia and the Stellarum fata, bearing his name, are certainly apocryphal.

In the Antipocras and in the Experimenta alike, the Greek-Arabic knowledge of the time is smothered under a mass of popular and magical lore and personal charlatanry. To justify the word charlatanry, it will suffice to quote a part of the incipit: "Incipiunt Experimenta fratris Nicolai . . . . qui tante fuerat experiencie quod ante ipsum non creditur similis ei fuisse nec operatur de futuro, ut patet in miris operibus suis in diversis provinciis et regionibus curas magnas et subitas faciendo." It is well to bear in mind that the word experimenta in such literature, and in the majority of mediaeval writings, covers the roughest kind of empiricism, occultism, and superstition. Nicholas' medical "experimenta" dealt mainly with serpents, toads, frogs, scorpions, etc., and he claimed to have wrought marvelous cures with his remedies, most of which were strange, irrational and disgusting. We may mention his reference to the occult virtue of the magnet. Among his sources he quotes Hermes, Tobias, Ptolemy, master Albert. He attacks the physicians steeped in Hippocrates and Galen in almost the same vein as one of our contemporary quacks would express his disdain of the teachings of our medical schools.

Some critics would place Nicholas in the fourteenth century, even in the second half. It is certain that the writings ascribed to him would have been written in the same way a century later, or for that matter at almost any time.

Text—J. W. S. Johnsson: Les Experimenta magistri Nicolai (Bull. de la Société franç. d'hist. de la médecine, vol. 10, 269–290, 1911).

The Antipocras, 327 leonine verses, was first published by K. Sudhoff: Antipocras, Streitschrift für mystische Heilkunde in Versen des Magisters Nikolaus von Polen (Archiv für Geschichte der Medizin, vol. 9, 31–52, 1915). Better edition by H. Diels: Über die Schrift Antipocras (Sitzungsberichte der preuss. Ak. der Wiss., 376–394, Berlin 1916; Isis, 3, 327; 4, 137).

R. Ganszyniec: Brata Mikolaja z Polski pisma lekarskie (The medical writings of brother Nicholas of Poland, 236 p., Poznan 1920). Critical edition of the Antipocras, the Experimenta, also of the German Cyrurgia, and of related texts, the Experimenta XII de serpentis corio by John Paulinus, and the Tractatus de oleo philosophorum, together with Polish translations, commentaries, list of drugs, glossary. The author was planning to publish a second volume of which I have not yet heard.

Criticism—Alex. Brückner: Antipocras. Zabytek trzynastego wieku (A literary monument of the thirteenth century; Pamietnik literacki, vol. 16, 284–288, 1918). Stan. Witkowski: Lekarz Mikolaj z Polski nowoodkryty pisarz lacinski XIII wieku (The physician Nicholas of Poland, a newly discovered Latin writer of the thirteenth century; Memoirs of the scientific academy of Cracow, philol. section, vol. 58, 38 p., 1919). Both papers reviewed in Mit. zur Gesch. d. Medizin (vol. 19, 282–284, 1920). Lynn Thorndike: History of magic (vol. 2, 768–770, 794, 796, 1923).

II. EASTERN CHRISTIANS

BONIFACE OF GERACE

Author of a treatise on horse medicine, who flourished probably in Gerace, Calabria, during the rule of Charles I of Anjou (1265–1282). It is not known whether his treatise, De equis eorumque curandis morbis, was originally written in Latin or in Greek. His name is Latin, and the Greek text is lost, yet the Greek hypothesis is not unplausible. There were still Greek speaking people in Calabria at that time, and at least two MSS. state that the text was translated from Greek into Latin (or into Italian) by the friar, master Antonio Dapera.

There is a beautiful Italian MS. of Boniface's treatise in the Pierpont Morgan Library, New York (no. 735). It was written and limned in South Italy c. 1345. It is explicitly stated (on fol. 48r) that it was translated from the Greek into Latin by maestro Antonio de Pera, a Dominican friar, and that king Charles I loved Boniface so much that he knighted him, gave him estates in Gerachi, Calabria, etc. There are many crude figures illustrating horses' ailments and how to treat them; a zodiac horse, etc. Other MSS. of this treatise (e.g., in Naples, Mannheim, and Wolfenbüttel) are also illustrated. It would be worthwhile to compare the text and illustrations of these MSS.[3a], and to examine other MSS. of the same kind, for example, the Spanish treatises on farriery mentioned on p. 1091. Though the Pierpont Morgan MS. dates only from the fourteenth century, the style of its illustrations suggests that there must have been an earlier prototype; indeed, they are related to the illustrations of the Manfred Bible (Vat. lat. 36) and of the Book of falconry of Frederick II (Vat. Pal. lat. 1071).

The MSS. of this treatise also include the pseudo-Hippocratic treatise on the veterinary art translated from the Arabic into Latin by Moses of Palermo, c. 1277.

Text—The text is unpublished. A critical edition of it and a comparison with the pseudo-Hippocratic treatise above mentioned are desirable.

[3a] I hope to publish such a study in Isis in the near future.

Criticism—Léon Moulé: Histoire de la médecine vétérinaire en Europe au moyen âge (30, 1900). Belle da Costa Greene: The Pierpont Morgan Library, 1924–1929 (59, New York 1930; Isis, 16).

MYREPSOS

Nicholas Myrepsos. Νικόλαος Μυρεψός (Myrepsos means unguentarius, a maker of ointments). Byzantine physician, born in Alexandria; flourished at the court of Nicaea, being physician (ἀκτουάριος) to Joannes III Ducas Batatzes (emperor from 1222 to 1254); traveled extensively; lived long enough to quote Nicholas III (pope from 1277 to 1280).

He compiled a large collection of pharmaceutical recipes called Δυναμερόν; this was completed toward the end of his life, c. 1280. It is primarily derived from the Antidotarium (parvum) of Nicholas of Salerno, but is far more elaborate. Against the 140–150 recipes of that Antidotarium, it contains no less than 2656 classified into 48 groups according to their medical properties (e.g., antidota, 511 recipes; salia 21; unguenta 98; enemata 51; hepatica et hemicranica 24; collyria 87; somnifera 12; ad scabiem, psilothra, 15; auricularia 23). It contains even more proofs of Arabic influence than the Antidotarium parvum; e.g., many mentions of musk, ambergris, camphor, senna.[4] No reference to distillation, nor to abortives. Use of mercurial ointments for itch and other skin troubles; use of common salt and salmiac. The recipes include many superstitious practices.

An abridged text of the Δυναμερόν was translated into Latin (or a Latin translation was abridged) by the Calabrian physician, Nicholas of Reggio (d. 1350), and recombined with the Salernitan antidotary into a single alphabetical order; the whole containing 1065 recipes. The full Latin text was not available until 1549. It remained the standard pharmacopoeia in Paris until the seventeenth century.

Text—There are at least 6 MSS. of the Greek text, which is still unpublished.

First Latin edition by Johann Agricola Ammonius (d. 1570): Nicolai Alexandrini liber de compositione medicamentorum secundum loca, translatus e graeco in latinum a Nicolao Rhegino Calabro, antehac nusquam impressus cum brevissimis annotationibus locorum difficilium (Ingolstadt 1541). This is the abridged Latin text referred to above.

A far more complete translation (or the translation of a more complete Greek text) was made or edited by Leonhard Fuchs (d. 1566): Nicolai Myrepsi Alexandrini medicamentorum opus in sectiones quadraginta octo digestum, hactenus in Germania non visum (Basel 1549). Reprinted in Lyon 1549, 1550. Also in the Medicae artis principes, edited by H. Stephanus (Paris 1567). The Stephanine collection was reprinted in Francfort 1625 or 1626, and in Nuremberg 1658 (Theatrum medico-practicum).

Criticism—E. H. F. Meyer: Geschichte der Botanik (vol. 3, 381–386, 1856). K. Krumbacher: Geschichte der byzantinischen Litteratur (615, 617, 1897). John Ferguson: Bibliotheca chemica (vol. 2, 103, 1906). M. Neuburger: Geschichte der Medizin (vol. 2, 133, 1911). F. H. Held: Nicolaus Salernitanus und Nikolaos Myrepsos (Diss., 46 p., Leipzig 1916). Calling into question Myrepsos' very existence. E. Jeanselme et L. Oeconomos: Un dispensaire médical à Byzance au temps des Paléologues (Aesculape, vol. 15, 26–30, 1925; Isis, 8, 541). Hermann Lehmann: Zu Nicolaus Myrepsus (Archiv für Geschichte der Medizin, vol. 17, 299–306, 1925; Isis, 11, 427). Continuing more aggressively Held's thesis; there was but one Nicholas, he of Salerno (and even this is not entirely certain); Nicholas

[4] These were Arabic drugs; witness the Arabic names musk, anbar, kāfūr, sanā.

of Alexandria is a myth! For the history of the Pharmacopoeia Augustana (Nuremberg 1546) and other early pharmacopoeias, see Isis (vol. 10, 69–71, 4 facsim., 1928).

DEMETRIOS PEPAGOMENOS

Δημήτριος ὁ Πεπαγωμένος. Demetrios of Constantinople. Byzantine physician, veterinary, and naturalist. He flourished in Constantinople, being physician to Michael VIII Palaeologos, emperor from 1259 to 1282. He wrote:

1. A very sensible treatise on gout, *Σύνταγμα περὶ τῆς ποδάγρας*, which he considers a diathesis caused by defective elimination of excreta.

2. A treatise on the feeding and nursing of hawks, *Περὶ τῆς τῶν ἱεράκων ἀνατροφῆς τε καὶ θεραπείας.* This is one of the earliest treatises of its kind in Christian Europe; the earliest in Greek. It is very elaborate, and according to the author's own statement, derived from earlier writings on the subject. It contains remarkable helminthological observations, and abundant information on everything that a good falconer ought to know; e.g., how to catch and train hawks, and how to treat them when they are well or ill. No mention is made of the hood, which was introduced into Europe from the East by Frederick II; on the other hand, Demetrios speaks of the curtain of which Frederick II had apparently no knowledge (the curtain is a screen of canvass depending from the underside of the perch to prevent a hawk from swinging after bating off). This shows that the sources of Frederick II and of Demetrios were independent.

3. A book on dogs, *Κυνοσόφιον* or *Περὶ κυνῶν ἐπιμελείας.* The authorship of this is very uncertain; it has also been ascribed to one Phaimon (*Φαίμων*) ancient philosopher. It is of little importance, being very inferior to ancient works of the same kind. It is divided into 50 chapters.

Apropos of no. 2, it is worthwhile to mention the existence of three other Greek treatises on falconry, dating presumably from the same time. (a) *Ὀρνεοσόφιον ἀγροικότερον*; (b) *Ὀρνεοσόφιον κελεύσει γεγονὸς τοῦ ἀοιδίμου βασιλέως κυρίου Μιχαήλ*; (c) *Ἱερακοσόφιον εἰς ἰατρείαν ὀρνέων καὶ εἰς κοπὰς καὶ κρῶμα, οἷον ζαγάνων, φαλκονίων, πετριτῶν, ἱερακίων, τζουρακίων καὶ ὀξυπτερύγων.* The last named is extracted from the second; it is probably younger. The second was written for Michael Palaeologos. The first deals only with pathology and therapeutics.

Text—The Liber de podagra was first published in Latin by Marcus Musurus (Rome 1517?); then in Greek and Latin, by Adr. Turnebus (Paris 1558). It was translated into French by Frédéric Jamot (70 p., Paris 1567; again, 56 p., Paris 1573), and that French version was retranslated into Latin by Jean Bourgeois (St. Omer 1619). It is included in vol. 10 of R. Chartier's edition of Hippocrates, with Latin translation (Paris 1679). New Greek-Latin edition by J. St. Bernard (Leiden 1743). C. G. Kühn: Opera medicorum graecorum (Additamentum VI, Leipzig 1826).

Kynosophion ac opusculum de cura et conservatione canum, edited in Greek and Latin by Rudbertus a Moshaim, i.e., Ruprecht von Mosham (1493–1543), (Vienna 1535). Phaemonis cynosophion seu de cura canum liber. New Greek and Latin edition by Andreas Aurifaber, i.e., Andreas Goldschmid (1512–1559) of Breslau, professor of medicine in Königsberg (Wittenberg 1545). Greek and Latin edition together with Claudios Aelianos (Lyon 1562). Phaemonis seu potius Demetrii Pepagomeni liber de cura canum, new Latin edition by Andreas Rivinus, based upon the earlier ones (36 p., Leipzig 1654).

The treatise on falconry was edited by Nicholas Rigault, librarian to Louis XIII: Ierakosophion. Rei accipitrariae scriptores nunc primum editi. Accedit kynosophion (i.e., the treatise on dogs above mentioned). (Paris 1612.) This contain-also the texts of the treatises (a) and (b), and a Latin translation of (a) by Petrus Gillius. (c) was edited by Jos. von Hammer-Purgstall: Falknerklee (81–85, Wien 1840; with commentary by Joseph von Eichenfeld, 86–88).

Demetrios' treatises on falconry and on dogs are included in Rudolf Hercher's edition of Claudios Aelianos (vol. 2, Leipzig 1866). German translations of both treatises are given in the theses of Kraenner and Omieczynski, quoted below.

Criticism—Ludwig Choulant: Handbuch der Bücherkunde (155–156, 1841). James Edmund Harting: Bibliotheca accipitraria (181–184, London 1891). K. Krumbacher: Geschichte der byzantinischen Litteratur (2d. ed., 615, 617, 631, 1897). Léon Moulé: La médecine vétérinaire en Europe au Moyen âge (63–64, Paris 1900). J. Ch. Huber: Demetrios über die Würmer in den Augen der Jagdfalken (Zoologische Annalen, 1908). M. Neuburger: Geschichte der Medizin (vol. 2, 132, 1911). Max Omieczynski: Hundezucht und Hundekrankheiten in der Literatur des klassischen Altertums mit besonderer Berücksichtigung des Kynosophion (Diss., 95 p., Berlin 1924). Paul Kraenner: Falkenheilkunde (Diss., 76 p., Berlin 1925).

See my notes on Maximos Planudes and Abū-l-Faraj.

III. WESTERN JEWS

ABRAHAM BEN SHEM-ṬOB

Abraham the Jew of Tortosa; Abraham Judaeus Tortuosensis. Born probably in Marseilles about the middle of the thirteenth century, son of the physician Shem-ṭob ben Isaac of Tortosa, dealt with above among the translators. He studied medicine probably in Italy and wrote a small medical treatise in Hebrew (91 paragraphs), Ḥibbur refuah be derek qaẓerah (Short road to the adjustment of health).

With the collaboration of a Christian, Simon Cordo of Genoa, he translated at least two medical works from Arabic, or more probably from Hebrew, into Latin; (1) the materia medica (book 28) of the Kitāb al-taṣrīf of Abū-l-Qāsim, Liber servitoris, Sefer ha-shimmush; (2) the Kitāb al-adwiya al-mufrada, Liber de simplici medicina of Ibn Sarābī.

A pseudo-Galenic treatise, De plantis or De medicinis occultis, containing some 46 recipes, was translated from Arabic into Latin by one Abraham (possibly Abraham ben Shem-ṭob?) together with Grumer (?) judge in Piacenza. That treatise had been translated into Arabic by Ḥunain ibn Isḥāq.

Text—For the translation of Abū-l-Qāsim and Ibn Sarābī, see my note on Simon of Genoa. The pseudo-Galenic text is included in at least some of the Juntine Latin editions of Galen (e.g., the sixth, Venice 1586; and the ninth, Venice 1625), and in the Greco-Latin edition by René Chartier (Paris 1679).

Criticism—L. Leclerc: Médecine arabe (vol. 2, 469–471, 1876). M. Steinschneider: Hebraeische Übersetzungen (657, 737, 972, 1893); Europaeische Übersetzungen (32, 1904). Moise Schwab: Jewish encyclopaedia (vol. 1, 119, 1901).

NATHAN BEN JOEL FALAQUERA

Falaquera or Palaquera, Palqera, Palqira. Hispano-Jewish physician who flourished in the second half of the thirteenth century. He compiled the Ẓori ha-guf, meaning, according to his own explanation, Balsam (for the pains) of the body. This is a very large Hebrew collection of medical quotations, derived from Arabic sources, and representing the medical knowledge accumulated by Hippocrates, Galen, Ibn Sīnā, Ibn Rushd, Maimonides, etc. After a long introduction devoted to God, the first cause and true physician, to the faculties of man, his three souls (vegetative, animal, and intelligent), to mystical comparisons of the various organs with this and that, begins the collection itself divided into four parts: (1) theory of medicine, 28 chapters; (2) practice including hygiene, 17 chapters; (3) diseases and their cures, a capite ad calcem, 12 chapters; (4) herbs and other drugs, their preparation and use. For the expression of medical or botanical ideas he used as many Biblical and Talmudic terms as possible; failing these, he quoted the Arabic terms but added Hebrew equivalents.

A treatise on celestial spheres is also ascribed to him.

He may be identical with Nathan of Montpellier, a pupil of whom wrote a Hebrew treatise on pathology, Sefer ha-yashar, divided into 150 paragraphs and appendices.

Criticism—Pietro Perreau: Della medicina teorico-pratica del rabbi Natan ben Joel Palquera (Atti del IV Congresso internazionale degli orientalisti, vol. 1, 189–197, Florence 1880). Analysis of the Ẓori ha-guf, including many chapter headings in Hebrew script. M. Steinschneider: Hebraeische Übersetzungen (842, 1893). J. S. Raisin: Jewish encyclopaedia (vol. 9, 183, 1905).

See my notes on Solomon ibn Ayyub, Shem-ṭob ben Isaac, Zeraḥiah Gracian, Moses Ibn Tibbon, Nathan ha-Me'ati, Samuel ben Jacob of Capua, Hillel ben Samuel, Solomon ben Moses of Melgueil.

IV. EASTERN JEWS AND SAMARITANS

AL-KŪHĪN AL-'AṬṬĀR

Abū-l-Munā Ibn abī Naṣr ibn Ḥaffāẓ al-Kūhīn al-Hārūnī al-'Aṭṭār al-Isrā'īlī. Kūhīn is the Hebrew Kohen, priest (hence the Jewish name Cohen and its variants); al-Kūhīn al-Hārūnī, descendant from the high priest Aaron. Al-'Aṭṭār means the druggist; al-Kūhīn al-'Aṭṭār might be translated the Jewish druggist of priestly descent. Many titles of honor prove his popularity; e.g., Aflāṭūn zamānihi wa rā'īs 'awānihi (the Plato of his time and the leader of his age).

Judeo-Egyptian pharmacist who flourished in Cairo c. 1260. He wrote in 1259–1260 for his son an Arabic treatise on pharmacy, entitled Minhāj al-dukkān wa dastūr al-a'yān (manual for the officine and canon for the great men), which is one of the best Arabic works of its kind with regard both to substance and to form. It enjoyed considerable popularity and is still used in many parts of the Muslim East to this day. It is divided into 25 parts: (1) deontology; (2) beverages (this covers one-sixth of the whole); (3) robs; (4) conserves; (5) narcotics, ma'jūn (pl. ma'ājīn); (6) electuaries, etc.; (20) succedanea; (21) synonyms; (22) weights and measures; (23) practical advice to pharmacists; (24) how to collect and preserve herbs; (25) provenience of drugs; how to test simple and compound drugs. This work was based upon previous Arabic writings, many of which are quoted, also upon the author's personal experience; he seems to have been in touch with Ibn al-Baiṭār.

Text—Many oriental editions; Cairo 1870, 1883, 1887, 1912, etc.

Criticism—L. Leclerc: Médecine arabe (vol. 2, 215–217, 1876). M. Steinschneider: Eine arabische Pharmakopie des XIII. Jahrhunderts von abu-l-Muna und die Quellen derselben (Z. der deutschen morgenländischen Gesellschaft, vol. 56, 74–85, 1902); Arabische Literatur der Juden (237–238, 1902). Eilhard Wiedemann: Über von den Arabern benutzte Drogen (Beiträge 49, Sitzungsber. d. physik. med. Sozietät, vol. 48, 16–60, Erlangen 1918; Isis, 4, 431). H. Rudy: Encyclopaedia judaica (vol. 1, 657, 1928; short and inaccurate). Max Meyerhof: Notes sur quelques médecins juifs égyptiens (Isis, vol. 12, 130, 1929).

SOLOMON KOHEN

Abū Manṣūr Sulaimān ibn Ḥaffāẓ al-Kūhīn. Jewish (Qaraite?) physician flourishing in Egypt, died in 1295–1296 (?). He wrote in Arabic a medical encyclopaedia, Kitāb al-muntakhab, divided into seven main parts: (1) generalities; (2) simples; (3) general diseases; (4) diseases of particular members of the body; (5) poisons and cosmetics; (6) antidotary; (7) medical aphorisms of Galen and others. There are many points in common between the Muntakhab and the Minhāj al-dukkān of al-Kūhīn al-'Aṭṭār, dealt with above.

M. Steinschneider: Arabische Literatur der Juden (233, 1902).

IBN AL-BISHR

Mufaḍḍal ibn Mājid Ibn al-Bishr al-Isrā'īlī (according to Ḥājī Khalīfa, vol. 6, 380, no. 13974, Mājid ibn Mufaḍḍal, popularly called Ibn al-Bishr al-Kātib). Jewish physician who composed in 1268–1269 a medical poem (arjūza fī-l-ṭibb) entitled Naq' al-ghalal wa-l naf' al-'ilal (Quenching of the thirst and advantage of the second drink!)

C. Brockelmann: Arabische Literatur (vol. 1, 492, 1898). M. Steinschneider: Arabische Literatur der Juden (239, 1902).

See my note on Ibn Kammūna.

MUWAFFAQ AL-DĪN

Muwaffaq al dīn Abū Yūsuf Ya'qūb ibn abī Isḥāq ibn Ghanā'im, al-Sāmirī al-Dimashqī. Samaritan physician and philosopher who flourished in Damascus, and died in 1282–1283. He wrote in Arabic a commentary (sharḥ) on the general part (kullīyāt) of Ibn Sīnā's Qānūn, and an introduction to the study of logic and theology, Madkhal ilā 'ilm al-manṭiq wal-ilahī.

Ibn abī Uṣaibi'a (vol. 2, 272). Ḥājī Khalīfa (vol. 4, 498; 5, 160, 472). F. Wüstenfeld: Arabische Aerzte (144, 1840). L. Leclerc: Médecine arabe (vol. 2, 176, 1876). M. Steinschneider: Arabische Literatur der Juden (330, 1902). Moses Gaster: Samaritan literature (Encyclopaedia of Islām, supp. to vol. 4; 10, 1925).

V. EASTERN MUSLIMS

IBN AL-QUFF

Abū-l-Faraj Ya'qūb ibn Isḥāq ibn al-Quff al-Masīḥī (the Christian) al-Karakī, Amīn al-daula. Christian physician; born in 1232–1233; brought up in Karak;[5]

[5] I take this to be the fortress east of the Dead Sea in ancient Moab?

died in Damascus 1286 (he has been confused with another and greater Abū-l-Faraj—Bar Hebraeus—who died in the same year). He was a pupil of Ibn abī Uṣaibi'a who devoted a note to him at the end of the revised edition of his 'Uyūn al-anbā'.

His main works are a medical compendium, Kitāb jāmi' al-gharaḍ fī ḥifẓ al-ṣiḥḥa wadaf' al-maraḍ (Compendium of what one should know to preserve one's health and avoid disease), and a treatise on surgery, Kitāb al-'umda fī ṣinā'at al-jirāḥa (The pillar of surgery). The second of these works is divided into two parts, theory and practice, each of which contains ten chapters. The first part begins with an elaborate anatomical introduction, then deals with pathology, and a classification of diseases according to the theory of four humours. In chapter 19 the author explains four methods of circumcision, and a new method of lithotomy applicable to women.

He also wrote an elaborate commentary on Hippocrates' Aphorisms, Kitāb al-uṣūl fī sharḥ al-fuṣūl, which is extant; and commentaries on the Qānūn and the Kitāb al-ishārāt of Ibn Sīnā, which are lost. Various other medical works are ascribed to him.

Criticism—Ibn abī Uṣaibi'a (Müller's edition, vol. 2, 273, 1884).

Antoine Barthélémy Clot (Clot bey): Note sur la fréquence des calculs vésicaux en Egypte et sur la méthode employée par les chirurgiens arabes pour en faire l'extraction (28 p., Marseilles 1830). F. Wüstenfeld: Arabische Aerzte (146, 1840). L. Leclerc: Médecine arabe (vol. 2, 203–204, 1876). C. Brockelmann: Arabische Litteratur (vol. 1, 493, 1898). E. Gurlt: Geschichte der Chirurgie (vol. 1, 662, 1898). E. Wiedemann: Beschreibung von Schlangen bei Ibn Qaff (Beiträge 50, Sitzungsberichte der phys. med. Sozietät, vol. 48, 61–64, Erlangen 1918). Translation with commentary of a chapter of the Jāmi'.

IBN AL-NAFĪS

'Alā' al-dīn Abū-l-Ḥasan 'Alī ibn abī-l-Ḥazm Ibn al-Nafīs al-Qarshī (or Qurashī) al-Miṣrī al-Shāfi'ī. Egyptian or Syrian physician who studied under Ibn al-Dakhwār[6] in Damascus, and in the course of time inherited his teacher's fame; he died at Damascus, being about 80 years of age, in 1288–1289 (the date 1296–1297 is unlikely). He wrote a number of commentaries on the ḥadīth and on the medical writings of Hippocrates (Aphorisms, Prognostics), Ḥunain ibn Isḥāq, and Ibn Sīnā (generalities and anatomy of the Qānūn, and the whole Qānūn). His independent medical works include a treatise on eye diseases, and another on diet, Kitāb al-mukhtār min al-aghdiya.

[6] I ought to have spoken before of this Ibn al-Dakhwār who was one of the most famous physicians of his time. Muhadhdhib al-dīn Abū Muḥammad 'Abd al-Raḥīm ibn 'Alī al-Dimashqī (Ibn) al-Dakhwār. Born at Damascus in 1169–1170, where his father 'Alī was a well known eye doctor; appointed chief of the physicians of Egypt and Syria by the Ayyūbid al-'Ādil (ruled from 1196 [1199] to 1218); al-'Ādil's successor in Damascus, al-Mu'aẓẓam, put him at the head of the hospital of Damascus, where he did considerable teaching, and where Ibn abī Uṣaibi'a was one of his pupils; he was called to Mesopotamia by the Ayyūbid al-Ashraf Mūsā (ruled there from 1210 to 1230), but he returned to Damascus in 1228–1229, and died there in 1230 (not 1250). He composed many medical writings, of which only one seems to have survived, a commentary on Hippocrates' Aphorisms. Ibn abī Uṣaibi'a devoted an exceptionally long note to him (A. Müller's edition, vol. 2, 239–246).

F. Wüstenfeld: Arabische Aerzte (123, 1840). L. Leclerc: Médecine arabe (vol. 2, 177–179, 1876). C. Brockelmann: Arabische Litteratur (vol. 1, 491, 1898).

By far the best known of these writings in his commentary on the Qānūn, Kitāb mūjiz al-qānūn (also called Al-mūjiz fī-l-ṭibb). It is divided into four parts: (1) generalities on the theory and practice of medicine; (2) victuals and drugs, simple and compound; (3) diseases relative to separate members or organs; (4) other diseases, their causes, symptoms and cures.

The great and lasting popularity of the Mūjiz is proved by a whole collection of supercommentaries[7] and translations. The earliest of these supercommentaries was composed by Abū Isḥāq Ibrāhīm ibn Muḥammad al-Ḥakīm al-Suwaidī (d. 1291). Another entitled Ḥall al-mūjiz (Key to the Mūjiz) was written by Jamāl al-dīn Muḥammad ibn Muḥammad al-Aqṣarā'ī (d. bef. 1397). A third one was prepared in Kirmān and completed in Samarqand, 1437, by Nafīs ibn 'Iwaḍ al-Kirmānī; notes were added to it by Ghars al-dīn Aḥmad ibn Ibrāhīm al-Ḥalabī in 1563–1564. A large commentary called Al-munjiz was composed by Maḥmūd ibn Aḥmad al-Amshāṭī al-Ḥanafī (born in 1407–1408). Still other commentaries were written at unknown times by Shihāb al-dīn ibn Muḥammad al-Ījī al-Bulbulī and by al-Sadīdī (or Sadīd al-dīn) al-Kāzirūnī. This last one was entitled Al-sharḥ al-mughnī or Al-mughnī fi sharḥ al-mūjiz.

The Mūjiz was translated into Turkish apparently twice, by Muṣliḥ al-dīn Muṣṭafā ibn Sha'bān al-Surūrī (d. 1561), and by Aḥmad ibn Kamāl, physician in Adrianople. There is also a Hebrew translation, Sefer ha-mugiz, probably made in Greece.

Another work of Ibn al-Nafīs, his commentary on the anatomical part of the Qānūn, the Sharḥ tashrīḥ ibn Sīnā,[8] seems to be extremely interesting from the physiological point of view. In five different places Ibn al-Nafīs quotes Ibn Sīnā's views on circulation in heart and lung and repeats the Galenic fragments included in Ibn Sīnā's account, and then proceeds to contradict these views with the utmost vigor. Five times does he state in unmistakable terms that the venous blood cannot pass from the right to the left ventricle through visible or invisible pores in the septum, but must pass through the "veinous artery" to the lungs, be mingled there with air, pass through the "arterious vein" into the left ventricle and there form the "vital spirit." If the authenticity of Ibn al-Nafīs' theory is confirmed his importance will increase enormously; for he must then be considered one of the main forerunners of William Harvey and the greatest physiologist of the Middle Ages. But we need confirmation. The relevant Arabic text was edited (on the basis of Berlin MSS.) together with a partial German translation full of mistakes, by an Egyptian physician, Muḥyī al-dīn al-Ṭaṭāwī, in the form of an inaugural dissertation of the faculty of medicine of Freiburg i. Br. (1924). Unfortunately it was not printed but only handwritten in five copies, none of which was available to me. One copy is in the Staatsbibliothek, Berlin; another, in the possession of Max Meyerhof to whose courtesy I owe all I know on the subject (private letter dated August 22, 1930).

Text—Ebenefis philosophi ac medici expositio super quintum canonem Avicennae ab Andrea Alpago bellunensi ex arabico in latinum versa. This is a part of the Latin Ibn Sīnā edition of Venice 1547.

Edition of the Mūjiz by Moulovee Mohammad Solyman of Herat and Rooh-ool-Ameen of Boolea (230 p., Calcutta 1828). Lithographic edition with various

[7] After Ḥājī Khalīfa, whose information I was not always able to check.

[8] This is quite independent of the Mūjiz, which does not deal at all with anatomy and physiology.

notes (154 p., Lucknow 1871). Lith. ed. with Persian commentary, Kāshif al-rumūz by Aḥmad al-dīn Lāhaurī, edited by Muḥammad Fīrūz al-dīn (part 1, 192 p., Lahore 1905). Lith. ed. with notes by Muḥammad 'Abd al-Razzāq (524 p., Delhi 1905). Lith. ed. with notes (286 p., Lucknow 1906).

Ḥall al-mūjiz by Muḥammad ibn Muḥammad al-Aqṣarā'ī. Lith. ed. with marginal notes (2 vols., Delhi c. 1870). Lith. reprint of the Delhi ed. (494 p. in 3 parts, Lucknow 1877).

Sharḥ al-mūjiz by Nāfis ibn 'Iwaḍ al-Kirmānī, with a supercommentary (707 p., lith., Lucknow 1865). Other ed. with another supercomm. (490 p., Cawnpore 1872); same reprinted (Lucknow 1895). Other partial edition (Lucknow 1894).

Sharḥ al-mughnī, or al-Sadīdī, by Sadīd al-dīn al-Kāzirūnī. Edited by Raḥmān-bakhsh (520 p., lith., Calcutta 1828). Ashshurh-ool Moognee, commentatio absoluta. A commentary on the Moojuz-ool Kanoon . . . . edited by Hukeem Mouluvee Abdool Mujeed, Mouluvee Gholam Mukhdoom, and Mouluwee Abdool-lah (860 p., Calcutta 1832). This edition includes the Greek equivalents of a few technical names. Other editions of the Mughnī, with various additions and notes: (390 p., Lucknow 1878); partial ed. with a list of weights and measures explained in Persian (Lucknow 1890); with a glossary of drug names explained in Persian (Lucknow 1894).

Criticism—Ḥājī Khalīfa (Fluegel's edition, vol. 6, 251–253, 1852). J. E. Sarkis: Dictionnaire de bibliographie arabe (268, Cairo 1928).

F. Wüstenfeld: Arabische Aerzte (146, 1840). L. Leclerc: Médecine arabe (vol. 2, 207–209, 264, 1876). M. Steinschneider: Hebraeische Übersetzungen (721, 1893). C. Brockelmann: Arabische Litteratur (vol. 1, 493, 1893). J. Hirschberg: Die arabischen Lehrbücher der Augenheilkunde (Abhdl. d. preuss. Ak., 92, 1905). Muḥyī al-dīn al-Ṭaṭāwī: Der Lungenkreislauf nach el-Koraschi (Diss., Freiburg i.Br., 1924; only five MS. copies, see above).

KHALĪFA IBN ABĪ-L-MAḤĀSIN

Khalīfa ibn abī-l-Maḥāsin al-Ḥalabī (i.e., of Aleppo). Syrian oculist who flourished c. 1256. Author of a very elaborate treatise on eye diseases, entitled Kitāb al-kāfī fī-l-kuḥl (The sufficient treatise on the collyrium) or fī-l-kiḥālat (on the art of making collyria, i.e., oculistics) or fī-l-ṭibb (on medicine). It mentions an incident experienced by the author in 1256; a MS. of it was written by another hand in 1275 (Bibliothèque nationale, Paris). The author was a Muslim; the copyist, 'Abd al-'Azīz, was a Christian. Taking the average of these two dates, we may assume that the Kāfī al-kuḥl was written c. 1265.

It is divided into two main parts: (1) the anatomy of the eye; (2) its treatment; The first part is subdivided as follows: (a) definitions, color of the eye; (b) tunics of the eye; (c) fluids of the eye; (d) visual power and its nerves; (e) motive nerves; (f) muscles of the eye, eyelids and eyelashes. The second part is also divided into six chapters: (a) generalities; (b) hygiene of the eye, things which are useful and things which are harmful; (c) how to open the eye and introduce drugs into it; (d) the best kind of probe and its use; (e) tools for the handling of the collyria; (f) best garments for the eye doctor. Followed by synoptic tables relative to the diseases of eyes and eyelids, giving for each disease the definition, description, varieties, causes, symptoms, treatment, drugs including narcotics; and other tables relative to surgical cases. Finally a list of drugs. The whole work is preceded by a long list of earlier Arabic works on the subject, and much of it is borrowed from other authors, chiefly Galen, Aḥmad al-Ṭabarī, and 'Alī ibn 'Īsā; though Khalīfa was obviously a practitioner of great experience, who was so sure of himself that he did not fear to operate the cataract of a one-eyed man. Some operations are minutiously described by him.

The illustrations found in MSS. of this treatise are very remarkable; chiefly a schematic figure representing the brain with its membranes, together with the eyes and eye nerves (the latter are shown crossed—i.e., the right eye is controlled by the left part of the brain and vice versa), and also 36 figures representing the 36 instruments needed by the eye doctor; each of these instruments is named and briefly described. The schema of brain and eyes occurs only in a late MS., but it goes back undoubtedly to an old Arabic tradition and is the earliest drawing of its kind which has come down to us.

Julius Hirschberg: Die arabischen Augenärzte (vol. 2, Leipzig 1905).

L. Leclerc: Médecine arabe (vol. 2, 145–147, 1876). C. Brockelmann: Arabische Litteratur (vol. 2, 364, 1902; incorrect). J. Hirschberg, J. Lippert, and E. Mittwoch: Die arabischen Lehrbücher der Augenheilkunde (Abhdl. der preussischen Akademie, chiefly p. 12, 73–84, 1905).

ṢALĀḤ AL-DĪN IBN YŪSUF

Ṣalāḥ al-dīn ibn Yūsuf, al-Kaḥḥāl bi-Ḥamā (meaning the eye doctor of Ḥamā). Syrian oculist who flourished, presumably in Ḥamā, c. 1296. He wrote for his son a very elaborate treatise on ophthalmology entitled Nūr al-'uyūn wa jāmi' al-funūn (Light of the eyes and collection of rules), wherein he refers to a case dealt with by him in 1296–1297.

The treatise is divided into ten books as follows: deontological introduction; (1) definition of the eye, anatomy in 22 chapters, including a schematic section (taqāṭu' al-ṣalībī) of the eye; (2) vision, including the geometrical theory of it. No mention is made of Ibn al-Haitham. Discussion of various theories of vision, largely derived from Aëtios of Amida and Ibn Sīnā; (3) eye diseases, their causes, treatment, drugs; (4) hygiene; affections of the eye-lids; (5) affections of the canthi; (6) affections of the conjunctiva; (7) affections of the cornea; (8) affections of the uvea, and cataract; (9) intangible affections; (10) simple drugs after Ibn al-Baiṭār.

This plan is identical to that of the Tadhkirat al-kaḥḥālīn of 'Alī ibn 'Īsā, and the Nūr al-'uyūn contains many verbatim extracts from the Tadhkira. The chapter on cataract is very full, but most of it is borrowed from 'Alī ibn 'Īsā and from 'Ammār ibn 'Alī.

Julius Hirschberg: Die arabischen Augenärzte (vol. 2, Leipzig 1905).

Ḥājī Khalīfa: Lexicon (vol. 6, 393, no. 14040, 1852). L. Leclerc: Médecine arabe (vol. 2, 205–206, 1876). Pierre Pansier: Collectio ophtalmologica veterum auctorum (part 2, 89, Paris 1903). J. Hirschberg, J. Lippert, and E. Mittwoch: Die arabischen Lehrbücher der Augenheilkunde (Abhdl. der preussischen Akademie, chiefly 14, 85–91, 1905).

See my notes on Ibn Ṭarkhān, Nāṣir al-dīn al-Ṭūsī, Quṭb al-dīn al-Shīrāzī.

QALĀ'ŪN'S HOSPITAL

The Baḥrī Mamlūk sulṭān al-Malik al-Manṣūr Saif al-dīn Abū-l-Ma'ālī al-Alfī al-Ṣāliḥī al-Najmī Qalā'ūn, who ruled Egypt and Syria from 1279 to 1290, distinguished himself not only as a great general and statesman, but also as a great builder. The most famous of his buildings is still partly extant. It is the great hospital of Cairo called after him Bīmāristān al-Manṣūrī. This was a very elaborate structure including different wards for special groups of patients, storerooms, a mosque, a school, Qalā'ūn's tomb, etc. The Bīmāristān al-Manṣūrī was not by any means the earliest Muslim hospital, but it is the earliest extant. For the earlier history of hospitals, including Muslim ones, see my note on mediaeval hospitals above. It may be recalled that hospitals were of Judeo-Byzantine origin; they were transmitted to Islām through the school of Jundīshāpūr (vol. 1, 435).

Qalā'ūn was the only Mamlūk sulṭān who founded a dynasty; that dynasty lasted five generations, until 1382.

Sobernheim: Qalā'ūn (Encyclopaedia of Islām, vol. 2, 685–687, 1924). For bibliography relative to his bīmāristān, see the note on mediaeval hospitals (p. 245–247).

VI. HINDUS

VOPADEVA

Or Bopadeva. Hindu poet, physician and grammarian. Born in Berār, the son of Keśava, a physician, he flourished at the court of Mahādeva, ruler of Devagiri from 1260 to 1271; he was protected by the minister Hemādri (dealt with below).

He wrote a commentary on the Śarṅgadharasaṃhitā, and other medical works, chiefly the Śataślokī (Hundred verses); dealing with the preparation and use of powders, pills, etc.

He also composed a Sanskrit grammar, with commentary, called Mugdhabodha. It was different in arrangement and terminology from Pāṇini's and was exceedingly popular in Bengal. Finally he wrote the Kavikalpadruma (Poet's wishtree), i.e., a dhātupāṭha (dictionary of roots) in verse, with a commentary.

Texts—The Śataśloki has often been printed (Madras 1860, Bombay 1889).

The Mugdhabodha has been edited by Otto Böhtlingk (480 p., St. Petersburg 1847).

The Dhātupāṭha was published in Calcutta 1830.

Criticism—C. Mabel Duff: Chronology of India (201, 310, 1899). Julius Jolly: Medicin (4, Strassburg 1901). M. Winternitz: Geschichte der indischen Litteratur (vol. 3, 402, 551, 1922).

TĪSAṬĀCĀRYA

Hindu physician who flourished before the fourteenth century. He is placed here on the assumption that he was possibly a contemporary of Vopadeva. He wrote a treatise entitled Cikitsākalikā, dealing with anatomy, physiology, general pathology and therapeutics. Tīsaṭa's son, Candraṭa, wrote a commentary upon it.

Text—Julius Jolly: Zur Quellenkunde der indischen Medizin, 4. Die Cikitsākalikā des Tīsaṭācārya (Z. der deutschen morgenländ. Ges., vol. 60, 413–468, 1906). Extracts in Sanskrit and German, with notes.

Criticism—M. Winternitz: Geschichte der indischen Litteratur (vol. 3, 551, 1922).

See my note on Hemādri.

VII. CHINESE

LI KAO

Li^{3} Kao^{3} (6884, 5950). Style name, Ming^{2}-chih^{1} (7946, 1787); nickname, Tung^{1} Yüan^{2} (12248, 13762). Northern Chinese physician. Flourished at the end of the Sung and the beginning of the Yüan dynasty. He wrote various medical works, mainly, in 1232 (?) the Nei^{4}-wai^{4}-shang^{1} pien^{4}-huo^{4*} lun^{4} (8177, 12442, 9742, 9207, 5320, 7475) in three chüan; the P'i^{2} wei^{4} lun^{4} (9078, 12574, 7475), also in 3 chüan; in 1276, the Lan^{2}-shih^{4*} pi^{4}-ts'ang^{4} (6721, 9974, 8932, 11601).

Li Kao was a pupil of Chang^{1} Yüan^{2}-su^{4} (416, 13744, 10348). The latter had started to point out the disharmonies between the old and the new, and did not use any more the ancient recipes. Li's medicine was based, like Chang's, upon the recognition of the importance of the stomach and the spleen. These are two correlative and opposite organs: the stomach is a fu^{3} (3685) organ, corresponding to the male and moving principle yang^{2} (12883); the spleen is a tsang^{4} (11584) organ corresponding to the female and passive principle yin^{1} (13224). The spleen corresponds also to the earth. Li Kao and his disciples paid special attention to it. The main idea of his therapeutics was to protect the spleen, earth organ, against the yang. It is not necessary to analyze these fantastic conceptions any further.

F. Hübotter: Guide (9, 36, 42, Kumamoto 1924; Isis, 7, 259); Die chinesische Medizin (11, 23, 349–351, Leipzig 1929; Isis, 14, 255). Hübotter gives an exceptionally long account of Li's theories (p. 349–351).

See my note on 'Īsā the Mongol.

VIII. JAPANESE

SEIA

Japanese veterinary who, aided by an artist, produced in 1267 the Bai zu kan, illustrations of seventeen plants used for horse diseases. These illustrations are excellent from the scientific as well as the artistic point of view.

Mitsutaro Shirai: Scientific Japan (215, Tokyo 1926; Isis, 10, 83–88).

See my note on Koremune Tomotoshi.

CHAPTER LIII

HISTORIOGRAPHY

(Second Half of Thirteenth Century)

I. WESTERN CHRISTENDOM

ROLANDINO

Rolandinus Patavinus, Rolandino de Romanciis. Italian chronicler. Born at Padua in 1200; obtained his doctor's degree at Bologna in 1221; became professor of grammar and rhetoric in Padua; succeeded his father as notary; died in Padua in 1276.

In 1262 he completed a Latin chronicle of Italian events from 1200 to 1260, dealing mainly with Ecelino III da Romano (1194–1259), the cruel Ghibelline tyrant. Though poorly written, it is remarkably clear and trustworthy. His account was partly based upon his father's diary, and after 1223 upon his own.

Text—First edition by Felix Osius (Venice, 1636). Better one in L. A. Muratori: Rerum italicarum scriptores (vol. 8, 169–360, 1726) etc.

Pietro Gherardo: Vita et gesti d'Ezzelino terzo da Romano (Venice 1544, 1560; Vicenza 1610; Venice, 1622; Padua 1668; Bassano 1677). Gherardo's work is derived essentially from Rolandino.

Criticism—G. Tiraboschi: Storia della letteratura italiana (2d ed. modenese, vol. 4, 62, 348, 478, 1788). Potthast (981, 1895).

SALIMBENE

Fra Salimbene de Adam; Ognibene, son of Guido di Adamo, a nobleman; born at Parma in 1221; died in Italy soon after 1288. Italian Franciscan and chronicler.

He entered the Franciscan order in 1238 and made his noviciate in Fano and Pisa; was influenced by the ideas of Joachim de Floris; sent to France in 1247, went to Lyon, met Giovanni Pian del Càrpine; proceeded to Paris and other cities; was in Ferrara from 1249 to 1256, then in Modena and Parma. He traveled much in Italy, gradually lost his Joachimite tendencies and became more conservative; in 1281 he seems to have settled down in Reggio, where he wrote his chronicle; he died soon after 1288.

He completed in 1284 and revised c. 1288 a Latin chronicle dealing with the period 1167–1287. It is a very personal chronicle containing many autobiographical items. It is a valuable mirror of contemporary life in Italy and France; one of the earliest accounts of French customs by a foreigner. It is especially valuable for the history of Lombardy, and for the history of the Franciscan order; e.g., the dissensions caused by the radical elements within the order, the so-called Fraticelli. It contains also very interesting information on miscellaneous subjects, such as Franciscan music, and the first unmistakable reference to a post-mortem examination. During the plague of 1286 a physician of Cremona opened the chest of a victim to examine the heart. For the next post-mortem, in 1302, see my note on Bartolomeo da Varignana (vol. 3).

Salimbene was very pious and credulous, but honest and outspoken; he had traveled considerably and met many people of all kinds including some of the protagonists of the century, Frederick II, Saint Louis, popes and tyrants.

Text—Incomplete and bowdlerized edition by Antonio Bertani (Parma 1857). Better edition by Oswald Holder-Egger (Monumenta Germaniae historica, Hanover 1905).

Italian translation by Carlo Cantarelli from the edition of 1857 (2 vols., Parma 1882). German translation by Alfred Doren from the edition of 1905 (2 vols., Leipzig 1914). English translation by G. G. Coulton (1906, see below). Italian translation by F. Bernini: La bizzarra cronaca (Lanciano 1926).

Criticism—L. Clédat: De fratre Salimbene et de ejus chronicae auctoritate (116 p., Paris 1878). Contains a part of the text omitted by Bertani in 1857. Ugo Balzani: Le cronache italiane nel medio evo (325 p., Milan 1884). Published previously in English (London 1883); later Italian editions (1900, 1909). Emil Michael: Salimbene und seine Chronik (Innsbruck 1889). Potthast (994, 1898). Auguste Molinier: Les sources de l'histoire de France (vol. 3, 57–60, Paris 1903). George Gordon Coulton: From St. Francis to Dante; a translation of all that is of primary interest in the chronicle of Salimbene, together with notes and illustrations from other medieval sources (370 p., London 1906; 2d ed. enlarged, 460 p., 1907). Ephraim Emerton: Fra Salimbene and the Franciscan ideal (Harvard Theological Review, vol. 8, 1915). E. Irenaeus Prime Stevenson: Grove's Dictionary of music (vol. 4, 509, 1928).

JAMES OF VORAGINE

Jacobus de Voragine (Varagine), Giacomo da Varaggio. Born at Varazze near Genoa c. 1230; assumed the Dominican habit in 1244; provincial of Lombardy from 1267 to 1286; archbishop of Genoa 1292; died in Genoa 1298–1299. Italian chronicler and hagiographer. His main works are the Chronicon januense and the Legendae sanctorum, both of which were completed after 1292. The Chronicon is a history of Genoa from mythical times down to 1293 (1297), including information on social and domestic life and ethical developments.

The Legendae sanctorum (alias Lombardica historia, because it includes a Lombard chronicle), was one of the most popular works of mediaeval times. Its popularity is attested by the existence of early translations in many vernaculars, by the fact that it was one of the earliest books to be printed, by its familiar name, the Golden Legend. That name—Legenda aurea—was given to it very early, before the end of the thirteenth century. The scientific value of this work is negligible, but it is a very precious witness to the age, and the historian of thought must take into account its wide and long popularity.

The Legenda was derived from a large number of written sources (e.g., Vincent of Beauvais' Speculum historiale), from unwritten folk-tales, and from the author's fertile imagination. The earliest printed Latin edition (c. 1470) contains 244 stories; Caxton's English translation (1483) almost 450 (including new stories of English saints).

Text—Earliest Latin edition of the Golden Legend, s.l. et a. (Ulm c. 1469). First dated edition, 1474. First edition with date and place, Paris 1475. Many other incunabula (more than 140 in 7 languages), entitled in various ways: Legenda aurea sanctorum, Liber passionalis, Lombardica historica, etc. Modern edition by J. G. Theodor Graesse: Legenda aurea vulgo Historia lombardica dicta. (Ed. 2, 967 p., Leipzig 1850).

Italian translation by Niccolò Manerbi or Malermi (1422–1500?) (Venice 1475). Stefano Rossi: Leggende di S. Jacopo Maggiore e di S. Stefano, volgarizzate nell' aureo secolo XIV (228 p., Firenze 1834). Giuseppe Manuzzi: Quattro leggende del beato Jacopo da Varagine volgarizzate nel secolo XIV (36 p., Accademia della Crusca, Firenze 1849). Luigi Razzolini: Legenda di S. Silvestro papa volgarizzata nel buon secolo (32 p., Firenze 1871). Wilhelm Friedmann: Altitalienische Heiligenlegenden (Gesellschaft für romanische Literatur, Bd. 14, 244 p., Dresden 1908).

French translation by Jean Bathalier (Lyon 1476), by Jean de Vingle (Lyon 1491), by J. B. M. Roze (3 vols., Paris 1902), by Teodor de Wyzewa (776 p., Paris 1902).

English translation by Caxton (Westminster 1483). Partial facsimile reproduction, with introduction by Alfred Aspland (Holbein Society, London 1878). Caxton's translation reprinted by William Morris and F. S. Ellis (3 vols., Kelmscott Press, 1892), also in the Temple Classics (7 vols., London 1900). Selection edited by G. V. O'Neill (Cambridge 1914).

Dutch translation (Gouda 1478), etc.

German translation first published in 1485. Translation by Richard Benz (2 vols., Jena 1917–1921).

Bohemian translation (Pilsen, s.a., c. 1477; Prague 1495).

Chronicon genuense, printed in Muratori: Rerum Italicarum scriptores (vol. 9, 5–56).

Criticism—Vincenzo Marcolino Pelazza: Vita del beato Giacomo da Varazze (110 p., Genova 1867). Marie Pellechet: Jacques de Voragine. Liste des éditions de ses ouvrages publiées au XVe siècle (Revue des bibliothèques, vol. 5, 89–98, 225–227, 1895). Potthast (634–635, 1896). Pierce Butler: Legenda aurea. A study of Caxton's Golden legend with special reference to its relations to the earlier English prose translation (160 p., Johns Hopkins thesis, Baltimore 1899). Marguerite, comtesse de Waresquiel: Le bienheureux Jacques de Voragine (Paris 1902). Francesco Luigi Manucci: La cronaca di Jacopo da Varagine (90 p., Genova 1904). Ernst Tiedemann: Passional und Legenda aurea (Palestra, 87, 161 p., Berlin 1909). V. Bugiel: La pathologie et la thérapeutique dans la Légende dorée (Bull. soc. franç. hist. méd., vol. 17, 320–349, 1923).

See notes on Brunetto Latini; also on Ricoldo di Monte Croce and other travelers.

JAIME EL CONQUISTADOR

En Jacme lo Conqueridor. James I the Conqueror. Born in Montpellier, 1208, the son of Peter II and Mary of Montpellier, king of Aragon from 1213 to his death in Valencia, 1276. He was a strong king who subdued his vassals, conquered the Balearic islands, and in 1238, Valencia. Later he was engaged in a long war against the Moors of Murcia in behalf of his son-in-law, Alphonso the Wise.

He wrote a chronicle of his deeds in Catalan.

Text—The first edition of Jaime's chronicle appeared in Valencia, 1557. Mariano Aguiló y Fuster: Libre del feyts es deuengutsen en la vida del molt alt senyor rey En Jacme lo Conqueridor (Biblioteca catalana, Barcelona 1879.)

Mariano Flotats and Antonio de Bofarull: Historia escrita en lemosin traducida al castellano (Barcelona 1848). Raymond Foulché-Delbosc: Gestas del rey D. Jayme (336 p., Sociedad de bibliófilos madrileños, Madrid 1909). This is an old Spanish adaptation.

The Chronicle of James the Conqueror written by himself. Englished by John Foster, with introduction and notes by Pascual de Gayangos (2 vols., London 1883).

Libre de saviesa (Santander 1908).

Criticism—Charles de Tourtoulon: Etudes sur la maison de Barcelone. Jacme ler le Conquérant (2 vols., Montpellier 1863–1867). Otto Denk: Einführung in die Geschichte der altcatalanischen Litteratur (548 p., München 1893). Francis Darwin Swift: The life and times of James the First (330 p., Oxford 1894). Congrès d'historia de la corona d'Aragó, Barcelona 1908 (2 vols., album of 50 pl.; Barcelona 1909–1913). Joaquín Miret y Sans: Itinerari de Jaume I (530 p., Barcelona 1918). Enciclopedia universal ilustrada (vol. 28, 2404–2408, 1926).

BERNAT DESCLOT

Bernard d'Esclot, de Sclot. Catalan chronicler. The facts of his own life (birth, death, etc.) are unknown.

He composed before the end of the century in Catalan a chronicle of the kings of Aragon from the twelfth century on, dealing mainly with Peter III the Great, whose life and exploits are told in detail until his death in 1285 (king of Aragon from 1276 to 1285). He quotes no sources but was an eyewitness of many of the events. His account is impersonal and terse, but vivid and sometimes intense. It includes descriptions of the final conquest of Valencia, and of the Sicilian Vespers, of the invasion of Catalonia by the French, and their defeat, etc.

Text—J. A. C. Buchon: Chroniques étrangères relatives aux expéditions françaises pendant le XIIIe siècle (Paris 1840; first edition of the Catalan text; reprinted in 1851, 1875). J. Coroleu: Cronica del rey En Pere e dels seus antecessors passats ab un prolech sobre 'ls cronistas catalans (Barcelona 1885).

Spanish translation by Raphael Cervera (Barcelona 1616; incomplete and imperfect).

Italian translation by Filippo Moisè: Cronache catalane del sec. XIII e XIV (Florence 1844).

English translation by Frank Linley Critchlow (404 p., Princeton University 1930).

Criticism—Potthast (372, 1896). A. Molinier: Sources de l'histoire de France (vol. 3, 181, 1903).

See notes on Alfonso X, and on Vincent of Beauvais.

WILLIAM OF PUYLAURENS

Guilelmus de Podio-Laurentii. Puylaurens is a place in Languedoc, equally distant from Lavau and Castres (Tarn). Born about the beginning of the thirteenth century. Chaplain to Raymond VII, count of Toulouse, from 1242 to the latter's death in 1249. He wrote in Latin a history of the Albigensian crusade and following events down to 1272, which is not as valuable as the history written by Peter of Vaux Cernay (first half of the thirteenth century), yet is very important; it is based to some extent upon his own observations and the accounts of other witnesses and is relatively moderate; besides its scope is wider and its perspective better. William was a good Catholic but loyal to the counts of Toulouse; he realized the need of the Crusade, but was not blind to the greed and cruelty of the Crusaders.

Text—Guil. Catel: Histoire des comtes de Toulouse (Toulouse 1623). Mart. Bouquet: Recueil des historiens des Gaules (vol. 19, 193–225; vol. 20, 764–776).

New edition by J. Beyssier in Achille Luchaire: Mélanges d'histoire du moyen âge (vol. 3, 85–175, 1904; vol. 4, 233).

French translation in Guizot: Collection des mémoires (vol. 15, 205–329). Translation by Charles Lagarde, with introduction and notes (354 p., Béziers, 1864).

Criticism—Paul Meyer: La Chanson de la croisade contre les Albigeois (vol. 2, p. xiii–xix, 1879). Potthast (555, 1896). A. Molinier: Les sources de l'histoire de France (vol. 3, 57, 66, 1903).

WILLIAM OF NANGIS

Guilelmus de Nangiaco. (Nangis is a place in Seine-et-Marne, half way between Melun and Provins). Monk of Saint Denis, archivist and librarian of the monastery from 1285 to 1300; died in or after 1300. French annalist. He compiled official biographies of the kings Louis IX and Philip III; an abbreviated chronicle to 1300; a longer universal chronicle to the same year; a French translation of the abbreviated chronicle, all other works being of course in Latin. His most important work is the universal chronicle, mostly composed before 1297; down to 1113 it is mainly derived from Sigebert of Gembloux (first half of the twelfth century); the sequel contains valuable first-hand information. It was often copied and thrice continued: in 1304, to 1303; later, from 1304 to 1340; finally from 1340 to 1368 by John of Venette (q.v., second half of the fourteenth century).

Text—Chronique latine de Guillaume de Nangis, de 1113 à 1300, avec les continuations de 1300 à 1368. Nouvelle édition par H. Géraud (Société de l'histoire de France; 2 vols., Paris 1843).

French translation in Guizot: Collection de mémoires (vol. 13).

For other works see Potthast (554–555, 1896).

Criticism—Léopold Delisle: Mémoire sur les ouvrages de Guillaume de Nangis (Mém. de l'Acad. des Inscriptions, vol. 27; 86 p., 1873). A. Molinier: Sources de l'histoire de France (vol. 3, 102–104, passim, 1903).

MATTHEW PARIS

Matthaeus Paris, Parisiensis, de Parisio, etc. Monk of St. Albans (21 miles from London on the road to Liverpool) since 1217; most of his life was spent there except for travels in England with his abbot and for a journey to Norway in 1248–1249; died in 1259. English historian, cartographer, artist. He was the most illustrious representative of the monastic school of St. Albans and his work represents the climax of English monastic historiography.

His main work is the Chronica magna; he wrote the part dealing with the years 1235 to 1259, but revised the previous parts, chiefly that contributed by Roger de Wendover (d. 1236) dealing with the years 1189 to 1235. Paris' account is far more comprehensive than the local annals which it continued; it contains information on many European events on which he was sometimes very well informed; it is a chronicle of Europe as seen from a St. Albans' window. He was credulous and biassed against foreigners and the Roman curia, but independent. He had a good deal of scientific knowledge and curiosity. He recorded the weather of each year, floods, earthquakes, falling stars, good and bad harvests, famines, sicknesses, natural curiosities (e.g., invasion of crossbills). His Historia minor (1067–1253) is an abridgment of the former work, but contains some new information.

His works contain maps designed by himself: (1) a world-map in two forms (this is rather a map of Europe and the Mediterranean basin); (2) a sketch of the

English Heptarchy in the form of a windrose; (3) a plan of the Roman roads of the same country; (4) an itinerary from the English court to Apulia (c. 1252); (5) a map of Palestine; (6) a map of England, in four forms. The last named map is the earliest known detail map of England; it is perhaps the most remarkable specimen of scholarly cartography, as opposed to the contemporary experimental cartography of the portolani, of the Christian Middle Ages; incidentally this map of England is the first example of late mediaeval work wherein the north (and not the east or south) is at the top of the sheet. The maps (4) and (5) are entirely unconnected, but they have been wrongly supposed to be parts of an itinerary from London to the Holy Land. Paris' information on Palestine was probably based upon a guide book of c. 1231, "Les pèlerinages pour aller en Jérusalem," or upon another contemporary work of the same type and origin.

Paris was an expert designer and limner. The MSS. of his works contain a large number of drawings ascribed to him. A painted panel (St. Peter) in the Oslo Museum is probably a work of his hand.

Text—First edition of the Chronica magna by Archbishop Matthew Parker (London 1571). French translation by A. Huillard-Bréholles: Grande Chronique de Matthieu Paris (9 vols., Paris 1840–1841). English translation by J. A. Giles (Bohn's Library, 3 vols., London 1852–1854.)

Excellent edition by Henry Richards Luard in the Rolls series (London 1872–1883; 7 vols., of which the last contains a copious index and glossary).

The Historia minor was edited by Sir Frederic Madden: Historia Anglorum, sive Historia minor (Rolls series, 3 vols., 1866–1869).

Maps—Four maps of Great Britain by Matthew Paris about 1250. Reproduced from three manuscripts in the British Museum and one at Corpus Christi, Cambridge (11 p., 4 maps, British Museum, London 1928; Isis, 13, 162).

Illustrations of his drawings—W. R. L. Lowe and E. F. Jacob: Illustrations to the life of St. Albans, in Trinity College, Dublin, reproduced in collotype facsimile, with description by Montague Rhodes James (39 p., Oxford 1924; Isis, 10, 129). A memoir by Montague Rhodes James in the Fourteenth Volume of the Walpole Society (1925–1926) contains reproductions of the 143 drawings ascribed to Paris, brought together from 6 MSS.

Criticism—William Hunt: Dictionary of national biography (vol. 43, 207–213, 1895). R. Röhricht: Bibliotheca geographica Palaestinae (52, 1890). A French itinerary from London to Jerusalem is ascribed to Paris. Potthast (778–779, 1896). C. R. Beazley: Dawn of modern geography (vol. 2, 217, 584–590, 1901; the best maps are reproduced). A. Molinier: Sources de l'histoire de France (vol. 3, 154–155, 1903). Charles Gross: Sources of English history (2d. ed., 384–385, 1915).

See notes on Jacob van Maerlant and Giles of Lessines.

HERMANN OF NIEDER-ALTAICH

Hermannus Altahensis. Born in 1200–1201. Abbot from 1242 to 1273 of the monastery of Nieder-Altaich, between Ratisbon and Passau; he died in 1275. German annalist. He compiled annals dealing with the period 1137–1273 which are valuable for the history of Bavaria, Austria and Bohemia, in spite of the author's political timidity. There are continuations down to 1303. He wrote historical accounts of the abbey of Nieder-Altaich (741–1271) and of his very successful administration of it.

Text—Best edition of the annals by Philipp Jaffé in the Monumenta Germaniae historica (scriptores, vol. 17). German translation by Ludwig Weiland in Geschichtschreiber der deutschen Vorzeit (134 p., Berlin 1871; revised edition, 208 p., Leipzig 1898).

Criticism—W. Wattenbach: Allgemeine deutsche Biographie (vol. 12, 164, 1880). Potthast (589, 1896; where Hermann's other works are quoted).

MARTIN OF TROPPAU

Incorrectly called Martin the Pole. Martinus Polonus, Oppaviensis. Bohemian annalist. Born at Troppau, Silesia, of a Bohemian family; assumed the Dominican habit in Prague; after 1265 he flourished in Rome where he was chaplain and penitentiary to the popes; in 1278 he was appointed archbishop of Gnesen, but he died in the same year, in Bologna, on his way to his see. The popular name, Martin the Pole, was given to him probably because the Bohemian Dominicans belonged to the Polish province of the order.

He compiled an index to Gratian's Decretum and to the Decretales, called Margarita decreti. By his time chronological parallels between the popes and emperors had already been attempted by various chroniclers, but Martin prepared a new one which put all the others in the shade in spite of its mediocrity. He began his Chronicon pontificum et imperatorum at the request of Clement IV (pope from 1265–1268), and the first edition was sent by him to his monastery in Prague before Clement's death. It is a chronology in two columns, allowing a page to each half-century, and a line to each year. The last edition went as far as 1277. The purpose was humble enough; Martin wanted simply to prepare a summary for the use of canonists, which they could bind with their Decretum or with the Historia scholastica of Peter the Eater. From the purely historical point of view it is worthless, or worse, for it was not simply superficial but superstitious, and it became the main vehicle of many fables; e.g., the story of the female pope Joan was, if not introduced, at least established by its means. Yet it must be taken into account because of its immense popularity and the influence it exerted down to the sixteenth century; it was translated into many languages; there is even an Armenian version for which see my note on Nerses Bakhon (second half of the fourteenth century).

Various continuations of Martin's chronology were compiled; e.g., by Bernard Guidonis (first half of the fourteenth century); and some of these are far more valuable, if only for the local information they include.

Text—First edition by Joannes Oporinus (Basel 1559). Edition by L. Weiland in the Monumenta Germaniae historica. Pierre Champion: Chronique martiniane. Edition critique d'une interpolation originale pour le règne de Charles VII restituée à Jean Le Clerc (Paris 1907).

Criticism—Reinhold Röhricht: Bibliotheca geographica Palaestinae (52, 1890). Apropos of a Descriptio terrae sanctae ascribed to Martin by mistake. W. Wattenbach: Deutschlands Geschichtsquellen (vol. 2, 466–472, 1894). Potthast (771–772, 1896.)

SIMON OF KÉZA

Hungarian annalist. Secretary to Leszek III Czarny (the Black), king of Poland from 1279 to 1288. He was himself of Magyar origin, and wrote in Latin a history of Hungary from the mythical days of Nimrod down to 1282 (1290); the first book deals with the Huns; the second with the Magyars.

Text—First edition by Alexius Horányi (Vienna, 1782; reprinted same year in Buda). New edition by Joseph Podhradczky (Buda, 1833).

Criticism—Ignace Kont: La Hongrie littéraire et scientifique (7, Paris 1896). Potthast (698, 1896). E. Jakubovich: Communication to the Hungarian Academy (Nov. 9, 1927) on the anonymous Gesta Ungarorum dating from the first half of the twelfth century (Journal des Savants, 142, 1928).

STURLA THÓRDARSON

In Icelandic: Sturla Þórðarson. Sturla son of Þórðr, who was the brother of Snorri Sturluson (q.v.). Icelandic historian; one of the greatest historians of mediaeval times.

He was born in 1214, and in 1250–1251 was the "speaker of laws," i.e., the president of the Icelandic Republic. In 1262 Iceland submitted to Norway, and in the following year Sturla went to Norway where he became a personal friend of King Magnus "the law-mender." He was then made lögmaðr (lawman), i.e., supreme judge of all Iceland, 1272–1276, and later when the office of lawman was divided, of Northern and Western Iceland, 1277–1282. He died in 1284.

He continued the task so admirably begun by his uncle, the writing of historical sagas of Iceland and Norway—a real prose epic.

He wrote a large part of the Sturlúnga saga, i.e., the saga of his own family (the house of the Sturlungs, named after his grandfather Sturla of Hvamm), dealing with the period 1116–1264. Later he composed the Hákonar saga gamla Hákonarsonar, the saga of the Norwegian king Hákon Hákonarson (1217–1263), and toward the end of his life he began the Magnús saga lagabaetis, the saga of Magnús Hákonarson the Law-mender (king of Norway, 1263–1280). Of this last work only some fragments have been preserved.

These writings are remarkable for their objectivity, impartiality, and the sober excellence of their Icelandic prose.

Many other biographical sagas date from about the same time, and are almost equally remarkable, but their authors are unknown; e.g., the Orkneyinga saga (or Jarla saga, or Jarla sögur), dealing with the earls of the Orkneys from c. 872 to 1170 (written c. 1200 or soon after); and the Knýtlinga saga, dealing with the Danish kings from Haraldr blátönn to Knútr the sixth, c. 930 to c. 1190 (this was composed somewhat later, c. 1270). Considered together these historical and biographical sagas form the finest body of historical writing of mediaeval Christendom.

Text—Sturlúnga saga. First Icelandic edition (4 thin vols., Kaupmannahöfn, 1817–1820). Gudbrand Vigfusson: Sturlunga saga, including the Islendinga saga of lawman Sturla Thordsson, and other works. (2 vols., Oxford 1878.) This includes a very elaborate introduction on the historical sagas (200 p.), genealogical tables, indices, and 2 maps. Critical edition by Kr. Kålund (Copenhagen 1906–1911).

Hákonar saga gamla Hákonarsonar and Magnús saga Hákonarsonar. Edited by Birgerus Thorlacius and Erich Christian Werlauff (Copenhagen 1818). Gudbrand Vigfusson: Icelandic sagas (Rerum britannicarum medii aevi scriptores, no. 88, vol. 2, 1887). Latin translation in the Scripta historica Islandorum (vols. 9 and 10, Copenhagen 1840–1841).

English translation by G. W. Dasent: Icelandic sagas and other historical documents relating to the settlements and descents of the Northmen on the British

Isles. Vol. 4. The saga of Hakon and a fragment of the saga of Magnus (Rerum brit. medii aevi scriptores, London 1894).

Orkneyinga saga. Edited and translated into Latin by the Icelander Jón Jónsson (Copenhagen 1780). Also in G. Vigfusson's Icelandic sagas (London 1887). English translation by Jón A. Hjaltalín and Gilbert Goudie, edited with notes by Joseph Anderson (358 p., 5 pl., 3 maps, Edinburgh 1873); also in G. W. Dasent: Icelandic sagas (vol. 3, 1894). Critical ed. by S. Nordal (Copenhagen 1913–1916).

Knýtlinga saga. Aefi Dana-konunga eda Knýtlinga saga, Historia Cnutidarum regum Daniae (268 p., without place or date, c. 1748). Edited by Hans Gram, with a Latin version by Árni Magnússon, revised by Gram. It was printed in Copenhagen before or about Gram's death in 1748, but was never published; the sheets, abandoned in the printer's attic, were most of them eaten up by mice; only a very few copies are extant. Latin version by Sveinbjörn Egilsson: Scripta historica Islandorum (vol. 11, 168–364, 1842). Extracts in Icelandic and Latin, in Monumenta Germaniae historica, Scriptorum tomus xxix (271–322, 1892).

Extract in French by L. S. Borring: Kanut Lavard (Mémoires de la Société royale des antiquaires du Nord, 193–209, 1836–1839).

Criticism—Potthast (p. 1037, 568, 759, 882, 699, 1896). William Paton Ker: Sturla the historian (Romanes lecture, 24 p., Oxford 1906). Hálldor Hermannsson: Bibliography of the Icelandic sagas (Islandica, vol. 1, 126 p., Ithaca 1908); Bibliography of the sagas of the kings of Norway (Islandica, vol. 3, 75 p., Ithaca 1910).

II. EASTERN CHRISTENDOM

GEORGIOS ACROPOLITES

Γεώργιος ὁ Ἀκροπολίτης. Byzantine historian. Born at Constantinople in 1217; in 1233 went to the Nicaean court, where he was educated partly by Nicephoros Blemmydes and trained for the diplomatic service; in 1244, John III Ducas Batatzes (1222–1254) made him his great chancellor (λογοθέτης); in 1257 he was entrusted the command of an army by his former pupil Theodoros II Lascaris, but failed and was made prisoner; Michael VIII Palaeologos freed him in 1260 and used him as a diplomat. After 1261 he flourished in Constantinople. In 1273 he was sent to Gregory X (pope, 1271–1276), to negotiate the reconciliation of the Latin and Greek churches, and in the following year, at the council of Lyon, he acknowledged in the emperor's name the supremacy of the Roman pontiff. In 1282 he was sent to John II, emperor of Trebizond. He died soon after his return to Constantinople in the same year, a few months before Michael VIII.

His main work is a chronicle, the Χρονικὴ συγγραφή, continuing that of Nicetas Acominatos. It deals with the period extending from the conquest of Constantinople by the Latins to the Byzantine restoration (1204–1261). It is largely based upon the valuable first-hand knowledge which his position as logothet, general, and ambassador had given him. The account is not impartial, but it is sober and matter of fact. The language is somewhat affected but very clear.

In 1252 he edited the letters of his pupil Theodoros Lascaris; in 1254 he wrote the funeral oration of John Ducas Batatzes; finally some small theological treatises are ascribed to him.

Text—We have three versions of the Chronicle: the original version, an abridged one, and an expanded one. First edition of the shorter version by Theod. Douza (Leyde 1614). Greek and Latin editions of the original and shorter versions by Leo Allatius (Paris 1651). Edition by Im. Bekker in the Bonn corpus (vol. 28,

1836). Also in Migne's Patrology (vol. 140, 969–1220, 1865). Opera edited by August Heisenberg (2 vols., Leipzig 1903). Volumen prius continens Historiam, breviarium historiae, Theodori Scutariotae additamenta; volumen alterum continens scripta minora; praecedit dissertatio de vita scriptoris.

Criticism—Potthast (498, 1896). K. Krumbacher: Byzantinische Litteratur (286–288, 1897).

MICHAEL VIII PALAEOLOGOS

Born in 1234. Emperor of Constantinople from 1261 (1259) to 1282. He resided at Nicaea until 1261; in June of that year he retook Constantinople from the Latins; he died in Thrace, 1282. He was excommunicated in 1262 by the patriarch Arsenios Autorianos because of his evil deeds. He tried to bring about the reconciliation of the Latin and Greek churches and sent deputies to the second council of Lyon, 1274, to accept the papal supremacy (see my note on Georgios Acropolites above). He did this in the face of his own people, not for any religious reason, but only for political reasons, for he was a scoundrel of the first order. He was one of the secret artisans of the Sicilian Vespers. He debased the Byzantine coinage.

This man would not deserve to be mentioned here except for the following facts. In 1280 he reestablished the monastery of the archangel Michael near Chalcedon, at the entrance of the Bosporus; in 1282 he reestablished the monastery of St. Demetrios in Constantinople. The acts of foundation (τυπικά) of these monasteries are of special interest because they contain autobiographical and other historical information.

In general such τυπικά (rules, formularies, rituals) are documents of great cultural interest and constitute valuable sources for Byzantine history, because they include not only liturgical and conventual regulations, but also historical facts concerning the monasteries and their founders, inventories of movables and immovables, dietetic and economic data, etc. The earliest example of a τυπικόν is the one written in 969 by St. Athanasios, founder of the great Laura of Mt. Athos.

Text—The typicon of 1280 was first edited by Manuel Joannes Gedeon: Τυπικὸν τῆς ἐπὶ τοῦ βουνοῦ τοῦ Αὐξεντίου σεβασμίας μονῆς Μιχαὴλ τοῦ Ἀρχαγγέλου (80 p., Athens 1895).

The typicon of 1282 was edited, incompletely, by G. Troickij: Imperatoris Michaelis Paleologi de vita sua opusculum necnon regulae quam ipse monasterio S. Demetrii praescripsit fragmentum (Khristianskoye chteniye, vol. 2, 529–579, Petersburg 1885; with Russian translation and commentary).

Criticism—K. Krumbacher: Byzantinische Litteratur (314–319 and by index, 1897). Conrad Chapman: Michel Paléologue, restaurateur de l'empire byzantin (Thèse, 204 p., 2 figs., 2 maps, Paris 1926).

See notes on Theodoros II Lascaris, Georgios Pachymeres, Nicholas Blemmydes, Maximos Planudes.

CYRIACUS OF GANDZAK

Ciracos (or Kirakos) Gandzakeci. Armenian historian. He was born in Gandzak (Kandsag; modern Elizabethpol) and flourished at the monastery of Kadig in Great Armenia; he studied under John Vanagan at the same time as Vardan the Great; he died in 1272.

He wrote a summary of Armenian history from the time of Gregory the Illuminator (302–325) to that of King Hayton I. This chronicle, which as usual is chiefly valuable for the latest period, contains much information of Arabic, Turkish, and Mongolian origin. It includes an account of King Hayton's journey to Mongolia and back. Cyriacus had some knowledge of the Mongolian language. He gives us a vivid description of the destruction of the Armenian city of Ānī by the Mongols in 1239; the few Armenian men who survived took refuge in Caffa, Trebizond, Astrakhan, etc.

Another contemporary chronicle of the Mongolian invasions into Armenia down to 1272 was written in Armenian by a monk called Malachiah (Malachi), said to be a schoolmate of Cyriacus.

Text—Marie Félicité Brosset: Deux historiens arméniens: Kiracos de Gantzac, Histoire d'Arménie; Ouakhtanès d'Ourha, Histoire en trois parties (St. Pétersbourg 1870).

Criticism—C. F. Neumann: Geschichte der armenischen Literatur (189, 1836).

VARDAN THE GREAT

Vardanes, Bardanes, Vartanes Partzerpertsi (Pardserpetsi, etc.). Armenian historian, theologian and grammarian. Born at Partzerpert (Arabic, Barsbart), a fortified place in the Taurus, north of Sis; after becoming a monk he went to Jerusalem c. 1238, thence to Cilicia where he was well received by Hayton (king of Armenia from 1225 to 1269); he lived there at least five years and attended the council of Sis in 1243; he returned to Greater Armenia but after a while came back again to Cilicia, for he attended the third council of Sis in 1251; he seems to have witnessed the sack of Baghdād in 1258; in 1264 he was summoned by Hūlāgū and had various interviews with him; he spent the rest of his life in the monastery of St. Andrew at Kaludsor (Kaïledsor-vankh, in the district Vaïots-dsor, province of Siunikh); he died in 1271.

While Vardan was in Greater Armenia, after 1243, he caused the Syriac chronicle of Michael the Elder (d. 1199) to be translated into Armenian; he may have made a part of that translation himself. He was very learned and knew many languages: Greek, Syriac, Persian (Arabic?), Hebrew, and Mongolian. He wrote in Armenian a universal chronicle, or rather a sort of chronology (for it is extremely abbreviated), from the creation to Hayton's reign and the death of the catholicos Constantine I of Partzerpert (1267). The earlier part was largely derived from Michael's Syriac chronicle and from many Armenian chronicles some of which are now lost. It is one of the most important works of its kind in Armenian literature.

He also wrote Biblical commentaries, homilies, an Armenian grammar, etc.

A collection of 144 animal fables (Book of the fox) is ascribed to him. The geography of Armenia bearing his name is apocryphal (it contains a reference to his own tomb!);[1] it was probably composed by one of his disciples; it is very valuable for the study of Armenian topography.

Text—Chronicle. Armenian editions by Nikita Osipovich Emin (Moscow 1861), and by L. Alishan (S. Lazzaro, Venice 1862). Russian translation with abundant notes by Emin (Moscow 1861).

J. Muyldermans: La domination arabe en Arménie, extrait de l'histoire universelle de Vardan (176 p., 2 pl., Louvain 1927). Critical edition of the Armenian

[1] P. 420 in Saint Martin's edition. Of course this may be an interpolation.

text with French translation and commentary (Rev. in American historical review, vol. 33, 428, 1928; and Journal des savants, 185–186, 1930).

Commentary on the Psalms (Astrakhan 1797). Collected edition of Biblical commentaries (Constantinople 1826).

Edition of selected fables with French translation by Jean Saint-Martin (Paris 1825).

The geography was first edited in Armenian by Diratsu Murad, under the following title (in Armenian): Brief and abridged geography, composed by the vartabed Vardan, the new interpreter of the Scriptures and our second illuminator (Constantinople 1728), at the end of a small Armenian Biblical dictionary. This was a wretched edition. A better one, together with a French translation and 140 very valuable geographical notes, was included by Jean Saint-Martin in his Mémoires historiques et géographiques sur l'Arménie (vol. 2, 406–471, Paris, 1819). Saint-Martin's work, completed by a geographical index, but unfortunately without maps, is an excellent tool for the study of Armenian topography. The names are given in Armenian script and in various transcriptions.

Criticism—C. F. Neumann: Geschichte der armenischen Literatur (186–188, 1836). Marii Ivanovich (né Marie Félicité) Brosset: Analyse critique de l'histoire universelle de Vardan, édition princeps du texte arménien et traduction russe par M. N. Emin (Mémoires de l'Académie des sciences de St. Pétersbourg, vol. 4, no. 9, 30 p., 1862). Including many quotations of the text in Russian or in Armenian. Karekeen Zarbhanelian: Armenian bibliography (in Armenian; 639–643, Venice 1883). This was kindly abstracted for me by R. P. Blake. Heinrich Gelzer: Sextus Julius Africanus (vol. 2, 482–496, 1898). Nikolai Iakovkevich Marr: The collection of Vardan's fables (in Russian; 3 vols., Petersburg and Tiflis, 1894–1899).

STEPHEN ORBELIAN

Stephanos Orbelian (or Orpelian) Siunetsi. Armenian historian and theologian. Born about the middle of the thirteenth century in Siunikh (i.e., the country around Lake Sevan or Gukchah, and a part of Karabagh (Qārā bāgh), Transcaucasia). His paternal uncle Sempad and later his father Darsaij were the lords of Orodn in Siunikh and the chiefs of the Orbelian family. In 1280 Stephen was ordained priest in the monastery of Noravankh (i.e., the new monastery) in the district of Vaïotsdsor; in 1287 he traveled to Cilicia, visited Leon II (king of Armenia from 1270 to 1289) in Sis and was consecrated archbishop of Siunikh. He made himself very unpopular with his flock and had to ask Arghūn (Īl-Khān from 1284–1291) to confirm him in his dignity. He died in 1304.

The Orbelian family was one of the most ancient and greatest of Armenia; according to its own claim, it was established in Armenia before Alexander's invasion of Persia (331 B.C.), and originated from the country called, in Armenian, Jenasdan (China?).

Stephen's main work was a history of the Orbelians down to 1290. The beginning of it is in fact a history of Armenia from the creation; the main part is a valuable chronicle of Siunikh. It is not a continuous narrative, but rather a collection of historical fragments divided into 9 chapters. In 1299 he composed an elegy dealing with the misfortunes of his country.

The new kingdom of Armenia in Cilicia (1196–1375) was enfeoffed to the Holy See and the Holy Empire. Under the influence of the Armenian kings, the catholicoi became more friendly to the Roman church, and finally Gregory VII (catholicos from 1293 to 1307) proclaimed publicly their allegiance to it. Stephen remained loyal to the Armenian church and to the doctrine of Monotheletism,[2] and fought with equal energy his countrymen who joined the Greek or the Roman faith. He addressed in 1302 to Gregory VII a theological treatise entitled Dserhnarg (Manual), directed against the Roman church; it contains valuable data concerning the political and ecclesiastical history of Armenia, Georgia, and Albania.

Text—The History of the Orbelians was first edited by Eleazar of Shamīrān, an Armenian merchant established in India (Madras 1775). However this text is very different from the MS. text kept by the Mekhitarists of Vienna. Fragments translated into Latin by V. Lacroze: Excerpta ex libro Stephani, Synensis archiepiscopi, ... cui titulus est Historia satraparum Orbelensium in majore Armenia (Archiv für asiatische Litteratur, Geschichte und Kunst, vol. 1, part 1 (the only one published) p. 114–118, Petersburg, 1810). The Madras text was reprinted and translated into French by Jean Saint-Martin: Mémoires historiques et géographiques sur l'Arménie (vol. 2, 56–175, Paris 1819). Followed by abundant notes (p. 176–300). Saint-Martin corrected the Madras text which was very imperfect, but his corrections were made without reference to MSS. A critical edition is badly needed.

Fragments of the Dserhnarg in Michael Chamchian: History of Armenia (Calcutta 1827).

Criticism—J. Saint-Martin's introduction to the edition above mentioned (p. 1–55). The largest part (p. 15–55) is a Dissertation sur l'origine et la famille des Orpélians et de plusieurs autres colonies chinoises établies en Arménie et en Géorgie. C. F. Neumann: Geschichte der armenischen Literatur (196–200, 1836).

VAHRAM OF EDESSA

Vahram Rhapun (i.e., magister); Vahram of Urfa (Urfa being the Armenian or Turkish name of Edessa, al-Ruhā in Arabic; in Jazīrah). Armenian poet, historian, and theologian. Secretary to Leon II, king of Armenia from 1270 to 1289. He continued the rhymed chronicle of Armenia begun by Nerses the Graceful (second half of the twelfth century), down to 1289. He wrote also homilies and a treatise on the Trinity.

Text—Second edition (Madras 1810).

English translation by C. F. Neumann: Vahrams chronicle of the Armenian kingdom in Cilicia during the time of the Crusades (London 1831; translation of the Madras text). Sahag Bedrosian: Chronique du royaume arménien de la Cilicie composée par Vahram Rapoun (24 p.; reprint from an unidentified journal, Paris 1864).

Criticism—C. F. Neumann: Geschichte der armenischen Literatur (191, 1836).

MEKHITAR OF AÏRI-VANKH

Mekhitar of Ayrivankh (Aïri-vankh means the monastery of the cave; it was located N.E. of the very ancient town of Karhni (or Garni), in the district of Ervian, Siunikh). Mekhitar was a doctor (vardapet) and historian. He composed c. 1297 a chronicle or chronology in Armenian, from the creation down to 1289. It is largely derived from the Armenian chronicle of Samuel of Ānī (to 1177) and from the Syriac chronicle of Michael the Elder (to 1196).

I have not been able to date exactly the activity of another historian called Mekhitar of Ānī (Ānī was an ancient city, the capital of Greater Armenia, on the

[2] The human and divine will of Christ is but one will.

Arpa Cai, not far from its confluence with the Araxes). This Mekhitar was a priest in the cathedral of Ānī who flourished in the thirteenth century. Could these two Mekhitars be identical? Of course Mekhitar of Aïri-vankh might have flourished in Ānī. At any rate Mekhitar of Ānī was very learned. A book dealing with Armenian, Georgian and Persian antiquities and the translation of an astronomical treatise (a treatise on the calendar?) from the Persian (or Arabic?) are ascribed to him. These works have not yet been discovered.

Text—Armenian edition of the chronology by Nikita Osipovich Emin (Moscow 1860). French translation by Marii Ivanovich Brosset (Mémoires de l'Académie de St. Pétersbourg, vol. 13, 133 p., 1869).

Criticism—For Mekhitar of Ānī, C. F. Neumann: Geschichte der armenischen Literatur (182, 1836).

For Mekhitar of Aïri-vankh, Heinrich Gelzer: Sextus Julius Africanus (vol. 2, 469–500, 1898).

See note on Abū-l-Faraj.

III. WESTERN ISRAEL

BENJAMIN 'ANAV

Benjamin ben Abraham 'Anav. (The word 'anaw means meek, modest; hence the Italian forms of that name: degli Mansi, Piatelli, Pietosi, Umani.) Benjamin delli Mansi. Roman Jewish scholar. Dates of birth and death unknown. He composed many poems, ethical, satirical, liturgical. The Roman maḥzor includes some of the last named and also calendrical rules put together by Benjamin between 1276 and 1294. He wrote notes on Rashi's commentary on the Pentateuch, etc. His most interesting writings from our point of view are his messages (sheliḥot) which contain information on the defamation of the Talmud by Nicholas Donin (1239), on its burning (1244), on the distinctive badges or garments which Jews were obliged to wear (1257), on the desecration of tombs in the Jewish cemetery of Rome (1267), etc.

Benjamin's brother, Zedekiah ben Abraham 'Anav, was the author of a famous ritual, Shibbole ha-leqeṭ. Zedekiah was about 70 years old in 1297; he was probably younger than Benjamin, whom he often quotes.

Text—The Shibbole ha-leqeṭ was often printed: Venice 1546, Vilna 1886. Abridged edition, Mantua 1514; etc.

Criticism—Moses Beer: Jewish encyclopaedia (vol. 1, 566, 568, 1901). U. Cassuto: Encyclopaedia judaica (vol. 2, 798, 801, 1928).

See note on Moses ben Naḥman.

IV. WESTERN ISLĀM

IBN AL-'IDHĀRĪ

Ibn al-'Idhārī (or 'Adhārī? 'Adsārī?) al-Marrākushī. Moroccan historian who flourished about the end of the thirteenth century. He wrote a history of Africa and Spain, Kitāb al-bayān al-mughrib, which contains the most detailed account of the Umayyads of Cordova. It is largely derived from the chronicle of 'Arīb ibn Sa'd (second half of the tenth century).

Text—R. P. A. Dozy: Histoire de l'Afrique et de l'Espagne intitulée al-Bayano 'l-Mogrib par ibn Adhārī et fragments de la Chronique d'Arīb (2 vols., Leyde, 1848–1851). Editio princeps with introduction and glossary. Partial Spanish translation by Francisco Fernandez Gonzalez: Historias de al-Andalus (vol. 1, Granada 1860). No more published; this corresponds to p. 2–161 of Dozy's Arabic text. Histoire de l'Afrique et de l'Espagne, traduite et annotée par E. Fagnan (2 vols., Alger 1901–1904).

Criticism—F. Wüstenfeld: Geschichtschreiber der Araber (no. 373, p. 151, 1881; only a few lines). C. Brockelmann: Arabische Litteratur (vol. 1, 337, 1898; 4 lines). Francisco Pons Boigues: Ensayo bio-bibliográfico sobre los historiadores y geógrafos arábigo-españoles (414, Madrid 1898). J. E. Sarkis: Dictionnaire de bibliographie arabe (172, Cairo 1928).

See notes on Ibn al-Abbār, Muḥammad ibn Rushaid, and Ibn Sa'īd al-Maghribī.

V. EASTERN ISLĀM

ABŪ SHĀMA

Shihāb al-dīn Abū-l-Qāsim 'Abd al-Raḥmān ibn Ismā'īl. Born at Damascus 1203; studied in Damascus and Alexandria; returned to Damascus where he taught at the madrasa al-Ruknīya; mobbed and murdered there in 1268.

Muslim historian, whose main work is the Kitāb al-rawḍatain fī-akhbār al-dawlatain (Book of the two gardens dealing with the history of the two reigns), which is a history of the two sultans Nūr al-dīn (Zangid atābeg of Syria, 1146–1173) and Salāḥ al-dīn ("Saladin," Ayyūbid ruler of Egypt, 1169–1193). The biography of the latter is largely a reproduction of the lost one by Ibn abī Ṭaiy'. He wrote a continuation of this work, Dhail al-rawḍatain, down to 1266–1267, and a summary and continuation of Ibn 'Asākir's History of Damascus (q.v., second half of the twelfth century).

Text—The Kitāb al-rawḍatain was printed in Cairo (2 vols., 1287–1292 H.). Saladin's biography had been partly edited and translated by E. P. Goergens and R. Röhricht: Arabische Quellenbeiträge zur Geschichte der Kreuzzüge (vol. 1, Berlin 1879). Arabic text with French translation by Barbier de Ménard: Abou Chamah, Le livre des deux jardins (Recueil des historiens des Croisades, Paris 1898, 1906).

Criticism—F. Wüstenfeld: Geschichtschreiber der Araber (p. 132–133, 1881). C. Brockelmann: Arabische Litteratur (vol. 1, 317, 1898); Encyclopaedia of Islām (vol. 1, 106, 1908). J. E. Sarkis: Dictionnaire de bibliographie arabe (317, Cairo 1928).

IBN WĀṢIL

Abū 'Abdallāh Muḥammad ibn Sālim ibn Wāṣil, Jamāl al-dīn. Born in 1207–1208; flourished in Ḥamāt; in 1260–1261 he was called to Cairo by the Mamlūk sulṭān Baybars (ruled from 1260 to 1277) and sent by him as an envoy to king Manfred of Sicily (ruled from 1258 to 1266); he remained a long time at Manfred's court, then returned to Ḥamāt, where he was chief qāḍī and professor in the madrasa, and where he died in 1298. Shāfi'ite doctor, historian, philosopher, mathematician. He taught Abū-l-Fidā' mathematics and prosody.

He dedicated to Manfred a treatise on logic which he called in his honor Al-impirūrīya, but after his return home he entitled it Nukhbat al-fikr fī-l-manṭiq (Selected thoughts on logic). He wrote a history of the Ayyūbids, entitled Kitāb mufarrij al-kurūb fī akhbār banī Ayyūb (The book which dispels sadness with the tales of the Ayyūbids); this was continued down to 1295–1296 by 'Alī ibn 'Abd al-Raḥmān, secretary to al-Muẓaffar III, Abū-l-Fidā's predecessor as prince of Ḥamāt. Finally he composed a commentary on the treatise on prosody of Ibn al-Ḥājib (d. 1249), Sharḥ al-maqṣad al-jalīl.

Criticism—Adolf Friedrich von Schack: Poesie und Kunst der Araber in Spanien und Sizilien (2 vols. Berlin 1865). F. Wüstenfeld: Geschichtschreiber der Araber (149, 1881). C. Brockelmann: Arabische Litteratur (vol. 1, 322, 1898). H. Suter: Mathematiker und Astronomen (157, 1900). Encyclopaedia of Islām (vol. 2, 428, 1918; short unsigned note).

IBN KHALLIKĀN

Shams al-dīn Abū-l-'Abbās Aḥmad ibn Muḥammad ibn Ibrāhīm ibn abī Bakr Ibn Khallikān al-Barmakī al-Irbilī al-Shāfi'ī. Muslim historian. Born in 1211 at Irbil (Arbela), Jazīrah, east of the Tigris; he received his first training from his father who was a teacher in the madrasa of Irbil; he continued his studies in Irbil until 1228, then in Ḥalab, Damascus, and Egypt. From 1260 to 1270, then again after 1277, he was chief qāḍī of Syria with residence in Damascus (for a time he was chief qāḍī for the four rites); he taught in various colleges, chiefly at the Fakhrīya madrasa in Cairo (1270–1277) and the Amīnīya madrasa in Damascus; he was professor at the last named madrasa at the time of his death in Damascus, 1282.

His only work, Kitāb wafayāt al-a'yān wa-anbā' abnā' al-zamān (The deaths of great personages and histories of the leading people of the time), is a large biographical dictionary of the great men of Islām, excepting roughly those of the first century of the Hegira. It contains 865 biographies. It is one of the most important works of its kind in the world literature. The redaction of it was begun during his first stay in Cairo in 1256, but was interrupted at the time of his appointment in Damascus; the last biography (no. 817) of this first edition was that of his ancestor, Yaḥyā ibn Khālid al-Barmakī (de Slane, vol. 4, 103–114). During the ten years (1260–1270) which he spent in Damascus as chief qāḍī he had little if any time to devote to his studies, but he did not cease to think of the biographies and planned to continue them on a much larger scale. When he returned to Cairo in 1270 he did not rewrite the whole work but added some fifty biographies (those relative to the letter y, the last of the Arabic alphabet) which are much longer than the preceding ones. He completed these additional biographies in 1274. He took considerable pains to give accurate information; e.g., to trace genealogies, to establish the right spelling of names, to indicate the main traits of each personality and illustrate them by anecdotes, to fix the dates of birth and death. In fact, he omitted many biographies because he was unable to ascertain the exact date of death.

As opposed to other biographical collections in Arabic, Ibn Khallikān's was the first to be extended to all classes of distinguished people. He tried to write it as well as possible in order that the reader might be entertained as well as informed. He has been compared (by Sir William Jones) to Boswell; the comparison is inadequate but the fact that it was made at all is noteworthy. The holograph MS. of the Wafayāt is in the British Museum.

Ibn Khallikān's dictionary was continued twice; (a) by al-Muwaffaq Faḍlallāh ibn abī Muḥammad Fakhr al-Ṣaqā'ī who wrote the Tālī kitāb wafayāt al-a'yān, containing biographies of Egyptian and Syrians who died between 1261 and 1325; (b) by Muḥammad Ibn Shākir al-Kutubī (d. 1363), the Fawāt al-wafayāt (Omissions from the deaths).

Extracts from the Wafayāt were compiled by various authors; to begin with, by Ibn Khallikān's own son, Mūsā ibn Aḥmad (born in Cairo 1253). The Wafayāt was twice translated into Persian: (a) by Yūsuf ibn Aḥmad ibn Muḥammad ibn 'Uthmān (completed 1490); (b) by Kabīr ibn Uwais ibn Muḥammad al-Laṭīfī under Selīm 1 (1512–1520).

Text—Ibn Challicani Vitae illustrium hominum nunc primum edidit F. Wüstenfeld (Göttingen 1835–1850; with valuable index). Another edition by Baron MacGuckin de Slane (Paris 1838–1842; left incomplete; stops at no. 678). Many oriental editions.

Jan Pijnappel: Vitae ex lexico biographico Ibn Callicanis quae non exstant nisi in codice Amstelod. 106 (48 p., Amsterdam 1845). Including 24 biographies missing in other MSS.

Excellent English translation with abundant notes by Baron MacGuckin de Slane: Ibn Khallikan's Biographical dictionary (4 vols. quarto, Paris, 1842–1871). Separate indexes for each volume; introductions in vol. 1 and 2; life of Ibn Khallikān in vol. 4.

Criticism—F. Wüstenfeld: Über die Quellen Ibn Khallikans (Gelehrte Anz., 45 p., Göttingen 1837); Die Geschichtschreiber der Araber (Abhandl. der Göttingen Ges. der Wiss., vol. 28, 139–145, 1881). This is an exceptionally long notice. E. Strandman: De cod. MS. vitas veterum poetarum Arabum sub nomine Ibn Challikani exhibente (Helsingfors 1666). C. Brockelmann: Arabische Litteratur (vol. 1, 326–328, 1898); Encyclopaedia of Islām (vol. 2, 396, 1918). J. E. Sarkis: Dictionnaire encyclopédique de bibliographie arabe (98–99, Cairo 1928).

IBN AL-RĀHIB AL-QIBṬĪ

Abū Shākir Buṭrus (Peter) ibn abī-l-Karam ibn al-Muhadhdhib al-Ma'rūf ibn al-Rāhib al-Qibṭī (meaning the Copt). Christian Egyptian historian who flourished c. 1270–1282.

In 1270–1271 he was deacon in the Monophysitic monastery of the Virgin, called Dair al-mu'allaqat, in Fusṭāṭ; he was still living in 1282. He wrote in Arabic a chronicle (Ta'rīkh) of eastern history from the creation down to 1258–1259, including an account of the seven oecumenical councils.

Text—Chronicon orientale, nunc primum latinitate donatum ab Abr. Ecchellensi (Script. hist. Byz., Paris 1651, again 1685). Abraham Ecchellensis was a Maronite who died in Rome, 1664. The part of the text dealing with the seven councils is not included. Jos. Sim. Assemani: Chronicon Petri Rahebi primum ex Arabico latine redditum ab Abr. Ecchellensi nunc nova interpretatione donatum (in the new Byzantine corpus, Venice 1729). Louis Cheikho: Interpretationem olim ab Abrahamo Ecchellensi institutam tum ab I. S. Assemano revisam iterum ad fidem Arabici textus recognovit (Corpus scriptorum Christianorum Orientalium, Scriptores Arabici, series III, tomus I, Paris 1903). A critical edition of the Arabic text is very desirable.

Criticism—F. Wüstenfeld: Geschichtschreiber der Araber (p. 145, 1881). C. Brockelmann: Arabische Litteratur (vol. 1, 349, 1898). J. E. Sarkis: Dictionnaire de bibliographie arabe (106, 1928).

AL-MAKĪN

Jirjīs al-Makīn (George Elmacin). 'Abdallāh ibn Abī-l-Yāsir ibn Abī-l-Makārim Ibn al-'Amīd (in the East he is generally called Ibn al-'Amīd). Born in Cairo 1205–1206, of an old Cairene Christian family; died in Damascus 1273–1274. Both he and his father were employed in the government service in Syria; when their patron, the governor of Syria, 'Alā al-dīn Ṭībars, fell into disgrace, they were recalled and put into prison; the father, Abū-l-Yāsir, died in 1238–1239; the son was reinstated, but reimprisoned some time later; when he regained his freedom he quitted the government service and established himself in Damascus, where he died in 1273–1274.

He composed a chronicle (to c. 1260) which is of great importance for intrinsic reasons, but also because it was one of the earliest Arabic works of its kind to be known in the West, and thus one of the earliest channels through which some accurate knowledge of Muslim history became available in Europe. It was entitled Kitāb al-majmū' al-mubārak (The blessed collection) and aimed to be universal. It deals mainly with Muslim history, but contains valuable information on eastern Christendom.

It is divided into two main parts; the first from the creation to Muḥammad, the second from Muḥammad to 1259–1260. The second part is naturally the most important. Apart from cosmological and geographical considerations at the beginning, the account is mainly in the form of biographies of the leading personalities, the first of these being Adam. For the earlier part, the account is largely derived from the Bible, from al-Ṭabarī (to 915) and Eutychios (to 937); his Christian contemporary Ibn al-Rāhib is quoted. He also made use of some earlier sources neglected by the majority of his predecessors; e.g., in the chapter on Alexander the Great, the pseudo-Aristotelian hermetical treatise Kitāb al-isṭamākhīs, previously included in the Ghāyat al-ḥakīm ascribed to Maslama ibn Aḥmad al-Majrīṭī (d. c. 1007).

The Majmū al-mubārak was continued by another Egyptian Christian, Mufaḍḍal ibn abī-l-Faḍā'il, for the period 1260–1348, under the title Kitāb al-nahj al-sadīd wal durr al-farīd fī mā ba'd ta'rīhh Ibn al-'Amīd. This is a very valuable continuation especially for the history of the Jacobite patriarchs of Egypt, the Muslims in Yaman and India, and the Mongols.

A part at least of the Majmū' al-mubārak was translated into Ethiopic.

Text—The second part only of al-Makīn's chronicle has been edited. Thomas Van Erpen (1584–1624): Historia saracenica . . . . arabice olim exarata a Georgio Elmacino et latine reddita (340 p., Leyden 1625). Arabic and Latin in parallel columns. Quotations from the first part with Latin translation in J. H. Hottinger: Smegma orientale (Heidelberg 1658). A critical edition of the whole work is badly needed.

English translation of the second part by Samuel Purchas (London 1626). French translation by Pierre Vattier: L'histoire mahométane de Macine (Paris 1657).

Chapter on Alexander the Great edited in Ethiopic and translated from Ethiopic into English by Sir Ernest A. Wallis Budge: The life and exploits of Alexander the Great (2 vols., London 1896).

Mufaḍḍal's continuation is being edited and translated into French by Edgar Blochet: Histoire des sultans mamlouks (Patrologia orientalis; part 1 in vol. 12, part 2 in vol. 14, 1920; part 3 in vol. 20, 1928). Part 3 extends to the year 1317, it includes a note préliminaire and notes additionnelles. I have not seen part 1.

Criticism—Interesting reference in Ibn Khaldūn's Prolegomena (de Slane's translation, vol. 1, 475). M. Steinschneider: Die arabischen Übersetzungen aus dem Griechischen (Centralblatt für Bibliothekswesen, Beiheft 5, Jahrgang 6, p. 88, 1889). F. Wüstenfeld: Geschichtschreiber der Araber (134, 1881). C. Brockelmann: Arabische Litteratur (vol. 1, 348, 1898). C. F. Seybold: Zu El Makīn's Weltchronik. Das Breslauer Schlussfragment und der Codex Gothanus Arabicus (Karshūnī)[3] 1557 des 1. noch unedierten Teils (Zeitschrift der deutschen morgenländischen Gesellschaft, vol. 64, 140-153, 1910). J. E. Sarkis: Dictionnaire de bibliographie arabe (191-193, Cairo 1928). M. Plessner: Encyclopaedia of Islām (vol. 3, 172, 1929).

VI. PERSIANS

MINHĀJ-I-SIRĀJ

Abū 'Umar-i-'Uthmān Minhāj-i-Sirāj of Jūzjān (near Balkh, in Khurāsān). Persian historian, born c. 1193; died after 1260. Like his father and grandfather he was first in the service of the Ghūrids, rulers of Afghānistān; in 1226 he joined the governor of Sind, Nāṣir al-dīn Qubācha, and in 1227 passed into the service of the latter's conqueror, Shams al-dīn Īltutmish (Altamish), sulṭān of Dehlī from 1210 to 1235.

He completed in 1260 and dedicated to Īltutmish's son, Nāṣir al-dīn Maḥmūd Shāh (ruled 1246-1265), a general history of the Muslim dynasties of Asia to 1260, in Persian, entitled Ṭabaqāt-i-Nāṣirī. It is divided into twenty chapters, of which the first is devoted to the Patriarchs and Prophets, and the last to the Mongol invasion. This last chapter is apparently the most important.

Text—The parts of the text dealing with India have been edited by Captain Nassau Lees in the Bibliotheca Indica and translated into English by Major Henry George Raverty: A general history of the Muhammadan dynasties of Asia, including Hindustan from 194 to 658 and the irruption of the infidel Mughals into Islam (2 vols., London 1881).

Criticism—E. G. Browne: A literary history of Persia (vol. 2, 470, 1906).

AL-JUWAINĪ

'Alā al-dīn 'Aṭā Malik ibn Muḥammad al-Juwainī. One of the greatest Persian historians. Born at Āzādwār in the district of Juwain, western Khurāsān, c. 1233; died in Arrān,[4] 1283.

He traveled twice to Mongolia and back in 1249-1251, and in 1251-1253. He became secretary to Hūlāgū (Īl-khān from 1256 to 1265) and accompanied him in the expedition against the Assassins.[5] When the fortress of Alamūt was taken by the Mongols in 1256, the famous library which was kept there was saved from complete destruction upon al-Juwainī's entreaty and handed over to him; al-Juwainī caused the heretical books to be destroyed and the others to be removed to the newly founded observatory of Marāgha. In 1256 he was appointed governor of Khurāsān, and in 1262 governor of Baghdād. Under Hūlāgū's successor, Abāgā (1265-1281), he continued as governor of Baghdād and helped to restore and

[3] Karshūnī means Arabic written in Syriac script.

[4] Arrān is the country between the rivers Kur and Aras (Cyrus and Araxes), east of the Gukchah lake.

[5] For their early history, see vol. 1, 752.

increase its prosperity by the building of a new canal, etc. He gave proof of religious toleration in 1268 when the Nestorian patriarch Denha found an asylum in his house. After 1270 he was accused of peculation, and towards the end of Abāgā's rule was destituted, ruined, and persecuted in various ways. The persecution continued under Aḥmad (1281–1284), and finally he took refuge in Arrān where he died (1283).

Al-Juwainī's main work was a history of the Mongols, written in Persian, entitled Ta'rīkh-i-jahān gushā (or jihān-kushāi), Annals of the world conqueror (i.e., Chingiz Khān). He conceived it during his second Mongolian journey (1251–1253) and completed it by 1260. It is the main Persian authority on the subject. It is divided into three parts, of which the first deals with the rise and development of the Mongol power down to the destruction of the Shāhs of Khwārizm (1231) and of the Assassins (1256), while the second and third deal respectively with the history of these two dynasties. For the second part, al-Juwainī made use of the Arabic chronicle, Mashārib al-tajārib, of Abū-l-Ḥasan 'Alī ibn Zaid al-Baihaqī (fl. 1148–1168), and of the Persian encyclopaedia, Jawāmi' al-'ulūm, of Fakhr al-dīn al-Rāzī (d. 1210); this part includes a history of the governors of Khurāsān to 1258. For the third part, the most valuable, he was able to use the documents found in Alamūt; hence it contains information on the Assassins which cannot be found anywhere else.

This work exerted a deep influence upon Persian historiography. It is not free from errors and contradictions, but is largely based upon sources, and the author was the only Muslim historian having a personal knowledge of eastern Mongolia. His description of Qaraqorum completes Rubruquis' contemporary account.

During his period of tribulation—i.e., toward the end of his life—he wrote an Arabic letter to his brothers, Taslīyat al-ikhwān (Consolation of the brothers).

Text—An edition of the Ta'rīkh-i-jahān gushā, by Mīrzā Muḥammad Qazwīnī is in course of publication (Gibb memorial series, London, 1912–).

Criticism—Edward G. Browne: Notes on the contents of the Ta'rīkh-i-jahān-gushā, with an appreciation and comparison of some of the MSS. (Journal Asiatic Soc., 27–43, 1904); Literary history of Persia (vol. 2 and 3, 1906–1920). W. Barthold: Encyclopaedia of Islām (vol. 1, 1067–1070, 1913). Reuben Levy: The account of Ismā'īlī doctrines in the Jāmi' al-tawārīkh of Rashīd al-dīn Faḍlallāh (Journal R. Asiatic Soc., 509–536, 1930; Isis, 15, 410).

See notes on al-Baiḍāwī and on Sa'dī.

VII. CHINA

CHU MU

Chu^{4*} Mu^{4*} (2597, 8082). Chinese encyclopaedist, born at Hsi^{4*}-hsien^{4} (4134, 4545), in the prefecture Hui^{1}-chou^{1}-fu^{3} (5160, 2444, 3682), Anhui. Birth and death dates unknown. He obtained his doctor's degree, chin^{4} shih^{4} (2075, 9992), in 1256; he must have been then about 40 years old. He completed in 1246 (?) the encyclopaedia Shih^{4} wên^{2} lei^{4} chü^{4} (9990, 12633, 6853, 3061) in 130 chüan; the title may be translated Encyclopaedia of classified quotations and facts. Each subject is illustrated by means of quotations from standard works, by historical facts, and by various literary references.

Text—The Library of Congress has three different editions of this work. First the original Yüan edition, with the preface by the author dated 1246. This is a

Ma^{3} sha^{1} pan^{3} (7576, 9624, 8589) edition, so called after the place Ma sha, in Chien^{4}-yang^{2} (1592, 12883), Fuhkien, whence the banyan wood came which was used for printer's engravings. That wood was very convenient because of its softness, but the prints were soon broken and uneven. After 1488 its use was forbidden by the Chinese government. The two other editions in the Library of Congress are respectively Ming and Ch'ing. The Ming edition was printed in 1604; the Ch'ing in 1763. The latter is very beautiful, and includes several old prefaces missing in the other editions.

Criticism—A. W. Hummel: Report of the Librarian of Congress for 1928–1929 (294, 1929).

HSIEH WEI-HSIN

Hsieh^{4} Wei^{2}-hsin^{1} (4432, 12598, 4574). Author of the encyclopaedia Ku^{3} chin^{1} ho^{2*} pi^{4*} shih^{4} lei^{4} pei^{4} yao^{4} (6188, 2027, 3947, 8956, 9990, 6853, 8804, 12889) which might be translated Classified summary of important facts of ancient and modern times. This work was published in 366 chüan in 1257. At that time Hsieh had already obtained his chin^{4} shih^{4} (2075, 9992) degree; thus he must have been at least 40 years old. This encyclopaedia has been superseded by later ones, yet it is a valuable monument of its time and contains interesting information which has not always been included in later works; e.g., on Sung government and Sung poetry.

Text—The Library of Congress has a Ming edition with a preface by Ku^{4} k'o^{3}-hsüeh^{2} (6254, 6078, 4839), dated 1556; it includes the original preface dated 1257, and another by a contemporary, Huang^{2} Shu^{2*}-tu^{4} (5124, 10039, 12089).

Criticism—A. W. Hummel: Report of the Librarian of Congress for 1928–29 (p. 295, 1929).

See notes on Kublai Khān, Ch'ang Tê, and Chou Ta-kuan.

VIII. JAPAN

AZUMA-KAGAMI

The Azuma-kagami (Mirror of the east) is a chronicle of Japanese history in fifty-two volumes covering the period extending from 1180 to 1266. It contains many anecdotes which illustrate the manners and morals of that time. It is written in Chinese and must thus be distinguished from the other kagami, written in Japanese, for which see my note on Fujiwara Tamenari (first half of the twelfth century).

Examples of the kind of anecdotes found in the Azuma-kagami are quoted by F. Brinkley: History of the Japanese people (348, London 1914).

CHAPTER LIV

LAW AND SOCIOLOGY

(Second Half of Thirteenth Century)

I. ITALY

MARTINO DA FANO

Italian jurist. Pupil of Azo at Bologna; taught law in Arezzo and Modena in 1255; also in Naples and Milan. He wrote a quaint little tract wherein he explained to law students how to behave and how to study, De regimine et modo studendi quem debent habere scolares.

Text—L. Frati: L'epistola De regimine et modo studendi di Martino da Fano (Studi e memorie per la storia dell' Università di Bologna, vol. 6, 19–29, 1921).
Criticism—E. M. Meyers: Iuris interpretes saec. XIII (Naples 1924). Carlyle: History of mediaeval political theory (vol. 5, 357, 1928). C. H. Haskins: Studies in mediaeval culture (75, Oxford 1929; Isis, 14, 433).

See notes on St. Thomas Aquinas and Giles of Rome.

PTOLEMY OF LUCQUES

Bartolommeo dei Fiadoni, da Lucca. (Bartolommeo was erroneously transformed into Tolomeo, Ptolomaeus, etc.) Ptolemaeus de Fiadonibus Lucensis. Dominican. Bishop of Torcello, 1319. Died in 1328. Italian annalist and publicist. Pupil of St. Thomas.

He completed, c. 1274–1282, his master's treatise, De regimine principum, which is one of the most original and deepest political writings of mediaeval times. However it would seem that Ptolemy's task was chiefly that of an editor. He wrote annals from 1061 to 1303, and an ecclesiastical history from Christ to 1312.

Text—For the Regimen principum, see my note on St. Thomas.
Annales (Lyon 1619). L. A. Muratori: Rerum italicarum scriptores (vol. 11, 1249–1306, 1727). Critical edition by Carlo Minutoli (Florence 1876).
Historia ecclesiastica edited by Muratori (op. laud., vol. 11, 740–1249).
Marius Krammer: Determinatio compendiosa de iurisdictione imperii auctore anonymo ut videtur Tholomeo Lucensi O. P. (Fontes iuris germanici antiqui in usum scholarum ex Monumentis Germaniae historicis separatim editi; 128 p., Hannover 1909).
Criticism—Karl Krüger: Des Ptolomaeus Lucensis Leben und Werke (84 p.; Göttingen 1874). Dietrich König: Ptolomaeus und die Flores chronicorum des Bernardus Guidonis (72 p., Würzburg 1875); Tolomeo, ein biographischer Versuch (Progr., 13 p., Harburg 1878). Potthast (944, 1896). Carlyle: History of mediaeval political theory (vol. 5, 1928).

II. FRANCE

PETER OF AUVERGNE

Petrus de Alvernia. Pierre de Croc. Born probably in Crocq (Creuse), Auvergne; canon of the cathedrals of Clermont and Paris; rector of the University of Paris, 1275; bishop of Clermont from 1301 to his death, 1304. French theologian and philosopher; member of the Sorbonne; disciple of St. Thomas, whose Politics was completed by him. He wrote Quodlibeta and Thomist commentaries on Aristotle's Logic, Physics and Metaphysics.

Victor Le Clerc: Histoire littéraire de la France (vol. 25, 93–118, 1869). M. De Wulf: History of mediaeval philosophy (vol. 2, 53, 1926).

WILLIAM DURAND

Guilelmus Durandus, or Durantus, Duranti (Durandi filius). Nicknamed Speculator after his Speculum. Languedocian jurist, canonist, and liturgist.

Born at Puymisson, diocese of Béziers, c. 1230; studied law at Bologna; c. 1264 he was teaching it at Modena; c. 1265 appointed chaplain to the French pope Clement IV (1265–1268); bishop of Mende in Gévaudan, 1286; the best part of his active life was spent in the papal service in Italy; he died in Rome, 1296.

His main works are the Speculum iudiciale or Speculum iuris (1271; revised 1287; 1291); the Repertorium iuris canonici (Breviarium aureum), and the Rationale divinorum officiorum (begun bef. 1286).

The Speculum is a clear and methodical synthesis of Roman and canon law, the first of its kind and scope; it enjoyed considerable fame and was the subject of many commentaries. It is divided into four books dealing respectively with (1) judges and their jurisdiction, lawyers, witnesses, litigants, etc.; (2) civil and canonical procedure; (3) criminal procedure; (4) collection of legal formulas, dictamina.

The Repertorium iuris canonici is divided into five books the order of which follows closely that of the Decretales; it contains abundant references to Gratian's Decretum and to various glosses. It is simply an abridgment of canon law, while the Speculum is a complete treatise on civil and canonical procedure.

The Rationale is one of our fundamental sources for the history of western liturgy. It superseded all earlier books on the subject; in fact, it incorporated much of the earlier literature, the sources being carefully quoted. It attempts to interpret in many different ways each and every detail of the liturgy. It is divided into eight books: (1) symbolism of religious architecture and art; (2) clergy; (3) ecclesiastical vestments; (4) mass; (5) other religious offices; (6) Sundays and other holy days; (7) Saints' days (includes conclusions against the Immaculate Conception); (8) compotus. The popularity of the Rationale was even greater than that of the Speculum; it was the first non-Biblical book to appear in print (1459) and it was repeatedly reprinted for a long time.

This Guillaume Durand should not be mistaken for his namesake and nephew, also a canonist and his successor in the bishopric of Mende, who died in 1330; nor for Guillaume Durand of St. Pourçain, to be dealt with in vol. 3.

Text—The Speculum has often been published: Strassburg 1473, Padua 1478, Venice 1493. More complete edition with tables, 2 vols., Torino 1578. Reprinted in Francfort 1612, again 1668.

Repertorium. Rome 1474. Often printed together with the Speculum.

Rationale. The first edition is probably that of Mainz, 1459 (there are a good many incunabula editions, not a few of which are undated). Edition by John Beleth (890 p., Naples 1850). English translation of the first book with introduction and notes by John Mason Neale and Benjamin Webb: The symbolism of churches and church ornaments (387 p., Leeds 1843).

Criticism—V. Leclerc: Histoire littéraire de la France (vol. 20, 411–497, 1842). Joh. Friedrich Schulte: Geschichte der Quellen und Literatur des canonischen Rechts von Gratian bis auf die Gegenwart (3 vols., 1875–1880). Emile Mâle: L'art religieux au XIIIe siècle en France (Paris 1898). Carlyle: History of mediaeval political theory (vol. 5, 1928).

STEPHEN BOILEAU

Etienne Boileau or Estienne Boilesve (Bibens aquam). Born in the Orléanais in the beginning of the thirteenth century; married in 1225; followed St. Louis to the Crusade in 1248, made a prisoner in 1250 and ransomed. Some time later St. Louis appointed him provost of Paris; he was no longer provost in 1271; he died probably in that year or later.

While he was provost he collected (c. 1268) all the customs relative to the guilds, artisans, and trades of the city under the title Etablissements des métiers de Paris (or, Livre des métiers). This is a document of considerable value for the study of contemporary usages, technology, industry, commerce, and language.

Text—First complete edition by Georges Bernard Depping (Collection de documents inédits sur l'histoire de France, 560 p., Paris 1837). New edition by René de Lespinasse and François Bonnardot, with long introduction, glossary, tables, facsimiles (Histoire générale de Paris, collection de documents, 575 p., Paris 1879).

Criticism—Daunou: Histoire littéraire (vol. 19, 104–114, 1838).

ETABLISSEMENTS DE SAINT LOUIS

The Etablissements de Saint Louis is a "coutumier" (a collection of customs relative to civil and feudal law) compiled before 1273. It was not an official publication, and only the first nine chapters of the first book (out of two) are drawn from the ordinances of St. Louis. The customs collected did not belong to the whole of France but only to Anjou, Maine, and Orléanais. They are mixed with extracts from Justinian's Corpus iuris. The customs themselves reveal the influence of Roman law, especially as taught in the school of Orléans.

The ascription to St. Louis is natural enough. (Born in Poissy, 1215, died off Tunis in 1270; king of France, Louis IX, from 1226 to his death; under the regency of his mother Blanche of Castile until 1236; canonized in 1297.) St. Louis was one of the greatest mediaeval kings and a large amount of administrative and legal unification was actually accomplished by him.

Two other French legal writings of that time may be briefly mentioned: the Conseil à un ami (Advice to a friend), an unintelligent compilation drawn mainly from the Digest and Institutes, by Peter of Fontaines (d. c. 1289), bailiff of Vermandois (now part of the Aisne and Somme departments); and the Livre de justice et de plaid (Book of justice and pleading), a collection of 342 clauses, 197 of which are of Roman and 145 of local origin. Like the Etablissements de Saint Louis this second work reveals the influence of the school of Orléans.

Text—The Etablissements and the Conseil were first edited by Du Cange in his edition of Joinville's Histoire de St. Louis (Paris 1668).

Fourth and best edition of the Etablissements by Paul Viollet published by the Société de l'Histoire de France (4 vols., Paris 1881–1886).

Ange Ignace Marnier: Le conseil de Pierre de Fontaines ou Traité de l'ancienne jurisprudence française (576 p., Paris 1846). Paul Collinet: Une traduction néerlandaise inédite du Conseil (14 p., Bruxelles 1901).

Pierre Nicolas Rapetti: Li livres de jostice et de plet, publié pour la première fois d'après le MS. unique de la Bibliothèque nationale, avec un glossaire (Paris 1850).

Criticism—Paul Vinogradoff: Roman law in mediaeval Europe (66–68, 1909). Carlyle: History of mediaeval political theory (vols. 3 and 5, 1916, 1928).

BEAUMANOIR

Philippe de Remi, sire de Beaumanoir (Philippus de Bellomanerio). French jurist and poet; one of the greatest jurists of mediaeval times.

Born at an unknown date in Remi (or Remin), near Compiègne, Beauvaisis, of a noble family; he was for a time a page in England; in 1273 he was already royal bailiff of Vermandois, and in 1280 great bailiff of Clermont, Beauvaisis; he died in 1296.

He compiled between 1279 and 1283, in Picard dialect, a legal treatise of great value, the Livre des coutumes et usages de Beauvoisins, divided into 70 chapters, not in very good order. The main purpose was to codify the legal customs of his own "pays," Beauvaisis (Dept. de l'Oise), but he compared these customs with others and took advantage of many other sources, such as the Etablissements de Saint Louis, and—with great moderation—Roman and canon law. Thus his work set forth the fundamental principles of civil law, and it helped most effectively to tear down feudal institutions and prepare the organization of law on a national basis. It is also naturally an excellent mirror of contemporary society. It was admired by Montesquieu.

He wrote, c. 1270–1280, romantic tales in French verse (Picard dialect); his masterpiece in that line being the tale entitled Jehan et Blonde.

Text—First edition, Coustumes de Beauvoisis avec des notes et un glossaire, par Gaspard Thaumas de la Thaumassière (Bourges 1690). Appended to Assises et bons usages du royaume de Jérusalem. New edition by Arthur Auguste Beugnot published by the Société de l'Histoire de France (2 vols., Paris 1842). Amédée Salmon: Texte critique avec introduction, glossaire et table analytique (Collection de textes pour servir à l'étude de l'histoire; 2 vols., Paris 1899–1900).

Poems edited by Hermann Suchier (Société des anciens textes, 2 vols., Paris 1884).

Ch. V. Langlois: La vie en France au Moyen âge d'après des romans mondains du temps (2d ed., 177–209, 1926). Analysis of Jehan et Blonde, with extracts.

Criticism—Felix Lajard: Histoire littéraire de la France (vol. 20, 356–408, 1842). Auguste Morel: Etude sur les coutumes de Beauvaisis (Paris 1851). Eduard Schwan: Philippe de Remi und seine Werke (Diss., 52 p., Bonn 1880; also in Romanische Studien, vol. 4, 351–410, 1880). Ch. V. Langlois: Grande Encyclopédie (vol. 5, 1033–1034). Paul Vinogradoff: Roman law in mediaeval Europe (68–83, London 1909). Vinogradoff calls the Coutumes "one of the most refreshing legal treatises in existence." Carlyle: History of mediaeval political theory (vols. 3 and 5, 1916, 1928).

See note on Vincent of Beauvais.

III. SPAIN

See note on Alfonso el Sabio.

IV. LOW COUNTRIES

See notes on Gilbert of Tournay and William of Moerbeke.

V. ENGLAND

BRACTON

Henry de Bracton (or Bratton). English jurist, one of the greatest jurists of the Middle Ages.

Born probably in Devonshire at an unknown time; died in or near Exeter 1268. His main work is a treatise on the laws and customs of England, De legibus et consuetudinibus Angliae, compiled chiefly between 1250 and 1256 and left unfinished. It was an attempt to combine the empirical knowledge derived from the practice of an English court with the theories of Roman law as explained in the school of Bologna, especially by Azo;—the earliest attempt to digest the English common law. It exerted a deep influence upon the development of English law, partly through the intermediary of the great Elizabethan jurist, Edward Coke (1552–1634).

Two summaries of the De legibus were compiled during the reign of Edward I (1272–1307), the one in Latin, the other in French. The Latin abridgment, composed c. 1290, is called Fleta (reference to Fleet street or to the Fleet prison?). The French abridgment, called Britton, dates from the same time. It is put in Edward's name, as if the laws had been prepared by him or for him. It has been ascribed to John le Breton, bishop of Hereford, who died in 1275, but its name might be just as well a corruption of Bracton's.

Text—First complete edition of the De legibus published by Richard Tottell (London 1569), reprinted in London 1640. Next edition by Sir Travers Twiss: Henrici de Bracton de legibus et consuetudinibus Angliae. Libri quinque in varios tractatus distincti (Rolls series, 6 vols., London 1878–1883). Edition by George E. Woodbine (2 vols., New Haven 1915–1922).

F. W. Maitland: Bracton's Notebook. A collection of cases decided in the king's courts during the reign of Henry III (king from 1216 to 1272) annotated by a lawyer of that time, seemingly Henry of Bratton (3 vols., London 1887).

F. W. Maitland: Select passages from the works of Bracton and Azo (Selden Society, 8, London 1895). Showing the extent of Bracton's borrowings from Azo.

The Fleta was first edited by the great jurist and scholar John Selden (1584–1654) with a dissertation (555 p., London 1647). Second edition (555 p., London 1685). New edition of Selden's dissertation reprinted from the text of 1647, with parallel translation, introduction and notes by David Ogg (270 p., Cambridge 1925).

The Britton was first printed without date (London c. 1530–1540). New edition by Edm. Wingate (London 1640). English translation by Robert Kelham (London 1762). Critical edition with translation by Francis Morgan Nichols (Oxford 1865).

Criticism—Kark Güterbock: Henricus de Bracton und sein Verhältnis zum römischen Rechte (137 p., Berlin 1862). English translation by Brinton Coxe (182 p., Philadelphia 1866). J. M. Rigg: Bracton (Dictionary of national biography, vol. 6, 144–147, 1886). J. M. Maitland: John G. Breton (ibidem, 275). Felix Liebermann: Über die Leges Anglorum saeculo XIII ineunte Londoniis collectae (114 p., Halle a.S., 1894). Paul Vinogradoff: Roman law in mediaeval Europe (70, 88–90, 1909). Carlyle: History of mediaeval political theory (vols. 3 and 5, 1916, 1928).

VI. CENTRAL EUROPE

SCHWABENSPIEGEL

The main mediaeval code of Germany was the Sachsenspiegel (Saxon mirror) composed by Eike of Repgow c. 1230 in Latin and soon afterwards translated by himself into German. Among later codes inspired by the Sachsenspiegel, the most important were the Spiegel deutscher Leute (or Deutschenspiegel)—including not only the old customs, the folklaw, but also the imperial law[1]—and the Schwabenspiegel. The first of these belongs probably to the first half of the century. The Schwabenspiegel (Speculum alemannicum) is certainly of the second half (c. 1259, c. 1272–1283). It included the substance of the Sachsenspiegel, customary law of southern Germany, fragments of civil, canon, and imperial law. Like the earlier German codes it is divided into two main parts, Landrecht and Lehnrecht (or Lehenrecht), i.e., civil and feudal law.

Text—Schwabenspiegel. Four incunabula editions appeared in Augsburg, the earliest three undated, the fourth in 1480. Many later editions, some of them including only the Landrecht or the Lehnrecht. F. L. A. v. Lassberg: Der Schwabenspiegel nach einer Handschrift vom J. 1287 (Tübingen 1840). Wilh. Wackernagel: Landrecht (Zürich 1840). Later editions by A. v. Daniels (Berlin 1860–1863), G. Lindner (Klausenburg 1885), etc.

Georges Auguste Matile: Le miroir du Souabe d'après le MS. français de Berne, XIVe siècle (142 p., Neufchâtel 1843).

Criticism—Potthast (1004, 1028, 1896). Julius Hartmann: Schwabenspiegel aus alter und neuer Zeit (2 pts., Stuttgart 1901–1903). Ludwig Rockinger: Über den sogenanten Schwabenspiegel in einem Rechtshandschriftenbande aus dem 15. Jahrh. im Haus- und Staatsarchiv in Zerbst (Bayer. Akad., Sitzungsber., 505–520, 1902); Deutschenspiegel, sogenannter Schwabenspiegel, Bertholds von Regensburg deutsche Predigten in ihrem Verhältnisse zu einander (Bayer. Akad., Abh., vol. 23, 211–300, 1904); Über die Familienangehörigkeit der sogenanten Krafftschen Hdsch. des kaiserlichen Land- und Lehenrechts (Bayer. Ak., Sitzungsber., (281–313, 1905); Von der Zeit der Abfassung des kaiserlichen Land- und Lehenrechts (Bayer. Ak., Abh., vol. 24, 57–142, 1906).

See notes on Martin the Pole and Engelbert of Admont.

VII. EASTERN ISLĀM

AL-NAWAWĪ

Abū Zakarīyā Yaḥyā ibn Sharaf ibn Mirā al-Ḥizāmī al-Ḥaurānī Muḥyī al-dīn al-Nawawī. Muslim theologian and scholar (1233–1277).

Born at Nawā, not far from Damascus, 1233; educated in Damascus, studying theology at the Rawāḥīya; in 1253 he made the Pilgrimage, then returned to Damascus; after the murder of Abū Shāma 'Abd al-Raḥmān ibn Ismā'īl in 1268, he succeeded him as professor in al-Ashrafīya (one of the higher theological schools of Damascus); he died at Nawā in 1277. His tomb is visited by pilgrims to this day.

[1] The imperial diet which met at Mainz in 1235 promulgated the first imperial law.

His main works are:

1. Minhāj al-ṭālibīn (Guide of fervent believers), a manual of Shāfi'ī law, derived from the Kitāb al-muḥarrar of 'Abd al-Karīm ibn Muḥammad al-Rāfi'ī al-Qazwīnī (d. 1226). This work was very influential; witness the large number of commentaries, glosses, abridgments.

2. Kitāb al-arba'īn ḥadīthān (The forty traditions). A great many commentaries were devoted to it.

3. Tahdhīb al-asmā' wal-lughāt (Correction of proper names and words), a biographical dictionary of illustrious Muslims, chiefly of the earlier ones.

He wrote many other works on traditions, law, religion and history. Some are simply commentaries on, or extracts from, earlier writings by Muslim ibn al-Ḥajjāj, al-Khaṭīb al-Baghdādī, Ibn al-Ṣalāḥ. A collection of his responsa, Kitāb al-manthūrāt wa 'uyūn al-masā'il al-muhimmāt, was edited by his disciple Ibn al-'Aṭṭār (d. 1324); biographies of him were written by Ibn al-'Aṭṭār and al-Suyūṭī.

Text—L. W. C. van den Berg: Le guide des zélés croyants. Manuel de jurisprudence musulmane selon le rite de Chāfi'ī. Texte arabe avec traduction et annotations (3 vols., Batavia 1882–1884). English translation from the French by E. C. Howard (585 p., London 1914).

Ferdinand Wüstenfeld: Biographical dictionary of illustrious men chiefly at the beginning of Islamism (2 vols., Göttingen 1842–1847).

Kitāb al-arba'īn (Cairo 1861, 1882, 1883, 1887). All these Cairene editions include the commentary by Aḥmad ibn Ḥijāzī al-Fashnī (second half of the sixteenth century). Other commentaries are included in the following editions: Fez 1891, Delhi 1895; Cawnpore 1869 (with Hindustani translation), again 1896; Lahore 1896, Amritsar 1897.

Tadrīb al-rāwī, commentary by al-Suyūṭī on al-Nawawī's treatise on the science of tradition, entitled Kitāb al-taqrīb wal-taisīr (284 p., Cairo 1889). French translation by M. Marçais (Journal asiatique, vols. 16–18, 1893, etc.).

Criticism—F. Wüstenfeld: Über das Leben und Schriften des Nawawī (Abhd., Ges. d. Wiss., Göttingen, vol. 4, 1849; derived from the oriental biographies above mentioned); Geschichtschreiber der Araber (138, 1881). C. Brockelmann: Arabische Litteratur (vol. 1, 394–397, 1898). J. E. Sarkis: Dictionnaire encyclopédique de bibliographie arabe (p. 1871–1879, 1930).

JA'FAR AL-ḤILLĪ

Abū-l-Qāsim Ja'far ibn Muḥammad ibn Yaḥyā ibn Sa'īd[2] al-Ḥillī al-Muḥaqqiq Najm al-dīn. Shī'a theologian, who originated from al-Ḥilla on the lower Euphrates. He flourished in Baghdād, and exerted some influence upon the last days of the caliphate (the last caliph, al-Musta'ṣim, died in 1258). He died c. 1277.

He composed the most popular textbook of Shī'a law (fiqh), the Kitāb sharā'i' al-islām (The laws of Islām).

Text—There are naturally many oriental editions of that work and of commentaries upon it or abridgments. The Sharaya ool Islam, a treatise on lawful and forbidden things by Abool Kasim of Hoolla, edited by Moolvee Seyud Oulad Hosein and Moolvee Zuhoor Ulee (625 p., Calcutta 1839). Arabic text with Russian translation by Kasembeg (Petersburg 1862; incomplete). A. Querry: Droit musulman. Recueil de lois concernant les Musulmans Schyites. French translation; revised and edited by C. A. C. Barbier de Meynard (2 vols., Paris 1871–1872).

Sharā'i' al-islām. With the commentary, Masālik al-afhām, by Zain al-dīn ibn 'Alī al-Shahīd al-Thanī (2 vols., lithographed, Teheran 1893–1896). That commentary was composed about the middle of the sixteenth century.

[2] Or Ja'far ibn al-Ḥasan ibn Ya'qūb ibn Sa'īd. He is often called Ja'far ibn Sa'īd.

Another edition of the Sharā'i' with Hindustani translation and notes (4 parts, lithographed, Lucknow 1897–1899).

Criticism—C. Brockelmann: Arabische Litteratur (vol. 1, 406, 1898). R. Strothmann: Shī'a (Encyclopaedia of Islām, vol. 4, 355, 1926).

AL-NASAFĪ

Ḥāfiẓ al-dīn Abū-l-Barakāt 'Abdallāh ibn Aḥmad al-Nasafī (i.e., of Nasaf, south of Samarkand). Muslim theologian and jurist of the Ḥanafī school. He was in Bukhārā in 1285, and died in 1310–1311.

He wrote many works on law, tradition, and the Qur'ān, of which it will suffice to mention three.

1. Manār al-anwār fī uṣūl al-fiqh (Beacon of light on the principles of law). Judging by the number of commentaries and editions of this work it was immensely popular. It includes interesting views on the critical study of traditions (ḥadīth).
2. Al-wāfī fī-l-furū'. Completed in Bukhārā, 1285.
3. Kanz al-daqā'iq fī-l-furū'. Abridgment of (2). Both works being compendia of Ḥanafī law. (The study of law, fiqh, is divided into two main branches, uṣūl al-fiqh and furū' al-fiqh; i.e., the principles and the branches or applications; the first work deals with the principles, the second and third with the applications.)

This al-Nasafī should not be confused with an earlier one, 'Umar ibn Muḥammad, who wrote a very popular Ḥanafī catechism, Al-'umda fī-l-'aqā'id (first half of the twelfth century).

Text—Manār al-anwār. With a commentary by Muḥammad Manṣūr 'Alī al-Yūsufī (208 p., lith., Delhi 1870?). Arabic text with Hindustani version and glosses (2 vols., lith., Agra 1902–1903). Many other oriental editions.

Kanz al-daqā'iq (424 p., lith., Delhi 1870). Many other editions: Lucknow 1874, 1877; Bombay 1877, 1882; Delhi 1889, 1890–1892, 1894; Lahore 1889; Meerut 1891. With Pushtu paraphrase, Delhi 1884.

Madārik al-tanzīl, commentary on the Qur'ān (2 vols., Bombay 1862). Etc.

Criticism—C. Brockelmann: Arabische Litteratur (vol. 2, 196–197, 1902). Carra de Vaux: Penseurs de l'Islām (vol. 3, 287–296, 1923). Dealing with the commentary on the Manār al-anwār by 'Abd al-'Azīz ibn Firishta Ibn al-Malak al-Kirmānī, who died c. 1427. J. E. Sarkis: Dictionnaire de bibliographie arabe (p. 1852–1853, Cairo 1930). The author confuses the two al-Nasafī abovementioned.

See note on Nāṣir al-dīn al-Ṭūsī.

VIII. INDIA

HEMĀDRI

Hindu jurist and physician. Minister and secretary to two rulers of the Yādava dynasty in Devagiri (Dowlatabad in Haidarabad): Mahādeva (1260–1271) and Rāmacandra (1271–1309).

He compiled one of the most imposing collections of laws and customs (dharmanibandha), entitled Caturvargacintāmaṇi. It is of special interest, like other works of the same kind, because it contains abundant quotations from earlier works (smṛiti and purāṇa) many of which are lost.

He wrote a commentary on Vāgbhaṭa's Ashṭāṅgahṛidayasaṃhitā.

Text—The Caturvargacintāmaṇi was published in the Bibliotheca Indica in a great many parts, by many editors (1873–1911).

Criticism—Julius Jolly: Recht und Sitte (Strassburg, 35, 1896). M. Winternitz: Indische Litteratur (vol. 3, 502, 549, 1922).

WAGARU

Or Wareru. Shan pedlar born at Donwun in the Tha-tun district, Burma, who managed to become lord of Martaban in 1281, and six years later was the sole ruler of Lower Burma (capital, Martaban). He was murdered in 1306.

He introduced the code of law called Dhammasaṭṭham (= Sanskrit, Dharmaśāstra), or Manu-Dhammasaṭṭham. This reference to the mythical Manu would suggest that this code is more strictly Hindu than it really is. In fact it is derived entirely from Sanskrit elements, but is Buddhist rather than Hindu, all Brahmanical rules being left out. For example criminal law is based upon the doctrine of karman. The Dhammasaṭṭham is the earliest law book of Burma. I may add that the laws of Siam, Java and Bali were derived from the same sources.

Text—Edition of Wagaru's Dhammasaṭṭham, with English translation and notes by E. Forchhammer, preface by John Jardine (Rangoon 1892).

Criticism—Julius Jolly: Recht und Sitte (Grundriss der indo-arischen Philologie, Bd. 2, H. 8; 41–44, Strassburg 1896). M. Winternitz: Indische Litteratur (vol. 3, 494, 1922). G. E. Harvey: History of Burma (110–111, 1925).

IX. CHINA

See note on Kublai Khān.

CHAPTER LV

PHILOLOGY

(Second Half of Thirteenth Century)

I. LATIN

See notes on John Garland, Vincent of Beauvais, Boetius of Dacia, Duns Scot, Robert Kilwardby, Bacon, Simon of Genoa, and Gerard of Sabbioneta.

BALBI

Giovanni Balbi of Genoa. Joannes Balbus de Janua (or Januensis). Italian grammarian and lexicographer. Dominican. Died in 1298.

He completed in 1286 the Catholicon, that is, a large treatise for the study of the Latin tongue, divided into five parts: orthography, prosody, grammar, rhetoric, and etymology. The last part is a dictionary derived from Papias (second half of the eleventh century) and Hugutio (second half of the twelfth century). As this last part is four times larger than all the rest together, the four others might be considered a sort of introduction to it; in fact, the Catholicon is often called a dictionary, after that fifth part. Balbi had some infinitesimal knowledge of Greek.

The Catholicon enjoyed a very great popularity. MSS. of it were among the few books of reference kept chained in French and English churches. It was one of the first books to be printed, and the first edition (1460) was followed by many others, also by various abridgments and elaborations. A French translation was used in the Parisian schools as late as 1759.

Text—The 24 incunabula editions are analyzed in the Gesamtkatalog der Wiegendrucke (vol. 3, 278–291, 1928). The first edition, Summa quae vocatur Catholicon, was printed at Mainz 1460, probably by Johann Gutenberg (373 leaves, 2 col., 66 lines, printed in black and red).

Second and following editions: Augsburg 1469; Strassburg, two c. 1470, another not after 1483; Nürnberg 1483; Venice 1483; Lyon c. 1485; Strassburg c. 1485; Lyon c. 1486; Nürnberg 1486; Venice 1487; Lyon 1489; Venice 1490; Lyon 1491; Venice 1492; Lyon 1492, 1493, 1494; Venice 1495; Lyon 1496; Venice 1497–1498; Paris 1499; Lyon 1500. It is interesting to note that of these 24 editions the first 6 were printed in Germany; of the following 18 only 2 were printed in Germany, 9 in Lyon, 6 in Venice, 1 in Paris.

Criticism—Samuel Berger: De glossariis et compendiis exegeticis quibusdam (thesis, 56 p., Paris 1879). George Washington Moon: The oldest type-printed book in existence; a disquisition on the relative antiquity of the Pfister and Mazarin Bibles and the "65-line A" Catholicon. (47 p., London 1901). Gottfried Zedler: Das Mainzer Catholicon (75 p., 11 pl., Ver. der Gutenberg Ges., 4, Mainz 1905). Sandys: History of classical scholarship (vol. 1^3, 606, 666, 1921).

II. FRENCH

See my summary in Chapter XLII.

III. CASTILIAN, PORTUGUESE, AND CATALAN

See my summary in Chapter XLII; and the notes on Ramon Lull, Alfonso X, and Dinis.

IV. ICELANDIC

See note on Sturla Thórdarson and my summary in Chapter XLII.

V. GREEK

See my summary in Chapter XLII, and notes on Maximos Planudes and Bacon.

VI. ARMENIAN

See my summary in Chapter XLII, and the notes on Vardan the Great and John of Erzinjān.

VII. SYRIAC

See my summary in Chapter XLII, and my note on Abū-l-Faraj.

VIII. HEBREW

See notes on Raymond of Peñafort, Raymond Martin, Solomon ben Ayyub, Tanḥūm Yerushalmī, Aaron ben Joseph.

IX. ARABIC

IBN MANẒŪR

Jamāl al-dīn Abū-l-Faḍl Muḥammad ibn al-Mukarram ibn 'Alī ibn Manẓūr al-Anṣārī al-Khazrajī[1] al-Ifrīqī. Muslim lexicographer and historian. Born in 1232–1233; died in Cairo in 1311.

He devoted his life to the making of historical summaries and lexicographical extracts. He is immortalized by his immense and very convenient Arabic dictionary, Lisān al-'arab. It includes the substance of Ibn Duraid's Kitāb al-jamhara fīl-lugha (first half of the tenth century), of al-Jauharī's Kitāb al-ṣiḥāḥ fīl-lugha (second half of the tenth century), and of Ibn Sīda's Kitāb al-muḥkam wal-muḥīṭ al-a'ẓam (second half of the eleventh century), and considerably more.

He abstracted Ibn 'Asākir's history of Damascus (Mukhtaṣar ta'rīkh madīnat Dimashq libn 'Asākir), al-Sam'ānī's history of Baghdād (Mukhtaṣar ta'rīkh Baghdād lil-Sam'ānī), the Kitāb al-'iqd al-farīd (Unique necklace) of Ibn 'Abd Rabbihi, the Kitāb al-aghānī (Book of songs) of Abū-l-Faraj al-Iṣfahānī, etc. He may be the author also of a summary of the Jāmi' mufradāt al-adwiya wal-aghdhiya of Ibn al-Baiṭār. He composed an anthology relative to night and day, etc. (Nithār al-azhār fīl-lail wal-nahār . . . .)

Text—Lisān al-'arab. With marginal notes by the editor, and with a preface by Aḥmad Fāris (20 vols., Būlāq 1883–1891).

Nithār al-azhār (188 p., Constantinople 1881).

Criticism—Edward William Lane: Arabic English Lexicon (Book 1, part 1, p. xvi, London 1863). Lane calls him Ibn Mukarram, but the name Ibn Manẓūr is more usual; for example, he is always called Ibn Manẓūr in the great dictionary Tāj al-'arūs (The bride's crown) of Muḥammad al-Murtaḍā al-Zabīdī (d. 1791). F. Wüstenfeld: Geschichtschreiber der Araber (p. 154, 1881). C. Brockelmann:

[1] Khazraj is the name of an Arabian tribe, settled near al-Madīna, which took an important part in the foundation of Islām. The members of that tribe were called Anṣār (helpers), a title of honor. Hence the patronymic Anṣārī.

Arabische Litteratur (vol. 2, 21, 1902). J. E. Sarkis: Dictionnaire de bibliographie arabe (255, 1928).

See notes on Raymond Martin, St. Peter Paschal, Ramon Lull, Ricoldo of Monte Croce, Bacon, and Ṣafī al-dīn.

X. SANSKRIT

See note on Vopadeva.

XI. CHINESE

TAI T'UNG

Tai^{4} T'ung^{2} (10567, 12270). Born at Yung^{3}-chia^{1} (13504, 1158) in Chehkiang; governor of T'ai^{2}-chou^{1} (10583, 2444), Chehkiang, under the Sung. He retired into private life after their expulsion from that province by the Mongols in 1275. Chinese philologist. He wrote after 1275 a work on the Six classes of characters, Liu^{4*} shu^{1} ku^{4} (7276, 10024, 6190), according to their origin (pictorial, indicative, suggestive compounds, phonetic, adoptive, deflected). These six classes, liu shu, should not be confused with the six forms, liu^{4*} t'i^{3} (7276, 11025), which refer to different ways of writing the same character (seal, official, plain, cursive, grass, Sung dynasty style as used in printing).

Text—The Library of Congress has the Liu shu ku in 33 volumes, with a supplementary analysis published in 1784.

Criticism—Lionel Charles Hopkins: The six scripts (75 p., Amoy 1881). I understand that this work or memoir, which I have not seen, contains a translation of the Liu shu ku. Léon Wieger: Chinese characters (2 vols., Ho-chien-fu 1915). Herbert A. Giles: Chinese biographical dictionary (708, 1898). S. Couling: Encyclopaedia Sinica (518, 1917).

XII. MONGOLIAN

See notes on Kublai Khān, Rubruquis, John of Montecorvino.

PHAGSPA

Phags-pa or Phagpa, Bashpa, etc.; in Chinese transcription Pa^{1}-ssŭ^{1}-pa^{1} (8510, 10271, 8510). Phagspa is really a title (=ārya in Sanskrit, meaning noble); his original name was Blo-gros Rgyal-mtshan. Tibetan Buddhist priest, who died in 1279.

Spiritual adviser to Kublai Khān whom he converted to Buddhism. In 1260 he was appointed "state preceptor" and head of the Buddhist church. In 1269, at Kublai's request, he devised a new Mongol alphabet[2] derived from the Tibetan and written vertically. There are some 30 inscriptions in that script but no other writings.

The Tibetan-Mongol alphabet was superseded before the end of the Yüan dynasty by another derived from the Uighūr script, itself derived either from the Syriac Estranghelo writing propagated in Central Asia by the Nestorians, or from the Sogdian. The Uighūr-Mongol script has remained in use ever since; it was adopted by the Manchu for their own language in 1599.[3]

[2] See my note on Chingiz Khān (p. 1207).
[3] See my note on Manchu writing (p. 273).

H. A. Giles: Chinese biographical dictionary (608, 1898). Samuel Couling: Encyclopaedia sinica (44, 580, 1917). René Grousset: Histoire de l'Extrême-orient (364, 461–462, 1929; Isis, 14, 437).

XIII. JAPANESE

See my summary in Chapter XLII.

GENERAL INDEX

This index has been compiled in the same way as the index to volume I, with two exceptions mentioned below. It will repay students to read the preface to the index of volume I, and in every case to consult that index as well as this one. It is even more necessary for students of pre-twelfth century science to consult this index as well as the one to volume I. Indeed ancient and early mediaeval authors are repeatedly mentioned in volume II. For the reader's convenience, whenever a pre-twelfth century author, mentioned in volume II, has been the subject of a separate note in volume I, a brief reference to that note and to his time of activity has been added. For example:

Bīrūnī (xi–1), vol. I, 707–709; vol. II, etc.

This means that al-Bīrūnī flourished in the first half of the eleventh century, and that a note relative to him will be found in volume I, p. 707–709 (for minor references to him in volume I, the index to that volume should be consulted).

The two exceptions are, first, that a great many Latin titles have been included which were omitted in volume I; second, that no name is classified under abū, bar, ben, or ibn. For example, Ibn Gabirol is classified under Ibn Gabirol in volume I and under Gabirol in volume II. I was obliged to do so because as centuries went on, the "ibn" was so often dropped (especially in Judeo-Arabic names) that it tended to disappear altogether.

Variants of mediaeval Latin words have generally been disregarded in the index, the references to many variants being grouped under a single heading; however, in a few cases, when variants were too erratic or too distant in the alphabetic order from the main heading, additional references have been provided.

There are so many variants to the mediaeval proper names, especially to the oriental ones, that the number of cross references required to meet every conceivable emergency would be well nigh endless. Bearing in mind that the users of this book are likely to be trained scholars who may be trusted to make some efforts of their own and to take sufficient pains, I have reduced the number of cross references to one to three per name.

The main references to mediaeval authors will generally be found under the "given" name, such as John or William, Abraham or David, Muḥammad or 'Alī. Christian and Jewish names have been provided, whenever possible, with a topographical cross reference; e.g., under Meung for John of Meung, under Posquières for Abraham ben David. Arabic names are often provided with various topographical adjectives, among which it is not easy to choose, and in addition with so many other nisbas, kunyas, and laqabs, that the most resolute indexer is driven to despair. I have simply tried to meet the most obvious requirements.

With regard to the Christian mediaeval names, I first thought of grouping all the men named after the same saint, under the latter's Latin name, but this led to ludicrous consequences in the case of men who never wrote in Latin. I then decided to group them all as much as possible under the English forms of the names. For example, all the Williams will be found together (under William) irrespective of the forms of that name in a dozen different languages. This will be certainly more convenient—and not only for English readers—than if these Williams were scattered throughout the index. A sufficient number of cross references have been provided to facilitate the readers' search (e.g., Aegidius, see Giles; Giovanni, see John).

With regard to Semitic words, it is well to bear in mind that legitimate variations in the vocalization may easily change their place in the index; for example, manhāj versus minhāj, etc. Wary readers will try various possible vocalizations. In general, the same vocalizations have been kept in both volumes, but I have felt obliged to make a few slight modifications: to illustrate, in volume I, I wrote Māsawaih al-Mārdīnī (p. 728); in volume II, I introduced an additional vowel in the second word, Māridīnī, because such a vowel is almost a phonetic necessity. However, experts disagree on this point, and I attach too little importance to it myself to want to discuss it. I quoted this example rather to exhibit the unavoidable uncertainties and ambiguities which the author must solve in one way or another. In Arabic script the long vowels are always indicated, but the short ones are determined only by oral traditions involving not a few divergencies. Once more I must ask the gentle reader to meet me half way, and to give my index more than one chance.

The articles al and ha have always been omitted at the beginning of words, even if that amputation caused the remaining phrase to be grammatically incorrect. To suppress the incorrectness it will suffice mentally to reestablish the article.

Imperfect and incomplete as it is, this index will help old-fashioned mediaevalists to realize that the Latin documents reveal but a part of the Middle Ages and not by any means the largest.

The index was compiled under my direction by Miss Frances Siegel (Radcliffe, 1931). I examined the cards and did my best to standardize the cross references, etc., but was not able to read the typed and printed copies of it before my departure for Europe and the Near East. The typed manuscript and the proofs were read and collated with the original cards, and sometimes with the text itself, by Dr. A. Pogo. Moreover, Dr. Pogo helped me throughout the compilation of the index and I am indebted to him for many valuable suggestions. I am thankful to him and to Miss Siegel for the assistance extended to me in the accomplishment of a peculiarly ungrateful task.[1]

George Sarton

Cambridge, Mass.
July 24, 1931

[1] If the cards used for the index had been of the regular size and filed in the usual way, they would have filled at least twenty standard library drawers.

INDEX

A-lao-wa-ting (xiii–2), 1034; 765.
A su, 773, 982.
Aachen, 34.
Aachen, see Albert.
Aagesön, see Svend.
Aaron and Evax, 592.
Aaron, father of Barhebraeus, 975.
Aaron, high priest, 1097.
Aaron b. Elijah of Nicomedia, 875.
Aaron b. Joseph ha-Levi, 885.
Aaron b. Joseph the Qaraite (xiii–2), 875; 729, 805.
Aaron ha-Levi of Barcelona (xiii–2), 884; 731.
Aaron b. Meshullam of Lunel (xiii–1), 625; 19, 506.
Ab bet din, 365, 477.
Abaci, L., 5, 7, 8, 504, 611.
Abacists, 4.
Abaco, de, 212.
Abacus, 4, 5, 124, 125, 167, 169, 210.
Abaelard, see Peter (xii–1).
Abahrī, 867.
Abanim, 592.
Abano, see Peter.
Abāqā, Khān, 1010, 1123.
Abba Mari, see Isaac.
Abba Mari b. Moses ha-Yarḥi, 884.
Abbār, Ibn al, (xiii–1), 681; 527, 796.
'Abbas, see Judah b. Samuel.
'Abbās al-Nabātī, Abū-l-, 38, 51, 514, 517, 650, 663.
'Abbas, see Samuel b. Isaac.
'Abbās al-Sibtī, abū-l-, (xii–2), 361; 287.
Abbeville, see Gerard.
Abbreviatio Avicenne de animalibus, 580.
Abbreviationes chronicarum, 457.
Abbreviationes librorum Galeni, 1090.
'Abd al-'Alī b. Muḥammad al-Barjandī, 1006, 1008.
'Abd al-'Azīz, copyist, 1101.
'Abd al-'Azīz b. 'Alī al-Huwārī, 999.
'Abd al-'Azīz b. Firishta, 1133.
'Abd al-Dār b. Quṣaij, 1065.
'Abd al-Ḥaqq b. Ibrahīm b. Sab'īn, 598.
'Abd al-Karīm b. Muḥammad al-Rāfi'ī, 1132.
'Abd al-Karīm b. Muḥammad al-Sam'ānī, 444.
'Abd al-Laṭīf (xiii–1), 599–600; 31, 39, 51, 72, 500, 510, 511, 514, 517, 521, 527, 649, 685, 768, 1019.
'Abd al-Laṭīf b. Yūsuf b. Muḥammad, 599.
'Abd al-Malik b. Abī-l-'Alā' Zuhr, 232.
'Abd al-Malik, abū Marwān, 231.
'Abd al-Malik b. Muḥammad al-Shīrāzī (xii–2), 400.
'Abd al-Malik al-Shīrāzī, 10, 296.
'Abd al-Mu' min, 113, 232.
'Abd al-Mu' min b. 'Abd-al-Ḥaqq, 643.
'Abd al-Mu'min al-Dimyāṭī (xiii–2), 1072; 60, 780.
'Abd al-Mu'mīn b. Faqīr al-Urmawī, 1034.
'Abd al-Mu' min b. Khalaf, 1072.
'Abd al-Mu' min al-Muwaḥḥid, 165.
'Abd al-Qādir al-Jīlī (xii–1), 164; 113.
'Abd Rabbihi, b., 1136.
'Abd al-Raḥīm b. 'Alī al-Dakhwār, 624.
'Abd al-Raḥīm b. 'Alī al-Dimashqī, 1099.
'Abd al-Raḥīm b. 'Umṛar al-Dimashqī, 635.
'Abd al-Raḥmān b. 'Alī b. Muḥammad, 362.
'Abd al-Raḥmān b. 'Awf, 602.
'Abd al-Raḥmān b. Ḥasan al-Isnawī, 871.
'Abd al-Raḥmān b. Ismā'īl, 1119, 1131.
'Abd al-Raḥmān al-Khāzinī, 26.
'Abd al-Raḥmān al-Manṣūr al-Khāzinī, 128, 216.
'Abd al-Raḥmān b. Naṣr (xii–2), 463; 28, 44, 47, 298, 303, 316.
'Abd al-Raḥmān b. Naṣrallāh, 80, 288, 306, 431.
'Abd al-Raḥmān al-Shīrāzī (xii–2), 431.
'Abd al-Raḥmān al-Ṣūfī (x–2), vol. 1, 665; vol. 2, 836, 842, 843.
'Abd al-Raḥmān b. abī-l-Wafā' Muḥammad, 469.
'Abd al-Rashīd b. Ṣāliḥ, 869.
'Abd al-Razzāq, 868.
'Abd al-Razzāq b. Aḥmad al-Shaibānī, 1005.
'Abd al-Razzāq al-Qāshāni, 597.
'Abd al-Wahhāb b. Aḥmad al-Sha'rānī, 662.
'Abd al-Wāḥid, Almohade, 598.
'Abd al-Wāḥid b. 'Alī al-Tamīmī, 681.
'Abd al-Wāḥid al-Marrākushī (xiii–1), 681; 527.
'Abd al-Wāḥid b. Muḥammad, 1008.
'Abd Yeshua, Mar, 979.
Abdāl, 235.
'Abdallāh b. Aḥmad b. al-Baiṭār, 663.
'Abdallāh b. Aḥmad al-Nasafī, 164, 1133.
'Abdallāh b. al-Ḥafīd, 233.
'Abdallāh b. Muḥammad al-Baṭalyūsī, 182.
'Abdallāh b. Muḥammad b. al-Yāsmīn, 400.
'Abdallāh b. Salām, 173.
'Abdallāh b. 'Umar al-Baiḍāwī, 870.
'Abdallāh b. Abī-l-Yāsir, 1122.
'Abdarī (xiii–2), 1065.

Brienne, see John.
Bright's disease, 1078.
Bṛihad-Arhannītiśāstra, 474.
Bril, 1026.
Brit, see Walter.
Britton, 801, 1130.
Brocard, traveler to Persia, 1052.
Brothers of St. Nicholas, see Nicholas.
Broussais, François Joseph Victor, 77.
Browne, Richard, 959, 963.
Browne, Sir Thomas, 26.
Browning, 110.
Brucioli, A., 618.
Brünhildesage, 395.
Bruges, 49, 825, 938.
Bruges, see Rudolph.
Bruin the Bear, 393.
Brunetto Latini (XIII-2), 926–928; 737, 793, 924, 1058, 1084.
Brunfels, Otto, 229, 360, 1081.
Bruni, see Leonardo.
Bruno, see Gabriel.
Bruno, Giordano, 968.
Bruno of Cologne, 110, 153.
Bruno of Hildesheim, 435.
Bruno da Longoburgo (XIII-2), 1077; 74, 782, 787, 886.
Bruns, P. I., 977.
Brussels, see Gerard.
Brut, Roman de, 453.
Bryennios, see Nicephoros.
Bryson, Pythagorean, 364, 463, 832, 1011.
Bryte, see Walter.
Brythonic dialects, 257.
Buddha, the (VI B.C.), vol. 1, 68–69; vol. 2, 826.
Buddhism, 715, 1058.
Buddhism, Chinese, 1064.
Buddhism, Japanese, 558, 827.
Buddhism, Tibetan, in Mongolia (XIII-2), 827.
Buddhist Asia, 36.
Buddhist biographies, 558.
Buddhist relics, 422.
Buddhist schools, 558.
Buffereau, François, 591.
Bughyat al-mutalammis, 444.
Bughyat al-ṭālib, 683.
Bugia, see Bougie.
Buhahylyha Byngezla, 834.
Bukelare, see John.
Bukhārā, 1056.
Bukhārī (IX-1), vol. 1, 551; vol. 2, 1066.
Būlād, 1021.
Bulgars, 157.
Bulgarus, 141, 266.
Bulghār, 412, 1056.
Būndahishn (XII-2), 396; 294.
Bundārī (XIII-1), 686; 447, 493, 527.
Bungey, 962.
Būnī, al (XIII-1), 595; 7, 499, 505.
Bunko, 865.
Buono del Garbo, 1078.
Buralli, see John.
Burana, carmina, 391.
Burana, Giovanni Francesco, 359.
Burāq Khān, 1056.
Burchard Argentinensis, 420.
Burchard of Mt. Sion (XIII-2), 1052–1053; **35**, 420, 771.
Burchard of Strassburg (XII-2), 420; **35**, **302**, 1052.
Burchard, traveler to Persia, 1052.
Burchard of Ursperg, 258.
Burgensis, see William of Congenis.
Burghers and artisans, 932.
Burgos, see Vincent.
Burgundio of Pisa (XII-2), 348; 55, 65, 67, 116, 180, 284, 304, 310, 316, 321, 383, 1086.
Buridan, 890.
Burma, 776, 981, 1057, 1134.
Bury St. Edmunds, 54, 132, 226.
Burzūya (VI-2), vol. 1, 449; vol. 2, 590.
Buscarello de' Ghizolfi (XIII-2), 1054; 37, 772, 775, 1018, 1049, 1069.
Business methods, 38.
Bussaeus, Andreas, 260.
Bússola, 630.
Bustān, 872.
Bustrophedon, 879.
Buṭlān, b. (XI-1), vol. 1, 730; vol. 2, 71, **134**, 235, 240, 343, 447.
Buṭrus b. abī-l-Karam, 1121.
Buxtorf, Johann, 186, 377.
Byzantine coinage, 1114.
Byzantine culture, 670.
Byzantine renaissance, 162.
Byzantine restoration, 1113.
Byzantine, see sericulture.
Byzantium, see Philip.
Byzantium, see Stephen.

C. Including words beginning with Greek kappa, also some Jewish names beginning with kaph or qoph but traditionally Romanized with c (e.g., Crescas).

Cabala (or cabbala), see Qabbalah.
Cabret, see Isaac b. Abraham.
Cabret, see Jacob b. Judah.
Caelestis alchymia, 958.
Caen in Normandy, 162.
Caen, see Raoul.
Caesar, G. I. (I-1 B.C.), vol. 1, 216–217; vol. 2, 973.
Caesarea, see Eusebios.
Caesarean operation, 1073.
Caesarius, Joh., 237.
Çag, rabbi, 843.
Čaghatāi, 868.
Cairo, 523, 524, 793, 1005, 1066.

De'ot ha-filusufim, 876.
Derash, 188, 879.
Derek ṭobim, 346.
Derivationes, 472.
Derivationum, summa, 698.
Dermatology, see Skin diseases.
Dervish, see Darwīsh.
Descalzos, 549.
Descartes, 196, 380, 614, 762, 920, 1018.
Desclot, see Bernard.
Desconort, 907.
Descriptio cuiusdam instrumenti, 177.
Descriptio Hybernie, 418.
Descriptio rerum et diffinitiones earum, 340.
Descriptio Terrae Sanctae, 223, 1052, 1111.
Descriptio totius orbis, 637.
Deśī, 474.
Design in nature, 374.
Deśīnāmamālā, 474.
Deśīśabdasaṃgraha, 474.
Despars, see James.
Deudes de Prades, 648, 927.
Deulacres, see Hagin.
Deutsche Ritter, 333.
Deutschenspiegel, 529, 692, 1131.
Devagiri, 1133.
Devanāgarī script, 480.
Devise des chemins de Babiloine, 1052.
Devizes, see Richard.
Devorguilla, 863.
Dhail al-rawḍatain, 1119.
Dhakhā'ir al-a'lāq, 597.
Dhakhīra al-Khwārizmshāhī, 134, 234.
Dhakhīra of Thābit b. Qurra, 703.
Dhammasaṭṭham, 1134.
Dhanapāla, 474.
Dharma, 269.
Dharmanibandha, 1133.
Dharmaśāstra, 1134.
Dhātupāṭha, 1103.
Dhawāt al-asmā, 999.
Dhebbōrīthā, Kĕthābhā dhĕ, 602.
Dhikr, 26.
Dhiosqorīdhīs, Kĕthābhā dhĕ, 976.
Dhū-l-Nūn (IX–2), vol. 1, 592; vol. 2, 874.
Diaeta morborum acutorum, de, 242.
Diaetae universales, 890.
Diaetae, see Diet, Diete.
Diagrams printed in colors, 618.
Diagrams with movable parts, 902, 903.
Dialectices, summulae, 956.
Dialectics, 599.
Dialogi cum Iudaeo, 199.
Dialogi in quibus impiae Iudaeorum opiniones confutantur, 199.
Dialogorum, Libri tres, 180.
Dialogus de scaccario, 467.
Dials, see Sundials.
Diaphoretics, 79, 478.
Diaz de Vivar, see Roderic.
Dibre ḥakamim, 379.
Dibre Mosheh, 850.
Diceto, see Ralph.
Dicta Alani philosophi, 384.
Dictamen, 572, 1127.
Dictionaries, see Geographical.
Dictionarius, 696.
Dictionary, 530, 696, 930.
Dictionary, see Botanical.
Dictionary, see Glossary.
Dictionary, see names of languages.
Didascalicon de studio legendi, 193.
Diebus criticis, de, 642, 964, 995.
Diebus decretoriis, de, 890.
Diet, 88, 236, 439, 605, 856.
Diet, see also Diaetae.
Dietary laws, 97.
Diete super cyrurgiam, 890, 891.
Dietetic calendar, 88.
Dietmar von Aist, 392.
Dietrich, see Theodoric.
Dieulacresse, 857.
Differentia spiritus et animae, de, 171.
Differentiis febrium, de, 348.
Differentiis pulsuum, de, 348.
Differentiis topicis, de, 858.
Difficilium ad scientiam veram spectantium, 960.
Diffusion, see Science.
Digambara, 474.
Digest, 141, 265, 268, 348, 465, 1128.
Digestion, 1089.
Digestorum, summa, 689.
Digges, Leonard, 762, 957.
Dignoscendis pulsibus, de, 76.
Dimension, perception of third, 1027.
Dinant, see David.
Dinis the Liberal, of Portugal (XIII–2), 844; 55, 718, 726, 779, 804.
Dinis de Odivellas, São, 844.
Dino del Garbo, 1078.
Diocles, mathematician (II–1 B.C.), vol. 1, 183; vol. 2, 342.
Diodoros of Sicily (V–2 B.C.), vol. 1, 231; vol. 2, 760.
Dion Cassios (III–1), vol. 1, 327; vol. 2, 137, 251, 974.
Dion Chrysostomos, 974.
Dionysios the Areopagite (V–2), vol. 1, 406; vol. 2, 116, 193, 347, 348, 584, 915, 920, 922, 941, 944.
Dionysios Periegetes (I–2), vol. 1, 258; vol. 2, 43, 395, 971.
Dionysios, pseudo-, see Dionysios the Areopagite.
Dionysios Thrax (II–2 B.C.), vol. 1, 200; vol. 2, 998.
Dionysios, see also Denis, Dinis, Saint Denis.
Diophantine, see Equations.
Diophantine tradition, 756.

Faṣl al-maqāl, 359.
Fatḥ b. 'Alī al-Iṣfahānī, 686.
Fatḥ Allāh Shirwānī, 1007.
Fatḥ al-mannān, 1019.
Fatḥ al-qussī, 447.
Fatigue, 653.
Fāṭimid rule, 681.
Fausto appetente die, 917.
Fāwā'īd, 230.
Fawāt al-wafayāt, 1012.
Fazelli, Thomas, 452.
Febribus, de, 233, 357, 438, 656.
Febrium differentiis, de, 87.
Fechos de caballos, 1091.
Feeding, artificial, 233.
Feet, care of, 653.
Feet, compressed, 1058.
Fei-t'un, 1073.
Felix de les maravelles del mon, 906, 910.
Felix of Valois, 281, 334.
Ferdinand, St., 718, 834.
Ferdinand III of Castile, 573.
Ferdinand IV, 711.
Ferdinand of Toledo, 718, 837, 844, 852.
Ferrari da Gradi, see John Matthew.
Ferrarius, see John.
Ferrarius, alchemist, 439.
Ferrarius in Salerno, 439.
Ferrer, see Vincent.
Ferté, La, 156.
Fetellus (xii-2), 421; 35, 224, 302.
Feudal, see Law.
Feudal society, 802.
Feuillants, 156.
Feverfew, 667.
Fevers, 84, 86, 371, 434.
Fez, see Fās.
Fiadoni, see Bartholomew.
Fiadoni, see Ptolemy of Lucques.
Fibonacci, see Leonardo.
Fibonacci, see Series.
Fidā', abū-l, 27, 42, 1012, 1065, 1119.
Fide catholica contra haereticos, de, 158.
Fide orthodoxa, de, 585.
Fidenza, see John.
Fieschi, see Sinibaldo.
Fiduciae de simplicibus medicinis, L., 62.
Figs, 62.
Figura alchata, de, 341.
Figuras artis, lectura super, 902.
Figura cata, 1004.
Figuras, Libro de las, 842.
Figuris sphaericis, de, 341.
Fīhi mā fīhi, 874.
Fihrist, 444.
Filippo, see Philip.
Filosofiya, S. ha, 208.
Finé, Oronce, 170.
Fine in quo traditur modus, de, 904.
Fineschi, Vincenzio, 1061.
Finger reckoning, 401, 992.
Finibus rerum naturalium, de, 592.
Finland, 411.
Finzi, see Moses.
Fiore, see John.
Fiore, Fioris, see Joachim.
Fiqh, 703, 1011, 1132, 1133.
Firangistān, 138.
Firdawsī (xi-1), vol. 1, 705; vol. 2, 27, 142, 686.
Firearms, 29, 766, 1034, 1038.
Firenzuola, 578.
Fireworks, 958.
Firmament, see Spheres, celestial.
Firmin of Belleval, 996.
Firmon, Ẓaddiq b. Joseph, 184.
Firush ha-Torah, 188.
Fishes, 578, 930.
Fishing, 58, 447.
Fitz, 467.
Fitzherbert, Sir Anthony, 647.
FitzNeal, Fitz Nigel, see Richard.
Fixation of a volatile substance, 1043.
Flagellants (xiii-2), 821-823.
Flagellation, 821.
Flamel, Nicolas, 219.
Flamenca, 910.
Flavio Gioja of Amalfi, 630.
Flavius, see Joseph.
Flay, 253.
Flebotomia, 436, 657, 1079, 1088.
Flemish, see Dutch.
Fleta, 801, 1130.
Fleugaus, Gregorij, 1081.
Fleur-de-lis, 1049.
Fleury, see Hugh.
Floating specks, 704.
Floods, 1109.
Florence, 551.
Florence, bankers, 985.
Florence, cathedral, 825.
Florence, see Gueruccius son of Cion.
Florence, see Marc Emilio.
Florence, see Peter.
Florence, see Richard.
Florence, see Thaddaeus Alderotti.
Florence of Worcester (xii-1), 255; 139.
Florentius Wigorniensis, 255.
Flores astrologiae, 170.
Flores chronicorum, 1126.
Flores diaetarum, 439.
Flores de filosofia, 834.
Flores historiarum, 676.
Floridus, L., 131, 222.
Floris, see Joachim.
Flos, 8, 612.
Flos florum, 896.
Flos medicinae, 434.
Flos naturarum, 1044.
Fludd, Robert, 880.

Isaac Tzetzes (xii–1), 192; 20, 120, 124.
Isabel, queen of Portugal, 845.
Īsāghūjī, 867.
Isagogarum alchorismi, L., 114, 125, 167.
Isagoge, 867, 1086.
Isagoge ad Tegni, 65, 849, 890, 894.
Isagogicus Abdilazi, L., 170.
Isaiah (viii B.C.), vol. 1, 58–59; vol. 2, 188, 470.
Isaiah b. Elijah of Trani (xiii–1), 887; 556, 732.
Isaiah b. Mali of Trani (xiii–1), 556; 488, 887.
Isaiah of Trani the Elder, 556.
Isaiah of Trani the Younger, 887.
Isengrim the Wolf, 393.
Isfahānī, see 'Imād al-dīn.
Isḥāq, abū, 1003.
Isḥāq b. Barūn (xii–1), 272; 142.
Isḥāq b. Ḥunain (ix–2), vol. 1, 600; vol. 2, 340, 341, 561, 848, 851, 1003.
Isḥāq Ibrāhīm, abū-l (xii–2), 471; 292, 316, 319, 556.
Isḥāq al-Isrā'īlī (x–1), vol. 1, 639; vol. 2, 75, 84, 87, 340, 436, 437, 563, 890, 960, 1080, 1084, 1085, 1090.
Ishāra ilā maḥāsin al-tijāra, 462.
Ishārāt, 1099.
Ishārāt fī ma'rifat al-ziyārāt, 413.
Ishārāt wal-tanbīhāt, 875, 978, 1010, 1019.
Ishinhō, 78.
Ishrāq, 362.
Ishrāqī school, 500, 596.
Ishrāqīyūn, 362.
Isidore of Seville (vii–1), vol. 1, 471–472; vol. 2, 172, 201, 222, 237, 315, 588, 593, 927, 928, 929, 1085.
Iṣlāḥ al-akhlāq, 345.
Iṣlāḥ al-Majisṭī, 123, 206, 849, 852, 1018.
Islām, sects, 249.
Islām, treatise against, 806.
Islendingabók, 127, 260, 404.
Islendinga saga, 1112.
Ismā'īl, b., 598.
Ismā'īl, Chinese, 1034.
Ismā'īl b. Ḥammād, see Jauharī (x–2).
Ismā'īl b. al-Ḥusain al-Jurjānī (xii–1), 234; 69, 117, 134, 1010.
Ismā'īl b. Ibrāhīm al-Māridīnī (xiii–1), 703.
Ismā'īl b. al-Razzāz, 27, 632.
Ismā'īl, abū Ṭāhir, 69, 432.
Ismā'īlī, 769, 1001, 1124.
Ismā'īlīya (ix–2), vol. 1, 593; vol. 2, 113, 1045.
Isrā', 893.
Isrā' ilā maqām al-asrā, 596.
Israel Caslari, 894.
Israel b. Joseph ha-Levi, 894.
Isṭamākhīs, 1122.
Isṭaqisāt, 563.
Ister, see Aethicus.
Istidlāl, 701.
Istikmāl, 373.
Italian language, 150, 577, 815.
Italy, 328, 540, 710, 818.
Italy, map, 222.
Itch, 134, 233, 1094.
Itch-mite, 85, 132, 233.
Ithbāt al-jauhar, 1010.
Īthiqōn Kĕthābhā dh', 978.
I'tibār, 446.
I'timād fī-l-adwiya al-mufrada, 562.
Itineraries, 771.
Itinerarium Cambriae, 418.
Itinerarium mentis ad Deum, 922.
Itinerarium peregrinorum, 479.
Itinerarium Ricardi, 476, 479.
I'tiqād, 666.
'Ittim, 477.
'Iṭṭur, 465.
'Iṭṭur soferim, 465.
Iudaei super decimum Euclidis, L., 341.
Iudicia, 176.
Iudiciis, de, 994.
Iudiciis nativitatum, de, 170, 178.
Iudiciis et significatione stellarum, de, 563.
Iulius Africanus, see Sextus.
Iunctio partium solutarum, 1077.
Iuncturarum aegritudinibus, de, 343.
Iuris subtilitatibus, de, 266.
Iurisdictione imperii, de, 1126.
Ius ubique docendi, 572.
Iuventute et senectute, de, 829, 945.
Ivar Bodde, 594.
Ivar Utvik, 638.
Ivoire, see William.
Ivory, fossil, 412.
'Iyun shib'a kokabe lakot, 987.
Izzud-Din Muḥammad Pelásgúní, 425.

J. Representing Arabic letter jīm. For Latin words see under I. For Spanish words, see also X.
Jābir b. Aflaḥ (xii–1), 206; 7, 11, 13, 16, 18, 123, 145, 295, 296, 298, 341, 373, 380, 399, 604, 621, 849, 852, 1005, 1018.
Jābir b. Ḥaiyān (viii–2), vol. 1, 532–533; vol. 2, 33, 145, 206, 343, 769, 958, 1043, 1044.
Jabr, 662.
Jabr wal-muqābala, 999, 1002.
Jacme, see James.
Jacob, Nestorian, 975.
Jacob b. Abba Mari b. Simson, 565.
Jacob b. Abbassi (xiii–2), 853; 720, 729.
Jacob Anaṭoli (xiii–1), 565–566; 6, 17, 42, 341, 356, 359, 485, 492, 502, 506, 514, 532, 567, 580.
Jacob b. Asher, 375, 476, 477.
Jacob of Barṭallā, 603, 975.
Jacob de Coster van Maerlant, 947.
Jacob of Edessa (vii–2), vol. 1, 500; vol. 2, 977.

Medicinis occultis, de, 1096.
Medicinis simplicibus, de, 896.
Mediterranean coasts, 40.
Mediterranean lingua franca, 1047.
Medium demonstrationis, 923.
Megacosmus, see Microcosmos.
Megenberg, see Conrad.
Megillat ha-megalleh, 207.
Megrim, 388.
Meir b. Baruch of Rothenburg (XIII-2), 887; 732, 557, 888.
Meir b. Simon of Narbonne, 607.
Meissen, see Henry.
Meistersänger, 392.
Mekhitar of Aïri-vankh (XIII-2), 1117; 795.
Mekhitar of Ānī, 721, 752, 1117.
Mekhitar of Her (XII-2), 441; 70, 87, 310.
Mela, Pomponius (I-1), vol. 1, 239; vol. 2, 927.
Melabók, 260.
Melaka qeṭana, 564.
Melancholia, 85, 371, 1078.
Melanchthon, 103, 176, 618.
Melgueil, see Solomon b. Moses.
Melibeus, tale, 697.
Melitene, 975.
Melitene, see Elias Qindasī.
Melkhites, 501.
Melons, dried, 1058.
Melun, see David.
Memoria et reminiscentia, de, 936.
Memoria seculorum, 452.
Memoria technica, 266.
Memoriale, 696.
Memoriale omnium temporum, 930.
Mēmrōnē, 602.
Menageries, 576, 578.
Menahem Ashkenazi, 888.
Menaḥem b. Saruk (x-2), vol. 1, 690; vol. 2, 190.
Mĕnārath qudhshē, 978.
Mencken, J. B., 693.
Mendelssohn, Moses, 377, 848.
Mendicant orders, 486.
Menelaos of Alexandria (I-2), vol. 1, 253-254; vol. 2, 206, 341, 836, 851, 1002, 1003, 1004, 1016.
Menentillus of Spoleto, 1055.
Menescalia, Libro de, 1091.
Meng-hung, 610.
Meno, 347.
Menorat ha-maor, 878.
Mensa philosophica, 580.
Menstruation 80, 941.
Mensura circuli, de, 340.
Mensural, see Music.
Mensurandis distantiis, de, 957.
Mentelin, Joh., 931.
Me'or ha-golah, 887.
Meqize nirdamim, 887.
Meqor ḥayyim, 606, 876.
Mequbbalim, 733, 880.
Mer des hystoires, 1053.
Merced, 554.
Mercedarians (XIII-1), 550; 487.
Mercury, element, salts and ointments, 30, 84, 435, 655, 667, 958, 960, 1043, 1046, 1094.
Mercury, planet, 198, 206, 373, 837, 838, 991, 1007, 1008.
Mercury, see Salivation.
Meri, 237.
Merlac, see Daniel.
Merlin, book, 947.
Merlin, prophecies, 256.
Merton, 12, 725, 863.
Merton, see Walter.
Mesehella, 577.
Meshullam b. Jacob, 345.
Meshullam b. Jonah, 65, 787, 846.
Mesrop (V-1), vol. 1, 397; vol. 2, 137, 281, 319.
Messiah, 881.
Messina, see Bartholomew.
Messina, see John.
Mesuë junior, see Māsawaih al-Māridinī.
Mesuë major, see Māsawaih, b.
Mesuë I, pseudo- , see Māsawaih al-Māridīnī.
Mesuë II, pseudo-, see Mesuë the Third.
Mesuë the Third; pseudo-Mesuë II (XIII-1), 662; 66, 74, 522, 834, 854, 1080.
Metalogicon, 466.
Metals, preparations, 667.
Metals, seven, 593, 960.
Metals, six, 1045.
Metals, theory, 84, 1043.
Metals, transmutation, 1043.
Metals, see Unity.
Metamorphoses, 938, 973.
Metaphysica Aristotelis, see Metaphysics.
Metaphysica nova, 909.
Metaphysica textualis, 967.
Metaphysica de viciis contractis in studio theologiae, 954, 960.
Metaphysics, 356, 561, 568, 580, 830, 846, 848, 860, 876, 924, 936, 942, 945, 946, 950, 954, 955, 965, 967, 1127.
Metaphysics, twelfth book, 955.
Metempsychosis, 111, 158, 366, 517.
Meteora, 340, 579, 848, 936, 937, 942, 955.
Meteorologica, 23, 31, 33, 48, 347, 355, 509, 511, 915, 945.
Meteorology, 22, 299, 386, 509, 561, 564, 567, 586, 593, 761, 768, 830, 859, 928, 960, 967, 970, 989, 996, 1018.
Method, see Science.
Methodus imposturae, 902.
Methodus medendi, 348, 436.
Métiers, Livre des, 1128.
Metrica, 612.
Metz, see Gershon.

Moses Farachi, 833.
Moses Finzi, 848.
Moses b. Immanuel, 1087.
Moses b. Jacob of Coucy (xiii–1), 555; 488, 557.
Moses b. Jacob ha-Sallaḥ, 185.
Moses b. Joseph Qimḥi (xii–2), 469; 318.
Moses b. Joshua of Narbonne, 183, 354, 871.
Moses of León, 878.
Moses b. Maimon, see Maimonides.
Moses Maimunī, see Maimonides.
Moses b. Naḥman Gerondi (xiii–1), 883; 35, 367, 477, 554, 714, 730, 825, 876, 884, 888.
Moses of Palermo (xiii–2), 833; 89, 717, 782, 1093.
Moses Sephardi, 118, 199.
Moses b. Samuel b. Tibbon (xiii–2), 847; 6, 17, 29, 65, 66, 182, 206, 208, 359, 360, 370, 371, 372, 374, 377, 400, 565, 566, 719, 732, 752, 763, 787, 852, 855.
Moses b. Shem-ṭob b. Ḥabib, 940.
Moses b. Shem-ṭob of León (xiii–2), 878–881; 730.
Moses b. Zedaqa, 666.
Moses ha-zeman, 369.
Mosham, Ruprecht v., 1095.
Motibus animalium, de, 936.
Motibus liquidis, de, 344.
Motibus planetarum, de, 835.
Motion, 174, 952, 955, 995.
Motion, perpetual, 764, 1031, 1032, 1033.
Motions, see Celestial.
Motions, natural, 764, 1018.
Motions, see Planetary.
Motions, see Sublunar.
Motu, de, 629.
Motu accessionis et recessionis, de, 341.
Motu cordis, de, 561, 890.
Motu membrorum, de, 344.
Motu ocravae sphaerae, de, 341.
Motu stellarum, de, 178.
Motu et tempore, de, 340.
Mouches volantes, 704.
Mouhot, Henri, 1068.
Moulins, see Guiard.
Mount, see next word of geographical name.
Mountains, 423.
Mountains, generation, 49, 561, 938.
Mousket, see Philip.
Moxa, 78.
Moxibustion, 78.
Mozarabs, 114.
Mozene ha-'iyyunim, 852.
Mozene ẓedeq, 563.
Moznayim, 190.
Mu'ālaja al-buqrāṭīya, 233.
Mu'allim, 39, 221.
Mu'ārij, Sūrat, 844.
Mu'arrab min al-kalām al-'ajamī, 271.
Mu'ayyad al-dīn, see 'Urḍī.
Mu'aẓẓam, Ayyūbid, 631, 649, 686, 1099.
Mucius, A. and M., 180.
Mudawwar b. al (xii–2), 432; 94, 307, 666.
Mudejars, 114.
Münster, Sebastian, 207, 369, 377, 470, 556, 848.
Mufaḍḍal b. abī-l-Faḍā'il, 1122.
Mufaḍḍal b. Mājid, 1098.
Mufaḍḍal b. 'Umar al-Abharī (xiii–2), 867; 600, 727, 753, 759, 868, 978.
Mufarrij al-kurūb, 1120.
Mufaṣṣal, 271.
Mufīd al-'ulum, 182.
Mugdhabodha, 1103.
Mughannī, 294, 839.
Mughnī, 1035.
Mughnī fī-l-adwiya al-mufrada, 663.
Mughnī fi sharḥ al-mūjiz, 1100.
Mughrīb, 1065.
Mughrib 'an ba'ḍ 'ajā'ib al-Maghrib, 412.
Mugiz, 1100.
Muḥāḍarah, 137.
Muḥāḍarah wal-mudhākarah, 185.
Muhadhdhab, b. al-Nāqid, 432.
Muḥākamāt, 1019.
Muḥammad b. 'Abd al-Bāqī al-Baghdādī (xi–2), vol. 1, 761; vol. 2, 9, 122, 341.
Muḥammad b. 'Abd al-Karīm al-Shahrastānī (xii–1), 249; 113, 137.
Muḥammad b. 'Abd al-Malik al-Ḥafīd, 233.
Muḥammad b. 'Abd al-Malik, see Ṭufail, Ibn.
Muḥammad b. 'Abd al-Raḥīm al-Muḥammad, 412.
Muḥammad b. 'Abd al-Raḥmān, 1066.
Muḥammad b. 'Abd al-Raḥmān al-Qazwīnī, 701.
Muḥammad b. 'Abdallāh, abū-l-'Alā', 233.
Muḥammad b. 'Abdallāh b. al-Abbār, 681.
Muḥammad b. 'Abdallāh b. al-'Arabī (xii–1), 264; 118, 141, 142.
Muḥammad b. 'Abdallāh al-Ḥaṣṣar (xii–2), 400; 295, 505, 849, 998.
Muḥammad b. 'Abdallāh b. Masarra, 598.
Muḥammad al-'Abdarī, 35, 775.
Muḥammad b. Aḥmad, abū-l-Qāsim, 769.
Muḥammad b. Aḥmad al-'Irāqī, 1045.
Muḥammad b. Aḥmad b. Kamāl pāshā, 1011.
Muḥammad b. Aḥmad al-Khafarī, 1007.
Muḥammad b. Aḥmad al-Kharaqī (xii–1), 204; 16, 17, 123, 750, 956, 1018.
Muḥammad b. Aḥmad al-Kinānī, 412.
Muḥammad b. Aḥmad al-Mursī, 865.
Muḥammad b. Aḥmad al-Nasawī (xiii–1), 686; 527.
Muḥammad b. Aḥmad al-Qazwīnī (xii–1), 182; 117.
Muḥammad b. Aḥmad b. Rushd, 357.
Muḥammad b. Aḥmad al-Tamīmī (x–2), vol. 1, 679; vol. 2, 371.

* In vol. 1 this word was misspelled Nidhām.

Orah, 882.
Orandus, Eirenaeus, 219.
Oranges, 57, 428.
Orbe, de, 343.
Orbelian, see Stephen.
Orbelian family, 1116.
Orbits, see Planetary.
Orbs, see Spheres.
Orde de cavayleria, Libre de, 905.
Ordeal by water, 447.
Order of nature, 61.
Orderic Vital (XII–1), 254; 138, 252.
Ordination, priestly, 158.
Organi, L., 129.
Organi de graduali, L., 217.
Organon, 144, 146, 179, 563, 567, 568, 852, 956, 967.
Organotherapy, 1044.
Orḥot ḥayyim, 888.
Oribasios (IV–2), vol. 1, 372; vol. 2, 1085.
Orientalism, western, 911.
Orihuela, see Shākir b. Muslim.
Orkneyinga saga, 1112.
Orkneys, 1112.
Orlamünde, see Albert.
Orlando, see Roland.
Orléans, 465, 495, 572, 688.
Orléans, school, 267, 1128.
Ormuz, 1057.
Ornatu coeli et eclipsibus solis et lunae, de, 593.
Ornatu mulierum, de, 895.
Ornithology, Chinese, 1075; 60.
Ornithology, see also Birds.
Orogeny, see Mountains, generation.
Orontes, 27, 623.
Orosius (V–1), vol. 1, 395; vol. 2, 121, 139, 258, 1050.
Orpelian Siunetsi, see Stephen Orbelian.
Orthodoxa fide, de, 348.
Orthography, 100, 104.
Ortolan, see Martin.
Ortu et divisione philosophiae, de, 949.
Ortu et occasione signorum, de, 404.
Ortu scientiarum, de, 171.
Orvieto, cathedral, 824.
Osbern of Canterbury, 472.
Osca, see Martin.
'Osher, 48.
Osius, Felix, 1105.
Osma, see Bernard.
Ossetes of the Caucasus, 982.
Ostenta, 587.
Ostia, see Hugolinus.
Ostia, see Leo.
Otia imperialia, 637.
'Otot 'elyonot, 848.
'Otot ha-shamayim, 564.
Otto IV, emperor, 485, 637.
Otto of Freising (XII–1), 258; 121, 122, 139, 144, 180, 416.
Otto of Saint Blaise, 258.
Ottonian renaissance, 162.
Ou-yang Hsiu (XI–2), vol. 1, 777; vol. 2, 57, 315.
Ounces of time, 586.
Our Lady of Mercy, 487, 550.
Our Lady, see also Notre Dame, Nuestra Señora.
Ovid, 80, 932, 938, 973.
Oviedo, charter, 451.
Ovis argali, 1053.
Ovis poli, 1053, 1058.
Ownership, 462, 463.
Oxen, humped, 1058.
Oxford, 280, 285, 352, 544, 571, 573, 725, 806, 863, 911.
Oxford, Franciscan school, 583.
Oxford French algorism (XIII–1), 619; 505.
Oxford, see John.
Oẓar ha-'aniyim, 889.
Oẓar ha-kabod, 882.
Oẓar massaoth, 415.
Oẓerot ḥayyim, 478.

P. For Hebrew words see also under F.
Pa-ssŭ-pa, 981, 1137.
Pablo, see Paul.
Pace et animi tranquillitate, de, 865.
Pachymeres, see George.
Pacioli, Luca, 986, 1028.
Pacius, J. Erh., 577.
Padmanābha, 213.
Padmasambhava, 827.
Padua, 495, 571.
Padua, see Anthony.
Padua, see Christopher.
Padua, see David.
Padua, see Lazarus.
Padua, see Rolandino.
Padua, see Salio.
Padua, university, 985.
Paganis, see Hugh.
Pagnino, Sante, 470.
Pahlawī, 396, 590.
Pai ch'uan hsüeh hai, 422, 429.
Pai fu t'ang suan hsüeh ts'ung shu, 628.
Pai shih lei pien, 1024.
Painting, 30.
Painting, see also Oil colors.
Pāiyalacchī nāmamālā, 474.
Palaeologoi, 711, 745.
Palaeologos, see Andronicos.
Palaeologos, see Michael VIII.
Palaquera, 1096.
Palencia, 571, 573.
Palencia, see Andrew.
Palermo, 280, 855.
Palermo, see Aḥiṭub b. Isaac.

Salicor, 1041.
Ṣāliḥ Najm al-dīn Ayyūb, 624, 663, 704.
Ṣāliḥ b. al-Ḥusain al-Ja'farī, 557.
Salimbene de Adam of Parma (xiii-2), 1105; 97, 765, 783, 793, 1082.
Salio of Padua (xiii-1), 562; 6, 492, 505.
Salisbury, cathedral, 824.
Salisbury, see John.
Salivation caused by mercury, 84, 655.
Saljūq rule, 686.
Salmiac, 1094.
Salmon, William, 963, 1045.
Salome, son of Arit, 305, 430.
Ṣalt, abū-l (xii-1), 230; 25, 118, 123, 128, 129, 133, 137, 190, 896.
Salt, common, 1094.
Ṣalt Umaiya al-Andalusī, abū-l, 190.
Saltness of the sea, 960.
Saltpeter, 29, 766, 1036, 1040.
Salts, 1043.
Saltus lunae, 404, 993.
Salvation by faith, 715.
Salvino degl' Armati, 1024, 1025.
Salza, see Hermann.
Salzburg, see Virgil.
Salzinger, Ivo, 905, 912.
Samā', 599.
Sama' al-ṭabī'ī, 847.
Samā'wa aḥkāmuku, 634.
Samā wal-'ālam, 847.
Sam'ānī (xii-2), 444; 311, 312, 682, 1136.
Samaritan coins, 883.
Samaritans, 336, 471, 666, 729, 788, 1098.
Samarkand, 1005, 1006, 1064.
Samarqandī, Muḥammad b. Ashraf, 1020.
Sāmarrā, 30.
Sambuceto, see Lambert.
Samḥ, b. al (xi-1), vol. 1, 715; vol. 2, 837.
Saṃhitā, 667.
Sāmī fī-l-asāmī, 271.
Samos, see Pythagoras.
Sāmudratilaka, 397.
Samuel, rabbi, 699.
Samuel of Ānī (xii-2), 448; 313, 1117.
Samuel Ashkenasi, 377.
Samuel of Bamberg, 605.
Samuel b. Benveniste, 372.
Samuel b. Isaac Abbas, 184.
Samuel b. Isaac Sardi, 477.
Samuel b. Jacob of Capua (xiii-2), 854; 66, 79, 662, 720, 787.
Samuel b. Judah (fl. c. 1335), 206, 849, 852.
Samuel b. Judah b. 'Abbās, 401.
Samuel b. Judah b. Tibbon (xiii-1), 564–565; 66, 283, 291, 306, 319, 345, 359, 360, 370, 371, 373, 376, 377, 492, 502, 523, 532, 567, 604, 605, 850, 877.
Samuel ha-Levi Abulafia (xiii-2), 843; 718, 764, 836, 837, 842.
Samuel b. Meïr (xii-1), 189; 119, 143, 190.
Samuel b. Moṭoṭ, 182, 368.
Samuel b. Nathan ha-Me'ati, 720.
Samuel b. Samson (xiii-1), 643; 35, 514.
Samuel b. Simson, 643.
Samuel b. Solomon of Chateau-Thierry, 557.
Samuel b. Solomon b. Nathan, 853.
Samuel b. Tibbon, 564.
Samū'īl b. 'Abbās (xii-2), 401; 20, 26, 80, 281, 296, 298, 307.
Samū'īl b. Yaḥyā al-Maghribī, 401.
Samūm, 454
Samurai, 694.
San Concordio, see Bartholomew.
San Felice, see Andrew Polo.
San hsiao lun, 478.
San Hung, 262.
San kyō, 263.
San Severo, see Marc.
San T'ung, 983.
San tzŭ ching, 727, 983.
San-yin chi-i ping-chêng fang lun, 443.
Sanā, 1094.
Sanad b. 'Alī (ix-1), vol. 1, 566; vol. 2, 26, 128.
Sanan al-abyan, 1066.
Sánchez, see Gonzalo.
Sancho IV of Castile, 711, 835.
Sancho VI of Navarre, el Sabio (xii-2), 427; 59, 304, 305, 317.
Sanctis et pignoribus sanctorum, de, 253.
Sancto Spiritu, L., 904.
Sandarac, 220.
Sanguine, 85.
Sanguine humano, de, 895.
Sanhedrin, chapter X, 373.
Sanitate, de, 832.
Sanitate tuenda, de, 348.
Śaṅkara (ix-1), vol. 1, 561; vol. 2, 826.
Sanskrit botanical glossary, 53.
Sanskrit-Chinese dictionary, 321, 474.
Sanskrit dictionaries, 321, 473, 1103.
Sanskrit grammar, 320, 472, 473, 806, 1103.
Sanskrit roots, 806.
Sanskrit, transliteration, 100.
Santalla, see Hugh.
Santiago de Compostela, 34, 138, 254.
Santo Antonio, see Gabriel.
Santritter, Joannes Lucilius, 840.
Saphadin, see 'Ādil Sayf al-dīn.
Saphaea Arzachelis, 12, 831.
Saphena, 339.
Sapientiae, L., 342.
Sar ha-gadol, 477.
Sarābī, b., see Serapion, junior (xii-1).
Śāradā, 214.
Sarāfyūn, see Serapion, senior (ix-2), and Yaḥyā b. Sarāfyūn.
Saragossa, see Stephen.
Sarai, Franciscans in, 1056.
Sareshel, see Alfred.
Sarewel, 561.

Studiorum ducem, 917.
Stupor mundi, 578.
Sturla of Hvamm, 1112.
Sturla Thórtharson (XIII-2), 1112-1113; 260, 698, 794, 804.
Sturlubók, 260.
Sturlúnga saga, 1112.
Sturluson, see Snorri.
Stylization vs. naturalism, 54.
Su-chou, 39, 422, 423.
Su wên hsüan chi yüan ping shih, 478.
Su wên ping chi, 478.
Suan ching shih shu, 627.
Suan-p'an, 626.
Sublimation, 1043.
Sublimatione arsenici, de, 655.
Sublunar motions, 22, 46, 764, 1018.
Sublunar world, 993.
Substances, 662.
Substantia orbis, de, 357, 580, 993.
Substantiis physicis, de, 198.
Subtilitatum diversarumque creaturarum libri IX, 387.
Sūdān, 36, 411, 773, 906.
Sudorifics, 667.
Sueno Aggonis, 458.
Suffering, see Sisters.
Suffrage, 798, 916.
Ṣūfī saints, 597, 601.
Ṣūfism, 502, 879.
Ṣufism, see also Taṣawwuf.
Sugar, 244, 874.
Sugar cane, 57, 452.
Sugar plantations, 454.
Suger of Saint Denis (XII-1), 161; 55, 108, 112, 132, 139, 146.
Suggestion, cure by, 382.
Suhrawardī, 875.
Suidas (X-2), vol. 1, 691; vol. 2, 584.
Sulaimān b. Ḥaffāz al-Kūhīn, 1098.
Sulaimān b. Ḥārith, 430.
Sulaimān b. Ḥubaish al-Tamīmī, 378.
Sulaimān the Merchant (IX-1), vol. 1, 571; vol. 2, 409.
Sulaimān Naḥīfī, 874.
Sulaimān I of Turkey, 662.
Sullam al-murawniq, 867.
Sullāqā haunānāyā, 975.
Sullivan, Stephen, 873.
Sulphur, 958, 960, 1043.
Sulphur theory, 1044.
Sulse ractini, L., 244.
Sulṭān Walad, Bahā' al-dīn, 874.
Sulṭānīya, 1008.
Sumatra, 1057.
Sumer is icumen in (XIII-1), 634; 25, 510.
Summa aurea, 692.
Summa codicis, 266, 689.
Summa contra Gentiles, 892, 915.
Summa Lincolniensis, 960.
Summa medicinalis, 656.
Summa moralium philosophorum, 197.
Summa naturalium, 942.
Summa pastoralis, 554.
Summa quorundam Alexandrinorum, 833.
Summa Rolandi, 268, 688.
Summa theologica, 582, 915, 936, 945, 946, 950, 973.
Summaria expositio, 959.
Summo bono, de, 945, 970.
Sumūm wal-mutaḥarriz, 372, 832, 850.
Sun, 1008.
Sun Hsi, 645.
Sun Ssŭ-mo (VII-2), vol. 1, 498; vol. 2, 78.
Sun Tzŭ (III-1), vol. 1, 321; vol. 2, 625.
Sun, distance, 1014.
Sundials, 621, 1031.
Sung Ching-ch'ang, 627, 1023.
Sung government, 1125.
Sung Lien, 982, 1022.
Sung Lin-hsiang, 88.
Sung Tz'ŭ (XIII-1), 668; 97, 524, 530.
Sunnites, 164.
Super usibus feudorum, Summa, 689.
Superstition, denunciation, 375.
Superstitition, see Magic.
Superstition, see Occultism.
Suppositoriis, de, 434.
Ṣūrat al-aqālīm, 1009.
Surds, 622.
Surface, generation, 997.
Surface, measurement, 999.
Surface tension, see Oil, extension.
Surgery, 73, 79, 783, 792, 1099.
Surgery, Arabic, 74.
Surgeon, see Barber.
Ṣūrī, b. al (XIII-1), 649; 51, 54, 517, 522.
Surveying, 930.
Sūryasiddhānta, 128, 213.
Sūs al-Aqṣā', 221.
Suspendium clericorum, 573.
Suśruta (VI B.C), vol. 1, 76-77; vol. 2, 84.
Suśruta-saṃhitā, 137, 247.
Sutoku, 263.
Sūtram, 215.
Suwaidī, 1100.
Ṣuwar al-aqālīm, 1009.
Suyūṭī, 362, 445, 1132.
Suzdal, 638.
Suzdal chronicle, 458.
Svapna, 397.
Svapnacintāmaṇi, 397.
Svein Sigurdsson, 638.
Sveinbjörnsson, see Rafn.
Sveinsson, Brynjulf, 202.
Svend Aagesön, (XII-2), 458; 315, 317.
Swabia, 1131.
Syger de Foucaucourt, 1030.
Syllogismo, de, 339.
Syllogismo hypothetico, de, 858.

* See Encyclopaedia of Islām, vol. 4, 822–826, 8 pl., 1931.

Wang s'ih shu hua yüan, 1074.
Wang Shu-lo (III-2), vol. 1, 343; vol. 2, 76.
Wang Tê-yüan, 628.
Wang Wei-tê (XI-1), vol. 1, 732; vol. 2, 78.
Wang Ying-lin (XIII-2), 983; 727, 747.
Waqf, 1001.
War, art, 28, 765, 1040.
Ware, see William.
Wareru, 1134.
Wares, see Falsifications, Genuineness.
Wares, knowledge, 462.
Warrāq, 870.
Wāṣil, Ibn (XIII-2), 1119; 796.
Water, distilled, 239, 658.
Water lore, 96.
Water mills, 510, 623.
Water wheels, 27, 623, 870.
Waterford, see Geoffrey.
Waters, mineral, 438.
Waters, miraculous, 83.
Waters, strong and medicinal, 29, 767.
Waters, twelve, 84, 767, 889.
Waṭwāṭ (XIII-2), 870; 42, 47, 775, 780.
Wave theory, 762, 957.
Wealth, see Ownership.
Weather signs, 996.
Weert, see John.
Weidler, Joh. F., 616.
Weights and measures, 28, 29, 376, 381, 432, 463, 586, 612, 659, 667, 763, 847, 930, 1097, 1101.
Weights and measures, see also Decimal.
Wells, see Artesian.
Weltchronik, Sächsische, 692.
Wên An, 262, 398.
Wên Chêng, 1021.
Wên hsien t'ung k'ao, 983.
Wên miao, temple, 423.
Wên Mu, 422.
Wendover, see Richard.
Wendover, see Roger.
Wenrich of Treves, 265.
Wesham, see Roger.
Westminster Abbey, 162.
Whales, 595.
Whaling, 59, 939.
Wharton, Henry, 275.
White, J., 599.
White Canons, 157.
White Friars, 549.
White Monks, 155.
White Sea, 36, 515, 638.
Wikkuaḥ, 876, 883.
Wilbrand of Oldenburg (XIII-1), 639; 35, 512.
Will, ethical, see Ẓawwa'ah.
William Accorso, 528, 689.
William of Alnwick, 969.
William Anelier of Toulouse, 673.
William of Apulia, 385.
William of Aragon, 896.
William Arremon, see William Daspa.
William of Auvergne (XIII-1), 588; 173, 219, 497, 557.
William of Auxerre, 568.
William of Brescia, 1087.
William the Breton (XIII-1), 674; 525.
William Burgensis, 656.
William of Champeaux (XII-1), 192; 120, 194.
William the Clerk, 58, 702, 927.
William of Conches (XII-1), 197-198; 43, 109, 110, 121, 144, 127, 385, 593, 929, 988, 991.
William of Congenis (XIII-1), 656; 74, 519, 521.
William the Conqueror, 825.
William Corvi (XIII-2), 1087; 67, 70, 90, 94, 784, 856.
William Daspa (Guillen Arremon), 718, 836.
William of Dôle, 932.
William of Drogheda (XIII-1), 692; 529.
William Durand, speculator (XIII-2), 1127; 750, 757, 800.
William Durand of Saint Pourçain, 1127.
William of Durham, 573, 863.
William the Englishman (XIII-1), 620; 15, 18, 21, 92, 210, 505, 520, 991, 996.
William, falconer to Roger II, 59, 133, 227.
William the Fleming, 393.
William of Hirnkofen, 898.
William of Hirsau (XI-2), vol. 1, 762; vol. 2, 197.
William Ivoire, 1081.
William of Jumièges, 254, 314, 453, 455.
William Le Mire (XII-2), 347; 284.
William Little, 456.
William of Lorris, 738, 932.
William of Lunis (XIII-1), 563; 492, 498, 505, 567, 716.
William of Malmesbury (XII-1), 255; 139, 453.
William de la Mare (XIII-2), 950; 741.
William of Marseilles, 620.
William of Moerbeke (XIII-2), 829-831; 6, 27, 63, 65, 584, 716, 735, 739, 749, 751, 762, 764, 786, 798, 801, 860, 892, 914, 923, 994, 1027.
William of Nangis (XIII-2), 1109; 794, 1048.
William de Nassio, 982.
William of Newburgh (XII-2), 456; 314.
William of Norway, 594
William of Occam, 740, 903, 967, 968.
William of Paris, 588.
William Parvus, 456.
William Pérault, 58, 925, 927.
William de Périsse, 897.
William Petit, 456.
William the Physician 347.
William IX of Poitiers, 389.
William of Puylaurens (XIII-2), 1108; 794.

GREEK INDEX

This index is very meager because the Greek scientific literature of the twelfth and thirteenth centuries was exceedingly poor. Ancient writings, especially those of Hippocrates, Plato, Aristotle, Euclid, Archimedes, Ptolemy, and Galen are very often quoted in this volume, but their titles appear almost always in Latin, Arabic, or Hebrew, very seldom in Greek, and they will easily be found by means of the General Index. The Greek Index is a supplementary index, which is not self-sufficient; the General Index should be consulted in every case.

Articles and the preposition *περί* have been omitted; genitives imply the omitted preposition.

G. S.

CRAIGIE HOUSE, CAMBRIDGE, MASS.
Fourth of July, 1931